Nicholas HILLIARD (1).

Queen Elizabeth's Great Seal of Ireland.

THE BRITISH MUSEUM

DRAWINGS BY BRITISH ARTISTS

Volume one: XVI & XVII centuries

CATALOGUE OF BRITISH DRAWINGS

VOLUME ONE: XVI & XVII CENTURIES
by
EDWARD CROFT-MURRAY & PAUL HULTON

Supplemented by a list of foreign artists'
drawings connected with Great Britain

by

CHRISTOPHER WHITE

TEXT

PUBLISHED BY THE TRUSTEES OF THE BRITISH MUSEUM
LONDON
MCMLX

Sold at

THE BRITISH MUSEUM *and by*

H.M. STATIONERY OFFICE, *York House, Kingsway, London, W.C.* 2,

BERNARD QUARITCH LTD, 11 *Grafton Street, London, W.* 1,

CAMBRIDGE UNIVERSITY PRESS, 200 *Euston Road, N.W.* 1

and KEGAN PAUL, TRENCH, TRUBNER & CO,

43 *Great Russell Street, London, W.C.* 1

Printed at the University Press Glasgow
by Robert MacLehose and Company Limited

CONTENTS

CONTENTS

LIST OF ARTISTS

PREFACE

BETWEEN 1898 and 1907 the late Mr. Laurence Binyon compiled the four volumes of his pioneer *Catalogue of Drawings by British Artists and Artists of Foreign Origin working in Great Britain . . . in the British Museum*, which still remains an indispensable text-book for the student of the history of art in this country. The first volume of this publication has, however, been long out of print; and many important drawings have been added to the collection since the last volume appeared, while recent research has brought to light much valuable information about the artists concerned which was hitherto unknown. Moreover, since Mr. Binyon's time, the British drawings in the Department have been rearranged in sections on a chronological basis, thereby greatly facilitating the study of a particular period.

With these considerations in view, the Trustees decided that a new catalogue of British drawings, which included drawings by foreign artists working in this country, should be compiled. The present volume appears as the first of this projected publication. It covers roughly the span of the XVI and XVII centuries, and is prefaced by a historical introduction giving some account of drawing in this country from medieval times down to about 1700, together with a handlist of drawings of British interest by foreigners not included in the main Catalogue. The period covered is, indeed, one which is still rather unfamiliar, and every effort has been made to compile as full biographical notices as possible of the artists represented.

The work of preparing the volume could not have been undertaken without the encouragement and guidance of many kind friends. In particular, the authors would like to express their gratitude to the following for their assistance during the preparation of various sections of the work: Miss Erna Auerbach (biographical notices); Mr. C. F. Bell (entries to portrait draughtsmen); Mrs. Bernard Croft-Murray (preliminary compilation of the indexes); Dr. E. S. de Beer (biographical notices); Mr. Sven Gahlin (index to topography); Mrs. Leslie Ginsberg (index to costume); Mr. Hugh Honour (biographical notices, especially architects and sculptors); Mr. Philip Loszinski (entries to the Van de Veldes); Mr. Oliver Millar (biographical notices); the Hon. Michael Norton (biographical notices); Mr. David Piper (entries to Edward Byng); Professor D. B. Quinn (John White entries); Mr. Graham Reynolds (biographical notices); Mr. Michael Robinson (biographical notices, entries to the Van de Veldes and index to shipping); Mr. B. Siedlecki (entries to Charles Beale and Edward Byng); Miss Elizabeth Walsh (biographical notices and entries to Charles and Mary Beale); Mr. John Woodward (biographical notices); Professor Francis Wormald (introduction).

They would also like to express their great indebtedness to Miss Margot Holloway who for the past four years has taken a large share in the work involved in seeing this publication through the press, and to Mr. D. F. Snelgrove who has also devoted much of his time to this same task as well as assisting in the arrangement of the plates; to Mr. Iolo Williams for the encouragement which he has given throughout the work; to their colleagues in the British

PREFACE

Museum, Bloomsbury—especially to Dr. Bertram Schofield, Keeper of Manuscripts, Dr. Cyril Wright and Mr. Julian Brown and the Students' Room staff of that department, and to Mr. Peter Skelton, Superintendent of the Map Room—for their unfailing kindness in facilitating access to the various collections in their charge; and to past and present colleagues of the Natural History Museum, South Kensington, for expert advice on the natural history entries—the late Sir Norman Kinnear, former Director, Dr. H. W. Parker, former Keeper of Zoology, Dr. F. C. Fraser, Keeper of Zoology, and his colleagues in that department and the Department of Botany, and Mr. A. C. Townsend, Librarian.

Mention must also be made of the admirable survey, *English Art 1625–1714*, published in 1957 by Dr. Margaret Whinney and Mr. Oliver Millar, which unfortunately appeared too late for reference to be made to it in the present volume, but which has proved invaluable during the stages of correcting the proofs.

The printing of the text has been in the hands of Messrs. Robert MacLehose & Co. of Glasgow, and the monochrome plates have been produced by Messrs. L. Van Leer & Co. of Amsterdam. To both of these firms the authors extend their thanks for much help and guidance. The colour plates of the frontispiece to Part II, and of John White's drawing of grilling fish (Pl. VIII b), were supplied by Messrs. John Swain & Son of Barnet, who most generously presented the block of the latter subject.

INTRODUCTION

THE earliest drawing in the present Catalogue, a sheet of studies by an unknown Flemish visitor to England, only dates from about 1512 or even later. But the history of drawing in England begins, of course, at a much more remote period than this: it begins with medieval book illustrations for, as far as is known, no drawings or cartoons for large-scale pictures or glass-paintings—such as one finds in later periods—have survived in English medieval art, though, indeed, works of this kind did once exist.[1]

A detailed survey of English medieval book illustration would be out of place in the present Introduction; and, moreover, the subject has already been admirably covered by two pioneer works, *Early Drawings and Illuminations . . . in the British Museum* by W. de G. Birch and H. Jenner (1879) and *Illuminated Manuscripts* by J. A. Herbert (1911), as well as by Dr. E. G. Millar's *English Illuminated Manuscripts from the Xth to the XIIIth century* (1926) and *English Illuminated Manuscripts of the XIVth and XVth centuries* (1928), Miss Margaret Rickert's *Painting in Britain, The Middle-Ages* (1954), and, in a more limited sphere, by Professor Francis Wormald's *English Drawings of the Tenth and Eleventh Centuries* (1952) and Dr. C. R. Dodwell's *The Canterbury School of Illumination, 1066–1200* (1954).[2]

Nevertheless, so closely linked with the medieval tradition is English art of the XVI century that it will be found necessary to speak quite often in the following pages of the survival of manuscript illustration in the period. Many of the basic techniques and media of drawing—metal points (among them the so-called 'plummet'[3]), pen and ink, water-colour, body-colour or *gouache*—had also been long established and widely used throughout the Middle Ages. And even, in certain branches of subject matter—notably in portraiture, landscape and natural history—it has been possible to trace a continuity of development from as far back as Anglo-Saxon times, in nowise broken by the coming of the Renaissance. Moreover, even outside the field of book illustration, will be found many drawings in the Department of Manuscripts, some record of which would constitute here an important supplement to the admittedly rather meagre group of works listed under the XVI century in the present volume.

[1] John A. Knowles, *John Thornton of Coventry*, in *The Antiquaries Journal*, Vol. XXXIX, 1959, pp. 274–82

[2] The reader is also referred to the *Class Catalogue*, Vols. 92–3, *Art* in the Department of Manuscripts.

[3] This was a medium much in favour throughout the Middle Ages down to the XVI century. It was used for ruling lines, noting *marginalia* of all kinds and making preliminary drawings. It contains lead as its characteristic element which in the passage of time has acquired a brownish or brownish-red tint through the action of sulphur impurities in the atmosphere. As good examples of preliminary drawing in 'plummet', with finishing work in pen and ink, may be cited the *Beauchamp Pageants* (Cotton, *Julius E iv*).

I

MEDIEVAL—XVI CENTURY

Figure-subjects

To survey the complicated development of figure-drawing, in all its aspects, as represented in English medieval manuscripts, would be an impossible task here; and we must, therefore, confine ourselves in this first section to giving some slight account of the subject during the period which immediately precedes that covered by the present Catalogue.

In this country, at the end of the XIV and beginning of the XV century, there flourished a most elegant school of limning whose origin has generally come to be associated with the patronage of Richard II and his Queen, Anne of Bohemia. Dutch, Rhenish and very probably Bohemian elements combine to characterize it, and its most prominent figure is an artist signing himself HERMANN SCHEERRE.[1] Among its most important productions, all in the Museum, are the *Carmelite Missal* (*Add. 29704–5*), the so-called *Bible of Richard II* (*Royal E ix*), the *Beaufort Hours* (*Royal 2 A xviii*), the *Bedford Psalter and Hours* (*Add. 42131*), and a *Sarum Hours* (*Stowe 16*). The decoration of this last-mentioned book is unfinished; but three of the spaces for the miniatures are occupied by delicate pen and ink drawings which it would be tempting to regard as preliminary outline-studies of Scheerre's own time, though, from a stylistic point of view, they would seem rather to be later additions. Working at the same time as the Scheerre school, but independent of it, was the English Dominican brother, JOHN SIFERWAS (Cyfvewas) (*fl.* 1380–1421), the accomplished master of the *Sherborne Missal* (belonging to the Duke of Northumberland) and of the *Lovell Lectionary* (*Harley 7026*), who will be mentioned again in later sections. In the second quarter of the XV century we meet with two other important books, the exquisite *Desert of Religion* (*Cotton, Faustina B vi*) and a copy of Lydgate's *Life of St. Edmund* (*Harley 2278*). The former of these already shows traces of the soft and naturalistic modelling of the figures which is such a feature of fully developed Gothic painting in the Low Countries. Slightly later we meet with another recognizable limner, WILLIAM ABELL of London (*fl. c.* 1446–61?), who was employed to decorate charters for Eton College, King's College, Cambridge, and St. Bartholomew's Hospital, and who may also, according to Dr. Pächt, have had to do with the *Abingdon Missal* in the Bodleian Library and with a *Sarum Hours* in the British Museum (*Harley 2900*). During the later 1400's Flanders was, of course, to have the dominating influence on English illumination. This was largely due to Edward IV's importation of many sumptuous manuscripts from Ghent and Bruges, and to the subsequent arrival here of actual Flemish artists such as the anonymous, but accomplished, limner of *Royal 19 C viii* and *16 F ii*.

Of XV century figure-drawing outside the sphere of full colour-miniature there are some good specimens, mainly executed in pen and ink, in the Museum. Among the earliest, dating from about 1400, is a sketch in *Royal 10 B xiv, f. 3b*, by a Canterbury monk JOHN PRESTONE, of his patron saint John the Baptist standing within a Gothic niche formed of two oak-trees meeting at the top of a cusped Gothic arch, with birds perched on the branches and a lion

---

[1] Margaret Rickert, *The Reconstructed Carmelite Missal*, 1952.

couched at the foot. Another single drawing is the exquisite study, of about 1450, of John Lydgate presenting his 'Pilgrim' to Thomas Montacute, Earl of Salisbury (*Harley 4826*) which is closely related in style to the illustrations in Thomas Chaundler's *Liber-Apologeticus* at Trinity College, Cambridge. Also reminiscent in style of the Lydgate drawing are the vignettes in *Cotton, Tiberius A vii*, in which monochrome figures appear in landscape and other settings tinted in transparent colour-washes. Next, we may cite two works of an antiquarian-chival-resque complexion: the second version of the *Rous Roll* (*Add. 48976*), dating from between 1477 and 1485,[1] and the *Beauchamp Pageants* (*Cotton, Julius E iv*),[2] made at some time before 1493. The drawings in the former are probably copies, by a good 'professional' draughtsman, after JOHN ROUS's originals in the earlier roll now in the College of Arms; those in the *Pageants* strongly reflect, in their delicate ink hatching, the Flemish influence of their period. And, lastly, there is in *Add. 40742* a single drawing of the Almighty amidst clouds, with Christ on the Cross below, the composition and style of which is very reminiscent of a well known type of *grisaille* miniature peculiar to Dutch books of hours of the mid-XV century. It is in black chalk, certainly a rare medium in England at this period.

The opening years of the XVI century in England give us only a few sporadic hints of the influence of the Renaissance. Two manuscripts, both dating from about 1500, Filippo Alberico's *Tabula Cebetis* (*Arundel 317*) and an anonymous *System of Ideographic Writing* (*Royal 12 C iii*), are embellished with miniatures, borders and initials reflecting Italianate taste as interpreted in France by Jean Bourdichon and his school, here imported into England in a somewhat provincial form. But, generally speaking, English book decoration continues well into the century in the familiar late Gothic tradition of Flanders, as can be seen in such litur-gical manuscripts as *Harley 1892, 2838* and *2887*, and *Royal 2 B xiii*, all of which have minia-tures closely related in style to each other, while the *Pontifical of John Longland, Bishop of Lincoln* (*Add. 21974*), made at some time between 1521 and 1547, represents this same style in its most degenerate form. A secular work, the Pembroke-Northumberland copy of John Lydgate's *Troy Book* and *Story of Thebes* (*Royal 18 D ii*), originally written about 1455–62, con-tains a number of miniatures in Flemish taste added in about 1520, which are far superior in quality to any in those books immediately mentioned above, and have a further interest in that a number of them have Italianate Renaissance architectural backgrounds. It has been suggested that they may be the work of a certain LAMBERT BARNARD (*fl.* before 1514: D. 1567/8), court painter to Robert Sherborne, Bishop of Chichester from 1508 to 1536. Another manuscript to show quite good Renaissance miniatures is *Royal 2 A xvi*, a *Psalter* written for Henry VIII by a French humanist, Jean Mallard 'regius orator'. Lastly, we may mention among these late illuminated books a second *Psalter* (*Royal 2 B ix*) executed in 1565 by the Florentine PETRUCCIO UBALDINI for his patron Henry Fitzalan, 12th Earl of Arundel. Ubaldini was certainly responsible for its calligraphy, but the illuminated armorial frontis-piece and the one miniature of David in prayer is apparently by an accomplished French hand, near to that of the miniatures in the *Heures de Dinteville* in the Bibliothèque Nationale, Paris,

---

[1] C. E. Wright, *The Rous Roll: the English version*, in *B.M.Q.*, XX, 1956, pp. 77–80.

[2] Edward Maunde Thompson, *The Pageants of Richard Beauchamp, Earl of Warwick*, in *Burl. Mag.*, I, 1903, pp. 151–63.

and various copies of the *Statutes of the Order of St. Michael*, one of which is in the Public Record Office and another in the John Rylands Library, Manchester.

Two manuscripts may be cited here, in passing, as examples of book illustration copied from rather earlier engravings. One is again *Harley 1892*, a *Psalter*, which contains a group of miniatures and one drawing in pen and ink after Martin Schongauer's *Passion* (*Lehrs*, V, No. 122 Ec.). The other is the head-piece to a list, made about 1540, of lands of the attainted monastery of Colchester (*Egerton 2164*), and is presumably intended to represent the arrival of the King's surveyors to take up their duties. In reality, however, it is nothing but an exact copy of Lucas van Leyden's engraving of the Triumph of Mordecai (*Bartsch*, No. 32). Below are two initial *T s* enclosing respectively a portrait of Henry VIII and—somewhat irrelevantly —the Triumph of Venus (also probably copied from an engraving). The subsidiary decoration of *putti* and foliations belongs to a type of early Renaissance ornament which would have been known at the time as 'antique work' and which is often found in contemporary monochrome wall-paintings. This head-piece is almost certainly the work of the clerk who wrote out the document, and represents the tradition of the medieval calligrapher-draughtsman, such as Brother JOHN PRESTONE, persisting into this later period. The same hand appears again, with similar ornament, on a roll of the possessions of Glastonbury Abbey, 1539, in the Bodleian Library (*19; S.C. 27814*), in a pattern book, dated 1542, in the Victoria and Albert Museum (*L.2090–1937*) and in a collection of decrees and orders of the Court of Augmentation in the Public Record Office (*E.315/91*). An even later example of 'calligraphic' drawing in the British Museum, is in *Add. 34605*, the *Ordinary of the Bakers' Company at York*, the minutes of which were kept in 1595–9 by the then clerk, ADAM KETTLEWELL, who, besides embellishing them with elaborate grotesque-initials, inserted (*ff.* 24b and 25) eight drawings in pen and ink tinted in water-colour representing the different stages of baking. Other calligraphic ornament is referred to below in the section on *Antiquarian and Heraldic Draughtsmanship*.

It is much to be regretted that there is so little to show how far the new and freer style of drawing, in pen and ink and chalk, which came into being in Renaissance Italy, found a footing in early Tudor England. Only one very faint though spirited outline in black chalk of a rearing horse has come to light to show the probable draughtsmanship of TOTO DEL NUNZIATA, Henry VII's Florentine Sergeant-Painter: it is not in the British Museum, but on the back of a document relating to Toto among the Loseley Manuscripts now deposited in the Borough Muniment Room at Guildford (*No. 1893*). And in the Louvre is a project in pen and wash for the decoration of a wall at Nonsuch which is now generally accepted as the work of NICOLO BELLIN (Bellino or Bellini), a Modenese who arrived in England by 1532 after a period of employment under Primaticcio at Fontaincbleau. But no drawings have survived from the hands of the other Italians over here at the time: Pietro Torregiano, Vincenzo Volpe, Alexe Carmillian, Bartolomeo Penni, Giovanni da Majano, 'Nycholas Florentyner', Domingo; while the painter-engineer, GIROLAMO DA TREVISO, perhaps the most distinguished among them, is only represented as a draughtsman in Henry's service by some hurried notes on a siege-plan of Boulogne (*see* below under *Landscape and Topography*).

We must look to the Northerner HANS HOLBEIN for the richest expression of earlier Renaissance drawing in England. As one would expect, portraiture is his most outstanding achievement in this field; and the Museum's representation of his portrait-drawings will be noted in the next section. Holbein's other specifically 'English' drawings in the collection include two charming *genre* studies, one of a woman seated on a settle with four children, the other of a lady wearing a peaked head-dress so characteristic of Tudor costume (p. 558, Nos. 1 & 2). A third drawing, attributed to Holbein (p. 570, No. 190) of musicians in a balcony might be connected with a project for some triumphal arch such as that designed by him for the coronation procession of Anne Boleyn, or with part of an external illusionistic wall-painting such as that of the 'House of the Dance' at Basle, in which case it is doubtful whether it can be claimed as of English origin. Copies made in the XVII century of Holbein's famous decorations for the Hanseatic Steelyard in London, the *Triumphs of Riches and Poverty*, are listed on p. 571, Nos. 193–7.

It seems natural to pass from Holbein to two artists who occupied leading positions at Court in Elizabethan times, NICHOLAS HILLIARD and ISAAC OLIVER. Hilliard's surviving drawings are confined to portraiture and will be included in the section devoted to that subject. Oliver, on the other hand, had a wider sphere of activity as a draughtsman, and being of French origin was more susceptible to continental influences. Some of his drawings show an acquaintance with Parmigianino; others, as one would expect, with the school of Fontaine-bleau (pp. 20–24). His finished limnings in colour of biblical subjects can be regarded among the late survivals in technique of medieval illumination. As far as can be discovered, there are no known specimens of these in the Museum; but Pl. 16, the drawing of the Entombment, is a preliminary study for his masterpiece (now lost) in this field, and Pl. 14, the Adoration of the Magi, must reveal something of the limner's manner in its carefully stippled washes. Finally we may cite, as a rare instance (outside Oliver's work) of up-to-date Continental influence on English drawing of this period, the anonymous study of young Bacchanals carousing, reproduced on Pl. 3. JOHN WHITE's studies of the natives of Virginia are included below in the section dealing with *Antiquarian and Heraldic Draughtsmanship . . . and Ethnography*.

Portraiture

Portrait-drawing in England has a long and unbroken tradition, and its history can be very completely studied in the Museum. Medieval book illustration plays a very important part in this context: there are representations of contemporary or near-contemporary events, of benefactors to a foundation, of ancestors who sprout from a genealogical tree, of an author presenting his work to his patron, of the owners of a book and the members of his family, and sometimes even of the limner himself. And—less defined—there are the heads introduced into initials and borders which, from their lively characterization, may well be—as is probably the case with the *Bedford Psalter and Hours* (*Add. 42131*)—of men and women with whom the artist was acquainted.

A search for portraits of royalty among the Museum's manuscripts is particularly rewarding, and it would, indeed, be quite possible to produce from them a nearly complete series of English monarchs from Anglo-Saxon down to Tudor times.[1] At the outset, we may note that the contemporary representations of Edgar of Wessex in *Cotton, Tiberius A iii* and

---

[1] The interest of such portraits was realized by Joseph Strutt as long ago as 1773 when he published his *Regal and Ecclesiastical Antiquities of England*.

Vespasian A viii, and of Canute in *Stowe 944* have about them—always granting the stylized limitations of the time—an individuality which suggests an attempt at actual likeness. On the other hand, many of these early portraits would, of course, be imaginary like those, attributed to MATTHEW PARIS,[1] which preface his *Abbrevatio Chronicorum (Cotton, Claudius D vi)*. A *Roll Chronicle (Royal 14 B v)*, dating from just before 1300, has charming little medallions of sovereigns down to Edward I which again must be largely imaginary, but which, with their azure backgrounds, constitute a very early anticipation of the Tudor miniature. Highlights in later medieval royal portraiture include a probable Henry IV in the *Bedford Psalter and Hours (f. 76b)* and his son Prince Henry (later Henry V) in *Arundel 38*, both emanating from the school of HERMANN SCHEERRE, and the youthful and elegant Richard III (so different from the familiar and unflattering strap-mouthed Tudor presentation of him) in the *Rous Roll (Add. 48976)*.

Among members of the Church and nobility we may note the following: a youthful St. Dunstan in *Cotton, Tiberius A 111*; St. Edmund Rich (?) in *Royal 2 A xxii*; Sir Geoffrey Luttrell and the ladies of his family in the *Luttrell Psalter (Add. 42130)*; John Beaufort, Earl of Somerset and his Countess in the *Beaufort Hours (Royal 2 A xviii)*, again from the school of HERMANN SCHEERRE; and Warwick the Kingmaker and others in the *Rous Roll*. A famous constellation of Middle English poets can also be assembled: Chaucer in *Royal 17 D vi* and *Harley 4866*; John Gower in *Cotton, Tiberius A iv*; Thomas Hoccleve in *Arundel 38* and *Royal 17 D vi* (HOCCLEVE, has, incidentally, been credited with having actually limned the prototype of the portrait of Chaucer mentioned above);[2] and the pen and ink drawing, already mentioned, of John Lydgate presenting his 'Pilgrim' to the Earl of Salisbury in *Harley 4826*. There are even a few self-portraits of limners: MATTHEW PARIS (D. 1259) in *Royal 14 C vii*; W. DE BRAILES of Oxford (*fl. c.* 1225–50) in *Add. 49999*; the Dominican JOHN SIFERWAS (*fl.* 1380–1421) in *Harley 7026*, and ALAN STRAYLER (*fl. c.* 1380) in *Cotton, Nero D 7*. And finally, among the lower orders, Stephen the carpenter of St. Alban's Abbey, complete with his axe and square, as he was portrayed by STRAYLER in *Nero D 7*.

This native English taste for portraiture received a new stimulus during the first half of the XVI century mainly owing to the presence here of HOLBEIN. Holbein revolutionized portrait-drawing in this country with his large bust-length studies of his English contemporaries, of which the most splendid assemblage is of course in the Royal Library at Windsor, and of which there is in the Print Room one notable example (p. 558, No. 3) together with two good workshop copies (p. 570, Nos. 189 & 191). Their prototypes in conception must be looked for in XV century Italy, for instance in such drawings in the Museum's collection as those by Carpaccio (*P. & P. 36*), Lorenzo di Credi (*P. & P. 46*), Domenico Ghirlandaio (*P. & P. 72 & 73*), Perugino (*P. & P. 191*) and two anonymous Venetians (*P. & P. 328 & 330*). Nearer in time and place to Holbein are his countrymen Dürer (whose large portrait-studies in the Print Room actually include one of an Englishman, Henry Parker, Lord Morley, 1523 (p. 557, No. 1)), Aldegrever, Jörg Breu I, Burgkmair, Lucas Cranach I, Peter Gärtner and Georg Pencz. Also, we may mention in the Museum's collection, as providing contemporary

---

[1] M. R. James, *The Drawings of Matthew Paris*, in *Walpole Soc.*, XIV, 1926, pp. 1–26, frontispiece & Pls. I–XXX; Francis Wormald, *More Matthew Paris Drawings* in *Walpole Soc.*, XXI, 1946, pp. 109–12, Pls. XXVII–IX; and Richard Vaughan, *Matthew Paris*, 1958.

[2] M. H. Spielmann, *The Portraits of Geoffrey Chaucer*, 1900, pp. 5–10.

or near contemporary parallels to Holbein's work in this field, some fine heads by the Netherlanders Jan de Beer (*P. 4*) and Lucas van Leyden (*P. 2 & 8*), and the important series of drawings by the Clouets and their school.

In another branch of portraiture, the miniature in body-colour on vellum stuck on card, HOLBEIN continued the tradition of the medieval illuminated manuscript: he is said, indeed, to have been taught by one of the late Flemish limners to visit England, LUKE HORENBOUT. We have already noted, when speaking of medieval portraiture, how figures of persons connected with a book and its making—the author, the translator, the patron and the artist—are not infrequently depicted in it; and this usage still continues in the XVI century as, for example, in *Henry VII's Psalter* (*Royal 2 A xvi*) which contains two delightfully intimate portraits of the monarch, probably by a French artist, one of him sitting in his chamber reading (*f. 3*), the other of him harping, attended by his fool Will Sommers (*f. 63b*). We have also seen how the bust or half-length medallion portrait appears in manuscripts at least as early as about 1300; and, as its descendant in the XVI century, we may cite the first volume of Albert Pigghe's *Commentaires de la Guerre Gallique* (*Harley 6205*), which dates from 1519, and its second volume in the Bibliothèque Nationale, Paris, as examples of this, though they are wholly French in origin. On *f. 3* of Vol. I, of the *Commentaires* is a medallion portrait of François I, and in Vol. II occur others of the *Preux de Marignan*: these, with their rich azure backgrounds, one may regard as virtually the immediate prototypes of such early single portrait-miniatures as that of Henry VIII at the age of thirty-five (*c.* 1525/6), attributed to HORENBOUT, in the Fitzwilliam Museum, Cambridge, and HOLBEIN's Anne of Cleves (*c.* 1539) and Mrs. Pemberton (*c.* 1540–3) in the Victoria and Albert Museum, which in their turn set the style for those by HILLIARD and OLIVER in the next generation.

Another type of portrait to adorn manuscripts is the big initial letter containing the figure of the enthroned sovereign which occurs at the head of documents of royal import. On *f.* 12*b* of *Add. 36705* is a characteristic letter *H* (perhaps cut from some charter and inserted in the present volume) containing just such a figure of Henry VIII surrounded by his courtiers, dating from about 1542–3. It is very likely that HILLIARD's well-known three-quarter length of the young Queen Elizabeth in the collection of the Duke of Portland derives in spirit from this kind of 'charter-portrait'. A very fine, but later, example of documental illumination is a *Patent* creating James I's son Henry Prince of Wales and Earl of Chester in 1610 (*Add. 36/932*). The initial *F* at the head encloses a portrait-group of the enthroned King with his son, in coronet and blue mantle, kneeling before him. The work is so very much higher in quality than usual that one is tempted to ascribe it to one of the court limners of the time such as HILLIARD or OLIVER.[1] Another limning of Prince Henry, this time in armour on horseback, appears on *f.* 1 of Jacques Cleland's *Le Pourtrict de Monseigneur Le Prince* (*Royal 16 E xxxviii*): it bears the signature *Henr: Peacham f.*, the author of *The Compleat Gentleman*. Documents were also sometimes embellished with royal portraits of a more sober kind in pen and ink, no doubt in most cases the work of the scribe himself. The initial *T* with Henry VIII in it in *Egerton 2164*

[1] In the Museum there is now only one detached portrait-miniature of the Hilliard-Oliver school, a fine *James I* set in the so-called Lyte Jewel in the Department of British and Medieval Antiquities. Formerly there were others of this period in the collection which were transferred to the National Portrait Gallery and the Victoria and Albert Museum in 1939.

has already been noted. In a similar vein, but of later date, is a Queen Elizabeth, *c.* 1586, in *Egerton 2882, f.* 207, of which the scribe's initials, *T (or I) B,* occur in the decoration on *f.* 1. And as the frontispiece to the autograph of GEORGE GASCOIGNE's *The Tale of Hemetes the Heremete,* 1575 (*Royal A xlviii*) appears another 'calligraphic' portrait of the same sovereign with the author, who was also probably his own draughtsman, presenting the book to her.

Drawings by HILLIARD are extremely rare: in fact, only two which are considered to be completely authentic are known, one being the celebrated design for Elizabeth's Greal Seal of Ireland which is reproduced as a frontispiece to the present Catalogue, the other a study of a young woman in the Victoria and Albert Museum. A third drawing, in the British Museum, of a Queen and her son (Pl. 11) is inscribed *N.H.* but is more doubtful; if by Hilliard, it would be a late work. It is interesting to compare the Northern neatness of Hilliard's brush or pen work with the loose chalk of his Umbrian contemporary FEDERICO ZUCCARO to whom so many Elizabethan portraits used quite unwarrantably to be given. But here in the Department are two unimpeachable relics of Zuccaro's short stay in England in 1574, the full-length studies in black and red chalks of Queen Elizabeth and the Earl of Leicester, listed on p. 578, Nos. 1 & 2.

Natural History and Scientific Illustration. Cartography

Throughout the history of drawing it is perhaps the portrayal of natural history in which most continuity is shown. Especially is this true with plants. The need for accuracy and high finish in depicting those used in medicine was fully realized as early as the second quarter of the VI century by the draughtsmen of the famous Vienna *Dioscurides;*[1] and the very fact that the plants and their roots could easily be studied from the life at close quarters enabled this accuracy to be achieved. The Vienna *Dioscurides* can be considered as virtually the ancestor of all subsequent illustrated herbals, including such XI and XII century English examples as *Cotton, Vitellius C iii* and *Harley 1585* and *5294.* As far as animals are concerned the *Dioscurides* is less true to life, and this is reflected in its other spiritual descendants, the bestiaries of the XII and XIII centuries, such as *Royal 12 C xix, Harley 4751, Sloane 3544* and *Add. 11283,* where the draughtsman would have relied for his subjects on prototypes long since distorted from reality, or on imaginary monsters which represented the tallest of travellers' tales. But, happily, at least one English artist, MATTHEW PARIS, had an opportunity of studying an elephant at first hand, the one sent by St. Louis to Henry III in 1255. Paris's drawing of it appears on *f. 169b* of *Cotton, Nero D 1*: he was obviously struck by the flexibility of the animal's trunk, and made a supplementary sketch of this to show how it could turn inwards. An even closer study of animal life, especially of birds and insects, begins to manifest itself during the XIV century, paralleling the revival of interest in landscape at the same period. As Dr. Pächt has shown,[2] this seems to have originated in Lombardy, but it quickly spread northwards through the channels of what is now conveniently known as 'International Gothic'. An early

[1] Dioscurides, *Codex Amiciae Iulianae . . . Vindobonensis Med. Gr. I,* ed. Joseph von Karabacek and others, 1906.

[2] Otto Pächt, *Early Italian Nature Studies and the early Calendar Landscape,* in *Warburg Journal,* XIII, 1950, pp. 13–47.

English example, probably about 1300, is on *f.* 234 of *Royal 3 D vi* in the border of which are admirable studies on a minute scale of a jay, a bullfinch and a peacock. Rather later, there is the vivacious drawing of God creating the birds and beasts on *f.* 2*b* of the *Holkham Picture Bible* (*Add. 47682*), and, in the same vein, *ff.* 59*b* and 65 of the *Smithfield Decretals* (*Royal 10 E iv*).

This same tradition is still found flourishing at the end of the century and in the early 1400's, as can be seen in the exquisitely coloured studies of birds in the *Pepysian Library Sketchbook* (Magdalene College, Cambridge) and on *f.* 5 of the *Lovell Lectionary* (*Harley 7026*) by JOHN SIFERWAS. And, as recalling the style of the older functional herbals, we may note the studies of plants in a copy of John Ademe's *Opera Chirurgica* (*Add. 29301*). Finally, by the second half of the XVI century naturalism attained to the extremes of virtuosity in the *flora* and *fauna* which are such characteristic features of the borders of Flemish manuscripts of the time. As we have already noted, Flanders was to become, largely through Edward IV's patronage of Flemish art, the dominating influence in English illumination. Two royal books, *19 C viii* and *16 F ii*, dating respectively from 1496 and *c.* 1500 and both produced in England, offer excellent instances of these naturalistic borders; and we may follow the style into the next century in two books decorated for Henry VIII, *Cotton, Vespasian A xvii* and *Royal 8 G vii*, and in the *Pontifical of John Longland, Bishop of Lincoln* (*Add. 21974*). In the two royal books the decoration is occasionally well executed; but in the *Pontifical* it is far coarser than one would expect to find even in the most average book of hours produced in Flanders itself at this period. A border of flowers and foliage surrounding a *Grant of Arms to Matthew Parker, Archbishop of Canterbury,* 1559 (*Egerton 2581A*) marks a further stage in the degeneration of this type of ornament, which was slow in dying and persisted in the borders of documents for yet another hundred years or so.

As we shall see also when speaking of the section *Landscape and Topography*, the link between the old and new is provided by Dürer. A number of his drawings in the Print Room show this: in particular, his fir-tree of 1495–7 (*W. 121*) and his muzzle of a cow of 1523 (*W. 367 & 368*) still have something of the medieval technique of minutely brushed body-colour; but his elk of 1512 (*W. 242*) and his walrus of 1521 (*W. 823*) already display the freer and bolder pen-work and broader colour-washes of a more modern handling of the medium. In England, about sixty years later, JOHN WHITE in his remarkable studies of animal and plant life (pp. 33–51) represents, too, this meeting of the old and the new. We may also draw attention to the series of coloured drawings of garden flowers copied in England about 1600–10 from a Dutch *florilegium*, listed in the present Catalogue on pp. 68–77, which represent the conventionally competent handling and exact portrayal of such material without, of course, White's distinctive touch, and to the little album (Pl. 4) where the more decorative treatment of the contents seems to descend direct from the style of the manuscript border.

Scientific illustration has not had the same continuous development as the illustration of natural history. Nevertheless, there are some interesting examples of it, dating from various periods, in the Museum which should be recorded here. One of the earliest scientific books to have pictures is the *Treatise on Astronomy* by Aratus, two English XI century copies of which (*Cotton, Tiberius B v* and *Harley 2506*) contain, as symbols of the constellations, very competent drawings of animals, birds and fish, deriving no doubt from antique prototypes. Similar drawings of a slightly later date occur in *Royal 13 A xi*. But, whereas charting the heavens was attempted through this fancied semblance of the constellations to the silhouettes of animals and other beings, mapping the earth and its contours was, from the beginning, tackled (to the modern eye) from a far more directly representational point of view, even though theology frequently dictated the layout. Early English cartography is well represented in the Museum. We may notice first two *Mappae Mundi*: one, the famous XI century 'Anglo-Saxon Map', in *Cotton, Tiberius B v* in which we already meet with the well-known convention of depicting towns as walled and towered enclosures; the other, in a XIII century *Psalter (Add. 28681)* showing the strange monsters of the bestiary along its right-hand edge. Both of these maps in lay-out anticipate the great Hereford map of RICHARD OF HALDINGHAM. Later world maps include a curious diagrammatic section of the globe, dating from the early XIV century, in the *Arundel Psalter (Arundel 83)* divided up, according to the elements, into strata round a flaming *Infernus*, and a mid-XV century example, still in the old tradition and very crude in handling, in *Add. 37049*. MATTHEW PARIS, who counted cartography among his several learned interests, can be credited with having drawn the first scientifically conceived maps of Great Britain alone since the age of Ptolemy. These date from 1250, and are to be found respectively in *Cotton, Claudius D vi* and *Julius D vii*. They are followed, in the next century, by the so-called 'Gough Map' now in the Bodleian Library, which, considering its early date, is surprisingly accurate in describing the country's features and, in this respect, shows a considerable advance on Paris's attempts.

The age of discovery and instrumental measurement saw the foundation of modern map-making. We cannot go into the later development of the art here; but at least we may cite two most important and delicately rendered charts of the Elizabethan era, those by JOHN WHITE of the eastern coastline of North America, listed in the present Catalogue on pp. 51–2, Nos. 59–60. Other related material will be found in the next section, *Landscape and Topography*.

There remains a group of XV century medical and astrological works to be noted: John Aderne's *Opera Chirurgica (Add. 29301)* with quite well-executed marginal drawings of wounded limbs, surgical instruments and herbs; the *Guild Book of the Barber Surgeons of York (Egerton 2572)* with both emblematic and medical drawings of good quality, in handling rather reminiscent of those in the *Rous Roll (Add. 48976)*; and a collection of alchemical tracts with marginal drawings *(Harley 2407)*. Related in spirit to the last-mentioned is an alchemical roll dealing with the search for the Philosopher's Stone *(Add. MS. 32621)*, written and presumably illustrated by a certain JAMES STANDISH in the late Elizabethan period. The text, still in Gothic script, consists of instructions in almost doggerel verse for carrying out experiments, and the mystical drawings no doubt derive from some medieval prototype.

Landscape and Topography

Landscape drawing in England had a most lively beginning under the influence of the *Utrecht Psalter*.[1] This famous book, now thought to have been executed in the Abbey of Hautvilliers near Rheims about the year 850, was in Canterbury by the beginning of the XI

---

[1] *See* Edward Maunde Thompson *The Utrecht Psalter*. Complete facsimile in collotype. 1873; and Francis Wormald, *English Drawings of the Tenth and Eleventh Centuries*, 1952, p. 21.

century and exercised a profound influence on Anglo-Saxon book illustration. Many of its vignettes have quite extensively developed landscape-settings, deriving ultimately from the antique, which are characterized by trees with twisted trunks and feathery foliage, Italianate buildings, and phallic looking rocks, all sketched in by a nervous and rapid hand. These vignettes already display, too, a basic feature of medieval landscape: the convention adopted by the artist—who had little or no idea of perspective as we now know it—of treating the composition as a bird's-eye view with a sharply rising background, achieving by this means some degree of recession, a device which was to be in pretty general use, in Northern Europe at least, up to the beginning of the XVI century. A copy (*Harley 603*) of the *Utrecht Psalter* was made at Canterbury in about 1000, and the Anglo-Saxon draughtsman in his version interpreted the illustrations of the original, which are in monochrome, through a medium of coloured ink outlines and occasional wash, endowing the otherwise stylized forms with an impressionistic naturalism. Even atmospheric effects are attempted, notably in the rocky landscape threshed by the divine wind on *f.* 51, and the blue, pink and brown tints of the sky on *f.* 69 where, too, it may be noted, the artist has borrowed the contours of the phallic rock-forms to depict his clouds. Elements of the 'Utrecht-Canterbury' style are to be found in two other XI century manuscripts in the Museum, *Cotton, Tiberius B v* and *Royal 15 A xvi* (*f.* 84), both from Canterbury. And in an *Anglo-Saxon Genesis* (*Cotton, Claudius B iv*) there are other atmospheric effects, such as an admirable rainbow set here in a wavy purple and white sky (*f.* 16*b*). On the other hand, the trees in this last-mentioned book are far more consciously stylized than those in *Harley 603*, with trumpet foliage and branches bent into a formally scrolled pattern like the ironwork of an early medieval door.

For the next two hundred years landscape elements in book illustration became increasingly more stylized, or perhaps rather simplified, even to the point of elimination: the 'sky', for instance, in the XII century is treated as a plain coloured or gilded surface, and from the XIII even down to the early XV as a diaper-pattern, while trees are represented as clusters of formal trefoils or artichoke-like sprouts. For examples of this economical landscape we may turn to three bestiaries: *Royal 12 C xix* and *2 F xiii*, and *Harley 4751*.

With the early years of the XIV century, however, there is already some indication of a revived interest in landscape. It is true that in *Queen Mary's Psalter* (*Royal 2 B vii*) little more than a couple of trees, some pitted earth or wavy water suggest an out-of-door setting. But in its near contemporary, the *Luttrell Psalter* (*Add. 42130*), there is in the lower margin of *f.* 181 a pure landscape vignette of what is presumably Sir Geoffrey Luttrell's overshot mill at Irnham with its meadow-bordered race baited with eel-traps. Other vignettes of the English country scene, of about the same time, occur in the margins of the *Ridware Chartulary* (*Egerton 3041*). During the course of the century trees began to lose their patterned formality and to take on, instead, a kind of symbolic naturalism in which the species is indicated by gigantic leaves. A delightful example of this is on *f.* 14 of the *Arundel Psalter* (*Arundel 83*), a group of birds and beasts listening to the discourse of an owl in a woodland setting of oak, ivy and other quite identifiable species springing from grassy hillocks speckled with flowers. And, as belonging to this same period, we may note in a delicately illustrated *Roll-Genealogy of Our Lord*, executed at St. Albans in the Matthew Paris tradition (*Royal 14 B ix*), another admirable rainbow arching across the vellum from one side to the other.

Meanwhile, Continental limners were developing the concept of a true landscape background which, early in the next century, was to reach a state of perfection in the hands of Pol de Limbourg in the *Très Riches Heures* of the Duc de Berri, dating from about 1416 and now at Chantilly. In England we already meet with some realization of this fuller landscape background in the splendid series of miniatures, dating from *c.* 1401–10 and probably by a Northern French artist, prefacing the *Beaufort Hours* (*Royal 2 A xviii*), in which, amongst other features we can trace the transitional treatment of the 'sky' from a purely decorative diaper to a star-spangled azure firmament. Another manuscript, the *Bedford Psalter and Hours* (*Add. 42131*), dating from after 1414 and illuminated by the Anglo-Rhenish (?) master HERMANN SCHEERRE, also has fine landscape backgrounds in some of its historiated initials. A further stage is marked in three volumes of the second quarter of the XV century: *The Desert of Religion* (*Cotton, Faustina B vi*), *f.* 14*b* of which shows 'Wylde bestes' in a forest, the darkness effectively expressed by shades of intense green and dark blue; *The Pilgrimage of the Soul* (*Cotton, Tiberius A vii*) in which the landscapes are rendered as green islands, with prettily tinted trees and an occasional blue sky freely washed in transparent water-colour; and Lydgate's *Life of St. Edmund* (*Harley 2278*), in which some of the out-of-door settings of the illustrations are characterized by conical green or olive hillocks and mottled blue and white skies.

The Franco-Flemish school of Pol de Limbourg descended into the final and completely naturalistic phase of landscaped miniature-painting which found its most accomplished expression at Bruges and Ghent in the late XV and early XVI century. This can be fully studied in the many books decorated in this style which were imported by Edward IV, and which are still among the Royal MSS. One of them, *15 E iv*, is of unusual interest as it contains on *f.* 24*b* an extensive landscape without figures, a distinct rarity at this early date. Flemish artists themselves were also imported into England; and one of the most accomplished among them—alas his name is not known—painted for Henry VII in 1496, probably at Sheen (Richmond), the illustrations to an allegorical work *Imaginacion de la vraye noblesse* (*Royal 19 c viii*) several of which had admirable landscape backgrounds.

Strict topography in medieval landscape is something of a rarity; and, generally speaking, the draughtsman only took pains to be accurate when he was working for some functional purpose. Important early examples of this are the well-known pictorial plans of the water-works of the Cathedral and Priory of Canterbury, dating from *c.* 1150, in the *Eadwine Psalter*, at Trinity College, Cambridge. And much later, we find an excellent XV century view of Richmond Castle, Yorkshire, in a *Registrum Honoris Richmondiae* (*Faustina B vii*). More often, only an approximation was achieved: in MATTHEW PARIS's *Itineraries from London to Apulia* in *Cotton, Nero D i* and *Royal 14 C vii*; in the XIV century *marginalia* of *Royal 13 A iii*, in delicately sketched 'plummet', representing Old St. Paul's, the Tower of London and York Minster; in the delightful conception, also of the XIV century, of how Stonehenge was built with Merlin's aid, in *Egerton 3028*; and in the panorama of Venice, of about 1400, at the beginning of an English copy of Marco Polo's *Li Livres du Graunt Caam*, in the Bodleian Library. On the other hand, the late XIV century views of Rome and Jerusalem in *Royal 1 B x*, and the pretty early XV century vignettes of English towns in *Cotton, Claudius E iv*, are completely imaginary except, perhaps, for that on *f.* 3 of the latter book showing the Gothic pavilion over the King's Bath at Bath. Even with the precedent of Pol de Limbourg's splendid views of the Duc de Berri's castles in the *Très Riches Heures*, topographical features in the great age of landscape-miniature of the later XV century are still uncommon. Among the British Museum manuscripts of English origin, dating from this period, there are three only in which recognizably depicted places appear: the famous view of the Tower and London Bridge in *Royal 16 F ii*; the pilgrimage church of Notre Dame de Hal in Hainault in *Royal 19 C viii*; and the Mont St. Michel in *Royal 20 E vi*.

The Franco-Flemish type of minutely finished landscape in body-colour was to continue well into the first half of the XVI century; and good 'English' examples are to be found among the later miniatures of the Pembroke-Northumberland *Lydgate* (*Royal 18 D ii*), including one showing the pilgrims leaving Canterbury which, however, is shown, even at this late date, as an imaginary Flemish city. But a far more informal approach to landscape—in particular topographical landscape—had already manifested itself before the end of the XV century. Dürer is, of course, the most prominent figure in this new development, especially in the medium of water-colour in which, though occasionally using a highly finished technique having affinities with that of contemporary miniaturists, he also experimented quite early in his career—indeed as early as 1494-7—with far broader semi-transparent washes than had previously been known. Admirable specimens of his work as a landscapist are in the Department: notably the *Weier Haus* near Nuremberg (*W. 115*), the Study of Rocks (*W. 110*), the Study of Water, Sky and Pine Trees (*W. 114*) and the Castle of Trent (*W. 95*).

Nothing so advanced as Dürer's influence could have been felt in England during his lifetime; but at least something of the new trend in landscape-drawing, in this case emanating (it seems almost superfluous to say) from the Low Countries, is discernible in a remarkable series mainly of bird's-eye views of harbour and other fortifications made for Henry VIII about 1538, among the Cotton Manuscripts (*Augustus I i, 22-3, 70-1, ii 57 B & 70, & Augustus I, Suppt. 2 & 15*). All display the same able pen-work, the same use of rose or lilac wash to denote water, and the same combination of pictorial, decorative and naturalistic elements, with the practical delineation of the subject-matter. The draughtsman's masterpiece is a vast prospect or 'plat', as it would have been called at the time, of Dover (*Augustus I i, 22-3*), with a detailed view of the town and cliffs, rowing-boats drawn up on the beach, and His Majesty's ships splendidly dressed out with flags and streamers in the foreground. This artist was evidently employed in other spheres of military draughtsmanship, for in *Augustus III, 8*, is a study by him of a large boat manned by archers, gunners and halberdiers. He may have been responsible too for some curious quasi-diagrammatic 'plats' of battles also in *Augustus III, 5-7*.

Related in style to this draughtsman's work, but less accomplished in handling, is a long bird's-eye prospect of the coast from Land's End to Exmouth (*Augustus I i, 35-9*). The countryside is indicated by ridges topped by freely sketched-in trees tinted in light green. There is some degree of accuracy in the topographical features: Exeter with its Castle on a mound and its Cathedral twin-towered and spired, and a number of recognizable country houses, such as Dartington Hall. Recording the same part of the coast, but perhaps at a slightly later date (*c. 1540?*), is a quite skilfully drawn 'plat' of Mount's Bay in Cornwall (*Augustus I i, 34*) showing naturalistic topographical features, though some of the houses have Flemish crow-stepped gables, due presumably to the imagination of the artist.

Returning to views of Dover we may mention one (*Augustus I ii, 9*) which, though it possesses little pictorial quality, has a certain interest as it is signed by the artist, JOHN LUCKAS, presumbly an engineer in Henry VIII's service. Also in this section of the Cotton Manuscripts are 'plats' of Scarborough (*Augustus I ii, 1*) and again Dover (*Augustus I i, 19*), in pen and ink tinted in water-colour, this time by an anonymous Italian hand which is recognizable in the meridional character of the conventionalized houses and other architectural features. A rather similar hand, also Italian, is present in a view of an attack on Landrecies in N.E. France, in 1543 (*Augustus I i, 50*).

One of the best known Italians in Henry VIII's employ was the painter-engineer GIROLAMO DA TREVISO to whom may perhaps be attributed the inscriptions and additional notes of Italianate buildings on an otherwise very crudely drawn plan of Boulogne (*Augustus I ii, 67*). Girolamo was killed at the siege of that town in 1544. Yet another of Henry's Italians, GIOVANNI ROSETTI—otherwise unrecorded—executed a plan of the Castle of Ardres (*Augustus I ii, 74*). The castle itself is shown only as a diagram, but naturalistic features such as spiky rocks and feathery trees are introduced into the drawing. One more early Tudor view of a French castle, that of Guines (*Augustus I ii, 12*), should be mentioned, as though it clearly belongs—as do all the others—to the category of quasi-military topography, it shows the building at ordinary eye level and so anticipates the naturalistic prospects of Hollar and his contemporaries.

There is nothing of this period in the Museum of quite such pictorial or topographical interest as the Fleming ANTHONIS VAN DEN WYNGAERDE's noble long views of London (parent of all subsequent long views of that city) and of the Tudor royal palaces, dating probably from 1557, in the *Sutherland-Clarendon* now in the Ashmolean Museum at Oxford. But in the *Handlist* appended to the present Catalogue is listed on p. 557, No. 1, the view of a palace which does not appear in Wyngaerde's series, Nonsuch, drawn in 1568 by another Fleming, JORIS HOEFNAGEL. This is a straightforward human eye level view, and has additional interest in the person of Elizabeth I herself riding across the foreground in her open coach. Topographical landscape had, indeed, by this time taken on a much more informal and less functional quality, but this new quality was not generally to be met with in England till the next century.

JOHN WHITE's drawings of Virginia include both topography and landscape. All of them, in varying degrees, are influenced by the convention of the bird's-eye view; and some, indeed, by the very nature of their subject-matter, are treated as military 'plats'. Most striking of all, as showing White's sensitive observation and handling of water-colour, is undoubtedly the study of Indians fishing (Pl. VII). Nearer to the conventionalized bird's-eye 'plat' in style, yet again showing White's delicate and naturalistic treatment of trees and other objects is the village of Secoton (Pl. VI). Another Indian village, Pomeiooc (Pl. 31), is drawn more according to the matter of fact precepts of military topography, which precepts are even more strictly adhered to naturally in the two forts on Puerto Rico (Pls. 18 & 23). White has, as already remarked, his own very personal style. It is interesting, therefore, to compare with what is undoubtedly his own work the skirmish between English seamen and Eskimo (Frontispiece to Plates) which is presumed to be a copy of a lost original by him. This drawing is by an accomplished, but far more consciously traditional hand than White's, with a technique of pen and ink tinted in water-colour descending direct from that of the 'informal' book illustration of the Middle Ages.

In *Cotton-Augustus* we can find contemporary, if crudely executed, counterparts to White's topography. There are the 'plats' by JOHN THOMAS 'solder' [soldier] of incidents in the Irish campaign of 1593 (*Augustus I ii, 38–9*) which are full of lively and picturesque ethnographical details including the bagpipers of Hugh Maguire's army. In something of the same vein as White's Puerto Rico is the English attack on the Castle of Lancerotto (Lanzarote) in the Canary Isles, 1598 (*Augustus I ii, 111*) with the English ships at anchor and soldiers on the shore led by a commander mounted on a camel, the local *fauna* being shown in pairs, suggesting a direct descent from their ancestors of the Ark. A fourth drawing which can be conveniently included here is a bird's-eye view and chart of the mouth of the Garonne and attack on Blois (*Augustus I ii, 80*) by an English hand, working in a neat and minute technique reminiscent of late medieval illumination. Even more closely allied to White's drawings, but not belonging to *Cotton-Augustus*, is the well-executed 'plat' of Drake's attack on the Island of Santiago in 1585 (*Egerton 2579*) which is discussed in greater detail on p. 28.

Further examples of Elizabethan military topography include two neatly drawn surveys of Plymouth (*Augustus I i, 40 & 42*) by yet another unrecorded italian, FRANCESCO GENIBELLI, and the inevitable Dover (*Augustus I i, 45*), perhaps by a certain THOMAS MILLES, who has both practically and picturesquely demonstrated, with a vivid Turneresque sunset, in which direction lies the West.[1]

In this essentially utilitarian class of drawings we may also note two works by well-known civilian surveyors of the period, R. TRESWELL's plan of Cheapside (Pl. 17) and JOHN NORDEN's *Description of the Honour of Windsor* (*Harley 3749*) made for James I in 1607 and containing a highly decorative and conventionalized view of the Castle.

In contrast, as finally introducing the complete emancipation of pictorial topography, may be mentioned two early XVII century drawings, both anonymous but of Netherlandish origin, one of Windsor Castle (Pl. 5), the other of the interior of Westminster Hall (Pl. 6).

Architecture and Sculpture; Designs for Metalwork

At all stages during the development of medieval book illustration, architecture and architectural elements have played a very effective part in providing the framework and background to the miniature. But working drawings, such as might have been used by the medieval master-mason, are very rare: at Orvieto there are the drawings of the West front of the Cathedral attributed to Lorenzo Maitani; in the archives of Strasburg Cathedral there are projects for Gothic arcading and other details; and, best known of all, there is, in the Bibliothèque Nationale in Paris, the sketchbook of Villard de Honnecourt. In England, the only medieval drawings of this kind which have so far come to light are among the Cotton Manuscripts in the British Museum.[2] Earliest among them is a beautiful

---

[1] The attribution is suggested by another bird's-eye view of Dover by a rather similar hand in the archives at Hatfield House (*Topographical Drawings* Vol. I, *f. 58*). It is inscribed: *This Plott was drawn &/ coloured by Tho. Milles for Willm Lord Cobham.*

[2] John Harvey, *Early Tudor Draughtsmen*, in *The Connoisseur Coronation Book*, 1953, pp. 97–102.

canopied altar-tomb, c. 1500(?), 'intended for Kinge Henry the sixte' (*Augustus II, 1*), drawn in pen and ink with light brown wash on vellum. Next to it in date would come an interesting elevation of a late Gothic pinnacled tower for King's College Chapel, Cambridge (*Augustus I i, 3*), of which the handling of the pen and wash show a competent hand, though the realization of the perspective is very insecure. Another drawing connected with the same building is *Augustus I i, 2*, an elevation of the South side. The treatment of the architectural detail in this last-mentioned is still medieval, but in reality the drawing is probably later, as little figures in academic dress apparently of about 1560, appear in it (unless these are a subsequent addition). A third King's College drawing, not however forming part of the Cotton collection, is that already referred to at the beginning of this Introduction as the earliest entry in the present Catalogue (Pls. 1 & 2).

Also in *Cotton-Augustus* are architectural drawings which can specifically be connected with Henry VIII. *Augustus I, 4* is a bow-fronted gallery resting on an arcade surmounted by beasts holding vanes charged with the royal cypher H.R.; though Italianate details are present, the feeling of the whole is still Gothic. *Augustus I ii, 13* is a bird's-eye view of an early Tudor brick mansion, partly fortified, the gatehouse of which is surmounted by vanes bearing the rose and fleur-de-lis, suggesting royal ownership. *Augustus I i, 84* and *ii, 11* are plans of the royal manor-house of Hull, and are signed by a certain ROGERS, presumably a surveyor in Henry's service. Another interesting architectural drawing in this group is *Augustus I i, 5*, an elevation of a pedimented building in complete Renaissance taste. It shows no signs of having any direct royal connexions, but nevertheless may well have been intended as a design for a triumphal arch in some state procession, as on the centre is a tablet inscribed with moral sentences in English, whilst on the wings are emblematical reliefs or paintings.

But undoubtedly the most important architectural drawing connected with Henry VIII in the Museum's possession is HOLBEIN's great design, thought to be for a chimney-piece at Bridewell Palace (p. 570, No. 188). And, in passing, we may note in *Harley 41 (f. 5b)*, an *Account of the Coronation of Anne Boleyn*, containing a detailed description of *the pagyaunt of the Styliard* designed by Holbein for this occasion, the drawing for which is in the Berlin Print Room.

More directly related to the projects for harbour works and fortifications, described in the previous section on *Landscape and Topography*, are three drawings by Henry's German engineer, STEFAN VON HASCHENPERG, two of them being plans for the fortification of Carlisle (*Augustus I i, 69* and *Suppt. 8–9*) and one a concentric castle for coastal defence (*Augustus I, Suppt. 16*). Two other designs for a concentric castle (*Augustus I i, 20* and *i, 67*) also probably originated with Haschenperg, though the actual drawings are by a far more skilled hand than his, near in style to that of the accomplished 'plats' of Dover and Calais (*Augustus I i, 22–23 & C*). Another military work of the same period, but not connected with Haschenperg, is a neatly drawn view of the pier at Boulogne, dated *1549 Januarij 26* (*Cotton Roll xiii 43*) showing in particular detail its construction, with large blocks of unworked stone bonded into the masonry and a very new looking and functional fort of bright red brick as tasteless as any War Department erection of today.

Suitable for mention here, but of later date, is a *Description* [by John Nodes and Thomas Butler] *of the severall fire-workes inuented and wrought* for the marriage of Princess Elizabeth to Frederick, Elector Palatine, 1613 (*Royal 17 C xxxv*). It contains seven drawings, in pen and ink and water-colour, of the various machines which are very architectural in character and reminiscent of the triumphal arches erected by Stephen Harrison for the accession of James I.

No drawings of this period for sculpture alone have been found in the Museum collections, though we may recall in that context the carved detail indicated on such designs as HOLBEIN's Bridewell chimney-piece. It has been thought appropriate, however, to notice here some important designs for metalwork and jewellery. Earliest is a drawing of the XV century, in pen and ink with grey wash, for the top of a late Gothic processional cross in *Add. 40742 f.* 19. And, of course, in the Print Room there are Holbein's splendid designs for goldsmiths' work (pp. 558–70) which include those for a cup for Jane Seymour and a clock presented to Henry VIII by Sir Anthony Denny, as a New Year's gift in 1544 (the year after Holbein's death). They emphasize the scope of Holbein's versatility as a court artist which he was called upon to show in company with other masters of the Renaissance—and, indeed, with their predecessors of the Middle Ages—before the coming of the more specialized artist of later times. In the other group (pp. 8–14 & Pls. 7 & 8) are similar drawings, mainly emanating from Nuremberg, which have a particular interest as reflecting the taste for that school at the court of James I.

Antiquarian and Heraldic Draughtsmanship. Studies of Costume and Ethnography. Archaistic Calligraphy

Objects of antiquity were already being studied and drawn in what is now regarded in itself as a period of well-established Antiquity. One of the earliest and most curious examples of this is in an XI century Canterbury School Psalter (*Cotton, Tiberius C vi*) which contains what might be called an Anglo-Saxon *Grove's Dictionary* with vignettes and descriptions of what were thought to be the ancient musical instruments mentioned in the Psalms. Another but much later instance, dating from the XIV century, of biblical antiquities being depicted occurs in *Royal 3 D vii*: they include diagrammatic sections of Noah's Ark with its decks named after their prospective passengers, a plan of the Temple and drawings of its furniture.

British Antiquity, as one would expect, appears in various medieval chronicles. In one of the mid-XIII century St. Albans books associated with MATTHEW PARIS (*Cotton, Nero D i*) there is a catalogue of jewels in the abbey treasury illustrated by coloured drawings including one of a late IV century cameo of an emperor in the guise of Aesculapius. Two copies of another XIII century chronicle, that of Roger of Hovedon (*Royal 14 C ii* and *Arundel 150*), have *marginalia* of the standard on its wheeled machine which saved the day for the English at the Battle of Northallerton in 1138. The XIV century drawing of Merlin building Stonehenge in *Egerton 3028* has already been noted in the section on *Landscape and Topography*. To this group may be added, as examples of XII–XIII century ethnographical illustration, the lively vignettes of primitive Irish life on *ff.* 28b and 29 of Giraldus Cambrensis' *Topographia Hibernica* (*Royal 13 B viii*).

But undoubtedly the most important aspect of antiquarian draughtsmanship during the Middle Ages was the delineation of heraldry. From the XIII century onwards heraldic ornament played an increasingly important part in book decoration: it is, of course, one of the principal means whereby the original ownership of a manuscript can be determined. In the

XIII century, too, we first meet with neatly drawn and coloured heraldry collected and preserved as memoranda, like the roll dating from that period now in the possession of Mr. Anthony Wagner, Richmond Herald, a XV century copy of which, known as the *Dering Roll*, is in the Museum (*Add. 38537*). Among later medieval heraldic books is *Stowe 594*, which dates from after 1450. It contains a series of large figures, in pen and brown ink with watercolour, connected with the Order of the Garter: Sir William Brugges, first Garter King of Arms, kneeling before St. George; Edward III; and the original knights of the Order. These apparently corresponded with the subjects of some painted glass inserted by Sir William in the chancel of St. George's Church, Stamford. Rather in the same style is a collection of gaily tinctured armorial data collected by Sir Thomas Holme, Clarenceux King of Arms from 1476 to 1493. An important fragment of this manuscript, contained in *Harley 4205*, consists of a number of spirited drawings, again in pen and brown ink with water-colour, including one of Sir Thomas himself (?) stepping out of a ship to receive his banner, and a series of knights fighting on foot and on horseback. Another fragment, *Add. 45133*, shows similar combatants, as well as figures of ancestors and their ladies, and the more usual rows of shields of arms. Closely related to this type of illustration are two famous commemorative works, the *Rous Roll* (*Add. 48976*) and the *Beauchamp Pageants* (*Cotton, Julius E iv*), both of which have been already mentioned in previous sections of this Introduction.

The tradition of the antiquarian and heraldic draughtsman of the late Middle Ages is met with again in the XVI century in a most interesting group of heraldic collections in manuscript (*Add. 45131–3*) associated with Sir Thomas Wriothesley (Garter King of Arms, 1504–34). The drawings are in pen and ink—in style decidedly reminiscent of the technique of the *Beauchamp Pageants*, and outside the Museum, of the *Islip Roll* at Westminster Abbey, though less accomplished—sometimes washed in with thick water-colour. *Add. 4531* contains records of state funerals and allied material: sketches of the funeral procession of Elizabeth of York, 1503 (*ff. 41b–42*) showing her effigy lying on the car, and of Henry VII on his deathbed, 1509 (*f. 54*); banners carried on such occasions; and several altar-tombs with reclining figures (one of them, *f. 89b*, beneath a canopy resting on foliated balusters in Renaissance taste). We may note that these records of tombs have about them exactly the same rather dry and emphatic quality as the drawings of antiquities made for Sir William Dugdale in the mid-XVII century by 'Mr. William Sedgwick (a skilful Arms Painter)',[1] and of similar watercolours of memorial sculpture made by antiquarian draughtsmen of the XVIII century for the extra-illustration of county histories and similar works. *Add. 45132* is confined mainly to drawings of heraldic pennons. One handsome example of a single heraldic composition of the early XVI century we may note in the Department of Printed Books (*c. 37 1.8*): a limning of the arms of Cardinal Wolsey, set against an azure background within an ogee arch decorated with primitive Renaissance ornament in French taste. It is pasted inside the cover of Vol. I of the Cardinal's own copy of *Quatuor Conciliorum generalium* (ed. Jacques Merlin), Paris, 1524, and is generally considered to be the first known English bookplate.

Later heraldic material in the Museum includes a pictorial record of the *Coronation Pro-*

---

[1] Now in the collection of the Earl of Winchilsea, but placed on indefinite loan in the Department of Manuscripts, British Museum (*B.M. Loan 38*).

cession of Elizabeth I, Jan. 15th, 1559, (*Egerton 3320*) in which appears a view of Westminster Hall with the banquet in progress. The other items relate to state funerals: one (*Add. 5408*) is a roll with drawings of *Elizabeth's funeral*, 1603, by the hand of the great antiquary WILLIAM CAMDEN, and his use of pen and brown ink recalls that of the earlier herald-draughtsman mentioned above as having been associated with Sir Thomas Wriothesley; the other (*Add. 35324*) of processions copied in the early XVII century by two different hands (using respectively pen and ink with grey wash, and pen and ink with body-colour) after older drawings representing, among others, the funerals of Anne of Cleves (1557), Mary Queen of Scots at Peterborough (1587) and Sir Christopher Hatton (1591).

Allied in some respects to such heraldic material is a remarkable group of designs, in pen and ink and body-colour, for the *décor* of some tournament or pageant held by Henry VIII (*Cotton, Augustus III, 11 & 18–36, & I ii, 76*). Four are for royal tents, and the remaining twelve for the costumes and accoutrements of knights and foot-soldiers. These costume-studies recall in style a series of coloured drawings, one of which is in the Print Room (*1926–7–13–9*), recording the jousting exploits of the Emperor Maximilian under the *nom-de-guerre* of *Freydel*, which were published by Mr. Campbell Dodgson in the *Burlington Magazine*, XLVIII, p. 235, & LIII, p. 170. The *Freydal* drawings are said to be South German, and it is possible therefore that Henry's tournament drawings may also be by a South German hand. Other highly interesting costume figures of a rather later date (and of rather a different kind) are those made by the Ghent artist, LUCAS DE HEERE, to illustrate his *Corte beschryvinghe van England, Scotland ende Irland*, 1573–5 (*Add. MS. 28330*). They belong to the class of representations of costumes of the different nations of the world, which became very popular during the XVI and XVII centuries. To this same class of costume-drawing belong JOHN WHITE's famous studies of the natives of North America (pp. 40–8 & 53–4, Pls. I–VIII, 30–4 & 39–40); and White's connexion with De Heere's drawings will be noted in greater detail on p. 28. Another and even earlier draughtsman to have anticipated White in his ethnographical illustrations was JEAN ROTZ, a cartographer of Dieppe, who in 1542 made for Henry VIII a *Boke of Ydrographie* (*Royal 20 E ix*) which is embellished with many very lively vignettes of primitive life.

Another facet of antiquarianism in the XVI century is expressed in a conscious revival of interest in Romanesque book ornament—presumably an English extension of the universal Italianate adaptation of the Carolingian minuscule as a model for humanistic script. An early example of this neo Romanesque decoration occurs in *Add. 33376*, an *Exchequer Account Book* of 1531–2, in which there are initials in pen and ink on *ff. 9b–10b* and *78b* formed of winged dragons, twisted serpents and interlaced strapwork. Rather similar grotesque monsters are to be found in the penwork initials of *Harley 3739* and *Add. 37665*, two volumes of a *Chartulary of Waltham Abbey* which was actually written and decorated by the last Abbot himself, ROBERT FULLER, who reigned from 1526 to 1540. At a rather later date we find the manuscript of THOMAS OSBORNE's *The Perfect Worke and practice of Arethmeticke*, 1602 (*Harley 4924*), crudely enlivened in pen and ink and water-colour, with borders of interlaced and geometrical ornament and grotesque initials, which continue this taste. And, finally, there is a whimsical antiquary, JOSEPH LAWSON (perhaps a former Rector of North Barsham, Norfolk) who copied into his *Pennarum Nitor*, 1608–10 (*Add. 36991*), various specimens of medieval calligraphy and ornament including several (*e.g. ff.* 15 and 43) which again derive from Roman-esque sources.

II

XVII CENTURY

Figure-Subjects

It was only a hundred years or so after its original flowering that the Renaissance made its full influence felt on English art; and England at last drew abreast with Continental achieve-ment. The splendid role played by Charles I and the members of his Court in bringing about this new enthusiasm for, and sensibility towards, the Arts has been admirably set forth by Miss Whinney and Mr. Millar in their *English Art 1625–1714* to which the reader is here recommended for a full appreciation of the period.

But, considering the new contacts with Italy and the rest of Europe and the number of skilled artists of international repute, from Rubens and Van Dyck downwards, who visited this country during the first half of the XVII century, it is surprising how few drawings with English connexions outside the fields of portraiture and landscape, have survived from that period. In the present Catalogue figure-subjects—always excepting portrait-studies—are limited to a group of pen and ink sketches by INIGO JONES (Pls. 172–3) (some of which are reminiscent of Guercino, as are his masque designs at Chatsworth), to two works by the Baltic-German decorator and tapestry-designer FRANCIS CLEYN (Pls. 99 & 100) (one of them a study for part of a triptych certainly made in the Netherlands), and to two by Isaac Oliver's son PETER OLIVER (Pl. 240).

The second half of the century saw the introduction into England of a taste for Baroque wall-paintings and one of its early practitioners ISAAC FULLER (Pl. 130) is represented by two studies neither connected, however, with any of his known decorations. The foreigners, ANTONIO VERRIO (Pl. 267), LOUIS LAGUERRE (Pls. 193–4) and LOUIS CHÉRON (Pls. 89–94) brought a more sophisticated and Continental quality to the school which was to culminate in SIR JAMES THORNHILL who, however, belongs more to the XVIII century and whose drawings will in consequence be listed in the next volume of the Catalogue. CHÉRON, a true son of the Paris Academy and exponent of the style of the *Grand Siècle*, is particularly well represented in the Print Room by a long series of mythological subjects (among them some designs for ceilings at Boughton House, Pls. 89–92). Also within this category can be in-cluded SIR PETER LELY's crayon drawing of a nymph carried off by a satyr (Pl. 221).

Academic drawing in chalks also makes its first appearance in the later part of the period covered by the present volume, Sir Godfrey Kneller's Academy, the earliest of its kind in England, was founded in 1711, and evidence of its activities can be seen in the nude studies by, or attributed to CHÉRON (Pls. 95–8) who was a prominent member of the circle. But even earlier examples of academic drawing, not from the life but from sculpture and casts, are to be found in the work of CHARLES BEALE II (Pls. 66 & 81–4) and SIR JOHN BAPTIST MEDINA (Pl. 239).

Genre scenes and figures, which were such a feature of Dutch art in the XVII century, are occasionally to be met with in English drawing of the period. Nearest to their Netherlandish prototypes are the lively sketches of the amateur tavern artist FRANCIS LE PIPER (Pls. 223–4), and one of them, a man reading the *London Gazette* by candlelight, also looks forward, in handling and spirit, to Hogarth. FRANCIS BARLOW (Pls. 53, 56 & 59) and JAN WYCK (Pls. 295–6) illustrate the everyday life of the age of Evelyn and Pepys in the music room and the hunting field. Most unexpectedly attributed to the Bohemian topographer WENCESLAUS HOLLAR are two black-clothed ladies dramatically silhouetted against lamp-lit backgrounds (Pls. 163–4); and among other costume-studies of the time are two striking figures of Irish peasant women, in water-colour over red chalk, which are to be found not in the Print Room, but in an album formerly belonging to Sir Hans Sloane and now in the Department of Manuscripts (*Sloane 5253, ff. 3 & 4*). By MARCELLUS LAROON (Pls. 195 & 197–202), father of the better known Captain Marcellus Laroon III, are studies of men fencing and a lively series of characters from the *Commedia dell' Arte*.

It might not be too far-fetched to regard the miniatures of the late medieval manuscript as developing, by the XVII century, into carefully finished drawings intended as designs for engraved book illustration, though the latter are usually in pen and ink with monochrome wash. Good examples of such drawings will be found listed under BARLOW (Pls. 51–4 & 57–8), HOLLAR (Pl. 165) and MICHEL TOUROUDE (Pl. 255).

Portraiture

The great tradition of portraiture, as revived in England by HOLBEIN, found itself well-established in the XVII century with VAN DYCK and his successors. English portrait-drawing of this period, which is very fully represented in the Print Room's collection, can conveniently be divided into two categories:

    1. *Drawings used as part of the machinery of portrait-painting*

    2. *Drawings made as an end in themselves*

In the first category can be placed the life-size, or near life-size studies of heads which constitute the true face-painter's drawings, and would be one of the most important and intimate stages in the making of a portrait. These are usually executed in black and white chalks or coloured crayons; and we have already found their early prototypes in XV century Italy, and subsequently with Dürer, Holbein and the Clouets. An admirable example of the later XVI century, and also more closely related to the material about to be discussed, is Barocci's bearded young man (*1897–4–10–8*) which will be mentioned again below in connexion with another aspect of portrait-drawing. Coming into the XVII century we find Rubens evidently making use of the life-size face-drawing, as can be seen in two admirable studies in the Print Room of his first wife Isabella Brant (*H. 92*) and of her successor Hélène Fourment (*H. 96*). Oddly enough, his pupil SIR ANTHONY VAN DYCK, who closely followed his methods and who became one of the greatest figures in English portraiture, does not seem to have adopted this particular device; nor does Van Dyck's follower SIR PETER LELY appear to have used the life-size face-drawing. With the next in succession among English portraitists, however, SIR GODFREY KNELLER, this particular type of study played a very important part: he probably became acquainted with it as one of the initial stages of portrait manufacture when learning in Maratta's studio in Rome (excellent examples of large portrait heads by Maratta are in the Print Room, *1894–8–8–40* . . . *41* and *1952–10–11–11*). In the present volume are listed a number of large heads of this type by Kneller, including one of the Duke of Marlborough and another of his brother, Admiral Charles Churchill (Pls. 182–3). In the succeeding generation JONATHAN RICHARDSON I extensively used such studies, as will be seen in the next volume.

Another kind of portraitist's drawing is the complete figure-study in black chalk sometimes touched with white on blue-grey or buff paper. This would again have been executed by the master-painter with the prime intention of fixing the pose of the subject and relationship to his or her surroundings and within the confines of the canvas or panel.

The immediate originator of this type of study, as far as this country is concerned, was no doubt Rubens, as is evinced by his Pieter van Hecke (*H. 91*) and his Hendrick van Thulden (*H. 91a*). But one might look for earlier, though, of course, less direct prototypes in XVI century Italy, such as the figure of a nobleman by the Florentine Agnolo Bronzino (*1958–12–13–1*) which, however, is tighter in handling than are Rubens's figures. VAN DYCK follows his master Rubens, in an almost identically loose handling of the chalk, in studies for portraits made both before settling in England in 1632 (*e.g. H. 36, 37, 40, 42 & 43*) and after (pp. 573–5, Nos. 1–30). LELY picks up the Rubens-Van Dyck tradition in his splendid series of figures in the Garter Procession (Pls 203–12). But, oddly enough, only one other drawing of this type by him outside this series is apparently known; it is listed at No. 19 on p. 417. KNELLER seems occasionally to have used the whole-length or near whole-length figure-study, as in the three drawings listed at Nos. 12–14 on p. 391.

Other drawings emanating from the XVII century portrait painter's studio were in the nature of copies used in the process of turning out replicas. They would doubtless have been invaluable to the hard-pressed assistants employed on such work, and would have represented, in the portraitist's stock-in-trade, what were known in the XVI century as 'patrons' (i.e. patterns), a word frequently appearing in artists' wills of the period. These 'replica-drawings' are of two kinds. One consists of full-size tracings, usually in chalk on varnished paper, after the faces and hands of an original picture. Such use of varnished paper goes back, in England, at least to HOLBEIN's day; and in the National Portrait Gallery are a number of tracings in this manner from his drawings, presumably from his workshop. In the present Catalogue (p. 267, Nos. (99)–(114) & Pl. 87) is a group of tracings in red chalk, sometimes heightened with white, of heads and hands from KNELLER's studio: they belong to a large collection of material retained after his death by his chief assistant, EDWARD BYNG. The second kind of studio-copy is a complete figure-study corresponding in size with those described above as having been made by the master as a pose-drawing. The object of making such a drawing was no doubt twofold: to keep a record of a portrait as a guide to repeating the original; and to use it as a model for a ready-made pose when painting a new sitter. The medium is inevitably black chalk or pen and ink with grey or brown wash, heightened with white, on blue-grey or buff paper. The Sebastiano Venier attributed to Titian, in the Department (*Fawkener 5211–63*), in chalks on blue-grey paper, may perhaps be an early example of this type of drawing. The supposed self-portrait of CORNELIUS JOHNSON (Pl. 169) represents an early use of the same manner in England, and the tightness of the handling might well suggest a copy from an oil-painting. The lady listed as No. 33 on p. 423, this time in grey wash on grey paper, shows this kind of drawing in the LELY period. But the largest and most revealing group of these pose-drawings is contained in some six sketchbooks and an album once belonging to EDWARD BYNG who has already been mentioned as Kneller's principal assistant. These are fully described on pp. 206–58 of the present Catalogue. In two instances the style of these drawings was adopted by a certain JOHN BULFINCH (pp. 203–4), one of the first recorded copyists to make reductions of portraits for extra-illustrating historical books. And it was also used by engravers when making preliminary studies for their portrait-plates after oil-paintings. ABRAHAM BLOOTELING's Charles II and Earl of Sandwich (p. 556, Nos. 1 & 2) are studies for mezzotints by him after Lely, and have in themselves, both in size and appearance, much of the quality of mezzotints about them. This same affinity with the mezzotint is also noticeable in the case of so many pose-drawings of the type mentioned above which, however, are not known to be related to engravings. And, in this connexion, it is not inappropriate to add that a large number of mezzotints by Lely's and Kneller's engravers are known to have been shipped to the American colonies during the first half of the XVIII century and were used as pose-models by the early portraitists over there.

We now pass to the portrait-drawing as an end in itself. A characteristic development in England of this particular branch of the art during the XVII century was in the technique of pastel or crayons. The polychromatic use of chalks—black, red, white and other colours together—was evidently known in mid-XVI century France and Germany, as shown in several drawings of the Clouet school, in Jörg Breu I's bust of a young man (1895-9-15-970), and—a little later—in Barocci's elaborating the same medium in his bearded man already alluded to. Barocci's head, as already stated, was itself probably a face painter's drawing intended only as a preliminary study for an oil-painting; but the very technique of coloured chalks as displayed in it was eminently suited in its completeness—like that of water-colour—for use in producing a finished work of art. And so, indeed, the qualities of this technique came to be fully realized by portraitists of the succeeding century. In the 1620's the Roman Ottavio Leoni was making smallish half-length studies of his acquaintances which are noticeable for the liveliness of their expression, the faces being worked up in something very near the 'crayon' manner in red and white, occasionally with an additional colour, over a black chalk foundation (See in the Print Room the series 1854-6-28-85 . . . 7 and 1866-7-14-34). Leoni's heads were of such finished quality that they lent themselves for engraving and the artist himself executed a number of plates after them. In France the tradition of the Clouets descended, in the late XVI and early XVII century, to Nicolas Lagneau who produced many finished drawings of heads, in various sizes and various combinations of chalk worked up with stump. And by the second half of the century the small crayon drawing reached a full development with another Frenchman, Robert Nanteuil, who, like Leoni, was also a skilled portrait engraver. As we shall see presently, Nanteuil had a considerable influence on English portraiture, both in drawing and engraving.

The Netherlander LUCAS VORSTERMAN, who visited England in about 1624(?)–30, was doubtless influenced by Rubens in his handling of chalks as is shown by his studies of Sir Francis Crane and the aged Countess of Arundel (pp. 577–8, Nos. 1–4). It is interesting to note in these how near he comes—presumably quite fortuitously—to his Italian contemporary Leoni. At a later date, Vorsterman's fellow-countryman LELY, developing the same technique but in a freer and softer manner, and on a slightly larger scale, produced some charming and very characteristic crayon portraits (Pls. 213–6, 218 & 220), the style of which was closely imitated by such of his pupils and followers as MARY BEALE (Pl. 107), MICHAEL DAHL (Pls. 108–10), RICHARD GIBSON (Pls. 139–40) and JOHN GREENHILL (Pls. 141–2).

The Lely school of crayon drawing mainly used a technique of three chalks—black, red and white—on a background of buff paper, relying on the stump for modelling and for achieving a graduation and blending of tints. Occasionally, however, some of its members like GREEN-HILL, GIBSON, T. THRUMTON (Pl. 261) and HENRY TILSON (Pls. 262–3) extended their technique to working in a wider range of colours applied not only to the figure but also to the background. This new manner descended direct from Nanteuil; and it would be tempting to regard it as having been imported into England by WILLIAM FAITHORNE who, when exiled during the Commonwealth, appears to have worked with Nanteuil in Paris. Nanteuil, however, does not appear to have drawn in full coloured pastel until about 1659, some nine years or so after Faithorne's return home; but this influence on his English contemporaries can quite easily be accounted for by the close artistic ties between France and England during the later Stuart period. EDMUND ASHFIELD (Pls. 47–8) came nearest to Nanteuil's virtuosity and richness in the handling of coloured chalks. He was followed by his pupil EDWARD LUTTERELL (Pls 232–3), a less able draughtsman, whose productions are often marred by an unpleasant fierceness of colour. Lutterell was an early practitioner of mezzotint, and also applied something of that technique to crayon-portraiture by roughening the surface of a copper plate and using this as a ground on which to work up his chalks. The Museum possesses no good original portraits by Lutterell; but its representation of his work includes some adaptations of etchings by Rembrandt which have a certain curiosity as early instances of the interest for that master in England. Nanteuil's erstwhile friend FAITHORNE is, oddly enough, further away in style from him than are either Ashfield or Lutterell. He too worked in full-coloured crayons; but his subjects are smaller in scale, and he sometimes uses for his backgrounds a recognizable convention—not found with them—of an oval 'niche' in which his portraits are set (See Pl. 124). Like Lutterell he also experimented in drawing on copper roughened with a mezzotint rocker to hold the chalks, as in his little portrait of John Sturt (Pl. 123).

Interesting contemporary parallels with English XVII century pastels may be found in Eglon van der Neer's bust of his wife Maria Duchâtel (H. 1) and Bernard Vaillant's man in black (H. 1). In both cases the subjects are on a larger scale than is found in this country.

The style of the Ashfield-Lutterell school persisted well into the first half of the XVIII century in the hands of such draughtsmen as WILLIAM BELLERS, GEORGE WHITE and JOHN WOOTTON who will appear in the next volume of the present Catalogue. There is no doubt also that the fully developed pastel in colour came more and more to be used for making small replicas of life-size portraits for cadet members of a family—an alternative, in fact, to the small replica in oils like that by LELY of Sir Charles Cotterell reproduced in Pl. 219. Such a practice was indeed in being as late as GAINSBOROUGH, who himself made reduced copies in pastel (now respectively in the British Museum and the Victoria and Albert Museum) of his life-size portraits of the 3rd Duke of Montague (1951–1–29–1) and the 4th Earl of Chesterfield.

Another form of finished portrait-drawing was the monochrome miniature, variously executed in pen and ink, metal-point, black lead, fine black chalk, and black and dark grey wash. This has a very well-defined Northern origin which can be traced back to the XV century and which can be fully studied in the Print Room. The early Flemish school includes notable examples in silver-point by, or in the style of Jan van Eyck (*P. 1*), Roger van der Weyden (*P. 1*), and Gerard David (*P. 1*); while the German school is represented by Dürer (*W. 903–5*) and Hans Holbein I (*1854–6–28–113 & 1895—9—15—988*). In the later XVI century the Netherlandish school includes works by Goltzius (*P. 1, 10 & 12*), Crispin van de Passe I (*P. 2 & 3*) and Wierix (*P. 30*), and the French school is represented by Thomas de Leu (*1920–11–18–17*).

Passing into the XVII century, we find the tradition continuing unbroken, though black lead[1]—usually on vellum—replaces the older silver or other metal-point on prepared paper; and highly finished modelling in black or grey wash, over a chalk or lead foundation, also makes its appearance. In the Netherlandish schools we may single out the following as having produced portraits throughout the century in the different varieties of monochrome technique: BLOOTELING (p. 556, & H. 2 & 3) Jan de Bray (*H. 3 & 4*), CHRISTIAN HAGEN (p. 557, & H. 1), Koogen (*H. 3*), Mierevelt (*H. 1*), QUEBORN (p. 572, & H. 1 & 2), Cornelis Visscher (*H. 1 & 2*) and Jan Visscher (*H. 1*). In France Nanteuil brought the technique of drawing in black lead to a high degree of perfection (*1854–6–28–68 & 1895–9–15–948 . . . 9*); and as a latish instance of a German draughtsman using this same method we may notice Michael Thiel (*1928–10–16–8*).

As far as the present Catalogue is concerned, the two earliest examples of this type of portraiture listed are the Queen and her son attributed to HILLIARD (Pl. 11) and the young lady by ISAAC OLIVER (Pl. 12). The former is in pen and ink, and is rather reminiscent of Wierix's handling of that medium; the latter is in metal-point on prepared paper. In the first half of the XVII century SIR BALTHAZAR GERBIER (Pls. 133–4) also used Wierix's method of fine pen and ink; and, rather later, in the 1640's, we find HOLLAR occasionally attempting portraiture both in black lead and in pen and ink (Pl. 166). The second half of the century saw well established the taste for characteristic *ad vivum* miniature in black lead on vellum. Earliest of its exponents must have been the Danziger-Scotsman DAVID LOGGAN (Pls. 228–31) who had a Netherlandish training. Loggan was followed by a whole school of draughtsmen in this medium, including his direct pupil ROBERT WHITE (Pls. 286–9), T. DACKETT (Pl. 127) and THOMAS FORSTER (Pls. 126–7). Loggan's manner became immensely popular and was even imitated by amateurs such as EDWARD ARGALL (Pl. 45). Like other forms of XVII century portrait-drawing it survived well into the 1700's in the hands of JONATHAN RICHARDSON I, GEORGE VERTUE and THOMAS WORLIDGE.

FAITHORNE, like his friend Nanteuil, worked not only in coloured chalks but also in monochrome. His portrait of Sir Orlando Bridgeman (Pl. 123) in the latter style shows Nanteuil's influence, though he elaborates the Frenchman's handling of black lead by strengthening it with softly modelled washes of black or grey in a manner somewhat reminiscent of their Dutch contemporaries (*e.g.* HAGEN's portrait of Sir William Davidson listed on p. 557). The elder

---

[1] 'Black lead' (graphite or plumbago) was not generally used in Europe till the second half of the XVI century. As far as England is concerned, it was first discovered about 1550 in Borrowdale where a mine was subsequently opened.

JOHN FABER (Pls. 120–2), though he is known to have followed Loggan in his use of black lead on vellum, is only represented in the Department by examples in the older technique of pen and ink. As might be inferred, the miniature in monochrome was closely connected with the development of the engraved portrait; and frequently LOGGAN, WHITE, FAITHORNE and FABER made engravings from their *ad vivum* drawings.

Lastly, in this section, may be mentioned the characteristically intimate studies in red chalk by the younger CHARLES BEALE (Pls. 63–5 & 67–80). These appear to be unique in native English art of their period; and their importance in themselves and their relationship to contemporary Dutch portrait and figure-studies are fully discussed in Beale's biography and the note which precedes the series in the Catalogue (pp. 148–52). Only one other drawing listed below approaches them in feeling, the seated lady attributed to WILLEM WISSING, which is reproduced in Pl. 297.

Grotesque and Caricature

The grotesques of the Middle Ages descend through Jerome Bosch and Pieter Breughel to the well-known drolleries of Dutch art, so well expressed by such artists as Adriaen Brouwer, Egbert van Heemskerck and Isaac van Ostade. Their manner is strongly reflected in the drawings of FRANCIS LE PIPER (Pl. 223) who has already been referred to when speaking of *genre* subjects in England at this period. And, in passing, we may note a profile in pen and ink, obviously from the life, of a hook-nosed ecclesiastic in an academic 'mortar-board', in the collection of Sir Bruce Ingram, which is given to Isaac Oliver by Mr. Michael Ayrton in his *British Drawings*, 1946, p. 18, though the handling and date seem much nearer to Le Piper's. If this later attribution is correct, this sketch would form an interesting link between English drawing of this period and the more personal variety of caricature which came into being in Baroque Italy.

Another aspect of grotesque art is represented by the entertaining series of drawings of figures from the *Commedia dell' Arte* attributed to the Netherlandish *genre* painter MARCELLUS LAROON II (Pls. 199–202). They recall contemporary Parisian engravings of personages from the *Commedia* published by Nicholas Bonnart and also Laroon's own series of *The Cryes of the City of London*.

As early manifestations of political satire may be cited the Dutch anti-Cromwellian composition (p. 556, No. 1) and BARLOW's original designs for packs of playing cards illustrating the Rump Parliament, the Popish Plot, and the Meal Tub Plot (Pls. 61–2).

Natural History

The traditionally minute technique of water-colour for depicting natural history is found everywhere in Europe during this period, and in England is represented in the work of ALEXANDER MARSHALL, two of whose sprays of flowers, tied with ribbons, are reproduced in Pl. 237. A far more informal approach to plant life is seen in VAN DYCK's pen and ink sketch, made in this country, of *soufissels, nettels* [and] *gras* (p. 576, No. 34) and in some studies by an anonymous Englishman of bindweed (Pls. 43–4).

Highly finished water-colour was also widely used at this period for depicting animals and birds; but the only example in the Department of its use by an English artist of the time is MARMADUKE CRADOCK's studies of poultry and ducks (Pls. 105–6). BARLOW, who is the best known of native English draughtsmen of animal and sporting subjects, hardly ever worked in full colour, and confined himself almost entirely to brush drawings in monochrome wash often with characteristic fat pen outlines. In the presentation of his subject-matter he is more stylized and simplified than are his perhaps more naturalistic contemporaries; but nevertheless he infuses considerable liveliness into his figures (Pls. 51 & 54–6). He derives his style, of course, from the Netherlands, and his prototypes are touched upon in the biographical notice of him on pp. 96–7. Not unlike Barlow is the landscapist and sporting artist JAN WYCK, a native of Haarlem, who settled in England soon after the Restoration and collaborated with Barlow in the illustrations to Richard Blome's *Gentleman's Recreation*, 1686. Two of Wyck's original drawings for this book, both of sporting subjects, are reproduced in Pls. 295–6. Two other Anglo-Dutchmen of the time, JAN GRIFFIER and ABRAHAM HONDIUS are represented by good chalk studies respectively of a turkey-cock (Pl. 144) and of dogs (Pls. 167–8).

'Favourite' animals and birds have always been part of the portrait painter's accessories, so it is not surprising to find VAN DYCK making the admirable studies of a greyhound listed on p. 575, No. 25, which he introduced into his portrait of James Stuart, 4th Duke of Lennox. KNELLER, in his turn, also used animals to add a touch of graceful intimacy to his formal portraits, and for this purpose drew the hound and the doe, reproduced in Pls. 186–7, which appear in two of his groups of children. It is more difficult to determine into what kind of portrait his brother, JOHN ZACHARY KNELLER, might have introduced his hog (Pl. 189); but, at least, in the illustrations to the present Catalogue, this has been made to act as a not inappropriate companion to Sir Godfrey's sketch of the well-fed tavern-keeper Lebeck (Pl. 188). One of the assistants in the Kneller studio, MARCELLUS LAROON II, also produced the spirited horse's heads, still in Van Dyck's manner, reproduced in Pl. 196.

Landscape, Topography and Seascape

The XVII century saw the final emergence in England of two schools of draughtsmanship, one of pictorial topography, the other of pure landscape.

Of pictorial topography there is more to show, and a more continuous development. One of the first recorded Netherlandish topographers to come here in the XVII century was CLAUDE DE JONGH (Pls. 174–9). His English drawings, carried out with a very personal and recognizably curly calligraphy, are dated between 1615 and 1628; and he seems to have worked almost entirely in Kent. He obviously enjoyed portraying ancient and ruined buildings, and had a real feeling for the picturesque side of antiquity which anticipates the artists of a hundred and fifty years later. But as records of the buildings which they represent De Jongh's drawings are far from accurate. Two other Dutch topographers to visit England in the first half of the XVII century were CORNELIS BOL and ALEXANDER KEIRINCX, authors of little views respectively of a blockhouse at Gravesend (Pl. 46) (which was also drawn by De Jongh, Pl. 175), and of the Tower of London from Bermondsey (p. 571, No. 1). Both of these drawings are more true to life than are any of De Jongh's.

The period following on De Jongh's is, of course, dominated by the Bohemian WENCESLAUS

HOLLAR (Pls. 146–61), by whom there is in the Museum a large and very representative collection of drawings of both English and Continental views, as well as his Tangier series. His very precise and delicate touch goes right back in style to the first half of the XVI century, to the time of the 'Master of the Dover and Calais plats' (*Cotton, Augustus, 1 i, 22–3* &c.), with such drawings as WYNGAERDE's views of London and the Tudor royal houses in the Ashmolean, and HOEFNAGEL's Nonsuch and Hans Bols's Amsterdam (*P. 5*) in the British Museum marking the intermediate stage in the story. HOLLAR used both the human eye and the bird's-eye view points, with the former finally establishing the taste and pattern for the naturalistic topographical picture in England, and with the latter continuing, as he did in his Tangier series, the older tradition of the 'plat'.

HOLLAR had a largish band of followers. Among them were DANIEL KING with his dry delineations of ecclesiastical buildings done for Dugdale's *Monasticon* (Pl. 180), JOHN DUNSTALL with his naive little views of Bethlehem Hospital and West Hampnett Place (Pls. 117–18) both in a very old-fashioned technique of body-colour on vellum, THOMAS JOHNSON with his fascinating prospect of the Baths at Bath (Pl. 171), and WILLIAM LODGE (Pls. 225–7). Related to Hollar's views of Tangier are two panoramas by military engineers, one of Malaga by SIR MARTIN BECKMAN (Pl. 162*a*), the other of Tangier by THOMAS PHILLIPS (Pl. 162*b*). Both of these last-mentioned draughtsmen are better represented in the volumes of *The King's Topography* in the Map Room. But by far the most interesting personality in Hollar's school was FRANCIS PLACE, who comes nearest to Hollar in the delicacy and liveliness of his handling of pen and wash, as can be seen in the drawings reproduced in Pls. 246–9 and 252.

Working through the same period as the members of the Hollar school was a succession of visitors from the Low Countries, some of whom spent the remainder of their lives here, while others came only for brief sojourns. All made their contributions towards building up the English school of topographical illustration. Among the first to come was WILLEM SCHELLINKS (pp. 572–3, Nos. 1–16) who between 1661 and 1663 travelled extensively in Southern England and drew many panoramic views of places so far apart from each other as Dover, Fowey and Stonehenge.[1] He also recorded the Dutch attack on the shipping in the Medway in 1667 (Nos. 8 & 10); but there is no evidence that he actually witnessed the event. HENDRICK DANCKERTS, who finally established himself in England by 1666 and remained here till about 1678, also did long views, two being of St. James's Park (Pl. 111) and two of Badminton House (Pl. 112). And a third visitor in the 1660's must have been JACOB ESSELENS who executed a fine panorama of Canterbury listed on p. 557, No. 1. Rather later, by 1681, arrived LEONARD KNYFF who came to be well-known as the delineator of many bird's-eye prospects of the seats of the nobility and gentry, which were engraved by Jan Kip in his *Britannia Illustrata*, 1720. Knyff had two distinct styles of drawing: one seen in his views of Berkeley Castle (Pl. 191) in which he uses soft monochrome washes rather reminiscent of the work of his fellow-countrymen Jan Asselyn, Bartholomeus Breenbergh and Thomas Wyck; the other more precise, with every feature defined in pen and ink, as in his bird's-eye prospect of Whitehall and St. James's Park (Pl. 190) and his Old Palace Yard, Westminster (Pl. 192). A more sombre and richer use of pen and wash in the Rembrandtesque manner is exemplified

[1] P. H. Hulton, *Drawings of England in the Seventeenth Century*, in *Walpole Soc.*, XXXV, 1959.

in drawings of Westminster and Margate by the obscure, but easily recognizable M. VAN OVERBECK (p. 571, Nos. 1 & 2).

As a single instance of a French topographical draughtsman in England we may cite FRANÇOIS(?) GASSELIN, whose London views (Pls. 131–2) are characterized—as are his drawings in other collections—by most oddly spelt inscriptions in his native language.

Turning to pure landscape drawing, the other main category dealt with in this section, we may put forward, as the earliest and most outstanding examples of this, the fine series of studies by, or attributed to, VAN DYCK (p. 576, Nos. 32–8). It must be admitted that only one of these, the group of plants (No. 34) already mentioned above in the section on *Natural History*, can definitely be said to have been made in England. But a quite convincing case has been presented for including also in the master's English period the lovely woodland and meadow scenes, in body-colour on blue-grey paper, listed on p. 576, Nos. 35–8. Obviously related to these is a study of trees on a river bank, not in the Museum but formerly in the Heseltine collection,[1] which might well be intended for a view across the Thames from Lambeth Marsh with Old St. Paul's in the distance. In style these body-colours attributed to Van Dyck derive from Rubens—they come very near to Rubens's study, in the Hermitage, of trees on the bank of a stream.[2] And ultimately, no doubt, they descend through Rubens from Barocci, as shown by the latter's sketch of a wooded bank, touched in always with this same medium of freely used body-colour, in the Print Room (*Pp. 3–202*).

After Van Dyck, it is rare to find in England pure landscape-studies until the second half of the XVII century. The inspiration—and indeed the production—is still in the main Netherlandish, and a number of artists mentioned in the present Catalogue illustrate this: COLONIA (Pl. 103), DANCKERTS (Pls. 113–14), GRIFFIER (Pl. 143). SIBERECHTS (Pls. 158–9), VAN DIEST (Pl. 264), VAN DER VAART (Pl. 265), JAN VAN DER VINNE (p. 577, No. 1), and JAN WYCK (Pl. 290). What one may assume to be direct study from nature, in the Rubens-Van Dyck tradition, is represented by the glimpses of woodland by Colonia, Griffier and Van Diest, and by the studies of known localities—all of them very expressive of the English countryside—by Danckerts, Siberechts, Van der Vinne and Wyck. Siberechts and Wyck are also of considerable interest for the direct influence which they seem to have had on native English landscapists in water-colour such as WILLIAM TAVERNER and PAUL SANDBY. The picturesquely 'composed' scene, made up from elements in part observed, in part imagined, is shown in Van der Vaart's view of a quarry and cottage.

Three Englishmen, FRANCIS BARLOW (Pl. 52), THOMAS MANBY (Pls. 234–6) and FRANCIS PLACE (Pls. 250–1) derive much of their style from the Netherlands, the last two mentioned especially showing the influence of Jan Asselyn, Bartholomeus Breenbergh and Thomas Wyck (*See H., III, Pls. II, III, XXXI & LXVII*) in their treatment of contrasting light and shade on masses of old and broken masonry. In Barlow's case the Netherlandish influence is almost detrimental, as he relies too much on conventional Dutch sources for his landscape backgrounds and accessories for one to trust him completely as a delineator of the contemporary English scene. Nevertheless, in the two illustrations to *Aesop* reproduced in Pl.

---

[1] *Reproductions of Original Drawings in colours, from the collection of J.P.H.*, 1903, No. 22.
[2] M. V. Drobroklonsky, *Catalogue of Drawings of the Flemish School, in the Hermitage*, Leningrad, 1955, p. 137, No. 659, Pl. LXI.

52 one senses his keen appreciation of the bleakness of a winter's day and the movement of a tempest.

The French school of landscape drawing of Claude and Gaspard Poussin (Dughet) is represented in a solitary example by JACQUES ROUSSEAU (Pl. 254).

Finally, in this section may be included the work of the VAN DE VELDES, father and son (Pls. 269–85 & 290a) who founded the great tradition of the English sea-piece which lasted in an unbroken line at least down to the time of Turner. The Van de Veldes brought with them from Holland a style of marine drawing well established there, as can be seen in the work of their countrymen Ludolf Backhuysen, Simon de Vlieger and Reinier Zeeman, all three of whom are well represented in the Department. Vlieger is known actually to have been a friend of the elder Van de Velde's; and, in this context, we may compare the younger Van de Velde's sketches in pen and brown ink of ships, dated 1693, to show how these should be placed in a composition (p. 513, No. 53) with Vlieger's little studies of perspective in the same medium (H. 14).

Architecture and Sculpture

The representation in the present Catalogue of drawings relating to architecture and sculpture is of considerable interest. INIGO JONES dominated the second quarter of the XVII century, both as an architect and as an arbiter of taste, and it was his interpretation of the neo-Palladian style of architecture which is undoubtedly one of the most characteristic expressions of the English Renaissance. Listed here is an important series of plans and elevations connected with Inigo's great project for Whitehall Palace, together with another set of plans for another extensive building also thought perhaps to have emanated from his office (pp. 377–81, Nos. 11–18).

In the second half of the century SIR CHRISTOPHER WREN is represented by a sketch, very probably by his own hand, for a section of the dome of St. Paul's (Pl. 294). Also connected with well-known works by him, the Monument and Hampton Court, are two drawings which seem, from the high finish of their handling, to have been executed by assistants in his office: one shows an alternative treatment for the finial of the Monument, substituting a phoenix for the present familiar fire-ball (Pl. 293); the other is a design for a reredos in the Chapel at Hampton Court (Pl. 292). By Wren's contemporary, the soldier-architect CAPT. WILLIAM WINDE, is a design for a door at Hampstead Marshall (Pl. 291), the house which he largely built for the first Lord Craven. And a curious combination of the fashionable Franco-Netherlandish taste of the Wren school with pepper-pot towered 'Scottish Baronial' is shown in a bird's-eye elevation of the Palace of Holyrood House which was built to the designs of SIR WILLIAM BRUCE for Charles II (Pl. 42). The drawing is probably by one of Bruce's assistants. As an example of the later development of English Baroque architecture there are sumptuous ideas for yet another Whitehall Palace, this time for Queen Anne (Pl. 119), put forward by WILLIAM EMMETT who was also the owner of the projects by Inigo Jones for that same palace mentioned above.

Two distinguished English sculptors of the late XVII century, GRINLING GIBBONS and EDWARD PIERCE, also appear in the present Catalogue. By the former are studies for the statue

xl

in Roman armour of Charles II at Chelsea Hospital or its better-known successor, the James II outside the National Gallery (Pls. 135–6), and a design for an elaborate Baroque monument to William III and Queen Mary to be carried out in gilded bronze (Pl. 137). Pierce is represented by an even more exuberant project for a monument, also in marble and gilded bronze, to the second Duke of Buckingham (Pl. 242), and by three in black and white marble (Pls. 243–5) including alternative designs for the commemoration of a bishop. All of these sculptors' drawings are executed with a high degree of care and precision. They follow closely an archetype of drawing probably already known in Italy by the second half of the XV century—witness the studies after Antonio Rossellino's tomb of the Cardinal of Portugal (P. & P. No. 232)—and certainly well in use by the mid-1500's, as exemplified by Giovanni Antonio Dosio's design for a monument to Pope Paul IV (1861–8–10–34). In this context it may be noted that an early English collector John Talman (See p. 586) owned a large collection of sculptors' drawings, among which were both the design by Dosio and those by Pierce mentioned above. In their turn such drawings as these initiated a tradition in England which can be traced through RYSBRACK down to neo-classics like FLAXMAN and the BACONS. Another study for sculpture illustrated in the present Catalogue (Pl. 181) is of a rather different quality, being carried out in loosish chalk, more in the nature of a small cartoon. It is presumed to be KNELLER's preliminary design for his own monument subsequently adapted by Rysbrack for the marble now in Westminster Abbey.

———————

Volume II of this Catalogue will continue the history of drawing in England into the first half of the XVIII century, when art in this country already takes on a more native quality. In portraiture the gap between Kneller and Reynolds is bridged by JONATHAN RICHARDSON I, WILLIAM HOARE OF BATH and JOHN VANDERBANK. SIR JAMES THORNHILL, our only native Baroque painter, closes the school of decoration initiated by Verrio. The school of landscape in water-colour makes its way forward through GEORGE LAMBERT, SAMUEL SCOTT, JONATHON SKELTON, and WILLIAM TAVERNER, towards the Sandbys. Barlow's and Wyck's portrayal of country life and sport is continued by JOHN WOOTTON and JAMES SEYMOUR. GRAVELOT and PHILIPPE MERCIER effectively contribute the elegance of the French Rococo. And the early Georgian scene, as a whole, is vividly studied in both high and low life by THOMAS HIGHMORE, MARCELLUS LAROON III, and by the presiding genius of the age, WILLIAM HOGARTH.

EDWARD CROFT-MURRAY

ABBREVIATIONS

AQT.	Aquatint
B.M.	British Museum
ENGR.	Engraving or engraved
ETCH.	Etching or etched
H.L.	Half length
Inf.	Information
INSCR.	Inscription or inscribed
N.G.	National Gallery
N.G. Ireland	National Gallery of Ireland
N.M. Wales	National Museum of Wales
P.R.O.	Public Record Office
PROV.	Provenance
r.	*recto*
REPR.	Reproduction or reproduced
R.I.B.A.	Royal Institute of British Architects
T.Q.L.	Three quarter length
v.	*verso*
V. & A. M.	Victoria and Albert Museum
WCT.	Woodcut
W.L.	Whole length

PART I
XVI and early XVII CENTURY

ANON. FLEMISH DRAUGHTSMAN

Working early XVI c.

Probably from Antwerp. Worked in England, perhaps at Cambridge and Winchester

1. *Recto.* **STUDIES OF ARCHITECTURAL AND SCULPTURAL DETAILS.**
In the upper l.-hand corner, the plan and elevation of an English fan vault, with attendant window tracery. Below, a body draped in a cloak, with the r. hand showing; a man's head with a long pointed nose in profile to l., and the capital and spurs from the base of a Romanesque column.   **Plate 1**

Metal-point; 13·3 × 9·4 cm. (5¼ × 3¾ in.).

INSCR.: In the upper r.-hand corner, in metal-point, with the ingredients for some aromatic preparation, partly in Latin and partly in Flemish (or perhaps, rather, Low German), *sarmentum* [twigs or oil of juniper] / *draconardum* or *diacarardum* [not identified] / *abrotanum* [southern wood] / *hartstrauck* [resin smoke] / *binzenmarck* [rush-pith, this having been used occasionally as material for candlewicks in former times] / *bisanynce* (?) [not identified] / *claudicus* (?) [lame (?) (but this seems irrelevant)]; and across the centre, also in metal-point,

$$Dat\ De\ coninck\ gheft\ selft\ \frac{jjo6z}{jj6z}\ [z=2(?)].$$

bergstenen s / *daechs* (?) [That the King himself gives 1162 (corrected to 11062(?)) 'mountain stones' daily (?)] ; and in the upper r.-hand corner in ink, in a much later hand, *171*.

Verso. **STUDIES OF HEADS OF MEN AND WOMEN.** Five of warriors in variously shaped helmets; seven of old and bearded men in turbans or conical hats; three of other men in hats and hoods; and two of women in head-dresses with high curving peaks.   **Plate 2**

Pen and ink.

INSCR.: At the foot, in ink, in an XVIII c. hand, *tsie.*

PROV.: Lady Jane Dundas. Lady Anne Charteris. Mrs. V. Frere, from whom it was purchased by the B.M., 1951.
1951–8–4–1.

BIBL. & REPR.: Croft-Murray, *Flemish Sketchbook*, passim. Inf. from Mr. John H. Harvey, and Dr. I. Q. van Regteren Altena.

This drawing was originally *f.* 171 in a sketchbook used by a draughtsman of the Antwerp school. Stylistically the heads in pen and ink on the *verso* have some affinities

A   I   C.E.D.

with a sheet of heads by the Antwerp artist Jan de Beer (B. *c.* 1475: D. before 1536) in the Department (**1886-7-6-7**). They should also be compared with the studies in a dismembered sketchbook attributed to Gerard David (published by Sir Martin Conway in *Burlington Magazine*, XIII, 1908, p. 155, and by Prof. F. Winkler in *Pantheon*, III, 1929, p. 271).

The present leaf shows that the draughtsman was taking notes for future reference, and is of especial interest as he was taking them in England. The fan vaulting on the *recto*, distinctly a novelty to continental eyes, is of a late type, with rows of cinquefoil arched panels surmounted by fleur-de-lis cresting, which can be associated with the royal mason, John Wastell, in the eastern chapels of Peterborough Cathedral (*c.* 1496–1508), the central tower of Canterbury Cathedral (*c.* 1505), and the nave and side-chapels of King's College Chapel, Cambridge (1512–15). The vaulting in the present drawing does not fit exactly any of these, but the peculiar window-tracery which accompanies it, with its four-lobed compartments, has something in common with that of several of the side-chapel windows at King's College (though these are four-centred instead of two-centred as in the drawing), and the juxtaposition of this tracery with a Wastell type of fan-vault certainly suggests a possible connexion with this building. The main inscription has, too, a distinctly royal flavour, and suggests a personal gift by the King of building materials. The list of words relating apparently to an aromatic preparation does not seem to have any connexion with the architectural sketches.

The Romanesque details are thought to be S. English in character, and are very near to a capital and spurs found in the Hospital Church of St. Cross near Winchester. The capital is on the S. respond of the arch from the S. transept to the S. choir chapel. The spurs are respectively on one of the bases of the first pier to the W. of the crossing, and on one of those of the N.E. crossing pier.

The head-dresses on the *verso* are typical of the fantastic costumes in which the Antwerp Mannerists of the early XVI c. delighted to dress their biblical and classical personages in order to give them an exotic or eastern appearance. Here again, with the association of fan vaulting and Antwerp Mannerism, it would be tempting to see some connexion with King's College. The later glass there, in the windows of the choir and E. end, executed under the direction of the Flemish glazier, Gallyon Hoone of Southwark, between 1526 and 1531, certainly contains figures with these types of head-dresses—for instance, in the E. window there are several old men in conical hats or turbans and soldiers in fantastic helmets, and in window IX, S. side (Robert Willis and J. W. Clark, *The Architectural History of the University of Cambridge*, 1886, I, p. 506), one of the Maries at the Sepulchre wears a high curving peak and eye-veil. But none of the heads in the glass corresponds exactly with any of those in the drawing; and it must be remembered that such types are the common property of the Antwerp school.

It is difficult to say whether the sketches on the *verso* are copies after some existing composition or are original studies. Certainly the latter is suggested by the two heads in the lower r.-hand corner, which appear to be of the same man seen full face with the front of his head-dress arranged in two different ways; and, to the left of these, by the three bearded old men in conical hats, which also seem to be essays for a single figure in different positions. On the other hand, one of these very heads of old men, as well as another in a hood nearer the top of the page, is cut off sharp by a vertical line on the right, as if looking out from a window or from behind a pillar, thus giving the impression of having been copied from something else.

ANON. ENGLISH DRAUGHTSMAN

Working *c.* 1596

1. *Recto.* **YOUNG BACCHANALS CAROUSING.** **Plate 3**

Pen and brown ink, with brown wash;
10·7 × 19·8 cm. (4¼ × 7¾ in.).

Verso. **A *PUTTO* AND TWO STUDIES OF BEARDED HEADS.** A *putto* reclining beside an urn, in the attitude of a river god. Two bearded heads above and to the r. **Plate 3**

Pen and brown ink.

INSCR.: *Verso*, in the same ink as the drawing, *In my beginning*, and by the same hand, but less carefully written and in a different ink, with memoranda of payments . . . *pd in pt* [part] *12ˢ kept 20 to be pd the 9 of aprell* [April] / . . . *6 aperell be a*

byll / *the 15 of aprell 1597* [altered from 6], and *Bought of John bresenders the 9 of october 1596* / . . . *297* (?) *c.* . . . *12–0–0.*

PROV.: R. G. Mathews (*Lugt*, No. 2213). Dr. A Scharf, from whom it was purchased by the B.M., 1947.
1947–7–12–5.

ANON. ENGLISH FLOWER DRAUGHTSMAN

Working late XVI—early XVII c.

1. SKETCHBOOK. Now containing 37 leaves, filled mainly with drawings of flowers and other plants, and birds. Both in handling and colouring these have much in common with some of the drawings of plants in the album described on pp. 59–60 under John White, No. 78 (*ff.* 27–73). The present book belonged to a certain Ellen Power, and at one time the drawings themselves were even thought to be by her (*See f.* 2r.); but this seems unlikely, as the note of ownership on *f.* 37v. is in a different and somewhat later calligraphy than that of the inscriptions accompanying the drawings. Ellen Power was probably a relation of the naturalist Henry Power, many of whose papers passed to Sir Hans Sloane, Bart., who subsequently owned the book, and may therefore have acquired it from this source; he also owned another volume of drawings (Add. MS. 5298), ascribed this time to a 'Mr. Power' in the *Catalogue of Add. MSS. 4324–6 & 5015–5832*, which contains studies of tulips and (on *ff.* 125–32) copies of some of the drawings in the present book.

A subsequent and equally untenable attribution of the present drawings to the Huguenot artist Jacques le Moyne (*See* p. 26) was put forward by Henry Stevens of Vermont (*Stevens, Hariot,* p. 65), no doubt because at one time they were bound up with a copy of Le Moyne's series of wood-engravings, *La Clef des Champs,* 1586.

3

14·5 × 20·4 cm. (5¾ × 8 in.).

f. 1*r.* CRIMSON DAMASK ROSE AND BUD.
Water-colours and body-colours.

INSCR.: To the r. of the drawing, in ink, in a XVII c. hand, *Damask Rose / 1*, and above it, in a later hand, with former catalogue numbers, *Min. 34 (34* struck out) */ 273.* and *104* (struck out). At the top, in the centre, *Bibliothecæ Sloanianæ. Min : 273 :*, and at the bottom, in black lead, *5 Pa* and *50*.

f. 2*r.* [Added later] BLANK, except for inscription.

INSCR.: On a separate slip of paper attached to the leaf, in black lead, *Mem.ᵐ made / 12/55*, and in ink, *Min. 273 / Several Flowers, Fruits, Birds, Insects / painted in water colours by Mrs. Ellen Powers / It begins with the damask rose, & ends / with the Robin red Breast; should contain / 37 leaves, but wants leave 11ᵗʰ. / At the end is a loose leafe of figures of / solid bodies from the globe to the Cube.*

f. 3*r.* A SPRAY OF FILBERTS.
Water-colours and body-colours over black lead.

INSCR.: To the r., in ink, in a XVII c. hand, *Filberds / 2.*, and above it, *9Z*a.*

f. 4*r.* RED LILY AND BUD.
Water-colours and body-colours over black lead.

INSCR.: To the r., in ink, in a XVII c. hand, *Red Lillie /3.*

f. 5*r.* CRIMSON EGLANTINES AND BUD.
Water-colours and body-colours over black lead.

INSCR.: To the r., in ink, in a XVII c. hand, *Eagllentine /4 :*

f. 6*r.* CRIMSON ROSE CAMPION AND BUD.
Water-colours and body-colours over black lead.

INSCR.: To the r., in ink, in a XVII c. hand, *Rosecampion / 5 :*

f. 7*r.* COWSLIPS.
Water-colours and body-colours over black lead.

INSCR.: To the r., in ink, in a XVII c. hand, *Cowslip / 6 :*

f 8*r.* RED AND YELLOW PEARS ON A BOUGH.
Water-colours and body-colours over black lead.

INSCR.: To the r., in ink, in a XVII c. hand, *Peares / 7 :*

f. 9*r.* RED CARNATION AND BUD.
Water-colours and body-colours over black lead.

INSCR.: To the r., in ink, in a XVII c. hand, *Cloue gilliflower/ 8 :*

f. 10*r.* PRIMROSES AND A FROG.
Water-colours and body-colours over black lead.

INSCR.: To the r., in ink, in a XVII c. hand, *Primrose / 9 :*

f. 11*r.* A SPRAY OF GOOSEBERRIES.
Water-colours and body-colours over black lead.

INSCR.: To the r., in ink, in a XVII c. hand, *Goosberries / 10 :*

The leaf with drawing No. 11 has been torn out.

f. 12r. DAFFODIL AND BUD.
Water-colours and body-colours over black lead.

INSCR.: To the r., in ink, in a XVII c. hand, *Daffodilly* / 12 :

f. 13r. BLUE IRIS AND BUD.
Water-colours and body-colours over black lead. **Plate 4**

INSCR.: To the r., in ink, in a XVII c. hand, *Flowerdeluce* / 13 :

f. 14r. A SPRAY OF RED CHERRIES.
Water-colours and body-colours over black lead.

INSCR.: To the r., in ink, in a XVII c. hand, *Cherries* / 14 :

f. 15r. BORAGE AND BUD.
Water-colours and body-colours over black lead.

INSCR.: To the r., in ink, in a XVII c. hand, *Burrage* / 15 :

f. 16r. A BUNCH OF GRAPES.
Water-colours and body-colours over black lead.

INSCR.: To the r., in ink, in a XVII c. hand, *Grapes* / 16

f. 17r. PINK AND BUD.
Water-colours and body-colours over black lead.

INSCR.: To the r., in ink, in a XVII c. hand, *Pinck* / 17 :

f. 18r. A SPRAY OF BARBERRIES.
Water-colours and body-colours over black lead.

INSCR.: To the r., in ink, in a XVII c. hand, *Barberries* / 18 :

f. 19r. PURPLE COLUMBINE AND BUD.
Water-colours and body-colours over black lead.

INSCR.: To the r. of the drawing, in ink, in a XVII c. hand, *Colobine* / 19 :

f. 20r. A SPRAY OF HAZEL NUTS.
Water-colours touched with body-colour over black lead.

INSCR.: To the r., in ink, in a XVII c. hand, *Nutts* / 20

f. 21r. PINK CARNATION AND BUD.
Water-colours and body-colours over black lead.

INSCR.: To the r., in ink, in a XVII c. hand, *Carnation gi* [lliflower (?)] / 21 :

f. 22r. SINGLE MARIGOLD AND BUD HALF OPENED.
Water-colours and body-colours over black lead.

INSCR.: To the r., in ink, in a XVII c. hand, *Marygold* / 22:

f. 23r. CORNFLOWER OR BLUE-BOTTLE AND BUD.
Water-colours and body-colours over black lead.

INSCR.: To the r., in ink, in a XVII c. hand, *Bothell* / 23 :

f. 24r. A POMEGRANATE ON A BOUGH, WITH A SLICE FROM IT TO SHOW THE SEEDS.
Water-colours and body-colours over black lead.

INSCR.: To the r., in ink, in a XVII c. hand, *Poundgarnet* / 24 :

f. 25*r.* PURPLE AND YELLOW PANSY.
Water-colours and body-colours over black lead.

INSCR.: To the r., in ink, in a XVII c. hand, *Paunsey / 25 :*

f. 26*r.* CRIMSON FOXGLOVE.
Water-colours touched with body-colour over black lead.

INSCR.: To the r., in ink, in a XVII c. hand, *Foxefingers / 26 :*

f. 27*r.* WILD STRAWBERRIES, WITH FLOWER AND FRUIT.
Water-colours touched with body-colours over black lead.

INSCR.: To the r., in ink, in a XVII c. hand, *Strauberries / 27 :*

f. 28*r.* CRIMSON STOCKS AND BUDS.
Water-colours and body-colours over black lead.

INSCR.: To the r., in ink, in a XVII c. hand, *Stockgilliflower / 28 :*

f. 29*r.* BLUE AND PINK EVERLASTING PEA, WITH PEASCODS AND FLOWER.
Water-colours and body-colours over black lead.

INSCR.: To the r., in ink, in a XVII c. hand, *Peasscodes / 29*

f. 30*r.* MEDLARS ON A BOUGH.
Water-colours and body-colours over black lead.

INSCR.: To the r., in ink, in a XVII c. hand, *Medlers / 30 :*

f. 31*r.* A SPRIG OF HOLLY, WITH RED BERRIES AND LEAVES.
Water-colours and body-colours over black lead.

INSCR.: To the r., in ink, in a XVII c. hand, *Holly / 31 :*

f. 32*r.* ARTICHOKE.
Water-colours over black lead.

INSCR.: To the r., in ink, in a XVII c. hand, *Artichoak / 32 :*

f. 33*r.* A TITMOUSE PERCHED ON A SPRAY OF BERRIES, PERHAPS PYRA-CANTHA. **Plate 4**
Water-colours and body-colour.

INSCR.: To the r., in ink, in a XVII c. hand, *Titmouse / 33 :*

f. 34*r.* A PEACOCK STANDING TO R., WITH TAIL SPREAD.
Body-colours, touched with pen and ink and heightened with gold.

INSCR.: To the r., in ink, in a XVII c. hand, *Peacock / 34 :*

f. 35*r.* A YELLOW, GREEN, RED AND BLUE PARROT, PERCHED ON A BOUGH PECKING AT CHERRIES.
Water-colours and body-colours over black lead.

INSCR.: To the r., in ink, in a XVII c. hand, *Parrat / 35 :*

f. 36*r.* A GOLDFINCH PERCHED ON A THISTLE.
Water-colours and body-colours over black lead.

INSCR.: To the r., in ink, in a XVII c. hand, *Goldfinch / 36*

f. 37*r.* A ROBIN PERCHED ON A STUMP, WITH A FLY FLYING TOWARDS HIM
Water-colours touched with body-colour over black lead.

INSCR.: To the r., in ink, in a XVII c. hand, *Robinredbrest / 37*

f. 37v. BLANK, except for inscription.

INSCR.: At the top, in ink, *Ellen Power Booke.*

f. 38r. GEOMETRICAL SOLIDS, INCLUDING A CUBE, A SPHERE, A PYRAMID, A PRISM, etc.

Pen and brown ink, heightened with white (oxidized?) and gold; on two conjoined sheets.

PROV.: Ellen Power. Henry Power (?). Sir Hans Sloane, Bart., by whom it was bequeathed to the B.M., 1753.

Old Crown (L.B.1).

ANON. DUTCH DRAUGHTSMAN

Working in the early XVII c.

1. **WINDSOR CASTLE FROM THE N.E.** View over undulating ground to the Castle, the full extent of which is seen from the N. range of the Upper Ward, l., to St. George's Chapel and Julius Caesar's Tower, r. **Plate 5**

Black lead, with grey wash; 27·1 × 44·2 cm. (10⅝ × 17⅜ in.).

INSCR.: *Recto*, at the top, in black lead, *de Begraefenis der Coningen van Engelant* [the burial place of the Kings of England], and over the Round Tower, in brown ink, *Winchester Touer.*

PROV.: Ralph Bernal (Sale, Sotheby, 21:11:1855, Lot 450). Purchased at the Bernal Sale by the B.M., 1855.

1855-4-14-227.

BIBL. & REPR.: *Hind, Dutch & Flemish*

Drawings, IV, p. 132, No. 42, Pl. LXXIX, No. 42.

Considered by Mr. Hind to be near in style to Jan Wyck (*q.v.*), but probably somewhat earlier than Wyck's period, as the N. range of buildings on the l. are shown in their medieval state, before Charles II's reconstruction of 1674–82. The view should be compared with that by Joris Hoefnagel in Braun & Hogenberg's *Civitates Orbis Terrarum,* 1573–1618, Pt. II, Pl. 2, and may indeed be based on it. Some of the towers have been much exaggerated in height.

ANON. DRAUGHTSMAN, PERHAPS DUTCH

Working in the early XVII c.

1. **WESTMINSTER HALL, THE N. END WITH THE COURTS OF CHANCERY AND KING'S BENCH IN SESSION.** On the floor of the Hall, groups of men, some of them lawyers in their gowns, standing in conversation. In the background, the two courts in session on a dais, with the judges seated under canopies

and some of the spectators housed in a temporary two-tiered wooden gallery on the l. **Plate 6**

Pen and brown ink, with brown wash; an additional slip, presumably with an alteration on it, in the upper r.-hand corner; 29·7 × 19·6 cm. (11¾ × 7¾ in.).

INSCR.: *Recto,* in the lower l.-hand corner, *HOLLAR.*

PROV.: W. & G. Smith, from whom it was purchased by the B.M., 1848.
1848–9–11–748.

From the costumes, this drawing would date from the early part of the XVII c. The old attribution to Hollar cannot, of course, be maintained; on the other hand, from the point of view of topography, the view should be compared with Hollar's etching of Westminster Hall during the trial of the Earl of Strafford (*Parthey,* No. 551. Hind, *Hollar,* No. 91, p. 76), which shows much the same kind of wooden galleries as in the present drawing.

ANON. DRAUGHTSMAN, PROBABLY GERMAN

Working early XVII c.

The following twenty ornamental drawings for goldsmith's and jeweller's work were originally bound up with another group of designs, also for goldsmith's work, engraved by or after Paul Flindt, Hans Collaert, Daniel Mignot, Paul Birckenhultz and other German and Flemish masters of the XVI and early XVII c. Some at least of these drawings date from the reign of James I, whose arms appear in No. 1. No. 3, drawn by the same hand, includes the Prince of Wales's feathers and must therefore have been commissioned by one of James's sons, Henry or Charles, and must be dated between 1610, when the title was bestowed, and 1612 when Henry died.

It is probable that two or three different hands are involved in the drawings below. Many of them show a strong Germanic influence, in particular, that of Paul Flindt of Nuremberg (*See* Nos. 3, 4, 5, and 20) and a Germano-Slav inscription is found on the *verso* of No. 8. Another artist, possibly the author of No. 5 and therefore of others close to it in style (Nos. 4, 6, and 7), is Aegidius (Gillis) Loidt, the Danish goldsmith, a note on whom appears at No. 5 below.

1. **DESIGN FOR A SECTION OF THE RIM OF A DISH.** Neptune in a chariot, r., drawn towards the l. by a sea-unicorn and two sea-horses, and preceded by two mermaids playing on the harp and trumpet and a *putto* riding on a lion. Above, from r. to l.: a *putto* with a wreath, a sword and a crown; the Royal Arms of James I supported by *putti*; and a *putto* with a sword. **Plate 8 (b)**

Pen and light brown ink; fan shaped; 6·4 × 24·3 cm. (2½ × 9⅝ in.).

PROV.: E. Peter Jones of Chester, from whom it was acquired by the B.M. in exchange for duplicates, 1917.
1917–6–9–1.

BIBL. & REPR.: *Proc. Soc. Ant.*, 2nd Ser., XXIX, 1917, pp. 3–4, & Fig. 3. *Inf.* from Mr. J. F. Hayward.

This drawing and Nos. 2, 3, 9 and 14 and perhaps others are probably by the same hand.

2. DESIGN FOR A PANEL FORMING PART OF THE BOWL OF A CUP.
The upper part decorated with an oval panel containing the same mermaids with harp and trumpet who appear in No. 1. Below, grotesque ornament with a mask.

Plate 7 (a)

Pen and light brown ink; cut to the outline; 11·9 × 7·4 cm. (4⅝ × 2⅞ in.).

PROV.: As for No. 1.
1917–6–9–2.

BIBL.: As for No. 1.

See note to No. 1.

3. *Recto.* DESIGN FOR A KNIFE. The handle surmounted by a royal crown and decorated with a festoon containing a shield of arms left blank, a mask, a pair of kettle-drums, and the Prince of Wales's feathers.

Plate 8 (a)

Pen and light brown ink; 22 × 3 cm. (8⅝ × 1⅛ in.).

Verso. A DIAGRAM AND INTERLACED LETTERS.

Pen and light brown ink.

INSCR.: In ink, near the r.-hand edge, *Esk . . . flind* (?) . . . (not fully legible).

PROV.: As for No. 1.

BIBL. & REPR.: As for No. 1, & Fig. 4.

The drawing on the *recto* is the only known

English design for a knife of this early period. The decoration would be applied to the handle in translucent enamel and gold or silver and niello. The word *fllind* (?), contained in the inscription on the *verso*, may possibly relate to Paul Flindt (*Fl.* Nuremberg, 1601–about 1618), the German ornamental engraver. (*See* also note to No. 1.)

4. PANEL OF GROTESQUE ORNAMENT PROBABLY FOR THE BOWL OF A CUP.

Black lead; the lower corners cut off; 8·2 × 10·6 cm. (3⅛ × 4⅛ in.).

PROV.: As for No. 1.
1917–6–9–1.

BIBL.: As for No. 1.

Similar in style to No. 7.

5. DESIGN CONSISTING OF ALTERNATIVE SECTIONS FOR THE FOOT OF A STANDING CUP. Decorated with interlaced strapwork and fruit in the manner of Paul Flindt.

Plate 7 (b)

Black lead; trapeze-shaped; 8·9 × 13·4 cm. ($3\frac{1}{2} × 5\frac{1}{4}$ in.).

INSCR.: *Recto*, on the foot of the cup, in black lead, *loidt*.

PROV.: As for No. 1.

1917–6–9–5.

BIBL.: As for No. 1.

From the inscription *loidt* it would appear that this cup was designed by the well-known Danish goldsmith Aegidius (Gillis) Loidt (*Fl.* 1569–77) (*See Olrik*, p. 15, No. 10, *Jones*, pp. 223–31. *T.-B.* XXIII, 1929, p. 333 (with *Bibl.*)). Olrik suggests, but without giving his reason, that Loidt may have been of English origin, in which case it is possible that his name was in reality Giles Lloyd, but there is nothing in existing records of English goldsmiths to confirm this. The name could also, on the other hand, derive from the S. Jutland village of Løjt. Loidt, whose mark is a shield containing the initials *A E*, became a master goldsmith in Copenhagen in 1569, and in 1577 made the large silver-gilt cup, known as the Rosenblomen (now in the National Museum, Copenhagen), for presentation to the Crown Prince Christian (later Christian IV) on his christening. Other works by, or attributed to Loidt, are a cup (now used as a chalice) in the church at Kävling in Sweden, and a plaque of copper *repoussé* in the Historiska Museum in Stockholm. *Inf.* from Mr. Erik Lassen.

6. DESIGN FOR THE BOWL OF A CUP in the form of a lady's skirt of the early XVII c. The front indicated by frogged ornament impressed in the paper. On the l. side, floral ornament representing embroidery.

Black lead and pen and ink; cut to the shape of the bowl; 15·4 × 13·6 cm. (6 × $5\frac{3}{8}$ in.).

INSCR.: *Recto*, along the l.-hand edge, in ink, a sentence in Latin (?) containing the word *Norinbirgiensis* (?).

PROV.: As for No. 1.

1917–6–9–6.

BIBL.: As for No. 1.

The rest of the cup (not shown) would consist of the bust and head of a woman, and when empty would stand bowl downwards. The design is of a teutonic type (*See* Pls. III and IV of Flindt, *Entwürfe*).

7. DESIGN FOR A EWER. Chased and embossed with figures of harpies and grotesques.

Black lead; oval; 15·5 × 8·7 cm. ($6\frac{1}{8} × 3\frac{3}{8}$ in.).

PROV.: As for No. 1.

1917–6–9–7.

BIBL.: As for No. 1.

8. DESIGN FOR THE INSIDE OF A BASIN. Chased and embossed with swags of birds and fruit, and on the rim with insects. In the upper l.-hand corner, a greyhound (?) springing to r.
Plate 10

Pen and ink with washes of brown and grey; made up in the upper r.-hand corner; 16·1 × 15·4 cm. ($6\frac{3}{8} × 6$ in.).

INSCR.: *Verso*, with mutilated notes in what appears to be a mixture of Germanic and Polish or Czech dialects in which the

following words or phrases may be indenti-
fied: *Seyr* [cheese (?)], *maso* [meat], *peczene*
[baked], *knau wertutz wysen* [*genau wer tuts
wissen* (?)], *kanknau ysset yskut werkons wysen
obs kut ist* [*kann genau—ist gut Werkens ob das
gut ist*(?)].

PROV.: As for No. 1.
1917-6-9-8.

BIBL.: As for No. 1.

9. *Recto*. DESIGN FOR A CUP, A PENDANT, AND A DECORATIVE TROPHY.

The cup engraved with grotesque ornament including the figure of a harpy. The
pendant composed of two hearts surmounted by a royal crown, and a cupid flying
with a bow and arrow. The trophy composed of a shield, arquebus, banner and
drum, surmounted by a grotesque swag of drapery with monsters swinging on it.

Plate 9

Pen and ink, with washes of grey and light
brown; made up in the upper and lower
r.-hand corners and in the l. margin;
16 × 14·9 cm. (6¼ × 5⅞ in.).

Verso: AN ORNAMENTAL DESIGN WITH THE PRINCE OF WALES'S FEATHERS.

Pen and brown ink.

PROV.: As for No. 1.
1917-6-9-9.
BIBL.: As for No. 1.

The trophy represented on the *recto* is
English in form and similar to the work of
Arnold Lulls, the Dutch goldsmith and
jeweller at the Court of James I. This is
probably by the same hand as No. 1.

10. *Recto*. STUDIES OF HANDS, A HORSE, THE PLAN AND BIRD'S-EYE ELEVATION OF A CRUCIFORM JACOBEAN BUILDING, AND THE ARMS OF THE CECIL FAMILY SURROUNDED BY THE GARTER AND SURMOUNTED BY A CORONET, SUPPORTED BY WINGED BOYS PLAYING ON THE HARP AND VIOL.

Black lead; 16·4 × 17·8 cm. (6½ × 7 in.).

The arms may be those of Thomas, 1st
Earl of Exeter or his younger brother Robert,
1st Earl of Salisbury (both created 1605.)

Verso: STUDY OF A CROWNED WOMAN, AND DETAILS OF JACOBEAN CRESTING WITH BLANK SHIELDS.

Pen and light brown ink with grey wash, and
black lead.

PROV.: As for No. 1.
1917-6-9-10.

BIBL.: As for No. 1.

11

11. *Recto.* **A BLANK SHIELD SURMOUNTED BY A HELMET, A NYMPH SEATED ON A ROCK (?) BELOW A HERALDIC HELMET, AND A HERALDIC LION'S HEAD.**

Black lead, with grey wash; made up in the lower r.-hand corner; $16 \cdot 1 \times 14 \cdot 2$ cm. ($6\frac{3}{8} \times 5\frac{5}{8}$ in.).

Verso: **JUSTICE.**

Pen and ink with grey wash.

BIBL.: As for No. 1.

PROV.: As for No. 1.
1917–6–9–11.

12. *Recto.* **FORTUNA POISED ON A WINGED GLOBE, HOLDING A WIND-FILLED VEIL.**

Black lead; made up in the l. and r. margins; $16 \cdot 7 \times 8 \cdot 8$ cm. ($6\frac{5}{8} \times 3\frac{3}{8}$ in.).

Verso: **AN INLAID OCTAGONAL TABLE.**

Pen and brown ink.

BIBL.: As for No. 1.

PROV.: As for No. 1.
1917–6–9–12.

The figure of Fortuna is a characteristically Germanic convention.

13. DESIGNS FOR CANDLE-BRACKETS. The arm of the upper bracket foliated and incorporating a crowned eagle, the lower of similar form but incorporating a lion with the Imperial Crown.

Pen and brown ink with grey wash, and black lead; made up in the lower r.-hand corner; $18 \cdot 8 \times 12 \cdot 1$ cm. ($7\frac{3}{8} \times 4\frac{3}{4}$ in.).

BIBL.: As for No. 1.

These designs are of unquestionably German character.

PROV.: As for No. 1.
1917–6–9–13.

14. *Recto.* **A NARROW PANEL OF GROTESQUE ORNAMENT.**

Black lead; $15 \cdot 3 \times 2 \cdot 5$ cm. (6×1 in.).

Verso: **DESIGN FOR A PENDANT.** Two winged hearts pierced by arrows on an anchor.

Pen and brown ink.

BIBL.: As for No. 1.

PROV.: As for No. 1.
1917–6–9–14.

This design is probably by the same hand as No. 1.

15. DESIGN FOR A CUP WITH A GADROONED BOWL.

Pen and brown ink; 7·3 × 4·1 cm. (2⅞ × 1⅝ in.).

PROV.: As for No. 1.
1917–6–9–15.

BIBL.: As for No. 1.

This design is possibly intended for manufacture in glass and appears to be a rather weak copy.

16. DESIGN FOR A STANDING CUP AND COVER. The bowl engraved with figures of classical warriors supporting a shield.

Black lead; the lower corners cut off; 8·5 × 5·7 cm. (3⅜ × 2¼ in.).

PROV.: As for No. 1.
1917–6–9–16.

BIBL.: As for No. 1.

17. PANEL OF GROTESQUE ORNAMENT.

Rubbing from a plate of pierced ornament; 8·3 × 6·5 cm. (3⅜ × 2½ in.).

PROV.: As for No. 1.
1917–6–9–17.

BIBL.: As for No. 1.

The shape, type and rivet holes at the sides suggest that the plate may have formed a book cover.

18. DESIGN FOR THE RIM OF A DISH. Three oval compartments: the central one upright, containing a coat of arms flanked by the initials *R* and *H*, (quarterly, 1 and 4 a bend, 2 and 3 a fleur-de-lis. A crest on a coronet, between two buffalo's horns, a demi-man wearing a cap and holding a scimitar, charged on the breast with a fleur-de-lis) the l.-hand one, oblong, containing the story of Daedalus and Icarus; and the r.-hand one, also oblong, the story of Hero and Leander (?). The whole topped by swags of drapery and fruit.

Pen and grey wash; fan-shaped; on two conjoined slips; 7·2 × 24 cm. (2⅞ × 9½ in.).

PROV.: As for No. 1.
1917–6–9–18.

BIBL.: As for No. 1.

The coat-of-arms, though not identified, is certainly German.

19. HERALDIC AND OTHER DETAILS. A lion rampant. A shield with a lion rampant, surmounted by a coroneted helm. Two shields conjoined: 1 quarterly and 4 per fess, a bordure below, 2 and 3 an eagle displayed; 2 quarterly, in each quarter a lion rampant. A scrolled oval shield, surmounted by a helm crested with a lion sejant. A figure of Minerva in a niche. A winged figure in a niche and a circular foliated ornament.

Pen and ink, with washes of brown and grey; 15·5 × 16·5 cm. (6⅛ × 6⅜ in.).

PROV.: As for No. 1.
1917–6–9–19.

BIBL.: As for No. 1.

The details of heraldry are certainly Germanic.

20. BOYS SPORTING WITH MILITARY EMBLEMS AND SWAGS OF DRAPERY.

Pen and ink, with washes of brown, blue, green and pink; made up in the upper l.- and r.-hand corners; 17·2 × 18·2 cm. (6¾ × 7⅛ in.).

PROV.: As for No. 1.
1917–6–9–20.

BIBL.: As for No. 1.

The execution of the figures is closely similar to that of Pl. XVIII in Flindt, *Entwürfe*.

HILLIARD, NICHOLAS

[HILLYARDE, HILDYARD, HILLIART, HELIARD, HELIER, BELIART, OEILLARDE]

B. 1547 : D. 1619

Limner and goldsmith

Born at Exeter, son of Richard Hilliard, goldsmith (and High Sheriff of that city) and Laurence, daughter of John Wall, goldsmith of London. Apprenticed to a London jeweller and goldsmith, perhaps his grandfather. The art of limning or miniature painting being often at this period complementary to the jeweller's craft, it was natural that Hilliard should have practised it at an early age, and a self-portrait dated 1560 (Welbeck Abbey) shows an unusually precocious talent. It is executed in water-colours and body-colours on vellum, the traditional medium for portrait miniature used by Hilliard, his contemporaries and immediate successors. By 1569 was already a person of standing in his craft, when a foreign goldsmith, Gualter Reynoldes, who 'cam for to increase his knowledge in that arte' was taken in that year 'under bayle of Nicholas Hilliard, goldsmith'. Became a member of the Goldsmiths' Company and is first recorded in its minutes, on Feb. 23rd, 1570–1, in connexion with a certain 'Agnes Rutlinger' (probably the wife of Jan Rutlinger [*See* below]) who 'promised to delyuer unto Thomas Clerke [a Warden of the Company]

a book of portraitures within this sennyght wholle and perfect, which is now in ye handes of Nicholas Helliard'. Was associated with the goldsmith-engravers Dericke Anthony (D. 1599) and Jan Rutlinger (D. 1609), gravers to the Mint, the former of whom lived as did Hilliard in St. Foster's Parish, Cheapside, in the 1560's. Was appointed, at some date unknown, goldsmith and limner to Elizabeth, and painted before 1570 the most youthful extant portrait of her as Queen (Welbeck Abbey), which in style recalls the traditional royal portraits done by English limners for charter headings from the end of the XV or beginning of the XVI c. His earliest dated portrait of her is that of 1572 (N.P.G., No. 108). Exchequer accounts for 1573 record Hilliard as having received on Jan. 9th a grant of reversion for a lease and on Oct. 11th the sum of £100 under a warrant of the Privy Seal. As the royal goldsmith, may have been the creator of the famous Armada and Phoenix Jewels. Also practised woodcut, a fact less well known as so little of his work in this medium has been identified. Cut two small portraits in wood of Louis de Gonzague, Duke of

Nevers (B. 1539: D. 1595) and his wife, for a small quarto volume, *Fondation du Duc de Nivernois*, printed in Paris in 1579. According to a letter written to the duke on Feb. 20th, 1577/8, probably by his secretary, Blaise de Vigenère, two other artists, a Frenchman and a Fleming, had previously failed in this task. Also probably executed or designed the woodcut title-borders of the *Psalmes of David*, 1571, and the *Common Places . . . of Peter Martyr*, 1574. In 1576 married his first wife, Alice Brandon, daughter of Robert Brandon, goldsmith and chamberlain of London, and according to the registers of St. Vedast's, Foster Lane, had at least seven children by her up to 1588. Her date of death not known. Visited France with her in 1577–8 'to increase his knowledge by this voyage' and 'to get a piece of money from the lords and ladies.' Quickly gained a considerable reputation to judge from the eulogy of Blaise de Vigenère. Also found a patron in the Duke of Alençon. In a list of the latter's court servants, Hilliard is described as 'Nicolas Beliart, peintre anglois, valet du chambre du duc d'Alençon en 1577', with a salary of 200 livres. Established contact with writers and artists at the French court such as Ronsard, Georges de Gand, portrait painter to the French queen (perhaps identifiable as Joris van der Estraten) and Germain Pilon (B. *c.* 1535: D. 1590), the royal medallist and limner, whose work at this time shows affinities with that of Hilliard. Hilliard's chronic lack of thrift and the imminent birth of a son probably accounted for his return to England in 1578. His portraits at this time, such as that of his wife (1578) and those of the Duke and Duchess of Nevers, previously mentioned, reflect the influence of François Clouet and his school which persists throughout his finest period during the 1580's. In 1583–4 a draft patent made George Gower Sergeant-Painter, but reserved for Hilliard the exclusive right of painting the Queen 'in small'. In the following year designed and engraved the

Queen's second Great Seal in conjunction with Derick Anthony and received in reward the grant of the manor of Poyle, Middlesex, in 1587, together with the lease of other properties. In spite of numerous grants and commissions, including an annual pension for life of £40 in 1599, complained more than once to Elizabeth's secretary, Robert Cecil, of financial difficulties. In 1598 was obliged to solicit the Queen's support for the renewal of the lease of his house in Gutter Lane, offering on July 4th, 1600, in part-payment to the Goldsmiths' Company, as landlords, 'a faire picture of the queen in greate', which must mean that he undertook life-size portraiture in oil, though no portrait in this medium can now be attributed to him with certainty. His reputation shown by his being compared to Raphael in the introduction to Richard Haydocke's translation of Lomazzo's *Trattata dell' Arte della Pittura, Scultura ed Architettura*, 1598. About 1600, was persuaded by Haydocke to write the *Treatise concerning the Arte of Limning*, the first work of its kind in English, important from a technical point of view and for the light it throws on Hilliard's career and personality. His training as a jeweller shown in his classification of colours, his preference for clear bright pigments and his care to avoid shadow which caused him to paint the Queen in the 'open alley of a goodly garden'. Speaks of meeting and conversing with such important figures of his time as Sir Philip Sidney, Sir Francis Bacon, Sir Christopher Hatton, and Queen Elizabeth herself. Laments the inability of the native-born artist to succeed without private means, and cites as instance John Bossam, 'the most rare English drawer of story works', who was forced to give up painting to become 'a reading minister'. In 1600 the Queen issued a new warrant for a third Great Seal to be designed jointly by Hilliard and Charles Anthony (D. 1615) and on which the former was still working in 1603 when the Queen died. Continued in his position as court limner under James I, although Isaac Oliver, his most talented pupil, had begun to supplant him in fashionable opinion. His later miniatures, with one or two notable exceptions, do not have the high qualities of his earlier work. In 1610–11 was employed by the first Earl of Salisbury as jeweller and limner, and was paid £10 for 'iii limned pictures maid for my lady Clifford'. As late as 1617, received from James I the exclusive right 'during the terme of 12 yeares . . . to invent, make, grave, and ymprint (and sell) any picture or pictures of our image or other representation of our Pson, . . . as well in paper and parchment as in any other thing or things whatsoever fitt and necessary for shewing of his skill and invention in this art or mystery . . .'. Was in the same year imprisoned in Ludgate Gaol for failing to meet a debt for which he had given surety. Also in 1617, brought an action against his creditor, William Pereman, in the Court of Requests. Died two years later, aged 72, in the parish of St. Martin-in-the-Fields, where he is buried. His other pupils and followers included his son Laurence (by his first wife Alice) who succeeded him in his position as court limner, Sir William Segar and his brother Francis, and Rowland Lockey (*Fl.* 1590–8). Commented to Robert Cecil 'I have taught divers both strangers and English'. Later members of the Hilliard family, Thomas, Edward and Henry Hilliard, appear in the minutes of the Painter-Stainers' Company between 1640 and 1691.

BIBL.: *Buckeridge*, pp. 383–4. *Walpole*, I, pp. 171–6. *D.N.B.*, 1891, pp. 429–30 (with *Bibl.*). *Norman, Hilliard. Norgate*, pp. 20, 34, 40, 72 & 90. *T.-B.*, XVII, 1924, p. 97 (with *Bibl.*). *Long*, p. 207. *Vasari Soc.*, Ser. II, Pt. XI, 1930, No. 11. *McKerrow & Ferguson*, pp. XXXVI & XXXVII, pp. 116–18 (No. 133) and pp. 127–8 (No. 148) and Reps. No. 133 and 148. *Winter, passim. Pope-Hennessy. Winter, Hilliard. Blakeston, Documents. Auerbach, Hilliard, Studies. Pope-Hennessy, Hilliard. Vertue, Index,* pp. 111–12. *Vertue*, VI, pp. 47–9. *Reynolds, passim. Woodward*, pp. 15–16. *Auerbach, passim. Inf.* from Miss E. Auerbach. *Piper, Lumley Inventory*, pp. 299–300.

1. DESIGN FOR THE OBVERSE OF QUEEN ELIZABETH'S GREAT SEAL OF IRELAND.

W.L. figure of the Queen, seated in a cushioned X chair, to front. Crowned and holding a sceptre, tipped with a fleur-de-lis, and an orb, her mantle being held up on either side by hands appearing from clouds. On the l., a scrolled shield bearing the Irish harp, and on the r., another bearing three crowns *in pale* (the old arms of Ireland). The Queen's head framed in a semi-circular shell-like canopy, flanked by crowned Tudor roses also in semi-circular arched compartments. Another Tudor rose in the centre of her footstool. The whole composition enclosed by a circular band inscribed *ELISABET D.G. ANGLIE FRAN. ET HIBERNIE REGINA* (the letters barely legible). **Frontispiece**

Pen and black ink, strengthened with wash, over black lead, on vellum; 12·9 × 12·9 cm. (5⅛ × 5⅛ in.); diam. 12·7 cm. (5 in.).

PROV.: Peter Gellatly. Mrs. Peter Gellatly, by whom it was presented to the B.M., 1912–7–17–1.

BIBL. & REPR.: *Dodgson, Irish Seal.*

Vasari Soc., Ser. I, Pt. III, No. 32. *Farquhar. Long*, p. 209. *Jenkinson*, pp. 314–23. *Winter*, front cover & p. 2.

The attribution to Hilliard of this drawing has been unreservedly accepted. Mr. Dodgson regards it definitely as a design for the Great Seal of Ireland. Miss Farquhar (*op. cit.*, p.

347), on the other hand, whilst accepting this view, also offers the alternative that it might be a rejected design for Elizabeth's second Great Seal of England, which of course is known to have been executed by Hilliard; and quotes in support of this the original royal letter, dated 15:vii:1584 (P.R.O., XXVIII, No. 86), charging Derick Anthony, graver of the Mint, and Hilliard to emboss patterns 'for a great Seale according to the last pattern made upon parchment by you our servant Hellyard delivered unto us . . .'. The present drawing, however, bears two essentially Irish emblems, the Harp (adopted by Henry VIII as the official arms of Ireland) and the Three Crowns (the exact significance and origin of which are unknown, though they were in use as the arms of Ireland for many hundreds of years and were confirmed as such by Edward IV). These would point to the first identification as being the correct one.

The design does not appear to have been carried out. Sir Hilary Jenkinson (*op. cit.*, p. 319) mentions that Elizabeth had two Great Seals for Ireland: the first, in use from at least 1569, being replaced in 1592 by the second which is so dated on the reverse. Both differ considerably from, and indeed are much inferior to, Hilliard's drawing, though they possess certain features in common with it: the devices of the Harp and the Three Crowns in both Seals, and the shell-like canopy behind the Queen's head in the second. But these features had already been introduced into the Seals of Edward VI and Mary I (*Jenkinson*, Pl. LXXXV (5), LXXXVI (4) & LXXXVII (4)), and cannot be regarded as an innovation due to Hilliard's design: rather do Elizabeth's Irish Seals

appear to derive direct from these earlier models.

The present drawing has, not unnaturally, far more in common with Elizabeth's second Great Seal of England which, as already mentioned, was designed by Hilliard in 1584 (*Farquhar*, Pl. XXIV). In fact, the two coincide so closely in general composition and in the arrangement of accessories, that one is even tempted to ascribe the drawing to about the same date, especially when one takes into account that it is executed on parchment, as was the 'pattern' for the English Seal, mentioned in the Queen's letter quoted above. In both Elizabeth is shown as seated to front in an X chair, whilst on either side of her are Tudor roses and hands holding up her mantle which issue from clouds. Even the details of her dress (in particular the folds of her farthingale) are very similar. In the English Seal, in place of the Harp and the Three Crowns on either side of the Queen, are the Royal Arms. It is interesting to note that the present drawing apparently shows the Queen as a much younger woman than she appears in the English Seal (she would have been 51 in 1584). A possible explanation is that Hilliard sought to flatter her inordinate vanity in the 'pattern' which he would have submitted for her approval. If this was so, presumably the royal features would have been likewise flattered in the 'pattern' for the Great Seal of England, and it is strange that the flattery was not carried out in the Seal itself. Another possible explanation (hinted at in *Farquhar*, p. 347) is that Hilliard made this 'pattern' for the Irish Seal at some time previous to 1584, and then later adapted the design, with necessary modifications, for the English Seal.

2. A QUEEN AND HER SON. She standing, turned half-l., wearing the costume of about 1610–15, with jewels in her hair, lace closed standing bands and a circular French farthingale. Before her, standing on a footstool, her son, wearing a diadem on his head, a doublet patterned with Tudor roses, petticoats and apron, and holding in his l. hand an orb and in his r. a sceptre, tipped with a fleur-de-lis, which he receives from his mother. In an architectural setting (unfinished), with part of a sarcophagus, l., and a pillar, r.   **Plate 11**

Pen and ink over black lead, on two slips of vellum, the one pasted over the other to enlarge the composition; 12·7 × 8·9 cm. (5 × 3½ in.).

INSCR.: *Recto*, in the lower l.-hand corner, *N.H.*

PROV.: Uncertain, but in the B.M. by 1837.

T 15–18.

BIBL.: *Vasari Soc.*, Ser. II, Pt. XI, p. 13, No. 11.

The attribution to Hilliard of this drawing rests mainly on the initials inscribed on it, which appear to be contemporary, though in a different ink from that used in the drawing itself. If the attribution is correct, the date of the costumes would point to a period late in the artist's life, but unfortunately there are no known drawings by him of that time with which a comparison might be made. There are, however, certain points in common with the two accepted drawings by Hilliard, notably in the treatment of the hands with their characteristically long and slender fingers. Mr. Binyon (*Vasari Soc.*) says of the present drawing: 'it is rather insensitive in its neatness and looks more like a copy.' The tightness of its handling suggests that it might have been intended as an engraver's design, but so far no related engraving has appeared to confirm this.

The Departmental Inventory of 1837 describes the subject as 'Mary Queen of Scots and her son'. If this identification is correct, the drawing must be a memorial representation of the Queen passing on the sceptre to the young King James, the sarcophagus perhaps being intended for that of either Darnley or Queen Elizabeth. Nearly all the portraits of Mary, which have any claims to authenticity (including even the memorial portraits) show her in the costume of the period in which she lived. The one exception is apparently a silver counter (whereabouts unknown), engraved by Simon van de Passe with a portrait of Mary 'in a high collar, similar to those worn by Anne of Denmark' (*See* Cust, *Mary Queen of Scots*, p. 112).

A more likely suggestion is that the present drawing represents Elizabeth, Queen of Bohemia (B. 1596: D. 1662) and her small son, Frederick Henry (B. 1614: D. 1629). This young prince was at one time considered to be not only heir to his father's throne, but also a likely heir to those of England and Scotland, as Prince Charles (later Charles I) suffered from very indifferent health as a boy. The sarcophagus might be considered to be that of Prince Henry, eldest son of James I, who had died in 1613 and to whom Elizabeth was greatly attached.

LOIDT, AEGIDIUS

[GILLIS]

Fl. 1567–77
Goldsmith

See pp. 9–10, No. 5

OLIVER, ISAAC

[Oliver, Ollivier, Oliviero, Isacke, Izack]
B. *c.* 1556(?) : D. 1617
Limner

Son of Peter Oliver (Pierre Ollivier), Huguenot goldsmith and pewterer of Rouen, who with his wife Typhan (or Tyffen) is known, from several entries in returns of aliens, to have settled in Fleet Lane, London, about 1568, Isaac having been born some time before that date. Vertue implies a connexion with a family of printers named Olivier living in Caen in the early XVI c. Early writers like Sandrart, Hondius and Peacham refer to the artist as English, but he did not become naturalized until late in 1606, generally spelling his name in the French style and referring to himself on the reverse of a portrait of 'Sir Arundell Talbot' (1596) as *Isacq Oliviero Francese* (*See Reynolds*, No. 149). Was the pupil of Nicholas Hilliard (*q.v.*) whose technique in limning he at first followed so closely that his earlier miniatures are not easily distinguishable from his master's. Is also stated by Buckeridge and Vertue to have received instruction 'as a good oil painter in little', from Federico Zuccaro (B. *c.* 1542: D. 1609), presumably when the latter visited England in 1574–5. Though no oil paintings can now be definitely attributed to him, Oliver certainly worked in this medium, for the Exchequer accounts of 1610–12 show payments made to him for several 'great pictures', and Vertue describes a *St. John* by Oliver painted on panel which was a portrait of the artist's gardener from the life. An entry in the Lord Chamberlain's accounts for Nov. 6th, 1612, the occasion of Prince Henry's funeral, when Oliver was one of the mourners, refers to him simply as 'Paynter' and to another, Mark Bedford, as 'Lymner'. Became famous not only for portrait miniature but also for history pieces executed in

the same medium, the best known of which was a limning of the Entombment dated 1616, but finished after the artist's death by his son, Peter for Charles I. The study for this work is in the Department (*See* No. 11 below). Many of his history pieces were copies of Italian or Flemish masters. At least one drawing of a decorative composition after Primaticcio is known (*See* No. 1 below), and a number of others are in the style of Parmigianino, whose work in the collection of Alessandro Vittoria he must have come to know when he visited Venice in 1596. Probably travelled in the Low Countries in 1588 from the evidence of a Dutch inscription on a portrait of an unknown man (Dutch Royal Coll.; *Reynolds*, No. 121). His ties with the Netherlands strengthened by his second marriage in 1602 to Sara Gheeraerts, probably daughter of the painter Marcus Gheeraerts the elder, and a relative of John de Critz, Sergeant-Painter to Queen Elizabeth. Seems to have married three times, his son Peter (*q.v.*) being by his first wife, whose portrait is in the Duke of Portland's collection. His marriage to his third wife, Elizabeth (his executrix), seems to have resulted in his connexion with the Russell family and through them with the portraitist Cornelius Johnson (*q.v.*), brother-in-law of Nicasius Russell, jeweller to James I. Was godfather to a son of Nicasius, whose grandson, Anthony Russell (B. 1663(?): D. 1743), the portrait-painter, possessed some of Oliver's work and was Vertue's main source of information about the artist. Left no account of his work (though Vertue saw pages of a sketch-book with entries in French and English) but Edward Norgate, limner and writer of the treatise on miniature, may well have received some technical information from the artist. Oliver's later reputation rests almost entirely on his miniature portraits. Vertue, on the inconclusive evidence of a roll of awards by the sovereign in 1579, where Oliver's name did not appear, concluded that he was out of favour with the Queen, of whom the artist's pen-drawing (c. 1590–5; engraved by Crispin van de Passe) and an unfinished miniature of about 1600, survive. Had gained important commissions by 1590 when he executed the famous portrait known traditionally as that of Sir Philip Sidney (*Reynolds*, No. 124). Though Hilliard enjoyed the official monopoly of royal portraiture in miniature, Oliver was nevertheless made 'her Ma^tes [Queen Anne's] painter for the Art of Lymning' in 1604. Seems by this period to have become more fashionable than Hilliard. Was paid by warrant, dated 1617, for 'four several pictures drawn for the Prince's [Charles] highness'. His portraits provide a most important record not only of individuals but of costume both at Court and for the masque designed by Inigo Jones (*Reynolds*, No. 182). A number of self-portraits also exist, one at Windsor and another in the collection of the Earl of Derby (*Reynolds*, Nos. 135 and 136). Vertue saw a model of the artist's bust in marble, destroyed in the Fire, together with his monument, at St. Anne's, Blackfriars, where Isaac and Peter Oliver were buried.

In his Will, dated June 4th, 1617, bequeathed to his wife, Elizabeth, one-third of his property and the lease of his house in Blackfriars Precinct (where he died), and to his son Peter, his 'drawings and limnings'. Vertue states that he was 61 or 62 years old at death. His drawings for the most part executed in pen and ink or dark washes, but he also worked in chalks. His studies notable for the fineness of the pen and brush strokes and the careful gradation of the tones of the washes in the modelling of the figures.

BIBL.: *Peacham*, p. 6. *Sanderson*, pp. 73 and 76. *Buckeridge*, pp. 406–7. *D.N.B.*, XLII, 1895, pp. 145–6. *Norgate*, pp. 20, 55 and 72. *Sandrart*, p. 191. *Long*, pp. 316–20. *T.-B.*, XXV, 1931, p. 598 (with *Bibl.*). *Winter*, *passim*. *Pope-Hennessy*. *Reynolds*, pp. 11–12 and *Bibl.* (on pp. 21–2). *Vertue*, *Index*, pp. 193–4. *Pope-Hennessy, Hilliard*, pp. 20, 25–9. *Woodward*, pp. 18–20. *Waterhouse*, pp. 28–9. *Auerbach*, pp. 133 and 179–80. *Vertue*, VI, pp. 37 and 53–5.

DRAWINGS IN OTHER COLLECTIONS: V. & A. Museum. Fitzwilliam Museum. Oppé, coll. Examples of his miniatures are in the collections of H.M. the Queen (Windsor), the V. & A. Museum, the Duke of Buccleuch, the Marquis of Exeter. In the N.P.G. is an oil painting of John Donne, perhaps by Oliver (No. 1849).

1. APOLLO AND THE MUSES. A pedimental composition, with Apollo, a viol between his knees, seated on a knoll upon Mount Parnassus and the Muses and two river gods grouped on either side of him. At the foot of the knoll, the Nymph of the Castalian Spring.

Black and red chalks; 22·7 × 59·5 cm. (9 × 23½ in.).

PROV.: P. H. Lankrink (*Lugt*, No. 2090). Sir Hans Sloane, Bart., by whom it was bequeathed to the B.M., 1753.

5214–243 (L.B.7).

BIBL.: *Sloane Cat.*, p. 160, No. 243.

In the manner of Primaticcio, though not connected with any known work by him.

2. DIANA. The goddess, leaning with her arms crossed upon a bank, r., and with head turned l., her bow and quiver beside her, r.   **Plate 13**

Pen and brown ink, with grey wash, over red chalk; 10·6 × 7·9 cm. (4¼ × 3⅛ in.).

PROV.: The Rev. C. M. Cracherode (*Lugt*, No. 606), by whom it was bequeathed to the B.M., 1799.
   G.g. 3–360. (L.B.1b).

BIBL.: *Cracherode Cat.*, p. 84, No. 360.

Described in the *Cracherode Cat.* as 'after Parmegianino'. It does not appear to be connected, however, with any known composition by that master.

3. AN ALLEGORICAL FIGURE (?). A draped female figure seated to front and looking to l., her l. hand resting on a cushion and holding a book, her r. hand outstretched.

Pen and brown ink, with grey wash; 10 × 7·7 cm. (4 × 3 in.).

PROV.: As for No. 2.
   G.g. 3–361. (L.B.1a).

BIBL.: *Cracherode Cat.*, p. 84, No. 361.

Like No. 2, described in the *Cracherode Cat.* as 'from Parmegianino', though no composition by that master can be associated with it.

4. THE PENITENT MAGDALEN. The Saint, half reclining on a wooded bank beneath a tree, looking up towards a ray of light descending from the sky, holding with her l. hand a skull and crucifix. In the background, l., a demon taking flight.

Pen and brown ink with brown wash; 19·4 × 12·5 cm. (7⅝ × 5 in.).

PROV.: Hon. John Spencer and the Earls Spencer (*Lugt*, No. 1530. Sale, Philipe, 29:v:1799, Lot 72). Richard Payne Knight,

by whom it was bequeathed to the B.M., 1824.
   P.p. 5–128 (L.B.2).

BIBL.: *Payne Knight Cat.*, p. 69, No. 128.

5. A COMPOSITION ON FOUR H.L. FIGURES. An elderly bearded man in the foreground, half turning towards a turbaned woman behind him, who points with her r. hand towards some object unseen. On the r., a youth with long hair and another figure.

Pen and brown ink; 7·9 × 10·5 cm. (3⅛ × 4⅛ in.).

PROV.: Sir Peter Lely (*Lugt*, No. 2092). Woodburn (Sale, Christie, 16–27:vi:1854, but not identifiable). Purchased, through W. B. Tiffin, at the Woodburn Sale by the B.M., 1854.
   1854–6–28–95.

Described in the *Departmental Register* as by 'A. Carralio', an artist of whom there is no record. The attribution to Isaac Oliver, which is due to Mr. A. E. Popham, has been suggested by its similarity in handling to No. 4 above.

6. THE ADORATION OF THE MAGI. The Virgin seated inside a roofless shed, l., the Child on her lap and Joseph behind. On the l. the first of the Magi kneeling to offer his gift. On the r. the other Magi attended by pages and a throng of followers.

Plate 14

Purplish brown wash, touched with pen and ink and heightened with white, over black lead; highly finished; 22·8 × 16·8 cm. (9 × 6⅝ in.).

INSCR.: *Recto*, in the lower r.-hand corner, by the artist, *Is: Ollivier.*

PROV.: W. B. Tiffin, from whom it was purchased by the B.M., 1855.
1855–7–14–55 (L.B.3).

BIBL.: *Reynolds*, p. 46, No. 203.

7. ANTIOPE. Antiope, naked and asleep, reclining towards the l. on drapery, with Cupid beside her, r., his head pillowed on his quiver. On the l., Jupiter disguised as a satyr, half seen.

Plate 15

Black chalk, touched with pen and ink and heightened with white, on buff paper; 19·5 × 27·9 cm. (7⅝ × 11 in.).

INSCR.: *Recto* in the lower r.-hand corner, by the artist, *Isa: Ollivier.*

PROV.: W. B. Tiffin, from whom it was purchased by the B.M., 1869.
1869–6–12–295.

8. A SEATED WOMAN. Seated in a chair to r., the forefinger of her l. hand lifted as if addressing a child.

Pen and brown ink; 8·4 × 6·9 cm. (3¼ × 2¾ in.).

PROV.: Hugh Howard. Dr. Robert

Howard, Bishop of Elphin. The Earls of Wicklow. Charles Howard, 5th Earl, from whom it was purchased by the B.M., 1874.
1874–8–8–2268 (L.B.6a)

9. A WOMAN ASLEEP. Seated to front, her arms folded, her head nodding. Wearing full sleeves, and cap.

Pen and ink; 11·4 × 7·6 cm. (4½ × 3 in.).

PROV.: As for No. 7.
1874–8–8–2269 (L.B.6b).

10. THE HOLY FAMILY. The Virgin, in a half-kneeling posture, holding on her lap the Infant Christ, who with outstretched hand offers some object to the young St. John kneeling on the r. In the background, r., St. Joseph leaning over a sculptured altar and touching the Virgin on the shoulder. Behind her, l., St. Elizabeth contemplating the Child.

Pen and brown inks, with grey wash over black lead; the upper corners cut off; 13·2 × 10·7 cm. (5⅛ × 4¼ in.). Old mount, 22·6 × 17·2 cm. (8⅞ × 6¾ in.).

INSCR.: *Recto*, on the old mount, in the lower r.-hand corner, *I Oliver*.

PROV.: John Campbell, 5th Duke of Argyll (Sale, perhaps Philipe, 23:v:1798, Lot 240). Woodburn (?) (not identified in any sale catalogue). Fairfax Murray (not in Sale, as purchased privately by F. Sabin). Victor Koch, by whom it was presented to the B.M., 1921.

1921–3–18–1.

11. THE ENTOMBMENT.

11. THE ENTOMBMENT. In the centre, the body of Our Lord, supported by four of the Disciples, being carried to the tomb, l., where Joseph of Arimathea (?) stands with outstretched arms to receive Him. In the r. foreground, a group of mourning followers about the figure of the Virgin, who, prostrated with grief, is supported by the youthful St. John.   **Plate 16**

Black chalk, pen and dark brown ink and wash, heightened with white; 29·5 × 37·7 cm. (11⅝ × 14⅞ in.).

INSCR.: *Recto*, in the lower r.-hand corner, by the artist, *Isa : Olliuier*

Verso, by Vertue, with some words partly erased, *This* [is] *the original design for the large limning begun by | Isaac Oliver & finisht by his Son Peter Oliver for | which limning when finisht, King Charles the first | settled an annuity of a hundred pounds a year | on Peter Oliver | this being a just* [next word illegible] *of the famous work | vid. the King's Catalog.* On a separate slip of paper, also by Vertue, *This original design, was first done | by Isaac Oliver to paint a large limning | which being not finisht 1616. when he died. Aº. 1617. | It was afterwards compleated by his Son Peter Oliver (by appointment of the King) who was also a most excellent limner, which he presented to | King Charles first. he settled an annuity of an hundred | pounds a year on the sd. P. Oliver. | vide Catalog of K. Charl. I. pictures. | item . . . .* [There follows an almost verbatim transcription of Vanderdoort's catalogue entry relating to the limning (*See* G. Vertue, *A Catalogue and Description of King Charles the First's Capital Collection,* 1757, pp. 32 & 33)].

PROV.: Theodore Russell (?). Anthony Russell. George Vertue (Sale, Ford, 19:v:1757, Lot 81). Thomas Hollis I. Thomas Hollis II (Sale, Sotheby, 30:iv:1817, Lot 1688). Charles Carnegie, 11th Earl of Southesk. Presented by the N.A.C.F. to the B.M., 1945.

1945–9–24–2.

BIBL.: *Vertue*, I, p. 130. N.A.C.F., 1946, p. 37. No. 1439. *Reynolds*, p. 46, No. 202.

The limning, for which this drawing is a study, was last recorded as being in the collection of James II but its whereabouts is not now known. Its dimensions must have been approximately those of the present drawing. The main figures and groups described by Vanderdoort (*op. cit.*) correspond exactly with those depicted in the drawing but Oliver must have added other figures to the background, making 'twenty-six lesser and bigger'.

A related composition, smaller and with differences in the disposition of the subsidiary figures, is in the Fitzwilliam Museum.

12. A WOMAN WITH OUTSTRETCHED ARM.

12. A WOMAN WITH OUTSTRETCHED ARM. Standing to front, looking downwards over her l. shoulder, her r. arm outstretched, her l. hand holding up part of the drapery which forms her dress.

Pen and brown ink, with blue-grey wash; 10·3 × 8·4 cm. (4 × 3¼ in.).

INSCR.: *Verso*, on the old mount, *C A 15 Feb 1736/7*.

23

PROV.: E.B. (*Lugt*, No. 827). John Thane (*Lugt*, No. 1544). Sir Thomas Lawrence. Samuel Woodburn (Sale, Christie, 5:vi:1860, Lot 215 (20)). Sir Thomas Phillipps, Bart.

T. F. P. Fenwick. Presented anonymously to the B.M., 1946.

BIBL.: *Popham, Fenwick*, p. 241, No. 1.
1946–7–13–1170.

13. A WOMAN WITH HER ARMS CROSSED. H.L., turned half r., her eyes looking to front, her arms crossed before her. Wearing drapery. **Plate 12**

Metal-point on prepared paper; 10·3 × 7·2 cm. (4 × 2⅞ in.). Old mount, 19·7 × 14·7 cm. (7¾ × 5¾ in.).

INSCR.: *Recto*, on the old mount, at the foot, by Jonathan Richardson I, *Is: Oliver*.
Verso, also probably by Richardson, various inventory numbers (?).

PROV.: Jonathan Richardson I (*Lugt*, No. 2184. Sale, Cock, 23:i:1746–7, Lot 48, or 5:ii:1746–7, Lot 7). Mrs. E. Yaxley, from whom it was purchased by the B.M., 1952.
1952–11–22–1.

14. A SYBIL (?). A woman seated to front, her head in profile to r., looking down at a book to which she points with her l. hand, her r. hand pointing outwards. Wearing drapery, her breast bare.

Pen and brown ink, with grey wash; 7·8 × 6·3 cm. (3 × 2½ in.).

PROV.: E B (*Lugt*, No. 827). Lord James

Cavendish. Charles Compton-Cavendish, 1st Lord Chesham. L. Colling Mudge, from whom it was purchased by the B.M., 1952.
1952–1–21–8.

15. A SEATED WOMAN. Seated to front, looking upwards towards the r., her l. arm resting across her knees, her r. hand on a stone plinth. Wearing drapery, her breast bare.

Pen and brown ink, with blue wash; 8 × 6·6 cm. (3⅛ × 2⅝ in.).

PROV.: As for No. 14.
1952–1–21–9.

INSCR.: *Recto*, on the old mount, below the drawing, *Isaac Oliver*.

'TRESWELL, R.'

Identifiable with one of the following:

TRESWELL, Ralph I (Radulphus)
Fl. 1566–1612(?)
Surveyor

Descended from a family already established at St. Albans in the reign of Edward IV. Son of Robert Treswell, 'alias Baker', of St. Albans, and Margaret Langley. Described as a 'citizen of London'. Acted as steward to Sir Christopher Hatton for whom he made in 1580–7 a series of 11 plans of the Hatton estates at Kirby Hall, Northants (County Record Office, Northampton). These are executed in pen and wash, and include a plan and elevation of the house enlivened with such naturalistic details as figures of game-keepers and deer and rabbits in the surrounding park. Also drew for Hatton a survey of his estates of Wimbledon (c. 1580–90, Earl Spencer, Althorp), Corfe Castle, 1588 (Northampton), and Teeton, 1591 (Northampton). Other maps by him of estates in Essex, Herts. and Northants. (Mr. Kenney, Mr. G. Harvey and the Earl of Winchelsea). As 'R. Treswell', drew plans of the London parishes of St. Martin-in-the-Fields and St. Giles's, 1586–7 (Public Record Office), and of Cransley, Northants, 1598 (Northampton Record Office). Probably accompanied Sir John Norris on his second expedition to Brittany in 1593–4, when he executed a map of that territory, 1594 (B.M., *Cotton MS., Augustus I*, ii, 58). As 'Ralph Treswell Senior', signed surveys of lands owned by the Clothworkers' Company, 1612 (Clothworkers' Co.). Married firstly Cecily Cresley by whom he had three sons, Robert Treswell (*See* below), Ralph II (Rafe) (*See* below) and Christopher. Does not appear to have had children by either his second wife, Anne Kentish, or his third wife, Elizabeth Bachelor.

TRESWELL, Ralph II (Rafe)

Fl. 1606–10

Surveyor

Second son of Ralph Treswell I and his first wife, Cecily Cresley. Followed his father's profession as a surveyor, and, as 'Ralph Treswell Junior', drew plans of lands adjoining Dulwich College, 1606 (P.R.O.), the Manor of Isleworth, 1607 (Syon House), the Sussex and Yorkshire estates of Henry Percy, 13th Earl of Northumberland, 1608 and 1610 (Petworth). Married Susan Peterson by whom he had four children.

TRESWELL, Robert

B. 1566: D. after 1631

Surveyor and Somerset Herald

Eldest son of Ralph Treswell I and his first wife Cecily Cresley. Bluemantle Pursuivant 1588–9 and Somerset Herald, 1597–1624. As 'Robert Treswell Blewmantle', drew for Sir Robert Colton a plan of the Manor of Carington, Northants, c. 1590 (Carington), and, as 'Robert Treswell', a plan of houses and lands from Charing Cross to Westminster, 1610 (P.R.O.). Married firstly Susan Lyons (D. 1590), secondly Anne Gadbury, and thirdly (at the age of 35 in 1601, when he was living in the parish of St. Botolph's, Aldersgate), Mary Castle. Apparently last recorded in 1631 when he supplied information which led to the grant of the forest of Shotover and Stowwood to the Earl of Lindsey.

BIBL.: *Cooke*, p. 92. *C.S.P., Dom., 1631–3*, p. 127. *Foster Licences*, p. 1358. *Brooks*, pp. 113 and 162. *Inf.* from Mr. R. A. Skelton.

1. **WEST-CHEAP, LONDON.** Bird's-eye view ('plat'), looking down on the W. end of Cheapside, branching, l., into the Shambles (later Newgate St.) and Paternoster Row, with the Church of St. Michael's-in-the-Querne dividing them. At the E. end of the Church, the Little Conduit, surrounded by water-jugs, with pipes leading from it. On the r., respectively to N. and S., Foster Lane and the Old Change, and on the l., to S., St. Paul's Gate. The church and red-roofed houses shown in elevation. On the r., a *Scale of feete*. **Plate 17**

Pen and ink, with water-colours; 27·1 × 39·3 cm. (10⅝ × 15½ in.).

INSCR.: *Recto*, on the r., below the scale, in ink, by the artist, *R. Treswell. 1585:*, and on other landmarks, *Paternoster rowe, St Mitchell in ye querne, ye lytte cundit, con pipes, foster lane, The Olde Change,* together with the points of the compass, *NORTHE, SOVTHE, EAST, WEST,* and notes of distances in feet.

PROV.: Frederick Crace. John Gregory Crace, from whom it was purchased by the B.M., 1880.

1880–11–13–3516.

ENGR.: By Howlett, 1814.

BIBL.: *Crace Cat.,* p. 436, Ptf. XXI, No. 1.

The area shown is N.E. of St. Paul's Cathedral, and occupies the exact centre of Ralph Aggas's map, *CIVITAS LONDINVM,* 1560–70.

WHITE, JOHN

Fl. 1585–93

Cartographer and draughtsman

Date and place of birth unknown, but described in his grant of arms of 1587 as 'John White of London, Gentleman', the quarterings possibly suggesting a S. Western origin. Nothing recorded of the artist until 1585, but the possibility that he sailed with Frobisher on his second voyage for a N.W. Passage (1577) cannot be excluded (*See* introductory note to Nos. 63 and 64). If the statement in his letter of 1593 to Richard Hakluyt (*See* below) that the 1590 voyage to Virginia was his '5th and last' is correct, may have made his first voyage with Amadas and Barlowe in 1584. In the following year sailed as draughtsman-surveyor with the expedition dispatched by Sir Walter Raleigh to establish the 'First Colony' of Virginia. Worked in close co-operation with Thomas Hariot, the astronomer and mathematician, who went as scientific observer. The frontispiece to the plates of the latter's *Briefe and true report of the new found land of Virginia* (published by Theodor de Bry in *America,* Pt. I, 1590) mentions 'the true pictures and fashions of the people . . . . Diligentlye collected and drawne by Ihon White who was sent thiter speciallye and for the same purpose by the said Sir Walter Raleigh. . .'. An idea of White's duties may

be gathered from instructions issued to a certain Thomas Bavin who as draughtsman was to have accompanied an expedition planned by Sir Humphrey Gilbert or associates to the south part of New England in 1582 (*See* Professor E. G. R. Taylor's discussion of Sir Thomas Hoby's commonplace-book in the *Mariner's Mirror,* XXXVII, 1951, pp. 48–62). White, like Bavin, expected to make a graphic record not only of coasts, harbours and encampments, but also of all unfamiliar flora and fauna, and the types and customs of the natives encountered on the voyage. Had an accomplished predecessor in the French artist, Jacques le Moyne, who probably worked in England for some years before 1588 when he died in Blackfriars, and whose position on the French expedition to Florida of 1564 closely anticipated White's. Like White, he later enjoyed Raleigh's patronage. Raleigh's expedition left Plymouth in April, 1585, under command of Sir Richard Grenville, and a Spanish source refers to its members as making drawings of plants in May of that year on the island of Puerto Rico, and Spanish names indeed found in a number of White's drawings of animals, fish and fruit observed in the Spanish West Indies. The colonists

26

finally reached the island of Roanoke in Croatoan Sound and there established the first English colony on N. American soil, under the governorship of Ralph Lane. White, one of the leaders of a group sent to explore the neighbouring Indian villages of Pomeiooc, Aquascogoc and Secoton, but his name not actually included in Hakluyt's list of 108 settlers, unless either the 'John Twit' or the 'William White' who appear there can be identified with him. Little doubt that he stayed with the colony from August, 1585 until June, 1586, when all its members returned to England. The identification of the artist with the governor of the second colony is confirmed by a passage in Gerard's *Herball* where he describes the sarsaparilla plant. He writes of 'Master *White* an excellent painter who caried very many people into Virginia (or after some Norembega) there to inhabite . . .'. Raleigh licensed White and his associates to settle part of the territory in his grant, i.e. the city of Raleigh in Chesapeake Bay. The expedition reached Roanoke (where White's licence did not extend) in July, 1587, but soon encountered difficulties and, after less than two months, White returned to England for further supplies. Left behind his daughter, Elinor Dare and a grand-daughter, Virginia, the first child born of English parents in North America. Early in 1588, met the Flemish engraver and publisher, Theodor de Bry, who had come to England to acquire Le Moyne's drawings in connection with his proposed publication, *America*. On that occasion de Bry also obtained some of White's drawings of Virginia which were used to illustrate the first part of this famous work. After an abortive attempt with two pinnaces to relieve the colony in April, 1588, arranged with William Sanderson, Raleigh's man of business, and John Watts, a London merchant, for a small fleet of privateers to accompany him to Roanoke with supplies and reinforcements, but eventually forced to set sail without them. His account of their failure to find the colonists when eventually

two of the ships reached Virginia in August, 1590, told in an account which he sent to Richard Hakluyt with the letter (mentioned above) dated Feb. 4th, 1593. Writes of finding on the island of Croatoan 'the frames of some of my pictures and Mappes, rotten and spoyled with rayne'. The letter was written 'from my house at Newtowne in Kylmore' and indicates that White, after his last failure, had retired to Munster and settled near the great estates granted to Raleigh by the Queen in 1586. Nothing more heard of him. The date for White's death, 'March 27, 1598', given in Sir William Musgrave's *Obituaries* (Harleian Soc., XLIX, p. 254) is a misreading of that author's MS. note and refers to the death of White's engraver and publisher, Theodor de Bry. The artist may possibly be identified with a John White 'late of parts beyond the seas', whose sister Brigit White, was appointed administratrix of his estate on May 22nd, 1606 (*See* Somerset House, Admin. Act Book, 1606).

An examination of White's drawings tends to qualify Mr. Binyon's opinion (*See* his *English Watercolours*, 1944, p. 2) that he was a founder of the English water-colour school. That much of his work survives in contrast to contemporary or earlier English artists, helps to obscure the fact that he must have been one of a line of topographical and documentary draughtsmen. In addition to Gerard's statement there is Thomas Moffet's opinion of the artist given in *Insectorum Theatrum*, p. 112, as 'pictor peritissimus'. Probably this represents the general view of White's contemporaries. For convenience White's work may be divided into the following groups:

I. *Maps and Topography*. White clearly a highly-trained and experienced cartographer, and familiar with such contemporary Flemish work as the maps of Ortelius, engraved by Hogenberg, or Waghenaer's *Spiegel*, 1586, engraved by the elder Jan van Deutecum. May have used some such model for his conventional decorations of ships, sea-monsters, etc., but his whales with their vertical spouts and his flying-fish and dolphins not found elsewhere, must be the result of direct observation. In his map of part of the E. coast of N. America (*See* No. 59 below), used the cartographical work of Jacques le Moyne, executed twenty years previously, for the area south of Cape Lookout which was not surveyed during the 1585 voyage. White's topographical drawings show a degree of competence which exceeds that of his English contemporaries. A comparison may be made of these with an exactly contemporary drawing of the same kind by an unknown hand representing Drake's attack on Santiago in the Cape Verde Islands in 1585 (B.M., Egerton MS. 2579). Here the draughtsmanship is of a high quality and the technique more in keeping with that of the earlier illuminators both in the application of pigments and in the conventions used; the turtle included in the scene is no doubt drawn from nature. The plate in Walter Bigges, *A summarie and true discourse of Sir Frances Drakes West Indian voyage*, 1589 (B.M. copy, G. 6509) is engraved after this drawing whose author must have seen White's work (*See* Nos. 9, 10, 26 and 27 below) and who must have executed the drawings for the other plates in Bigges' account. White's comparable work (*See* Nos. 3 and 36) is freer and the observation more direct and realistic. It is also allied to that of other military topographers and draughtsmen of estate maps of the period, particularly of 'Solder' (Soldier) John Thomas (working in the late XVI c.) whose drawing of the defeat of Hugh Maguire (B.M., Cotton MS., Aug. I.ii.38) though much cruder, also forms a parallel to White's drawing of Grenville's fort on Puerto Rico (No. 3). There is the same use of the convention of the half plan, half birds-eye-view and of figures and objects out of scale.

II. *Figures and Costume*. White's figure and costume studies representing primitive types, belong to a tradition which goes back at least to Dürer (*See* Winkler, *Dürers Zeichnungen*, IV, No. 825). The drawings of Hungarian warriors by Roelandt Savery (B. 1576: D. 1639) in the Department (*See* Hind, *Dutch and Flemish Artists*, IV, p. 55, Nos. 1–3) are later examples of the same tradition. English examples, both earlier and contemporary with White, also found, *e.g.* the woodcut in the Ashmolean Museum, Oxford, of Irish chieftains (*See* Hind, *Studies*, II, Fig. XI, p. 230) and the water-colour drawings in the Dept. of MSS., of an Irish woman (Add. MS. 5253, Nos. 3 and 4). White's figure drawings may be divided into those taken from the life and those derived from earlier sources. The first group includes the studies of Indians of Virginia (Nos. 32–49), remarkable for their sensitive characterization and careful rendering of detail. The Eskimo (Nos. 63 and 64) also appear to have been drawn from the life, and show strong affinities with the studies of Frobisher's Eskimo drawn in this country by the contemporary Dutch artist, Lucas de Heere (B. 1534: D. 1584) who worked in England between 1567 and 1577. In the second group are the Orientals (Nos. 72–6) which apparently derive from earlier costume books, and the 'Ancient Britons' (Nos. 67–71) taken, according to de Bry, from an 'Oold English Cronicle', showing marked Flemish influence and a strong similarity to de Heere's drawings of 'Picts' (*See* B.M., Add. MS. 28.330, *f.* 8v.). Both artists express the general and increasing interest in antiquity characteristic of their age. De Bry adds that the 'Picts' were intended 'to showe how that the Inhabitants of the great Bretannie haue bin in times past as sauuage as those of Virginia'. Also included in this group must be two drawings of Indians of Florida (Nos. 61 and 62), almost certainly taken from drawings by Jacques le Moyne (*See* above) though to judge from the only extant drawing by that artist (formerly coll. J. H. Hyde, New York) White seems to owe little to him stylistically.

III. *Natural History*. The drawings of

natural history subjects (Nos. 5–31, 50–58, 65, 66) and the mentions of White in Moffet (*See* above) show him to have been an unusually accurate scientific draughtsman. The Swiss naturalist, Conrad Gesner (B. 1516: D. 1565), had used and admired a generation previously drawings of fauna by the Cambridge physician and historian John Caius (B. 1510: D. 1573) and White again seems to have carried forward a tradition already well established and which goes back to the English medieval bestiary and herbal.

BIBL.: *De Bry, America*, Pt. I, Epistle and frontispiece to plates. *Hakluyt*, III, pp. 251–95. *Gerard, Herball*, pp. 709–10. *Moffet*, p. 112. *Stevens*, p. 224–6. *Weeks. Eggleston. D.N.B.*, LXI, 1900, pp. 54–5 (with *Bibl.*). *Stevens, Hariot, passim. Binyon, White. Bushnell, White. Taylor*, pp. 42–4. *Adams. D.A.B.*, XX, 1936, pp. 110–11. *Rowse*, pp. 213, 225, 238–43. *Cumming. T.-B.*, XXXV, 1942, pp. 497–8 (with *Bibl.*). *Woodward*, pp. 16–17. *Kendrick*, pp. 123–5. *Lorant*, pp. 180–4. *Williams*, pp. 3–4. *Van der Waal*, I, p. 92. *Andersen. Lemaitre*, pp. 17–18. *Quinn, passim* (with full *Bibl.*).

The following drawings, together with three of insects in the Dept. of MSS. (*See* Nos. 7 and 58), make up the known total of White's original work. None are signed but there can be little doubt of White's authorship. The draughtsman whose work was engraved by Theodor de Bry is stated by the latter to have been 'Ihon White' (*See* p. 26 above). The quality of the drawings in itself would almost preclude their being copies. In addition there is the evidence provided by the inscription on the drawing in the Dept. of MSS. of the Swallow-tail Butterfly, apparently by the same hand as No. 58 below (*See* note to that entry). If 'Candidus' (White) was the 'pictor' or author of this drawing, as stated, then it follows for reasons of style that the whole set here described is also by him.

A study of these drawings by the side of De Bry's engravings in *America*, Pt. I, reveals that the engraver used variants of the present drawings sometimes with considerable, though always secondary, differences. There are also engravings of five drawings (Pls. II, XII, XXI and XXIII, and *Picts*, Pl. III), for which no original or variant now exists. It is clear that White executed a number of different sets of fair copies of his drawings, as well as extra copies of individual drawings, for the use of professional colleagues such as Hariot (*See* p. 26), whose account of the colony they were originally intended to illustrate, for the publisher Theodor de Bry, patrons like Raleigh or naturalists like Thomas Penny (*See* note to No. 58). The relationship of the different sets of originals, surviving or presupposed, and of copies by other hands is discussed by Professor D. B. Quinn in his *Roanoke Voyages*, I, pp. 392–8.

The present drawings must be dated after White's return from Virginia in July, 1586, though many of the preliminary sketches would have been made during the outward voyage in 1585, the date given on the title-page, or perhaps in 1584 (*See* biographical notice above). 1587, the year inscribed on the drawing of the Swallow-tail Butterfly already referred to, can be taken only as a date *post quem non* for that drawing. The uniformity of style and finish throughout the set suggests that all the drawings were executed at one period including those unconnected with the Virginian venture (Nos. 63–76). The set made for De Bry must have been executed before 1590, the date of publication of *America*, Pt. I.

The history of the drawings requires some amplification beyond the provenance given at No. 1 below. No mention of White's originals is found after De Bry's references in *America*, Pt. I, until the appearance in 1788 of the annual catalogue of the London book-seller, Thomas Payne the elder. No. 284 of his list is described in the words of its title-page (No. 1) and also as 'seventy-five drawings, coloured, in the original binding. Folio.—Fourteen guineas.' Edmund Malone, in a letter of March 12th, 1788, brought this item to the notice of the 1st Earl of Charlemont. The latter replied by return on March 15th requesting Malone to buy it for him. The album remained in the Charlemont family until August, 1865, when the library of the 3rd Earl came up for sale at Sotheby's. On June 30th fire broke out in a warehouse adjacent to the auction-rooms in Wellington Street where the drawings were stored. Though the album was only slightly charred by the flames, it lay saturated with water and under pressure for three weeks. The damage suffered was minor: slight running of the colours and blurring of lines in a few drawings. A more curious result was the formation of off-prints on the intervening leaves. The album was purchased by Henry Stevens, the American writer, and the drawings removed from the damaged album and remounted in a new volume while the off-sets were bound up in a second volume (No. 77). Both were offered to the American collector James Lenox who declined to buy them allowing the Trustees of the British Museum to acquire them in 1866 for £225. They were placed in the Grenville Library and were finally transferred to the Dept. of Prints and Drawings in 1906. The drawings were subsequently remounted, numbered and described separately for the first time in the late Laurence Binyon's *Catalogue of Drawings by British Artists*, IV, pp. 326–33.

The arrangement adopted for the drawings follows fairly closely the order chosen by Professor Quinn in Chapter VI of the *Roanoke Voyages*. The subjects connected with the voyage of 1585 and the exploration of the Roanoke area are described where possible in the order of events and discoveries which they illustrate. A more detailed catalogue of the drawings is in preparation.

[1–31]. DRAWINGS CONNECTED WITH THE W. INDIES. The original studies for these would have been executed on the outward voyage to Virginia.

1. TITLE-PAGE. *The pictures of sondry things collected and counterfeited according | to the truth in the voyage made by S.* *Walter Raleigh knight | for the discouery of La Virginea. In the 27th yeare | of the most happie reigne of our Souereigne lady Queene | Elizabeth. And in the yeare of o.* *Lorde God. | 1585.*

Pen and brown ink; 8 × 16·4 cm. (3⅛ × 6½ in.).

PROV.: Thomas Payne I. Purchased by James Caulfield, 1st Earl of Charlemont, 1788. James-Molyneux, 3rd Earl (Sale, Sotheby, 11:viii:1865, Lot 228). Henry Stevens from whom it was purchased by the B.M., 1866. Placed in the Grenville Library and transferred to the Dept. of P. & D., 1906.

1906–5–9–1 (1) (L.B.1).

BIBL.: *Payne Cat.*, 1788, p. 9, No. 284.

Stevens Report. Hist. MSS. Comm., Charlemont MSS., II, p. 73. *Binyon, White*, p. 19. *B.M., Eng. Topographical and Landscape Drawing*, p. 4. *B.M., Raleigh and Hakluyt*, p. 26, No. 111. *Hind, Engraving in England*, I, pp. 128–31. *Quinn*, p. 398, No. 1.

The inscription, by the same hand as those which appear throughout the following drawings, may be White's own. If so, it is curious that the artist should have used the word 'by' in line 2 which is incorrect since Raleigh did not himself travel to Virginia.

2. THE ISLANDS OF DOMINICA AND SANTA CRUZ (SAINT CROIX).

Above, a distant view of Dominica as it appears from the sea; below, a similar view of Santa Cruz; between, a scale of miles.

Pen and brown ink over black lead, the scale tinted in water-colours; 24·4 × 21·7 cm. ($9\frac{5}{8} \times 8\frac{5}{8}$ in.).

INSCR.: *Recto*, at the top, above the coast of Dominica, *The Risinge of the Ilande of Dominica*; in the centre, above the scale marked off from *1* to *30*, *This scale contaynethe XXX: myles*; at the foot, above the coast of Santa Cruz, *The Risinge of the Ilande of Santicruse*.

PROV.: As for No. 1.

1906–5–9–1 (36) (L.B.1 (37)).

BIBL.: *Quinn*, p. 403, No. 1, A. & B.

Dominica, 'wherewith we fell the 7. day of Maye' (1585), but not Santa Cruz, is mentioned in *Hakluyt* (III, p. 251). Santa Cruz would probably have been sighted on May 9th.

3. PLAN OF A FORTIFIED CAMP AT MOSQUETAL (TALLABOA BAY), PUERTO RICO.

The area enclosed by a river on the W. side, l., and on the N.E. and S. sides by a series of entrenchments. A small lake, r., completes the N.E. corner of the defences. The S. line of entrenchments which has three masked entrances, runs just N. of the sea shore. Within the fort, woodland except for clearings near the water-filled trenches manned by sentries. Among the trees, at the N. edge of the wooded area, a row of huts and enclosures forming the Governor's quarters. On the S. edge, similarly, the General's quarters. In the clearing between the latter and the S. entrenchments, a pinnace nearly completed, timber spars, and in the S.E. corner, a wood fire. In a clearing, towards the E. edge of the camp, r., two horses. On the lake, land crabs, a heron and two species of duck. Approaching the S.E. corner of the camp from the wood to the N.E., a party of men hauling in a tree trunk on a four-wheeled carriage protected from the rear by two files of harquebusiers. In the lower l.-hand corner, another column of armed men moving E. and beginning to ford the river, with a figure mounted on horseback near the rear; on the E. bank, a sentry discharging his musket in reply to a shot fired by one of the party to signal arrival. At the top, l., a small boat manned by four men carrying barrels of water, being rowed across the river to the E. bank just N. of the fort. Emerging from the wood in the N.E. corner, r., another party of armed men marching S. towards the fort. In the upper l.-hand corner, a square with a heavy red border to frame an inscription and at the foot, an English ship riding at anchor off-shore. In the lower r.-hand corner, a scale of yards ('paeces').
Plate 23

Pen and brown ink over black lead, and water-colours; some of the stronger features off-printed on either side of a central fold; on two conjoined sheets; 36·3 × 44·5 cm. 14¼ × 17½ in.).

INSCR.: *Recto*, in the upper l.-hand corner, within the square, *THE xj^{th} of Maie the Generall in the | Tyger arriued | at St Iohñs Iland where | he fortified in this manner, toke in fresh | water, and buylt a Pynnes, And then | departed from thence the xxiij^{th} of the | same moneth. 1585.*; to the r. of the timber carriage, *The manner of | drawing in of tymber, | into the fort for the | buylding of a Pynnes*; on the river, *A fresh ryuer*; beneath the N. entrenchments, *Mr Lanes quarter* and *Northe | Syde*, and, above the S. entrenchments, *The Generalls quarter*; In the lower r.-hand corner, beneath the scale, marked off from 5 to 40, *PÆSCES*.

PROV.: As for No. 1.

1906–5–9–1 (4) (L.B.1 (3)).

BIBL.: *B.M., Eng. Topographical and Landscape Drawing*, No. 11. *B.M., Raleigh & Hakluyt*, p. 23, No. 97. *Quinn*, p. 403, No. 2.

The drawing shows White's ability as a surveyor draughtsman. It represents events described in *Hakluyt* as taking place between 12th (not 11th, as stated on the drawing) and 22nd May, 1585. The ship portrayed is Grenville's flagship, the *Tiger*. The mounted figure of 'The Generall', on the l., is Grenville himself returning on the 22nd May after a meeting with the Spaniards to arrange a truce. His quarters are those on the S. side of the camp, the Governor's (Ralph Lane's) on the N. side. The two horses were captured from the Spaniards and the fire may be the site of a forge which, according to Spanish sources, was used to make nails for the building of a pinnace. The crabs represented in the lake are the species described at No. 5 below. The unit used for the scale is probably the 'geometrical pace' of 5 feet.

4. PLAN OF AN ENTRENCHMENT NEAR CAPE ROJO, PUERTO RICO.

Bounded by a moat and a rampart in form basically square but with large arrow-shaped bastions on the N., E. and W. sides, the entrance being on the S. side, very close to the sea. Within the N. bastion, at the top, the smaller of two mounds of salt, the larger of which, in the centre of the fort, is being demolished by a party of men with pickaxes and carried in sacks to a boat drawn up in the entrance of the fort. Within each bastion an armed sentry. Another sentry stands guard on top of the larger salt mound and at least one other supervises the work. Off-shore, in the lower l.-hand corner, a captured Spanish frigate riding at anchor. **Plate 18**

Pen and brown ink over black lead, and water-colours; 31·5 × 22 cm. (12⅜ × 8¾ in.).

INSCR.: *Recto*, in the upper l.-hand corner, *The forme of a fort wch was made by M^r | Ralfe Lane in a parte of St Iohñs Ilande | neere Capross where we toke in salt | the xxvj^{th} of May. 1585.*

PROV.: As for No. 1.

1906–5–9–1 (5) (L.B.1 (4)).

BIBL.: *B.M., Eng. Topographical and Land-scape Drawing*, p. 4, No. 10. *B.M., Raleigh & Hakluyt*, p. 23, No. 98. *Quinn*, p. 404, No. 3.

Lane's discovery of the Spaniard's salt mounds and the making of the entrenchment is described in *Hakluyt* (III, p. 252). The narrative mentions only one mound, the drawing shows two. Professor Quinn points out the similarity of the defences to those on Roanoke Island and considers that the fort here represented was located at Salinas Bay (*Quinn*, pp. 905–6).

5. LAND CRAB (probably *Cardisoma guanhumi* Latreille). Seen from above.

Water-colours over black lead, heightened with white (oxidized); 23·2 × 27·7 cm. (9⅛ × 10⅞ in.).

INSCR.: *Recto*, at the top, *A lande Crab*.

PROV.: As for No. 1.
1906–5–9–1 (**56**) (L.B.1 (58)).

COPY: From another version, at No. 78 below, *f.* 16 r.

BIBL.: *Quinn*, p. 405, No. 4.

The West Indian land crab also appears on the lake in No. 3 above and was evidently drawn by White in Puerto Rico in May, 1585.

6. PURPLE-CLAWED (OR LAND) HERMIT CRABS (*Coenobita clypeatus* Herbst). The upper is shown protruding, r., from a long arrow-shaped shell (*Turritella variegata* Linn.); the lower, l., from a snail-like shell (*Natica canrena*, Linn.).
Plate 29

Water-colours over black lead, touched with white (oxidized); 18·8 × 15·5 cm. (7⅜ × 6⅛ in.).

INSCR.: *Recto*, at the top, above the upper drawing, *Caracol*; in the centre, above the lower, *Caracol*; at the foot, *Thes lyve on land neere the Sea syde, and breede in sondry shells / when they be empty.*

PROV.: As for No. 1.
1906–5–9–1 (**57**) (L.B.1 (59)).

COPY: From another version, at No. 78 below, *f.* 17r. (*b*), the shells being relatively in different positions.

BIBL.: *Quinn*, p. 405, No. 5 (a).

Caracol in XVI c. Spanish means a twisted shell and is here applied to the shells used by the hermit crabs.

7. STUDIES OF FIREFLIES (*Pyrophorus noctilucus*) **AND A GADFLY** (*Tabanus* species). Three studies of a firefly: l., with wings closed, head to r.; top centre, with wings open and head uppermost; and r., with wings slightly open, head to l. Below, a gadfly, head uppermost.

Water-colours over black lead, touched with white; 19·8 × 18·7 cm. (7⅞ × 7¾ in.).

INSCR.: *Recto*, beneath the top insect, *A flye which in the night / semeth a flame of fyer.*; at the bottom, beneath the gadfly, *A dangerous byting flye.*

PROV.: As for No. 1.
1906–5–9–1 (**67**) (L.B.1 (69)).

WCT.: By an unknown artist, in Thomas Moffet's *Insectorum Theatrum* (1634), p. 112

and of a gadfly, in the same edition, p. 61 (*See* note below).

BIBL.: *Raven*, p. 185. *Quinn*, p. 406, No. 7 (a) & p. 459, No. 108 (a).

The fireflies are W. Indian. Another version of two of the studies of these insects, with wings open and wings closed, and after which the above woodcut was executed, is found in the manuscript of Moffet's 'Insectorum Theatrum' (B.M., Sloane MS., 4014, *f.* 109 r.). They are drawn on separate slips of paper and pasted in. White's authorship is virtually certain both on grounds of style and from the reference in the accompanying text 'Hanc Cicindelam una cum icone a Candido pictore [the artist, White] peritissimo, qui diligentissime eam tam in Hispaniola quam in Virginiâ obseruauit, accepi. Another version of the gadfly, from which the

above mentioned woodcut was probably executed, appears in the same MS. (f.69 v.) with the reference (f. 63) 'Duas Asilorum rariores species Pennius descripsit, quarum unam ex Virginia Indorum Candidus, alteram ex Russia Elmerus chirurgus diligens ad eum misit'.

8. TWO STUDIES OF SCORPIONS (*Tityus tityinae*). On the l., a specimen on its back facing l., on the r., another with its tail curled up, facing r.

Water-colours over black lead, touched with white (oxidized); 10·3 × 18·5 cm. (4 × 7¼ in.).

INSCR.: *Recto*, at the top, *Scorpions*.

PROV.: As for No. 1.

1906–5–9–1 (73) (L.B.1 (75)).
BIBL.: *Quinn*, pp. 405–6, No. 6.

A West Indian species.

9. IGUANA (*Cyclura* species). Seen from the side and above, facing l. **Plate 19**

Water-colours over black lead, heightened with white (oxidized) and silver (?); 14·4 × 21 cm. (5⅝ × 8¼ in.).

INSCR.: *Recto*, at the top, *Igwano. Some of thes are . 3 . fote in length. / and lyue on land.*

PROV.: As for No. 1.
1906–5–9–1 (71) (L.B.1 (73)).

ENGR.: By an unknown artist, as an inset, in the plate of Cartagena in *Bigges*, reproduced in *Wright* at p. 54.

COPY.: From another version, at No. 78 below, f. 13 r (a).

BIBL. & REPR.: *Binyon, White*, Pl. XXIX a. *B.M., Raleigh & Hakluyt*, p. 28. No. 126. *Quinn*, p. 406, No. 8.

This is the first known English drawing of an iguana, no doubt made in the West Indies as *igwano* is a word of Spanish West Indian origin. The author of the inset in the Cartagena plate referred to above, must surely have known White's drawing and may well have sailed with White on the voyage from Port Ferdinando to England in June, 1586.

10. CROCODILE (*Crocodylus acutus* Cuvier) **OR ALLIGATOR** (*Alligator mississipiensis* Daudin). Seen from the side and above, facing l. **Plate 20**

Water-colours over black lead, touched with white (oxidized); 11·1 × 23·3 cm. (4⅜ × 9⅛ in.).

INSCR.: *Recto*, at the top, towards the r., *Allagatto. This being but one moneth old was 3 . foote / 4 . ynches in length. and lyue in water.*

PROV.: As for No. 1.
1906–5–9–1 (72) (L.B.1 (74)).

ENGR.: By an unknown artist in the plate of Santo Domingo in *Bigges*, but with modifications.

COPY: From another version, at No. 78 below, f. 13 r. (b).

BIBL.: Quinn, p. 407, No. 9 (a).

The reptile as represented shows characteristics common both to the crocodile and alligator, but if the drawing was made on one of the West Indian islands, as its Spanish inscription suggests, it would probably represent the former. Allagatto is a corruption of the Spanish El lagarto, often misapplied to both crocodiles and caimans. The inscription is quite misleading as a reptile of this size would be about two years old.

11. PINEAPPLE (*Ananas comosos*). The fruit with tuft uppermost.

Water-colours over black lead, touched with white; 25·9 × 14·1 cm. (10⅛ × 5½ in.).

INSCR.: Recto, in the top l.-hand corner, The Pyne frute.

PROV.: As for No. 1.
1906–5–9–1 (41) (L.B.1 (43)).

COPY: From another version, at No. 78 below, f. 24 r.

BIBL.: Quinn, p. 407, No. 10 (a).

12. MAMMEE APPLE (*Mammea americana*). The fruit seen from the side and above, with stalk below.

Water-colours over black lead; 21 × 18·4 cm. (8¼ × 7¼ in.).

INSCR.: Recto, at the top, Mammea.

PROV.: As for No. 1.
1906–5–9–1 (40 (a)) (L.B.1 (42)).

COPY: From another version, at No. 78 below, f. 23 r.

BIBL.: Quinn, p. 408, No. 11 (a).

13. BANANA (*Musa paradisiaca*). A single fruit, l., stalk uppermost, with part of another in cross-section, r.

Water-colours over black lead; 29·4 × 17·7 cm. (11½ × 7 in.).

PROV.: As for No. 1.
1906–5–9–1 (40) (L.B.1 (41)).

COPY: From another version, at No. 78 below, f. 25 r.

INSCR.: Recto, at the top, Platano. or Planten.

BIBL.: Quinn, p. 408, No. 14 (a).

See also note to No. 14.

14. STALK AND FRUIT OF THE BANANA (*Musa paradisiaca*). The top part of a plant with six bunches of fruit growing from it.   Plate 21

Water-colours over black lead; 32·4 × 22·1 cm. (12¾ × 8¾ in.).

Don Fernando de Altamirano, a Spaniard captured by Grenville off Puerto Rico,

INSCR.: *Recto*, near the top r.-hand corner, *Platano.* or *Planten.*

PROV.: As for No. 1.
1905–9–1 (39) (L.B. 1 (40)).

BIBL.: *Quinn*, p. 408, No. 13.

specifically mentions banana plants as having been taken away from that island by the Englishmen in May, 1585. He also says that they made sketches of other fruits and trees along the coast of Puerto Rico (*See Quinn*, p. 742).

15. FLAMINGO (*Phoenicopterus ruber* Linn.). Standing, in profile, facing r.

Plate 24

Water-colours over black lead, touched with white (oxidized); 29·6 × 19·7 cm. ($11\frac{5}{8} \times 7\frac{3}{4}$ in.).

INSCR.: *Recto*, at the top, *A Flaminco.*

PROV.: As for No. 1.
1906–5–9–1 (60) (L.B. 1 (62)).

BIBL.: *Allen*, p. 446. *B.M., Raleigh & Hakluyt*, p. 27, No. 122. *Quinn*, p. 409, No. 15.

The bird is common in the W. Indies but is only occasionally found in N. Carolina. The drawing is therefore grouped with the W. Indian section.

16. FRIGATE BIRD (*Fregata magnificans* Mathews). In flight, seen from below, with wings outspread.

Water-colours over black lead, touched with white; 13·6 × 22·3 cm. ($5\frac{3}{8} \times 8\frac{3}{4}$ in.).

PROV.: As for No. 1.
1906–5–9–1 (62) (L.B. 1 (64)).

BIBL.: *Quinn*, p. 409, No. 16.

The drawing probably represents the female specimen as seen from a ship's deck. The bird nests in the W. Indies but sometimes reaches the N. Carolina coast in summer and was probably drawn by White on the voyage from the W. Indies to Virginia.

17. RED-BILLED TROPIC BIRD (*Phaethon aethereus mesonauta* Peters). In flight, seen from below, with wings outspread.

Water-colours over black lead, touched with white; 16·2 × 20·4 cm. ($6\frac{3}{8} \times 8\frac{1}{8}$) in.).

PROV.: As for No. 1.
1906–5–9–1 (65) (L.B. 1 (67)).

BIBL.: *Quinn*, p. 409, No. 17.

As with No. 16, the bird was apparently drawn while in flight above the ship's deck.

18. BROWN BOOBY (*Sula leucogaster leucogaster* Boddaert). Sitting on the ground, in profile, facing r.

Water-colours over black lead, heightened with white; 13·2 × 23·1 cm. ($5\frac{1}{4} \times 9\frac{1}{8}$ in.).

INSCR.: *Recto*, towards the top, above the bird, *Bobo.*

PROV.: As for No. 1.
1906–5–9–1 (63) (L.B. 1 (65)).

BIBL.: *Quinn*, p. 409, No. 18.

Bobo is the Spanish for gannet or booby. The bird is found in the W. Indies.

19. COMMON NODDY TERN (*Anoüs stolidus stolidus* Linn.). Standing in profile, facing l.

Water-colours over black lead, touched with white (oxidized); 15·7 × 23·4 cm. (6¼ × 9¼ in.).

INSCR.: *Recto*, at the top, *Tinosa*.

PROV.: As for No. 1.
1906–5–9–1 (59) (L.B.1 (61)).

BIBL. & REPR.: *Allen, XVI c. American bird paintings*, Pl. I. Quinn, p. 409, No. 19.

20. MOONFISH (*Selene vomer* Linn.). In profile, facing r.

Water-colours over black lead, heightened with gold and white (oxidized); 14·8 × 22·2 cm. (5⅞ × 8¾ in.).

INSCR.: *Recto*, at the top, *Polometa. A foote long*.

PROV.: As for No. 1.
1906–5–9–1 (47) (L.B.1 (49)).

BIBL.: *Quinn, p. 409, No. 20.*

The specimen was probably drawn in the W. Indies.

21. MOONFISH (*Selene vomer* Linn.). In profile, facing l.

Water-colours over black lead, touched with white (oxidized); 19·1 × 21 cm. (7½ × 8¼ in.).

INSCR.: *Recto*, at the top, *Crocobado*.

PROV.: As for No. 1.
1906–5–9–1 (49) (L.B.1 (51)).

COPY: From another version, at No. 78 below, *f.* 19 *v.* (*b*).

BIBL. & REPR.: *Andersen, p. 105. Quinn*, p. 410, No. 21 (a).

The word *crocobado* is not found in Spanish.

22. GROUPER (probably *Epinephelus ascencionis* Osbeck). In profile, facing l.

Water-colours over black lead, heightened with gold and touched with white (oxidized); 9·2 × 21·9 cm. (3⅝ × 8⅝ in.).

INSCR.: *Recto*, at the top, *Garopa*.

PROV.: As for No. 1.
1906–5–9–1 (48) (L.B.1 (50)).

COPY: From another version, at No. 78, *f.* 18 *r.* (*b*).

BIBL.: *Quinn, p. 410, No. 22 (a).*

The word *garopa* is from the Portuguese *garoupa*. The specimen represented is one of the Grouper family, probably the Rock Hind.

23. GROUPER (probably *Mycteroperca* Gill). In profile, facing l.

Water-colours over black lead, heightened with gold and white (oxidized); 13·1 × 21·4 cm. (5⅛ × 8⅜ in.).

INSCR.: *Recto*, at the top, *Mero*.

PROV.: As for No. 1.
1906–5–9–1 (50) (L.B.1 (52)).

COPY: From another version, at No. 78 below, *f.* 22 *r.* (*a*).

BIBL.: *Quinn, p. 410, No. 23 (a).*

The Spanish *mero* is used for several different fish but the French *mérou* is confined to the Grouper.

24. BLUE-STRIPED GRUNT (*Haemuleon sciurus* Shaw). In profile, facing r.

Water-colours over black lead, heightened with blue body-colour and white (oxidized); 11·2 × 21·4 cm. (4⅜ × 8⅜ in.).

INSCR.: *Recto*, at the top, *Pefe pica*.

PROV.: As for No. 1.
1906–5–9–1 (52) (L.B. 1 (54)).

COPY: From another version, at No. 78 below, *f.* 17 r. (*a*).

BIBL.: *Quinn*, p. 410, No. 24 (a).

Pefe in the inscription is no doubt meant to read *Pefe* (i.e. *Pese*). *Péce pica* in Spanish means lance-fish.

25. SQUIRREL-FISH OR SOLDIER-FISH (*Holocentrus ascencionis* Osbeck). In profile, facing r.

Water-colours over black lead, heightened with gold and white (oxidized); 13·2 × 19·9 cm. (5¼ × 7¾ in.).

INSCR.: *Recto*, at the top, *Oio de buey*.

PROV.: As for No. 1.
1906–5–9–1 (42) (L.B. 1 (44)).

COPY: From another version, at No. 78 below, *f.* 22 r. (*b*).

BIBL.: *Quinn*, p. 411, No. 25 (a).

Ojo de buey is the Spanish for ox-eye.

26. DOLPHIN (*Coryphaena hippurus* Linn.). In profile, facing l.   Plate 26

Water-colours and blue body-colour over black lead; 12·6 × 22·8 cm. (5 × 9 in.).

INSCR.: *Recto*, at the top, *Duratho. Of thes some are . 5 . foote long.*

PROV.: As for No. 1.
1906–5–9–1 (44) (L.B. 1 (46)).

ENGR.: By an anonymous artist in the plate of San Agustin in *Bigges*, reproduced in *Wright* at p. 166.

COPY: From another version, at No. 78 below, *f.* 20 r. (*a*).

BIBL.: *Quinn*, p. 411, No. 26 (*a*).

The Spanish *dorado* (from the fish's golden glow at night) is still used. A drawing of a dolphin chasing flying-fish is also found in White's general map (No. 59).

27. FLYING-FISH (probably *Exocoetus volitans* Linn.). Seen from the side and above, facing l.   Plate 27

Water-colours over black lead, heightened with blue body-colours and gold (oxidized); 27·7 × 23·4 cm. (10⅞ × 9¼ in.).

INSCR.: *Recto*, above the fish, *Bolador.*, and below, *The flyeng fishe.*

PROV.: As for No. 1.
1906–5–9–1 (46) (L.B. 1 (48)).

ENGR.: By an unknown artist in the plate of Santiago in *Bigges*, reproduced in *Wright*, at p. 6. Though not close to White's drawing, may have been taken from a derivative.

COPY: From another version, at No. 78 below, *f.* 21 r.

BIBL.: *Quinn*, p. 412, No. 27 (a).

Pez volador is the modern Spanish for a flying-fish.

28. REMORA OR SHARK-SUCKER (*Echeneis naucrates* Linn.). Dorsal view, facing l.

Water-colours over black lead, heightened with blue body-colour and white; 15·3 × 19·7 cm. (6 × 7¾ in.).

INSCR.: *Recto*, at the top, *Rebeso. Two fote and a halfe long.*

PROV.: As for No. 1.
1906–5–9–1 (53) (L.B.1 (55)).

COPY: From another version at No. 78 below, *f.* 20 r. (*b*).

BIBL.: *Quinn*, p. 412, No. 28 (a).

The Spanish *rébeza*, now superseded by *rémora*, means thick lip.

29. REMORA (*Remora remora* Linn.). Ventral view, facing r.

Water-colours over black lead, touched with white (oxidized); 12 × 15·5 cm. (4¾ × 6⅛ in.).

INSCR.: *Recto*, in the centre, above the fish, *Rebeso*.

PROV.: As for No. 1.
1906–5–9–1 (43) (L.B.1 (45)).

COPY: From another version, at No. 78 below, *f.* 15 r. (*a*).

BIBL.: *Quinn*, p. 412, No. 29 (a).

30. QUEEN TRIGGER-FISH (*Balistes vetula* Linn.). In profile, facing r.

Water-colours over black lead, heightened with blue body-colour and white; 14·3 × 22·3 cm. (5⅝ × 8¾ in.).

INSCR.: *Recto*, in the top r.-hand corner, *Pefe porco. Of this, some are . 2 . fote in length.*

PROV.: As for No. 1.
1906–5–9–1 (55) (L.B.1 (57)).

ENGR.: By an unknown artist, in reverse, as a *Sea Connye* in the general map in *Bigges* reproduced in *Wright* as the frontispiece

COPY: From another version, at No. 78 below, *f.* 19 v. (*a*).

BIBL.: *Quinn*, p. 413, No. 30.

Again, as for No. 23, the ƒ should read ſ (s). *Péce puerco* in modern Spanish means pig-fish. A drawing of the Queen Trigger-fish appears in White's general map (No. 59).

31. PORTUGUESE MAN-O'-WAR (*Physalia physalis*). In a floating position with tendrils extended below.
Plate 28

Water-colours over black lead, heightened with blue body-colour and white (oxidized); 30·5 × 17·6 cm. (12 × 7 in.).

INSCR.: *Recto*, at the top, *This is a lyuing fish, and flote vpon the Sea, Some call them Caruels.*

PROV.: As for No. 1.
1906–5–9–1 (45) (L.B.1 (47)).

COPY: From another version, at No. 78 below, *f. 19 r.*

BIBL.: *Quinn*, p. 413, No. 31 (a).

This medusa was formerly known as *caravella caravella* from its common name, Portuguese Man-o'-War.

[32–60]. DRAWINGS CONNECTED WITH THE ROANOKE COLONY.

32. THE VILLAGE OF POMEIOOC. A bird's-eye view of an Indian village consisting of eighteen huts laid out in two rows round the perimeter of a circular palisade of long stakes. In the centre, a number of figures sitting or squatting round a fire, others standing in groups or walking about, one at the far side accompanied by a dog. Towards the lower l.-hand corner, an entrance through the palisade approached by a path bordered by overlapping bamboos fixed into the earth.

Plate 31

Water-colours over black lead, heightened with gold and touched with white; 22·2 × 21·5 cm. (8¾ × 8½ in.).

INSCR.: *Recto*, at the foot, *The towne of Pomeiock and true forme of their howses, couered | and enclosed some wth matts, and some wth barcks of trees. All compassed | abowt wth smale poles stock thick together in stedd of a wall.*

PROV.: As for No. 1.
1906–5–9–1 (8) (L.B.1 (7)).

ENGR.: By Theodor de Bry in *America*, Pt. I, Pl. XIX, with a landscape background. Described as *The Tovvne of Pomeiooc.*

COPY: From another version, at No. 78 below, *ff. 2 v.* and 3 *r.*

BIBL. & REPR.: *Binyon, White*, Pl. XXVII (a). *B.M., Eng. Topographical and Landscape*

Drawing, p. 5, No. 13. *B.M., Raleigh and Hakluyt*, p. 27, No. 114. *Quinn*, p. 415, No. 33 (a).

Both De Bry and the author of the variant copy mentioned above must have used versions of the present drawing, nearer to one another than to this original, both, for example, having a pond or group of ponds in the upper r.-hand corner. Pomeiooc is the most generally used of the contemporary forms of the name. The huts are of the Algonkian long house type with arched roofs (similar to those represented at Secoton (No. 36 below), except for the large hut near the upper r.-hand corner which has a ridged roof rising to a point in the middle. For further information *see* Swanton, *Indians*, pp. 386–439. A detailed drawing similar to the central group round the fire of the present drawing is found at No. 40 below.

33. A WOMAN AND CHILD OF POMEIOOC. The woman standing, her body turned half l., her head half r. Wearing her hair in a fringe across her forehead, longer at the sides and caught up in a knot at the neck. Her forehead, cheeks and chin tattooed. Wearing a long, three-string pearl necklace through which her r. wrist is thrust; and, painted on her neck, a pattern simulating a shorter necklace of three strings with a pendant. Her upper arms elaborately painted to simulate bands of woven material. Round her loins a fringed skin apron reaching in front almost to her knees. In her l. hand a gourd vessel. On her l., a small girl, naked except for a pad of moss between her legs supported by a thong tied at the waist. Her hair worn in a fashion similar to the woman's and around her neck a two-string necklace of copper (?) beads, through which her r. hand is placed. In her l. hand, an English doll in contemporary female costume. **Plate II**

Water-colours over black lead, touched with white; 26·3 × 14·9 cm. (10⅜ × 5⅞ in.).

INSCR.: *Recto*, at the top, *A cheife Herowans wyfe of Pomeoc. | and her daughter of the age of . 8 . or . | 10 . yeares.*

PROV.: As for No. 1.

1906–5–9–1 (13) (L.B.1 (14)).

ENGR.: By Theodor de Bry in *America*, Pt. I, Pl. VIII, in reverse, with the lettering, *A cheiff Ladye of Pomeiooc*, a landscape background and modifications. The figure of the woman is also incorporated in the frontispiece to the same work.

BIBL. & REPR.: Binyon, *White*, Pl. XXVIII (b). *B.M. Postcard*, B. 429. *B.M., Raleigh and Hakluyt*, p. 27, No. 118; Quinn, p. 417, No. 34 (a).

The original sketch for the present drawing was doubtless made on the expedition referred to at No. 32. Again, differences in the De Bry engraving (in which the child holds a rattle in her r. hand and the doll in the l.,) point to a different original and not to the kind of modification introduced by the engraver.

34. AN OLD MAN OF POMEIOOC. Standing to front, with legs apart, his head turned half l. Wearing a cockscomb down the middle of his head, his hair shaven at the sides and caught up in a knot at the neck, and a fringed deerskin mantle slung over his l. shoulder leaving his r. bare arm and reaching below his knees.

Water-colours over black lead, touched with white (oxidized); 26·1 × 15 cm. (10¼ × 5⅞ in.).

INSCR.: *Recto*, at the top, *The aged man in his wynter garment.*

PROV.: As for No. 1.

1906–5–9–1 (19) (L.B.1 (20)).

ENGR.: By Theodor De Bry in *America*, Pt. I, Pl. IX, with the lettering, *An ageed manne in his winter garment*, modifications of dress and, in the background, a view of Pomeiooc.

COPY: From another version, at No. 78 below, f. 10 v.

BIBL.: Quinn, p. 418, No. 35 (a).

35. A WOMAN OF POMEIOOC CARRYING A CHILD. Seen from behind, walking away towards the l., her head looking round over her l. shoulder, her child on her back holding on to her shoulders, its l. leg resting in the crook of her l. arm. Wearing her hair fringed in front and falling behind to her neck, tattooed or painted bands round her upper arms, and a fringed deerskin skirt reaching to her thighs.

Water-colours over black lead, touched with white; 25·7 × 14·1 cm. (10⅛ × 5⅝ in.).

INSCR.: *Recto*, at the top, *The wyfe of an Herowan of Pomeiooc.*

PROV.: As for No. 1.

1906-5-9-1 (15) (L.B.1 (16)).

ENGR.: By Theodor de Bry in *America*, Pt. I, Pl. X, in reverse and with the addition of a front view of the same woman. With the lettering, *Their manner of careynge ther Childern and a tyere of the cheiffe Ladyes of the towne of Dasamonquepeuc.*

BIBL.: *Quinn*, p. 419, No. 36 (a).

The discrepancy between the inscription and the printed title seems to indicate that White relied on his memory in describing his finished drawings made from the same sketch. Certainly de Bry was again using a different original, no doubt with the two figures. As stated in Hariot's narrative printed with Pl. X in *America*, Pt. I, the village of Dasemunkepeuc was about four miles from Roanoke (i.e. the fort on Roanoke Island).

36. THE VILLAGE OF SECOTON. A bird's-eye view of an Indian village consisting of a cluster of huts with other single huts scattered among surrounding trees. At the top, part of a lake or river, joined by a path leading to the main group of huts, centre, from which a wide road runs down through the settlement. To the r., three fields of maize at different stages of growth, in the top one of which is a small shelter on a raised platform where a watcher sits to scare birds from the ripe crop. In the village, Indians engaged in various activities: in the upper part, within the cluster of huts, tending a fire and walking about in pairs; below, eating from three large bowls placed on matting in the roadway; near the foot, squatting in a line to the l. of a group of figures dancing round a ring of wooden posts, waving rattles. Towards the bottom l.-hand corner, a large log fire within a circle of posts, and in the corner, a hut larger than the rest. **Plate VI**

Water-colours over black lead, heightened with white (oxidized); 32·4 × 19·9 cm. (12¾ × 7⅞ in.).

INSCR.: *Recto*, in the top r.-hand corner, on the first of the fields of maize, *Their rype corne.*; below, on the second field, *Their greene corne.*; on the third and lowest field, *Corne newly sprong.* In the centre, below the figures feeding, *Their sitting at meate.* In a semi-circle about the camp-fire, near the bottom l.-hand corner, *The place of solemne prayer*, and below it, above the hut, *The howse wherin the Tombe of their Herounds / standeth.* To the r., below the line of squatting figures, *SECOTON.*, and to the r. again, below the dancing figures, *A Ceremony in their prayers w^{th} / strange iesturs and songs dansing / abowt posts carued on the topps / lyke mens faces.*

PROV.: As for No. 1.

1906-5-9-1 (7) (L.B.1 (6)).

ENGR.: By Theodor de Bry in *America*, Pt. I, Pl. XX, with the addition of plots of tobacco, sunflowers, Indians shooting at deer with bows and arrows, etc. Described as *The Tovvne of Secota.*

BIBL. & REPR.: *Binyon, White*, Pl. XXIV. *B.M. Postcard*, B.427. *Rowse, Grenville*, Pl. V. *B.M., Eng. Topographical & Landscape Drawing*, p. 5, No. 12. *B.M., Raleigh and Hakluyt*, p. 27, No. 113; *Quinn*, p. 420, No. 37 (a).

The original drawing was probably made on the expedition which reached Secoton on July 15th, 1585 (*See Hakluyt*, III, p. 253). The circle of dancing figures is represented, with modifications, in a separate drawing (No. 39). For detailed observations on the separate features of the drawing and engraving, *see Quinn*, pp. 420-22.

37. A WOMAN OF SECOTON. Standing, turned half r., with her arms folded and her r. foot slightly forward. Wearing her hair as in No. 35 but without the knot and with a twisted head-band, tattoo or painted marks on her forehead, cheeks and chin, a simulated neck ornament ending at a point between her breasts and bands painted about her upper arms, fore-arms, calves and insteps. Round her loins, a fringed deer-skin, inset with pearls or beads, in the form of a double apron reaching, before and behind, half way down her thighs.

Water-colours over black lead, touched with white (oxidized) and light blue body-colour; 26 × 13·9 cm. (10¼ × 5½ in.).

INSCR.: *Recto*, at the top, *The wyfe of an Herowan of Secotan.*

PROV.: As for No. 1.
1906–5–9–1 (18) (L.B.1 (19)).

ENGR.: By Theodore De Bry in *Virginia*, Pl. IV, with the lettering, *On of the chieff Ladyes of Secota*, and the addition of a back view of the same figure against a background of Indians fishing.

COPY: From another version, at No. 78 below, *f. 5 r.*

BIBL.: *Quinn*, p. 423, No. 38 (a).

As for No. 35, the engraver must have used the more elaborate original with the woman represented both from the front and from behind.

38. AN OSSUARY TEMPLE. A building made chiefly of reed matting, raised several feet above the ground on wooden posts and consisting of a single chamber open at the front. Within, ten dessicated human bodies placed side by side, their feet towards the back of the hut against four bundles of matting. By the r. wall, a seated image facing front. Above the front opening, mat hangings tied back. Beneath the hut, two skins lying on the ground, and in front, a log fire.   **Plate 30**

Water-colours over black lead, touched with gold; 29·5 × 20·4 cm. (11⅝ × 8 in.).

INSCR.: *Recto*, at the top, *The Tombe of their Cherounes or cheife personages, their flesh clene taken of from the bones saue / the skynn and heare of theire heads, wch flesh is dried and enfolded in matts laide at theire / feete. their bones also being made dry, ar couered wth deare skynns not altering / their forme or proportion. With theire Kywash, which is an / Image of woode keeping the deade.*

PROV.: As for No. 1.
1906–5–9–1 (9) (L.B.1 (8)).

ENGR.: Unsigned, in *America*, Pt. I, Pl. XXII, with modifications and the addition of a much larger and loftier outerstructure of poles and matting, with an arched roof, and a priest attending the fire. Described as *The Tombe of their Werovvans or Cheiff Lordes.*

BIBL.: *Quinn*, p. 425, No. 40 (a).

An exterior view of the temple is found in the drawing of Secoton (No. 36) and is identified by the inscription *The howse wherein the Tombe of their Herounds standeth*. The *Kiwash* or *Kiwasa*, the image watching over the dead, was evidently the subject of a separate drawing now lost but also engraved for *America*, Pt. I (Pl. XXI). A similar interior of a high chamber of reed matting, supported by poles, with an arched roof is found in the representation of Powhatan holding court in John Smith's map of Virginia, engraved by William Hole, first published in 1612 (?).

39. A FESTIVE DANCE. A ring of fourteen Indians of both sexes carrying leafy sprays, arrows and rattles and dancing about a circle of seven wooden posts, the tops of which are carved in the shape of human heads. Wearing fringed skin aprons or loin-cloths, necklaces, and for the most part, feathers in their hair. Some also wearing sprays of leaves and some tattooed. In the centre of the circle, three women facing inwards, their arms clasped tightly about each other. **Plate 32**

Water-colours over black lead, touched with white; many details offprinted on either side of a central fold; 27·4 × 35·8 cm. (10¾ × 14⅛ in.).

PROV.: As for No. 1.
1906–5–9–1 (10) L.B.1 (9)).

ENGR.: Unsigned, in *America*, Pt. I, Pl. XVIII, in reverse, with small modifications. Described as *Their danses vvhich they vse att their hyghe feastes*.

BIBL. & REPR.: *Binyon, White*, Pl. XXV. *B.M., Raleigh and Hakluyt*, p. 27, No. 115. *Quinn*, p. 427, No. 41 (a).

The dance is shown on a smaller scale in No. 36 (lower r.-hand corner). It was evidently associated with the corn festival, the carved faces perhaps representing minor deities.

40. A CAMP FIRE CEREMONY. Ten Indians of both sexes sitting in various postures, in a circle round a log fire, one facing outwards. Dressed similarly to the dancers in No. 39. Some waving gourd rattles, others apparently singing. The figure seated behind the flames perhaps conducting the ceremony. **Plate VIII [a]**

Water-colours and crimson body-colour over black lead, heightened with white and gold; 21·8 × 20·2 cm. (8⅝ × 8 in.).

PROV.: As for No. 1.
1906–5–9–1 (11) (L.B.1 (10)).

ENGR.: By Theodor De Bry in *America*, Pt. I, Pl. XVII, in reverse, with one seated figure omitted and two standing figures and a background of Indians fishing in a lagoon, added.

Described as *Their manner of prainge vvith Rattels abowt te fyer*.

BIBL. & REPR.: *Quinn*, p. 429, No. 42 (a).

The drawing may be compared with the group in the view of Pomeiooc (No. 31) but is probably connected with the *place of solemne prayer* depicted in the drawing of Secoton (No. 36).

41. A MAN AND A WOMAN EATING. Two Indians, a man l. and a woman r., squatting, facing one another on a rush mat, eating fruit (?) from a large round wooden dish placed between them. The man dressed as in No. 34, his head shaven at the sides and back (?), with a cockscomb along the middle and a single upstanding feather at the back. Wearing an ornament, probably of leather, in the lobe of his l. ear. The woman, dressed as in No. 33, wearing a three-string necklace of pearls or beads. **Plate 34**

Water-colours over black lead, touched with white; 20·9 × 21·4 cm. (8¼ × 8½ in.).

INSCR.: *Recto*, at the top, *Theire sitting at meate*.

PROV.: As for No. 1.

1906–5–9–1 (20) (L.B.1 (21)).

ENGR.: By Theodor de Bry in *America*, Pt. I, Pl. XVI, with some additions and modifications and with the lettering, *Their sitting at meate.*

BIBL. & REPR.: *Binyon, White*, Pl. XXV (b). *B.M., Raleigh and Hakluyt*, p. 27, No. 120. *Quinn*, p. 429, No. 43 (a).

42. A PRIEST. Standing, facing half r., his r. foot slightly forward, his r. forefinger pointing to the ground. His hair shaven at the sides with a cockscomb along the middle of his head and a short fringe in front bristling up above the forehead. Wearing a leather ornament in the lobe of his r. ear as in No. 41, and a tunic of rabbit-skins, the fur on the outside, reaching to his thighs, covering his l. arm and fastened at the r. shoulder with a knot. **Plate 33**

Water-colours over black lead, touched with white (oxidized); 26·2 × 15·1 cm. (10⅜ × 5⅞ in.).

INSCR.: *Recto*, at the top, *One of their Religious men.*

V, with the lettering, *On of the Religeous men in the towne of Secota*, and a back view of the same figure against a background of a lagoon. In quite a different posture in the frontispiece to the same work.

PROV.: As for No. 1.

1906–5–9–1 (14) (L.B.1 (15)).

ENGR.: By G. Veen in *America*, Pt. I, Pl.

BIBL. & REPR.: *Hakluyt* (MacLehose edn.), VIII, p. 376. *Binyon, White*, Pl. XXVIII (a). *B.M., Raleigh and Hakluyt*, p. 27, No. 119. *Quinn*, p. 430, No. 44 (a).

43. INDIANS FISHING. A wide, shallow channel of the sea. In the foreground, a canoe paddled by two Indians standing at the bow and the stern, with two other figures squatting in the centre by a small fire and surrounded by a pile of fish; against the prow, a fishing net. In the middle distance, a fish-weir of stakes stretching obliquely towards the far side of the lagoon, with a square cage attached in which a number of fish, including a skate, are trapped. To the r., two figures wading in the water spearing fish. In the distance, another canoe with two occupants and beyond, low hills surmounted by trees. In the water, numerous fish and marine creatures, including, lower r., a Hammer-headed Shark and, by the shore line, two shells with Hermit Crabs (No. 6) and a King Crab. Behind the canoe, another Hammer-headed Shark, and to the r., near the stern, a Striped Mullet or Striped Bass (No. 78, *f.* 104v.). Between the two figures with spears, two Trigger-fish (No. 30) and, furthest, an unidentified large fish; below the fish-trap, a Catfish and to the right of it, a Spiny Box-fish (No. 53); on the extreme l., near the bow of the canoe, a Mud-fish (?). Along the shore, various plants, some in flower. In the sky, in the upper l.-hand corner, a Brown Pelican (No. 52) with two Trumpeter Swans (No. 78, *f.* 81r.) flying below; and near the r.-hand edge, a flight of nine duck. **Plate VII**

Water-colours touched with white and gold; 35·3 × 23·5 cm. (13⅞ × 9¼ in.).

INSCR.: *Recto*, at the top, *The manner of their fishing.*; and on the canoe, *Cannow.*

PROV.: As for No. 1.
1906–5–9–1 (6) (L.B.1 (5)).

ENGR.: By Theodor de Bry in *America*, Pt. I, Pl. XIII, with many additions and modifications (*See* note). Described as *Their manner of fishynge in Virginia*.

BIBL. & REPR.: *Binyon, White*, Pl. XXVI. *B.M., Eng. Topographical and Landscape Drawing*, p. 5, No. 14. *B.M., Raleigh and Hakluyt*, p. 26, No. 112. *Quinn*, p. 433, No. 46 (a).

An example of a composite drawing in which the artist has brought together from his numerous individual sketches, a number of fish, marine creatures, plants and birds not necessarily all appropriate to the area (Cape Hatteras, N. Carolina), as for example, the W. Indian Hermit Crabs (and shells) and the Hammer-headed Shark. The word *Cannow* (canoe) is itself of W. Indian origin. The appearance of the King-crab (*Limulus polyphemus*) is of special interest as one of the earliest known representations of this creature (*See Science* (N.S.), XXVII, 1908, p. 669). The engraving by de Bry includes many additional features such as the three fish weirs in the background and a quite different kind of fish-trap—a feature almost certainly derived from a variant of the present drawing. Among the additional fish, reptiles, etc., in the engraving, which are found elsewhere among the White drawings or copies, are a White Cat-fish (No. 78, *f.* 107 *v.*), a Garfish (No. 78, *f.* 105 *v.*), a Diamond-back Terrapin (No. 57), and a W. Indian Land Crab (No. 5).

44. COOKING IN A POT. A large earthenware pot with pointed base, containing meat, maize etc., resting on the logs of a fire.

Water-colours over black lead, touched with gold and white; 15 × 19·5 cm. ($5\frac{7}{8}$ × $7\frac{5}{8}$ in.).

INSCR.: *Recto*, to the l. and r. of the cooking vessel, *The seething——of their meate.* | *in Potts——of earth.*

PROV.: As for No. 1.
1906–5–9–1 (11a) (L.B.1 (11)).

ENGR.: By G. Veen in *America*, Pt. I, Pl. XV, with the lettering, *Their seetheynge of their meate in earthen pottes* and the addition of a man, r., fanning the flames, and a woman, l., holding a ladle.

BIBL.: *B.M., Raleigh and Hakluyt*, p. 27, No. 116. *Quinn*, p. 437, No. 48 (a).

45. GRILLING FISH. Two fish cooking on a grill built of wooden stakes, over a log fire. At the r., close to the fire, two more fish, impaled on sticks. **Plate VIII [b]**

Water-colours over black lead, heightened with white (oxidized) and gold; 14·6 × 17 cm. ($5\frac{3}{4}$ × $6\frac{3}{4}$ in.).

INSCR.: *Recto*, at the bottom, *The broyling of their fish ouer th' flame of fier.*

PROV.: As for No. 1.
1906–5–9–1 (11b) (L.B. 1 (12)).

ENGR.: By Theodor De Bry in *America*, Pt. I, Pl. XIV, in reverse, with the lettering, *The brovvyllinge of their fishe ouer the flame*, and the addition of two men, dressed as in No. 46, one to the l. of the fire, holding a pronged fork, the other to the r. carrying a basket of fish.

BIBL.: *B.M., Raleigh and Hakluyt*, p. 27, No. 117. *Quinn*, p. 435, No. 47 (a).

46. A CHIEF (POSSIBLY WINGINA). Standing, facing half l., with legs slightly apart, his r. foot placed on a stone and his arms folded. His hair dressed as in No. 34

and his skin apron, with pearls inset in the fringe, worn as in No. 37. In his l. ear, a bead ornament hanging from a loop at the lobe. Around his neck, a short single necklace of pearls and a thong supporting a square gorget of copper (?) which hangs on his chest. On his r. wrist, a pearl bracelet.

Water-colours and gold over black lead, touched with white; 26·2 × 14·7 cm. (10⅜ × 5¾ in.).

INSCR.: Recto, at the top, A cheife Herowan.

PROV.: As for No. 1.
1906–5–9–1 (21) (L.B.1 (22)).

ENGR.: By Theodor De Bry in America, Pt. I, Pl. VII, in reverse, with the lettering, A chieff Lorde of Roanoac, and the addition of a back view of the same figure against a landscape of Indians fishing as in No. 43.

BIBL.: Quinn, p. 438, No. 49 (a).

If the lettering on the De Bry plate is correct, the figure must represent the chief, Wingina (or Pemisapan).

47. AN INDIAN WOMAN. Standing, facing half l., her hands resting on her shoulders, her r. leg twisted round her l. so that the toes are obscured by the heel of her l. foot. Wearing her hair and head-band as in No. 41, a blue ear-ornament, a short two-string pearl (?) necklace with a pendant, and a fringed deerskin apron as in No. 37. Her cheeks, chin and upper arms painted as in No. 37 and her wrists and calves similarly ornamented.

Water-colours over black lead, touched with white (oxidized) and blue body-colours; 23·4 × 13·5 cm. (9¼ × 5¼ in.).

INSCR.: Recto, at the top, One of the wyues of Wyngyno.

PROV.: As for No. 1.
1906–5–9–1 (17) (L.B.1 (18)).

ENGR.: By G. Veen in America, Pt. I, Pl. VI, in reverse, and the addition of a back view of the same figure against a landscape of a lagoon. With the lettering, A younge gentill woeman daughter of Secota.
COPY: From another version, at No. 78 below, f. 6 r.

BIBL.: Quinn, p. 439, No. 50 (a).

The disparity between the inscription above, the lettering of the engraving and the inscription on the copy, Of Aquascogoc, confirms the belief that White's memory was unreliable when he was working up his finished drawings from the original sketch and that there existed at least three versions of the same subject, all differently inscribed. It will be observed that the artist has treated the left foot as a right foot, as a result, no doubt, of the twisting of the right leg round the left.

48. AN INDIAN PAINTED FOR THE HUNT. Standing to front, his head turned half l., with feet apart, his l. hand holding a six-foot bow, his r. resting on his hip. His hair worn as in No. 46 with the addition of three feathers, one standing upright on his forehead, the others stuck behind his ears. At his l. ear, a pendant copper and bead ornament, a long six-string pearl or bead necklace about his neck and a double bracelet of the same kind on his r. wrist, his l. wrist supported by a leather

47

guard. Wearing a fringed deerskin apron as in No. 37 but without the pearls inset, a quiver partly visible at his l. hip and a puma's (?) tail behind reaching almost to the ground. His face, neck, chest, arms and calves painted in strong lineal and circular patterns. **Plate III**

Water-colours and black lead, touched with white; 26·3 × 15 cm. (10⅜ × 5⅞ in.).

INSCR.: *Recto*, in the top l.-hand corner, *The manner of their attire and | painting them-selues when | they goe to their generall | huntings, or at theire | Solemne feasts.*

PROV.: As for No. 1.
1906–5–9–1 (12) (L.B.1 (13)).

ENGR.: By Theodor de Bry in *America*, Pt. I, Pl. III, in reverse, with the lettering *A weroan or great Lorde of Virginia*, variations, and the addition of a back view of the same figure against a landscape background of a hunting scene. Also in the title-page to the

same work, with considerable modifications. By William Hole, in John Smith's map of Virginia, first published in 1612 (?), the figure reversed, wearing a skin jerkin, a club in the l. hand, the lower end of the quiver showing a fox's head.

COPY: From another version, at No. 78 below, *f.* 6 *v.*

BIBL. & REPR.: *B.M. postcard*, B. 428. *Rowse, Grenville*, Pl. VI. *Kendrick*, Pl. XII a. *B.M., Raleigh and Hakluyt*, p. 27, No. 121. *Quinn*, p. 440, No. 51 (a).

Pl. XXIII of *America*, Pt. I, shows a back view of the same figure.

49. A MEDICINE MAN. In a dancing posture, facing half r., with both arms raised, his l. hand above his head, his r. turned up at the wrist to shoulder level, his l. leg half bent behind him and the back of his r. foot touching the ground in front. His head adorned at the r. side with a small bird, its wings outstretched. About his waist, a leather girdle over which a skin breach cloth hangs down in front, the mask of the animal at the top. Tucked through the girdle at his r. hip, a skin bag with long tassels hanging down to his knees. **Plate I**

Water-colours over black lead, touched with white (oxidized); 24·6 × 15·1 cm. (9¾ × 6 in.).

INSCR.: *Recto*, in the top l.-hand corner, *The flyer.*

PROV.: As for No. 1.
1906–5–9–1 (16) (L.B.1 (17)).

ENGR.: By G. Veen in *America*, Pt. I, Pl. XI, with the lettering, *The Coniuerer*, and a

landscape background of a river with Indian fishing and hunting water-fowl. Also in the frontispiece to the same work, the posture quite different.

BIBL. & REPR.: *B.M. Postcard*, B.430. *Allen*, p. 446. *Quinn*, p. 442, No. 52 (a).

For the significance of the bird worn on the head, see *Flannery, Analysis*, No. 95. The inscription seems suggestive of a dancing ceremonial.

50. COMMON MILKWEED (*Asclepias syriaca*). Section of the plant, l., showing five pairs of leaves and the terminal fruit, and r., the root. **Plate 22**

Water-colours over black lead, touched with white; 35·6 × 20·9 cm. (14 × 8¼ in.).

INSCR.: *Recto*, in the upper r.-hand corner, *Wysauke*, and in the upper l.-hand corner, *The hearbe wch the Sauages call Wysauke | wherewth theie cure their wounds w^{ch} | they receaue by the poysoned arroes | of theire enemyes.*

PROV.: As for No. 1.
1906–5–9–1 (37) (L.B.1 (38)).

WCT.: By an unknown artist in Gerard, *Herball* (1597), p. 752 (*See* note).

COPY: From another version, at No. 78 below, *f.* 26 r.

BIBL. & REPR.: *Blunt*, p. 84. *Quinn*, p. 444, No. 54 (a).

The woodcut referred to above, from its similarity to the present drawing, was doubtless executed after another version by White. Gerard's description shows his familiarity with some of the details of the Virginia enterprise (*See also* p. 68). The Indian word *wysauke* derives from an Algonkian root meaning bitter.

51. ROSEGENTIAN (*Sabbatia stellaris* Pursh). Stem of the plant bearing three flowers and two buds. **Plate 25**

Water-colours over black lead, heightened with white; 34·9 × 18 cm. (13¾ × 7⅛ in.).

PROV.: As for No. 1.
1906–5–9–1 (38) (L.B.1 (39)).

BIBL.: *Quinn*, p. 447, No. 55.

The Saltmarsh Rosegentian is common along the coasts of N. Carolina and Virginia. As with the Milkweed (No. 50), White drew it for its reputed medicinal properties.

52. EASTERN BROWN PELICAN (*Pelicanus occidentalis occidentalis* Linn.). Decapitated head, in profile to r. **Plate 35**

Water-colours over black lead, heightened with white; 18·5 × 22·4 cm. (7¼ × 8⅞ in.).

INSCR.: *Recto*, at the top, *Alcatrassa. This fowle is of the greatnes of a Swanne. | and of the same forme sauing the heade, wch is in length . 16 . ynches*; and, at the foot, towards the r., *Tanboril.*, being the title for the drawing, now separated, of the Swell-fish (No. 54). At the extreme lower edge, the tips of the letters of the inscription on No. 54.

PROV.: As for No. 1.
1906–5–9–1 (58) (L.B.1 (60)).

BIBL.: *Quinn*, p. 447, No. 57 (a).

The bird is found on the coasts of N. Carolina in the summer where doubtless White drew it as it also appears in No. 43. The drawing of the Swell-fish (No. 54) was originally on the same sheet as the present drawing and must later have been cut away separating the drawing from its heading.

53. BURRFISH (*Chilomycterus schoepfi* Walbaum). In profile facing l. Inflated.

Water-colours over black lead, heightened with white; 13 × 20·5 cm. (5⅛ × 8⅛ in.).

INSCR.: *Recto*, at the top, *Gallo.*

PROV.: As for No. 1.
1906–5–9–1 (54) (L.B.1 (56)).

COPY: From another version, at No. 78 below, *f.* 18 r. (a).

BIBL.: *Quinn*, p. 455, No. 96 (a).

54. SWELL-FISH (*Spheroides testudineus* Linn.). In profile, facing l. Inflated.

Water-colours over black lead, touched with white (oxidized); 9·9 × 16·8 cm. (3⅞ × 6⅝ in.).

INSCR.: *Recto*, at the top [Tanboril], *A fresh ryuer fish.*, the top of some of the strokes cut away (*See* No. 52).

PROV.: As for No. 1.
1906–5–9–1 (51) (L.B.1 (53)).

COPY: From another version, at No. 78 below, *f.* 14 r. (*b*).

BIBL.: *Quinn*, p. 456, No. 100 (a).

This Swell-fish is more common in W. Indian waters and may have been drawn there.

55. LOGGERHEAD TURTLE (*Caretta caretta* Linn.). Seen from above, facing l.

Water-colours over black lead, heightened with white; 18·7 × 25·9 cm. (7⅜ × 10¼ in.).

PROV.: As for No. 1.
1906–5–9–1 (70) (L.B.1 (72)).

BIBL. & REPR.: *Binyon, White,* Pl. XXIX (b). *Quinn*, p. 456, No. 101 (Nos. 101 and 103 having the references in the footnotes crossed).

The Atlantic Loggerhead Turtle is the only sea turtle to breed on the Carolina Banks.

56. COMMON BOX TORTOISE (*Terrapene carolina* Linn.). Seen from above, facing l. **Plate 37**

Water-colours over black lead, touched with white; 14·4 × 19·7 cm. (5¾ × 7¾ in.).

INSCR.: *Recto*, at the top, *A land Tort wch the Sauiages esteeme aboue all other Torts.*

PROV.: As for No. 1.
1906–5–9–1 (68) (L.B.1 (70)).

BIBL.: *Quinn*, p. 456, No. 102.

See Hariot's reference to tortoises and turtles in *America*, Pt. I, p. 21.

57. DIAMOND-BACK TERRAPIN (*Malaclemys terrapin* Latreille). Seen from above, the head facing r. **Plate 38**

Water-colours over black lead, heightened with white; 17·4 × 25·2 cm. (6⅞ × 10 in.).

PROV.: As for No. 1.
1906–5–9–1 (69) (L.B.1 (71)).

BIBL. & REPR.: *B.M., Raleigh and Hakluyt,* p. 28, No. 125. *Quinn*, p. 457, No. 103 (Nos. 103 and 101 having the references in the footnotes crossed).

58. SWALLOW-TAIL BUTTERFLY (*Papilio turnus*). Seen from above, with wings outspread, head uppermost. **Plate 36**

Water-colours over black lead, with blue body-colour and touched with white; 13·9 × 19·8 cm. (5½ × 7¾ in.).

PROV.: As for No. 1.
1906–5–9–1 (66) (L.B.1 (68)).

WCT.: By an unknown artist, in Thomas Moffet's *Insectorum . . . Theatrum*, 1634, p. 98, after another version of the drawing (See note).

COPY: From another version, at No. 78 below, *f.* 14 r. (*a*).

BIBL. & REPR.: *Holland. Adams. B.M., Raleigh and Hakluyt*, p. 28, No. 123; *Quinn*, p. 458, No. 107 (a).

The other version by White from which the above woodcut was taken, appears in Thomas Moffet's 'Insectorum . . . Theatrum' (B.M., Sloane MS., 4014) *f.* 96 r. It bears the inscription, *Hanc è Virginiâ | Americanâ Candidus* [White] *ad me* [Thomas Penny the naturalist] *Pictor detulit. | 1587*. This note establishes White as the author. The date 1587 might equally refer to the time of presentation as to the time of the artist's return from America and there is nothing inconsistent with White's having executed the drawing in 1585/6. The discovery of the Moffet drawing makes the evidence for White's authorship of the present set of drawings even stronger since the hand is almost certainly the same.

59. MAP OF THE E. COAST OF N. AMERICA: CHESAPEAKE BAY TO THE FLORIDA KEYS.

On the mainland, towards the top, the arms of Sir Walter Raleigh. To the r., along the coast of N. Carolina, Indian villages indicated by red dots. Off the coast, outside the Banks, two English vessels with their sails furled, lying at anchor, and further S., two sailing W. towards S. Carolina. Further E., two other vessels, sailing away from and towards the coast. In the sea, dolphins, both fish (No. 26) and mammal, flying-fish (No. 27), a Queen Trigger-fish (No. 30), whales, sea-monsters, etc. In the centre, to the r., the points of the compass and to the r. again, running from top to bottom, a scale of degrees of latitude marked off from 24 to 40.

Pen and brown ink over black lead, and water-colours, heightened with white (oxidized) and gold, over grey and brown wash; many details offset on either side of the central fold; on two conjoined sheets; 37 × 47.2 cm. (14⅝ × 18⅝ in.).

INSCR.: *Recto*, in the top r.-hand corner, on a promontary (?), *NORAM* [Norambega]. To the l., on the mainland, above and below the Raleigh arms, *LA | VIRG | ENIA | PARS*. Along the coast-line from the top, the names of numerous villages and physical features: *Scicoac., Chesepiuc., Weapemeoc., Tetipano, Masquetuc., Chawanooc, Moratuc, Tramaskecooc., Dasemunkepeuc, Mentso., Pomeiooc.*, a lake, *Paquip., Aquascogoc, Secoton.*; and the names of islands along the same stretch of coasts, *Croatamung., Etacrewac., Port Ferdinando., Roanoac, Hatarask., Paquiac., Croatoan., Wococon.* Continuing down the coast westwards: *R: Iordano.* (?), *C: de S. Helene., Toupa., STALAME | HOIA., Port Royal., ADVSTA MAION., MACEOV., R. Grande., R: Belle., R: de Gironde., R. de Garonne., R. de Charente., R. de Loyre, R. de Somme., VTINA., R. de Seine., R: de May., Machiaca., Carline, SATVRIONA., R: Des Daufins., C: des Francoys., C: do Mont., C: Canaueral., Les Iardinetz., Coste des Feuz., CATOS., C: DE FLORIDE.*, and below the islands, off the tip of Florida, *Les Martirs.* Up the W. coast of Florida: *Baye des Isles., R. d la Paix., Port de Repoy., Baye de La Ponce.* [C.], *de Rapare.*, and to the r., a lake, *Secrope.* Continuing up the W. coast, several mutilated names, the sheet having been cut down: [. . .] *raburg.*, and to the r., *OATCHAQVA.*, [B. de la]. *Haulte., R. d. Ianpones,* [ ] *h.*, [ ] *rueiles.*; above a representation of a mountain,

[M]ountaigne Pallassi. Down the peninsula of Florida, [T] ER/R/A [F]L/O/R/I/D/A. The islands shown lying across the lower part of the sheet, from l. to r., Bahama., (an illegible name), CIGATEO, IANI, GVANIMA., and at the bottom, IABO. and Moyagora. At the centre of the r.-hand edge, a mutilated name, La Be[rmuda].

Prov.: As for No. 1.

1906–5–9–1 (2) (L.B.1 (1)).

Bibl. & Repr.: Fite & Freeman, pp. 92–4. Quinn, p. 460, No. 109 and Pl. VI.

For White's use of earlier maps in the areas S. of N. Carolina see Professor Quinn's notes referred to in the bibliography above.

60. MAP OF THE E. COAST OF N. AMERICA FROM CHESAPEAKE BAY TO CAPE LOOKOUT. On the mainland, towards the top, the royal arms (damaged by water and offset above). Lower, below the central inlet (Albemarle Sound) and to the l. of the lake inscribed Paquippe, the arms of Sir Walter Raleigh. To the r., between the coastline and the Caroline Banks, in the area inscribed Mentso, three pinnaces, a fourth being represented in Albemarle Sound. To the r., just E. of the Banks, three English vessels, the most northerly (off Hatrask) lying at anchor, the others sailing N. At various points along the coast and in entrances to rivers, etc., Indian canoes. The position of Indian villages indicated by red dots. In the upper section, on the sea, the points of the compass offset above, and in the lower r.-hand corner, a scale of 10 leagues.

Pen and brown ink and water-colours over black lead, heightened with silver (?) (oxidized) and gold and touched with white over grey and brown wash; repaired at two points; 47·8 × 23·5 cm. (18⅞ × 9¼ in.).

Inscr.: Recto, on the land, from the upper l.-hand corner to the lower l.-hand corner, L/A./VI/R/G/I/NEA./P/A/R/S. Along the coastline from the top, the names of villages and physical features: Combec, Mashawatec., Skicóac., Chesepiuc., Sho., Titepano.; then to the l., along the N. coast of Albemarle Sound, Masequetuc., Ricahokene., Cautaking., Weapemeoc., Mascomenge., Warowtani., Chawaonac. R., along the S. coast of Albemarle Sound, Moratuc., Tramaskecooc., Dasemunkepeuc, Roanoac. S., along the coast, Nausegoc., Pomeyooc. and l., on a lake, Paquippe. Continuing S., Mentso., Aquascogoc., Seco, Secoton., Secotaóc., Newasiwac. and to the l., Marasanico. Along the Carolina Banks, S. from the mouth of Albemarle Sound, Croatamung., Etacrewac., Hatrask, Páquiac., Croatoan, and Wococon.

Prov.: As for No. 1.

1906–5–9–1 (3) (L.B.1 (2)).

Engr.: By Theodor de Bry in America, Pt. I., Pl. I, with the lettering, Autore Ioanne With Sculptore Theodoro de Bry, and with a considerable additional area westwards (See note).

Bibl. & Repr.: Hakluyt (MacLehose edn.), VIII, at p. 320. Quinn, p. 461, No. 110 and Fig. 7, pp. 847–8 and 854–72.

Professor Quinn describes the present map as 'the most careful detailed piece of cartography for any part of North America to be made in the sixteenth century, and the first to be based, at least by an Englishman, on a survey made on the ground'. For further notes by this author see the above bibliography. De Bry's engraving is based on a more extensive map closely similar to the above in the E. areas which White himself surveyed, but is otherwise conjectural.

WHITE

[61–2.] INDIANS OF FLORIDA AFTER JACQUES LE MOYNE.

61. INDIAN OF FLORIDA. Standing with feet apart, his body turned half r., his head half l. Wearing his hair caught up in a knot above his head from which a long plume falls down behind, heavy ornaments of silver in the lobes of his ears, a circular gorget of brass (?) from a thong about his neck, similar plaques in sets of four round his elbows and knees, a quiver full of arrows on his back supported by a band over his l. shoulder, and a loin-cloth fringed with tassels. His limbs elaborately painted with horizontal and vertical bands of a chain-like pattern, his neck and torso with flame-like shapes including the same pattern. Holding an arrow in his r. hand and a six-foot bow in his l., the wrist bound by a leather guard and the thumb nail of that hand conspicuously long.   **Plate V**

Pen and brown ink and water colours over black lead, with blue and red body-colours, touched with silver (?) (oxidized), gold and white; the bow string in pen and ink; 26·8 × 13·7 cm. (10½ × 5⅜ in.).

INSCR.: *Recto*, at the top, *Of Florida*.

PROV.: As for No. 1.
1906–5–9–1 (22) (L.B.1 (23)).

BIBL. & REPR.: *Hakluyt* (MacLehose edn.), VIII, at p. 448. *B.M. Postcard*, B.431. *Quinn*, p. 462, No. 1.

As White did not touch Florida on the voyage to Virginia in 1585, it seems certain that the present drawing as well as No. 62 was not done from the life. The type of Indian represented belongs to the Timucua group from the St. John River area of Florida. The resemblance to the figures in De Bry's engravings in *America*, Pt. II (Pls. VIII and XVIII) strongly suggests that White used the same source, namely the drawings of Jacques le Moyne, artist to the French expedition to Florida in 1564 (*See* biographical note above). It has also been remarked that White's Indians of Florida, though taken from Le Moyne, do not have the faces of Europeans as Le Moyne's tend to have judging from the one extant drawing by that artist of Indians (reproduced in *Lorant*, p. 32). The improvement by White on his originals must have resulted from his own close observation of the Indians of N. Carolina.

62. WOMAN OF FLORIDA. Standing to front, her head turned slightly to l. Wearing her hair long on her shoulders, a painted head-band, ear ornaments as in No. 61, a single string necklace of brass beads within which is a simulated necklace painted or tattooed, and a scanty blue garment passing over her r. shoulder leaving her l. breast and shoulder bare, and cut in long points reaching to her knees. Her body and limbs painted as in No. 61 and her face possibly tattooed. In her l. hand, of which the nails are conspicuously long, a bowl held close to her body. In her r., held out from the elbow at her side, a number of corn cobs.   **Plate IV**

Pen and brown ink and water-colours over black lead, with blue body-colour, touched with gold and silver (?) (oxidized); 26·1 × 13·5 cm. (10¼ × 5⅜ in.).

INSCR.: *Recto*, at the top, *Of Florida*.

PROV.: As for No. 1.
1906–5–9–1 (23) (L.B.1 (24)).

BIBL. & REPR.: *B.M. Postcard*, B.432. *Quinn*, p. 462, No. 2.

See note to No. 61.

53

[63–4]. ESKIMO. The following two drawings may well have been made, as Dr. Birket-Smith suggests (*Folk* (Danish Ethnological Association) I, 1959, pp. 25–7), in 1577, on Frobisher's second voyage to the N.W. This view is supported by the existence of the drawing showing English seamen fighting Eskimo, described below (*See* No. 78, *f*. 12 *v*.), but there is no documentary evidence for this. The drawings could have been executed in England, for Frobisher brought back to this country a man, and a woman with a baby. George Best's report of the second voyage says: 'We shewed him [an Eskimo] ye picture of his Countreymā, which yᵉ last yeare was brought into England (whose counterfet we had drawne, with boate, & other furniture, both as he was in his own, & also in english apparell)'. Both White's drawings certainly seem to have been done from the life.

63. AN ESKIMO MAN. Standing facing front, his l. hand resting on a bow, his r. on his hip. Wearing sealskin clothes consisting of a hood or close-fitting cap, a short jacket reaching to the hips, with a long 'tail' visible behind, trousers and long fur-lined boots to his knees. **Plate 39**

Pen and brown ink and water-colours over black lead, touched with white (oxidized); 22·5 × 16·3 cm. (8⅞ × 6½ in.).

PROV.: As for No. 1.
1906–5–9–1 (29) (L.B.1 (30)).

COPY: From another version, at No. 78 below, *f*. 11 r.

BIBL.: *Quinn*, p. 463, No. 1. *Inf.* from Dr. Helge Larsen and Dr. K. Birket-Smith of the National Museum, Copenhagen.

The Eskimo portrayed is a native of Baffin Island. The bow is authentic but somewhat distorted. A similar drawing of a native of the same region by Lucas de Heere, at Ghent (MS. 2466) is inscribed *Homme sauage amené des pais septentrionaux par M. Furbisher L'an 1576* and is reproduced in *Chotzen & Draak* (Plate XXIX).

The drawing emphasises the Mongolian features of the Eskimo, a fact remarked on by the early voyagers who, in search of Cathay, were ready to identify them as Asiatics. White also made a drawing of the back view of this figure (*See* No. 78 below, *f*. 5 *v*.).

64. AN ESKIMO WOMAN. Standing, facing front, her l. hand held behind her hip. Dressed as in No. 63 but with the jacket coming down to a point in front and boots reaching to her thighs. Carrying a baby on her back whose face peeps out of her hood. **Plate 40**

Pen and brown ink and water-colours over black lead, touched with white (oxidized); 22·3 × 16·6 cm. (8¾ × 6½ in.).

PROV.: As for No. 1.
1906–5–9–1 (30) (L.B.1 (31)).

COPY: From another version, at No. 78 below, *f*. 11 v.

BIBL. & REPR.: *B.M.*, *Raleigh and Hakluyt*, p. 13, No. 55. Andersen, p. 112. *Quinn*, p. 464, No. 3.

See note to No. 63.

[65–6]. N. AFRICAN OR EUROPEAN BIRDS.

65. COMMON ROLLER (*Coracias garrulus*). Standing, in profile, facing l.

Water-colours over black lead, with blue body-colour, touched with white; made up in the lower r.-hand corner; 16 × 22·6 cm. (6¼ × 8⅞ in.).

PROV.: As for No. 1.
1906–5–9–1 (64) (L.B.1 (66)).

BIBL.: *Quinn*, p. 464, No. 5.

INSCR.: *Recto*, in the upper r.-hand corner, by a later hand, in black lead, *The Roller*.

A N. African bird migrating to N. Europe.

66. HOOPOE (*Upupa epops*). Standing, in profile, facing r.

Pen and brown ink and water-colours over black lead, heightened with white (oxidized); made up in the upper l.-hand corner; 15·1 × 21·2 cm. (6 × 8¾ in.).

BIBL.: *Quinn*, p. 464, No. 6.

A N. African bird migrating to N. Europe and occasionally England.

PROV.: As for No. 1.
1906–5–9–1 (61) (L.B.1 (62)).

[67–71]. ANCIENT BRITONS. Theodor De Bry in Pt. I of *America* adds five plates to those of Indians and their villages under the title, 'Som Picture of the Pictes which in the olde tyme dyd habite one part of the great Bretainne'. These engravings, as with those of Virginia, are after originals by White which are variants, in four instances, of the following drawings. The engraver also adds, 'The painter of whom, I haue had the first . of . the Inhabitans of Virginia, give my allso thees 5. Figures following, fownd as he did assured my in a oolld English cronicle, the which I wold well sett to the ende of thees first Figures, for to showe how that the Inhabitans of the great Bretannie haue bin in times past as sauuage as those of Virginia'. No such 'cronicle' has in fact been discovered though White may well have been working from older models. His 'Picts' form a close parallel to those of Lucas de Heere in that artist's *Corte beschryvinghe van England, Scotland, ende Irland* (B.M., Add. MS., 28, 330, *f*. 8*b*.) and reproduced in *Kendrick*, Pl. XIII (b). *Cf.* similar illustrations by Nicholaes van Geilenkercken for Cluverius, *de Germania Antiqua* (1616).

67. A 'PICT' WARRIOR. Nude figure standing to front, with feet apart and head turned half l., carrying a circular shield in his l. hand and in his r., a man's head. Wearing his hair reaching to the shoulders, a moustache, a scimitar at his back, his body stained blue and painted with grotesque heads of birds, animals and serpents.

Water-colours touched with white over black lead, with pen and brown ink on the feet and hair; 24·5 × 17 cm. (9⅝ × 6¾ in.).

1906–5–9–1 (24) (L.B.1 (25)).

ENGR.: By Theodor de Bry in *America*, Pt. I (*Picts*), Pl. I, with the lettering, *The Trvve picture of one Picte*. Also by John Speed, with considerable modifications, in his *Historie of Great Britaine*, p. 180, reproduced in *Kendrick*, Pl. XV.

BIBL. & REPR.: *Kendrick*, pp. 123–5 and Pl. XIII (a). *Van de Waal*, I, p. 92; II, Pl. XXXVI (2). *Quinn*, p. 463, No. 3 (a).

68. A 'WOMAN NEIGHBOUR TO THE PICTS'.

Standing, facing front, her feet slightly apart and her head turned half r. Wearing long hair falling over her shoulders, a kind of short apron tunic laced up in front, leaving her breasts bare, a long scimitar with a hilt in the form of a bird's head at her back and hanging from a leather belt round her waist. Holding a long spear in her r. hand and resting her l. hand on her hips.

Pen and brown ink and water-colours over black lead, touched with white (oxidized); 22·2 × 15·4 cm. (8¾ × 6⅛ in.).

PROV.: As for No. 1.

1906–5–9–1 (25) (L.B.1 (26)).

ENGR.: By Theodor de Bry in *America*, Pt. I (*Picts*), Pl. V, with modifications and the lettering, *The Trvve picture of a women nigbour to the Pictes*. Also by John Speed with considerable modifications, in his *Historie of Great Britaine*, p. 181, as Boadicea, reproduced in *Kendrick*, Pl. XV.

BIBL.: *Kendrick*, p. 124, and *Quinn*, p. 463, No. 4 (a).

69. A 'PICT' WARRIOR.

Nude figure, standing to front, with his feet apart and head turned half r., carrying a circular shield over his l. forearm and holding a spear in his r. hand. Wearing his hair long reaching to his shoulders, a moustache, a thick cord as a necklace and a girdle of similar material from which a scimitar hangs by a chain at his back. His body stained blue and painted with star-shaped and other patterns simulating neckbands, bracelets and hose.

Pen and ink and water-colours over black lead, touched with white (oxidized); 24·3 × 15·2 cm. (9½ × 6 in.).

PROV.: As for No. 1.

1906–5–9–1 (26) (L.B.1 (27)).

BIBL. & REPR.: *Kendrick*, Pl. XII (b). *Quinn*, p. 463, No. 5 (a).

70. A WOMAN 'PICT'.

Nude figure, walking to r., looking back over her r. shoulder. Wearing her hair long reaching to her hips, a thick cord as a necklace and a double girdle of the same material round her waist from which a scimitar hangs at her back. Holding in her r. hand two spears horizontally and in her l. a third resting on the ground. Her body stained blue and painted with grotesque beasts' heads at the shoulders and knees, with half moons, stars and net-like patterns to simulate material on her legs.

Pen and brown ink and water-colours over black lead, touched with white; 23 × 17·9 cm. (9 × 7 in.).

PROV.: As for No. 1.

1906–5–9–1 (27) (L.B.1 (28)).

ENGR.: By Theodor de Bry in *America*, Pt. I (*Picts*), Pl. II, with the lettering, *The Trvve picture of a women Picte*. Also by John Speed, much modified in his *History of Great Britaine*, p. 180, reproduced in *Kendrick*, Pl. XV.

BIBL. & REPR.: *Andersen*, p. 99. *Quinn*, p. 463, No. 6 (a).

71. A 'WARRIOR NEIGHBOUR OF THE PICTS'. Standing to front, with feet apart, his head turned l. Wearing his hair long at the back, a moustache, a short tunic and a leather belt from which a small round shield hangs at his r. side. Holding in his r. hand a long sword which rests on his r. shoulder, his l. hand placed on his hip. His body stained blue.

Pen and brown ink and water-colours over black lead, heightened with white; 23·6 × 15·4 cm. (9¼ × 6 in.).

PROV.: As for No. 1.
1906–5–9–1 (28) (L.B.1 (29)).

ENGR.: By Theodor de Bry in *America*, Pt. I (*Picts*), Pl. IV, with modifications.

BIBL.: *Quinn*, p. 463, No. 7 (a). *Inf.* from Mr. M. Kinnard.

The small shield is certainly English and of a type in use in the early Tudor period. The sword may also be English but is too indefinite to date. It is not impossible that White drew both sword and shield from surviving models. The present drawing is distinct from the others and lacks the imaginative ornamentation found in them.

[72–76]. ORIENTALS. The following drawings of oriental figures are no doubt copies from earlier costume or travel books. Connected illustrations which point to a common source are noted under the drawing in question. There is no evidence that White travelled to the East.

72. AN UZBEK (?). Standing facing front, his head turned half l. Wearing a conical fur cap, a beard, and a long striped sleeveless cloak over a blue coat, white trousers and red shoes.

Water-colours and blue body-colour over black lead, heightened with black; 24·3 × 13·9 cm. (9⅝ × 5½ in.).

PROV.: As for No. 1.
1906–5–9–1 (33) (L.B.1 (34)).

BIBL.: *Quinn*, p. 464, No. 9.

73. A TURK (?). Standing to front, his head facing r. Wearing a flat hat secured by a band covering his ears and passing under his chin, a long sleeveless striped cloak over white trousers, the upper part of his body being bare, shoes of a yellowish brown and a short scimitar hanging from his waistband.

Water-colours over black lead; 22·5 × 15·5 cm. (8⅞ × 6⅛ in.).

PROV.: As for No. 1.
1906–5–9–1 (31) (L.B.1 (32)).

BIBL.: *Quinn*, p. 464, No. 7.

74. A TURKISH WOMAN. Standing facing front, with feet apart, her l. hand on her hip, her r. holding in front a loose diaphanous outer garment wrapped round her and draped over her l. shoulder. Wearing also a head-dress of white cloth falling down behind, a black veil covering her face, a long coat caught up in front to reveal a red under-garment tied about her waist with a sash, and red shoes.

Water-colours over black lead, heightened with black and white; 21·1 × 16·3 cm. (8¼ × 6⅜ in.).

PROV.: As for No. 1.
1906–5–9–1 (34) (L.B.1 (35), as a man).

BIBL.: *Quinn*, p. 464, No. 10, as 'A man, possibly Levantine'. *Inf.* from Mrs. O. Kurz.

Nicolas de Nicolay in *Les Quatres Premiers Livres des Navigations et Peregrinations Orientales*, 1568, includes a plate (B.M. copy, p. 68 C) sufficiently close to the present drawing to suggest a common prototype. It is entitled *Femme Turque vestue a la Moresque* and differs in the following particulars: the veil is raised, the r. hand lies on the buttoned under-garment, the outer garment lying open about the shoulders; the l. hand, instead of resting on the hip, holds up the under-garment from the ground. The stance and posture are however essentially the same. An English edition of Nicolay appeared in 1585 with a smaller version of the illustration at p. 56, entitled *A Turkie woman apparrelled after the Moorish fashion*.

75. A TURKISH WOMAN. Standing, facing half r., with feet apart. Wearing a head-dress and veil of white material leaving only the eyes visible, a long red coat buttoning down the front with side openings into which both hands are thrust, and yellow shoes.

Water-colours over black lead; 22·2 × 15·3 cm. (8¾ × 6 in.).

PROV.: As for No. 1.
1906–5–9–1 (32) (L.B.1 (33)).

BIBL.: *Quinn*, p. 464, No. 8. *Inf.* from Mrs. O. Kurz.

Another plate (B.M. copy, p. 76 A) in Nicolay (*See* No. 74), entitled *Femme Turque allant par la ville* is somewhat similar to the present drawing although the head-dress is quite different and there is a shawl or cloth about the face, neck and shoulders. There is also a veil of some stiff material. But the stance and close similarity of the rest of the costume suggest a common prototype. Again, a smaller version of the illustration appears in the English edition, entitled *A woman Turke going through the Citie* (p. 63).

76. A GREEK WOMAN (?). Standing facing half l., holding a rose to her face in her r. hand, her l., which holds a pomegranate, resting on her hip. Wearing a close fitting red cap, a short red tunic with frogged ornament in front, a white belt over a loose garment of white cloth, and trousers worn in the Mohammedan manner.

Water-colours over black lead, touched with silver (?) (oxidized); 21 × 9·4 cm. (8⅜ × 3¾ in.).

PROV.: As for No. 1.
1906–5–9–1 (35) (L.B.1 (36)).

BIBL.: *Quinn*, p. 464, No. 11.

The stance and the tunic perhaps have a remote connexion with the *Fille de Joye Turque* of Nicolay (B.M. copy, p. 160 C; *See* No. 74).

77. ALBUM. Containing seventy-two offsets from the above drawings (*See* introductory note) but lacking Nos. 1, 3, 39 and 59, the last three being large folding drawings offprinting on to themselves. After the cutting out of the original drawings, the offsets remaining in the original album have in a number of instances made faint counter-proofs through the intervening spaces on the backs of the adjoining offsets. It may thus be possible, by identifying these counter proofs, to reconstruct the original order of the drawings.

36·5 × 22·7 cm. (14$\frac{3}{8}$ × 9 in.).

PROV.: From Aug. 1865, *See* introductory note, p. 30, then as for No. 1.

BINDING: XIX c. red morocco, gilt, by F. Bedford, London.

1906–5–9–2.

78. ALBUM. Containing 113 leaves of drawings of Indians of Virginia and fauna and flora after John White, Indians of Brazil after Jean de Léry, European or W. Asiatic flora, after Dutch originals, and miscellaneous costume studies, etc. All are copies except for those (mounted at some later date (?)) on *f.* 41*v.* and *f.* 70*v.* The quality of the drawings is somewhat unequal being generally competent but occasionally becoming crude as for example in the drawing of the skink (*f.* 109*v.*). The White copies are probably by one or at the most two hands and the fact that one watermark (close to *Heawood*, Nos. 2877 and 2878) occurs almost consistently throughout the first section of White copies (*ff.* 3–26) and only two others (*Briquet*, Nos. 13148 and 13163) throughout the last section of copies of lost drawings by White (*ff.* 75–113) tends to support this view. Whilst there is no direct evidence of authorship, some light is thrown on the problem and on the history of the present album by the draft letter of Sir Hans Sloane to Abbé Bignon recently discovered by M. Jean Jacquot in the Dept. of MSS. (Sloane MS. 4069, *ff.* 112*v.*–113). Though undated it must have been written between July 1st and October 30th, 1709 and contains this passage:

'Vous n'ignorez pas que Theodore de Bry a fait un receuil de voyages aux Indes Orientales et Occidentales avec de fort bonnes tailles douces. Les planches de la Iere partie, qui appartiennent a la Virginie sont tres-belles, et a vous parler franchement si belles et si curieuses que je ne croyois pas qu'elles fussent naturelles mais que cet illustre graveur y avait adjouté du sien. Le hazard m'a tiré de cet erreur, car il y a deux ou trois ans que chez les descendans d'un Peintre et dessinateur nommé White, lequel avoit voyagé avec Sr Walter Raleigh, je vis le livre original d'ou toutes ces planches ont esté tirées. Il y en avoit aussi beaucoup d'autres tres-curieuses que Theodore de Bry a negligé de nous donner. Parmi celles ci sont toutes les Plantes, tous les Oiseaux, les Poissons &c. Il y en a aussi plusieurs qui regardent les manieres et les moeurs des Indiens, et que j'estime dautant plus curieuses qu'ils etoient naturels avant leur communication avec les Europeans. Theodore de Bry nous dit dans le proeme qu'il a mis au devant de ses planches qu'ils les avoit de White. Ne pouvant pas acheter ce livre je l'ai tout fait copier par un assez habile homme. L'original etoit un peu gaté parce que de jeunes gens s'en servoient pour apprendre a dessiner . . . .'

59

'Le livre original' can only be identified with the present album of drawings which by the time the above letter was written Sloane had not yet acquired from its owner. The copies he had made are evidently those found scattered among the Sloane MSS. and noted beneath the relevant drawings below. When at some later date the album passed into Sloane's collection, he added an explanatory note on *f. 4r.* in which he again describes the drawings as 'originall draughts . . . by M.' John White'. According to the letter, Sloane discovered the album in 1706 or 1707 when it still belonged to the White family and was being used as a copy book by the children. As it must be presumed that the drawings had remained in the family since they were executed, the meaning of the phrase inscribed on *f. 2r.* 'This Lent to my soon whit' can only be the straightforward one, 'This lent to my son White'. A widow who had previously been married to a White, could, after remarriage, have referred to a son by her former husband's name. The supposition is that someone of the generation following John White, perhaps a son, executed the copies *c.* 1610, and that during the next hundred years the album was passed down through his descendants until its acquisition by Sloane sometime after 1709. The same hand can perhaps be distinguished in one or two copies in Edward Topsell's MS. 'The Fowles of Heauen' (Huntington Library, Ellesmere MS., 1142), noted below, in particular that 're- ceived from . . . *Master* Hakluyt' (See *f. 91r.*). If so, Hakluyt presumably obtained one or several drawings directly from the artist of the present series, which he presented to Topsell before *c.* 1614, the probable date of that author's work.

39 × 28·5 cm. (15⅜ × 11¼ in.).

BINDING: Modern half blue morocco by the B.M., with the Sloane Library book stamp blocked in gold on the covers.

f. 1r. BLANK.

f. 1v. INSCR.: In a XVII c. hand (?), *W. Raughleys Book* and then by Sloane, *by White. M.' Catesbys* ———— and again, in the first hand near the r.-hand edge, *VO* [L. I] / *Nat Hi* [st of F]*lori* [da] / *p* [ag]*e*, and near the l.-hand edge, *page.* Beneath, *141 Bald Eagle* ———— *i.* The next line deleted. Continuing down the page, *150 Red head Woodpecker* ———— *20* / *152 large Woodpecker* ———— *17* / *153. Blue bird* ———— *47* / *154 Hairy Woodpecker* ———— *19* / *155* (next words deleted) *The yellow Woodpecker Nat Hist Jam* [aica] / *vol : 2ᵈ 201* / *Tab : 25* / *156 Red Wing'd* (*Woodpecker* deleted) *Starling* ———— *13* / *157. Towhee Bird* ———— *34* / *158 Redbird*

of Virg : ———— *38* / *159 Gold Wing'd Woodpecker* ————*18* / *160 blue Jay* ———— *15* / *162 Fox colour'd Thrush 28* / *151. Purple Jackday* ———— *12* / *19* ———— *flying fish* ———— and lower down, on the r., *Vol 2.* Following on beneath, as before, *16* (*Squirrel fish* deleted) *Hind 14* / *18 Old Wife 22* (?) (partly torn away) / *20 Squirrel fish* (number torn away) and page here cut off short.

Sloane has collated a number of the natural history subjects below with plates in Mark Catesby's *Natural History of Carolina, Florida and the Bahama Islands,* 1731–43 and, in one instance, with his own *Natural History of Jamaica.*

f. 2r. INSCR.: In a XVII c. hand, *There is in this Book a hondred and 12 Leaues / with flowers and Pickters and of fish and of fowles / beside wast Paper / this Lent to my soon whit 11 Aprell 1673*; and in an XVIII c. hand, *5270* (the Sloane MS. number), and again in a different hand of that period *Min. 79* (the number deleted), and *Min. 56* (the whole deleted). In Sloane's hand, *The originall draughts of yᵉ habits, towns | customs &c of the West Indians, and of the plants | birds fishes &c found in Groenland, Virginia, | Guiana &c. by M. John White who was a Painter | & accompanied Sʳ Walter Ralegh in his voyag[e]. | See the preface to the first part of America of Theodore de Bry or | the description of Virginia where some of these/draughts are curiously cutt by that Graver/.* In another XVIII c. hand, *Many are | duplicates* and again, in another hand of the same period, *Bibliothecæ Sloanianæ Min: 111.* and *Jamaica,* spelt variously and deleted, on four different parts of the page.

The first inscription, in a semi-literate hand, must have been written about sixty years after the drawings were executed and, as suggested in the introductory note, probably by a descendant of John White. In stating that there were 112 leaves, the writer was perhaps referring to the original pagination of the album which can still be traced up to *f.* 110. Sloane's inscription which follows should be read together with his letter to Abbé Bignon quoted in the introductory note.

ff. 2*v.* & 3*r.* THE VILLAGE OF POMEIOOC. As for No. 32 but on a larger scale with the addition, outside the stockade, of corn fields, l. and r., and three small ponds in the upper r.-hand corner.
  Pen and brown ink and water-colours, heightened with white or silver (oxidized?).

INSCR.: At the top, *POMEIOOC,* in the upper l.-hand corner, *1* and in the upper r.-hand corner, in an XVIII c. hand, *1.*

  L.B.3 (1).

COPY: In Sloane MS. 5253, No. 14.

BIBL.: *Quinn,* p. 416, No. 33 (b).

With its additional features, this drawing is nearer to De Bry's engraving than to No. 32 and must have been copied from another version closer to that used by the engraver.

f. 3*v.* OFFSET OF No. 4*r.*

INSCR.: In the upper l.-hand corner, *z.*

f. 4*r.* ENGLISH COURTIER (?) OF THE XV c. Walking to l., his head turned half l., his hands raised in front. Wearing a long purple gown reaching to the ground with high, fur-lined (?) collar and hood lined with dark red.
  Pen and brown ink and water-colours with purplish and dark red body-colours, touched with white (oxidized); mounted.

INSCR.: In the upper l.-hand corner, in an XVIII c. hand, *17.*

  L.B.3 (16).

f. 4*v.* OFFSET OF A MALE FIGURE IN TUDOR COSTUME, WEARING A BONNET. From a folio now lost.

f. 5*r.* A WOMAN OF SECOTON. As for No. 37.
  Water-colours heightened with white (oxidized); mounted.

INSCR.: Above, *Of Secoton,* at the upper r.-hand corner, *i* and in the upper l.-hand corner, in an XVIII c. hand, *10.*

  L.B.3 (8).

BIBL.: *Quinn,* p. 423, No. 38 (b).

A copy from another version very close to No. 37.

f. 5*v.* AN ESKIMO MAN. Seen from the back, the face turned half r. Wearing a close-fitting fur cap or hood dividing on his shoulders, a sealskin jacket with a 'tail', trousers and long fur-lined boots reaching above the knee. Holding a bow in his l. hand, and a paddle in his r. Behind him, on the ground, an arrow.

Pen and brown ink and water-colours.

INSCR.: In the upper l.-hand corner, *4* and in an XVIII c. hand, *11*.

L.B.3 (10).

BIBL.: *Quinn*, p. 463, No. 2.

This is a copy of a lost drawing representing the back view of the figure at No. 63 but the paddle is an additional feature.

f. 6r. AN INDIAN WOMAN. As for No. 47 but much more crudely drawn and with differences in the tattoo or painted marks on the face and calves.

Water-colours touched with white (oxidized).

INSCR.: At the top, *Of Aquascogoc* and, in an XVIII c. hand, *8*.

L.B.3 (6).

COPY: In Sloane MS. 5253, No. 17.

BIBL.: *Quinn*, p. 439, No. 50 (b).

f. 6v. AN INDIAN PAINTED FOR THE HUNT. As for No. 48 without tattoo or painted marks or a tail, and with other minor differences.

Water-colours touched with white (oxidized).

INSCR.: In the upper l.-hand corner, *5* and in an XVIII c. hand, *9*.

L.B.3 (9).

COPY: In Sloane MS. 5253, No. 15.

BIBL.: *Quinn*, p. 440, No. 51.

This is a rather weak copy of another version of No. 48 and the distinctly European features in contrast with those of White's original may be noted.

f. 7r. BRAZILIAN NATIVES MOURNING OVER A DEAD MAN. A group of five naked savages, four crouching women, and one man holding a gourd rattle, wailing over the body of a man lying, partly visible, in a hammock in the centre.

Pen and brown ink and water-colours.

INSCR.: In the upper l.-hand corner, in an XVIII c. hand, *3*.

L.B.3 (3).

This is closely related to, and is perhaps a copy of, the woodcut illustration in Jean de Léry, *Histoire d'un Voyage fait en la terre du Brésil*, 1578 (p. 335). It may also be compared with a woodcut on *f. 85v.* of A. Thevet, *Les Singularitez de la France Antarctique, autrement nommée Amerique*, 1558. The figure of a woman squatting with her hands over her face is also found in Thevet, *f. 76v.*, entitled *Ceremonies aux massacres des prisonnieres.*

f. 7v. BRAZILIAN HEAD-HUNTER. A naked savage standing, facing front, head half l. with feet apart. He holds a club in his r. hand, his l. resting on his hip. His chest, arms, thighs and calves, bear long parallel scars or painted marks. At his feet, a severed human head.

Pen and brown ink and water-colours.

INSCR.: In the upper l.-hand corner, *6* and in an XVIII c. hand, *2*.

L.B.3 (2).

This drawing is also related to a woodcut illustration in Léry p. 249 (*See* note to *f. 7r.*).

f. 8r. A ROMAN SOLDIER. Standing in profile to r., holding a bow and arrow. Wearing a helmet, scale cuirasse, tunic and calf-high leather sandals which are bound around the lower legs with thongs. At his back, a quiver full of arrows and, at his r. side, a short sword.

Pen and brown ink and water-colours, touched with white (oxidized).

INSCR.: In the upper l.-hand corner, *15*.

L.B.3 (14).

COPY: In Sloane MS. 5253, No. 1.

f. 8v. A DOGE OF GENOA. Standing to front, his head turned half r. Bearded, wearing a coronet, a robe lined with ermine, an ermine hood and black shoes. Holding in his r. hand a sceptre, his l. hand raised.

Pen and dark brown ink and water-colours, heightened with gold and white (partly oxidized).

INSCR.: At the top, *Duca de Genoua 1575.*, in the upper l.-hand corner, *7* and in an XVIII c. hand, *16*.

L.B.3 (15).

COPY: In Sloane MS. 5253, No. 2.

The present drawing is related to Pl. XXX in Abraham de Brüyn, *Habits de Diverses Nations*, 1581.

f. 9r. FRENCHMAN WELCOMED BY BRAZILIAN SAVAGES. A Frenchman in XVI c. costume, seated in a hammock, covering his face with his r. hand. Opposite him a naked Brazilian woman crouching, her face also hidden in her hands. Behind the hammock stands a naked man breaking an arrow.

Pen and dark brown ink and water-colours, heightened with white (oxidized).

INSCR.: In the upper l.-hand corner, in an XVIII c. hand, *4*.

L.B.3 (4).

COPY: In Sloane MS. 5253, No. 29.

As with the drawings at *ff. 7r.* and *v.* the present drawing is related to the woodcut illustration in Léry, p. 315. The ceremony of welcome is described on pp. 314–17 of that work.

f. 9v. A BRAZILIAN WITH HIS WIFE AND CHILD. A naked savage holding a bow in his l. hand and arrows in his r. Standing in front of a woman with a child supported by a sling.

Pen and brown ink and water-colours.

INSCR.: In the upper l.-hand corner, *8* and in an XVIII c. hand, *5*.

L.B.3 (5).

COPY: In Sloane MS. 5253, No. 24.

This drawing is also closely related to a woodcut in Léry, p. 121.

f. 10r. BRAZILIANS DANCING. A savage bending towards a monkey on the ground, r. He is naked except for variously coloured plumage worn at his back and bands of ornamental material round his calves. Behind him, a woman wearing a feather head-dress, dancing and holding a rattle in her r. hand. In the upper l.-hand corner, on a separate piece of paper inlaid, a parrot perched on a tree, spreading its wings.

Pen and brown ink and water-colours.

INSCR.: In the upper l.-hand corner, in an XVIII c. hand, *6*.

L.B.3 (5A).

COPY: In Sloane MS. 5253, No. 23.

This is again related to the woodcut illustration in Léry, p. 275, which however shows a parrot with wings folded suggesting that the drawing was not copied direct from it.

f. 10*v*. AN OLD MAN OF POMEIOOC. As for No. 34 but with many minor differences including the wearing of feathers in the hair.
Pen and brown ink and water-colours.

INSCR.: In the upper l.-hand corner, *9* and in an XVIII c. hand, *7*.

L.B.3 (7).

COPY: In Sloane MS. 5253, No. 16.

BIBL.: *Quinn*, p. 419, No. 35 (b).

f. 11*r*. AN ESKIMO MAN. As for No. 63, but in reverse, and holding a paddle in his l. hand.
Pen and brown ink and water-colours.

INSCR.: In the upper l.-hand corner, in an XVIII c. hand, *12*.

L.B.3 (11).

COPY: In Sloane MS. 5253, No. 9.

This drawing represents the same figure as at *f.* 5*v*., seen from the front.

f. 11*v*. AN ESKIMO WOMAN. As for No. 64 with minor variations.
Pen and brown ink and water-colours.

INSCR.: In the upper l.-hand corner, *10* and in an XVIII c. hand, *13*.

L.B.3 (12).

COPY: In Sloane MS. 5253, No. 11.

f. 12*r*. BLANK.

f. 12*v*. ENGLISH SAILORS IN A SKIRMISH WITH ESKIMO. An inlet of the sea with icefloes in which a boat, fully manned, and flying a flag showing the cross of St. George and the royal arms, exchanges fire with four Eskimo, armed with bows and arrows, on top of a cliff, r. In the foreground, an Eskimo paddling a kayak, a number of other kayaks being visible in the distance. Beyond the boat, l., a steep headland surmounted by tents with groups of Eskimo above and below, armed with harpoons and bows and arrows. **Frontispiece to plates**
Pen and brown ink and water-colours.

INSCR.: In the upper l.-hand corner, *11* and in an XVIII c. hand, *14*.

L.B.3 (13).

COPY: In Sloane MS. 5253, No. 8, inscribed, *The English in Queen Elizabeth's Reign discouer GRONELAND, land there & are oppos'd by ye Natives.*

BIBL. & REPR.: *Binyon, White*, Pl. XXX. *Quinn*, p. 464, No. 4.

The drawing probably represents an incident on Frobisher's second voyage (1577) (*See* introductory note to Nos. 63 and 64), the original either executed by White from the life or at second hand to illustrate an account. There seems to be a definite relation between the Eskimo in the kayak, in the foreground, and the same in reverse in the woodcut frontispiece to the German and Latin editions of Dionysius Settle's account of Frobisher's last voyage, published in 1580.

f. 13*r*. (*a*) IGUANA. As for No. 9 but darker in colour.
Pen and brown ink and water-colours, heightened with white (oxidized).

INSCR.: Above, *The Gwanoo*, and in the upper l.-hand corner, in an XVIII c. hand, *18*.

L.B.3 (17 (a)).

COPY: In Sloane MS. 5272, No. 22.

BIBL.: *Quinn*, p. 407, No. 8 (b).

(b) CROCODILE OR ALLIGATOR.
As for No. 10, but darker in colour.
Pen and brown ink and water-colours,
touched with white.

L.B.3 (17 (b)).

BIBL.: *Quinn*, p. 407, No. 9 (b).

f. 13*v.* BLANK.

INSCR.: In the upper l.-hand corner, beneath a strip of paper used as strengthening,
12.

f. 14*r.* (a) SWALLOW-TAIL BUTTERFLY.
As for No. 58.
Pen and black ink, water-colours and blue
body-colour.

INSCR.: Below, *MAMANKANOIS* and in
the upper l.-hand corner, in an XVIII c.
hand, *19.*

L.B.3 (18 (a)).

COPY: In Sloane MS. 4014, *f.* 96r.

BIBL.: *Quinn*, p. 458, No. 107 (b).

This is probably a copy of a third version
of the drawing (*See* No. 58).

(b) SWELL-FISH. As for No. 54,
but in reverse, slightly enlarged and darker in
colour.
Pen and brown ink and grey wash, touched
with white.

INSCR.: Below, *TANBOREL.*

L.B.3 (18 (b)).

COPY: In Sloane MS. 5267, No. 42.

BIBL.: *Quinn*, p. 456, No. 100 (b).

f. 14*v.* BLANK.

INSCR.: In the upper l.-hand corner, *13.*

f. 15*r.* (a) REMORA. As for No. 29 but
enlarged and brown in colour.
Water-colours heightened with white.

INSCR.: Below, *REBESO,* and in the upper
l.-hand corner, in an XVIII c. hand, *20.*

L.B.3 (19 (a)).

BIBL.: *Quinn*, p. 412, No. 29 (b).

(b) REMORA. As for No. 28 but in
reverse, enlarged and brown in colour.
Water-colours heightened with white.

L.B.3 (19 (b)).

COPY: In Sloane MS. 5267, No. 9.

BIBL.: *Quinn*, p. 412, No. 28 (b).

f. 15*v.* BLANK.

INSCR.: In the upper l.-hand corner, *14.*

f. 16*r.* LAND CRAB. As for No. 5.
Pen and brown ink and water-colours.

INSCR.: Above, *A LANDE CRABE* and in
the upper l.-hand corner, in an XVIII c.
hand, *21.*

L.B.3 (20).

COPY: In Sloane MS. 5262, No. 10.

BIBL.: *Quinn*, p. 405, footnote 1.

f. 16*v.* BLANK.

INSCR.: In the upper l.-hand corner, *15.*

E

C.E.D.

f. 17r. (*a*) BLUE-STRIPED GRUNT. As for No. 24 but enlarged.

Pen and brown ink, water-colours and blue body-colour, touched with white.

INSCR.: Below, *PEFFE PICA* and in the upper l.-hand corner, in an XVIII c. hand, *22*.

L.B.3 (21 (a)).

COPY: In Sloane MS. 5267, No. 128.

BIBL.: *Quinn*, p. 411, No. 24 (b).

(*b*) LAND HERMIT CRABS. As for No. 6 but slightly enlarged and with the snail-like shell to the l. of the other.

Pen and black ink and water-colours, touched with white.

INSCR.: Below, *CARACOL . CARACOL.*

L.B.3 (21 (b)).

COPY: In Sloane MS. 5262, No. 19.

BIBL.: *Quinn*, p. 405, No. 5 (b).

f. 17r. BLANK.

INSCR.: In the upper l.-hand corner, *16*.

f. 18r. (*a*) BURRFISH. As for No. 53.
Water-colours touched with white.

INSCR.: Below, *GALLO*, and in the upper l.-hand corner, in an XVIII c. hand, *23*.

L.B.3 (22 (a)).

COPY: In Sloane MS. 5267, No. 32.

BIBL.: *Quinn*, p. 455, No. 96 (b).

(*b*) GROUPER. As for No. 22 but enlarged.

Water-colours over black lead, touched with white.

INSCR.: Below, *GAROPA*.

L.B.3 (22 (b)).

COPY: In Sloane MS. 5267, No. 104.

BIBL.: *Quinn*, p. 410, No. 22 (b).

f. 18v. BLANK.

INSCR.: In the upper l.-hand corner, *17*.

f. 19r. PORTUGUESE MAN-O'-WAR. As for No. 31, but with modifications.
Water-colours over black lead with blue body-colour.

INSCR.: In the upper l.-hand corner, in an XVIII c. hand, *24*.

L.B.3 (23).

COPY: In Sloane MS. 5262, No. 27.

BIBL.: *Quinn*, p. 413, 31 (b).

f. 19v. (*a*) QUEEN TRIGGER-FISH. As for No. 30.

Pen and brown ink and water-colours with blue body-colour, touched with white.

INSCR.: In the upper l.-hand corner, *18* and in an XVIII c. hand, *25*. In the upper r.-hand corner, on a separate piece of paper attached, in Sloane's hand, *Old wife . Cat.* [esby].

L.B.3 (24 (a)).

COPY: In Sloane MS. 5267, No. 51 and, in reverse, No. 44.

BIBL.: *Quinn*, p. 413, footnote 1.

(b) MOONFISH. As for No. 21.
Pen and brown ink, tinted with water-colour washes.

L.B.3 (24 (b)).

COPY: In Sloane MS. 5267, No. 88.

BIBL.: *Quinn*, p. 410, No. 21 (b).

f. 20r. (a) DOLPHIN. As for No. 26 but enlarged and in reverse.
Pen and brown ink, water-colours and blue body-colour, touched with white.

INSCR.: Above, *DEORATHO* and in the upper l.-hand corner, in an XVIII c. hand, *26*.

L.B.3 (25 (a)).

COPY: In Sloane MS. 5267, No. 68.

BIBL.: *Quinn*, p. 412, No. 26 (b).

(b) REMORA. As for No. 28 but much enlarged and darker in colour.
Pen and brown ink and water-colours, heightened with white.

INSCR.: Beneath, *REBESO*.

L.B.3 (25 (b)).

COPY: In Sloane MS. 5267, No. 9.

BIBL.: *Quinn*, p. 412, No. 28 (b).

f. 20v. BLANK.

INSCR.: In the upper l.-hand corner, *19*.

f. 21r. FLYING-FISH. As for No. 27 but enlarged.
Water-colours over black lead, heightened with white (oxidized).

INSCR.: Above, *BOLADORA* and in the upper l.-hand corner, in an XVIII c. hand, *27*.

L.B.3 (26).

COPY: In Sloane MS. 5267, No. 84.

BIBL.: *Quinn*, p. 412, No. 27 (b).

f. 21v. BLANK.

INSCR.: In the upper l.-hand corner, *20*.

f. 22r. (a) GROUPER. As for No. 23 but enlarged.
Water-colours over black lead, touched with white (oxidized).

INSCR.: Above, *MERO* and in the upper l.-hand corner, in an XVIII c. hand, *28*.

L.B.3 (27 (a)).

COPY: In Sloane MS. 5267, No. 102.

BIBL.: *Quinn*, p. 410, No. 23 (b).

(b) SQUIRREL-FISH OR SOLDIER-FISH. As for No. 25 but much enlarged.
Pen and brown ink and water-colours over black lead.

INSCR.: Below, *OIO DEBVEY* and above, on a separate piece of paper attached, in Sloane's hand, *Squirrell fish Cat.*[esby].

L.B.3 (27 (b)).

COPY: In Sloane MS. 5267, No. 115.

BIBL.: *Quinn*, p. 411, No. 25 (b).

f. 22v. BLANK.

INSCR.: In the upper l.-hand corner, *21*.

f. 23r. MAMMEE APPLE. Similar to No. 12

but somewhat larger and with the addition of a cross-section of the fruit on a smaller scale below.

Washes of brown and pale yellow over black lead.

INSCR.: Above, *MAMEA*, and in the upper l.-hand corner, in an XVIII c. hand, *29*.

L.B.3 (28).

BIBL.: *Quinn*, p. 408, No. 11 (b).

The drawing of a Mammee Apple in Sloane MS. 5289, No. 158 may not be after White.

f. 23v. OFFSET. Outlines of the tuft of the pineapple at *f. 24r*.
Black lead.

INSCR.: In the upper l.-hand corner, *22*.

f.24r. PINEAPPLE. As for No. 11 but much more strongly and crudely coloured.
Water-colours and white and pink body-colours over black lead.

INSCR.: Above, *PINE*, and in the upper l.-hand corner, in an XVIII c. hand, *30*.

L.B.3 (29).

BIBL.: *Quinn*, p. 407, No. 10 (b).

f. 24v. OFFSET. Faint outlines of the banana at *f. 25r*.

INSCR.: In the upper l.-hand corner, *23*.

f. 25r. BANANA. As for No. 13 but

slightly enlarged and more strongly coloured (a greenish yellow).
Water-colours over black lead.

INSCR.: Below, towards the l., *PLATANO* and in the upper l.-hand corner, in an XVIII c. hand, *31*.

L.B.3 (30).

BIBL.: *Quinn*, p. 408, No. 14 (b).

Unlike most of the other drawings in the volume, this is possibly a direct copy of No. 13 for the flecks of colour on the skin are, positionally, exactly reproduced.

f. 25v. OFFSET. The outlines of the milk-weed at *f. 26r*.
Black lead.

INSCR.: In the upper l.-hand corner, *24*.

f. 26r. COMMON MILKWEED. As for No. 50 but considerably enlarged and showing four pairs of leaves instead of five.
Water-colours over black lead.

INSCR.: At the top, towards the r., *WISAKON*, and in the upper l.-hand corner, in an XVIII c. hand, *32*.

L.B.3 (31).

ENGR.: In Gerard, *Herball* (1597), p. 752.

BIBL.: *Quinn*, p. 444, No. 54 (b).

f. 26v. BLANK.

INSCR.: In the upper l.-hand corner, *25*.

[ff. 27r.–74r.]. Flowers. Copies, probably from a Dutch florilegium (c. 1600) of European or Western Asiatic plants.

f. 27r. HYACINTH (*Hyacinthus orientalis*).
Water-colours and blue and white body-colours (oxidized?).

INSCR.: Beneath, *Hyacinthus orientalis*, and in the upper l.-hand corner, in an XVIII c. hand, *33*.

L.B.3 (32).

f 27*v*. APENNINE ANEMONE (*Anemone apennina*).

Water-colours and blue and white body-colours.

INSCR.: Beneath, *Anemone flore cœruleo.* and in the upper l.-hand corner, *26* and, in an XVIII c. hand, *34*.

L.B.3 (33).

f. 28*r*. (*a*) GRAPE HYACINTH (*Muscari botryoides*).

INSCR.: Beneath, *Hyacinthus Botroydes cœruleus.* and in the upper l.-hand corner, in an XVIII c. hand, *35*.

(*b*) GRAPE HYACINTH (*Muscari botryoides albus*).

INSCR.: Beneath, *Hyacinthus Botroydes albus.*

(*c*) SPRING CROCUS (*Crocus vernus*).

INSCR.: Beneath, *Crocus vernus.*

(*d*) and (*e*) HEPATICA (*Anemone hepatica*).

Water-colours over black lead, with blue and white body-colours.

INSCR.: Beneath, *Hepatica regalis.*

L.B.3 (34).

f. 28*v*. MUSK HYACINTH (*Muscari Muscarimi*).

Pen and ink and water-colours.

INSCR.: Towards the foot, on either side of the bulb, *Muscari . sine Hyacinthus racemosus | alter.*; and in the upper l.-hand corner, *27* and in an XVIII c. hand, *36*.

L.B.3 (35).

f. 29*r*. (*a*) ANEMONE (*Anemone coronaria*).

INSCR.: Beneath, *Anemone,* and in the upper l.-hand corner, in an XVIII c. hand, *37*.

(*b*) and (*c*) GRAPE HYACINTH (*Muscari botryoides*).

Water-colours over black lead, touched with white.

INSCR.: Beneath (*c*), *Hyacinthus Botroydes.*

L.B.3 (36).

f. 29*v*. BLANK.

INSCR.: In the upper l.-hand corner, *28*.

f. 30*r*. PASQUE FLOWER (*Pulsatilla vulgaris*).

Water-colours over black lead, heightened with white.

INSCR.: Beneath, *Pulsatilla.* and in the upper l.-hand corner, in an XVIII c. hand, *38*.

L.B.3 (37).

f. 30*v*. (*a*) LARKSPUR (*Delphinium ajacis* or *D. consolida*).

Water-colours over black lead, heightened with white (oxidized?).

INSCR.: Beneath, *Consolida regalis* and in the upper l.-hand corner, *29* and, in an XVIII c. hand, *39*.

(*b*) GRASS PINK (*Dianthus plumarius*).

Water-colours and pink and red body-colours.

INSCR.: Beneath, *Amerius flos.*

L.B.3 (38).

f. 31*r.* TULIP (*Tulipa* cultivar).
Water-colours over black lead, touched with white.

INSCR.: Beneath, *Tulipa Bononiensis*. and in the upper l.-hand corner, in an XVIII c. hand, *40*.

L.B.3 (39).

f. 31*v.* BLANK.

INSCR.: In the upper l.-hand corner, *30*.

f. 32*r.* JONQUIL (*Narcissus jonquilla*).
Water-colours over black lead, touched with white (oxidized).

INSCR.: Beneath, *Narcissus juncifolius* and in the upper l.-hand corner, in an XVIII c. hand, *31*.

L.B.3 (40).

f. 32*v.* OLIVER CROMWELL. Engraving by William Trevillian.

INSCR.: In the upper l.-hand corner of the folio, *31*.

Mounted at a later date.

f. 33*r.* PERSIAN FRITILLARY (*Fritillaria persica*).
Water-colours.

INSCR.: Beneath, *Liliū persicum*. and in the upper l.-hand corner, in an XVIII c. hand, *42*.

L.B.3 (41).

f. 33*v.* BLANK.

INSCR.: In the upper l.-hand corner, *32*.

f. 34*r.* CHRISTMAS ROSE (*Helleborus niger*).
Pen and tinted inks and water-colours.

INSCR.: Beneath, *Helleborus niger*. and in the upper l.-hand corner, in an XVIII c. hand, *43*.

L.B.3 (42).

f. 34*v.* OFFSETS. Outlines of tulips (*Tulipa* cultivar) at *f.* 40*r*.
Black lead.

INSCR.: In the upper l.-hand corner, *33*.

f. 35*r.* (*a*) SUMMER SNOWFLAKE (*Leucojum aestivum*).
　　　　(*b*) SPRING SNOWFLAKE (*Leucojum vernum*).
Pen and tinted inks and water-colours, touched with white (oxidized).

INSCR.: Beneath, *Leucojū bulbosum maius*. and in the upper l.-hand corner, in an XVIII c. hand, *44*.

L.B.3 (43).

f. 35*v.* BLANK.

INSCR.: In the upper l.-hand corner, *34*.

f. 36*r.* TULIP (*Tulipa* cultivar).
Pen and brown ink, water-colours and bluish body-colour.

INSCR.: Beneath, *Tulipa lutea mixta rubro*, and in the upper l.-hand corner, in an XVIII c. hand, *45*.

L.B.3 (44).

f. 36*v.* BLANK.

INSCR.: In the upper l.-hand corner, *35*.

f. 37*r.* TWO STUDIES OF A TULIP (*Tulipa* cultivar).
Pen and red ink and water-colours.

INSCR.: Beneath and between, *Tulipæ.* and in the upper l.-hand corner, in an XVIII c. hand, *46.*

L.B.3 (45).

f. 37*v.* BLANK.

INSCR.: In the upper l.-hand corner, *36.*

f. 38*r.* TULIP (*Tulipa* cultivar).
Pen and red ink and water-colours.

INSCR.: Beneath, *Tulipa.*

L.B.3 (46).

f. 38*v.* BLANK.

INSCR.: In the upper l.-hand corner, *37.*

f. 39*r.* STUDIES OF THE TULIP (*Tulipa* cultivar).
Pen and tinted inks and water-colours, touched with white.

INSCR.: Beneath, *Tulipæ diuersimodæ. et variores colorum.* and in the upper l.-hand corner, in an XVIII c. hand, *48.*

L.B.3 (47).

f. 39*v.* BLANK.

INSCR.: In the upper l.-hand corner, *38* and in the lower l.-hand corner, *Richard Crooft* (?).

f. 40*r.* TULIP (*Tulipa* cultivar). Coloured drawing and, upside down, an outline drawing.
Pen and red ink, water-colours and black lead outlines.

INSCR.: Beneath, *Tulipa.* and in the upper l.-hand corner, in an XVIII c. hand, *49.*

L.B.3 (48).

The outlines have been offset, or vice versa, on *f.* 34*v.*

f. 40*v.* BLANK.

INSCR.: In the upper l.-hand corner, *39.*

f. 41*r.* STUDIES OF TWO TULIPS (*Tulipa* cultivar).
Pen and tinted inks touched with white (oxidized).

INSCR.: Beneath and between, *Tulipæ.* and in the upper l.-hand corner, in an XVIII c. hand, *50.*

L.B.3 (49).

f. 41*v.* VENUS AND CUPID. The goddess reclining on her l. elbow, Cupid holding the drapery about her waist.

Grey wash; mounted.

INSCR.: In the upper l.-hand corner, *40* and on the drawing, in the upper r.-hand corner, in an XVIII c. hand, *51.*

L.B.3 (50).

A later Dutch (?) drawing.

f. 42*r.* DOG'S TOOTH VIOLET (*Erythronium dens-canis*).
Water-colours and purplish red body-colour, touched with white.

INSCR.: Beneath, *Dens caninus.* and in the upper l.-hand corner, in an XVIII c. hand, *52.*

L.B.3 (51).

f. 42*v.* CLAMMY PRIMULA (*Primula viscosa*, entire-leaved form).
Pen and tinted and black ink and water-colours.

INSCR.: Beneath, *Auricula Ursi. | Paralitica Alpina maior.*, in the upper l.-hand corner, *41* and in an XVIII c. hand, *53*.

L.B.3 (*52*).

f. 43r. CLAMMY PRIMULA (*Primula viscosa*).
Pen and tinted and black ink and water-colours.

INSCR.: Beneath, *Auricula Ursi. | Paralitica Alpina maior.* and in the lower r.-hand corner, *42* (inverted).

L.B.3 (*53*).

f. 43v. SWEET FLAG (*Acorus calamus*).
Pen and dark brown ink and water-colours, touched with white.

INSCR.: Beneath, *Acorus verus cū suo Juli* and in the upper l.-hand corner, in an XVIII c. hand, *55*.

L.B.3 (*54*).

f. 44r. LADY'S SLIPPER ORCHID (*Cypripedium calceolus*). Separate studies of flower and plant.
Pen and black ink and water-colours.

INSCR.: Beneath the flower, *Calceolus Mariæ.*; in the upper l.-hand corner, in an XVIII c. hand, *56* and in the upper r.-hand corner, *10*.

L.B.3 (*55*).

f. 44v. SNAKE'S HEAD FRITILLARY (*Fritillaria meleagris*).
Water-colours over black lead.

INSCR.: Beneath, *Fritillaria*; in the upper l.-hand corner, *43* and in an XVIII c. hand, *57*.

L.B.3 (*56*).

f. 45r. TWO STUDIES OF SNAKE'S HEAD FRITILLARY (*Fritillaria meleagris*).
Pen and black ink and water-colours, touched with white.

INSCR.: Beneath, *Fritillaria.* and in the upper l.-hand corner, *58* partly covered.

L.B.3 (*57*).

f. 45v. SPRING SNOWFLAKE (*Leucojum vernum*).
Water-colours.

INSCR.: Beneath, *Leuconī bulbosū maius.*, in the upper l.-hand corner, *44* and in an XVIII c. hand, *59*.

L.B.3 (*58*).

f. 46r. SNOWDROP (*Galanthus nivalis*).
Water-colours touched with white.

INSCR.: Beneath, *Leuconī bulbosū minus* and in the upper l.-hand corner, in an XVIII c. hand, *60*.

L.B.3 (*59*).

f. 46v. TWO STUDIES OF SPRING SNOWFLAKE (*Leucojum vernum*).
Water-colours over black lead, heightened with whitish body-colour.

INSCR.: Beneath, *Leuconī bulbosū alterū*, in the upper l.-hand corner, *45* and in an XVIII c. hand, *61*.

L.B.3 (*60*).

f. 47r. POET'S NARCISSUS (*Narcissus poeticus*).
Water-colours over black lead, heightened with white (oxidized).

INSCR.: Beneath, *Narcissus medio purpureus.* and in the upper l.-hand corner, in an XVIII c. hand, *62*.

L.B.3 (*61*).

f. 47v. BLANK.

INSCR.: In the upper l.-hand corner, *46*.

f. 48r. POLYANTHUS NARCISSUS (*Narcissus tazetta mediterraneus*).
Pen and black ink and water-colours, touched with white.

INSCR.: Beneath, *Narcissus medio luteus* and in the upper l.-hand corner, in an XVIII c. hand, *63*.

L.B.3 (62).

f. 48v. BLANK.

INSCR.: In the upper l.-hand corner, *47*.

f. 49r. QUEEN ANNE'S DOUBLE DAFFODIL (*Narcissus pseudonarcissus eystettensis*).
Pen and black ink and water-colours, touched with white (oxidized).

INSCR.: Beneath, *Narcissus syluestris multiplex*. and in the upper l.-hand corner, in an XVIII c. hand, *64*.

L.B.3 (63).

f. 49v. JONQUIL (*Narcissus jonquilla*).
Pen and black ink and water-colours over black lead, touched with white (oxidized).

INSCR.: Beneath, *Narcissus juncifolius*., in the upper l.-hand corner, *48* and in an XVIII c. hand, *48*.

L.B.3 (64).

f. 50r. SPRING ADONIS (*Adonis vernalis*).
Pen and tinted inks and water-colours.

INSCR.: Beneath, *Veratri nigri species.* / *Buphthalimī* . *Dod*. and in the upper l.-hand corner, in an XVIII c. hand, *66*.

L.B.3 (65).

f. 50v. BLANK.

INSCR.: In the upper l.-hand corner, *49*.

f. 51r. HYACINTH (*Hyacinthus orientalis*).
Pen and tinted inks and water-colours, touched with white.

INSCR.: Beneath, *Hyacinthus orientalis maior*. and in the upper l.-hand corner, in an XVIII c. hand, *67*.

L.B.3 (66).

f. 51v. BLANK.

INSCR.: In the upper l.-hand corner, *50*.

f. 52r. BLANK.

f. 52v. STUDIES OF SNOWDROP (*Galanthus nivalis*).
Pen and brown and black ink and water-colours.

INSCR.: Beneath, *leuconī bulbosum tryphillon*. and in the upper l.-hand corner, *51* and, in an XVIII c. hand, *68*.

L.B.3 (67).

f. 53r. BLANK.

f. 53v. STUDIES OF GRAPE HYACINTHS (*Muscari botryoides* and *m. botryoides album* (?)).
Pen and tinted inks and water-colours, touched with white or yellowish body-colour.

INSCR.: Beneath, *Hyacinthus racemosus cœruleus et albus*., in the upper l.-hand corner, *52* and in an XVIII c. hand, *69*.

L.B.3 (68).

f. 54r. BLANK.

f. 54ᵛ. MOURNING IRIS (*Iris susiana*).
Pen and dark brown ink and water-colours.

INSCR.: Beneath, *Iris variegatus.*, in the upper l.-hand corner, *53* and in an XVIII c. hand, *70*.

L.B.3 (*69*).

f. 55ʳ. TWO STUDIES OF GERMAN IRIS (*Iris germanica*).
Water-colours heightened with white.

INSCR.: In the upper l.-hand corner, in an XVIII c. hand, *71*.

L.B.3 (*70*).

f. 55ᵛ. BLANK.

INSCR.: In the upper l.-hand corner, *54*.

f. 56ʳ. BLANK.

f. 56ᵛ. SPANISH IRIS (*Iris xiphium*).
Pen and tinted inks and water-colours, touched with white.

INSCR.: In the upper l.-hand corner, *55* and in an XVIII c. hand, *72*.

L.B.3 (*71*).

f. 57ʳ. BLANK.

f. 57ᵛ. ENGLISH IRIS (*Iris xiphioides*).
Pen and tinted inks and water-colours.

INSCR.: In the upper l.-hand corner, *56* and, in an XVIII c. hand, *73*.

L.B.3 (*72*).

f. 58ʳ. SIBERIAN IRIS (*Iris sibirica*).
Pen and tinted inks, and water-colours.

INSCR.: In the upper l.-hand corner, in an XVIII c. hand, *74*.

L.B.3 (*73*).

f. 58ᵛ. BLANK.

INSCR.: In the upper l.-hand corner, *57*.

f. 59ʳ. SEASHORE IRIS (*Iris spuria*).
Pen and tinted inks and water-colours, touched with white.

INSCR.: In the upper l.-hand corner, in an XVIII c. hand, *75*.

L.B.3 (*74*).

f. 59ᵛ. BLANK.

INSCR.: In the upper l.-hand corner, *58*.

f. 60ʳ. SEASHORE IRIS (*Iris spuria*).
Pen and tinted inks and water-colours, touched with white.

INSCR.: In the upper l.-hand corner, in an XVIII c. hand, *76*.

L.B.3 (*75*).

f. 60ᵛ. BLANK.

INSCR.: In the upper l.-hand corner, *59*.

f. 61ʳ. SEASHORE IRIS (*Iris spuria*).
Pen and tinted inks and water-colours, touched with white.

INSCR.: In the upper l.-hand corner, in an XVIII c. hand, *77*.

L.B.3 (*76*).

f. 61ᵛ. BLANK.

INSCR.: In the upper l.-hand corner, *60*.

f. 62ʳ. TWO STUDIES OF IRISES. On the l., a species of Iris (*Iris pumila* (?)). On the

r., the Moraea Iris (*Gynandriris sisyrinchium*).
Water-colours and black lead, touched with white.

INSCR.: Beneath the first, *Sisynrichiū maius.* and beneath the second, *Sisynrichiū minus.* Above, in the upper l.-hand corner, in an XVIII c. hand, *78.*

L.B.3 (77).

f. 62v. BLANK.

INSCR.: In the upper l.-hand corner, *61.*

f. 63r. TWO STUDIES OF HUNGARIAN IRIS (*Iris variegata*).
Pen and brown ink and water-colours, touched with white.

INSCR.: In the upper l.-hand corner, in an XVIII c. hand, *79.*

L.B.3 (78).

f. 63v. BLANK.

INSCR.: In the upper l.-hand corner, *62.*

f. 64r. PEACOCK TIGER FLOWER (*Tigridia pavonia*).
Pen and tinted inks and water-colours.

INSCR.: Below, *Tigridis flos.* and in the upper l.-hand corner, in an XVIII c. hand, *80.*

L.B.3 (79).

f. 64v. BLANK.

INSCR.: In the upper l.-hand corner, *63.*

f. 65r. BUSH NASTURTIUM (*Tropaeolum minus*).
Pen and tinted inks and water-colours.

INSCR.: Beneath, *Nasturtiū Indicum.* and in the upper l.-hand corner, in an XVIII c. hand, *81.*

L.B.3 (80).

f. 65v. BLANK.

INSCR.: In the upper l.-hand corner, *64.*

f. 66r. INDIAN SHOT (*Canna indica*).
Pen and tinted inks and water-colours, heightened with white.

INSCR.: Beneath, *Canna Indica.* and in the upper l.-hand corner, in an XVIII c. hand, *82.*

L.B.3 (81).

f. 66v. BLANK.

INSCR.: In the upper l.-hand corner, *65.*

f. 67r. BIRD'S EYE PRIMROSE (*Primula farinosa*).
Pen and tinted inks and water-colours, heightened with white.

INSCR.: Beneath, *Paralytica Alpina minor.* and in the upper l.-hand corner, in an XVIII c. hand, *83.*

L.B.3 (82).

f. 67v. BLANK.

f. 68r. (*a*) TWO STUDIES OF DOG'S TOOTH VIOLET (*Erythronium dens-canis*).
(*b*) TWO STUDIES OF SPRING CROCUS (*Crocus vernus*).
Pen and tinted inks and water-colours, heightened with white.

INSCR.: In the centre, below (*a*), *Dens caninus.* and below (*b*), *Crocus vernus.*, in the upper l.-hand corner, in an XVIII c. hand, *84* and in the upper r.-hand corner, *13.*

L.B.3 (83).

f. 68v. BLANK.

INSCR.: In the upper l.-hand corner, *66.*

f. 69r. TWO STUDIES OF HEPATICA (*Anemone hepatica*).
Pen and tinted inks and water-colours, touched with yellow and whitish body-colour.

INSCR.: Beneath the upper, *Hepatica regalis flore rubro.* and beneath the lower, *Hepatica regalis flore cœruleo,* and in the upper l.-hand corner, in an XVIII c. hand, *85.*

L.B.3 (84).

f. 69v. BLANK.

INSCR.: In the upper l.-hand corner, *67.*

f. 70r. DOUBLE PEACOCK ANEMONE (*Anemone pavonina*).
Pen and tinted inks and water-colours, touched with white.

INSCR.: Beneath, *Anemone flore rubro multiplex.* and in the upper l.-hand corner, in an XVIII c. hand, *86.*

L.B.3 (85).

f. 70v. FOUR *PUTTI* PLAYING WITH A GOAT. Two *putti* leading the animal, one astride its back and one behind it.
Black chalk; oval; mounted along the upright folio.

L.B.3 (86).

A later addition.

f. 71r. TULIP (*Tulipa* cultivar).
Pen and tinted inks and water-colours, touched with white.

INSCR.: Beneath, *Tulipa.* and, in the upper l.-hand corner, in an XVIII c. hand, *88.*

L.B.3 (87).

f. 71v. CHALCEDONIAN LILY (*Lilium chalcedonicum*). Separate studies of bulb, and of stem and flower.
Pen and tinted inks and water-colours, heightened with white (oxidized?).

INSCR.: Beneath, *Liliũ Byzantinũ.* and above, towards the l., just visible through the reinforced edge of the paper, 69. Below, r., in an XVIII c. hand, *89.*

L.B.3 (88).

f. 72r. APENNINE ANEMONE (*Anemone apennina*).
Pen and tinted inks and water-colours, touched with white.

INSCR.: Beneath, *Anemone flore cœruleo simplici.* and in the upper l.-hand corner, in an XVIII c. hand, *90.*

L.B.3 (89).

f. 72v. BLANK.

INSCR.: In the upper l.-hand corner, *70.*

f. 73r. STAR ANEMONE (*Anemone hortensis*).
Pen and tinted inks and water-colours, touched with white.

INSCR.: Beneath, *Anemone simplex flore rubro.* and in the upper l.-hand corner, in an XVIII c. hand, *91.*

L.B.3 (90).

f. 73v. BLANK.

INSCR.: In the upper l.-hand corner, *71.*

76

f. 74r. YELLOW MUSK HYACINTH (*Muscari macrocarpum*).

Pen and tinted inks, water-colours and mauve body-colour.

INSCR.: Beneath, *Hyacinthus spurius racemosus alter : sine Muscari.* and in the upper l.-hand corner, in an XVIII c. hand, *92.*

L.B.3 (91).

f. 74v. BLANK.

INSCR.: In the upper l.-hand corner, *72.*

[ff. 75r.–113r.]. Copies of lost drawings by John White. Birds, fishes and reptiles of Virginia.

f. 75r. BALD EAGLE (*Halieaetus leucocephalus leucocephalus* Linn.). In profile, facing l., perched on a tree trunk.

Pen and brown and black ink and water-colours, heightened with white.

INSCR.: At the top, *Nahyápuw. The Grype. almost as bigg | as an Eagle.* and in the upper l.-hand corner, in an XVIII c. hand, *93.*

L.B.3 (92).

BIBL.: *Quinn,* p. 449, No. 65.

f. 75v. BLANK.

f. 76r. SANDHILL CRANE (*Grus canadensis* Linn). In profile, walking to l.

Water-colours touched with white.

INSCR.: At the top, *Taráwkow. The Crane.* and in the upper l.-hand corner, in an XVIII c. hand, *94.*

L.B.3 (93).

COPY: In Sloane MS. 5265, No. 87 and in Edward Topsell, 'The Fowles of Heauen' (Huntington Library, Ellesmere MS. 1142), *f.* 206v., with the inscription *Tarawkow | Konikantes | The Crane of | Virginia | 19.*

BIBL. & REPR.: *Allen,* p. 446, Fig. 17. *Quinn,* p. 447, No. 56.

f. 76v. BLANK.

INSCR.: In the upper l.-hand corner, *73.*

f. 77r. COMMON LOON (*Gavia immer*). On water, in profile to l.

Water-colours heightened with white.

INSCR.: Above, *Peeáwkoo. As bigg as a Goose.* and in the upper l.-hand corner, in an XVIII c. hand, *95.*

L.B.3 (94).

COPY: in Sloane MS. 5265, No. 35, and after the above or another version in Edward Topsell, 'The Fowles of Heauen' (Huntington Library, Ellesmere MS. 1142), *f.* 86r. with the inscription *Chungent.*

BIBL.: *Quinn,* p. 448, No. 60.

f. 77v. BLANK.

INSCR.: In the upper l.-hand corner, *74.*

f. 78r. SURF SCOTER (*Melanitta perspicillata* Linn.). On water, in profile to l.

Water-colours heightened with white.

INSCR.: Above, *Iawéepuwes. Somewhat bigger then | a Duck.* and in the upper l.-hand corner, in an XVIII c. hand, *96.*

L.B.3 (95).

COPY: In Sloane MS. 5625, No. 4.

BIBL.: *Quinn*, p. 448, No. 62.

f. 78v. BLANK.

INSCR.: In the upper l.-hand corner, *75*.

f. 79r. RED-BREASTED MERGANSER (*Mergus serrator* Linn.). On water, in profile to l.
Water-colours and red body-colour, heightened with white.

INSCR.: Above, *Qvúnziuck. of the bignes of a Duck*, and in the upper l.-hand corner, in an XVIII c. hand, *97*.

L.B.3 (96).

COPY: In Sloane MS. 5265, No. 20.

BIBL.: *Quinn*, p. 448, No. 63.

f. 79v. BLANK.

INSCR.: In the upper l.-hand corner, *76*.

f. 80r. BUFFLEHEAD DUCK (*Bucephala albeola* Linn.). On water, in profile to l.
Water-colours and purplish body-colour, heightened with white.

INSCR.: Above, *Weewraamánqueo. As bigg as a Duck.* and in the upper l.-hand corner, in an XVIII c. hand, *98*.

L.B.3 (97).

COPY: In Sloane MS. 5265, No. 17.

BIBL.: *Quinn*, p. 448, No. 61.

f. 80v. BLANK.

INSCR.: In the upper l.-hand corner, *77*.

f. 81r. COMMON LOON (*Gavia immer*). On water, in profile to l. Adult specimen.
Water-colours touched with white, light blue and reddish body-colours.

INSCR.: Above, *Asanamáwqueo. As bigg as a Goose.* and in the upper l.-hand corner, in an XVIII c. hand, *99*.

L.B.3 (98).

COPY: In Sloane MS. 5265, No. 62.

BIBL.: *Quinn*, p. 448, No. 59.

f. 81v. BLANK.

INSCR.: In the upper l.-hand corner, *78*.

f. 82r. TRUMPETER SWAN (*Cygnus buccinator*). On water, in profile to r.
Water-colours heightened with white.

INSCR.: Towards the top, *Woanagusso. The Swann.* and in the upper l.-hand corner, in an XVIII c. hand, *100*.

L.B.3 (99).

COPY: In Sloane MS. 5265, No. 8.

BIBL.: *Quinn*, p. 448, No. 58.

f. 82v. BLANK.

INSCR.: In the upper l.-hand corner, *79*.

f. 83r. GULL. Possibly an immature specimen of the Glaucous Gull (*Larus hyperboreus* Gunnerus) or an immature Herring Gull (*Larus argentatus*). On water, in profile to l.
Water-colours touched with white.

INSCR.: Above, *Kaiauk. A Gull as bigg as a Duck.* and in the upper l.-hand corner, in an XVIII c. hand, *101*.

L.B.3 (100).

COPY: In Sloane MS. 5265, No. 63.

BIBL.: Quinn, p. 448, No. 64.

The name *Kaiuk* also appears in Topsell (*f.* 31*v.*).

f. 83*v.* BLANK.

INSCR.: In the upper l.-hand corner, *80*.

f. 84*r.* RED-HEADED WOODPECKER (*Melanerpes erythrocephalus* Linn.). Standing, in profile to l.
Pen and black ink and water-colours, heightened with white.

INSCR.: Towards the top, *Maraseequo. A woddpicker. | Of this bignes.* and in the upper l.-hand corner, in an XVIII c. hand, *102*.

L.B.3 (101).

COPY: In Sloane MS. 5263, No. 121.

BIBL. *Quinn*, p. 449, No. 69.

f. 84*v.* BLANK.

INSCR.: In the upper l.-hand corner, *81*.

f. 85*r.* PURPLE GRACKLE (*Quisqualus quiscula*). Standing, in profile to l.
Water-colours and purple, heightened with greenish body-colour and touched with yellow and white.

INSCR.: Above, *Tummaihumenes. Of this bignes.* and in the upper l.-hand corner, in an XVIII c. hand, *103*.

L.B.3 (102).

COPY: In Sloane MS. 5263, No. 96.

BIBL.: Quinn, p. 452, No. 79.

f. 85*v.* BLANK.

INSCR.: In the upper l.-hand corner, *82*.

f. 86*r.* SOUTHERN PILEATED WOODPECKER (*Drycopus pileatus pileatus* Linn.). Standing, in profile to l.
Pen and black ink and water-colours, heightened with white.

INSCR.: At the top, *Memeo. As bigg as a Croo.* and in the upper l.-hand corner, in an XVIII c. hand, *104*.

L.B.3 (103).

COPY: In Sloane MS. 5263, No. 166 and, probably from another version, in Edward Topsell, 'The Fowles of Heauen' (Huntington Library, Ellesmere MS. 1142), *f.* 31*v.*, with the inscription, *Aushousetta*.

BIBL.: Quinn, p. 449, No. 67.

f. 86*v.* BLANK.

INSCR.: In the upper l.-hand corner, *83*.

f. 87*r.* (*a*) EASTERN BLUEBIRD(?) (*Sialia sialis sialis* Linn.). Perching on a branch, in profile to l.
Pen and black ink and water-colours, touched with white.

INSCR.: Above, at the top, *Iachdwanjes. Of this biggnes.* In the upper l.-hand corner, in an XVIII c. hand, *105*, and in the upper r.-hand corner, *152*.

L.B.3 (104 (a)).

COPY: (?) In Edward Topsell, 'The Fowles of Heauen' (Huntington Library, Ellesmere MS. 1142) *f.* 31*v*, with the inscription *Aupseo*.

BIBL.: Quinn, p. 451, No. 75.

If the Eastern Bluebird is intended, and there appears to be no other likely identification, a number of features such as the shape of the head and length of tail and the light colour of the breast are inaccurately represented.

(b) TOWHEE (*Pipilo erythrophthalmus erythrophthalmus* Linn.). In profile to l., perching on a head of Indian corn at which it is pecking.
Pen and brown and black ink and water-colours, touched with white.

L.B.3 (104 (b)).

COPY: In Sloane MS. 5264, No. 104.

BIBL.: *Quinn*, p. 452, No. 82.

Probably a female Red-eyed Towhee.

f. 87v. BLANK.

INSCR.: In the upper l.-hand corner, *84*.

f. 88r. (a) BLUE-GREY GNAT-CATCHER (?) (*Polioptila caerulea caerulea* Linn.). Perching on a branch, in profile to l.
Pen and brown and black ink and water-colours, touched with white.

INSCR.: Above, at the top, *Meemz. of this bignes*. In the upper l.-hand corner, in an XVIII c. hand, *106* and in the upper r.-hand corner, *154*.

L.B.3 (105 (a)).

COPY: In Sloane MS. 5266, No. 151.

BIBL.: *Quinn*, p. 449, No. 70.

Possibly a female specimen.

(b) HAIRY WOODPECKER (*Dendrocopos villosus villosus* Linn.). Perching on a branch, in profile to l.

Pen and black ink and water-colours, heightened with white.

INSCR.: Above, *Chacháquises. A wodpicker of this bignes*.

L.B.3 (105 (b)).

BIBL.: *Quinn*, p. 449, No. 68.

Possibly a Yellow-bellied Sapsucker (*Sphyrapicus varius varius* Linn.).

f. 88v. BLANK.

INSCR.: In the upper l.-hand corner, *85* and to the r., in an early hand, *Lomas* (?), partly cut off.

f. 89r. (a) BROWN THRASHER (?). Perching on a spray of honeysuckle, the body in profile to l., the head turned to the r.
Pen and brown and black ink and water-colours, touched with white.

INSCR.: In the upper l.-hand corner, in an XVIII c. hand, *107* and in the upper r.-hand corner, *155*.

L.B.3 (106 (a)).

COPY: In Sloane MS. 5264, No. 105.

BIBL.: *Quinn*, p. 453, No. 83.

Probably the female Brown Thrasher (*Toxostoma rufum* Linn.).

(b) BALTIMORE ORIOLE (*Icterus galbula* Linn.). Standing, in profile to r.
Pen and black ink, water-colours and scarlet body-colour, heightened with white.

L.B.3 (106 (b)).

COPY: In Sloane MS. 5263, No. 87 and, fairly closely, in Edward Topsell, 'The

Fowles of Heauen' (Huntington Library, Ellesmere MS. 1142), *f.* 86r. with the inscription *Chawancus* and the caption *A Virginia bird w!out description.*

BIBL.: *Quinn,* p. 451, No. 78.

f. 89v. BLANK.

INSCR.: In the upper l.-hand corner, *86.*

f. 90r. (*a*) EASTERN RED-WING (*Agelaius phoeniceus phoeniceus* Linn.). Perching on a branch, in profile to l.
Pen and black ink and water-colours touched with yellow body-colour and white.

INSCR.: Above, at the top, *Chúwquaréo. The blackbyrd.* In the upper l.-hand corner, in an XVIII c. hand, *108* and in the upper r.-hand corner, *156.*

L.B.3 (107 (a)).

COPY: In Sloane MS. 5264, No. 91.

BIBL.: *Quinn,* p. 451, No. 77.

The drawing in the Edward Topsell MS., 'The Fowles of Heauen', mentioned above, *f.* 85r., inscribed *Chuquareo,* is in reverse and too unlike the above to be a copy.

(*b*) AMERICAN BARN SWALLOW (*Hirundo rustica erythrogaster* Boddaert). In profile to l.
Pen and black ink and water-colours, heightened with white.

INSCR.: Above, *Weeheépens. The Swallowe.*

L.B.3 (107 (b)).

COPY: The Sloane MS. 5264, No. 140.

BIBL.: *Quinn,* p. 450, No. 71.

f. 90v. BLANK.

INSCR.: In the upper l.-hand corner, *87.*

f. 91r. TOWHEE (*Pipilo erythrophthalmus erythrophthalmus* Linn. or *Pipilo erythrophthalmus alleni*). Perching on a branch, in profile to l.
Pen and black ink and water-colours, heightened with white.

INSCR.: At the top, *Chúwhweeo. Somthing bigger then a Blackbyrd.* In the upper l.-hand corner, in an XVIII c. hand, *109* and in the upper r.-hand corner, *157.*

L.B.3 (108)

COPY: In Sloane MS. 5264, No. 108, probably in Sloane MS. 5266, No. 142 and, close enough to be by the same hand, Edward Topsell, 'The Fowles of Heauen' (Huntington Library, Ellesmere MS. 1142), *f.* 85v., with the inscription *Chuwheeo.*

BIBL.: *Quinn,* p. 452, No. 81.

The copy of this drawing in the Topsell MS. mentioned above was, as stated in the text, 'receiued, from that worthye, industrious, & learned . . . Master Hackluyt' (for the full MS. description *see Quinn,* p. 452, note 3).

f. 91v. BLANK.

INSCR.: In the upper l.-hand corner, *88.*

f. 92r. CARDINAL (*Richmondena cardinalis cardinalis* Linn.). Perching on a branch, in profile to l.
Pen and black ink and water-colours, touched with white body-colour.

INSCR.: Above, towards the top, *Meesquouns. Almost as bigg as a Parratt.* In the upper l.-hand corner, in an XVIII c. hand, *110* and in the upper r.-hand corner, *158.*

L.B.3 (109).

F

C.E.D.

COPY: In Sloane MS. 5264, No. 77.

BIBL.: *Quinn*, p. 452, No. 80.

f. 92*v*. BLANK.

INSCR.: In the upper l.-hand corner, *89*.

f. 93*r*. NORTHERN FLICKER (*Colaptes auratus luteus* Bangs). Standing in profile to l.
Water-colours touched with white.

INSCR.: Above, towards the top, *Quurúc-quaneo.* | *A woodpicker.* | *As bigg as a Pigeon.* In the upper l.-hand corner, in an XVIII c. hand, *111* and in the upper r.-hand corner, *159* (the top of the number cut away).

L.B.3 (110).

COPY: In Sloane MS. 5263, No. 112 and, crudely, in Edward Topsell, 'The Fowles of Heauen' (Huntington Library, Ellesmere MS. 1142), *f.* 31*v*, with the inscription, *Aiussaco.*

BIBL. & REPR.: *Allen*, p. 447, Fig. 18. *Quinn*, p. 452, No. 81.

f. 93*v*. BLANK.

INSCR.: In the upper l.-hand corner, *90*.

f. 94*r*. FLORIDA BLUE JAY (*Cyanocitta cristata*). Perching on a branch, in profile to l.
Water-colours heightened with white.

INSCR.: At the top, *Artamóckes. The linguist. A birde that imitateth* | *and vseth the sounde and tunes almost of* | *all the birdes in the contrie.* | *As bigg as a Pigeon.* and in the upper l.-hand corner, in an XVIII c. hand, *112*.

L.B.3 (111).

COPY: In Sloane MS. 5263, No. 70.

BIBL.: *Quinn*, p. 450, No. 72.

The drawing in the Topsell MS., *f.* 32*r*., inscribed *Artamokes* is a feeble caricature of the above but may be a copy of it by a very unskilled hand.

f. 94*v*. BLANK.

INSCR.: In the upper l.-hand corner, *91*.

f. 95*r*. (*a*) CUCKOO. Perching on a branch, in profile to l.
Pen and black ink and water-colours, heightened with white.

INSCR.: In the upper l.-hand corner, in an XVIII c. hand, *113* and in the upper r.-hand corner, *161*.

L.B.3 (112 (a)).

COPY: In Sloane MS. 5264, No. 103.

BIBL.: *Quinn*, p. 451, No. 74.

Possibly the Yellow-billed Cuckoo (*Coccyzus americanus americanus* Linn.).

(*b*) JUNCO (?). Perching on a branch, in profile to l.
Pen and black ink and water-colours, heightened with white.

L.B.3 (112 (b)).

BIBL.: *Quinn*, p. 451, No. 76.

Possibly the Slate-coloured Junco (*Junco hyemalis hyemalis* Linn.).

f. 95*v*. BLANK.

INSCR.: In the upper l.-hand corner, *92*.

f. 96*r*. THRASHER (?). Perching on a branch, in profile to r.

Pen and brown and black ink and water-colours touched with white (oxidized).

INSCR.: Above, *Poócqueo. Bigger then a Thrush*. In the upper l.-hand corner, in an XVIII c. hand, *114* and in the upper r.-hand corner, *162* (partly cut away).

L.B.3 (113).

COPY: In Sloane MS. 5264, No. 66.

BIBL.: *Quinn*, p. 450, No. 73.

Probably the Brown Thrasher (*Toxostoma rufum* Linn.).

f. 96*v.* BLANK.

INSCR.: In the upper l.-hand corner, *93*.

f. 97*r.* BLANK.

f. 97*v.* FLOUNDER. In profile to l.
Pen and brown ink and water-colours, touched with white or silver (oxidized).

INSCR.: Above, and to the r., down the lower r.-hand border of the upright folio, *Pashockshin. The Playse. | A foote and a halfe in length*. Towards the upper l.-hand corner, *94* and in an XVIII c. hand, *115*.

L.B.3 (114).

COPY: In Sloane MS. 5267, No. 9.

BIBL.: *Quinn*, p. 454, No. 88.

Either the Southern Flounder (*Paralichthys lethostigmus* Jordan & Gilbert) or the Summer Flounder (*Paralichthys dentatus* Linn.).

f. 98*r.* BLANK.

f. 98*v.* BOW-FIN (*Amia calva* Linn.). In profile to l.

Pen and brown ink and water-colours with touches of white and silver (?) (oxidized).

INSCR.: Above, down the r.-hand border of the upright folio, *Marangahockes. 3. or 4. foote in length*. Towards the upper l.-hand corner, *95* and in an XVIII c. hand, *116*.

L.B.3 (115).

COPY: In Sloane MS. 5267, No. 119.

BIBL.: *Quinn*, p. 454, No. 89.

f. 99*r.* BLANK.

f. 99*v.* FISH. In profile to l.
Pen and blue and black ink and water-colours, touched with white.

INSCR.: Above, down the r.-hand border of the upright folio, *Ribuckon. A foote in length*. In the upper l.-hand corner, *96* and in an XVIII c. hand, *117*.

L.B.3 (116).

COPY: In Sloane MS. 5267, No. 127.

BIBL.: *Quinn*, p. 454, No. 92.

Probably intended for the White Perch (*Morone americana* Gmelin).

f. 100*r.* BLANK.

f. 100*v.* ALEWIFE OR SHAD (*Pomolubus pseudoharengus* Wilson). In profile to l.
Water-colours heightened with white.

INSCR.: Above, down the r.-hand border of the upright folio,
Chaham ⎱
Wundúnãham ⎰ *The hearing . 2 . foote in length*.
In the upper l.-hand corner, *97* and in an XVIII c. hand, *118*.

L.B.3 (117).

COPY: In Sloane MS. 5267, No. 110.

BIBL.: *Quinn*, p. 453, No. 85.

f. 101r. BLANK.

f. 101v. STRIPED BASS (*Roccus saxatilis* Walbaum). In profile to l.
Pen and blue ink and water-colours, touched with yellow body-colour and white.

INSCR.: Above, down the r.-hand border of the upright folio, *Mesickek. Some 5 or 6 foote in lengthe*. In the upper l.-hand corner, *98* and in an XVIII c. hand, *119*.

L.B.3 (118).

COPY: In Sloane MS. 5267, No. 120.

BIBL.: *Quinn*, p. 454, No. 90.

f. 102r. BLANK.

f. 102v. CHANNEL BASS (*Sciaenops ocellatus* Linn.). In profile to l.
Water-colours touched with white and silver (oxidized).

INSCR.: Above, down the r.-hand border of the upright folio, *Chigwusso. Some 5. foote in length*. In the upper l.-hand corner, *99* and in an XVIII c. hand, *120*.

L.B.3 (119).

COPY: In Sloane MS. 5267, No. 126.

BIBL.: *Quinn*, p. 454, No. 91.

f. 103r. BLANK.

f. 103v. SEA LAMPREY (*Petromyzon marinus* Linn.). Head to l.
Water-colours.

INSCR.: Above, down the r.-hand border

of the upright folio, *Kokohockepúweo. The Lampron, a foote in lengthe*. In the upper l.-hand corner, *100* and in an XVIII c. hand, *121*.

L.B.3 (120).

COPY: In Sloane MS. 5267, No. 2.

BIBL.: *Quinn*, p. 456, No. 99.

f. 104r. BLANK.

f. 104v. MULLET (*Mugil cephalus* Linn. (?)).
Water-colours touched with white.

INSCR.: Above, down the r.-hand border of the upright folio, *Tetszo. The Mullett, some 2 foote in length*. In the upper l.-hand corner, *101* and in an XVIII c. hand, *122*. On a slip of paper attached to the top r.-hand corner, in Sloane's hand, *Mullet Cat*. [esby].

L.B.3 (121).

COPY: In Sloane MS. 5267, No. 92.

BIBL.: *Quinn*, p. 454, No. 87.

f. 105r. BLANK.

f. 105v. GARFISH (either *Tylosurus acus* Lacépède or *Tylosurus raphidoma* Ranzani). In profile to l.
Water-colours touched with white or silver (oxidized).

INSCR.: Above, down the r.-hand border of the upright folio, *Arasémec. Some 5. or 6. foote in length*. In the upper l.-hand corner, *102* and in an XVIII c. hand, *123*.

L.B.3 (122).

COPY: In Sloane MS. 5267, No. 80.

BIBL.: *Quinn*, p. 455, No. 93.

f. 106r. BLANK.

f. 106v. GAR PIKE (*Lepisosteus osseus* Linn.).
In profile to l.
    Water-colours touched with white or
silver (?) (oxidized).

    INSCR.: Above, down the r.-hand border
of the upright folio, *Kowabetteo. Some 5. or 6.
foote in length*. In the upper l.-hand corner,
103 and in an XVIII c. hand, *124.*

    L.B.3 (123).

    COPY: In Sloane MS. 5267, No. 96.

    BIBL.: *Quinn*, p. 455, No. 94.

f. 107r. BLANK.

f. 107v. CATFISH (probably *Ameiurus catus*
Linn.). In profile to l.
    Water-colours touched with white.

    INSCR.: Above, to the r., down the r.-
hand border of the upright folio, *Keetrauk.
Some 2. foote and a halfe in length*. In the upper
l.-hand corner, *104* and in an XVIII c.
hand, *125.*

    L.B.3 (124).

    COPY: In Sloane MS. 5267, No. 33.

    BIBL.: *Quinn*, p. 455, No. 95.

f. 108r. BLANK.

f. 108v. SHEEPSHEAD BREAM (*Archosar-
gus probatocephalus* Walbaum). In profile to l.
    Body-colours and water-colours, height-
ened with white (oxidized).

    INSCR.: To the r., down the r.-hand
border of the upright folio, *Masunnehockeo.
The olde wyfe, | 2. foote in length*. In the upper
l.-hand corner, *105* and in an XVIII c. hand,

126. On a slip of paper attached to the top
r.-hand corner, in Sloane's hand, *Pork fish.
Cat.* [esby].

    L.B.3 (125).

    COPY: In Sloane MS. 5267, No. 117.

    BIBL.: *Quinn*, p. 453, No. 86.

f. 109r. BLANK.

f. 109v. SKINK (genus *Eumeces*). Head to l.
    Pen and brown ink and water-colours over
black lead.

    INSCR.: Above, down the r.-hand border
of the upright folio, *Meméskson. A foote in
length*. In the upper l.-hand corner, *106* and
in an XVIII c. hand, *127.*

    L.B.3 (116).

    COPY: In Sloane MS. 5272, No. 45.

    BIBL.: *Quinn*, p. 457, No. 105.

    Probably a mature male specimen of the
Five-lined Skink (*Eumeces fasciatus* Linn.) but
it could be *Eumeces inexpectatus* or *Eumeces
laticeps* for the drawing is extremely crude.

f. 110r. BLANK.

f. 110v. SNAKE. Head to l.
    Pen and brown and black ink and water-
colours, touched with white and silver
(oxidized).

    INSCR.: Above, down the r.-hand border
of the upright folio, *Tesicqueo. A kinde of
Snake which the Saluages (being | rost or sodden)
doe eate. Some an ell long*. In the upper l.-hand
corner, *107* (overlaid) and in an XVIII c.
hand, *128.*

    L.B.3 (127).

Copy: In Sloane MS. 5272, No. 52.

Bibl.: *Quinn*, p. 457, No. 104.

The crude drawing makes identification difficult but the specimen is perhaps one of the non-poisonous King-snakes (genus *Lampropeltis*), possibly either the Scarlet King-snake (*L. triangulum elapsoides*) or the Milk-snake (*L. triangulum triangulum*).

f. 111r. SHARP-NOSED STURGEON (*Acipenser oxyrhynchus* Mitchill (?)). In profile to l.
   Pen and brown ink and water-colours, touched with white, silver (oxidized) and blue body-colour.

Inscr.: Above, down the r.-hand border of the upright folio, *Coppáuseo. The Sturgeon some 10. 11. 12. or 13 foote in length.*

L.B.3 (128).

Copy: In Sloane MS. 5267, No. 95.

Bibl.: *Quinn*, p. 453, No. 84.

Possibly the smaller Sharp-nosed Sturgeon, *Acipenser brevirostrum* Le Sueur.

f. 111v. BLANK.

Inscr.: In the upper l.-hand corner, part of the figure *8* of the number *108* (partly overlaid).

f. 112r. BURRFISH (*Chilomycterus schoepfi* Walbaum). In profile to l. Inflated.
   Water-colours heightened with white (?).

Inscr.: Above, down the r.-hand border of the upright folio, *A swelling fish : 8 ynches in lengthe.* In the upper l.-hand corner, in an XVIII c. hand, *130.*

L.B.3 (129).

Copy: In Sloane MS. 5267, No. 45.

Bibl.: *Quinn*, p. 455, No. 97.

The same fish as at No. 53 above but a copy from another drawing.

f. 112v. BLANK.

Inscr.: In the upper l.-hand corner, *109* (overlaid).

f. 113r. COMMON CROAKER (*Micropogon indulatus* Linn. (?)). In profile to l.

Pen and dark blue ink and water-colours, touched with white and silver (oxidized); the paper much foxed.

Inscr.: Above, down the r.-hand border of the upright folio, *Manchauemec. Some a foote in length.* In the upper l.-hand corner, in an XVIII c. hand, *131.*

L.B.3 (130).

Copy: In Sloane MS. 5267, No. 122.

Bibl.: *Quinn*, p. 455, No. 98.

The poorness of the drawing and colouring makes identification uncertain.

f. 113v. BLANK.

Inscr.: In the upper l.-hand corner, *110* (?) (overlaid).

Prov.: Descendants of John White until after 1709 when purchased by Sir Hans Sloane, Bart., who bequeathed it to the B.M., 1753. Placed in the Dept. of MSS. and transferred to the Dept. of Prints & Drawings, 20:vi:1893.

Sloane 5270.

Bibl.: *Quinn*, pp. 394–7.

PART II
XVII CENTURY

ANON. DRAUGHTSMAN, PERHAPS DUTCH
Working mid XVII c.

1. LONDON AND OLD ST. PAUL'S FROM NEAR ARUNDEL HOUSE. View looking E., probably from the roof of part of Somerset House, the parapet of which crosses the foreground. Beyond, the trees in the garden of Arundel House, and, in the centre, the exterior of the famous gallery of Thomas Howard, 2nd Earl of Arundel. To the l., the turrets of the main block of the house. In the background the city, with, from l. to r., Old St. Paul's, the tower of St. Mary-le-Bow, the spires of St. Lawrence-Poulteney and St. Dunstan-in-the-East, the Tower, and London Bridge. **Plate 41**

Brush drawing in grey wash; 22·4 × 38·3 cm. ($8\frac{7}{8}$ × $15\frac{1}{8}$ in.).

INSCR.: *Verso*, at the foot, in ink, *26*, and in pencil, *£ s d* and *London before the Fire* 0 *15 0* by . . . (the remainder perhaps cut away). On Crace's mount, *This drawing by Thomas Van Wyck 1654. . . . From the Stowe Collection the Duke gave T. T. Smith £2. 2.*

PROV.: T. T. Smith. Richard Grenville, 1st Duke, and Richard Grenville, 2nd Duke of Buckingham (Sale, Sotheby, 8:viii:1849, Lot 221 or 223 (?)). Frederick Crace. John Gregory Crace, from whom it was purchased by the B.M., 1880.

1880–11–13–1149 (L.B., as by Jan Wyck, Vol. IV, p. 371).

BIBL.: *Crace Cat.*, p. 154, Ptf. I, No. 41.

This drawing was catalogued by Mr. Binyon as 'Attributed to Jan Wyck', but it has nothing in common with the known work of that draughtsman. The older attribution to the father, Thomas Wyck, is perhaps nearer the mark, and the handling of the wash in the architecture and foliage is not unlike that in two drawings by him in the Department (*See* Hind, *Dutch and Flemish Drawings*, IV, p. 117, Nos. 1 & 2). The evidence, however, is too slight to warrant giving the drawing definitely to the elder Wyck.

In the view, the S. transept of St. Paul's is apparently shown roofless which suggests that it might have been taken after the Great Fire of 1666. On the other hand, the roof of the nave and the cap of the tower, as well as the line of the houses along the river-front towards the bridge are shown intact, whereas according to Hollar's view of London after the Fire (*Parthey*, No. B. 1015, Hind, *Hollar*, No. 19, p. 49) all roofs of the Cathedral, including the cap of the tower, were destroyed, and most of the houses on the water devastated.

ANON. ENGLISH (?) FLOWER DRAUGHTSMAN

Working mid or later XVII c.

The following drawings are mounted in a large folio volume, originally belonging to Sir Hans Sloane, containing several hundred drawings of plants. They have been selected as being the work of one, probably English, hand of the middle or later XVII c.

1. HOLLY SPRAYS.

Oil-colours on canvas; $24 \cdot 8 \times 19 \cdot 7$ cm. ($9\frac{3}{4} \times 7\frac{3}{4}$ in).   PROV.: Sir Hans Sloane, Bart., by whom it was bequeathed to the B.M., 1753. **Sloane 5283 (85).**

2. PLANTS. Sprays of several unidentified species.

Oil-colours; $20 \cdot 5 \times 32$ cm. ($8 \times 12\frac{5}{8}$ in.).   PROV.: As for No. 1. **Sloane 5283 (86).**

3. PLANTS. Sprays of two unidentified species.

Oil-colours and body-colours; $29 \cdot 3 \times 21 \cdot 7$ cm. ($11\frac{5}{8} \times 8\frac{5}{8}$ in.).   PROV.: As for No. 1. **Sloane 5283 (87).**

4. PLANT. Unidentified species.

Oil-colours and body-colours; 32×21 cm. ($12\frac{5}{8} \times 8\frac{1}{4}$ in.).   PROV.: As for No. 1. **Sloane 5283 (88).**

5. ACANTHUS.

Oil-colours; a much mutilated sheet; $33 \cdot 5 \times 48$ cm. ($13\frac{1}{4} \times 18\frac{7}{8}$ in.).   PROV.: As for No. 1. **Sloane 5283 (89).**

6. AFRICAN MARIGOLD. Sixteen studies of the flower.

Body-colours and water-colours; $36 \times 25 \cdot 2$ cm. ($14\frac{1}{8} \times 9\frac{7}{8}$ in.).   PROV.: As for No. 1. **Sloane 5283 (90).**

7. SUNFLOWER.

Body-colours and water-colours; $28 \cdot 3 \times 20 \cdot 2$ cm. ($11\frac{1}{8} \times 8$ in.).   PROV.: As for No. 1. **Sloane 5283 (91).**

8. BINDWEED. Clusters of leaves.

Plate 44

Water-colours and body-colours; $20 \cdot 7 \times 33$ cm. ($8\frac{1}{4} \times 13$ in.).   PROV.: As for No. 1. **Sloane 5283 (123).**

9. BINDWEED. Studies of leaves. Plate 43

Water-colours and body-colours; 20·3 × 32 cm. (8 × 12⅝ in.).

PROV.: As for No. 1.
Sloane 5283 (137).

10. IVY SPRAYS.

Oil-colours and body-colours; 18·3 × 29 cm. (7¼ × 11⅜ in.).

PROV.: As for No. 1.
Sloane 5283 (125).

11. IVY.

Oil-colours and body-colours; 19 × 29·3 cm (7½ × 11½ in.).

PROV.: As for No. 1.
Sloane 5283 (126).

12. QUINCE. Branch with two fruits.

Water-colours; 23·7 × 21·7 cm. (9⅜ × 8½ in.).

PROV.: As for No. 1.
Sloane 5283 (127).

13. PLANT. Spray of unidentified species.

Black chalk; 19·7 × 19·3 cm. (7¾ × 7⅝ in.).

PROV.: As for No. 1,
Sloane 5283 (128).

14. QUINCE. Branch with two fruits.

Water-colours; 30·5 × 19·5 cm. (12 × 7⅝ in.).

PROV.: As for No. 1.
Sloane 5283 (129).

15. PLANTS. Several unidentified species.

Water-colours and body-colours; 11·5 × 18·5 cm. (4½ × 7¼ in.).

PROV.: As for No. 1.
Sloane 5283 (130).

16. PLANT. Unidentified spray.

Black chalk and light wash; irregularly cut; 8·5 × 19 cm. (3⅜ × 7½ in.).

PROV.: As for No. 1.
Sloane 5283 (131).

17. PLANT. Unidentified spray.

Black chalk on blue-grey paper; irregularly cut; 11·7 × 9·7 cm. (4⅝ × 3¾ in.).

PROV.: As for No. 1.
Sloane 5283 (132).

18. PLANT. Unidentified spray.

Black chalk; 14·7 × 19·9 cm. (5¾ × 7⅞ in.).

PROV.: As for No. 1.
Sloane 5283 (133).

19. CHERRY LAUREL BRANCH.

Water-colours and body-colours; irregularly cut; 48·2 × 52·7 cm. (19 × 20¾ in.).

PROV.: As for No. 1.
Sloane 5283 (134).

20. ALDER BRANCH.

Water-colours and body-colours; irregularly cut; 33 × 24·2 cm. (13 × 9¼ in.).

PROV.: As for No. 1.
Sloane 5283 (135).

21. LAUREL LEAVES.

Water-colours and body-colours; irregularly cut; 30·5 × 29 cm. (12 × 11⅜ in.).

PROV.: As for No. 1.
Sloane 5283 (136).

22. IVY SPRAYS.

Oil-colours; upper and lower r.-hand corners cut; 15 × 25·3 cm. (5⅞ × 10 in.).

PROV.: As for No. 1.
Sloane 5283 (124).

ANON. ARCHITECTURAL DRAUGHTSMAN

Working *c.* 1671–9

Probably an assistant in the office of Sir William Bruce, the architect of Holyrood House

1. EDINBURGH, HOLYROOD HOUSE. Bird's-eye elevation from the W., showing the quadrangle.   **Plate 42**

Pen and brown ink with grey washes, indented for transfer; 24·5 × 43·8 cm. (9⅝ × 17¼ in.).

INSCR.: *Recto*, in the upper r.-hand corner, in black lead, *Holyrood House*.

PROV.: A. W. Thibaudeau, from whom it was purchased by the B.M., 1880.
1880–6–12–340.

ENGR.: By Pierre Fourdrinier in Maitland, *Edinburgh*, Bk. II, p. 152.

In the opinion of the late Mr. James Brotchie of the National Gallery of Scotland, this drawing 'is almost certainly from the workshop of Sir William Bruce', though unfortunately no drawings from Bruce's workshop are known with which it can be compared. The palace is shown more or less as it is today, though the main gateway differs in detail and there are now no statues on the pediment in the quadrangle.

ANON. ENGLISH DRAUGHTSMAN

Working after 1677

1. PROSPECT OF LONDON, SOUTHWARK, WESTMINSTER AND THE THAMES, FROM THE N. BANK. View, perhaps from Northumberland House or York House, looking S. over the Thames. On the l., the City, various landmarks including, from l. to r., the towers of St. Mary-le-Bow and the Royal Exchange, and the Monument. In the centre, Southwark with, from l. to r., the towers of St. Olave's and St. Mary Overy (now Southwark Cathedral), the smoking kiln of a glass factory, the spire of St. George's, the houses along Bankside, St. George's Fields, and Lambeth Palace. On the r., Westminster and the Abbey.

Plates 45 and 46

Pen and brown ink, with grey wash; 6·9 × 37·3 cm. (2¾ × 14¾ in.).

INSCR.: *Recto*, with the names of landmarks from l. to r., *St Pauls* [the building not seen as the paper is cut away]—*St Mary Bow*— *Royall Exchange*—*Monyment*—*Tower-Bridg*—*St Mary overs*—*Glass Hous*—*St Georg feil* [ds]— *Lambeth Hous*—*Westminster Hall*—*Great Toms Tower*—*west^m Aby*—[(?)w]^t[(?) *sic* for White] *Hall* [the building not seen as the paper is cut away].

    Verso, with recipes for colours in face-painting, *tervert India read | & White for a middle coller | or shadow in ye face of a l* [ady (?)] *reflections of lake*
*Flake white spruce oaker virm | * [i]*lion to make ther ye 2 littest coller | Flacke white oaker virmilion & | lake for ye 3 & 4 Coller | and for a 5 Coller some other reds and Ind* [ia] *| Read. Tervert for to brake y* [e] *| other darker Reds or shadow | wth some brown pink & black as is ne | sesary*
to Make Varnish for face: take | . . . mastick to 1 pint of tirpintine pound it | and lett it desoulf jently by y [e] *fir* [e (?)] *shake it often when it desoulfe* [(?) it] *is done.* On the old backing, in a much later hand, *St. George's Fields and distant hills | from Whitehall,* and *13 £1 1 0.* On Mr.

Crace's mount, *From the Stowe Collection the Duke gave £1-1-.*

PROV.: T. T. Smith. Richard Grenville, 1st Duke, and Richard Grenville, 2nd Duke of Buckingham (Sale, Sotheby, 8:viii:1849, (?) Lot 221 or 223). Frederick Crace. John Gregory Crace, from whom it was purchased by the B.M., 1880.
 1880–11–13–1152.

BIBL.: *Crace Cat.*, p. 155, Ptf. II, No. 44. *Croft-Murray, Rubens*, p. 90, *note 9.*

This drawing must date from after the erection of the spire of the new Church of St. Mary-le-Bow and of the Monument, both of which are seen on the l. of the view and were completed in 1677. The *Glass Hous* is no doubt one of the glass factories for which Southwark and Blackfriars were once famous, and the predecessor, in the former place, of the well-known Falcon works of the XVIII and early XIX c. *Great Toms Tower* at Westminster evidently indicates the Clock Tower there, the bell of which was known as Great Tom. This bell was subsequently transferred to St. Paul's Cathedral when the Clock Tower was demolished in 1715.

ANON. DRAUGHTSMAN

Working *c.* 1680 (?)

1. **EXECUTION OF CHARLES I.** The King between groups of figures on the scaffold, his arms raised. Above him, an angel descending with the martyr's crown. In the foreground, below the scaffold, a musketeer and a halberdier, and in the background, part of the Banqueting House, Whitehall.

Pen and ink, with grey wash; 7·6 × 4·8 cm. (3 × 1⅞ in.).

PROV.: Messrs. Hogarth, from whom it was purchased by the B.M., 1887.
1887–10–10–7 (L.B. 4 a).

This and the following drawing appear to be designs for engraving, perhaps for playing cards such as those designed by Barlow (*See* pp. 135–48). Previously attributed to Faithorne, they are not sufficiently close to his style to be grouped with his work.

2. CAVALRY AND FOOT SOLDIERS IN ORDER OF BATTLE. Four cavalrymen in front of massed foot soldiers carrying pikes and banners, one with the cross of St. George.

Pen and ink, with grey wash; 7·5 × 4·8 cm. (2⅞ × 1⅞ in.).

PROV.: As for No. 1.
1887–10–10–8 (L.B. 4b).
See No. 1 (note).

ANON. ENGLISH DRAUGHTSMAN

Working c. 1700

An unknown portrait draughtsman working in crayons in the tradition of Ashfield (q.v.) and Lutterell (q.v.)

1. A GENTLEMAN. Bust turned half-r., with eyes to front. Wearing a long curling brown wig, cravat, and black drapery. On a greenish-grey ground.

Crayons; oval; rubbed and damaged at the sides; 28·3 × 23 cm. (11 × 9 in.).

PROV.: Sir Hans Sloane, Bart., by whom it was bequeathed to the B.M., 1753.
Sloane, 5214–263. T. 10–263.

BIBL.: *Sloane Cat.*, p. 162. No. 263.

ARGALL, EDWARD

Fl. 1682

Amateur portrait draughtsman

Nothing known of this amateur, but no doubt a member of a family which owned the manor of East Sutton, Kent, from Henry VIII's reign till 1610 when the property was sold by John Argall, then living at Colchester, to his brother-in-law Sir Edward Filmer (*See* PROV. of drawing described below).

BIBL.: *Hasted*, II, p. 418. *Metcalfe, Essex*, pp. 137 & 335.

1. EDWARD ARGALL. Bust to front, with head turned slightly to l. Wearing long curling hair or wig, slight moustache, falling bands of lace, a coat buttoned under his gown. **Plate 45**

Black lead on vellum; within an oval; $11 \times 8 \cdot 3$ cm. ($4\frac{1}{4} \times 3\frac{1}{4}$ in.).

INSCR.: *Recto*, on the r., in black lead, by the artist, *E A / 1682*, and on a separate slip of paper from the back of the old frame, *Edward Argall Esqr 168* [2].

PROV.: Filmer family of East Sutton Park,

Kent. Joseph Ceci, by whom it was presented to the B.M., 1952.

1952–10–14–3.

Presumably, from the signature and later inscription, a self-portrait. Its technique is a pale reflection of that used by the professional artists of the Loggan-White school.

ASHFIELD, EDMUND (OR EDWARD)

Fl. from 1669: D. 1690 (?)

Portrait painter and draughtsman in crayons

According to Buckeridge was 'a Gentleman well descended' and probably belonged to the Bucks. branch of the Ashfield family, several members of which were significantly named Edmund. Is said by Thomas Hearne to have been 'a sober Person & suspected to be a Roman Catholick'. May thus perhaps be identified with the 'Edmund Ashfeild' who acted as one of the witnesses at the marriage, in the Catholic Chapel Royal at St. James's, on Sept. 8th, 1669, of Walter Blum (*sic*, but presumably Walter Blunt of Mapledurham) and Elizabeth Plowden (probably daughter of Edmund Plowden of Plowden Hall, Salop). At some time unknown became a pupil of the portraitist, John Michael Wright. The earliest contemporary reference to Ashfield as an artist provided by a MS. volume, at Welbeck Abbey, containing poems by Sir Thomas Lawrence (B. 1645: D. 1715(?)), 3rd Bart. of Iver (Bucks.) and Chelsea, amongst which are *Verses sent with the Musick Speech to my Cousin Edward* [*sic*] *Ashfeild an Ingenious Painter*, the speech in question having been delivered at Oxford on July 11th, 1669. Began probably as a copyist in oils in which capacity he made versions of an imaginary portrait of Duns Scotus (now at

Hampton Court) by Ribera or a follower which was apparently in Wright's possession before it passed into Charles II's collection by *c.* 1666–7. One of these copies acquired by the Bodleian Library in 1670 for £3 8s., another at Merton College, and a third, according to Anthony à Wood, 'In Lambeth Gallery' (presumably Lambeth Palace, though no such picture exists there now). Another copy by Ashfield at Oxford is the portrait of James Butler, 1st Duke of Ormonde, after an original by Lely in the collection of the Duke of Devonshire. Also painted reduced copies of portraits of Penelope, Lady Herbert, after Vandyck, and Lady Warwick, both at Burghley. Subsequently took to crayons. In connexion with Ashfield's use of this medium Buckeridge (*Dedication*) says: 'Our countryman, Mr. Ashfield, *multiply'd the number and variety of* tints, *and painted various complexions in imitation of oil; and this* manner *has been so much improved among us, that there is no subject which can be express'd by oil, but the crayons can effect it with equal force and beauty*'. Gave instruction in this medium to Edward Lutterell (*q.v.*). Extant examples of Ashfield's crayons, which are very uneven in quality, are limited to a period between 1673 and 1676. Among them is the finely preserved portrait of a young man, dated 1673, in the Ashmolean Museum, Oxford. Two others, in the collection of Mr. R. G. Plowden, a lady, dated 1675 and a gentleman, dated 1676, both no doubt members of the Plowden family, are of interest in relation to Ashfield's Catholic connexions (See above). As a curiosity may be mentioned too 'a coloured drawing by Ashfield' of 'Oliver Cromwell at the age of 30' (no doubt a copy of an earlier picture and not an *ad vivum* portrait) which was in Sir Joshua Reynolds's Sale (Phillips, 26:v:1798, Lot 1946). Some miniatures have been attributed to Ashfield, but no documented examples are known. According to Hearne, lived at the 'red ball in Lincoln Inn field in Holben row, the first house'. Sir William Musgrave gives the date of Ashfield's death as 1690, but neither of the authorities quoted by him, Walpole and Pilkington, support this. It is possible, however, that Sir William may have based his information on an advertisement in *The London Gazette*, No. 2642, for March 5th–9th, 1690–1, announcing that on 'the 9th. instant & the following day . . . will be sold by Auction a very fine and entire Collection of the

Paintings of *Mr*. E. A. lately deceased, fit for Chimnies, Halls, Stair-cases, Chambers, Closets, &c. with some other Goods, at John's Coffee-house next the Nags-head-Tavern in Cheapside . . . .' It must be admitted that the pictures mentioned suggest that they were rather 'histories' or landscapes than the portraits which were Ashfield's speciality; on the other hand he might perhaps have owned, like other painters of the time, a collection of pictures by other masters. The statement, made by Thieme-Becker, that Ashfield died in 1700, is apparently without authority.

BIBL.: *Buckeridge, Dedication* & p. 355. *Musgrave*, I, p. 56. *Turner, passim. Rylands,* pp. 4 & 81. *Baker, Lely,* I, p. 188 & II, p. 187. *Baker, Ashfield, passim. Bell & Poole,* pp. 5–6. *Baker & Constable,* p. 53, Pl. 67a. *T.-B.,* II, 1908, p. 179 (with *Bibl.*). *Long,* p. 9 (with *Bibl.*). *B.F.A.C., British-born Artists,* pp. 24–5. *Weale,* p. 12. *Woodward, passim. Burghley Cat.,* Nos. 189 & 195. *Ashmolean Mus. Report,* 1955, pp. 68–9, Pl. XVI. *Inf.* from Mr. Francis Needham.

DRAWINGS IN OTHER COLLECTIONS: Those mentioned above, and lists in *Baker, Ashfield,* and *B.F.A.C. British-born Artists.*

1. A GENTLEMAN. Head and shoulders turned half-l., with eyes looking to front. Wearing a light brown wig, lace cravat with black strings, and armour.   **Plate 48**

Crayons; 28·2 × 22·5 cm. (11 × 8⅞ in.).

PROV.: William Anderson, from whom it was purchased by the B.M., 1908.
1908–7–14–47.

BIBL. & REPR.: *Baker, Lely,* II, p. 187. *Baker, Ashfield,* pp. 84, 86, & Pl. LXXV. *Foster, Cooper,* p. 70. *Baker & Constable,* p. 53 & Pl. 67a.

Though unsigned, the attribution of this drawing to Ashfield has been generally accepted, and Mr. Collins Baker even refers

to it as the painter's masterpiece. It is certainly, in the admirable handling of the medium and the characterization of the sitter, far superior to most of Ashfield's other works, and is, indeed, one of the finest English XVII c. crayon drawings extant. Mr. Collins Baker assigns it to about 1675, the date of Ashfield's portrait of James Maitland, 1st Duke of Lauderdale, at Ham House. Mr. Collins Baker also sees in it 'a kind of family likeness' to this latter portrait. It has little in common, however, with Lely's portrait drawing of Lauderdale in the Department (1874–8–8–2263).

94

2. A YOUNG MAN. H.L., turned half-r., with eyes looking to front and l. hand to his breast. Wearing a light auburn wig, lace cravat, and purple drapery.   **Plate 47**

Crayons and black lead; 29·3 × 20·3 cm. (11½ × 8 in.).

PROV.: P. & D. Colnaghi, from whom it was purchased by the B.M., 1902. 1902–8–22–12.

When acquired by the B.M., this drawing was attributed to Sir Peter Lely. It is, however, clearly not by him, and is much nearer both in handling and colouring to the work of Edmund Ashfield.

BACKER, JOHN JAMES
Working from 1697: D. after 1705 (?)
Portrait and drapery painter

Was of Dutch or Flemish origin, and probably connected with one of the several families of artists of this name recorded in the Low Countries. Actually said by Walpole to have been a brother of the Amsterdam painter Adriaen Backer (B. 1635 or 36: D. 1684), though no authority is given for this statement. Worked as assistant to Sir Godfrey Kneller (*q.v.*), and, according to Vertue, accompanied his master to Brussels about 1697 when he went to paint the equestrian portrait of the Duke of Bavaria. Also made a small copy of the self-portrait by Kneller which was presented to the Uffizi, *c.* 1705. With another of Kneller's assistants, John Peters (Jan Pieters) of Antwerp, gave instruction in drawing to Vertue when a boy. Painted a good portrait, in Kneller's manner, of Sir Stephen Fox (now in the collection of the Earl of Ilchester) which was engraved in mezzotint by John Simon after 'I. Baker', and lettered, with reference to the sitter, *Aged 75. Anno 1701* (*Chaloner Smith*, III, No. 60). In *Thieme-Becker* and elsewhere, has been confused with a certain Nicolas de Backer (B. *c.* 1648: D. 1697) of Antwerp, referred to by Vertue (I, pp. 142 & 146) as 'Baker who painted insides of churches & buildings very neat . . .' and as 'old Baker, who painted church perspective', some of whose pictures, including 'those of churches & chappels at *Rome*', were in Mr. Sykes's sales of 1724. It is not clear whether this other Backer was ever in England.

BIBL.: *Walpole*, II, p. 598. T.-B., II, 1908, p. 324 (as Nicolas de Backer). *Vertue*, *Index*, p. 12 (as Baker).

DRAWINGS IN OTHER COLLECTIONS. Miss Agnes Mongan, *A Woman's l. Forearm*, inscribed: *Jefrow Agnes van Brakel | no Rings nor Braeslet*.

1. AN OLD WOMAN. Head covered with drapery, in profile to l., looking upwards and smiling.   **Plate 88**

Black chalk, heightened with white, on grey paper; 39·7 × 26·9 cm. (15⅝ × 10⅝ in.).

INSCR.: *Recto*, in the lower r.-hand corner, in black ink, *Backer invent*ʳ.

Verso, in black ink, inventory letters and numbers (?).

PROV.: Edward Byng. C. W. B. W. Roberts, his great-great-nephew. G. R.

Harding, from whom it was purchased by the B.M., 1897.

1897–8–13–9 (95).

The present drawing formed part of a large collection of sketchbooks and studies mainly by Edward Byng (*q.v.*) who worked, like Backer, as a drapery painter in Kneller's studio. Included in this series was also a drawing by Marcellus Laroon the elder, another of Kneller's assistants (*q.v.*).

BARLOW, FRANCIS

B. 1626(?): D. 1704

Painter and etcher, principally of animal and sporting subjects

Date and place of birth uncertain, the year 1626 being given by Redgrave but without known authority. Is called by Vertue 'Barlow of Lincolnshire' no doubt repeating an established tradition, but on the frontispiece to his *Multae et Diversae Avium Species* (1671)(?) is styled *Indigenam Londinensem*. Said by Vertue to have been apprenticed to 'Shepherd, a Face Painter'—perhaps identical with the William Sheppard who painted the portrait of Thomas Killigrew (1650), now at Woburn Abbey, and with the 'Mr. Sheppard, A picture maker by Creechurch' (St. Catherine Cree), who appears in the minutes of the Painter-Stainers' Company for Feb. 28th, 1640–1, as promising 'to pay for his admittance into the Companye'. Nine years later Barlow, together with Robert Walker, the Commonwealth portrait painter, and 'Sir' Edmund Marmion, the amateur etcher, was given the freedom of the Company (March 4th, 1649/50). Early in his career, seems to have turned his attention to the branch of art for which he is best known. Richard Symonds also notes between 1650 and 1652 that Barlow was 'living near the Drum in Drury Lane . . . for a quadro of fifishes he made he had 8l¹ he uses to make fowle and birds and colour them from life'. By 1656, Evelyn could write of the artist as 'the famous painter of Fowle, Beasts & Birds'. An early work with which his name can be associated, Edward Benlowes' *Theo-*

phila (1652), reveals him as a skilled portraitist in the etched bust of the author appearing in the frontispiece.

Secured the patronage and friendship of a number of eminent men: General Monck (afterwards 1st Duke of Albemarle), whose portrait he painted and whose elaborate funeral ceremonial he was commissioned to design in 1670; Sir Francis Prujean, physician to Queen Catherine, to whom the first edition of *Æsop's Fables* was dedicated; William, 3rd Earl of Devonshire, to whom he dedicated the second and third editions and for whom he designed a book plate; Denzil Onslow, who commissioned from the artist six paintings of birds, animals and fish (now in the collection of Lord Onslow at Clandon Park), four of them being large decorative compositions for the hall of his house at Purford and noted by Evelyn in 1681; and John Hervey, later 1st Earl of Bristol. Attempted unsuccessfully, despite the diarist's approval of Barlow as an animal painter, to obtain Evelyn's patronage by dedicating to him in 1656 an engraving of Titian's *Venus*. Vertue also mentions that he 'drew some Ceilings of Birds for Noblemen & Gentlemen' and refers to a painting of a flock of birds at Burghley. His earliest known work is dated 1648 (*See* No. 1 below).

Besides *Theophila* and the *Multae et Diversae Avium Species*, designed, and sometimes etched, many other book illustrations, including those to James Howell's *The Parly of Beasts* (1660), Sir Robert Stapylton's *Juvenal* (1660), John Ogilby's *Æsop's Fables* (2nd edition, II, 1668; *See* note to Nos. 17–103 below) and *Britannia* (1675), *Severall Wayes of Hunting, Hawking and Fishing, according to the English Manner* (1671), and Richard Blome's *Gentleman's Recreation* (Part II, 1686). Also drew some of the tombs in Westminster Abbey for Francis Sandford's *Genealogical History of the Kings of England* (1677). His most important published work was undoubtedly *Æsop's Fables* (for a full account of this see notes to Nos. 17–103 and 104–30 below). His work as a book illustrator resulted in his co-operation with some of the best draughtsman-engravers then working in England, his drawings being etched or engraved by Hollar (*q.v.*), Griffier (*q.v.*), Place (*q.v.*), Faithorne (*q.v.*), and Simon Gribelin, as well as by lesser men like Richard Gaywood, Thomas Dudley, Nicholas Yeates, Thomas Neale and Arthur Soly. Was the author of a large etching, *The Last Horse Race Run before Charles the Second* (published in 1687) showing the King attending a race at Dorset Ferry near Windsor in 1684. It is the first known English print of this sport. A late reference to the artist occurs in the Earl of Bristol's accounts for 1702 when £35 was paid to Barlow for pictures by Carlotto (Carlo Dolci or Carlo Maratti) and Guido (Guido Reni). Vertue says he died a poor man in 1702, but this date has been proved incorrect, as he is now known to have been buried on August 11th, 1704, in St. Margaret's, Westminster. Is not known to have made a Will.

His etched plates for *Æsop's Fables* and other original etchings place him on a level with the best of his contemporaries, although he himself in his introduction to that work rated his powers in this medium over-modestly. As an etcher also appears to have earned a reputation outside England, for the introduction to the 4th edition of his *Æsop*, published in Amsterdam (1714) speaks of *des animaux et des oiseaux dessinez d'un gout exquis et d'une touche savante*, and of his work as *tres utile aux peintres, sculpteurs, graveurs, et autres artistes ou amateurs de dessin*. As a painter also gained wide recognition. Vertue considered that 'had his Colouring and Pencilling been as good as his Draught; which was most exact, he might have easily excelled all that went before him in that kind of Painting [of Fowls, Fish and Beasts]'. According to Symonds, 'In his Paeses he used Speklis for ye skye & has no good greene for his ground & grasse.'

As a painter of animal and sporting subjects, belongs to the circle mainly of Dutch artists working in England, like Hondius (*q.v.*), Griffier and Thomas and Jan Wyck (*q.v.*), and, as a painter of birds, has affinities with Melchior Hondecoeter (B. 1636: D. 1695), James Bogdany (D. 1720) and Pieter Casteels (B. 1684: D. 1749), and may be regarded as a precursor of his younger contemporary, Marmaduke Cradock (*q.v.*).

BIBL.: *Painter-Stainers' Minutes*, II, p. 8. *Buckeridge*, p. 357–8. *D.N.B.*, III, 1885, pp. 219–20. *Evelyn, Diary*, III, pp. 166–7. *T.-B.*, II, 1908, pp. 505–6 (with *Bibl.*). *Shaw Sparrow, British Sporting Artists*, pp. 21–51, with *Plates*. *Shaw Sparrow, British Etching*, pp. 92–109, with *Plates*. *Shaw Sparrow, Barlow*. *Shaw Sparrow, Earliest Sporting Artist*. *Vertue, Index*, p. 13. *Ogden, Index*, p. 219.

DRAWINGS IN OTHER COLLECTIONS: List in *B.F.A.C. British Born Artists*.

The following drawings are arranged in their probable order of execution.

1. *Recto.* **DAVID SLAYING THE LION.** David raising his sword against a lion surprised with a sheep. In the distance, r., David's flock beneath a tree.   **Plate 49**

Pen and brown ink; the corners cut off; 20·6 × 29·5 cm. (8⅛ × 11⅝ in.).

INSCR.: *Recto*, on a stone at the foot, r., *Franc Barlow | inventer | 1648.*

Verso : STUDIES OF A LION'S HEAD.

Black chalk.

PROV.: H. S. Reitlinger (Sale, Sotheby, 27:i:1954, Lot 132). Purchased at the Reitlinger Sale by the B.M., 1954.

1954–2–13–3.

This drawing is Barlow's earliest known dated work. Its deliberate penwork can be considered as characteristic of the artist's first manner (*See* also No. 2 below).

2. NINE STUDIES OF HEADS ARRANGED IN TWO ROWS. The upper row of men, the lower of women, drawn in various poses.
Plate 50

Pen and brown ink; the corners cut off; 17·2 × 27·8 cm. (6¾ × 11 in.).

INSCR.: *Recto*, at the top, by the artist, *Invention*; and below eight of the heads, though not in sequence, *1–8*.

PROV.: H. S. Reitlinger (Sale, Sotheby, 27:i:1954, Lot 133). Purchased at the Reitlinger Sale by the B.M., 1954.

1954–2–13–4.

Similar in style to, and no doubt of the same date as, No. 1.

3. ILLUSTRATION TO CANTO II OF EDWARD BENLOWES' *Theophila, or Loves Sacrifice*, 1652. Theophila kneeling in prayer towards the r. before a fountain surmounted by a cross, emblematic of Christ's sacrifice. Around her, the seven Deadly Sins, in the guise of animals, threatening her. In the background, the Garden of Eden with the temptation and expulsion of Adam and Eve.
Plate 51

Brush drawing in grey wash; 19 × 14·2 cm. (7⅜ × 5⅝ in.).

PROV.: A. E. Evans & Sons, from whom it was purchased by the B.M., 1859.

1859–7–9–3.

ETCH.: By Barlow, in reverse, in *Theophila*, p. 23, the subject illustrating the lines which appear below the etching:

Satan caus'd Eves, Eve Adams Fall,
Whose Lapse hath brought a Curse on All :
No marvaile then THEOPHILA
Beseig'd with deadly sinnes does pray,
And kneeling lifteth up her Hands
To CHRIST, the Fount that streaming stands :
Which Laver all her Wounds doth cure,
And of polluted, makes HER pure.

BIBL.: *Lowndes*, I, p. 153. *Walpole*, III, pp. 899–900. *Shaw Sparrow, British Etching*, pp. 93–4. *Vertue*, II, p. 72.

Theophila, or Loves Sacrifice. A Divine Poem is the best known work of Edward Benlowes (B. 1603 (?): D. 1676) of Brent Hall, Essex, a patron of letters and himself a man of literary pretensions. The book is now better known for its rarity and bibliographical interest than for its poetic content. Most copies extant have been mutilated by the removal of many of the illustrations, and the very few recorded copies which are thought to be complete are said not to agree in the collation of the plates. Barlow's etchings, which include a portrait of Benlowes, are probably the only illustrations designed expressly for the book, and speaking of them

Vertue says 'it appears that Barlow was then a man of some fame or reputation. the Animals that are etched are done with Spirit & judgment'. The remaining illustrations consist of impressions from rather earlier plates or woodblocks, including Hollar's

Four Seasons (Parthey, Nos. 614–17), two engravings by Thomas Cecill emblematic of the Passion and Resurrection, dated 1632, and a woodcut with the Tree of Knowledge originally belonging to Robert Barker's folio edition of the Bible of 1633.

4. A PELICAN IN HER PIETY. A pelican standing with wings outspread, feeding three of her young with the drops of blood which she draws from her breast.

Grey wash with brush outline; 14·9 × 17·2 cm. ($5\frac{7}{8} \times 6\frac{3}{4}$ in.).

PROV.: Henry Graves & Co., from whom it was purchased by the B.M., 1858.
1858–6–26–408.

A similar subject, but a different composition, was etched by Barlow as the title-page to Sir William Denny's *Pelicanicidium*, 1653 (*See Johnson*, p. 1, No. 1).

5. DESIGN FOR THE FRONTISPIECE TO JOHN BROWN'S *The Description and use of the Carpenters-Rule*, **1656.** W.L. figure of an elderly bearded man standing within a doorway, above which are garlands suspended from a mask. Wearing a broad-brimmed hat and doublet girt with a sash, and holding in his l. hand the carpenter's rule, and in his r. a compass. On the ground and on a pedestal beside him, geometrical solids of various forms. **Plate 53**

Brush drawing in grey wash; indented for transfer; 11·5 × 6·9 cm, ($4\frac{1}{2} \times 2\frac{3}{4}$ in.).

PROV.: Richard Bull (Sale, Sotheby, 25:v:1881, Lot 52). Purchased at the Bull Sale, through A. W. Thibaudeau, by the B.M., 1881.

1881–6–11–155 (L.B., as by Richard Gaywood, 1).

ETCH.: By Richard Gaywood, in reverse, as the frontispiece to John Brown's *The Description and Use of the Carpenters-Rule* . . . . *To which is added, The use of a (portable) Geometrical Sun-dial, with a Nocturnal on the backside . . .*, 1656 [2nd edn. 1688.] An impression of this etching is in the Dept. (1883–5–12–55). With it, on the same sheet of paper, is an impression of the etched diagram of the 'Geometrical Sun-dial', which in the book faces p. 143.

BIBL.: *B.M. Engraved Portraits*, I, 1908, p. 260.

John Brown or Browne, who describes himself as a 'Philomath' of scientific instruments and the author of a number of small treatises on mathematical and other kindred subjects, published between 1656 and 1671. According to an inscription on the diagram of the 'Geometrical Sun-dial' mentioned above, he lived in 'Dukes place neere Aldgate', while his later publications give his address as 'The *Sphear* and *Sun-Dial* in the *Minories*'. Pepys, who mentions him frequently in his Diary between 1663 and 1669, had a high opinion of Brown's instruments and purchased several of them, including the 'Carpenters-Rule'.

According to Bromley (*A Catalogue of Engraved British Portraits*, 1793, i, p. 106), the Catalogue of the Bull Sale and O'Donoghue (*See* Bibl. above), the figure of the man in the frontispiece to *The Description and Use of the Carpenters-Rule* is a portrait of John Brown himself. Mr. Binyon also accepts this view. Like Nos. 6 and 16, this drawing has previously been ascribed to Richard Gaywood, presumably on the strength of his name appearing on the etching which he made after it. There is no doubt, however, that the drawing in reality is by Barlow.

6. DESIGN FOR THE TITLE-PAGE TO SAMUEL CLARKE'S *A Geographical Description of all the Countries in the Knowne World, 1657.* A central panel, left blank for the title, surrounded by compartments, two on each side and one below. At the top, a globe in a niche decorated with garlands. On the l., in compartments, two female figures, symbolizing respectively Asia with an elephant, and America with a camel (though perhaps intended for the more appropriate llama). On the r., two other figures, Europe with a horse, and Africa with a lion. At the foot, a rhinoceros and an elephant, in a landscape with a palm tree.   **Plate 54**

Brush drawing in grey wash; indented for transfer; 23·7 × 15 cm. ($9\frac{3}{8} × 5\frac{7}{8}$ in.).

INSCR.: Within the central panel, *the original | Drawing by | Gaywood to | . . . Frontispiece | 15 . . . 13.*

PROV.: E. Daniell, from whom it was purchased by Dr. John Percy, 1881 (Sale, Christie, 17:iv:1890, Lot 844). Purchased at the Percy Sale, by the B.M., 1890.

   1890–5–12–85 (L.B., as by Richard Gaywood, 2).

ETCH.: By Richard Gaywood, in reverse, as the title-page to Samuel Clarke's *A Geographical Description of all the Countries of the Knowne World*, 1657, forming a second part to *A Mirror or Looking-Glass Both for Saints & Siners*, 1656, the title-page of which is also etched by Gaywood (*See* Johnson, p. 21, No. 8).

BIBL.: *Percy Cat.*, p. 44(2).

   Though traditionally ascribed to Gaywood, there is no doubt that in reality this drawing is by Barlow (*See* notes to Nos. 5 and 16).

[7–15] DRAWINGS CONNECTED WITH *Variae Quadrupedum species*, etched by Wenceslaus Hollar, 1659–63 (*Parthey*, Nos. 2080–89).

7. SWINE AND DONKEYS. Scene in a yard. In the centre, a boar, his forelegs planted on a mound, confronting two donkeys on the r. On the l., a sow lying on the ground, suckling her young, and beyond her, three other pigs, one coming out of a sty. Over the fence in the background, a countryman with a pitchfork, his l. arm raised.

Brush drawing in grey wash; indented for transfer; 14·3 × 20·2 cm. ($5\frac{5}{8} × 8$ in.).

   PROV.: W. B. Tiffin, from whom it was chased by the B.M., 1855.
   1855–7–14–63 (L.B.2*b*).

ETCH.: By Hollar, in reverse, in *Variae quadrupedum species*, Pl. 2 (*Parthey*, No. 2081).

8. BEARS. Two bears confronting each other in the foreground, a third half-hidden on the l., and a fourth climbing a palm-tree on the r. Landscape background.

Brush drawing in grey wash; indented for transfer; 14·7 × 21·2 cm. (5¾ × 8⅜ in.).

ETCH.: By Hollar, in reverse, in *Variae quadrupedum species*, Pl. 4, (*Parthey*, No. 2083).

PROV.: As for No. 7.
1855–7–14–64 (L.B.3*a*).

9. GOATS AND SHEEP.

A he-goat standing on a mound in the centre, with two she-goats on the l., one looking up at him, the other turned away. On the r., a ram and two sheep, and perched above them on a tree, a magpie and two tits. In the foreground, a mole.

Brush drawing in grey wash; indented for transfer; 14·3 × 20·3 cm. (5⅝ × 8 in.).

ETCH.: By Hollar, in reverse, in *Variae quadrupedum species*, Pl. 5 (*Parthey*, No. 2084).

PROV.: As for No. 7.
1855–7–14–62 (L.B.2*a*).

10. HORSES.

In the foreground, a horse standing in profile to l., and behind him another horse on his hind legs. Beyond, other horses, seen in different characteristic poses, in an undulating meadow bordered by distant trees.

Brush drawing in grey wash, indented for transfer; 14·2 × 20·2 cm. (5⅝ × 8 in.).

ETCH.: By Hollar, in reverse, in *Variae quadrupedum species*, Pl. 6, (*Parthey*, No. 2085). In the etching the principal horse is shown black to contrast with the others.

PROV.: Mr. Whitehead, from whom it was purchased by the B.M., 1876 (registered in error as 1875).
1875–6–12–561 (L.B.5).

11. DEER, HARES, RABBITS AND SQUIRRELS.

A buck and a doe moving across the foreground from the r. On the l., another buck feeding, and a hare sitting on its haunches listening. On the extreme r., two rabbits feeding on the ground, and in a tree beyond, two squirrels. In the distance, a stretch of open country with a building on a hill, and five wild duck crossing the sky. **Plate 55**

Brush drawing in grey wash; indented for transfer; 14·6 × 21·7 cm. (5¾ × 8½ in.).

ETCH.: By Hollar, in reverse, in *Variae quadrupedum species*, Pl. 8 (*Parthey*, No. 2087).

PROV.: As for No. 7.
1855–7–14–61 (L.B.4).

12. CATTLE.

A cow turned to r., grazing in the foreground. Beyond her, l., a bull, and r., another cow. Further off, r., two other cows, one lying down, the other grazing near a tree. In the distance, a hill crowned with a church spire.

Brush drawing in grey wash, indented for transfer; 14·2 × 20·2 cm. (5⅝ × 8 in.).

ETCH.: By Hollar, in reverse, in *Variae quadrupedum species*, Pl. 9, (*Parthey*, No. 2088).

PROV.: As for No. 10.
1875–6–12–562 (L.B.6).

13. HOUNDS. In the foreground five hounds, four of them coupled in pairs, and the man in charge of them standing with raised stick on the extreme r., hallooing. Beyond, an undulating landscape, with a hare running across a hillock towards the r.

Plate 56

Brush drawing in grey wash; indented for transfer; 14·2 × 20·2 cm. (5⅝ × 8 in.).

ETCH.: By Hollar, in reverse, in *Variae quadrupedum species*, Pl. 10 (Parthey, No. 2089).

PROV.: As for No. 10.
1875–6–12–560 (L.B.7).

14. DOGS AND CATS. A mastiff, his jaws open, sitting on the l., chained to his kennel. In the centre, a greyhound looking at an angry cat who stands with arched back on the top of a wall, while a spaniel with forepaws on the wall barks at her. In the lower r.-hand corner, another cat appearing at an opening. Landscape background.

Brush drawing in grey wash; indented for transfer; 14·2 × 20·2 cm. (5⅝ × 8 in.).

INSCR.: *Recto*, at the foot in the centre, by the artist, *F. Barlow*.

PROV.: As for No. 10.
1875–6–12–559 (L.B.8).

ETCH.: By Hollar, in the same sense (Parthey, No. 2042), and by Richard Gay-

wood, in reverse. Parthey, evidently not knowing that the original design was by Barlow, has incorrectly placed it as Pl. 2 of the series of twelve etchings of hounds and other animals after Peeter van Avont, dated 1646–7 (Parthey, Nos. 2041–52). In style, however, both the present drawing and the etching after it resemble *Variae quadrupedum species* (See Nos. 7–13 above & No. 15 below) and may really form part of that series.

15. LEOPARDS AND LYNXES. Two leopards, one moving across the foreground from the l., the other turning away to retaliate against two lynxes who are snarling at him from a bank, r. Landscape background, with a leopard chasing a stag, centre, and a rocky hill, l., crowned by trees.

Brush drawing in grey wash; indented for transfer; 14·5 × 20·9 cm. (5¾ × 8¼ in.).

ETCH.: By Richard Gaywood, in reverse.

PROV.: As for No. 7.
1855–7–14–65 (L.B.3*b*).

In style this drawing belongs to those connected with the series of etchings by Hollar, *Variae quadrupedum species*.

16. DESIGN FOR THE FRONTISPIECE TO JOHN PLAYFORD'S *Musick's Delight on the Cithren*, 1666. A young man playing the cithern, seated at a table on which is an open music-book in which he reads. On the wall behind him, l., another cithern, a bass viol, and a *pochette* or kit.

Plate 53

Pen and brown ink, with grey wash; indented for transfer; 7·6 × 13 cm. (3 × 5⅛ in.).

PROV.: Archibald Russell, Lancaster Herald (Sale, Sotheby, 2:iv:1928, Lot 50).

Purchased at the Russell Sale by the B.M., 1928.

1928–7–16–10.

ETCH.: By Richard Gaywood, in reverse, as the frontispiece to John Playford's *Musick's Delight on the Cithren*, 1666.

BIBL. & REPR.: *Dodgson, Barlow*, p. 285.

The Cithern or Cithren (Ital. *Cetera*), an instrument shaped like a lute, but with a flat back and only four pairs of wire strings, enjoyed great popularity from the XVI down to the XVII c., especially for accompanying the voice. The etching, being in the reverse sense to the drawing, shows the instrument correctly held. It has been suggested that the man shown playing it represents John Playford (B. 1623: D. 1686) himself, but the features have little in common with the authentic portraits of him, one of which, etched by Gaywood, appears as the frontispiece to *A. Brief Introduction to the Skill of Music for Song and Viol*, 3rd edn., 1660 (*B.M., Engraved Portraits*, III, p. 479).

Though traditionally ascribed to Gaywood, there is no doubt that in reality this drawing is by Barlow (*See* notes to Nos. 5 & 6).

[17–103]. TITLE AND ILLUSTRATIONS TO ÆSOP'S FABLES WITH HIS LIFE. *In English, French & Latin. The English by Thos. Philipott Esq.; The French and Latin by Rob. Codrington, M.A., Illustrated with One hundred and Twelve Sculptures By Francis Barlow*, 1666, a second edition of which appeared in 1687 with thirty-one extra plates designed by Barlow illustrating Æsop's Life. Both of these editions, and a third which appeared in 1703, were published by Barlow himself. A fourth and last edition, in French, was bought out by Etienne Roger in Amsterdam in 1714. For a full bibliographical account *see Hofer*.

As Mr. Hofer points out, Barlow was much indebted for the sources of his illustrations to the etchings by the elder Gheeraerts in *Esbatement Moral, des Animavx*, Antwerp, 1578. Another source was John Ogilby's *The Fables of Æsop Paraphras'd in Verse, and adorn'd with Sculpture*, 1651, of which the frontispiece is signed by Francis Cleyn, though it is uncertain whether he is also the author of the plates to the *Fables*.

A second edition of Ogilby's *Æsop*, published in 1665–8, should also be mentioned here, as (in company with Hollar and R. Stoop) Barlow contributed several of the plates to it. These appear in Vol. ii, published in 1668, and illustrate Fables xiv (etched by Richard Gaywood), xvi, xx, xxi, xxxi, xxxix, xli, xliii, xliv, xlvi, xlix, together with *Androcleus or the Roman Slave*, opposite pp. 129, 138, 142 (?), 146 (?), 153, 157, 162, 164, 166, 168, 172, 176, 182 (?), 186, 188, 192 (?). Not unnaturally some of them have features in common with the plates in Barlow's own editions of *Æsop*.

In the following list of drawings any possible connexion between them and Gheeraerts or Ogilby is noted.

The drawings were acquired from three different sources: one (No. 75) was purchased from Mr. Tiffin in 1855, thirty-six from Messrs. Graves in 1858, and the remaining seventy-seven from Miss E. Hanks in 1867. When acquired, the last mentioned series was mounted in an album, the leaves of which are watermarked *1794 / J WHATMAN*, bound in white vellum gilt and lettered on the spine *BARLOW'S / DRAWINGS*. All the original designs for Barlow's *Æsop* in the collection have now been mounted together in this album following the order of the plates of the second edition of the work, 1687. For strict chronological reasons, however, those illustrating the *Life* are listed (Nos. 104–30) after the *Fables*.

BIBL.: *Walpole*, II, p. 371. *Vertue*, II, p. 136. *Hofer*, pp. 279–95 (with full *Bibl.*).

17. DESIGN FOR THE ETCHED TITLE-PAGE. An oval cartouche surmounted by an eagle and supported at the sides, l., by a leopard and a boar, and r., by a lion and a bear, with a fox in the centre at the foot.

Pen and brown ink, with grey wash; indented for transfer; 23·3 × 15·6 cm. (9¼ × 6⅛ in.).

INSCR.: *Recto*, on the cartouche, *Original | DRAWINGS | Design'd and Executed By | Mʳ Francis Barlow | From which he Etched | The Prints for his | Æsop Fables.*

PROV.: Miss E. Hanks, from whom it was purchased by the B.M., 1867.
1867–4–13–320A (L.B.13(1)).

ETCH.: By Barlow, in reverse.

18. FABLE I: 'THE COCK AND PRECIOUS STONE'. Scene in a farmyard, with the cock standing on a dunghill, centre, looking down at the jewel. To r. and l., four hens with their chicks. In the background, r., two pigs being fed by an old woman at a door in the farmhouse, and l., a stable, with a man holding a pitchfork at the entrance and an ox and a horse at the windows.

Pen and brown ink, with grey wash; 13 × 16·1 cm. (5⅛ × 6⅜ in.).

PROV.: As for No. 17.
1867–4–13–347 (L.B.13(29)).

ETCH.: By Barlow, in reverse.

[The drawing for Fable II: 'The Wolf and Lamb' is missing.]

19. FABLE III: 'THE LYON AND FOUR BULLS'. The lion, seen from the back, standing on a bank in the foreground, r., looking down at the four bulls who are grazing in a meadow, l. Wooded hills in the distance, l.

Pen and brown ink, with grey wash; 12·5 × 15·9 cm. (4⅞ × 6¼ in.).

PROV.: As for No. 17.
1867–4–13–348 (L.B.13(30)).

ETCH.: By Barlow, in reverse.

20. FABLE IV: 'THE FOX AND THE FROG'. The fox heading a group of animals, including the horse, the goat, the hart and the ox, below a tree, r., looking down at the frog seated, l., under a clump of bulrushes. Wooded hills, surmounted by a building with a tower in the distance, l.

Pen and brown ink, with grey wash; 13 × 16·3 cm. (5⅛ × 6⅜ in.).

PROV.: As for No. 17.
1867–4–13–349 (L.B.13(31)).

ETCH.: By Barlow, in reverse, with modifications including the position of the horse's head and the addition of a monkey and a squirrel in the tree, r.

[The drawing for Fable V: 'The Ass eating Thistles' is missing.]

21. FABLE VI: 'THE LARK'S NEST IN THE CORN'. The owner of the field and his son, with sickles in their hands and with their dog, standing, r., and conversing near a tree. In mid-distance, centre, the cornfield, with the parent larks hovering over their young who are on the ground. Further off, l., two men beside a gate, beyond which is a cottage amidst trees backed by distant hills.

Pen and brown ink, with grey wash; 12·9 × 16·3 cm. (5 × 6⅜ in.).

PROV.: As for No. 17. 1867–4–13–350 (L.B.13(32)).

ETCH.: By Barlow, in reverse.

22. FABLE VII: 'THE FOX AND COCK IN A TREE'. In the centre, the fox gazing up at a tree in which the cock and two hens have taken refuge, l. In mid-distance, a farm-house, standing behind a fence with a gate in it. Beyond, r., a huntsman and hounds descending a hill in pursuit of a stag.

Pen and brown ink, with grey wash; 12·5 × 16 cm. (4⅞ × 6¼ in.).

PROV.: As for No. 17. 1867–4–13–351 (L.B.13(33)).

ETCH.: By Barlow, in reverse.

23. FABLE VIII: 'THE FOX IN THE WELL'. The wolf resting his forepaws on the parapet of the well, l., and looking down at the fox within. On the r., a gate in a fence leading to a meadow with distant trees and hills beyond.

Pen and brown ink, with grey wash; 12·9 × 16·3 cm. (5 × 6⅜ in.).

PROV.: As for No. 17. 1867–4–13–352 (L.B.13(34)).

ETCH.: By Barlow, in reverse.

24. FABLE IX: 'THE WOLVES AND SHEEP'. The wolves attacking the sheep in the foreground. In mid-distance, l., a clump of trees, and further off, r., open country with distant hills.

Pen and brown ink, with grey wash; 12·9 × 16·3 cm. (5 × 6⅜ in.).

ETCH.: By Barlow, in reverse, with slight modifications in the distance.

PROV.: As for No. 17. 1867–4–13–353 (L.B.13(35)).

Perhaps inspired by *Gheeraerts*, p. 11, *Des Brebis, Loups & Chiens*.

[The drawing for Fable X: 'The Eagle's Nest' is missing.]

25. FABLE XI: 'THE WOLF IN SHEEPS CLOTHING'. Two shepherds standing on the l. and looking up at the wolf with his sheepskin hanging from the branch of a tree, r. Landscape background with a flock of sheep.

Pen and brown ink, with grey wash; 12·9 × 16·1 cm. (5 × 6⅜ in.).

ETCH.: By Barlow, in reverse, with slight modifications in the distance.

PROV.: As for No. 17.
1867–4–13–354 (L.B.13(36)).

Perhaps inspired by *Gheeraerts*, p. 75, *Le Loup en habit de Brebris*.

26. FABLE XII: 'THE RINGDOVE AND FOWLER'. The fowler kneeling, r., with a spaniel at his side, and taking aim at the ringdove perched on a tree, l. On the extreme r., the adder biting the fowler's heel. In the background, a cottage amidst trees.

Pen and brown ink, with grey wash; 13 × 16·3 cm. (5⅛ × 6⅜ in.).

PROV.: As for No. 17.
1867–4–13–355 (L.B.13(37)).

ETCH.: By Barlow, in reverse.

27. FABLE XIII: 'THE SOW AND HER PIGS'. The sow with her litter before the sty, r., turning in defiance to the wolf who appears on the l. Within the sty, r., another pig, and on the roof, two doves.

Pen and brown ink, with grey wash; 12·8 × 15·9 cm. (5 × 6¼ in.).

ETCH.: By Barlow, in reverse, with the addition of an owl on the paling of the sty, l.

PROV.: As for No. 17.
1867–4–13–356 (L.B.13(38)).

Perhaps inspired by *Gheeraerts*, p. 18, *Du Loup & d'une Truye*.

28. FABLE XIV: 'THE HORSE AND THE ASS'. The horse coming into the foreground from the r., and the ass going away towards the l. In the background, a stretch of open country, with a pack-horse and another ass, r.

Brush drawing in brown wash over black lead, touched with pen and ink; indented for transfer; 13 × 15·4 cm. (5⅛ × 6 in.).

ETCH.: By Barlow, in reverse.

The above, with its rather thin pen outline, differs considerably from the majority of drawings in this series.

PROV.: As for No. 4.
1858–6–26–372 (L.B.13(39)).

[The drawing for Fable XV: 'The Wolf and Goat' is missing.]

29. FABLE XVI: 'THE DOVES AND HAWK'. Two hawks descending on a farmyard with a dovecote on the r. of it. In the foreground, a third hawk attacking a dove, and the bodies of two others lying nearby. On the r., another dove perched on a basket. In the background, a gate in a wall, beyond which are trees and a domed building.

Pen and brown ink, with grey wash; 13·1 × 16·2 cm. (5⅛ × 6⅜ in.).

PROV.: As for No. 17.
1867–4–13–357 (L.B.13(40)).

ETCH.: By Barlow, in reverse.

Probably inspired by *Gheeraerts*, p. 40, *Des Colombes & l'Esprenier*.

In the 1st edn. of Barlow's *Æsop*, 1666, the etching of this subject occurs on p. 209, with the title *The Doves, Kite, and Sparhawk*, illustrating Fable CIV. In the 2nd edn., 1687, it occurs on p. 33, with the title *The Doves and Hawk*, illustrating Fable XVI, which has much the same text as Fable CIV in the 1st edn. (*See* note to No. 99). The present drawing has been more conveniently listed here according to this latter arrangement.

30. FABLE XVII: 'THE CITY MOUSE AND COUNTRY MOUSE'. A larder interior with a quantity of meat and dead game lying on a ledge and hanging from the ceiling, l. At the corner of the ledge, l., the two mice scampering away on the entry of a servant who appears at the top of a flight of steps, r. In the background, through the open window, a cottage amidst trees.

Pen and brown ink, with grey wash; 13 × 16·3 cm. (5⅛ × 6⅜ in.).

PROV.: As for No. 17.
1867–4–13–358 (L.B.13(41)).

ETCH.: By Barlow, in reverse.

31. FABLE XVIII: 'THE SWALLOW AND OTHER BIRDS'. A countryman walking towards the r., sowing in a field, his plough and harrow laid aside beneath a tree, r., in which five birds are perched. Overhead, l., the swallow flying away. In the distance, a hilly landscape with a cottage and a ruin.

Pen and brown ink, with grey wash; 12·9 × 16·3 cm. (5⅛ × 6½ in.).

PROV.: As for No. 17.
1867–4–13–359 (L.B.13(42)).

ETCH.: By Barlow, in reverse.

32. FABLE XIX: 'THE HUNTED BEAVER'. The beaver on the bank of a stream, centre, turning to bite off his stones, as a pursuing couple of hounds and their huntsman, winding his horn, rush on their prey from the r. Landscape background with distant hills, l., and a heron and other birds in flight overhead.

Pen and brown ink, with grey wash, over black lead; 12·8 × 16·2 cm. (5 × 6⅜ in.).

PROV.: As for No. 17.
1867–4–13–360 (L.B.13(43)).

ETCH.: By Barlow, in reverse.

[The drawing for Fable XX: 'The Fox and Cat' is missing.]

33. FABLE XXI: 'THE CAT AND MICE'. Interior of a shed with the cat sitting on top of a hutch within an alcove, r., and looking down at the mice, centre, with their bell. On the l., a yard with a fence, with fields and trees beyond.

Pen and brown ink, with grey wash, over black lead; 12·8 × 16·2 cm. (5 × 6⅜ in.).

ETCH.: By Barlow, in reverse, with the addition of two oxen in the yard, r.

PROV.: As for No. 17.
1867–4–13–361 (L.B.13(44)).

34. FABLE XXII: 'THE LYON AND OTHER BEASTS'. The lion, surrounded by the other animals, standing in the centre with his paw resting on the dead hart. Landscape background with distant hills.

Pen and brown ink, with grey wash; 12·8 × 16·2 cm. (5 × 6⅜ in.).

ETCH.: By Barlow, in reverse, with the addition of an ape sitting astride the ass on the r.

PROV.: As for No. 17.
1867–4–13–362 (L.B.13(45)).

Probably based on *Gheeraerts*, p. 60, *Du Lion & d'autres bestes*.

[The drawing for Fable XXIII: 'The Lyon and Mouse' is missing.]

35. FABLE XXIV: 'THE LION AND THE MOUSE'. In the centre, the lion's daughter unconcernedly crushing with her paw the presumptuous mouse who has pretended to her hand. On the l., the lion and his lioness, and on the r. the entrance to their den overhung by trees.

Pen and brown ink, with grey wash; 13 × 16 cm. (5⅛ × 6¼ in.).

ETCH.: By Barlow, in reverse, with the addition of two swallows in the centre background.

PROV.: As for No. 4.
1858–6–26–373 (L.B.13(46)).

Perhaps inspired by *Gheeraerts*, p. 12, *Du Lion & le Rat*.

36. FABLE XXV: 'THE DOG WITH A CLOG'. The aggressive dog, put under restraint with a bar and a weight hanging from his neck, standing on the r., surrounded by his companions. In the background, below, a stretch of flat and open country.

Brush drawing in grey wash, over black lead; 13·1 × 15·7 cm. (5⅛ × 6⅛ in.).

In the drawing the second dog from the l. was originally intended to be shown with his head in profile to r. instead of turned away to the l. The outline in black lead of the profile can still be seen.

PROV.: As for No. 4.
1858–6–26–374 (L.B.13(47)).

ETCH.: By Barlow, in reverse.

37. FABLE XXVI: 'THE OXE AND TOAD'. The ox standing on the r. before a barn, while the toad and her daughter appear in the lower l.-hand corner. In mid-distance, two other oxen cropping the grass, and beyond them, a gate in a fence behind which is a cottage, l., backed by a wooded hill.

Pen and brown ink, with grey wash, over black lead; 13·2 × 16·3 cm. (5⅛ × 6½ in.).

PROV.: As for No. 4.
1858–6–26–375 (L.B.13(48)).

ETCH.: By Barlow, in reverse, with the addition of a countryman at the upper window of the barn, l., and three sheep and another countryman on the r. of the gate in the background.

Perhaps inspired by *Gheeraerts*, p. 38, *De la Grenouille & du Beuf*.

In the drawing the outlines in black lead showing a slightly different position of the forefeet and r.-hand horn of the ox can be seen.

38. FABLE XXVII: 'THE LION AND FOX'. The lion standing at the top of slightly rising ground, l., while the fox, looking up at him, crouches on the r. In the background, r., a clump of trees, and at some distance away, l., again the lion and the fox, and beyond them, a hill surmounted by a tower.

Pen and brown ink, with grey wash, over black lead; 13·3 × 16·6 cm. (5¼ × 6½ in.).

PROV.: As for No. 4.
1858–6–26–376 (L.B.13(49)).

ETCH.: By Barlow, in reverse, with the lion's head slightly inclined towards the l., and the distant hill modified in form and not surmounted by a tower.

39. FABLE XXVIII: 'THE APE AND FOX'. In the centre, the fox, seen from behind, looking at the ape who is seated, r., beneath a tree on the branches of which is another ape. Trees and hills in the distance, l.

Pen and brown ink, with grey wash; 12·9 × 16·3 cm. (5⅛ × 6⅜ in.).

PROV.: As for No. 17.
1867–4–13–363 (L.B.13(50)).

ETCH.: By Barlow, in reverse, with the addition of another ape and two squirrels in the tree on the l.

[The drawing for Fable XXIX: 'The Dog and Ox' is missing.]

[The drawing for Fable XXX: 'The Birds and Beasts' is missing.]

40. FABLE XXXI: 'THE TYGRE AND FOX'. The tiger springing upwards in his attempt to drag the arrow from his side, while the fox looks round at him from the r. Concealed in the bushes, r., the turbaned archer, and in the background, l., his other victims lying transfixed by his arrows.

Pen and brown ink, with grey wash; 13 × 15·7 cm. (5⅛ × 6¼ in.).

PROV.: As for No. 17.
1867–4–13–364 (L.B.13(51)).

ETCH.: By Barlow, in reverse, with the stripes more clearly indicated on the tiger, instead of the 'leopard's spots' which appear in the drawing.

[The Drawing for Fable XXXII: 'The Lioness and Fox' is missing.]

41. FABLE XXXIII: 'THE OAK AND REED'. A landscape threshed by a gale. On the l., the oak torn up by its roots and falling over, and r., the reeds bending before the wind. In the foreground, two herons, and overhead, l., a flight of wild duck.   **Plate 52**

Pen and brown ink, with grey wash; 12·7 × 15·8 cm. (5 × 6¼ in.).

ETCH.: By Barlow, in reverse.

Perhaps based on *Gheeraerts*, p. 16, *Du Fresne & du Roseau*.

PROV.: As for No. 17.
1867–4–13–365 (L.B.13(52)).

42. FABLE XXXIV: 'THE WIND AND THE SUN'. In the foreground, the traveller walking towards the r., huddled in his cloak against the blast directed at him by a wind, whose profile with puffed-out cheeks appears in the clouds above, l. In mid-distance, centre, the same traveller now divested of his cloak on account of the heat of the sun shining in the upper r.-hand corner. In the background, l., a church amidst trees.

Pen and brown ink, with grey wash, over black lead; 13 × 16 cm. (5⅛ × 6⅜ in.).

ETCH.: By Barlow, in reverse, with the two figures of the traveller completely altered in appearance (though retaining their original places in relation to the composition), becoming bearded old men in different costumes from those seen in the drawing.

PROV.: As for No. 4.
1858–6–26–377 (L.B.13(53)).

43. FABLE XXXV: 'THE KITE, FROG, AND MOUSE'. A semi-circular arena surrounded by frogs and mice all holding lances. In the foreground, the mouse champion, l., mounted on a weasel, facing the frog champion, r., mounted on a lobster, and at some distance away, the same champions fighting on foot. Overhead, the kite hovering above his prey.

Brush drawing in grey wash; 12·9 × 15·4 cm. (5⅛ × 6⅛ in.).

ETCH.: By Barlow, in reverse.

BIBL.: *Hofer*, p. 280 & Pl. IV, *a* & *b*.

Based on *Ogilby*, 1651 edn., Fable VI, *The Battaile of the Frog and Mouse*.

PROV.: As for No. 4.
1858–6–26–378 (L.B.13(54)).

44. FABLE XXXVI: 'JUPITER AND THE FROGS'. Two storks standing on a river bank, r., one bending to devour a frog, the other looking up towards Jupiter seated amidst clouds in the upper l.-hand corner. On the far side of the river, l., frogs climbing over a log.

Pen and brown ink, with grey wash, over black lead; 13·3 × 16·4 cm. (5¼ × 6½ in.).

PROV.: As for No. 4.
1858–6–26–379 (L.B.13(55)).

ETCH.: By Barlow, in reverse, with modifications to the figure of Jupiter and the addition of a stork flying upwards in the background.

The stork in the foreground, bending down to devour a frog, is reminiscent of a bird in the same position, also in the foreground, of *Ogilby*, 1651 edn., Fable XII, *Of the Frogs desiring a King*.

45. FABLE XXXVII: 'THE OLD WOMAN AND HER MAIDS'. A farmyard by moonlight with the two maids bending over the cock in the foreground, one being about to kill the bird with upraised hatchet. From a window of the house beyond, their mistress watching them. In the lower r.-hand corner, a dog, and in mid-distance, l., another cock perched on a fence beyond which is a church spire amidst trees.

Pen and brown ink, with grey wash, and slight alterations in black lead; 12·9 × 16·2 cm. (5 × 6⅜ in.).

PROV.: As for No. 17.
1867–4–13–366 (L.B.13(56)).

ETCH.: By Barlow, in reverse.

46. FABLE XXXVIII: 'THE LION AND BEAR'. The lion, l., and bear, r., resting after their hunt together, with the carcass of a deer between them, while the fox creeps upon them unawares from behind. In the background, l., a wooded hillock.

Pen and brown ink, with grey wash; 12·6 × 15·7 cm. (5 × 6¼ in.).

PROV.: As for No. 17.
1867–4–13–367 (L.B.13(57)).

ETCH.: By Barlow, in reverse.

47. FABLE XXXIX: 'THE CROW AND POT'. The crow, standing near a tree at the edge of a bank, r., dropping stones into the pot. Below, l., a valley with a cottage amidst trees on the far side and hills beyond.

Pen and brown ink, with grey wash; 12·5 × 15·9 cm. (5 × 6¼ in.).

PROV.: As for No. 17.
1867–4–13–368 (L.B.13(58)).

ETCH.: By Barlow, in reverse.

48. FABLE XL: 'THE PORCUPINES AND ADDERS'. A porcupine looking round threateningly at three adders coiled together at the entrance to the den, r., which is below a bank surmounted by trees.

Pen and brown ink, with brown wash; 13 × 15·5 cm. (5⅛ × 6⅛ in.).

PROV.: As for No. 4.
1858–6–26–380 (L.B.13(59)).

ETCH.: By Barlow, in reverse, with the head of the porcupine modified.

Probably based on *Gheeraerts*, p. 77, *L'Herisson & le Serpent*.
This drawing, with its less fluid penwork than usual, differs considerably from the other drawings in this series.

49. FABLE XLI: 'THE HARES AND STORM'. The hares checked at the edge of a stream in the foreground in their flight from a wood at the top of a bank, l. On the r., frogs on the bank of a stream. In the background, a tower surrounded by trees below a hill. A heron and other birds in flight overhead, r.

Pen and brown ink, with grey wash; 13·2 × 16·3 cm. ($5\frac{1}{8}$ × $6\frac{1}{2}$ in.).

PROV.: As for No. 4.
1858–6–26–381 (L.B.13(60)).

ETCH.: By Barlow, in reverse.

50. FABLE XLII: 'THE FOX AND WOLF'. A hunter, with his two hounds, r., raising his staff to strike the wolf who snarls at him from the entrance to his lair. In the background, l., the fox watching the scene from the top of a wooded bank.

Pen and brown ink, with grey wash; 13 × 16·2 cm. ($5\frac{1}{8}$ × $6\frac{3}{8}$ in.).

PROV.: As for No. 17.
1867–4–13–369 (L.B.13(61)).

ETCH.: By Barlow, in reverse.

Based on *Gheeraerts*, p. 93, *Le Loup et le Renard*.

51. FABLE XLIII: 'THE DOG AND SHEEP'. The sheep, seen from behind, standing between her accuser, the dog, r., and his witness, the wolf, l., while his two other witnesses, the vulture and the kite, sit on the bough of a tree, r.

Pen and brown ink, with grey wash; 12·6 × 16·1 cm. (5 × $6\frac{3}{8}$ in.).

PROV.: As for No. 17.
1867–4–13–370 (L.B.13(62)).

ETCH.: By Barlow, in reverse.

Perhaps based in part on *Gheeraerts*, p. 61, *Du Loup & de la Brebis*.

52. FABLE XLIV: 'THE CRANE AND PEACOCK'. The crane, centre, conversing with the peacock, l., in a landscape, with a tree on the r., a stile in mid-distance, and wooded hills in the background.

Pen and brown ink, with grey wash; 13·1 × 16·6 cm. ($5\frac{1}{8}$ × $6\frac{1}{2}$ in.).

PROV.: As for No. 4.
1858–6–26–382 (L.B.13(63)).

ETCH.: By Barlow, in reverse, with the position of the peacock modified, and the addition of a crane flying in the upper r.-hand corner.

53. FABLE XLV: 'THE VIPER AND FILE'. Scene inside a forge. On the r., the viper on a ledge gnawing at the file. In the centre, the same incident as it were magnified, with a dragon gnawing the anvil. In the background, l., the forge fire.

Pen and ink, with grey wash; 12·8 × 15·4 cm. (5 × $6\frac{1}{8}$ in.).

PROV.: As for No. 17.
1867–4–13–371 (L.B.13(64)).

ETCH.: By Barlow, in reverse.

54. FABLE XLVI: 'THE LYON, ASS, AND COCK'. The cock and the ass in the foreground, r., confronting the lion who stands at some distance away, l. In the background, r., on the slope of a hill, the lion devouring the ass.

Pen and brown ink, with grey wash; 12·7 × 16·2 cm. (5 × 6⅜ in.).

Prov.: As for No. 4. 1858–6–26–383 (L.B.13(65)).

Etch.: By Barlow, in reverse.

[The drawing for Fable XLVII: 'The Jay and Peacock' is missing.]

55. FABLE XLVIII: 'THE ANT AND FLY'. In the foreground, r., the ant and the fly conversing beneath a tree. On the l., in mid-distance, a palace with cupola-topped towers rising amidst trees.

Pen and brown ink, with grey wash; 13·2 × 16·2 cm. (5¼ × 6⅜ in.).

Etch.: By Barlow, in reverse, with other ants added beneath the tree.

Prov.: As for No. 4. 1858–6–26–384 (L.B.13(66)).

56. FABLE XLIX: 'THE ANT AND THE GRASSHOPPER'. A wintry landscape, with the grasshopper in the foreground, l., approaching a snow-covered anthill, above which is a leafless tree with two magpies perched on it. To the r., a frozen stream, on the far side of which a man, loaded with a faggot, trudges towards a cottage. Overhead, a flight of herons. **Plate 52**

Pen and brown ink, with grey wash; 13 × 15·3 cm. (5⅛ × 6 in.).

Etch.: By Barlow, in reverse.

Prov.: As for No. 4. 1858–6–26–385 (L.B.13(67)).

Perhaps based in general composition on *Gheeraerts*, p. 14, *De La Cigale & La Fourmy*, though the snowy landscape is Barlow's own innovation.

57. FABLE L: 'THE COUNTRYMAN AND SNAKE'. Interior of a cottage with the hearth on the l., before which is the snake threatening the countryman's wife and one of her children. On the r., the countryman about to attack the snake with his pitchfork, while the other child crawls away to safety near his father.

Brush drawing in grey wash; 13·1 × 15·4 cm. (5⅛ × 6⅛ in.).

Prov.: As for No. 4. 1858–6–26–386 (L.B.13(68)).

Etch.: By Barlow, in reverse.

58. FABLE LI: 'THE SICK LYON'. The lion lying in his den, r., beneath a wooded bank, with a sheep's carcass beside him. On the l., the fox looking at him.

Pen and brown ink, with grey wash; 13 × 16·3 cm. (5⅛ × 6½ in.).

PROV.: As for No. 17.
1867–4–13–372 (L.B.13(69)).

ETCH.: By Barlow, in reverse, with the addition of a rabbit at the foot of the tree above the lion's den.

59. FABLE LII: 'THE WANTON CALF'. The calf in the foreground, centre, turning to mock at the harnessed ox who plods past him with his carter from the r. Landscape background, with a priest about to sacrifice the calf before an altar, l.

Pen and brown ink, with grey wash; 12·9 × 16·1 cm. (5⅛ × 6⅜ in.).

PROV.: As for No. 17.
1867–4–13–373 (L.B.13(70)).

ETCH.: By Barlow, in reverse.

60. FABLE LIII: 'THE CLOWN AND CART'. The clown, l., lying on his back with arms raised invoking the aid of Hercules who is seated above on clouds. To the r., the horse and cart stuck in the quagmire.

Brush drawing in grey and brown washes over black lead; 13·2 × 15·5 cm. (5¼ × 6⅛ in.).

PROV.: As for No. 4.
1858–6–26–387 (L.B.13(71)).

ETCH.: By Barlow, in reverse, with slight modifications to the figure of Hercules.

61. LIV: 'THE BELLY AND MEMBERS'. The nude body of an old man lying exhausted on a bank, l., at the top of which is an altar and a grove of trees. On the r., an open prospect over fields towards distant hills.

Pen and brown ink, with grey wash; 13 × 16·2 cm. (5⅛ × 6⅜ in.).

PROV.: As for No. 17.
1867–4–13–374 (L.B.13(72)).

ETCH.: By Barlow, in reverse, with the addition of two stags in the grove and modifications to the tree on the r.

[The drawing for Fable LV: 'The Horse and Lion' is missing.]

62. FABLE LVI: 'THE STORK AND GEESE'. The countryman kneeling, centre, beside his net from which he takes by their throats the stork and one of the geese. On the r., his horse and dog. Landscape background, with a clump of trees, r., and a distant church-spire rising in wooded surroundings, l.

Pen and brown ink, with grey wash; 12·9 × 16·3 cm. (5⅛ × 6½ in.).

PROV.: As for No. 17.
1867–4–13–375 (L.B.13(73)).

ETCH.: By Barlow, in reverse, with the addition of two pheasants in the trees, l., and a flight of wild geese overhead, r.

Perhaps based on *Gheeraerts*, p. 111, *Le Laboureur & la Cigoigne*.

63. FABLE LVII: 'THE CAT AND COCK'. Scene in a farmyard. On the r., the cat attacking the cock. In the background, r., the farmhouse near which are two hens, one before the door, the other perched on a fence. On the l., a wooded prospect to distant hills.

Pen and brown ink, with grey wash; 12·6 × 16 cm. (5 × 6⅜ in.).

ETCH.: By Barlow, in reverse.

Perhaps based on *Gheeraerts*, p. 100, *Le Chat & le Poulet*.

PROV.: As for No. 17.
1867–4–13–376 (L.B.13(74)).

64. FABLE LVIII: 'THE LEOPARD AND FOX'. The leopard moving towards the r. foreground and looking back at the fox, who, seen from behind, l., returns his gaze. Landscape background with a tree on the r.

Pen and brown ink, with grey wash; 13·3 × 16·6 cm. (5¼ × 6½ in.).

ETCH.: By Barlow, in reverse, with the addition of a parrot in the tree, l.

PROV.: As for No. 4.
1858–6–26–388 (L.B.13(75)).

65. FABLE LIX: 'THE SHEPHERD'S BOY'. The shepherd boy and his dog pursuing from the l. the wolf, who is making his escape towards the r., with a sheep in his mouth. The remainder of the flock below, r., and beyond, on the side of a hill, two men ploughing.

Pen and brown ink, with grey wash; 13·3 × 16·4 cm. (5¼ × 6½ in.).

PROV.: As for No. 4.
1858–6–26–389 (L.B.13(76)).

ETCH.: By Barlow, in reverse.

66. FABLE LX: 'THE GOAT IN THE WELL'. The fox crouching on a broken wall, l., looking down at the goat, whose head appears at the mouth of the well, r. A tree in the background, l.

Brush drawing in brown wash, touched with pen and ink, over black lead; unfinished, the tree in the background being only in the latter medium; indented for transfer; 12·9 × 15·1 cm. (5⅛ × 6 in.).

PROV.: As for No. 17.
1867–4–13–377 (L.B.13(77)).

ETCH.: By Barlow, in reverse.

Based in part on *Gheeraerts*, p. 42, *Du Regnard & du Bone*.

67. FABLE LXI: 'CUPID AND DEATH'. Death, appearing at the door of a charnel-house, r., taking aim with his bow and Cupid's arrow at an elderly couple seated, l., making love on the edge of a newly-dug grave. In the grave, centre, a dog snarling at Death. In the background, two young lovers lying dead, transfixed by Death's shafts, shot by Cupid who appears in the clouds above aiming at another young man, who begs for mercy.

Pen and brown ink, with grey wash; 13 × 16·4 cm. (5⅛ × 6½ in.).

PROV.: As for No. 17.

1867–4–13–378 (L.B.13(78)).

ETCH.: By Barlow, in reverse.

68. FABLE LXII: 'THE OLD MAN AND HIS SONS'. The old man seated, r., with a bundle of osiers in his l. hand, addressing his three sons who stand before him, l. In the background, their cottage with an old woman at the door, r.

Pen and brown ink, with grey wash; touched with black lead; 12·9 × 16·2 cm. (5⅛ × 6¾ in.).

PROV.: As for No. 17.

1867–4–13–379 (L.B.13(79)).

ETCH.: By Barlow, in reverse, with the addition of a dog sitting beside the three sons, and two birds in the upper r.-hand corner, one sitting on the roof of the cottage, the other in flight.

In the drawing the faint outline in black lead of the dog beside the sons can be seen.

69. FABLE LXIII: 'THE OLD DEER AND FAWN'. The stag with a fawn beside him, standing near a thicket, r. On the l., a paling with a gate in it beyond which is a stretch of hilly and wooded country with a hunt in progress.

Pen and brown ink, with grey wash; 13 × 15·8 cm. (5⅛ × 6¼ in.).

PROV.: As for No. 4.

1858–6–26–300 (L.B.13(80)).

ETCH.: By Barlow, in reverse.

70. FABLE LXIV: 'THE OLD HOUND'. The huntsman standing at the top of a bank, l., threatening with his upraised cane the old hound who cringing looks up at him. Below, on the r., three other hounds pursuing a stag. In mid-distance, a gate in a paling, beyond which is a stretch of hilly and wooded country.

Pen and brown ink, with grey wash; 12·5 × 15·9 cm. (5 × 6¼ in.).

PROV.: As for No. 17.

1867–4–13–380 (L.B.13(81)).

ETCH.: By Barlow, in reverse.

Probably based on *Gheeraerts*, p. 102, *Le vieil Chien & son Maistre*.

[The drawing for Fable LXV: 'Jupiter and the Camels' is missing.]

71. FABLE LXVI: 'THE TAILLESS FOX'. The tailless fox standing on the l., conversing with his four companions who are sitting on the r. Landscape background with a wooded bank, r., and a prospect of wooded and hilly country with a cottage, l.

Pen and brown ink, with grey wash, touched with black lead; 12·7 × 16·2 cm. (5 × 6¾ in.).

PROV.: As for No. 17.

1867–4–13–381 (L.B.13(82)).

ETCH.: By Barlow, in reverse, with a sixth fox introduced, coming down the bank on the l.

72. FABLE LXVII: 'THE FOX AND CROW'. The fox looking up at the crow perched, with a cheese in his beak, on the branch of a tree, r., beneath which a horse and cart move away into the background. On the l., a fence beyond which are a tavern with a maypole (?) beside it, and distant wooded hills.

Pen and brown ink, with grey wash; 13·1 × 16·6 cm. (5⅛ × 6½ in.).

Prov.: As for No. 4. 1858–6–26–391 (L.B.13(83)).

73. FABLE LXVIII: 'THE DOVE AND HAWK'. The fowler seated, r., addressing the hawk, whom he holds on his knee. On the l., another bird caught in his net. In the background, a village green, with a church in the centre, a cottage on the r., and a distant windmill on a hillock, l.

Pen and brown ink, with grey wash; 12·7 × 16 cm. (5 × 6⅜ in.).

Etch.: By Barlow, in reverse.

Prov.: As for No. 4. 1858–6–26–392 (L.B.13(84)).

Based on *Gheeraerts*, p. 109, *L'Oiseleur & la Perdrix*, of which even the background has been adapted by Barlow.

74. FABLE LXIX: 'THE NURSE AND WOLF'. Interior of a cottage with the nurse, r., her back to the hearth, bending over a cradle with an infant in it and pointing with her r. hand towards the wolf, who appears at the door, l. By her side, another child clinging to her skirt. In the foreground, on the floor, a cat, a broom, and a wash-tub.

Brush drawing in grey wash; indented for transfer; 12·9 × 15·1 cm. (5 × 6 in.).

Etch.: By Barlow, in reverse, with the addition of a bowl and spoon to the objects in the foreground.

Prov.: As for No. 17. 1867–4–13–382 (L.B.13(85)).

[The drawing for Fable LXX: 'The Tortoise and Hare' is missing.]

75. FABLE LXXI: 'THE YOUNG MAN AND HIS CAT'. The young man fondling his cat and kneeling in supplication on a balcony towards the l., where is an altar with a smoking urn on it. Above, l., Venus newly alighted from her dove-drawn car and attended by Cupid, reclining on clouds and making a sign to grant his request. On the r., in an alcove, the young man in bed with his mistress who leaves him to pursue two mice running across the floor.

Brush drawing in grey wash; 12·3 × 15·5 cm. (4⅞ × 6⅛ in.).

Prov.: As for No. 7. 1855–7–14–66 (L.B.1).

A rejected design.

76. FABLE LXXI: 'THE YOUNG MAN AND HIS CAT'. The young man, l., fondling his cat and kneeling in supplication in profile to r. at the top of a flight of steps which leads down to a garden, r. Above, r., Venus with Cupid riding on the clouds in a dove-drawn car. In the background, l., the young man's mistress leaving her lover and bed to pursue three mice running across the floor.

Pen and brown ink, with grey wash; 13·2 × 16·3 cm. (5¼ × 6⅜ in.).

REPR.: *Hofer*, Pl. Va.

PROV.: As for No. 4.
1858–6–26–393 (L.B.13(86)).

ETCH.: By Barlow, in reverse.

The appearance and costume of the young man perhaps inspired by those of the same personage in *Ogilby*, 1651 edn., Fable LXXIII, *Of the Youngman and the Cat.*

77. FABLE LXXII: 'THE ASS IN A LION'S SKIN.' The ass, his back covered with the lion's skin, being chastised by his master, l., who holds him with a halter and beats him with a stick. In the background, l., a tree, and r., a field with cattle and horses in it.

Pen and brown ink, with grey wash; 12·5 × 15·9 cm. (5 × 6¼ in.).

PROV.: As for No. 17.
1867–4–13–383 (L.B.13(87)).

ETCH.: By Barlow, in reverse.

[The drawing for Fable LXXIII: 'The Birth of the Mountains' is missing.]

78. FABLE LXXIV: 'THE SATYRE AND CLOWN'. The satyr, r., and the clown, centre, both seated at a table at the entrance to a cave, the clown blowing on his broth to cool it, while the satyr converses. On the l., the clown's wife standing in profile to r., with a pot on the fire behind her. Near the satyr, a dog licking the ground.

Pen and brown ink, with grey wash; 13·2 × 16·3 cm. (5⅛ × 6⅜ in.).

siderable modifications to all three figures, and the addition of a hood over the fireplace.

PROV.: As for No. 4.
1858–6–26–394 (L.B.13(88)).

ETCH.: By Barlow, in reverse, with con-

REPR.: *Hofer*, Pl. VIa.

Perhaps inspired by *Gheeraerts*, p. 83, *Le Paysan & le Satyre.*

[The drawing for Fable LXXV: 'The Young Kite and his Mother' is missing.]

79. FABLE LXXVI: 'THE NIGHTINGALE AND HAWK'. The hawk, perched on the branch of a tree, holding in his talon the nightingale. Below, l., a hilly prospect with a tower.

Pen and brown ink, with grey wash; 13 × 16·4 cm. (5⅛ × 6½ in.).

PROV.: As for No. 4.
1858–6–26–395 (L.B.13(89)).

ETCH.: By Barlow, in reverse, with the addition of two other nightingales, one on a further branch of the tree, the other in the upper r.-hand corner.

In the drawing the second of the additional nightingales is indicated in black lead in the upper l.-hand corner.

80. FABLE LXXVII: 'THE PEACOCK AND NIGHTINGALE'. The peacock standing in profile to l., and looking at his rival, the nightingale, who sits singing on a tree, l. Above, Juno seated on clouds.

Brush drawing in grey wash, touched with pen and ink; 13·2 × 15·5 cm. (5⅛ × 6⅛ in.).

PROV.: As for No. 4.

1858–6–26–396 (L.B.13(90)).

ETCH.: By Barlow, in reverse, with

modifications to the peacock and the figure of Juno, and the addition of a cottage on the l.

Based on *Gheeraerts*, p. 10, *Paon & Rossignol*.

[The drawing for Fable LXXVIII: 'The Angler and Little Fish' is missing.]

[The drawing for Fable LXXIX: 'The Geese in the Corn' is missing.]

[The drawing for Fable LXXX: 'The Dog and the Peice of Flesh' is missing.]

81. FABLE LXXXI: 'THE ASS AND LITTLE DOG'. The ass trying to caress,with his forelegs, his master who is seated in the centre with the little dog on his knees. On either side, a servant with a stick, one of them beating the ass. In the background, l., a balustrade overlooking a garden.

Pen and brown ink, with grey wash; indented for transfer; 13·2 × 16·6 cm. (5¼ × 6½ in.).

PROV.: As for No. 4.

1858–6–26–397 (L.B.13(91)).

ETCH.: By Barlow, in reverse.

Perhaps inspired by *Gheeraerts*, p. 31, *De l'Asne & du Chien*. Barlow's figures, like *Gheeraerts's*, wear XVI c. dress.

[The drawing for Fable LXXXII: 'The Wolf and Crane' is missing.]

82. FABLE LXXXIII: 'THE COVETOUS AND ENVIOUS MAN'. In the centre, Apollo standing with his lyre resting on the ground at his r. side, and pointing with his l. hand towards the envious man and the covetous man, r., the former of whom makes signs that one of his own eyes should be removed so that his companion should lose both of his. Trees in the background, l.

Pen and brown ink, with grey wash; 13·4 × 16·5 cm. (5¼ × 6½ in.).

PROV.: As for No. 4.

1858–6–26–398 (L.B.13(92)).

ETCH.: By Barlow, in reverse, with

modifications to the figure of Apollo, whose head is shown in profile to l. looking directly towards the two men, while his lyre is carried under his l. arm, and his feet are bare instead of being covered by boots as in the drawing.

83. FABLE LXXXIV: 'THE TWO POTS'. A stream flowing into the foreground from r. to l., with an earthenware jar and cauldron being swept along on it. To l., a heron standing at the water's edge, and r., two kingfishers, one perched on a basket, near a clump of rushes and a willow. In the background, l., an open prospect with hills.

Pen and brown ink, with grey wash and additions in black lead; 12·7 × 16·3 cm. (5 × 6½ in.).

ETCH.: By Barlow, in reverse, with the addition of foliage on the l., and a flight of wild duck rising towards the r.

PROV.: As for No. 4.
1858–6–26–399 (L.B.13(93)).

In the drawing the additions apparent in the etching are indicated faintly in black lead.

[The drawing for Fable LXXXV: 'The Fox and Stork' is missing.]

[The drawing for Fable LXXXVI: 'The Bear and Bee-hives' is missing.]

84. FABLE LXXXVII: 'THE BEAR AND TWO TRAVELLERS'. The bear, l. sniffing at the head of one of the travellers who lies in the roadway, face downward, towards the l. In the background, r., a clump of trees with the other traveller appearing amidst the branches.

Pen and brown ink, with grey wash; indented for transfer; 13·2 × 16·3 cm. (5¼ × 6⅜ in.).

ETCH.: By Barlow, in reverse.

Based on *Gheeraerts*, p. 30, *De deux amys & de l'Ours*.

PROV.: As for No. 4.
1858–6–26–400 (L.B.13(94)).

85. FABLE LXXXVIII: 'THE CAPTIVE TRUMPETER'. The trumpeter on horseback captured, as he gallops towards the r., by two other horsemen, one in oriental dress, the other in a classical helmet. A battle in progress in the distance, r., and trees on the l.

Pen and brown ink, with grey wash; indented for transfer; 12·7 × 15·7 cm. (5 × 6¼ in.).

PROV.: As for No. 17.
1867–4–13–384 (L.B.13(95)).

ETCH.: By Barlow, in reverse.

86. FABLE LXXXIX: 'THE FIGHTING COCKS AND PARTRIDGE'. Scene in a farmyard, with the two cocks confronting each other in the foreground, centre, and the partridge standing beyond them, r., on a mound. In the background, r., a building serving as a hen-house, with two openings at the top, at which appear, l., a hen, and r., a man's head. To the l., a gate and a paling on which is perched another fowl.

Pen and brown ink, with grey wash; 12·9 × 15·6 cm. (5⅛ × 6⅛ in.).

PROV.: As for No. 4.
1858–6–26–401 (L.B.13(96)).

ETCH.: By Barlow, in reverse, with the

addition of two other fowls, one on the paling in the background, the other (whose head appears in the lower l.-hand corner of the drawing) in the lower r.-hand corner.

Based in part on *Gheeraerts*, p. 110, *La Perdrix & les Cocqs*.

[The drawing for Fable XC: 'The Fowler and Partridge' is missing.]

87. FABLE XCI: 'THE EAGLE AND CROW'. The shepherd seizing the crow from off the ram's back, while his children run towards him from their shelter on the l. On the r., part of the flock on the slope of a hill, and overhead, the eagle bearing off a lamb.

Pen and brown ink, with grey wash; 12·7 × 15·9 cm. (5 × 6¼ in.).

PROV.: As for No. 17.
1867–4–13–385 (L.B.13(97)).

ETCH.: By Barlow, in reverse.

88. FABLE XCII: 'THE LION, ASS, AND FOX'. In the centre, the lion with his forepaws planted on the thigh of his prey, a hart, which lies together with the dead ass on the r. On the l., the fox contemplating the two carcasses. In the background, r., a clump of trees, and l., a wooded and hilly prospect.

Pen and brown ink, with grey wash; 12·9 × 16·2 cm. (5⅛ × 6⅜ in.).

PROV.: As for No. 17.
1867–4–13–386 (L.B.13(98)).

ETCH.: By Barlow, in reverse, with the lion's head turned slightly towards the fox.

89. FABLE XCIII: 'THE FOX AND GRAPES'. The fox in the centre looking up at a vine growing near a fence, r. In the background, l., a wooded and hilly prospect.

Pen and brown ink, with grey wash; 12·8 × 16·1 cm. (5⅛ × 6⅜ in.).

PROV.: As for No. 17.
1867–4–13–387 (L.B.13(99)).

ETCH.: By Barlow, in reverse.

90. FABLE XCIV: 'THE HORSE AND HART'. The hart and the horse galloping on a road towards the r., the hart in advance of the other which is ridden by a man in armour. In the background, centre, a castle amidst trees.

Pen and brown ink, with grey wash; 12·9 × 16·1 cm. (5⅛ × 6⅜ in.).

PROV.: As for No. 17.
1867–4–13–388 (L.B.13(100)).

ETCH.: By Barlow, in reverse.

Based on *Gheeraerts*, p. 41, *Du Cerf & du Cheval*. The horseman in armour in Barlow's design is clearly inspired by a figure similarly equipped in *Ogilby*, 1651 edn., Fable XLV, *Of the Hart and Horse*.

[The drawing for Fable XCV: 'The Young Man and Swallow' is missing.]

[The drawing for Fable XCVI: 'The Man and his Goose' is missing.]

91. FABLE XCVII: 'THE WOLF AND DOG'. The wolf and dog walking beside each other along a road towards the l. and conversing. Landscape background with trees on the r. and a wooded and hilly prospect on the l.

Pen and brown ink, with grey wash; 12·9 × 16·2 cm. (5⅛ × 6⅜ in.).

PROV.: As for No. 17.
1867–4–13–389 (L.B.13(101)).

ETCH.: By Barlow, in reverse.

92. FABLE XCVIII: 'THE WOOD AND CLOWN'. The clown with raised hatchet felling a tree in the centre foreground. Behind him, his spaniel barking at two wild duck, r., and beyond, a hilly prospect.

Pen and brown ink, with grey wash; 13·1 × 16·4 cm. (5⅛ × 6½ in.).

PROV.: As for No. 4.
1858–6–26–402 (L.B.13(102)).

ETCH.: By Barlow, in reverse, with modifications to the figure and costume of the clown, who appears in the etching without a hat and bald-headed.

Probably based on *Gheeraerts*, p. 57, *Du Paysant & de la Forest*.

93. FABLE XCIX: 'THE OLD LION'. The lion lying on the ground, l., being kicked by the ass from the r., while his degradation is watched, from l. to r., by the horse, the hart, the ox, and the boar. A rock and shrubs in the background, l.

Brush drawing in grey wash; 12·9 × 15·5 cm. (5⅛ × 6⅛ in.).

PROV.: As for No. 4.
1858–6–26–403 (L.B.13(104)).

A rejected design.

94. FABLE XCIX: 'THE OLD LION'. The lion lying on the ground, r., being kicked by the ass from the l., while his degradation is watched, from l. to r., by the boar, the horse, the sheep, the hart, the ox, and the goat. Trees in the background, r.

Pen and brown ink, with grey wash; 12·6 × 15·8 cm. (5 × 6¼ in.).

PROV.: As for No. 17.
1867–4–13–390 (L.B.13(103)).

ETCH.: By Barlow, in reverse.

Perhaps inspired by *Gheeraerts*, p. 69, *Du Lion enuieilly*.

95. FABLE C: 'THE HORSE AND LOADED ASS'. The man on the r. driving along a road, towards the l., the horse and the ass, of whom the latter has sunk to the ground under his load, while the horse bears nothing on his back. In the background, trees to the r., and a prospect over open country to the l.

Pen and brown ink, with grey wash; 12·8 × 15·6 cm. (5 × 6⅛ in.).

ETCH.: By Barlow, in reverse.

Perhaps based on *Gheeraerts*, p. 35, *Du Cheval & de l'Asne*.

PROV.: As for No. 17.
1867–4–13–391 (L.B.13(105)).

96. FABLE CI: 'THE OLD MAN AND DEATH'. Death, l., appearing to the old man, who stands, r., with his arms outstretched towards his faggot on the ground. In the background, a line of trees and a distant church-spire, r.

Brush drawing in grey wash, touched with pen and ink; 12·9 × 15·6 cm. (5⅛ × 6⅛ in.).

ETCH.: By Barlow, in reverse, with slight modifications to the line of trees in the background.

PROV.: As for No. 4.
1858–6–26–404 (L.B.13(106)).

97. FABLE CII: 'THE BOAR AND ASS'. The ass, richly caparisoned, standing on the r., while the boar moves away towards the l., snarling at him. Trees in the background, l.

Pen and brown ink, with grey wash; 12·9 × 16 cm. (5⅛ × 6¼ in.).

ETCH.: By Barlow, in reverse.

Probably based on *Gheeraerts*, p. 115, *Le Cheual de guerre & la Truye*.

PROV.: As for No. 17.
1867–4–13–392 (L.B.13(107)).

98. FABLE CIII: 'THE DOLPHIN AND TUNIS'. In the foreground, the dolphin stranded on the shore, while on a rock at some distance away, l., is the tunis (tunny) in a similar plight. To the r., the sea with a ship on it. Gulls flying overhead.

Pen and brown ink, with grey wash; 12·9 × 16·3 cm. (5⅛ × 6½ in.).

PROV.: As for No. 17.
1867–4–13–393 (L.B.13(108)).

ETCH.: By Barlow, in reverse.

99. FABLE CIV: 'THE PEACOCK AND PIE'. The peacock, a crown above his head as king elect, standing on a slight eminence, surrounded by the other birds, among whom, l., is the magpie. On the r., a tree in which is perched the owl, and in the distance, l., a hilly and wooded landscape.

Pen and brown ink, with grey wash; 13·1 × 16·2 cm. (5⅛ × 6⅜ in.).

PROV.: As for No. 17.
1867–4–13–394 (L.B.13(109)).

ETCH.: By Barlow, in reverse.

Probably based on *Gheeraerts*, p. 47, *Du Paon, qu'on vouloit faire Roy des Oiseaux*.

In the 1st edn. of Barlow's *Æsop*, 1666, the etching of this subject occurs on p. 33 with the title *The Parliament of Birds* illustrating,

apparently incorrectly, Fable XVI: 'The Doves and Hawk'. In the 2nd edn., 1687, it occurs on p. 209 with the title *The Peacock and Pie*, correctly illustrating Fable CIV, which appears for the first time in this edn. The present drawing has been more conveniently listed here according to this latter arrangement.

100. FABLE CV: 'THE FORRESTER AND LION'. The lion vanquishing a man in ancient Roman armour, who falls back before him, r., this being the lion's version of the subject of a sculptured group in the background, l., which, erected by men, shows a man vanquishing a lion.

Pen and brown ink, with grey wash; 12·8 × 16 cm. (5 × 6¼ in.).

PROV.: As for No. 4. 1858–6–26–405 (L.B.13(110)).

ETCH.: By Barlow, in reverse.

[The drawing for Fable CVI: 'The Stag looking into the Water' is missing.]

[The drawing for Fable CVII: 'The Stag in the Ox-stall' is missing.]

101. FABLE CVIII: 'THE DOVE AND PISMIRE'. The dove, perched on the branch of a tree, l., turning her head to look at the fowler, who kneels, r., holding in one hand the string of his net while with the other he tries to catch the pismire (ant) which has bitten him in the leg.

Pen and brown ink, with grey wash; 12·9 × 16·5 cm. (5⅛ × 6½ in.).

PROV.: As for No. 4. 1858–6–26–406 (L.B.13(111)).

ETCH.: By Barlow, in reverse, with the position and costume of the fowler modified (he being shown bare-headed), and the addition of another dove flying in mid-distance, l.

102. FABLE CIX: 'THE LION IN LOVE'. On the r., a young woman standing in profile to l., looking down at the lion, who sits on the l., while his claws are cut by the woman's father who kneels beside him. Further to the l., the woman's mother, standing in an archway, also watching the scene. In the background, r., her father slaying the lion with a spear.

Pen and brown ink, with grey wash; 13·2 × 16·4 cm. (5¼ × 6½ in.).

PROV.: As for No. 4. 1858–6–26–407 (L.B.13(112)).

ETCH.: By Barlow, in reverse.

103. FABLE CX: 'THE TORTOISE AND EAGLE'. The eagle flying in mid-air holding the tortoise in his talons. Below, a stretch of water with ships on it, flanked on either side by rocky heights and by a castle to the l.

Pen and brown ink with grey wash over black lead; 13·2 × 16·6 cm. (5¼ × 6½ in.).

PROV.: As for No. 17.
1867–4–13–395 (L.B.13(113)).

ETCH.: By Barlow, in reverse.

Probably based on *Gheeraerts*, p. 86, *L'Aigle & le Limaçon*.

[104–130]. ILLUSTRATIONS TO ÆSOP'S LIFE IN *Æsop's Fables* . . . , 2nd edn., 1687. Five of these were probably etched by Barlow himself, the remainder by a disciple of Hollar's, Thomas Dudley, two of them being dated 1678, and two others 1679.

The costumes worn by the persons represented in the series are a curious admixture of oriental, semi-classical and apparently late medieval elements, and it is difficult to determine their prototypes, supposing these to exist. Mr. Hofer (p. 280 and Pl. 1 *a* and *b*) points out a general similarity in composition between Pl. 21, *Æsop before King Croesus*, and the woodcut representing the same subject on *f.* 30 *v.* of Francesco Tuppo's edition of *Æsop*, published at Naples in 1485. This may even suggest that Barlow actually saw a copy of Tuppo's edition, in which the costumes are late medieval with occasional oriental touches, and thus perhaps account for Barlow's use of these elements. Similiar costumes are to be found in the plate to Barlow's own *Æsop*, No. LXXIII, *The Birth of the Mountains* and certain plates to *Androcles* in Ogilby's *The Fables of Æsop*, II, 1668, pp. 164, 166 and 168. It may also be mentioned that Barlow's *Æsop's Life* drawings have a curious affinity, both in the treatment of the figures and the medium, with a series depicting the *Life of Joseph* by the Dutch glass designer Jan Swart (*fl.* 1522–53) in the Department (Popham, *Dutch and Flemish Drawings*, Nos. 17–20); and Swart's drawing of *Gluttony on his hog* (Popham, No. 13) also comes near to Barlow's work. There is, however, no evidence that this artist was known in England in Barlow's day.

No other earlier edition of *Æsop*, with illustrations to the Life, appears to have provided Barlow with a model. The inclusion, however, of a rectangular decorative tablet for explanatory verses at the foot of each plate (left blank in the actual drawings) may be traced back immediately to Francis Cleyn's frontispiece to Ogilby's *Æsop* of 1651 which also has a tablet with verses in a similar position (*See* Hofer, Pl. 3, *a* and *b*).

The following drawings were all acquired from Miss E. Hanks in 1867 and are mounted with the other drawings by Barlow for his *Æsop* in an album as described in the prefatory note to Nos. 17–103.

BIBL.: *See* Prefatory note to Nos. 17–103.

104. ÆSOP CONVICTING HIS FELLOW SERVANTS OF HAVING EATEN THE FIGS. Interior with Æsop kneeling, r., before his master who lays his hand on the hunchback's shoulder. On the l., the two other servants vomiting the figs. In the background a double window, through which trees are seen. The tablet bordered by birds and fish.

Pen and brown ink over black lead, with grey wash; 24·3 × 16·4 cm. (9½ × 6½ in.).

Prov.: As for No. 17.
1867–4–13–320 (L.B.13(2)).

Inscr.: *Recto*, on the tablet, *printing*, and *1*.

Etch.: By Barlow (?) (*See above*), in reverse and with slight modifications.

105. ÆSOP ENTERTAINING THE PRIESTS OF DIANA. Æsop approaching from the r. and offering a dish of fruit to the two priests who are seated on a bank, l. Landscape background with a shelter amidst trees on the r. The tablet bordered by birds and fruit.

Pen and brown ink over black lead, with grey wash; indented for transfer; 24·3 × 16·4 cm. (9½ × 6½ in.).

Prov.: As for No. 17.
1867–4–13–321 (L.B.13(3)).

Etch.: By Barlow (?) (*See above*), in reverse.

Inscr.: *Recto*, on the tablet, *printing*, and *2*.

106. ÆSOP ASKING THE MERCHANT TO TAKE HIM INTO HIS SERVICE. Æsop, l., detaining the merchant who is moving away towards the r., holding a money-bag. Behind Æsop, l., Zenas resting his hand on the hunchback, and an old woman. In the background, other figures, and a wall beyond which are trees and a gabled building. The tablet bordered by hounds, hares and squirrels.

Pen and brown ink, with grey wash; indented for transfer; 24 × 16·2 cm. (9⅜ × 6⅜ in.).

Prov.: As for No. 17.
1867–4–13–322 (L.B.13(4)).

Inscr.: *Recto*, on the tablet, *printing*, and *3*.

Etch.: By Barlow (?) (*See above*), in reverse.

107. ÆSOP CARRYING THE BASKET OF LOAVES. Æsop, with a dog beside him, trudging towards the l., bearing on his back a large basket filled with loaves. Behind him, r., his three fellow-servants following and pointing to the basket. Landscape background with a castle in the distance, l. The tablet bordered by grotesque masks and laurel.

Pen and brown ink, with grey wash; indented for transfer; 24·1 × 16·4 cm. (8½ × 6⅜ in.).

Prov.: As for No. 17.
1867–4–13–323 (L.B.13(5)).

Inscr.: *Recto*, on the tablet, *printing*, and *4*.

Etch.: By Thomas Dudley, in reverse.

108. ÆSOP BOUGHT BY THE PHILOSOPHER XANTHUS. The merchant, standing in the centre, being paid by Xanthus who appears on the r. with two other

men beyond him. On the l., Æsop between his fellow-servants, Cantor and Grammaticus. A group of buildings in the background. The tablet bordered by swans and dragons.

Pen and brown ink, with grey wash; indented for transfer; 24 × 16·3 cm. (9½ × 6⅜ in.).

INSCR.: *Recto*, on the tablet, *printing*, and 5.

PROV.: As for No. 17.
1867–4–13–324 (L.B.13(6)).

ETCH.: By Thomas Dudley, in reverse.

109. XANTHUS PRESENTING ÆSOP TO HIS WIFE. Xanthus standing in the centre and presenting Æsop, whom he holds by the hand, to his wife, who, seated l. in a canopied chair, turns away in horror. In the background, r., the two maidservants. In a richly decorated room. The tablet bordered by a dragon's mask, cockle-shells, and fish.

Pen and brown ink over black lead, with grey wash; indented for transfer; 24·3 × 16·3 cm. (9½ × 6⅜ in.).

INSCR.: *Recto*, on the tablet, 6.

PROV.: As for No. 17.
1867–4–13–325 (L.B.13(7)).

ETCH.: By Thomas Dudley, in reverse.

110. ÆSOP RESOLVING FOR XANTHUS THE GARDENER'S PROBLEM. The gardener standing, r., before an arch, his l. hand resting on his spade, his r. hand pointing downwards. On the l., Æsop enumerating on his fingers the points of his solution of the gardener's problem, while Xanthus stands beside him. In the background, a balustrade with the garden beyond. The tablet bordered by birds attacked by weasels (?).

Pen and brown ink, with grey wash; indented for transfer; 24·3 × 16·4 cm. (9½ × 6½ in.).

INSCR.: *Recto*, on the tablet, *printing . . . Mʳ Dolman*, and 7.

PROV.: As for No. 17.
1867–4–13–326 (L.B.13(8)).

ETCH.: By Thomas Dudley, in reverse.

'Mr. Dolman', whose name appears in the inscriptions on this and Nos. 111, 112, 118, 120, 124, 128, 129 & 130, has not been identified. It is just possible that he may have been the writing-master to whom the verses in the tablets beneath the engravings would probably have been entrusted, but there is no record of him in Sir Ambrose Heal's *The English Writing-Masters*, 1931.

111. ÆSOP ORDERED BY XANTHUS TO TAKE A DISH TO HER THAT LOVES HIM BEST. Xanthus seated at a table with his guests, l., handing to Æsop a dish of meat. In the background, l., musicians in a gallery, and r., Æsop before his master's wife, casting the meat to the bitch Lycaena. The tablet bordered by grotesque masks and fruit.

Pen and brown ink, with grey wash; indented for transfer; 24·1 × 16·3 cm. (8½ × 6⅜ in.).

INSCR.: *Recto*, on the tablet, *printing . . . Mʳ Dolman*, and 8.

PROV.: As for No. 17.
1867–4–23–327 (L.B.13(9)).

ETCH.: By Thomas Dudley, in reverse, 1678.

See note to No. 110.

112. ÆSOP PASSING THE HOUSE OF THE FATHER OF XANTHUS'S WIFE.
Æsop, loaded with market produce, walking from the r. and addressing one of the servants of the house who stands at the road-side. In the background, the house with Xanthus's wife appearing at an upper window and a maidservant looking over the garden wall. The tablet bordered by foliated scrolls with a grotesque mask in the centre.

Pen and brown ink, with grey wash; indented for transfer; 24·2 × 16·3 cm. (9½ × 6⅜ in.).

INSCR.: *Recto*, on the tablet, *printing . . . Mr Dolman, and 9.*

PROV.: As for No. 17.
67–4–13–328 (L.B.13(10)).

ETCH.: By Thomas Dudley, in reverse.

See note to No. 110.

113. ÆSOP, ORDERED TO SERVE A DINNER OF THE BEST, SERVES UP TONGUES AT EVERY COURSE.
Xanthus seated, r., beneath a canopy, with his guests at table, while Æsop approaches from the l. bearing a dish of tongues. The tablet bordered by dragons.

Pen and brown ink, with grey wash; indented for transfer; 24·1 × 16·3 cm. (9½ × 6⅜ in.).

INSCR.: *Recto*, on the tablet, *. . . was to bring . . .* (almost obliterated), *printing, and 10.*

PROV.: As for No. 17.
1867–4–13–329 (L.B.13(11)).

ETCH.: By Thomas Dudley, in reverse.

114. ÆSOP, ORDERED TO SERVE A DINNER OF THE WORST, SERVES UP TONGUES AGAIN.
Æsop, a dish of tongues in his hand, approaching from the l. the table where Xanthus is seated with his guests. In the background, an arcade beyond which are seen trees and a turreted building. The tablet bordered by owls and other birds.

Pen and brown ink, with grey wash; indented for transfer; 24 × 16·3 cm. (9⅜ × 6⅜ in.).

INSCR.: *Recto*, on the tablet, *printing, and 11.*

PROV.: As for No. 17.
1867–4–13–330 (L.B.13(12)).

ETCH.: By Thomas Dudley, in reverse.

115. XANTHUS ORDERS HIS WIFE TO BE BURNT.
Xanthus seated, r., at a table turns to look down at his wife who kneels beside him, l. On the far side of the table, a servant with his hand raised in surprise, and on the l., Æsop and the 'person Regardless'. Through the doorway and windows in the background, a wooded

landscape with Æsop bringing the 'person Regardless' to the house. The tablet bordered by hounds, hares, and rats.

Pen and brown ink, with grey wash; indented for transfer; 24·1 × 16·3 cm. (9½ × 6⅜ in.).

PROV.: As for No. 17.
1867–4–13–331 (L.B.13(13)).

INSCR.: Recto, on the tablet, printing, and 12.

ETCH.: By Thomas Dudley, in reverse.

116. ÆSOP AND THE BATHERS. Xanthus, on the r., being shown the stone at the entrance to the bath, l., by Æsop. In the background, the ruined classical arcade covering the bath, with the bathers on the l. The table bordered by cocks and fruit.

Pen and brown ink, with grey wash; indented for transfer; 24·1 × 16·3 cm. (9½ × 6⅜ in.).

PROV.: As for No. 17.
1867–4–13–332 (L.B.13(14)).

INSCR.: Recto, on the tablet, 13.

ETCH.: By Thomas Dudley, in reverse.

[The drawing for the plate showing Æsop taken to prison is missing.]

117. XANTHUS OFFERING TO DRINK THE SEA, IF THE RIVERS ARE PREVENTED FROM FLOWING INTO IT. Xanthus, attended by Æsop and the people of Samos, kneeling with a cup in his hand beside a stream, which flows into the sea, r. In the background, r., a whale spouting water, two ships, and a castle on a promontory. The tablet bordered by fish and shells.

Pen and brown ink, with grey wash; indented for transfer; 24 × 16·3 cm. (9½ × 6⅜ in.).

PROV.: As for No. 17.
1867–4–13–333 (L.B.13(15)).

INSCR.: Recto, on the tablet, printing, and 15.

ETCH.: By Thomas Dudley, in reverse, 1679.

[The drawing for the plate showing Æsop exposing Xanthus's wife to shame is missing.]

118. ÆSOP BEATEN BY XANTHUS FOR SAYING HE HAD SEEN TWO CROWS, WHEN ONLY ONE WAS IN SIGHT. Xanthus, seen from the back, centre, turning with upraised stick to beat Æsop, l., who bows before the blows he is about to receive. Overhead, l., the two crows, one perched on a branch, the other flying away. In the background, r., part of the house, with an open window through which is seen a feast in progress. The tablet bordered by hounds and grotesque beasts.

Pen and brown ink, with grey wash; indented for transfer; 24 × 16·2 cm. (9⅜ × 6⅜ in.).

INSCR.: Recto, on the tablet, printing . . . Mr Dolman, and 16.

PROV.: As for No. 17.
1867–4–13–334 (L.B.13(16)).

ETCH.: By Barlow (?) in reverse, with modifications, Xanthus being seen from the front with his stick pointing towards the ground.

See note to No. 110.

119. ÆSOP AT HIS MASTER'S GATE SENDS AWAY ALL THE GUESTS EXCEPT ONE. Æsop standing, r., with a dog near him, saluting three of the guests who depart towards the l., while a fourth passes through an archway into the house, r. The tablet bordered by grotesque masks and a gadrooned pattern.

Pen and brown ink, with grey wash; indented for transfer; 23·9 × 16·3 cm. (9⅜ × 6⅜ in.).

PROV.: As for No. 17.
1867–4–13–335 (L.B. 13(17)).

INSCR.: *Recto*, on the tablet, *printing*, and *18*.

ETCH.: By Thomas Dudley, in reverse, 1678.

120. ÆSOP INTERPRETING AN INSCRIPTION ON A TOMB, THEREBY DISCOVERING A TREASURE. Æsop and Xanthus, l., standing before a tomb, r., the former interpreting to his master the inscription which appears on its base: R · NQ · F · I / T · A · R · R · D / Q · I · T · A · E / D · Q · IT · A. In the background, another tomb and a building. The tablet bordered by grotesque animals and masks and swags of fruit.

Pen and brown ink, with grey wash; indented for transfer; 24·1 × 16·4 cm. (9½ × 6⅜ in.).

PROV.: As for No. 17.
1867–4–13–336 (L.B.13(18)).

INSCR.: *Recto*, on the tablet, *printing* . . . Mr *Dolman*, and *19*.

ETCH.: By Thomas Dudley, in reverse.
See note to No. 110.

121. ÆSOP INTERPRETING TO THE SAMIANS THE PORTENT OF THE EAGLE AND THE PUBLIC RING. Xanthus presenting Æsop to the rulers of Samos who are seated at a table on a raised platform, r. Below, l., other Samians, with buildings of the city beyond, above which flies the eagle with the ring in its beak. The tablet bordered by grotesque birds and otters devouring fish.

Pen and brown ink, with grey wash; indented for transfer; 24 × 16·2 cm. (9⅜ × 6⅜ in.).

PROV.: As for No. 17.
1867–4–13–337 (L.B.13(19)).

INSCR.: *Recto*, on the tablet, *printing*, and *20*.

ETCH.: By Thomas Dudley, in reverse, with modifications.

122. ÆSOP KNEELING BEFORE KING CROESUS. Croesus enthroned, r., surrounded by members of his court, with Æsop kneeling before him, l. The tablet bordered by monkeys.

Brush drawing in grey wash, partly outlined with pen and brown ink; indented for transfer; 24·2 × 16·4 cm. (9½ × 6⅜ in.).

INSCR.: *Recto*, on the tablet, *printing*, and *21*.

PROV.: As for No. 17.
1867–4–13–338 (L.B.13(20)).

ETCH.: By Thomas Dudley, in reverse, with additional detail.

Less finished than other drawings in this series.

123. ÆSOP WELCOMED ON HIS RETURN TO SAMOS FROM THE COURT OF LYDIA. The rulers of Samos, at the city gate, r., attended by a band of horns and trumpets, welcoming Æsop as he comes ashore, l., from the ship, a branch of olive in his hand. The tablet bordered by doves and fabulous monsters. **Plate 57**

Pen and brown ink, with grey wash; indented for transfer; 24·2 × 16·3 cm. (9½ × 6⅜ in.).

PROV.: As for No. 17.
1867–4–13–339 (L.B.13(21)).

INSCR.: *Recto*, on the tablet, 22.

ETCH.: By Thomas Dudley, in reverse.

124. ÆSOP FALSELY ACCUSED BY EUNUS, HIS ADOPTED SON, BEFORE LYCERUS KING OF BABYLON. Lycerus enthroned, l., resting his hand on Æsop's back, while Hermippus stands beside the throne on the extreme l. On the r., Eunus offering to the king the forged letter as evidence against Æsop, and indicating the treasure lying on the ground which Æsop is presumed to have amassed through bribery. In the background, r., a group of courtiers. The tablet bordered by dragons and other monsters.

Pen and brown ink, with grey wash; indented for transfer; 24 × 16·3 cm. (9⅜ × 6⅜ in.).

PROV.: As for No. 17.
1867–4–13–340 (L.B.13(22)).

ETCH.: By Thomas Dudley, in reverse.

INSCR.: *Recto*, on the tablet, *printing* . . . Mr *Dolman*, and 23.

See note to No. 110.

125. ÆSOP IN THE SEPULCHRE FED BY HERMIPPUS. Æsop from within the sepulchre, r., receiving food and drink from Hermippus who kneels on a bank, l. In the background, trees and a distant building with a tower, l. The tablet bordered by birds and spaniels.

Pen and brown ink, with grey wash; indented for transfer; 24·1 × 16·4 cm. (9½ × 6½ in.).

PROV.: As for No. 17.
1867–4–13–341 (L.B.13(23)).

INSCR.: *Recto*, on the tablet, *printing*, and 24.

ETCH.: By Thomas Dudley, in reverse.

126. ÆSOP BROUGHT OUT OF THE SEPULCHRE. The same setting as in No. 125, with Æsop, r., being assisted out of the sepulchre by Hermippus who kneels on the bank above, while three of the Babylonian courtiers approach from the l. The tablet bordered by eagles, partridges and spaniels, and masks of a lion and a goat.

Pen and brown ink, with grey wash; indented for transfer; 24 × 16·4 cm. (9½ × 6⅜ in.).

PROV.: As for No. 17.
1867–4–13–342 (L.B.13(24)).

INSCR.: *Recto*, on the tablet, *printing*, and 25.

ETCH.: By Thomas Dudley, in reverse.

127. EUNUS FORGIVEN BY ÆSOP. Æsop seated, l., in his bedchamber, taking by the hand Eunus who stands before him, r. In the distance, r., Eunus flinging himself, out of remorse, from a cliff. The tablet bordered by grotesque birds and beasts.

Pen and brown ink, with grey wash; indented for transfer; 24 × 16·2 cm. (9⅜ × 6⅜ in.).

PROV.: As for No. 17.
1867–4–13–343 (L.B.13(25)).

INSCR.: *Recto*, twice on the tablet, *26*.

ETCH.: By Thomas Dudley, in reverse.

[The drawing for the plate showing Æsop with the four eagles holding up children in baskets before King Nectenabo is missing.]

128. ÆSOP SHOWN HIS OWN STATUE ERECTED BY LYCERUS. Lycerus, attended by members of his court, l., showing Æsop his statue standing on a plinth in a niche, r. In the background, a portico and a building with a cupola. The tablet bordered by dragons and hounds.

Pen and brown ink, with grey wash; indented for transfer; 24·1 × 16·3 cm. (9½ × 6⅜ in.).

PROV.: As for No. 17.
1867–4–13–344 (L.B.13(26)).

INSCR.: *Recto*, on the tablet, *28*, and printing . . . Mr *Dolman*.

ETCH.: By Thomas Dudley, in reverse, 1679.

See note to No. 110.

[The drawing for the plate showing Æsop being charged with having stolen the gold cup is missing.]

129. ÆSOP FLUNG OVER A PRECIPICE BY THE DELPHIANS. A crowd of Delphians, some armed with pikes, hurrying up a steep slope to the summit of a precipice, from which Æsop is falling. The tablet bordered by serpents and dragons.

Pen and brown ink, with grey wash; indented for transfer; 24·1 × 16·4 cm. (9½ × 6⅜ in.).

PROV.: As for No. 17.
1867–4–13–345 (L.B.13(27)).

INSCR.: *Recto*, on the tablet, *30*, and printing . . . Mr *Dolman*.

ETCH.: By Thomas Dudley, in reverse.

130. THE DELPHIAN PRIESTS PRAYING AT THE MONUMENT ERECTED TO ÆSOP'S MEMORY. In the centre, the monument, a statue of Æsop beneath a baldachino with twisted columns on a plinth supported by satyrs. Before it, r. and l., four of the Delphian priests imploring Heaven to avert the plague, the victims of which are seen outside the city in the background. A storm overhead with lightning flashing from the clouds. The tablet bordered by laurel sprays, cockle shells, and stars. **Plate 58**

Pen and brown ink, with grey wash; indented for transfer; 23·9 × 16·2 cm. (9⅜ × 6¼ in.).

INSCR.: *Recto*, on the tablet, *31*, and printing . . . Mr *Dolman*.

PROV.: As for No. 17.
1867–4–13–346 (L.B.13(28)).

ETCH.: By Barlow (?) in reverse.

See note to No. 110.

131. ILLUSTRATION TO THE FABLE OF 'THE FOX AND THE EAGLE'. In the foreground, a vixen looking up at a rock, l., surmounted by an eagle's nest apparently in flames, from which fall her cub and one of the eaglets. Overhead, the two parent birds bringing back as food part of the sacrifice from a smoking altar seen amidst trees in the background, r.

Pen and brown ink, with grey wash; a modification of the design on another slip of paper inset on the r.; 8 × 9·6 cm. (3⅛ × 3¾ in.).

INSCR.: *Recto*, at the foot, *B I* (a collector's mark (?) but not identified).

PROV.: As for No. 3.
1859–7–9–4 (L.B.10).

This composition, besides being on a much smaller scale, is completely different from that of Barlow's etching in the *Æsop's Fables* of 1666, p. 21. The latter illustrates only the first of the three fables connected with the Fox and the Eagle, and follows the traditional details of this in showing, for instance, the Eagle's nest in a tree, whereas the present drawing apparently combines elements of all three fables, while the Eagle's nest is shown on a rock.

132. PARTRIDGE STALKING. A stretch of open countryside rising into a hillock in the distance. In the foreground, a covey of partridges watched by a man concealed behind a horse which is cropping the grass beneath a tree, r. Also on the r., a dog crouching. On the l., kingfishers at a river bank. **Plate 59**

Brush drawing in grey wash; 19·9 × 29·5 cm. (7⅞ × 11⅝ in.).

INSCR.: *Recto*, in the lower r.-hand corner, by the artist, *F. Barlow*, and in the lower l.-hand corner, *n D*, (a collector's mark (?), but not identified).

PROV.: As for No. 3.
1859–7–9–2 (L.B.11).

ETCH.: By Jan Kip, in reverse. Subsequently included in the re-publication by Bowles and Sayer of etchings after Barlow, *Various Birds and Beasts Drawn from the Life* . . . , Pl. 6.

133. A GROUP OF BIRDS IN A GARDEN. On the l., a peacock perched on a block of masonry at the foot of a column, with four peahens around him. In the centre, an ostrich and on the r., a cassowary, with two pheasants between them. On the extreme r., an ape squatting on the ledge of a pyramid. Across the background, a garden wall beyond which are cypress trees and two swallows flying overhead. **Plate 60**

Pen and brown ink, with grey wash; indented for transfer, 21·2 × 31·3 cm. (8⅜ × 12⅜ in.).

PROV.: Parkes & Co., from whom it was purchased by the B.M., 1920.
1920–4–20–19.

ETCH.: By Jan Griffier, in reverse, and subsequently included in the re-publication by Bowles and Sayer of etchings after Barlow, *Various Birds and Beasts Drawn from the Life* . . . , Pl. 14.

134. AN EAGLE CARRYING OFF A CHICKEN. An eagle flying towards the l., holding in its talons a chicken at which it tears with its beak. Below, on the r., a cottage flanked by trees.

Pen and brown ink, with grey wash; indented for transfer; 12·8 × 17·5 cm. (5 × 6⅞ in.).

PROV.: Hugh Howard. Dr. Robert Howard (Bishop of Elphin). The Earls of Wicklow. Charles Howard, 5th Earl, from whom it was purchased by the B.M., 1874.
1874–8–8–2257 (L.B.12).

ETCH.: By Francis Place, in reverse, apparently as one of a series of birds, after designs by Barlow published by P. Tempest, *Multae et Diversae Avium Species* . . . , 1694,

and later re-issued with a new title, *Birds & Fowles of Various Species* . . . (See *Walpole Soc.*, X, p. 55, No. 106) in the re-publication by Bowles and Sayer of etchings after Barlow, *Various Birds and Beasts Drawn from the Life* . . . , Pl. 50.

The composition of the present subject is not unlike that of Barlow's etching of an eagle with a cat in its talons, illustrating an incident which he witnessed in Scotland (See *Vertue*, I, p. 116).

135. DUCK SHOOTING. In the foreground, three ducks, one in flight, another on the edge of a pond, and a third with her ducklings in the water, l. On the r., behind a tree, a fowler taking aim with his gun.

Pen and brown ink, with grey wash, on brown paper; 12·9 × 18·3 cm. (5⅛ × 7¼ in.).

INSCR.: *Recto*, in the lower r.-hand corner, by the artist, *F. Barlow 1684*.

PROV.: Samuel Woodburn (Sale, Christie,

12:vi:1860, in Lot 1091). Sir Thomas Phillipps, Bart. T. Fitzroy Phillipps Fenwick. Presented anonymously to the B.M., 1946.
1946–7–13–1168.

BIBL.: *Popham, Fenwick*, p. 236, No. 1.

136. DESIGN FOR THE LABEL BELOW A PORTRAIT OF PETER THE GREAT. The label, with the inscription, simulating a bear's skin suspended from a hook on either side of the oval frame to the portrait. In the centre, the animal's head with a coat of arms indicated below it, and on either side, its four paws.

Pen and brown ink with grey wash; indented for transfer; the paper cut to fit the lower part of the oval frame; 8·6 × 23 cm. (3⅜ × 9 in.).

INSCR.: *Recto*, on the bear's skin, in pencil,

PETER . . . ALEXEEWITZ | THE GREAT . . . CZAR OF MOSCOW.

PROV.: Sir Hans Sloane, Bart., by whom it was bequeathed to the B.M., 1753.
5236–185.

BIBL.: *Sloane Cat.*, p. 265, No. 185.

In the *Sloane Cat.* this drawing is said to be French; but the inscription points to an English origin, and, indeed, the handling suggests Barlow. The engraved portrait for Peter the Great for which the label was intended has not been identified. The only English portrait of the Czar of a suitable date

is John Smith's mezzotint of 1697 after Kneller's painting (*Chaloner Smith*, III, p. 1214, No. 217). The label of the mezzotint is, however, of a completely different design, being a plinth surmounted by a crown and other regalia, and the present drawing would not appear to be an alternative for it. Rather do the proportions of the drawing suggest that it was meant for a smaller engraving.

137 (1)–(61). **ALBUM.** Containing 61 satirical designs for playing cards illustrating events from the period of the *Rump Parliament* (1648–53), the *Popish Plot* (1678) and the *Meal Tub Plot* (1680). The drawings are uniform in size, each contained within a ruled ink border with a small, rectangular space at the foot for a title or description. The attribution to Barlow rests purely on the style which is consistent throughout the series. This consistency of style, together with the uniformity of size and format, and in general of the costumes depicted (except where there is a definite attempt to depict an older fashion, as in some of the *Rump Parliament* illustrations), suggests that all the designs were completed within a limited period of time, in spite of the interval of thirty years between the first and last of the events illustrated. Fifteen of the *Popish Plot* designs are known to have been engraved and form part of a rare pack of cards (*See B.M. Playing Cards*, E. 186) in which the last event illustrated was the 'Tryall of Sr G. Wakeman, and 3 Benedictine Monks' (July 18th, 1678). It was probably this pack which was advertised in the *True Domestick Intelligence* for Dec. 26th, 1679, as representing 'to the life the several consults for killing the King, and extirpating the Protestant Religion, the manner of the murthering Sir Edmond-bury Godfrey, the Tryals and executions of the conspirators, and all other material designs relating to the contrivance and management of the said horrid Popish Plot'. . . . If so, at least fifteen of Barlow's designs were finished before the end of 1679. None of the later episodes connected with the *Popish* and *Meal Tub Plots* was, so far as is known, engraved. Two broadsides in the B.M. Print Room, entitled *A True Narrative of the Horrid Hellish Popish Plot to the tune of Packington's Pound* (*B.M. Satires*, Nos. 1092 & 1093), contain twenty-four designs similar to but larger than, and quite distinct from those here discussed. Though bearing no printed date, the broadsides are inscribed in an old hand, *A burlesq on the Popish Plott. 15 May. 1682.* This may well be the correct date of the publication for Oates is satirised in several of the designs in a way hardly possible three years before, when he had been acclaimed a national hero.

All the small group of *Rump Parliament* designs (Nos. 1–7), have been engraved to form part of an even rarer pack of cards (*B.M. Playing Cards*, E. 195). These were long thought to have been a royalist publication of the time of, or shortly after, the events they illustrate, but for reasons already indicated, there seems nothing except the subject matter to distinguish the originals from the *Popish Plot* designs.

If the designs listed below can safely be attributed to Barlow, he must almost certainly have been the author of the broadsides previously mentioned and of at least six other known packs of historical playing cards which cover a period extending into the reign of Queen Anne (*B.M. Playing Cards*, E.185, 189, 190 & 191; *B.M. Schreiber Cards*, p. 163, No. 56 & p. 165 No. 62).

All pen and brown ink; about 6·5 × 5·2 cm. (3 × 2 in.).

BINDING: Mid-XVIII c., red morocco, gilt tooled with the Fountaine crest of an elephant on the back and front covers.

INSCR.: On the *verso* of the upper fly-leaf, in two different XVIII c. hands, one in ink (the same as No. (15) *recto* below (?)), one in pencil, *Plott Cards, 1680*.

[(1)–(7)]. **Episodes connected with the Rump Parliament.**

(1) CHARLES WORSLEY AS A WEAVER AT A LOOM.

INSCR.: *Recto*, at the foot, in a XVII c. hand, *one a weaving at a | loome his Sworde & a | head peice lying by*

ENGR.: Anonymously, in reverse, for the six of hearts in the *Rump Parliament* pack (*B.M. Playing Cards*, E. 195), with the lettering, *Worsley an Inckle Weaver a man of Personal Valor.*

BIBL.: *Goldsmid*, p. 14, No. 21 & Pl. VI. *Hulton, passim.*

Charles Worsley, born of a Manchester family, was elected first M.P. for that city in 1654. In the following year he was appointed one of Cromwell's major-generals.

(2) COLONEL RAINSBOROUGH RIDING INTO THE CITY DRIVING A CROWD BEFORE HIM.

INSCR.: *Recto*, at the foot, in the same hand as No. (1), *The Army Entering Londō | threttning yᵉ prentices & sitizens*

ENGR.: As for No. (1), for the nine of clubs, with the lettering, *The Army entring the City persuing the Apprentices.*

BIBL.: *Goldsmid*, p. 18, No. 34 & Pl. IX. *Hulton, passim.*

In July 1647, the Army persuaded Parliament that the City militia should be controlled by commissioners of which it (the Army) approved. This broke with the tradition by which the City itself controlled the militia, and provoked riotous demonstrations. Colonel Rainsborough, in the name of law and order, seized the defences of London Bridge and marched into the City.

(3) DESBOROUGH GESTICULATING, WITH FIREARMS PROTRUDING FROM HIS POCKETS.

INSCR.: *Recto*, at the foot, in the same hand as No. (1), *Tall greatman | with a Canon in each | Pockett*

ENGR.: As for No. (1), for the six of clubs, with the lettering, *Desbrow Olivers Champion haueing a Cannon in each Pocket.*

BIBL.: *Goldsmid*, p. 14, No. 22 & Pl. VI. *Hulton, passim.*

The motion to make Cromwell king, which Parliament introduced in 1657, encountered strong opposition even from the Protector's own family, in particular from his brother-in-law, John Desborough.

(4) COLONEL HEWSON ENTERING LONDON AT THE HEAD OF A TROOP OF HORSE.

INSCR.: *Recto*, at the foot, in the same hand as No. (1), *Hewson. at yᵉ head of | his troop entring Londō. | pulling downe poles and | Chains*

ENGR.: As for No. (1), for the nine of hearts, with the lettering, *Huson the Cobler entring London.*

BIBL.: *Goldsmid*, p. 17, No. 33 & Pl. IX. *Hulton, passim.*

Colonel John Hewson, a shoemaker by origin, marched into London in Dec., 1659, to suppress opposition to the régime, particularly from the apprentices.

(5) SIR ARTHUR HASELRIGGE GESTICULATING.

INSCR.: *Recto*, at the foot, in the same hand as No. (1), *In a Distracted | Action or posture*

ENGR.: As for No. (1), for the eight of diamonds, with the lettering, *Don Haselrigg Kᵗ of yᵉ Codled braine.*

BIBL.: *Goldsmid*, p. 17, No. 32 & Pl. VIII. *Hulton, passim.*

Sir Arthur Haselrigge, a stubborn supporter of the principle of parliamentary government, was described by Clarendon as an 'absurd bold man' and as 'of a weak understanding'.

(6) CROMWELL CONVERSING WITH NYE AND GODWIN.

INSCR.: *Recto*, at the foot, in the same hand as No. (1), *Oliver Confessing to | Nye and Godwin*

ENGR.: As for No. (1), for the five of spades, with the lettering, *Nye and Godwin Olivers Confessors.*

BIBL.: *Goldsmid*, p. 13, No. 19 & Pl. V. *Hulton, passim.*

Dr. Thomas Godwin and Philip Nye were appointed in 1653 commissioners 'for approbation of Publique Preachers'.

(7) COLONEL FIENNES DESERTING THE COLOURS.

INSCR.: *Recto*, at the foot, in the same hand as No. (1), *An Officer | runing away from | his Colours*

ENGR.: As for No. (1), for the seven of hearts, with the lettering, *Nathaniel Fines whereby hangs a tale.*

BIBL.: *Goldsmid*, p. 15, No. 25 & Pl. VII. *Hulton, passim.*

Colonel Nathaniel Fiennes surrendered Bristol to the royalist forces under Prince Rupert, on July 26th, 1643. He is said by *Mercurius Aulicus* to have reached Southampton 'at the head of 80 horse, each of whom had a woman riding behind him'.

[(8)–(61)]. Episodes connected with the Popish and Meal Tub Plots.

(8) OATES AND TONGE BEFORE THE PRIVY COUNCIL. (?).

BIBL.: *Hulton, passim.*

The two gowned figures, shown speaking to the seated group, may represent Titus Oates and Ezerel Tonge, the imposters who testified before the Privy Council on Sept. 28th, 1678. Their information about the so-called *Popish Plot* resulted in a series of trials which continued during the course of the next few years.

(9) OATES RECEIVING LETTERS FROM THE JESUITS.

INSCR.: *Recto*, at the foot, in the same hand as No. (1), *Oates shewne letter* [s] | *to carry to France &* | *Spaine*

ENGR.: Anonymously, in reverse, somewhat modified, for the five of hearts, in the *Popish Plot* pack (*B.M. Playing Cards*, E. 186), with the lettering, *D*| *Oates receiues letters from y*[e] *Fathers to carry beyond Sea.*

BIBL.: *Schreiber*, Pl. X. *Hulton, passim.*

Oates confessed to having acted as a confidential agent for the Jesuits.

(10) SIR EDMUND BERRY GODFREY SHADOWED BY HIS MURDERERS.

Plate 61

INSCR.: *Recto*, at the foot, in the same hand as No. (1), *S*[r] *E. B. Godfry doggd* | *w*[th] *2 or three by S*[t]*.* | *Clement Church*

ENGR.: As for No. (9), for the knave of spades, with the lettering, *S*[r] *E. B. Godfree doggd by S*[t] *Clements Church.*

BIBL. & REPR.: *Schreiber*, Pl. XI. *Hulton, passim* & Pl. V(*b*).

Sir Edmund Berry Godfrey, the Westminster magistrate to whom Oates made his original disclosures concerning the Plot, was murdered between Oct. 12th and 17th, 1678, by persons unknown. Sir Miles Prance, a Catholic silversmith, made a confession in which he alleged that four men named Gerald, Green, Berry and Hill strangled Godfrey in the courtyard of Somerset House after shadowing him along the Strand from St. Clement Danes, on the evening of Oct. 12th.

(11) GODFREY'S BODY CARRIED INTO A ROOM AT SOMERSET HOUSE.

The inscription cut away.

ENGR.: As for No. (9), for the eight of spades, with the lettering, *S*[r] *E. B. Godfree Carrying up* | *into a Roome.*

BIBL.: *Schreiber*, Pl. XI. *Hulton, passim.*

After the murder of Godfrey (*See* No. (10)), according to the evidence of Miles Prance, the body was carried into a room at Somerset House.

(12) GODFREY'S BODY CARRIED AWAY ON HORSEBACK.

Plate 61

INSCR.: *Recto*, at the foot, in the same hand as No. (1), *They mount him astrid* | *before hill. 2 o 3 going* | *w*[th] *them*

ENGR.: As for No. (9), for the five of spades, with the lettering, *The body of S*[r] *E. B. G. carry'd to Primrose hill on a Horse.*

BIBL. & REPR.: *Schreiber*, Pl. XI. *Hulton, passim* & Pl. V(*c*).

The body, according to Prance's account, was removed in a sedan chair several days later to Soho and there placed on a horse and carried to the foot of Primrose Hill, where it was left, transfixed with a sword.

(13) THE EXECUTION OF GODFREY'S MURDERERS.

INSCR.: *Recto*, at the foot, in the same hand as No. (1), *The Execution of y*[e] | *3 murtherers*

ENGR.: As for No. (9), for the three of spades, with the lettering, *The Execution of the murtherers of S*[r] *E. B. Godfree.*

BIBL.: *Schreiber*, Pl. XI, *Hulton, passim.*

Green, Berry and Hill (*See* No. (10)) were

convicted of the murder of Godfrey and hanged, but not, in fact, all three together. Green and Hill were executed on Feb. 21st, 1679, Berry on the 28th.

(14) LONDON IN FLAMES.

INSCR.: *Recto*, at the foot, in the same hand as No. (1), *London a fire & peop*[le] | *stealing away goods* | . . . [word illegible] *kind of tumults*

ENGR.: As for No. (9) for the two of clubs, with the lettering, *London remember the 2ᵈ. of September. 1666.*

BIBL.: *Schreiber, Pl. XIII. Hulton, passim.*

The burning of London was one of the inevitable ingredients of the Plot. The Great Fire was still a recent memory and in times like these, the Catholics were naturally inculpated.

(15) A JESUIT OFFERING MONEY FOR ARSON.

INSCR.: *Recto*, at the foot, in an XVIII c. hand, *A Jesuit offers money* | *to burn houses*
          Verso, in another XVIII c. hand, *a Jesuit offers mon*[ey] | *to burn houses*

BIBL.: As for No. (8).

See No. (14).

(16) THE ARREST OF A JESUIT.

BIBL.: As for No. (8).

The incident represented has not been identified.

(17) JESUIT MEETING AT SOMERSET HOUSE.

INSCR.: *Recto*, at the foot, in the same hand as No. (1), *a Consult at* | *Somerset house* | *all within preists & Jes*[uits], and inserted between the first two lines, *all yᵉ consult case leaders*

ENGR.: As for No. (9), for the ace of spades, with the lettering, *The Consult att Somerset house.*

BIBL.: *Schreiber, Pl. XI. Hulton, passim.*

Oates, on more than one occasion, gave evidence that he had heard the Queen (Catherine of Braganza) give her consent, at her residence in Somerset House, to the murder of the King.

(18) POPE IN COUNCIL.

Plate 61

INSCR.: *Recto*, at the foot, in the same hand as No. (1), *A consult at Roome* | *the Pope & Cardinalls* | *yᵉ divell under yᵉ table*

ENGR.: As for No. (9), for the ace of hearts, with the lettering, *The Plot first hatcht at Rome by the Pope and Cardinalls & ᶜᵗ.*

BIBL. & REPR.: *Schreiber, Pl. X. Hulton, passim* & *Pl. V(a).*

The prime mover in the Plot can have been none other than the Pope himself !

(19) A JESUIT COUNCIL.

INSCR.: *Recto*, at the foot, in the same hand as No. (15) recto, *the Jesuits consult* | *to raise prentices*
          Verso, in the same hand as No. (15) verso, *the Jesuits consul*[t] | *to raise Prentices*

BIBL.: As for No. (8).

(20) THE DEVIL DROPPING PLOTTERS.

Plate 62

INSCR.: *Recto*, at the top, within a scroll,

in an XVIII c. hand, *my Paunch will never be | Emtyed;* and at the foot, in the same hand as No. (15) (recto), *the Devil supplying | the pope with plotters*

        Verso, in the same hand as No. (15) *verso, the devil supplying | the Pope wth plotters*

BIBL. & REPR.: *Hulton, passim* & Pl. V(*e*).

The Devil's appearance in this design is very close to that of another in the broadsheet referred to above (*B.M. Satires*, No. 1092, p. 649) and is particularly characteristic of Barlow's fantasy.

(21) THE POPE GIVING COMMISSIONS TO THE JESUITS.

INSCR.: *Recto*, at the foot, in the same hand as No. (15) *recto, the Pope gives fresh | commissions.*

        Verso, in the same hand as No. (15) *verso, the Pope gives | fresh Commissions*

BIBL.: As for No. (8).

Not engraved, but similar to a design engraved for the five of hearts in the pack known as *All the Popish Plots* (*Schreiber*, Pl. VI).

(22) JESUITS RECEIVING COMMISSIONS.

INSCR.: *Recto*, at the foot, in the same hand as No. (1), *Jesuitts receive Com̄ | issions* [t]*o move ye Peopl^e | to Rebell*

ENGR.: As for No. (9), slightly modified, for the five of diamonds, with the lettering, *Severall Iesuitts receiuing Commissions to stir the People to Rebellion in Scotland.*

BIBL.: *Schreiber*, Pl. XII. *Hulton, passim.*

The fomenting of rebellion against the King by Jesuit missionaries in the interests of the Duke of York, was said to have been another feature of the Plot.

(23) A JESUIT SPEAKING TREASON.

INSCR.: *Recto*, at the foot, in the same hand as No. (15) *recto, a Jesuit speaking Treason.*

        Verso, in the same hand as No. (15) *verso, a Jesuit speaking | Treason*

BIBL.: As for No. (8).

Not engraved, but close to the design for the queen of spades (*Schreiber*, Pl. XI).

(24) PROTESTANTS IN A MASQUERADE.

INSCR.: *Recto*, in the same hand as No. (15) *verso, Protestants in | Masquerade*

BIBL.: As for No. (8).

This probably represents a scene from one of the great anti-papal masquerades organized by the Whig Green Ribbon Club, which were held annually from 1679 for a period and which culminated in 'pope burnings'. *See B.M. Satires*, I, Nos. 1084 & 1085.

(25) COLEMAN DRAWN IN A SLEDGE TO EXECUTION.

Traces of black lead beneath the pen and brush lines; inscription cut away.

ENGR.: As for No. (9), for the six of hearts, with the lettering, *Coleman drawn to his execution.*

BIBL.: *Schreiber*, Pl. X. *Hulton, passim.*

A less finished drawing than the rest of the series.

    Edward Coleman was secretary both to James, Duke of York, and to his Catholic wife, Mary of Modena. He kept in close correspondence with Louis XIV's confessor, Père de la Chaize, and was one of the central figures in the *Plot*. He was tried and convicted of high treason on Nov. 27th, 1678, and executed on Dec. 3rd.

(26) GROVE AND IRELAND DRAWN IN A SLEDGE TO EXECUTION.

INSCR.: *Recto*, at the top, in the same hand as No. (1), *Grove & Ireland | in one sledge*

ENGR.: As for No. (9), with modifications, for the two of diamonds, with the lettering, *Ireland and Grove drawn to their execution.*

BIBL.: *Schreiber*, Pl. XII. *Hulton, passim.*

Father William Ireland, *alias* Ironmonger, a Jesuit who had come to England in 1677 as procurator of the province, and Grove, a lay brother, were named, among others, by Oates as principals in the plot to assassinate the King. They were tried, convicted on false evidence and executed at Tyburn on Jan. 24th, 1678/9.

(27) JENISON WHO IS ABOUT TO REVEAL THE *PLOT*, CHIDED BY MISTRESS ANNE IRELAND.

INSCR.: *Recto*, at the foot, in another XVIII c. hand, *M⁸ Ane Ireland Comes to Mʳ Jenˢ | Chamber to chide him for goeing | to disʳ (as she heard) the pop.ˢʰ plot*

BIBL.: As for No. (8).

Robert Jenison, educated at the Jesuit college at Douai, like Oates, turned informer and revealed in 1679 and 1680 before the Council and the House of Commons that he had been so appalled by the revelations of William Ireland (*See* No. (26)) as to be converted to Protestantism. The reference to Anne Ireland is presumably to William

Ireland's sister who gave evidence in his defence at his trial.

(28) JOHN SMITH FLYING FROM CATHOLICISM.

INSCR.: *Recto*, at the foot, in the same hand as No. (15) *recto, Mr Smith flying | from Church of Rome*
Verso, in the same hand as No. (15) *verso. Mr Smith flying frō | Ch of Rome*

BIBL.: As for No. (8).

The Mr. Smith is probably John Smith, a cousin of Robert Jenison (*See* No. (27)) who had previously been confessor to the Jenison family and who also turned informer, giving the same reasons for his sudden revulsion towards Rome.

(29) WHITEBREAD MADE PROVINCIAL.

INSCR.: *Recto*, at the foot, in the same hand as No. (1), *Whitebread made | Provinsiall of yᵉ Jesuitts*

ENGR.: As for No. (9), somewhat modified, for the four of diamonds, with the lettering, *Whitebread made Provintiall.*

BIBL.: *Schreiber*, Pl. XII. *Hulton, passim.*

Thomas Whitebread was appointed Provincial of the English Jesuits early in 1678.

(30) WHITEBREAD WRITING LETTERS ABOUT THE IRISH SITUATION.

INSCR.: *Recto*, at the foot, in the same hand as No. (1), *Whitebread writeing | letters concerning yᵉ stat*[e]*| of Ireland*

ENGR.: As for No. (9), for the seven of clubs, with the lettering, *Whitebread writeing letters concerning the state of Ireland.*

BIBL.: *Schreiber*, Pl. XIII. *Hulton, passim.*

Whitebread was alleged to have been concerned with the raising of a papal army in Ireland.

(31) DUGDALE READING LETTERS.

INSCR.: *Recto*, at the foot, in the same hand as No. (1), *Dugdale reading letters | Concerning yᵉ Plott several | lying before him*

ENGR.: As for No. (9), for the king of diamonds, with the lettering, *Mr Dugdale in Staffordshire reading several letters relating to the Plott.*

BIBL.: *Schreiber*, Pl. XII. *Hulton, passim.*

Stephen Dugdale was steward to Lord Aston, a Catholic peer, at Tixhall, Staffs. In Dec., 1678, he laid information before the Privy Council about alleged treasonable meetings held there and about incriminating letters discovered by him.

(32) DUGDALE LAYS INFORMATION BEFORE A MAGISTRATE.

INSCR.: *Recto*, at the foot, in the same hand as No. (15) recto, *Dugdale gives his | depositions*
       Verso, in the same hand as No. (15) verso, *Dugdale gives his depositions*

BIBL.: As for No. (8).

See No. (31).

(33) MRS. PRICE BRIBING DUGDALE.

INSCR.: *Recto*, at the foot, in the same hand as No. (15) *recto* (?), *Mrs Price persuades Dugdale to retreat*
       Verso, in the same hand as No. (15) verso, *Mᵗˢ Price psuades | Dugdale to retract*

BIBL.: As for No. (8).

In Jan., 1680, Anne Price, also a servant to Lord Aston (*See* No. (31)), together with one John Tasborough, was tried for having bribed Dugdale to retract evidence given by him against Father Harcourt, her confessor. Both were found guilty and fined.

(34) FLIGHT OF SIR GEORGE WAKEMAN.

INSCR.: *Recto*, at the foot, in the same hand as No. (15) recto, *Sir Geo. Wakeman | flyes —*
       Verso, in the same hand as No. (15) verso, *Sʳ Geo: Wakeman | flyes*

BIBL.: As for No. (8).

Not engraved, but the horseman in the background appears, only slightly modified, in the ten of clubs (*Schreiber*, Pl. XIII).

Sir George Wakeman, physician to Queen Catherine, was tried, together with three Benedictines, on July 18th, 1679, for conspiring to kill the King. Wakeman was alleged to have consented to poison the King for £15,000. The prisoners were acquitted by Chief Justice Scroggs—a most unpopular verdict, and Wakeman was forced to fly the country to escape the fury of the people.

(35) THE PORTUGUESE AMBASSADOR CONGRATULATING LORD JUSTICE SCROGGS.

INSCR.: *Recto*, at the foot, in the same hand as No. (15) recto, *the portugal Embassador | & & —*
       Verso, in the same hand as No. (15) verso, *the Portugell | Embassador &c*

BIBL.: As for No. (8).

The day following the acquittal by Lord

Justice Scroggs (*See* No. (34)), the first such verdict to be delivered in any of the *Plot* trials, the Portuguese ambassador, Henrique de Sousa Tavarez, Marquez d'Arronches, to Scroggs's embarrassment, called on him publicly to congratulate him on his conduct of the case.

(36) DANGERFIELD EXAMINED BY THE PRIVY COUNCIL.

INSCR.: *Recto*, at the top, within a scroll, in the same hand as No. (20) *recto* (within the scroll), *Drive to Tiburne*; and, at the foot, in the same hand as No. (15) *verso*, *Capt: Tom Examind | before yᵉ Councel*

BIBL.: As for No. (8).

Thomas Dangerfield, *alias* Willoughby, an attorney's son, gaol-bird and self-styled captain, played a prominent part in the invention of the sham Presbyterian plot known as the *Meal Tub Plot*. After his 'discovery' of the plot, he was found, on examination by the Privy Council in Oct., 1679, to have a criminal record and was imprisoned. He later saved himself by fixing the ultimate responsibility for the plot on the Catholic leaders, in particular the Earl of Castlemaine and the Countess of Powis.

(37) DANGERFIELD PRODUCING DOCUMENTS OF THE *MEAL TUB PLOT* BEFORE THE LORD MAYOR (?).

INSCR.: *Recto*, at the foot, in the same hand as No. (8) *recto*, *Dungerfield presents a boo* [k] *| of the sham presbi : Plott*

BIBL.: As for No. (8).

On Oct. 31st, 1679, Dangerfield (*See* No. (36)), was taken from prison to make fresh disclosures to Sir Robert Clayton, Lord Mayor, to the effect that the Presbyterian plot was a forgery and that it had been dic-tated to him by the Catholic Countess of Powis and approved of by other Catholic leaders including Lord Peterborough.

(38) DANGERFIELD OFFERED MONEY TO MURDER THE KING.

INSCR.: *Recto*, at the top, within a scroll, in the same hand as No. (15) *verso*, *Heaven yʳ reward*; and, at the foot, in the same hand as No. (15) *recto*, *Dungerfield offerd | money to kill the King*
　　　　　Verso, in the same hand as No. (8) *verso*, *Dangerfield offerd | money to kill yᵉ | king*

BIBL.: As for No. (8).

Dangerfield (*See* No. (36)) also confessed to Sir Robert Clayton that he had resisted a bribe of £2,000 offered to him by Lord Arundel to murder the King, but instead had undertaken to assassinate Lord Shaftesbury for £500.

(39) DANGERFIELD OFFERED THE SACRAMENT BY A JESUIT.

Plate 62

INSCR.: *Recto*, at the foot, in the same hand as No. (15) *recto*, *Dungerfield offerd | the sacram : to kill yᵉ King*
　　　　　Verso, in the same hand as No. (15) *verso*, *Dangerfield offerd | the sacramᵗ to | kill yᵉ King*

BIBL. & REPR.: *Hulton, passim* & Pl. V(*f*).

See No. (38) with which this subject is clearly connected.

(40) DANGERFIELD BRIBED TO MURDER LORD SHAFTESBURY.

INSCR.: *Recto*, at the foot, in the same hand as No. (15) *recto*, *Dungerfield offerd 500 | to kill Lᵈ Shaftsbury*
　　　　　Verso, in the same hand as No. (15)

verso, Dangerfield offerd | 500 to kill Ld | Shaftsbury

BIBL.: As for No. (8).

See No. (38).

(41) DANGERFIELD LAYS INFORMA-TION BEFORE PARLIAMENT (?).

INSCR.: *Recto*, at the foot, in the same hand as No. (15) *recto*, Dungerfield gives his *dep | ositions to the parliament*
        Verso, in the same hand as No. (15) *verso*, Dangerfield gives his Depositions to *yᵉ | Parliamt*

BIBL.: As for No. (8).

It is not known whether Dangerfield was called to the bar of either House of Parliament to disclose details of the *Meal Tub Plot*.

(42) DANGERFIELD UNDERGOING PENANCE.

INSCR.: *Recto*, at the foot, in the same hand as No. (15) *recto, Dungerfields pennance | for killing Sir. Ead. Godfrey*
        Verso, in the same hand as No. (15) *verso, Dangerfields penn | ance for killing | Sʳ Ead : G :*

BIBL.: As for No. (8).

It is not clear why Dangerfield is here connected with the murder of Godfrey. Perhaps, since the inscription is XVIII c. the writer's knowledge of the *Plot* was not precise.

(43) LORD CASTLEMAINE WRITING *THE COMPENDIUM.*

INSCR.: *Recto*, at the foot, in the same hand as No. (15) *recto, Castlemaine writing | the compendium*

Verso, in the same hand as No. (15) *verso, Castlemaine writing | the compendium*

BIBL.: As for No. (8).

Roger Palmer, 1st Earl of Castlemaine, was denounced by Oates as a Jesuit and arrested in Oct., 1678. Whilst in prison he wrote *The Compendium*, an account of the sufferings of his fellow Catholics as a result of the *Plot*. He was brought to trial in Nov., 1679, for complicity in the *Meal Tub Plot*, but defended himself so skilfully that he secured an acquittal.

(44) ANDERSON QUESTIONED IN NEW-GATE JAIL.

INSCR.: *Recto*, at the foot, in the same hand as No. (15) *recto, Anderson examined | in Newgate*, and in black lead, above the word *Anderson, chains*
        Verso, in the same hand as No. (15) *verso, Anderson Examin'd | in Newgate*

BIBL.: As for No. (8).

Lionel Anderson (*alias* Munson), a Catholic priest, with seven others, was charged in Jan., 1680, with having received orders from Rome. He was executed.

(45) LORD JUSTICE NORTH TAKES EVDENCE FROM THE DYING BEDLOE

INSCR.: *Recto*, at the foot, in the same hand as No. (15) *recto, Lᵈ North takes Bedloes | dying depositions*
        Verso, in the same hand as No. (15) *verso, Ld North takes | Bedloes dying | Depositions*

BIBL.: As for No. (8).

William Bedloe, an imposter of the same class as Oates, provided together with the latter the bulk of the evidence against the

Catholics, particularly in relation to the murder of Godfrey and the supposed plan to murder the King. He was the author of *A Narrative and Impartial Discovery of the Horrid Popish Plot* . . . and other pamphlets on the same theme. Sir Francis North, Chief Justice of the Common Pleas, took Bedloe's evidence as he lay dying in Aug., 1680, which turned out to be merely a repetition of what he had already given on numerous occasions. It was read to the assembled Commons on Oct. 28th.

(46) BEDLOE'S EVIDENCE PRESENTED TO PARLIAMENT.

INSCR.: *Recto*, at the foot, in the same hand as No. (15) *recto*, *Bedloes dying depositions*
Verso, in the same hand as No. (15) *verso*, *Bedloes dying | Depositions*

BIBL.: As for No. (8).

See No. (45).

(47) BEDLOE'S FUNERAL.

INSCR.: *Recto*, at the foot, in the same hand as No. (15) *recto*, *Bedloes funeral*
Verso, in the same hand as No. (15) *verso*, *Bedloes Funerall*

BIBL.: As for No. (8).

Not engraved, but similar to a design for the two of spades (*Schreiber*, Pl. XI, *Godfrey's funeral*).

William Bedloe (See No. (45)) died a natural death on Aug. 20th, 1680, at Bristol. His body lay in state in Merchant Taylors' Hall and he was buried with ceremony.

(48) SIR ROGER L'ESTRANGE WRITING AT A TABLE.

INSCR.: *Recto*, at the foot, in the same hand

as No. (15) *verso*, *Lestrange writing | to Rome.*

BIBL.: As for No. (8).

Sir Roger L'Estrange, tory journalist and pamphleteer, was Oates's most severe critic, and in his *Brief History*, 1680, sets out the Catholic case for the *Plot* being a pure fabrication. He was made J.P. for Middlesex in 1680, but was forced to flee the country because of popular feeling in support of the *Plot*.

(49) 'NOLL'S FIDDLER' RUNNING FROM PARLIAMENT.

INSCR.: *Recto*, at the foot, in the same hand as No. (15) *recto*, *Noll's fidler runns | from the parliament.*
Verso, in the same hand as No. (15) *verso*, *Nolls fidler runs | strangle* [strangely] *from yⁿ | parliamᵗ*

BIBL.: As for No. (8).

L'Estrange (See No. (48)), was bitterly attacked for his published disbelief in the *Plot*. On Nov. 17th, 1680, he was burnt in effigy. In the broadside, *The Solemn Mock Procession of the Pope* . . . (B.M. *Satires*, No. 1085) he is depicted as a dog holding a violin and the figure labelled 'Old Nol's Fidler'.

(50) GADBURY CASTS THE KING'S HOROSCOPE.

INSCR.: *Recto*, at the foot, in the same hand as No. (15) *verso*, *Gadbury declares the | King's Nativity*

BIBL.: As for No. (8).

Not engraved, but similar to a design for the queen of diamonds (*Schreiber*, Pl. XII).
John Gadbury, astrologer and possibly a convert to Roman Catholicism, was impli-

cated in the *Popish Plot* and brought before the Council in November, 1679, but released.

Verso. TWO MEN, ONE SEATED.

Black lead.

BIBL.: As for No. (8).

The figures, similar to the standing and seated men on the *recto*, are very roughly drawn.

(51) MRS. CELLIER WRITING TREASONABLE LETTERS.

INSCR.: *Recto*, at the foot, in the same hand as No. (15) *recto*, *Mrs Celliere writing to | her Spanyards*
    Verso, in the same hand as No. (15) *verso*, *Mrs Celiere writing | to her Spanyards*

BIBL.: As for No. (8).

Elizabeth Cellier, known as the 'Popish midwife', and represented in this and three following designs, was one of the central figures in the *Meal Tub Plot* (See No. (36)). The papers purporting to provide evidence for it were found in her meal tub. She was accused of high treason in June, 1680, but her chief accuser, Dangerfield, was so patently untrustworthy that she was acquitted.

(52) MRS CELLIER CONSPIRES TO BURN THE FLEET.

INSCR.: *Recto*, at the foot, in the same hand as No. (15) *recto*, *Mrs Celliere consults | to burn the fleet*
    Verso, in the same hand as No. (15) *verso*, *Mrs Celiere consult* [s] *| to burn y* ^{e} *fleet*

BIBL.: As for No. (8).

See No. (51).

(53) MRS CELLIER WRITING HER TRACT.

INSCR.: *Recto*, at the foot, in the same hand as No. (15) *recto*, *Mrs Celliere writing | her Narrative*
    Verso, in the same hand as No. (15) *verso*, *Mrs. Celiere writing | her narrative*

BIBL.: As for No. (8).

After her acquittal, Mrs. Cellier (See No. (51)) composed a pamphlet in her own vindication, *Malice defeated; or a brief Relation of the Accusation and Deliverance of Eliz. Cellier.*

(54) MRS CELLIER IN THE PILLORY.
Plate 62

INSCR.: *Recto*, at the foot, in the same hand as No. (15) *recto*, *Mrs. Celliere disgraces | the pillory*
    Verso, in the same hand as No. (15) *verso*, *Mrs. Celiere disgraces | the pillory*

BIBL.: As for No. (8) and *B.F.A.C.*, p. 27, No. 51.

Certain passages in Mrs. Cellier's pamphlet (See No. (53)) about the treatment of prisoners in Newgate, exposed her to a second trial for libel. She was convicted and sentenced to a fine of £1,000 and to stand three times in the pillory. Presumably the 'disgrace' is connected with the breeches (?) she is seen to be wearing beneath her coat.

(55) A WOMAN ENTERING A BUILDING.

INSCR.: *Recto*, at the foot, in the same hand as No. (15) *verso*, *No Protestant conceels*

BIBL.: As for No. (8).

The figure probably represents Mrs. Cellier though the significance of the inscription is uncertain.

(56) A ST. OMER WOMAN BEING SWORN IN.

INSCR.: *Recto*, at the foot, in the same hand as No. (15) *recto*, *a St Omers Lady | instructed to Swear*

Verso, in the same hand as No. (15) *verso, a St Omers lady | instructed to | swear*

BIBL.: As for No. (8).

This is presumably a reference to a witness brought over from St. Omer (where there was a large English Jesuit college) to give evidence in one of the many trials of Jesuit priests. Many of these witnesses were housed by Mrs. Cellier.

(57) SIR THOMAS GASCOIGNE OFFERS MONEY FOR A NUNNERY (?)

INSCR.: *Recto*, at the foot, in the same hand as No. (15) *recto, Gascoyne offers money | to erect a Nunnery*

Verso, in the same hand as No. (15) *verso, Gascoyne offers | money to erect | a Nunnery*

ENGR.: The design appears in several more or less modified forms in the *Popish Plot* pack (*B.M. Playing Cards*, E. 186), for the king of hearts, the queen of spades, the queen of diamonds and the king of clubs, but none of these with lettering which refers to Gascoigne.

BIBL.: *Schreiber*, Pls. X–XIII. *Hulton, passim.*

The inscription may represent a guess by the writer, since there seems no obvious reason why the drawing should refer to this matter. Sir Thomas Gascoigne, a Yorkshire baronet and landowner, took the advice of one John Pracid, a Jesuit, on his intended establishment of a nunnery. He was tried and acquitted on Feb. 11th, 1679/1680, of having signed a resolution to kill the king.

(58) FATHER RUSHTON ADMINISTERING THE OATH TO BOLRON.

INSCR.: *Recto*, at the foot, in the same hand as No. (15) *recto, Father R. gives the oath to | Baldron to kill | the king*

Verso, in the same hand as No. (15) *verso, Father R: gives the | oath to Baldron to | kill the king*

BIBL.: As for No. (8).

Robert Bolron had been manager of one of the collieries owned by Sir Thomas Gascoigne (*See* No. (57)). Threatened with prosecution for fraud by the baronet's daughter, he revenged himself, with Laurence Mowbray, or Mowbery, a servant in the family, who had been discharged for suspected theft, by turning informer and accusing Gascoigne of conspiracy against the life of the king. Bolron gave evidence that he himself received the oath to kill the king from Father Rushton, a Catholic priest, at the baronet's house, Barnbow Hall, Yorks.

(59) MOWBRAY GIVING EVIDENCE BEFORE THE LORD MAYOR.

INSCR.: *Recto*, at the foot, in the same hand as No. (27), *Mowbray & Sr Robt Clayton | Lord mayor*

BIBL.: As for No. (8).

Laurence Mowbray (*See* No. (58)) and Bolron (*See* No. (58)) were refused a hearing by the Yorkshire magistrates and were forced to go to London to make their depositions.

(60) MOWBRAY STABBED IN LEICESTER FIELDS.

INSCR.: *Recto*, at the foot, in the same hand as No. (15) *recto, Mowbray Stab'd in | Leicester fields.*

Verso, in the same hand as No. (15) *verso*, *Mowberry stabd | in Lecester fields*

BIBL.: As for No. (8).

An attempt was made on Mowbray's life on Oct. 15th, 1679, in Leicester Fields, but the fact that he was wearing two bodices and shammed dead saved him.

(61) IMPRISONMENT OF ARCHBISHOP PLUNKET.

INSCR.: *Recto*, at the foot, in the same hand as No. (8) *recto*, *the titular A. B^p of | Dublin sent to Newgate*

Verso, in the same hand as No. (8) *verso*, *ye titular A: Bi of | Dublin sent to | Newgate*

BIBL.: As for No. (8).

Oliver Plunket, Roman Catholic Archbishop of Armagh and titular primate of Ireland, was arrested in Dec., 1678, for complicity in the *Popish Plot* and conspiring to bring a large French army to Ireland. Found guilty on false evidence, he was hanged, drawn and quartered at Tyburn, in July, 1681.

PROV.: Sir Andrew Fountaine. H. S. Reitlinger (Sale, Sotheby, 12/13:iv:1954, Lot 215). F. B. Benger, from whom it was purchased by the B.M., 1954.

1954–7–10–4.

BEALE, CHARLES II

B. 1660: D. 1726 (?)

Portraitist and limner

Born on 16th June, 1660, at Hind Court, Fleet St., and baptised on the 23rd of the same month at St. Dunstans-in-the-West. Second son of Charles Beale I (*See* No. 1 (i) below) and Mary Beale (*q.v.*). In 1665 taken with the rest of the family to Albrooke, Hants., to avoid the Plague, and while there, appears to have contracted smallpox. According to Charles Beale I's *Diary* for 1676/7 (now in the Bodleian Library), both young Charles and his brother Bartholomew were put to copying the works of Van Dyck and Lely, and frequented the latter's studio. Drawings by Italian masters were also borrowed from the Royal Collection (apparently through the good offices of William Chiffinch, official 'cleaner' to the collection) for the boys to study. Bartholomew soon turned to medicine, but Charles continued his artistic career, and in March, 1676/7, began to practise limning under the guidance of Thomas Flatman. An entry in the diary referred to above for July 31st 1677, reads 'pd. Mr. Golbold for ye little Ebony frame and glass to the thing limned in Black by my son Charles after Jack How's pict: done by Mr. Lely ... 0–50–00.' Must have made rapid progress as a draughtsman to judge from the studies in his sketch-book of 1679, now in the Pierpont Morgan Library (*See Introductory Note* below). It is clear from the elder Beale's diary of 1680/1 (in the possession of the N.P.G.) that the young artist was busily engaged in assisting his mother in her prolific output of portraits by working on draperies and backgrounds. Against the date July 13th is the note, 'Charles got £100— for laying in drapery and dead colour of Marchioness of Dorchester's picture.' Vertue records that the artist suffered from a weakness of sight (perhaps the result of his early attack of smallpox) and was forced to give up working in miniature after four or five years, but the small portrait of Richard, 4th Earl of Lauderdale at the V. & A., dated *1688*, would seem to disprove this. Certainly continued to paint in oils, as a portrait, perhaps of Dryden, in the Fitzwilliam Museum, is signed and dated *1693*. According to an inscription in the artist's 'third' sketchbook, now belonging to Sir Samuel Beale (*see* below), would still have been living in *1721*. Vertue records his death in two different localities, 'Longacre' and 'against St. Clement's Church in the Strand'. If the former is correct, may be identified with a certain 'Charles Beal' who was buried on Dec. 26th, *1726*, at St. Martin-in-the-Fields in which parish Long Acre is situated. There is no record of him in the Registers of St. Clement Danes. Vertue also states that Beale died in debt to a Mr. Wilson, a banker (known to have been a friend of the family), at whose house the artist lodged and who thus came into possession of much of his work.

Though his oil paintings, in the Lely tradition, are not easily distinguishable from his mother's, his intimate figure studies in red chalk of members and friends of the family, have apparently no counterpart in the native English art of the time, though they are paralleled by the characteristic studies of Dutch *genre* painters of the 17th c., such as Gabriel Metsu, and Gerard van Honthorst. They have affinities too with the figure of the seated lady, attributed to Willem Wissing, described on p. *548* of the present Catalogue, No. 1. His technique of heavy red chalk may also have a Netherlandish origin and should be compared with the study of Grinling Gibbons by Sir J. B. Medina (*See* p. *447*, No. 1 r.) and at least three studies by Dutch artists also in the Department, the self-portrait by Carel du Jardin, the *Count Ferdinand Bocskai* by Moses van Uytenbroeck, and the *Peasant Woman and a Boy* by Adriaen van de Velde (Hind, *Dutch and Flemish Artists*, III, p. 123, No. 1; IV, p. 72, No. 1, Pl. XLIV; IV, p. 75, No. 2, Pl. XLV (*b*) 2).

BIBL.: *St. Martin-in-the-Fields, Register*, 1723–32, p. 71. *Walpole* (1786), III, p. 140. *Cracherode Cat.*, pp. 3, 99. *Hind, Dutch and Flemish Artists*, pp. 72, 75, 123. *Reitlinger. Long*, p. 20. *Reynolds. Vertue, Index*, p. 16. *Walsh*.

[1–177]. The following drawings, with the exception of Nos. 17 and 107, originally came from an album which is thus described for the first time in a footnote in the 4th edition of *Walpole* (1786), III, p. 140: 'Mr. G. Steevens has a quarto volume of studies in red chalk by Mrs. Beale and her son Charles. Several by her from nature, Van Dyck and Lely, are highly finished and very lively, tho' hard, and the drawing not very correct. There is nothing but human figures.' This note re-appears in Walpole's *Collected Works*, 1798, III, p. 337, but oddly enough was not included by Dallaway or Wornum in the later editions of the *Anecdotes*. 'Mr. G. Steevens' is probably identical with George Steevens (B. 1736: D. 1800) the Shakespeare commentator. According to the *Cracherode Catalogue* (*See Bibl.* below) the album was inscribed on a guard after the fly leaf *From Mr Stevens* [sic] *Decr 16th, 1788*, that presumably being the date when it was acquired by the Rev. C. M. Cracherode, by whom it was eventually bequeathed to the B.M. in 1799. The drawings were still in the album in 1845 when it was noted, without however the contents being listed, in the *Cracherode Cat.* Subsequently the drawings were taken out and mounted separately, but the volume itself most unfortunately was not preserved.

The old attribution of the contents of the album jointly to Mary Beale and her son

Charles has presented a problem. Those drawings bearing the signature *C B* in mono-gram (Nos. 115, 122, 158–60, 162–7, below) could definitely be given to Charles, and two others, unsigned (Nos. 112 & 144) appear also traditionally to have been attributed to him. The remainder would presumably have been assigned to Mary. Mr. Binyon in cataloguing the group accepted in principle these attributions, pointing out, however, that there was no discernible difference of style between many of the drawings ascribed to Mary and those signed by Charles. Thus it was that this type of drawing, with its technique of waxy deep-red chalk strengthened with black lead and black chalk, came to be accepted as characteristic of Mary Beale.

In the meantime, a sketchbook closely related to the British Museum drawings had been acquired by the Pierpont Morgan Library with the Fairfax Murray Collection. This book measures 22·7 × 17·3 cm. (8⅞ × 6¾ in.) and contains about 73 leaves watermarked with a *Fleur de Lis* (*Heawood*, No. 1785). At the beginning is the MS. title, *Charles Beale | 1ˢᵗ Book, 1679*, and again, in smaller lettering, with flourishes, *Charles: Beales | Book*. All the studies in it are in the same medium of red chalk, black lead and black chalk as are the B.M. drawings, with the exception of that on *f.* 8, which is in black lead only. It should be noted that none of them is signed.

Six of the leaves are reproduced in *J. Pierpont Morgan Collection of Drawings . . . formed by C. Fairfax Murray*, 1912, III, Pls. 6–11, and are listed under the name 'Charles Beale (XVII Century)' without other qualification. Subsequently Capt. H. S. Reitlinger drew attention to this sketchbook in an article primarily dedicated to the Beale drawings in the B.M. (*Burl. Mag.*, XLI, 1922, pp. 143–7), in which he suggests that 'son Charles' may in reality have been the author of all of them. Further re-search has indeed substantiated this. A number of miniatures by Charles Beale II are known, on which appears the characteristic monogram *C B*, and three of the subjects of these are also to be found in the group of drawings in the B.M. (Nos. 107, 117 & 130). Moreover, a bold form of cross-hatching which is used in varying degrees in many of the drawings (*e.g.* Nos. 8, 30, 72 & 100) occurs in the miniatures, more especially in the draperies and backgrounds (V. & A. M., *Sir Peter Lely*, dated *1669* (555–1905) and *Richard, 4th Earl of Lauderdale*, and *Anne, his Countess*, the former dated *1688* (P. 93 & 94, 1937), but sometimes in the face (Duke of Buccleuch, *Samuel Pepys*, dated *1688*)).

The generous action of the authorities of the Pierpont Morgan Library in presenting to the B.M. a complete set of photostats of all the studies in their sketchbook has established beyond doubt the origin of the Steevens-Cracherode drawings listed below. Though none of the studies in the Pierpont Morgan book is signed, the younger Charles Beale's authorship of it is proved by the *C* with curling ends which forms the initial letter of the title *Charles Beale 1ˢᵗ Book*; this is identical with the *C* of the monogram on his drawings in the B.M. and his miniatures. Its contents con-sist almost entirely of intimate studies from the life of exactly the same type and feeling as those described below (Nos. 1–99, all of them previously attributed to Mary Beale), and the same bold cross-hatching, already referred to, appears on a number of them, for example, on the study of a man on *f.* 15. Each leaf of the book has on the *verso* an offset from the drawing on the following leaf; and on lifting a number of the Steevens-Cracherode drawings from their mounts it was found that all of these too had offsets (Nos. 1, 13, 17, 31, 53, 55, 56, 85, 86, 90, 166, 172). This shows that the Steevens-Cracherode drawings were themselves originally leaves of a similar sketchbook (or perhaps a number of sketchbooks) which must have been cut out, trimmed, and mounted together in an album before, or at the time they passed into Steevens's collection. Another point in common with the Pierpont Morgan book is the similarity of the watermarks which are also variants of the *Fleur de Lis* of about the same period (apparently *Heawood*, Nos. 1781, 1781a, and 1784).

It is clear from the offsets that the registration numbers of the Steevens-Cracherode drawings, which doubtless follow the old order in the album, represent also the original order of the drawings in the sketchbook or sketchbooks. These offsets have also furnished additional proof that all the Steevens-Cracherode drawings are by the younger Charles Beale, for sheets bearing the monogram *C B* are shown thereby to have originally come next to ones without it (*i.e.* those formerly attributed to Mary Beale). Thus No. 166 (G.g.4. W.5–21) *Statuette of a Putto skating*, signed *C B*, has on its *verso* the offset from No. 13 (G.g.4. W.5–22) *A Young Man playing a Recorder*, which is not signed and was formerly given to Mary Beale; and this in its turn has the offset from No. 167 (G.g.4. W.5–23) another study from the *Putto skating*, which again is signed *C B*.

Though there would have been then complete justification in listing these drawings according to their registration numbers, it was felt that it would be more convenient, from the point of view of study, to classify them here in seven consecutive groups (Nos. 1–177), according to their types of subject. A concordance of their numbers in the present catalogue is, however, appended, should it be required at any time to reconstruct the original order.

More recently two further sketchbooks have come to light which afford additional proof of the younger Charles Beale's authorship of these drawings. They belong respectively to Sir Samuel Beale and Miss H. M. Beale, who are probably members of the same family as the artist, though the sketchbooks themselves have not descended to them direct in the family. Sir Samuel's book resembles the one in the Pierpont Morgan Library: it measures 26·1 × 20·3 cm. (10¼ × 8 in.), is bound in vellum and contains the same typical studies in red chalk from the life. On the first fly-leaf is inscribed by the artist, *Charles Beale | 3rd Book 1680*, and on the second, also by the artist, *Charles Beales | Book, | Ano Domini | 1721*, together with a later note of ownership, *J. Wakeford*. A number of subjects in this book have been named by the artist, and this has enabled some of the Steevens-Cracherode drawings which represent the same subjects also to be identified. Miss Beale's book measures 24·7 × 20·1 cm. (9¾ × 8 in.) and is bound in old marbled boards. It too contains studies in red chalk many of which are replicas—perhaps rather coarser in quality—of those in Sir Samuel's book.

Taken together the Pierpont Morgan sketchbook, the two Beale sketchbooks and the Steevens-Cracherode drawings in the B.M. (which may represent the contents of

'Charles Beale's 2nd Book'), probably constitute most of, but not all the artist's output in this characteristic use of red chalk. There are, however, at least three other drawings not immediately included in the group which are clearly connected with it. These comprise No. 15 below, the *Man with a slight Squint*, and two versions (respectively in the Royal Library at Windsor and in the collection of Sir Robert Witt) of the same study of the man who appears in Nos. 24–27. No. 107, the portrait of Lord Strafford after Van Dyck, though in much the same technique, does not belong to the group.

In conclusion may be noted another sketchbook, this time attributed to Mary Beale, in the V. & A. M. (E. 4528–1919). It is a quarto volume measuring 25·4 × 20·3 cm. (10 × 8 in.), bound in vellum and inscribed on the outside of each cover by a former owner, *J . . . Godsehall / 1668* (no artist of this name is known, but a certain John Godshall, merchant of London, and of East Sheen, who died in 1691, is recorded). The leaves are watermarked with a Fool's Cap (*Heawood*, Nos. 2002 or 2009), and a large number of them are stained grey or blue-grey, the others being left white. The contents include figure-subjects in various media, ranging from black, white, and coloured chalk to pen and ink, grey wash, and water-colour; and among them are studies from the life, sketches for or after portraits (early Lely period to late XVII or early XVIII c.) and copies from Van Dyck's *Iconographia*. There is no documentary evidence to connect the book directly with Mary Beale, and the early owner 'J . . . Godsehall' does not appear to have been a member of her circle. The attribution to her must, therefore, have been arrived at through the stylistic affinities of some of the drawings with those in the B.M. In particular, that on p. 204, a study of Pierre de Jode after Van Dyck—the head in red chalk highly finished, the body in black chalk lightly drawn—and other copies after Van Dyck in black chalk (pp. 112, 119 & 121) are reminiscent; and it is possible, therefore, that this book, though it probably has no connexion with his mother, may represent another side of the younger Charles Beale as a draughtsman.

In listing the present series of drawings, reference is made as follows, when occasion arises, to three of the related sketchbooks described above:

> *Beale I.* Charles Beale / 1st Book. 1679 (Pierpont Morgan Library).
> *Beale II.* Charles Beale / 3rd Book. 1680 (Sir Samuel Beale).
> *Beale III.* Charles Beale, Undated (Miss Helen M. Beale).

[1–42]. STUDIES FROM THE LIFE: MEN.

These drawings, as far as can be judged, are all taken direct from the life, and besides those identified as representing the elder Charles Beale (Nos. 1–8) and perhaps the younger (*i.e.* the artist himself, Nos. 9–11) are all probably of members of the Beale circle. In type they correspond with the drawings in the sketchbooks listed above. As intimate and informal studies they are unlike anything else known in native English art of the time; but they are paralleled by the drawings of contemporary or rather earlier Dutch painters of interior *genre* scenes (*See* Charles Beale biography, p. 149).

1. CHARLES BEALE I. Bust, turned half-r. Wearing curling hair and shirt open at the neck.

Red chalk, strengthened with black lead and black chalk; 21·3 × 17·1 cm. (8¼ × 6¾ in.).

INSCR.: Lettered on the modern mount, below the drawing, perhaps reproducing an inscription from the old album, *Charles Beale*.

PROV.: G. Steevens (before 1788). The Rev. C.M. Cracherode, by whom it was bequeathed to the B.M., 1799.
G.g.4. W.5–64 (L.B., as attributed to Mary Beale, 16).

BIBL.: *Walpole* (1786), III, p. 141. *Cracherode Cat.*, under G.g.4.W.5. *Reitlinger*.

[Charles Beale I (B. 1631: D. after 1681). Fifth son of Bartholomew Beale of Grays Inn and Walton Manor, Bucks., and Clerk of the Signets. Husband of Mary Beale (*q.v.* whom he married on Mar. 8th, 1651/2) and father of Bartholomew (*See* p. 199, No. 1) and Charles Beale II, author of the present drawings. Held an official post as Deputy Clerk of the Patents which he relinquished in 1665. Helped his wife in her professional work as a portraitist by purchasing materials for her and keeping a record of her sitters. Occasionally also tried his own hand at painting, and also dealt in pictures. The 'Mr. *Beale*' commended by Sir William Sanderson in his *Graphice*, p. 20, thought by Long to have referred to the elder Charles Beale, but is more likely in its context to be a misprint for 'Mrs. Beale.']

This and the following seven drawings (Nos. 2–8) evidently represent the same person. According to the identifications on some of the mounts (Nos. 1, 5, 6 & 8), perhaps reproducing inscriptions in the original album from which they came, they should be studies of Charles Beale I. One of the sitter's most prominent characteristics is the group of warts in the region of the mouth—three

on the upper lip (two to the l. and one to the r. of his nose), and one on his lower lip to the r., and one in the centre of the chin. These are clearly shown in the present drawing. They also occur in an oil painting of the same personage (*Cf.* in particular No. 4) attributed to Mary Beale, until recently in the collection of the Duke of Wellington (Sale, Sotheby, 26:xi:1947, Lot 18). This picture is said to represent the Poet Laureate, Thomas Shadwell, and on the strength of this identification Mr. Binyon tentatively suggested that the present group of drawings might also be studies of him. This picture bears, however, no resemblance whatsoever to the one portrait of Shadwell which can be considered as authentic, the bust on his monument in the Poets' Corner, Westminster Abbey, and the only apparent reason for connecting it with him is the fact that the sitter holds a laurel wreath. The intimate manner too in which the subject of the present drawings has been studied, shows that he was well-known to the artist; but there is nothing to suggest that Shadwell was ever a member of the Beale circle, nor even that he sat to Mrs. Beale or her son Charles.

Further evidence has since come to light, which indeed points to Charles Beale I as being the person concerned and thus to the old identification as being the correct one. In the V. & A. M. is a miniature definitely of Beale at the age of thirty-three painted by his friend Thomas Flatman in 1664 (*See* Graham Reynolds in the *Burl. Mag.*, LXXXIX, 1947, p. 67 & Pl. II E). This shows the sitter with an identical group of warts about his mouth; and his other facial characteristics are not inconsistent with those of the person represented in the drawings and in the portrait formerly belonging to the Duke of Wellington. The reason for the subject of the last mentioned picture holding a laurel wreath is certainly obscure, as Charles Beale does not

153

appear to have had any talent for verse—on the contrary he himself refers, with becoming modesty but ample justification, to some verses, addressed by him to his wife- to-be in a letter of 1651, as the work of a 'clod of earth'. But perhaps the laurel here merely denotes his general interest in the arts.

2. CHARLES BEALE I. Bust, nearly in profile to l. Wearing curling hair and shirt open at the neck.

Red chalk, strengthened with black lead and black chalk; 21·4 × 16·6 cm. (8⅜ × 6½ in.).

PROV.: As for No. 1.
G.g.4. W.5–59 (L.B., as attributed to Mary Beale, 18).

BIBL.: As for No. 1.

3. CHARLES BEALE I. Head, turned half-r., with eyes looking to front. Wearing curling hair.

Red chalk, strengthened with black lead and black chalk; 17·1 × 15·5 cm. (6¾ × 6⅛ in.).

PROV.: As for No. 1.
G.g.4. W.5–68 (L.B., as attributed to Mary Beale, 17).

BIBL.: As for No. 1.

The present drawing corresponds with a portrait, in the collection of the Earl Spencer at Althorp, said to be of Thomas Otway by Mary Beale.

4. CHARLES BEALE I. Bust, with body turned to front and head half-l. Wearing curling hair and shirt open at the neck. **Plate 64**

Red chalk, strengthened with black lead and black chalk; 21·3 × 18·1 cm. (8⅜ × 7⅛ in.).

PROV.: As for No. 1.
G.g.4. W.5–102 (L.B., as attributed to Mary Beale, 19).

BIBL.: As for No. 1.

5. CHARLES BEALE I. Bust, turned slightly to r., with eyes looking to front. Wearing curling hair and shirt open at the neck. **Plate 63**

Red chalk, strengthened with black lead and black chalk; 21·8 × 15·7 cm. (8½ × 6⅛ in.).

INSCR.: Lettered on the modern mount, below the drawing, perhaps reproducing an inscription from the old album, *Charles Beale*.

PROV.: As for No. 1.
G.g.4. W.5–115 (L.B., as attributed to Mary Beale, 15).

BIBL.: As for No. 1.

6. CHARLES BEALE I. Bust, turned half-r. Wearing curling hair and shirt open at the neck.

Red chalk, strengthened with black lead and black chalk; 24·2 × 16·2 cm. (9½ × 6⅜ in.).

INSCR.: Lettered on the modern mount, below the drawing, perhaps reproducing an inscription from the old album, *Charles Beale*.

PROV.: As for No. 1.
G.g.4. W.5–122 (L.B., as attributed to Mary Beale, 14).

BIBL.: As for No. 1.

7. CHARLES BEALE I IN A FUR-EDGED CAP. Bust, turned to front, with eyes looking to l. Wearing a fur-edged cap, curling hair, doublet and shirt open at the neck.

Red chalk, strengthened with black lead and black chalk; 21·9 × 16·8 cm. (8⅝ × 6⅝ in.).

PROV.: As for No. 1.
G.g.4. W.5–33 (L.B., as attributed to Mary Beale, 22).

BIBL.: As for No. 1.

8. CHARLES BEALE I IN A FUR-EDGED CAP. Head, turned half-l., with eyes looking to front. Wearing a fur-edged cap, curling hair, and shirt open at the neck.

Red chalk, strengthened with black lead and black chalk; 21·3 × 18·1 cm. (8¾ × 7⅛ in.).

INSCR.: Lettered on the old mount, below the drawing, perhaps reproducing an inscription from the old album, *Charles Beale*.

PROV.: As for No. 1.
G.g.4. W.5–106 (L.B., as attributed to Mary Beale, 20).

BIBL.: As for No. 1.

9. A YOUNG MAN WITH A WART ON HIS R. JAW, PERHAPS CHARLES BEALE II. Bust, turned half-r. Wearing curling hair and his shirt open at the neck.

Red chalk, strengthened with black lead and black chalk; 21·9 × 18·3 cm. (8⅝ × 7¼ in.).

INSCR.: Lettered on the mount, below the drawing, perhaps reproducing an inscription from the old album, *Charles Beale*.

PROV.: As for No. 1.
G.g.4. W.5–152 (L.B., as attributed to Mary Beale, 21).

BIBL.: As for No. 1.

This drawing was listed by Mr. Binyon, as a possible portrait of Thomas Shadwell, with those now identified as representing Charles Beale I (*Cf.* Nos. 1–8 in this Catalogue). The present sitter, however, is clearly not the same person, though like Nos. 1, 5, 6 & 8, the mount is lettered *Charles Beale*. It is possible, therefore, that it may be a self-portrait of the artist, Charles Beale II.

10. THE SAME YOUNG MAN WITH A WART ON HIS R. JAW, AS IN No. 9, PERHAPS CHARLES BEALE II. Bust, turned half-r. Wearing curling hair and his shirt open at the neck.

Red chalk, strengthened with black chalk; the shoulders lightly indicated; 22 × 18·1 cm. (8⅝ × 7⅛ in.).

PROV.: As for No. 1.
G.g.4. W.5–46 (L.B., as attributed to Mary Beale, 61).

BIBL.: As for No. 1.

See note to No. 9. The sitter's hair is shown lighter in colour in the present drawing.

11. THE SAME YOUNG MAN WITH A WART ON HIS R. JAW, AS IN Nos. 9 & 10, PERHAPS CHARLES BEALE II. Bust, turned half-r., leaning over to the l. Wearing curling hair.

Red chalk, strengthened with black lead and black chalk; 17·4 × 13·1 cm. (6⅞ × 5⅛ in.).

PROV.: As for No. 1.
G.g.4. W.5–50 (L.B., as attributed to Mary Beale, 62).

BIBL.: As for No. 1.

See note to No. 9. The sitter's hair is shown lighter in the present drawing.

12. A YOUNG MAN READING. H.L., seated to front at a table, looking down at the book which he is reading. Wearing a fur-trimmed *montero*, long curling hair, and a cravat. **Plate 65**

Red chalk, strengthened with black chalk; 22·4 × 17 cm. (8¾ × 6¾ in.).

PROV.: As for No. 1.
G.g.4. W.5–5 (L.B., as attributed to Mary Beale, 43).

BIBL.: As for No. 1.

13. THE SAME YOUNG MAN AS IN No. 12, PLAYING A RECORDER. Bust, turned half-r. Wearing a *montero*, long curling hair, and a long cravat, and holding a recorder to his lips.

Red chalk; the face alone finished; 20·5 × 16·1 cm. (8 × 6¼ in.).

PROV.: As for No. 1.
G.g.4. W.5–22 (L.B., as attributed to Mary Beale, 44).

BIBL.: As for No. 1.

14. A YOUNG MAN, PROBABLY THE SAME AS IN Nos. 12 & 13, ASLEEP. Head alone, turned half-l., lying in bed, with his eyes closed. Wearing a night-cap over his long curling hair, his shoulders covered by the bed-clothes. **Plate 72**

Red chalk, strengthened by black lead; 20·2 × 18·1 cm. (7⅞ × 7⅛ in.).

PROV.: As for No. 1.
G.g.4. W.5–37 (L.B., as attributed to Mary Beale, 92).

BIBL.: As for No. 1.

15. A MAN WITH A SLIGHT SQUINT. Head turned slightly to l. and looking down. Wearing a fur-edged cap over close-cropped hair, and his shirt open at the neck.

Red chalk; 16·5 × 13·6 cm. (6½ × 5¼ in.).

PROV.: As for No. 1.
G.g.4. W.5–47 (L.B., as attributed to Mary Beale, 24).

BIBL.: As for No. 1.

The same sitter also appears in *Beale II, ff.* 64*v*. & 67*v*., and *Beale III, f. 57v.*, as well as in a single drawing in the Ashmolean Museum.

16. THE SAME MAN WITH A SLIGHT SQUINT AS IN No. 15. Head turned half-l. and looking down. Wearing a fur-edged cap over close-cropped hair, and his shirt open at the neck.

Red chalk, with black lead and black chalk; 21·3 × 16·8 cm. (8⅜ × 6⅝ in.).

PROV.: As for No. 1.

G.g.4. W.5–70 (L.B., as attributed to Mary Beale, 23).

BIBL.: As for No. 1.

17. THE SAME MAN WITH A SLIGHT SQUINT AS IN Nos. 15 & 16, READING. Nearly H.L., turned slightly to r., seated at a table, reading a book. Wearing a fur-edged cap over close-cropped hair, and a long cravat.

Red chalk, touched with black chalk; the body only lightly indicated; 24·4 × 19·2 cm. (9½ × 7½ in.).

INSCR.: *Recto*, in the upper l.-hand corner, 60.

PROV.: Elhanan Bicknell (Sale, Christie, 1:v:1863, Lot 409, not mentioned, but with drawings by Nicholas Blakey). Purchased at the Bicknell Sale, through Marseille Holloway, by the B.M., 1863.

1863–5–9–933 (L.B., as attributed to Mary Beale, 89).

BIBL.: *Reitlinger.*

For another version *cf. Beale II, f. 67v.*

18. 'BAKER'. Head, turned half-l., with a long nose and a wart on his l. jaw. Wearing long wavy hair and falling bands.

Red chalk, strengthened with black lead and black chalk; 20·6 × 16·7 cm. (8⅛ × 6½ in.).

PROV.: As for No. 1.

G.g.4. W.5–66 (L.B., as attributed to Mary Beale, 26).

BIBL.: As for No. 1.

The same sitter, wearing a fur cap and inscribed *Baker*, also appears in *Beale II, f. 71v.*

19. 'BAKER'. Bust, turned half-l., with eyes looking to front. Wearing falling bands and his coat unbuttoned.

Red chalk, strengthened with black lead and black chalk; 24·6 × 18·6 cm. (9⅝ × 7¼ in.).

PROV.: As for No. 1.

G.g.4. W.5–167 (L.B., as attributed to Mary Beale, 27).

BIBL.: As for No. 1.

20. A MAN WITH A LONG CURLING PERIWIG. Nearly H.L., seated to l., with eyes looking to front. Wearing a slight moustache, and cravat.

Red chalk, strengthened with black lead and black chalk; the body lightly indicated; $23 \cdot 9 \times 17 \cdot 5$ cm. ($9\frac{3}{8} \times 6\frac{7}{8}$ in.).

PROV.: As for No. 1.

G.g.4. W.5–87 (L.B., as attributed to Mary Beale, 12).

BIBL.: As for No. 1.

21. THE SAME MAN WITH A LONG CURLING PERIWIG AS IN No. 20.
Head turned half-l., with eyes looking to front. Wearing a cravat.

Red chalk, strengthened with black lead and black chalk; $21 \times 17 \cdot 1$ cm. ($8\frac{1}{4} \times 6\frac{3}{4}$ in.).

PROV.: As for No. 1.

G.g.4. W.5–86 (L.B., as attributed to Mary Beale, 13).

BIBL. As for No. 1.

22. A YOUNG MAN, WITH A BROAD FACE, LOOKING OVER HIS SHOULDER. Nearly H.L., looking round over his r. shoulder, his body in profile to r. Wearing long curling hair.

Red chalk, strengthened with black lead and black chalk; the body lightly indicated; $23 \cdot 8 \times 16 \cdot 7$ cm. ($9\frac{3}{8} \times 6\frac{5}{8}$ in.).

PROV.: As for No. 1.

G.g.4. W.5–123 (L.B., as attributed to Mary Beale, 119).

BIBL.: As for No. 1.

23. THE SAME YOUNG MAN, WITH A BROAD FACE, AS IN No. 22. Head turned half-l.

Red chalk, strengthened with black lead and black chalk; the cravat lightly indicated; $21 \cdot 7 \times 17 \cdot 5$ cm. ($8\frac{1}{2} \times 6\frac{7}{8}$ in.).

PROV.: As for No. 1.

G.g.4. W.5–124 (L.B., as attributed to Mary Beale, 120).

BIBL.: As for No. 1.

24. 'T. PORTER' SMOKING A PIPE. Nearly T.Q.L., looking down towards the r., seated in a chair over the back of which he leans his l. arm, while smoking a pipe. Wearing long curling hair, falling bands, a narrow cross-belt and sash.

Red chalk, with black lead and black chalk; the body lightly indicated; $24 \cdot 5 \times 19$ cm. ($9\frac{5}{8} \times 7\frac{1}{2}$ in.).

PROV.: As for No. 1.

G.g.4. W.5–130 (L.B., as attributed to Mary Beale, 53).

BIBL.: As for No. 1.

The same sitter also appears in *Beale I, ff.* 21r., 23r. & 44 (?), *Beale II, ff.* 65v., 68v., 70v. (inscribed *T.P.*) & 77v. (inscribed *T. | Porter. | N*), and *Beale III, ff.* 58v., 61v., 63v. & 70v.

25. 'T. PORTER' SMOKING A PIPE. Nearly H.L., seated to front, looking half-r., and smoking a pipe which he holds in his l. hand. Wearing the cross-belt and sash as in No. 24 but the cravat tied in a bow as in No. 26. **Plate 76**

Red chalk, strengthened with black lead and black chalk; the body lightly indicated; 24·6 × 19·2 cm. (9⅝ × 7½ in.).

PROV.: As for No. 1.
G.g.4. W.5–171 (L.B., as attributed to Mary Beale, 52).

BIBL. & REPR.: *Walpole* (1786), III, p. 140. *Cracherode Cat.*, under *G.g.4. W.5. Reitlinger*, p. 144 & Pl. A.

26. 'T. PORTER'. Nearly H.L., turned slightly to r., and looking to front. Wearing a cravat as in No. 25.

Red chalk, strengthened with black lead and black chalk; 24·2 × 18·8 cm. (9½ × 7⅜ in.).

PROV.: As for No. 1.
G.g.4. W.5–163 (L.B., as attributed to Mary Beale, 51).

BIBL.: As for No. 1.

27. 'T. PORTER'. Nearly H.L. and in profile to r., leaning slightly forwards. Wearing a cravat as in Nos. 25 & 26.

Red chalk, strengthened with black lead and black chalk; the body lightly indicated; 23·6 × 17·6 cm. (9¼ × 6⅞ in.).

PROV.: As for No. 1.
G.g.4. W.5–168 (L.B., as attributed to Mary Beale, 54).

BIBL.: As for No. 1.

28. CARTER, THE COLOURMAN, LOOKING OVER THE BACK OF A CHAIR. H.L., looking half-l., and seated in a chair on the back of which he rests his r. hand. Wearing long wavy hair and broad falling bands. **Plate 68**

Red and brown chalks, strengthened with black lead and black chalk; 24·6 × 19·1 cm. (9⅝ × 7½ in.).

PROV.: As for No. 1.
G.g.4. W.5–161 (L.B., as attributed to Mary Beale, 47).

BIBL.: As for No. 1.

[Carter (*Fl.* 1680–1742). Colourman and son of a colourman, both of whom were, according to Vertue (IV, p. 65 & V, pp.

14–15) 'intimate in the Beals family'. Acquired from the Beales all their papers, account books and almanack-diaries from which Vertue made extracts.]

The same sitter appears in *Beale II, ff. 75v.*, 78v., 81v. & 82v. (all being inscribed *Carter | N*), and in *Beale III, ff* 68v., 71v. & 74v. In *Beale II, f. 76v.*, there is also an admirable study of *Mrs* Carter, an elderly woman with a twisted mouth, wearing a hood and holding a pipe, who was probably the mother of the subject of the present drawing.

29. CARTER, THE COLOUR MAN, LOOKING OVER THE BACK OF A CHAIR. Nearly H.L., turned half-l., looking to front and smiling. Seated in a chair, over the back of which he leans with his l. elbow, his r. hand extended as if receiving some object not shown. **Plate 67**

Red and brown chalks, strengthened with black lead and black chalk; 24·3 × 19·2 cm. (9½ × 7½ in.).

PROV.: As for No. 1.

G.g.4. W.5–165 (L.B., as attributed to Mary Beale, 50).

BIBL.: As for No. 1.

30. CARTER, THE COLOUR MAN, LOOKING UPWARDS. Nearly H.L., turned half-r., and looking to front and upwards.

Red chalk, strengthened with black lead and black chalk; 24·3 × 18·5 cm. (9½ × 7¼ in.).

PROV.: As for No. 1.

G.g.4. W.5–172 (L.B., as attributed to Mary Beale, 48).

BIBL.: As for No. 1.

31. A MAN WITH BUSHY HAIR. Bust, turned slightly to r., with eyes looking to front, smiling. Wearing a skull cap with a stud in the peak, and thick bushy hair.

Plate 70

Red chalk, strengthened with black lead and black chalk; the body only lightly indicated; 24·1 × 17·1 cm. (9½ × 6⅞ in.).

PROV.: As for No. 1.

G.g.4. W.5–174 (L.B., as attributed to Mary Beale, 56).

BIBL.: As for No. 1.

32. THE SAME MAN WITH BUSHY HAIR AS IN No. 31. Bust, seated in profile to r., his arms folded across his chest. Wearing the same peaked skull cap as in No. 31.

Plate 69

Red chalk over black chalk, strengthened with black lead and black wash; the body only lightly indicated; 24·8 × 18·9 cm. (9¾ × 7⅞ in.).

PROV.: As for No. 1.

G.g.4. W.5–175 (L.B., as attributed to Mary Beale, 57).

BIBL.: As for No. 1.

33. A YOUNG MAN, WITH LONG FLOWING HAIR, LIFTING THE LID OF A CHEST. H.L., looking to front, his r. shoulder hidden by the curved lid of a chest which he lifts with his l. hand.

Red chalk, strengthened with black lead and black chalk; 19·7 × 18·6 cm. (7¾ × 7¼ in.).

PROV.: As for No. 1.

G.g.4. W.5–2 (L.B., as attributed to Mary Beale, 46).

BIBL.: As for No. 1.

34. A MAN IN A BROAD-BRIMMED HAT. H.L., looking to front and leaning towards the l., his l. hand extended as if offering a letter, which, however, is not shown. Wearing a broad brimmed hat, long hair, falling bands and open coat.

Red chalk, touched with black lead; 28·3 × 18·1 cm. (9⅜ × 7⅛ in.).

PROV.: As for No. 1.
G.g.4. W.5–7 (L.B., as attributed to Mary Beale, 49).

BIBL.: As for No. 1.

35. A MAN IN A LONG CURLING PERIWIG. Head turned half-l. Wearing a cravat.

Red chalk, strengthened with black lead and black chalk; 21·2 × 17·4 cm. (8⅜ × 6⅞ in.).

PROV.: As for No. 1.
G.g.4. W.5–28 (L.B., as attributed to Mary Beale, 28).

BIBL.: As for No. 1.

36. WILLIAM (?) MORE. A YOUNG MAN. Bust, with head turned half-r. Wearing a loose gown open at the neck and hair to the shoulder.

Red chalk; 21·4 × 17·2 cm. (8⅜ × 6¾ in.).

PROV.: As for No. 1.
G.g.4. W.5–48 (L.B., as attributed to Mary Beale, 83).

BIBL.: As for No. 1.

[William More (*Fl.* 1680). Half-brother of Rev. John More, and close friend of the Beale family.]
The same sitter also appears in *Beale II*, ff 79*v*. (inscribed *More . N | yⁿ great*), 83*v*. & 84*v*. (both inscribed *More d*).

37. A YOUNG MAN WITH LONG CURLING HAIR. Head, turned half-l., with eyes looking to front. Wearing his shirt open at the neck.

Red chalk, strengthened with black lead and black chalk; the shoulders lightly indicated; 20 × 17·5 cm. (7⅞ × 6⅞ in.).

PROV.: As for No. 1.
G.g.4. W.5–80 (L.B., as attributed to Mary Beale, 60).

BIBL.: As for No. 1.

The same sitter appears in *Beale I*, *f*. 30.

38. A MAN IN A CLOSELY CURLED PERIWIG. Bust, turned half-l., with eyes looking upwards. Wearing a loose gown and shirt open at the neck.

Red chalk, strengthened with black lead and black chalk; 22 × 16·7 cm. (8⅝ × 6½ in.).

PROV.: As for No. 1.
G.g.4. W.5–93 (L.B., as attributed to Mary Beale, 99).

BIBL.: As for No. 1.

39. A YOUNG MAN WITH LONG CURLING HAIR. Head, turned half-l., with eyes looking to front, and a wart below his mouth, r. Wearing his shirt open at the neck.

Red chalk, strengthened with black lead and black chalk; 19·4 × 17·7 cm. (7⅝ × 7 in.).

PROV.: As for No. 1.
G.g.4. W.5–131 (L.B., as attributed to Mary Beale, 25).

BIBL.: As for No. 1.

Mr. Binyon has suggested that this may represent Thomas Otway, the dramatic poet, on the strength of a supposed likeness to Mary Beale's portrait of him engraved by Houbraken (*See B.M. Engraved Portraits*, III, p. 385. No. 1). A comparison of the two portraits, however, does not seem to justify such an identification.

40. A MAN WITH CURLING HAIR. Head, turned half-l., with eyes looking to front.

Red chalk, strengthened with black lead and black chalk; 18·7 × 16·9 cm. (7⅜ × 6⅝ in.).

PROV.: As for No. 1.
G.g.4. W.5–133 (L.B., as attributed to Mary Beale, 122).

BIBL.: As for No. 1.

41. A MAN WITH A BROAD FACE, SMILING. Bust, looking to front, his head inclined to l., wearing long curling hair and a cravat.

Red chalk, strengthened with black lead and black chalk; 23·7 × 18·7 cm. (9⅜ × 7⅜ in.).

PROV.: As for No. 1.
G.g.4. W.5–147 (L.B., as attributed to Mary Beale, 115).

BIBL.: As for No. 1.

42. A MAN, IN OUTLINE. Bust, turned to r., and looking upwards. Wearing long hair and falling bands.

Red chalk; in preliminary outline only; 23·6 × 17·9 cm. (9¼ × 7 in.).

PROV.: As for No. 1.
G.g.4. W.5–173 (L.B., as attributed to Mary Beale, 55).

BIBL.: As for No. 1.

[43–72]. STUDIES FROM THE LIFE: WOMEN.

43. A YOUNG WOMAN IN A FRILLED CAP. Bust, turned half-l., looking upwards over her l. shoulder. Wearing a cap frilled with lace.

Red chalk, strengthened with black lead and black chalk; 21·3 × 16·1 cm. (8⅜ × 6⅜ in.).

PROV.: As for No. 1.
G.g.4. W.5–6 (L.B., as attributed to Mary Beale, 33).

BIBL.: As for No. 1.

The same sitter appears in *Beale I, ff.56r.*, & 61r.

44. THE SAME YOUNG WOMAN AS IN No. 43, LYING DOWN. Head and shoulders, resting on a pillow, and looking upwards over her l. shoulder. Wearing a cap and bodice.

Red chalk; the cap, bodice and pillow lightly indicated; $17 \cdot 5 \times 18 \cdot 1$ cm. ($6\frac{7}{8} \times 7\frac{1}{8}$ in.).

PROV.: As for No. 1.
G.g.4. W.5–13 (L.B., as attributed to Mary Beale, 32).

BIBL.: As for No. 1.

45. THE SAME YOUNG WOMAN AS IN No. 43, SMILING. Bust, turned to front, her head inclined over her r. shoulder, her lips parted in a smile. Wearing a cap with a lace border, and her bodice open at the neck.

Red chalk, strengthened with black lead and black chalk; the body lightly indicated; $22 \times 17 \cdot 5$ cm. ($8\frac{5}{8} \times 6\frac{7}{8}$ in.).

PROV.: As for No. 1.
G.g.4. W.5–34 (L.B., as attributed to Mary Beale, 85).

BIBL.: As for No. 1.

46. 'DOWDY'. A YOUNG WOMAN. Bust, turned half-l., bare-headed, and looking over her l. shoulder.

Red chalk, strengthened with black lead and black chalk; $20 \cdot 1 \times 16 \cdot 7$ cm. ($7\frac{7}{8} \times 6\frac{1}{2}$ in.).

PROV.: As for No. 1.
G.g.4. W.5–10 (L.B., as attributed to Mary Beale, 37).

BIBL.: As for No. 1.

The same sitter appears in *Beale II, ff.* 12r. (inscribed *D. Dowdy. N.*), 16r. (inscribed *D. Doudy. | d.*), & 17r. (inscribed *Dowdy. d*), and in *Beale III, ff.* 8r. (inscribed *dowdy n*), 11r. & 12r.

47. 'DOWDY'. Bust, turned half-r., and looking upwards over her r. shoulder.

Red chalk, strengthened with black lead and black chalk; the body lightly indicated; $22 \cdot 1 \times 16 \cdot 2$ cm. ($8\frac{5}{8} \times 6\frac{3}{8}$ in.).

PROV.: As for No. 1.
G.g.4. W.5–77 (L.B., as attributed to Mary Beale, 38).

BIBL.: As for No. 1.

48. 'ANNE MEELES'. A FAIR-HAIRED YOUNG WOMAN. H.L., turned half-l., with eyes looking to front. Wearing a lace frilled cap, and bodice open at the neck.

Red chalk, strengthened with black lead and black chalk; $24 \cdot 4 \times 17 \cdot 5$ cm. ($9\frac{5}{8} \times 6\frac{7}{8}$ in.).

PROV.: As for No. 1.
G.g.4. W.5–15 (L.B., as attributed to Mary Beale, 40).

BIBL.: As for No. 1.

The same sitter appears in *Beale II, ff.* 86v. (inscribed *Meeles N.*), 93v. (inscribed *A Meeles. d* and *Mumping* [mumbling] *Nan*) & 96v. (inscribed *A. Meeles N.*).

49. 'ANNE MEELES'. Bust, turned to front, with eyes looking to front.

Red chalk, strengthened with black lead and black chalk; the body lightly indicated; 23·2 × 16·5 cm. (9⅛ × 6½ in.).

PROV.: As for No. 1.

G.g.4. **W.5–82** (L.B., as attributed to Mary Beale, 76).

BIBL.: As for No. 1.

50. 'SU: JAXON' (?) (*i.e.* **JACKSON(?)**). **A YOUNG WOMAN.** Bust, turned half-l. and head half-r., with eyes looking downwards. Wearing a cap with strings and a broad collar.

Red chalk, strengthened with black lead and black chalk; 20 × 16 cm. (7⅞ × 6⅜ in.).

PROV.: As for No. 1.

G.g.4. **W.5–26** (L.B., as attributed to Mary Beale, 36).

The same sitter appears in *Beale II, f.* 25r. (inscribed *Su: Jaxs. | N.*) and in *Beale III, f.* 18r.

51. 'SU: JAXON' (?). Bust, with body turned half-l. and head to front, and eyes looking to front. Wearing a cap with lappets.

Red chalk, strengthened with black lead and black chalk; the body lightly indicated; 21·4 × 16·9 cm. (8⅜ × 6⅝ in.).

PROV.: As for No. 1.

G.g.4. **W.5–39** (L.B., as attributed to Mary Beale, 34).

BIBL. & REPR.: As for No. 1. *Reitlinger,* p. 144 & Pl. B.

52. 'SU: JAXON' (?). Nearly H.L., with body in profile to r., head turned half-r., and eyes looking to front. Wearing a cap.

Red chalk, strengthened with black lead and black chalk; 20·6 × 16·2 cm. (8⅛ × 6⅜ in.).

PROV.: As for No. 1.

G.g.4. **W.5–42** (L.B., as attributed to Mary Beale, 35).

BIBL.: As for No. 1.

53. A YOUNG WOMAN WITH LIGHT-COLOURED HAIR. Bust, with body turned to front, head half-l., and eyes looking downwards. Wearing her hair loose on her l. shoulder, and a low-necked dress with a frill showing at the edge.

Red chalk, strengthened with black lead and black chalk; 23·8 × 18 cm. (9¼ × 7 in.).

PROV.: As for No. 1.

G.g.4. **W.5–79** (L.B., as attributed to Mary Beale, 77).

BIBL.: As for No. 1.

54. THE SAME YOUNG WOMAN AS IN No. 53. Bust, with bare shoulders, in profile to r., looking downwards. Wearing her hair knotted at the back.

Red chalk, strengthened with black lead and black chalk; 21·6 × 18 cm. (8½ × 7 in.).

PROV.: As for No. 1.

G.g.4. **W.5–99** (L.B., as attributed to Mary Beale, 97).

BIBL.: As for No. 1.

55. THE SAME YOUNG WOMAN AS IN No. 53, ASLEEP. Bust, with body turned half r., lying back with eyes closed, her hair falling on her bare shoulder. On the r., a boy with curly hair appearing from behind a curtain and tickling her nose with a spill to wake her. Plate 71

Red chalk, strengthened with black lead and black chalk; 19·2 × 17·4 cm. (7½ × 6⅞ in.).

PROV.: As for No. 1.

G.g.4. **W.5–148** (L.B., as attributed to Mary Beale, 126).

BIBL.: As for No. 1.

56. THE SAME YOUNG WOMAN AS IN No. 53, WEEPING. Head turned half-r. and looking upwards. Wearing her hair loose and falling on her shoulders.

Red chalk, strengthened with black lead and black chalk; 20·8 × 17·2 cm. (8⅛ × 6¾ in.).

PROV.: As for No. 1.

G.g.4. **W.5–150** (L.B., as attributed to Mary Beale, 128).

BIBL.: As for No. 1.

57. A DARK-HAIRED YOUNG WOMAN IN A LACE-TRIMMED CAP. Bust, with head turned half-r. and her shoulders bare. Plate 73

Red chalk, strengthened with black lead and black chalk; 21·7 × 17·9 cm. (8¾ × 7 in.).

PROV.: As for No. 1.

G.g.4. **W.5–126** (L.B., as attributed to Mary Beale, 109).

BIBL.: As for No. 1.

58. THE SAME DARK-HAIRED YOUNG WOMAN AS IN No. 57. Nearly H.L., turned half-l., her eyes looking to front. Wearing a lace cap with a hood over it. Plate 74

Red chalk, strengthened with black lead and black chalk; the body lightly indicated; 23·7 × 18·5 cm. (9¼ × 7¼ in.).

PROV.: As for No. 1.

G.g.4. **W.5–149** (L.B., as attributed to Mary Beale, 108).

BIBL.: As for No. 1.

59. THE SAME DARK-HAIRED YOUNG WOMAN AS IN No. 57, ASLEEP. H.L., leaning back in a chair, with head turned towards the l. her arms folded in her lap. A kitten on her l. shoulder.

Red chalk, strengthened with black lead and black chalk; 24·4 × 19 cm. (9⅝ × 7½ in.).

G.g.4. **W.5–154** (L.B., as attributed to Mary Beale, 31).

BIBL.: As for No. 1.

60. A YOUNG WOMAN WITH A HIGH FOREHEAD. H.L., turned half-r., with eyes looking to front. Wearing a cap with lace-trimmed lappets and a kerchief. Beside her, in the lower r.-hand corner, a cat.

Red chalk, strengthened with black lead and black chalk; the body lightly indicated; 24·4 × 19·1 cm. (9½ × 7½ in.).

PROV.: As for No. 1.
G.g.4. **W.5–143** (L.B., as attributed to Mary Beale, 111).

BIBL.: As for No. 1.

61. THE SAME YOUNG WOMAN WITH A HIGH FOREHEAD AS IN No. 60. Nearly H.L., turned half-l., with eyes looking to front. Wearing a hood.

Red chalk, strengthened with black lead and black chalk; the body lightly indicated; 23·3 × 17·8 cm. (9⅛ × 7 in.).

PROV.: As for No. 1.
G.g.4. **W.5–145** (L.B., as attributed to Mary Beale, 112).

BIBL.: As for No. 1.

62. THE SAME YOUNG WOMAN WITH A HIGH FOREHEAD AS IN No. 60. Nearly H.L., with body turned half-r., head to front, and eyes looking half-r. Wearing a lace-trimmed cap and hood.

Red chalk, strengthened with black lead and black chalk; 24 × 18·3 cm. (9⅜ × 7⅛ in.).

PROV.: As for No. 1.
G.g.4. **W.5–169** (L.B., as attributed to Mary Beale, 58).

BIBL.: As for No. 1.

63. AN ELDERLY WOMAN SEATED IN A CHAIR. T.Q.L., with body turned slightly to l., head to r., and hands folded in her lap. Wearing a plain hood and broad collar.

Red chalk, strengthened with black lead and black chalk; 23·2 × 17·4 cm. (9⅛ × 6⅞ in.).

PROV.: As for No. 1.
G.g.4. **W.5–12** (L.B., as attributed to Mary Beale, 41).

BIBL.: As for No. 1.

One of the comparatively rare studies from the life among these drawings where the body has been finished.

64. 'NORRICE'. A YOUNG WOMAN. H.L., seated, with body turned to front, head turned half-l., eyes looking downwards, and hands (not seen) in her lap. Wearing a veil over her hair and a bodice with sleeves reaching to her elbows.

Red chalk, strengthened with black lead and black chalk; 24·4 × 17·3 cm. (9⅝ × 6¾ in.).

PROV.: As for No. 1.
G.g.4. W.5–18 (L.B., as attributed to Mary Beale, 29).

BIBL.: As for No. 1.

The same sitter appears in *Beale II, ff.* 8r. & 18r. (both inscribed *Norrice. N.*), & 32r., and in *Beale III, ff.* 7r. (inscribed *Norrice N*), 11r., 12r., 13r. & 24r.

65. A YOUNG WOMAN. Bust, with body turned slightly to l., head half-r., and eyes looking slightly downwards. Wearing a kerchief over a cap.

Red chalk, strengthened with black lead and black chalk; the body lightly indicated; 21·3 × 18 cm. (8⅜ × 7⅛ in.).

PROV.: As for No. 1.
G.g.4. W.5–24 (L.B., as attributed to Mary Beale, 30).

BIBL.: As for No. 1.

66. A WOMAN SEATED AT A TABLE. H.L., with head turned half-l. and eyes looking downwards, resting her arm on the corner of a table. Wearing a cap with lace-trimmed lappets.

Red chalk, strengthened with black lead and black chalk; the body only lightly indicated; 23·9 × 17·5 cm. (9⅜ × 6⅞ in.).

PROV.: As for No. 1.
G.g.4. W.5–36 (L.B., as attributed to Mary Beale, 42).

BIBL.: As for No. 1.

67. A YOUNG WOMAN. Bust, with body turned to front, head half-r., and eyes looking downwards. Wearing a cap and a bodice open at the neck.

Red chalk, strengthened with black lead; 21·2 × 16·9 cm. (8¼ × 6⅝ in.).

G.g.4. W.5–51 (L.B., as attributed to Mary Beale, 84).

PROV.: As for No. 1.

BIBL.: As for No. 1.

68. A YOUNG FAIR-HAIRED WOMAN IN A LACE-TRIMMED CAP. Bust, turned half-l. The shoulders cut off at the line of the bodice.

Red chalk, strengthened with black lead and black chalk; 21·3 × 17·4 cm. (8⅜ × 6⅞ in.).

PROV.: As for No. 1.
G.g.4. W.5–132 (L.B., as attributed to Mary Beale, 116).

BIBL.: As for No. 1.

69. A YOUNG WOMAN RESEMBLING A NEGRESS. H.L., with body in profile to r., head turned half-r., and eyes looking to front, smiling. Wearing a frilled cap and two tight curls above her forehead. **Plate 75**

Red chalk, strengthened with black chalk and black lead; the body lightly indicated; 23·7 × 16·7 cm. (9⅜ × 6⅝ in.).

PROV.: As for No. 1.

G.g.4. W.5–146 (L.B., as attributed to Mary Beale, 86).

BIBL.: As for No. 1.

70. A YOUNG WOMAN WITH HER HAIR IN A LARGE KNOT. Bust, turned half-r., with eyes looking to front. Wearing her hair in curls in front and in a large knot at the back, and a low-necked gown cut in tabs on the shoulders.

Red chalk, strengthened with black lead and black chalk; 24 × 16·3 cm. (9⅜ × 6⅜ in.).

PROV.: As for No. 1.

G.g.4. W.5–134 (L.B., as attributed to Mary Beale, 110).

BIBL.: As for No. 1.

71. 'BUTTERMILK'. A YOUNG WOMAN. Bust, with body turned half-r., head turned half-l., and eyes looking downwards. Wearing her hair in curls, and a low-necked gown.

Red chalk, strengthened with black lead and black chalk; 23·3 × 16·3 cm. (9⅛ × 6⅜ in.).

PROV.: As for No. 1.
G.g.4. W.5–160 (L.B., as attributed to Mary Beale, 91).

BIBL.: As for No. 1.

The same sitter appears, seated, writing at a table to l., in *Beale II*, f. 89v. (inscribed *Buttermilk*).

72. A FAIR-HAIRED WOMAN, WITH A KERCHIEF OVER HER HEAD. Bust, turned to r., with eyes looking to front.

Red chalk, strengthened with black lead and black chalk; 23·4 × 18·2 cm. (9⅛ × 7⅛ in.).

PROV.: As for No. 1.

G.g.4. W.5–164 (L.B., as attributed to Mary Beale, 114).

PROV.: As for No. 1.

[73–99]. STUDIES FROM THE LIFE: CHILDREN.

73. 'THOMSON' OR 'THOMPSON', 'NORICE' OR 'NORRIS' (?). A SMALL BOY. Nearly H.L., with body turned half-l., head half-r., and eyes looking upwards. Wearing a cravat.

Red chalk, strengthened with black lead; the body lightly indicated; 21·4 × 17·5 cm. (8⅜ × 6⅞ in.).

PROV.: As for No. 1.

BIBL.: As for No. 1.

G.g.4. W.5–17 (L.B., as attributed to Mary Beale, 73).

[Thomson Norice. Probably the son of the Beales' porter Thompson Norice or Norris.]

The same sitter appears, at various ages, in *Beale II, ff.* 13r. (inscribed *Thomson. N. N.*), 21r. (inscribed *Thompson's | N.*), 24r. (in-scribed *T. N.*) & 38r. (?), and *Beale III, ff.* 9r. (inscribed *Thomson | N.N.*), 17r. & 28 (?).

74. 'THOMSON' OR 'THOMPSON', 'NORICE' OR 'NORRIS' (?). Bust, with body turned half-r. and head to front. Wearing a cravat.

Red chalk, strengthened with black lead and black chalk; the body lightly indicated; 21·2 × 15·5 cm. (8⅜ × 6 in.).

PROV.: As for No. 1.
G.g.4. W.5–32 (L.B., as attributed to Mary Beale, 72).

BIBL.: As for No. 1.

See note to No. 73.

75. 'THOMSON' OR 'THOMPSON', 'NORICE' OR 'NORRIS' (?). H.L., seated in a chair on the back of which he rests his r. elbow, with body turned to front and head half-r. Wearing his shirt open at the neck.

Red chalk, strengthened with black lead and black chalk; 24·5 × 18·4 cm. (9⅝ × 7¼ in.).

BIBL.: As for No. 1.

See note to No. 73.

PROV.: As for No. 1.
G.g.4. W.5–40 (L.B., as attributed to Mary Beale, 65).

76. 'THOMSON' OR 'THOMPSON', 'NORICE' OR 'NORRIS' (?). Head turned half-r., with eyes looking to front.

Red chalk; unfinished; 16·4 × 15·1 cm. (6⅜ × 5⅞ in.).

BIBL.: As for No. 1.

See note to No. 73.

PROV.: As for No. 1.
G.g.4. W.5–105 (L.B., as attributed to Mary Beale, 96).

77. 'THOMSON' OR 'THOMPSON', 'NORICE' OR 'NORRIS' (?). T.Q.L. seated, with body facing r., head to front, and eyes looking to l. over his shoulder, his r. arm akimbo.

Red chalk, strengthened with black chalk and black lead; 24 × 17·8 cm. (9⅜ × 7 in.).

BIBL.: As for No. 1.

See note to No. 73.

PROV.: As for No. 1.
G.g.4. W.5–127 (L.B., as attributed to Mary Beale, 66).

78. 'THOMSON' OR 'THOMPSON', 'NORICE' OR 'NORRIS' (?). ASLEEP. Head lying, with eyes closed, towards the r., on a pillow.

Red chalk; 16·4 × 15·6 cm. (6⅜ × 6⅛ in.).   Bibl.: As for No. 1.

Prov.: As for No. 1.   *See note to No. 73.*
G.g.4. W.5–128 (L.B., as attributed to Mary Beale, 69).

79. 'THOMSON' OR 'THOMPSON', 'NORICE' OR 'NORRIS' (?). H.L., seated, with body in profile to l., head turned half-l., and eyes looking to front.   **Plate 78**

Red chalk, strengthened with black chalk and black lead; 24·5 × 18·2 cm. (9⅝ × 7⅛ in.).

Bibl.: As for No. 1.

See note to No. 73.

Prov.: As for No. 1.
G.g.4. W.5–153 (L.B., as attributed to Mary Beale, 67).

80. 'THOMSON' OR 'THOMPSON', 'NORICE' OR 'NORRIS' (?). Nearly H.L., seated, with body turned to front, head half-l., and eyes looking slightly upwards, his r. arm resting on the back of the chair. Wearing his coat unbuttoned at the neck.

Red and brown chalks, strengthened with black lead and black chalk; 24 × 18·2 cm. (9⅜ × 7⅛ in.).

Bibl.: As for No. 1.

See note to No. 73.

Prov.: As for No. 1.
G.g.4. W.5–158 (L.B., as attributed to Mary Beale, 68).

81. 'THOMSON' OR 'THOMPSON', 'NORICE' OR 'NORRIS' (?), SMILING. Nearly H.L., turned half-l., looking upwards. Wearing a cravat.

Red chalk, strengthened with black lead and black chalk; the body lightly indicated; 23·7 × 17·3 cm. (9¼ × 6¾ in.).

Bibl. & Repr.: As for No. 1. *Reitlinger*, p. 144 & Pl. D.

See note to No. 73.

Prov.: As for No. 1.
G.g.4. W.5–170 (L.B., as attributed to Mary Beale, 71).

82. A BOY WITH THICK CURLING HAIR, HOLDING A SHELL. H.L., with body in profile to l., head turned half-l., eyes looking to front, and holding a shell in his right hand. Wearing his shirt open at the neck.

Red chalk, strengthened with black lead and black chalk; 24·5 × 18·6 cm. (9⅝ × 7⅜ in.).

Bibl.: As for No. 1.

The same sitter appears in *Beale III, f. 85v.*

Prov.: As for No. 1.
G.g.4. W.5–94 (L.B., as attributed to Mary Beale, 87).

83. THE SAME BOY AS IN No. 82, ASLEEP. H.L., lying back towards the l., in a chair or on a day-bed, with eyes closed, his r. hand holding a fold of the loose gown which he wears.

Red chalk, strengthened with black lead and black chalk; $21 \cdot 4 \times 18 \cdot 7$ cm. ($8\frac{3}{8} \times 7\frac{3}{8}$ in.).

PROV.: As for No. 1.

G.g.4. W.5–96 (L.B., as attributed to Mary Beale, 88.

BIBL.: As for No. 1.

84. A SMALL BOY. Head turned to front. Wearing curling hair.

Red chalk, strengthened with black lead and black chalk; $18 \cdot 2 \times 16 \cdot 4$ cm. ($7\frac{1}{8} \times 6\frac{3}{8}$ in.).

PROV.: As for No. 1.

G.g.4. W.5–136 (L.B., as attributed to Mary Beale, 74).

BIBL.: As for No. 1.

85. THE SAME SMALL BOY AS IN No. 84. Head turned half-r. Wearing his shirt open at the neck.   **Plate 79**

Red chalk, strengthened by black lead and black chalk; $20 \cdot 1 \times 17 \cdot 5$ cm. ($7\frac{7}{8} \times 6\frac{7}{8}$ in.).

PROV.: As for No. 1.

G.g.4. W.5–137 (L.B., as attributed to Mary Beale, 70).

BIBL.: As for No. 1.

86. A SMALL BOY WITH FAIR CURLING HAIR. Bust, with body turned slightly to r., and head to front. Wearing a loosely tied cravat.

Red chalk, touched with black lead; $20 \times 16 \cdot 8$ cm. ($7\frac{7}{8} \times 6\frac{5}{8}$ in.).

PROV.: As for No. 1.

G.g.4. W.5–30 (L.B., as attributed to Mary Beale, 64).

BIBL.: As for No. 1.

87. A YOUTH WITH THICK CURLING HAIR. Head to front. Wearing his shirt open at the neck.

Red chalk, strengthened with black lead and black chalk; $19 \cdot 1 \times 16 \cdot 4$ cm. ($7\frac{1}{2} \times 6\frac{1}{2}$ in.).

PROV.: As for No. 1.

G.g.4. W.5–72 (L.B., as attributed to Mary Beale, 81).

BIBL.: As for No. 1.

88. A BOY. H.L., with body nearly in profile to r., head turned half-r., with eyes looking to front. Wearing long curling hair and a cravat.

Red chalk, strengthened with black lead and black chalk; the body lightly indicated; 24 × 15·6 cm. (9⅜ × 6⅛ in.).

PROV.: As for No. 1.
G.g.4. W.5–81 (L.B., as attributed to Mary Beale, 75).

BIBL.: As for No. 1.

89. A BOY. Head turned slightly to r., with eyes looking to front. Wearing long curling hair and his shirt open at the neck.

Red chalk, strengthened with black lead and black chalk; 18·8 × 16·8 cm. (7⅜ × 6⅝ in.).

PROV.: As for No. 1.
G.g.4. W.5–140 (L.B., as attributed to Mary Beale, 59).

BIBL.: As for No. 1.

90. A SMALL BOY. Bust, turned half-l., with eyes looking to front, smiling. Wearing curling hair and a cravat.

Red chalk, strengthened with black lead and black chalk; 20·7 × 18·4 cm. (8⅛ × 7¼ in.).

PROV.: As for No. 1.
G.g.4. W.5–141 (L.B., as attributed to Mary Beale, 63).

BIBL.: As for No. 1.

91. A BOY. H.L., with body in profile to r., head turned half-r., and eyes looking to front. Wearing long curling hair and a cravat.

Red chalk, strengthened with black lead and black chalk; the body lightly indicated; 21·4 × 17·5 cm. (8⅜ × 6⅞ in.).

PROV.: As for No. 1.
G.g.4. W.5–151 (L.B., as attributed to Mary Beale, 113).

BIBL.: As for No. 1.

92. A FAIR-HAIRED YOUTH WEARING A *MONTERO*. Bust, with body turned to front, and head half-l. Wearing a *montero*, curling hair, and loose drapery over his partly bare shoulder.

Red chalk, strengthened with black lead and black chalk; the body lightly indicated; 22·2 × 17·9 cm. (8¾ × 7 in.).

PROV.: As for No. 1.
G.g.4. W.5–155 (L.B., as attributed to Mary Beale, 117).

BIBL.: As for No. 1.

93. A GIRL. Head, turned to front and leaning slightly to l., with eyes looking upwards. Wearing a lace-trimmed cap.

Red chalk, strengthened with black lead and black chalk; 19·8 × 16·9 cm. (7¾ × 6⅝ in.).

PROV.: As for No. 1.
G.g.4. W.5–139 (L.B., as attributed to Mary Beale, 39).

BIBL.: As for No. 1.

The same sitter, as the Magdalen, probably appears in *Beale II, f.* 60*v.*, & *Beale III, f.* 52*v.*

94. A GIRL WITH PEARLS IN HER HAIR. Bust nearly in profile to r. Her hair braided at the back and pearls twisted through the front. Wearing a low-necked dress.

Red chalk, strengthened with black lead and black chalk; 21·7 × 18 cm. (8½ × 7⅛ in.).

PROV.: As for No. 1.
G.g.4. W.5–43 (L.B., as attributed to Mary Beale, 93).

BIBL.: As for No. 1.

95. A SMALL GIRL. Bust, turned half-r., with eyes looking to front.

Red chalk, strengthened with black lead and black chalk; 21·3 × 16·6 cm. (8⅜ × 6½ in.).

PROV.: As for No. 1.
G.g.4. W.5–117 (L.B., as attributed to Mary Beale, 105).

BIBL.: As for No. 1.

96. A GIRL. Bust, with body turned half-r., head to front, and eyes looking half-l. Wearing her hair loose and a low-necked dress.

Red and brown chalks, strengthened with black lead and black chalk; the lower part of the body lightly indicated; 21·7 × 17·4 cm. (8½ × 6⅞ in.).

PROV.: As for No. 1.
G.g.4. W.5–156 (L.B., as attributed to Mary Beale, 94).

BIBL.: As for No. 1.

In its use of brown chalk in the hair this drawing should be compared with Nos. 28 & 29.

97. A GIRL. Head, turned half-l. Wearing her hair knotted behind. **Plate 80**

Red and brown chalks, strengthened with black lead and black chalk; 19·2 × 17·8 cm. (7½ × 7 in.).

PROV.: As for No. 1.
G.g.4. W.5–157 (L.B., as attributed to Mary Beale, 123*).

BIBL.: As for No. 1.

Like No. 96 this drawing should be compared with Nos. 28 & 29 in its use of brown chalk in the hair.

98. A GIRL IN A FRILLED CAP. Head, turned half-r.

Red chalk, strengthened with black lead and black chalk. 19·2 × 18·2 cm. (7⅝ × 7⅛ in.).

PROV.: As for No. 1.
G.g.4. W.5–162 (L.B., as attributed to Mary Beale, 90).

BIBL.: As for No. 1.

99. A SMALL GIRL WEARING A FUR-TRIMMED CAP. Bust, turned half-r., with bare shoulders.

Red chalk, strengthened with black lead and black chalk; $19\cdot5 \times 16\cdot6$ cm. ($7\frac{5}{8} \times 6\frac{1}{2}$ in.).

PROV.: As for No. 1.

G.g.4. W.5–121 (L.B., as attributed to Mary Beale, 95).

BIBL.: As for No. 1.

[100–124]. STUDIES FROM EARLIER PICTURES. The drawings in this section are apparently all copies from earlier pictures, and there is evidence to suggest that Charles Beale would have had access to at least three collections to enable him to make them. These would have been Charles II's (*See* Nos. 100–105 and 111), Sir Peter Lely's (*See* 113, 115 & 119), and his own father's (mentioned in *Vertue*, IV, pp. 168 & 174; *See* Nos. 112 & 116). Two of the subjects here represented (Nos. 112 & 117) are known also to have been copied by Charles Beale as miniatures.

100. PRINCE CHARLES, LATER CHARLES II, IN THE PORTRAIT GROUP OF THE THREE CHILDREN OF CHARLES I, BY VAN DYCK. Nearly H.L., turned half-r. Wearing a lace collar and doublet.

Red chalk, strengthened with black lead and black chalk; the body lightly indicated; $24\cdot2 \times 18$ cm. ($9\frac{1}{2} \times 7\frac{1}{8}$ in.).

PROV.: As for No. 1.
G.g.4. W.5–109 (L.B., as attributed to Mary Beale, 145).

BIBL.: As for No. 1.

The original picture, which was painted in 1635 for Charles I, was sold in 1649 to Col. Webb. It was back in the Royal Collection by 1687 when it appears in the Inventory of James II's collection quoted by Vertue (*See Cust, Van Dyck*, p. 266, No. 42. *Vertue*, IV, p. 92).

101. THE R. HAND OF PRINCE CHARLES, IN THE SAME PICTURE BY VAN DYCK AS No. 100.

Red chalk, strengthened with black lead; $18\cdot1 \times 14\cdot3$ cm. ($7\frac{1}{8} \times 5\frac{5}{8}$ in.).

PROV.: As for No. 1.
G.g.4. W.5–112 (L.B., as attributed to Mary Beale, 149).

BIBL.: As for No. I.

See note to No. 100.

102. PRINCESS MARY, LATER PRINCESS OF ORANGE, IN THE SAME PICTURE BY VAN DYCK AS No. 100. Bust, turned half l., with eyes looking to front. Wearing flowers in her curling hair and a necklace.

Red chalk, strengthened with black lead and black chalk; $19\cdot5 \times 17\cdot7$ cm. ($7\frac{5}{8} \times 7$ in.).

PROV.: As for No. 1.
G.g.4. W.5–108 (L.B., as attributed to Mary Beale, 146).

BIBL.: As for No. 1.

See note to No. 100.

103. THE HANDS OF PRINCESS MARY, IN THE SAME PICTURE BY VAN DYCK AS No. 100.

Red chalk; $12 \cdot 6 \times 17 \cdot 5$ cm. ($4\frac{7}{8} \times 6\frac{7}{8}$ in.).

BIBL.: As for No. 1.

PROV.: As for No. 1.
G.g.4. W.5–111 (L.B., as attributed to Mary Beale, 150).

See note to No. 100.

104. PRINCE JAMES, LATER JAMES II, IN THE SAME PICTURE BY VAN DYCK AS No. 100. Bust, turned half-l., with head looking back over his l. shoulder. Wearing a lace-edged cap.

Red chalk, strengthened with black lead and black chalk; $19 \cdot 4 \times 16 \cdot 7$ cm. ($7\frac{5}{8} \times 6\frac{1}{2}$ in.).

BIBL.: As for No. 1.

See note to No. 100.

PROV.: As for No. 1.
G.g.4. W.5–107 (L.B., as attributed to Mary Beale, 147).

105. THE HANDS OF PRINCE JAMES, ONE RESTING ON THE WRIST, THE OTHER IN THE L. HAND OF PRINCE CHARLES, IN THE SAME PICTURE BY VAN DYCK AS No. 100.

Red chalk, strengthened with black lead; $12 \cdot 3 \times 17 \cdot 3$ cm. ($4\frac{3}{4} \times 6\frac{3}{4}$ in.).

BIBL.: As for No. 1.

See note to No. 100.

PROV.: As for No. 1.
G.g.4. W.5–110 (L.B., as attributed to Mary Beale, 148).

106. PRINCESS ELIZABETH AND HENRY, DUKE OF GLOUCESTER, CHILDREN OF CHARLES I, AFTER THE SKETCH IN OILS BY VAN DYCK.
Heads. The Princess turned half r., looking down at her infant brother. Both wearing close-fitting caps, and she a necklace.

Red chalk, strengthened with black lead and black chalk; the Princess's shoulders lightly indicated; $15 \cdot 5 \times 23 \cdot 1$ cm. (6×9 in.).

PROV.: As for No. 1.
G.g.4. W.5–54 (L.B., as attributed to Mary Beale, 144).

BIBL.: As for No. 1.

The present drawing is clearly a copy of the oil-sketch, now in the collection of Lord Chesham (exhib. Agnew, *Loan Exhibition of Pictures by Old Masters*, 1922, No. 2. K. der K., *Van Dyck*, p. 384), which is a preliminary study for two of the figures in the portrait group of the five children of Charles I at Windsor Castle. (*See K. der K.*, p. 385.) The early history of this oil-sketch is not known.

**107. THOMAS WENTWORTH, 1st EARL OF STRAFFORD, IN THE POR-
TRAIT GROUP OF THE EARL AND HIS SECRETARY, SIR PHILIP MAIN-
WARING, BY VAN DYCK.** Bust, turned slightly to r., with eyes looking to front,
moustache and tufted beard. Wearing a broad falling band and buttoned doublet.

Red and black chalk; $11 \times 10 \cdot 2$ cm. ($4\frac{3}{8} \times 4$ in.).

PROV.: The Rev. C. M. Cracherode, by whom it was bequeathed to the British Museum, 1799.
G.g.1–445 (L.B., as attributed to Mary Beale, 136).

BIBL.: *Cracherode Cat.*, p. 99, No. 445.

The original picture is in the collection of Earl Fitzwilliam at Wentworth Woodhouse. It was apparently lent to the Beale family, as recorded by the elder Charles Beale in his Diary under May 22nd, 1677: 'Mr Francis Knollys came himself and fetched away the original picture of the old Earl of Strafford & Sr Philip Manwaring wch had been left here for some years . . . it was carried away by two of Lord Hollis's servant (*sic*) whome Mr Knollys brought with him for that purpose' (*See Vertue*, IV, p. 173). A list of copies is given in *Cust, Van Dyck*, p. 284, No. 201. The present drawing is reduced to the scale of a miniature, and does not belong to the main group of drawings here described. It is, however, in much the same medium and technique as they are, though rather less skilfully handled.

**108. THOMAS WENTWORTH, 1st EARL OF STRAFFORD, IN THE SAME
PICTURE BY VAN DYCK AS No. 107.** Head alone, turned half-r., with eyes
looking to front. Wearing a broad falling band.

Red chalk, strengthened with black lead and black chalk; $20 \cdot 8 \times 18 \cdot 4$ cm. ($8\frac{1}{8} \times 7\frac{1}{4}$ in.).

PROV.: As for No. 1.
G.g.4. W.5–90 (L.B., as attributed to Mary Beale, 134).

BIBL.: As for No. 1.

See note to No. 107.

**109. THE HANDS OF THOMAS WENTWORTH, 1st EARL OF STRAFFORD,
IN THE SAME PICTURE BY VAN DYCK AS Nos. 107 & 108.** The l. hand
holding a letter, the r. resting on the arm of the chair.

Red chalk, strengthened with black lead and black chalk; $16 \cdot 5 \times 22 \cdot 5$ cm. ($6\frac{1}{2} \times 8\frac{7}{8}$ in.).

PROV.: As for No. 1.
G.g.4. W.5–103 (L.B., as attributed to Mary Beale, 151).

BIBL.: As for No. 1.

See note to No. 107.

**110. SIR PHILIP MAINWARING, IN THE SAME PICTURE BY VAN DYCK
AS Nos. 107 & 108.** H.L., seated, and looking upwards to the l. as he writes at
Strafford's dictation.

Red chalk, touched with black chalk; 22 × 18·7 cm. ($8\frac{5}{8} \times 7\frac{3}{4}$ in.).

PROV.: As for No. 1.
G.g.4. W.5–100 (L.B., as attributed to Mary Beale, 135).

BIBL.: As for No. 1.

See note to No. 107.

111. M. DE SAINT ANTOINE, IN THE EQUESTRIAN PORTRAIT OF CHARLES I, BY VAN DYCK. Bust, turned half l., looking upwards. Wearing a skull cap, curling hair, moustache and pointed beard, and a broad falling band over his doublet.

Red chalk, strengthened with black lead; 23·6 × 18·7 cm. ($9\frac{1}{4} \times 6\frac{3}{8}$ in.).

PROV.: As for No. 1.
G.g.4. W.5–73 (L.B., as attributed to Mary Beale, 133).

BIBL.: As for No. 1.

The original picture, painted for Charles I about 1633, was sold in 1650 to Sir Balthazar Gerbier, subsequently passing to Remy van Leemput, from whom it was recovered in 1660 for the Royal Collection. It is now at Windsor Castle. A replica is at Hampton Court (See K. der K., Van Dyck, p. 372). A list of copies is given in Cust, Van Dyck, p. 263, No. 4.

112. ANTOINE TRIEST, BISHOP OF GHENT, AFTER THE PICTURE BY VAN DYCK. Head alone, turned half-l., with eyes looking to front. Wearing close-cut hair, moustache and pointed beard, and turned-up collar.

Red chalk, strengthened with black lead and black chalk; 18·8 × 17·4 cm. ($7\frac{3}{4} \times 6\frac{7}{8}$ in.).

PROV.: As for No. 1.
G.g.4. W.5–69 (L.B., as attributed to Charles Beale, 1).

BIBL.: As for No. 1.

In the Victoria and Albert Museum is a miniature by the younger Charles Beale, signed with the characteristic monogram C B and dated 1679 (Dyce Bequest, D. 132), doubtless copied from the same portrait of Bishop Triest as the present drawing. Several versions of the original picture are known or have been recorded, notably one in the Hermitage, Leningrad, and another, formerly in the collection of the Duke of Norfolk and (in 1952) in the possession of Messrs. Tomas Harris (See Cust, Van Dyck, p. 260, Nos. 120 & 121, & Burl. Mag., LXXIX, 1941, pp. 198, Pl. IB, 199–203). None of these is known to have been in England in the XVII c., but it is worth noting that the elder Charles Beale owned a 'Bishops picture of Van Dykes' to which he refers in his Diary under April 20th, 1672 (See Vertue, IV, p. 168), and this may perhaps have been a version of the portrait of Bishop Triest, and the original of the present drawing.

113. SIR ANTHONY VAN DYCK, AFTER THE SELF-PORTRAIT PAINTED ABOUT 1640–1. Bust, with body turned to right, head half-r., and eyes looking to front. Wearing long curling hair, moustache and tufted beard, a slashed doublet and a falling band.

M

C.E.D.

Red chalk, strengthened with black lead and black chalk; 24·3 × 18·3 cm. (9½ × 7⅛ in.).

INSCR.: *Recto*, in the lower r.-hand corner, twice, in black lead, *Vandyke* (almost obliterated) and *Vandyck*.

PROV.: As for No. 1.
G.g.4. W.5–63 (L.B., as attributed to Mary Beale, 137).

BIBL.: As for No. 1.

This drawing corresponds with the picture, until about 1941 in the collection of Mr. H. Eastwood, C.B., of the Admiralty (*See* Gustav Glück in *The Burl. Mag.*, LXXIX, 1941, p. 194, and Pl. facing p. 173). The original, however, is in an oval, instead of a rectangle as is the present copy which shows a certain awkwardness in finishing off the dress in the lower l.-hand corner, thus sug-

gesting that it was indeed made after an oval picture. Dr. Glück mentions a number of replicas of the portrait, among them one by Lely then in the possession of Messrs. Spink (*op. cit.*, p. 199 & Pl. IIA), and it is interesting to note that in Lely's sale was listed '*Of Sir Anthony Vandyke . . . His Own Picture in an Oval . . .*

	Foot.	Inch.	Foot.	Inch.'
	01.	10.	01.	06.

(*Burl. Mag.*, LXXXII, 1943, p. 187), which was purchased by the Earl of Newport for £34. The measurements for Mr. Eastwood's picture, given as 61 × 47 cm. or 1 ft. 2⅛ × 1 ft. 6½ in. do differ from those of the self-portrait in Lely's sale, but not so much as to preclude the possibility that they might be the same picture, a supposition strengthened by the fact that Lely did himself make a replica of the subject. The present drawing, therefore, may have been copied from the picture in Lely's collection.

114. THE INFANT JESUS BLESSING, IN SOME COMPOSITION CONNECTED WITH THE PICTURE OF THE VIRGIN AND CHILD WITH THE ABBÉ SCAGLIA, BY VAN DYCK. In profile to l., with His r. arm extended, blessing.

Red chalk, touched with black lead and black chalk; 16·5 × 23·6 cm. (6½ × 9¼ in.).

PROV.: As for No. 1.
G.g.4. W.5–55 (L.B., as attributed to Mary Beale, 152).

BIBL.: As for No. 1.

The prototype of the composition from which this detail is taken, is the picture formerly in the collection of Lord Anthony de Rothschild, and now in the National Gallery (No. 4889). This was still in Antwerp in 1791, and is not recorded as having been in

England before 1819 (*See Smith, Dutch, Flemish and French Painters*, Pt. III, p. 103), when it was sold with the collection of John Knight (Phillips, 24:iii:1819, Lot 80). A number of derivations from it are known, including three with a figure of St. Catherine substituted for that of the Abbé Scaglia, and a fourth, attributed to Lely (Sale, Robinson & Fisher, 20:i:1938, Lot 91), in which the head of the Virgin has been completely altered, the figure of Scaglia omitted, and a landscape introduced into the background, l. The present drawing, however, does not agree exactly with the Child in any of these.

115. THE HEAD OF CUPID, IN THE PORTRAIT-GROUP OF LADY ELIZABETH THIMBLEBY AND HER SISTER DOROTHY, VISCOUNTESS ANDOVER, BY VAN DYCK.

Red chalk, strengthened with black lead and black chalk; 21·8 × 18·2 cm. (8¼ × 7⅛ in.).

INSCR.: *Recto*, at the foot, in the centre, in red chalk, by the artist, *C B* (monogram).

PROV.: As for No. 1.
G.g.4. W.5–57 (L.B., as by Charles Beale, 11).

BIBL.: As for No. 1.

The original picture must have been painted about 1637, the year when Lady Dorothy Savage, daughter of the 2nd Earl of Rivers, married Charles Howard, Viscount Andover and later 2nd Earl of Berkshire of the 2nd creation. It was in the collection of Sir Peter Lely, and appeared in his Sale Catalogue (*Burl. Mag.*, LXXXII, p. 187) as 'My Lady *Thimbleby* and her Sister with a Cupid'. It was purchased at the sale by the 2nd Earl of Sunderland and from him descended to the present owner, Earl Spencer (*K. der K.*, *Van Dyck*, p. 502), wrongly called 'Catherine, Countess Rivers and her Sister'). Other versions of the picture are recorded: one noted by Vertue 'at Weston Warwickshire—Mr. . . . Sheldons . . . double ½ len. Countess of Berkshire, Mrs. Thimbleby Vandyke and a Cupid presenting a basket of Flowers'; a good copy formerly at Kimbolton Castle, called 'The Countess of Southampton and the Countess of Rutland'; another copy sold at Hengrave Hall in 1897; and a fourth version at Wardour Castle.

116. ADRIAEN HANNEMAN, AFTER THE SELF-PORTRAIT PAINTED IN 1656. H.L., seated, turning round to look over his l. shoulder and resting his l. hand on the back of the chair. Wearing long curling hair, moustache and tufted beard.

Red chalk, strengthened with black lead and black chalk; 22 × 18 cm. (8⅝ × 7⅛ in.).

PROV.: As for No. 1.
G.g.4. W.5–61 (L.B., as attributed to Mary Beale, 143).

BIBL.: As for No. 1.

In the inventory of pictures belonging to the elder Charles Beale (*See* note preceding Nos. 100–124) is mentioned 'Mr. Hannemans picture, & frame 18″', which may be the one copied in the present drawing. The subsequent history of this picture is not known, but the drawing does correspond with a self-portrait of Hannemann, signed and dated *1656*, which in 1857 was in the collection of Sir Hugh Hume Campbell, Bart., when it was exhibited in the Art Treasures Exhibition at Manchester (*Catalogue*, p. 62, No. 862). It was sold at Sir Hugh's sale at Christie's, 16.vi.1894, Lot 21, being identified there with the self-portrait mentioned in J. B. Descamp's *La Vie des Peintres Flamands* . . . 1754, II, p. 188, and is now in the Rijksmuseum, Amsterdam (*Catalogue*, 1927, p. 81, No. 1103). Another version of the picture was in 1952 in the possession of J. A. Tooth, 16 Cork Street, London, W.1 (*Catalogue*, *Exhibition of Paintings*, Oct.–Nov., 1951, p. 4, No. 6); it differs from the Amsterdam picture and the drawing in the rendering of the sitter's thumb, which is turned towards him instead of outwards, and in the simplification of the folds of his shirt-cuff.

117. AN ELDERLY MAN IN A SKULL CAP, AFTER AN UNIDENTIFIED PORTRAIT, *c.* 1640.

Head alone, turned to half-r., with eyes looking to front. Wearing a skull cap, curling hair, and tufted beard.

Red chalk, strengthened with black lead and black chalk; 18·6 × 16·8 cm. (7¼ × 6⅝ in.).

PROV.: As for No. 1.

G.g.4. W.5-125 (L.B., as attributed to Mary Beale, 125).

BIBL.: As for No. 1.

In the collection of Earl Beauchamp is a miniature by the younger Charles Beale, signed with the characteristic monogram *CB*, and clearly copied from the same portrait from which the present drawing is taken (*See* G. C. Williamson, *History of Portrait Miniatures*, 1904, I, Pl. V at p. 14, No. 9).

118. A BOY, PROBABLY AFTER A FIGURE IN AN UNIDENTIFIED PORTRAIT-GROUP, *c.* 1640.

H.L., turned half-r., with eyes looking to front. Wearing curling hair and a doublet buttoned to the neck, and holding a flower (?) in his l. hand.

Red chalk, strengthened with black lead and black chalk; the body lightly indicated; 22·8 × 17 cm. (8⅞ × 6⅝ in.).

PROV.: As for No. 1.

G.g.4. W.5-144 (L.B., as attributed to Mary Beale, 123).

BIBL.: As for No. 1.

119. A SHEPHERD HOLDING A PIPE, AFTER A PICTURE OF THE SCHOOL OF GIORGIONE.

Bust, turned to l., looking round over his l. shoulder. Wearing a large dark cap, short curling beard, fur cloak, and holding in his r. hand a pipe.

Red chalk, strengthened with black lead and black chalk; 23·6 × 18·8 cm. (9¼ × 7⅜ in.).

PROV.: As for No. 1.

G.g.4. W.5-74 (L.B., as attributed to Mary Beale, 154).

BIBL.: As for No. 1.

This drawing may be a copy of a picture

listed in Lely's Sale Catalogue as '*of Giorgione del Castel Franco . . . A Head of a Piper*

Ft.	In.	Ft.	In.'
01	08	01	04

(*Burl. Mag.*, LXXXI, p. 186). Several versions of the subject are recorded, one of the best known being that in the Pinacoteca at Naples (*See* Dr. Johannes Wilde in the *Wiener Jahrbuch*, New Series, VII, 1933, p. 124). None, however, can be identified with the picture in Lely's collection.

120. OUR LORD, AFTER AN UNIDENTIFIED PICTURE.

Bust, with Head turned half-r. Wearing drapery over His shoulders.

Red chalk, strengthened with black lead and black chalk; 21·8 × 18·2 cm. (8½ × 7⅛ in.).

PROV.: As for No. 1.

G.g.4. W.5-142 (L.B., as attributed to Mary Beale, 129).

BIBL.: As for No. 1.

121. A YOUNG BACCHUS ASLEEP, AFTER AN UNIDENTIFIED PICTURE. Head alone, nearly in profile to r. Wearing a wreath of vine.

Red chalk; unfinished: 20·7 × 15·6 cm. (8⅛ × 6⅛ in.).

PROV.: As for No. 1.

G.g.4. W.5–159 (L.B., as attributed to Mary Beale, 130).

BIBL.: As for No. 1.

122. A BEARDED MAN, AFTER A FIGURE IN AN UNIDENTIFIED PIC-TURE, BY RUBENS OR VAN DYCK (?). Head alone, looking down towards the r. With short curling hair, moustache and beard, and his shirt open at the neck.

Red chalk, strengthened with black lead and black chalk; 21·3 × 16·4 cm. (8⅜ × 6½ in.).

INSCR. *Recto*, at the foot, in the centre, in red chalk, by the artist, *CB* (monogram).

PROV.: As for No. 1.

G.g.4. W.5–56 (L.B., as by Charles Beale, 1).

BIBL.: As for No. 1.

Perhaps a study from the same picture as that copied in Nos. 123 & 124.

123. TWO MEN, ONE BEARDED, THE OTHER CLEAN SHAVEN, AFTER FIGURES IN AN UNIDENTIFIED PICTURE, BY RUBENS OR VAN DYCK (?). Heads, looking down towards the l., the bearded one with his shoulders bare.

Red chalk, strengthened with black lead and touched with black chalk; 23·6 × 18·7 cm. (9¼ × 7⅞ in.).

PROV.: As for No. 1.
G.g.4. W.5–76 (L.B., as attributed to Mary Beale, 153).

BIBL.: As for No. 1.

Perhaps a study from the same picture as that copied in Nos. 122 & 124.

124. A YOUNG MAN, AFTER A FIGURE IN AN UNIDENTIFIED PICTURE, BY RUBENS OR VAN DYCK (?). Head, looking down towards the r., his face lit from below. With short hair and slight moustache, and his shirt open at the neck.

Red chalk, strengthened with black lead and black chalk; 22·1 × 17·2 cm. (8⅜ × 6¾ in.).

PROV.: As for No. 1.
G.g.4. W.5–113 (L.B., as attributed to Mary Beale, 127).

BIBL.: As for No. 1.

Perhaps a study from the same picture as that copied in Nos. 122 & 123.

[125–137]. STUDIES FROM CONTEMPORARY PORTRAITS: MEN. The drawings in this section include copies from portraits by Mary Beale, among them a number of low church divines who appear to have been on friendly terms with the Beale family (Nos. 126, 131, 133, 135 & 136). Others are from portraits by Sir Peter Lely, including one, a self-portrait (No. 130), which Charles Beale also copied as a miniature.

125. A MAN, PERHAPS CHARLES BEALE THE ELDER. Nearly H.L., with body turned to front, head half-r. and eyes looking to front, his l. hand held to his breast. Wearing long curling hair, slight moustache, his shirt open at the neck and a cloak draped over his shoulder.

Red chalk, strengthened with black lead and black chalk; the body lightly indicated; 23·5 × 18·1 cm. (9¼ × 7⅛ in.).

PROV.: As for No. 1.

G.g.4. W.5–89 (L.B., as attributed to Mary Beale, 4).

BIBL.: As for No. 1.

This drawing was catalogued by Mr. Binyon as a portrait of the younger Charles Beale. It bears, however, some resemblance to the miniature by Flatman of the elder Charles Beale, dated 1664, in the V. & A. M. (See note to No. 1). Vertue mentions 'a double ½ lenght of Mr. Beale & his wife Mrs. Mary Beale by Sr. P L' (monogram) in the possession of 'Carter Colourin.' and that they were also painted, early in married life, by Robert Walker (See Vertue, IV., pp. 65 & 174).

It should be compared too with another drawing, apparently of the same man and in the same familiar technique, now in the collection of Mr. W. S. Lewis of Farmington, Connecticut. This originally belonged to Vertue who wrote on it, *M.ʳ Beale / son of M.ʳˢ Beale*. It later passed into the collection of Horace Walpole, who used it for the engraved portrait of the younger Charles Beale by T. Chambars in the 1st and 2nd editions of the *Anecdotes of Painting*. Subsequently, it was given by Walpole to Richard Bull. Despite Vertue's inscription, it must rather be regarded as a copy by Charles Beale II of yet another early portrait of his father.

126. HEZEKIAH BURTON, AFTER THE PICTURE BY MARY BEALE. Bust, turned half-r., with eyes looking to front. Wearing long curling hair and bands.

Red chalk, strengthened with black lead and black chalk; the body lightly indicated; 21·6 × 18·6 cm. (8½ × 7⅜ in.).

PROV.: As for No. 1.

G.g.4. W.5–138 (L.B., as attributed to Mary Beale, 5).

BIBL.: As for No. 1.

[Hezekiah Burton (D. 1681), divine. Was elected a Fellow of Magdalene College, Cambridge, when he was noted as a tutor, and became acquainted with Pepys and Sir Orlando Bridgeman, the latter appointing him Canon of Norwich in 1667. With Tillotson and Stillingfleet (See Nos. 135, 136 & 133) was one of the 'Latitude-men' who sought tolerant 'comprehension' of the Dissenters. Subsequently became Minister of St. George's, Southwark, and Vicar of Barnes.]

The original picture was painted, according to the elder Charles Beale, in 1673/4 (See Vertue, IV, p. 172). A version of it is at Magdalene College, Cambridge, and it is also known through an engraving by Robert White, forming the frontispiece to Burton's *Discourses*, published posthumously in 1684 (See B.M. Engraved Portraits, I, p. 302).

127. A YOUTH AS A SHEPHERD, TRADITIONALLY SAID TO BE ABRAHAM COWLEY, AFTER THE PICTURE BY SIR PETER LELY. Head, nearly in profile to l., with chin slightly tilted upwards. Wearing long flowing hair and shirt open at the neck.

Red chalk, strengthened with black lead and black chalk; 20·7 × 18·1 cm. (8⅛ × 7⅛ in.).

INSCR.: Lettered on the mount, below the drawing, perhaps reproducing an inscription from the old album, *Abraham Cowley*.

PROV.: As for No. 1.

G.g.4. W.5–65 (L.B., as attributed to Mary Beale, 131).

BIBL.: As for No. 1.

The original picture is now in the Dulwich College Gallery. It was said to represent Abraham Cowley, the poet (B. 1618: D. 1667) as early as 1766 when in the collection of a Mr. Lovibonde, and this identification was accepted by Walpole when the picture was at Strawberry Hill. It is now, however, considered to be incorrect (*See Beckett*, p. 42, No. 129).

128. A YOUTH, SAID TO BE ABRAHAM COWLEY. Head, turned half-l. Wearing long curling hair and shirt open at the neck.

Red chalk, strengthened with black lead and black chalk; 21 × 18 cm. (8¾ × 7 in.).

INSCR.: Lettered on the mount, below the drawing, perhaps reproducing an inscription from the old album, *Abraham Cowley*.

PROV.: As for No. 1.

G.g.4. W.5–52 (L.B., as attributed to Mary Beale, 6).

BIBL.: As for No. 1.

The identification of the sitter in this drawing as Abraham Cowley appears on the mount, probably reproducing an earlier inscription in the album. It is probably based on a superficial resemblance to the well-known supposed portrait of Cowley by Lely at Dulwich (*See* No. 127). Mr. Binyon sees some connection with the doubtful portrait of Cowley at the N.P.G., attributed to Mary Beale (No. 659).

129. SIR THOMAS ISHAM, BART., AFTER THE PICTURE BY SIR PETER LELY. T.Q.L., standing, with body turned to front, half-l., and his r. arm held in front of him and pointing to the r. Wearing a long curling periwig and antique dress.

Red chalk; in outline only; 21·7 × 18 cm. (8½ × 7 in.).

PROV.: As for No. 1.

G.g.4. W.5–45 (L.B., as attributed to (Mary Beale, 142).

BIBL.: As for No. 1.

[Sir Thomas Isham, 3rd Bart. of Lamport (B. 1657: D. 1681). During his short life travelled much in Italy and became an enthusiastic collector of works of art.]

The original picture, from which the present drawing is copied, is at Lamport (*See Beckett*, p. 48, No. 261 & Pl. 127).

130. SIR PETER LELY, AFTER THE SELF-PORTRAIT HOLDING A STATUETTE OF A *PUTTO*. Bust, with body in profile to r., head turned half-r., and eyes looking to front. Wearing long flowing periwig, moustache, and drapery over his shoulder.

Red chalk, strengthened with black lead and black chalk; the body lightly indicated; 20·8 × 17·5 cm. (8⅛ × 6⅞ in.).

INSCR.: Lettered on the mount, below the drawing, perhaps reproducing an inscription from the old album, *Sir Peter Lely*.

PROV.: As for No. 1.

G.g.4. W.5–62 (L.B., as attributed to Mary Beale, 132).

BIBL.: As for No. 1.

The original picture was in the collection of the Earl of Jersey at Osterley Park (*See Beckett*, p. 50, No. 291). It shows the sitter to r. at a table, on which he holds the statuette of a *putto* (not seen in the present drawing) which was doubtless among the works of art in his collection. Charles Beale may well have used such statuettes as this to draw from (*See* Nos. 158–177 below). Beale also painted a miniature after the complete picture, signed with the characteristic monogram *C B* and dated *1679*. It is now in V. & A. M. (*555–1905. See Foster, Cooper*, Pl. LXX).

131. A DIVINE, PROBABLY SIMON PATRICK, BISHOP OF ELY. Bust, turned half-l., with eyes looking to front. Wearing long curling hair or periwig, and bands.

Red chalk, strengthened with black lead and black chalk; the body lightly indicated; 20·1 × 16·2 cm. (7⅞ × 6⅜ in.).

INSCR.: On the mount, below the drawing, perhaps reproducing an inscription from the old album, *John Dryden*.

PROV.: As for No. 1.

G.g.4. W.5–104 (L.B., as attributed to Mary Beale, 7).

BIBL.: As for No. 1.

[Simon Patrick (B. 1626: D. 1707). Educated at Queen's College, Cambridge. Though at first a Presbyterian, was ordained into the Church of England, successively be-

coming Vicar of Battersea in 1658, Rector of St. Paul's Covent Garden, in 1662, Royal Chaplain in 1671, Dean of Peterborough in 1679, Bishop of Chichester in 1689, and of Ely in 1691. Was an opponent of Roman Catholicism, and an early supporter of the Societies for the Promotion of Christian Knowledge and the Propagation of the Gospel.]

The identification of the sitter in this drawing as John Dryden on the mount is incorrect. On the other hand, the sitter bears a fairly close resemblance to the portrait of Bishop Patrick by Lely in the N.P.G. (No. 1500, *Beckett*, p. 57, No. 412). The elder Charles has noted among the 'pictures done from the Life by Mrs. Beal since 1671/2,' one of Dr. Patrick's (*See Vertue*, IV, p. 170).

132. ANTHONY ASHLEY COOPER, 1st EARL OF SHAFTESBURY, AFTER ROBERT WHITE (?). Head, turned half-l., with eyes looking to front. Wearing a long curling periwig and lace cravat.

Red chalk, strengthened with black lead; 22·2 × 17·4 cm. (8¾ × 6⅞ in.).

INSCR.: Lettered on the mount, below the drawing, perhaps reproducing an inscription from the old album, *Anthony, First Earl of Shaftesbury*.

PROV.: As for No. 1.

G.g.4. W.5–44 (L.B., as attributed to Mary Beale, 8).

BIBL.: As for No. 1.

[Anthony Ashley Cooper, 1st Earl of Shaftesbury (B. 1621: D. 1683). The well-known politician and anti-papist of the later XVII c.]

The present drawing seems to be a copy in reverse of the head in Robert White's portrait of Shaftesbury engraved in 1680 (*See B.M. Engraved Portraits*, IV, p. 59, No. 13).

133. EDWARD STILLINGFLEET, BISHOP OF WORCESTER, AFTER THE PICTURE BY SIR PETER LELY. Bust, turned slightly to r., with eyes looking to front. Wearing curling hair or periwig, bands and gown.

Red chalk, strengthened with black chalk and black lead; the body lightly indicated; 21·4 × 17·7 cm. (8⅜ × 7 in.).

INSCR.: Lettered on the mount, below the drawing, perhaps reproducing an inscription from the old album, *Edward Stilling fleet, Bishop of Worcester.*

PROV.: As for No. 1.

G.g.4. W.5–98 (L.B., as attributed to Mary Beale, 138).

BIBL.: As for No. 1.

[Edward Stillingfleet (B. 1635: D. 1699). Successively Rector of Sutton, of St. Andrews, Holborn, Canon of St. Paul's in 1667, and of Canterbury in 1669, Dean of St. Paul's in 1678, and Bishop of Worcester in 1689. Noted for his learning and antiquarian interests, and for his toleration of Dissenters.]

The original picture was painted by Lely in 1676 for the elder Charles Beale, who records in his Diary under Sept. 26th (?) of that year, that he sent the painter one ounce of his 'richest lake' in part payment for it and two other portraits, one of 'Mr. Dean of Canterbury', the other of the younger Charles Beale (*See Vertue*, IV, p. 175). The picture has not been traced, but it is known through the engraving after it by Abraham Blooteling which was executed 'very probably by Mrs. Beals desire'. (*See B.M. Engraved Portraits*, IV, p. 195; *Vertue*, IV, p. 172). It may be noted that the present drawing, though in the reverse sense, corresponds almost exactly in size with this engraving. Another portrait of Stillingfleet by Mary Beale herself was engraved by Robert White as a frontispiece to his *Sermons*, 1696, and to his *Works*, 1710 (*See B.M. Engraved Portraits*, IV, pp. 194–5).

134. A MAN, WITH GREY OR LIGHT-COLOURED HAIR, PERHAPS DR. THOMAS SYDENHAM. Bust, turned half-r., with eyes looking to front. Wearing long curling hair, slight moustache and small tufted beard, bands and academic gown.

Red chalk, strengthened with black lead and black chalk; the body lightly indicated; 21·5 × 16·9 cm. (8½ × 6⅝ in.).

PROV.: As for No. 1.

G.S.4. W.5–101 (L.B., as attributed to Mary Beale, 11).

BIBL.: As for No. 1.

Mr. Binyon has pointed out a resemblance between this drawing and one of the portraits, by Mary Beale, of Dr. Thomas Sydenham (B. 1624: D. 1689), the celebrated physician, who was a friend of the Beale family.

The original of this is known only through an engraving after it by Abraham Blooteling, serving as the frontispiece to Sydenham's *Observationes Medicae*, 1676 (*See B.M. Engraved Portraits*, IV, p. 237, No. 2). A version of it in oils exists in the Royal College of Physicians, with, however, differences of dress.

135. JOHN TILLOTSON, ARCHBISHOP OF CANTERBURY, AFTER THE PICTURE BY MARY BEALE. Head, turned half-r., with eyes looking to front. Wearing long curling hair and bands.

Red chalk, strengthened with black lead and black chalk; $18 \cdot 8 \times 15 \cdot 6$ cm. ($7\frac{3}{8} \times 6\frac{1}{8}$ in.).

PROV.: As for No. 1.

G.g.4. W.5–60 (L.B., as attributed to Mary Beale, 10).

BIBL. As for No. 1.

[John Tillotson (B. 1630: D. 1694). Successively chaplain to Charles II, Dean of Canterbury in 1670, Canon of St. Paul's in 1675, Dean of St. Paul's in 1689, and Archbishop of Canterbury in 1691. Was noted in his day as a preacher, and for his toleration of the Dissenters.]

The original picture, from which the present is copied, is in The Deanery at Canterbury. It is no doubt the one noted there by Vertue as dating from 1672, and is thus probably identical with the 'Dr. Tillotson' listed by the elder Charles Beale among those 'pictures done from the Life by Mrs. Beal since $167\frac{1}{2}$ (*See Vertue*, I, p. 116, & IV, p. 170). Vertue also saw in the possession of one 'Carter Colourman . . . a Coppy in Water Colours of Dr. Tillotson' by the younger Charles Beale, signed with his characteristic monogram and dated *1680*. This is probably identical with the miniature of Tillotson by Charles Beale, now in the Royal Collection at Windsor, which indeed corresponds with the present drawing (*See Vertue*, IV, p. 65, & V, p. 20, *Long*, p. 20). It may be noted too that Lely painted a portrait of Tillotson for the elder Charles Beale in 1672 (*See Vertue*, IV, pp. 169–70), which was engraved by Abraham Blooteling, and has affinities with Mary Beale's picture of the same period. Mrs. Beale also painted Tillotson later as Archbishop, and this portrait was engraved successively by Robert White and P. Vanderbank (*See B.M. Engraved Portraits*, IV, pp. 284–5, Nos. 1–3 & 17.

136. JOHN TILLOTSON, ARCHBISHOP OF CANTERBURY, PROBABLY AFTER A PICTURE BY MARY BEALE. Bust, turned half-l., with eyes looking to front. Wearing long curling hair, bands and gown.

Red chalk, strengthened with black lead and black chalk; the body lightly indicated; $20 \cdot 1 \times 16 \cdot 8$ cm. ($7\frac{7}{8} \times 6\frac{5}{8}$ in.).

PROV.: As for No. 1.

G.g.4. W.5–97 (L.B., as attributed to Mary Beale, 9).

BIBL. & REPR.: As for No. 1. *Foster, Cooper*, Pl. LXVI.

The original picture has not been identified, but must clearly have been painted at the same time as the original of No. 135.

137. A BOY WITH A SPANIEL, PERHAPS AFTER A PICTURE BY LELY.

T.Q.L., standing, with body in profile to l., head turned half-l., and eyes looking to front, his l. hand resting on the head of a spaniel. Wearing fair curling hair and a belted doublet. A tree in the background.

Red chalk, strengthened with black lead and black chalk; the body lightly indicated; 24·5 × 18·6 cm. (9⅝ × 7¾ in.).

PROV.: As for No. 1.

G.g.4. W.5–71 (L.B., as attributed to Mary Beale, 141).

BIBL.: As for No. 1.

The spaniel is somewhat like that in Lely's portrait of William Cecil, 2nd Earl of Salisbury at Hatfield (See Beckett, p. 60, No. 462, & Pl. 12).

[138–157]. STUDIES FROM CONTEMPORARY PORTRAITS: WOMEN.

Hardly any of the portraits in this section have been identified. The originals seem mainly to have been by Sir Peter Lely, but some may have been by Mary Beale.

138. MARY BEALE, AFTER LELY. H.L., with body half-l. and eyes to front, her hands crossed on her breast. Wearing her hair falling in curls, a pearl necklace and drapery.

Red chalk, touched with black lead and black chalk; 22·7 × 17·5 cm. (8⅞ × 6⅞ in.).

INSCR.: Lettered on the mount, below the drawing, perhaps reproducing an inscription from the original album, *Mary Beale*.

PROV.: As for No. 1.

G.g.4. W.5–88 (L.B., as attributed to Mary Beale, 3).

BIBL.: As for No. 1.

Mary Beale (See pp. 198–9 for biographical note).

The present drawing appears to be after a portrait painted in early life. The attribution of the original to Lely is suggested by a replica of the drawing, now in the collection of Mr. W. S. Lewis of Farmington, Connecticut, which was inscribed by a former owner, George Vertue, *Mrs. Beal | Paintress. aft Lely*. Later this replica passed into the collection of Horace Walpole, who used it for the engraved portrait of Mrs. Beale by T. Chambars in the 1st and 2nd editions of the *Anecdotes of Painting*. In view of this inscription, it is possible that both drawings may be based on Lely's double portrait of Mrs. Beale and her husband together, which is mentioned by Vertue (See note to No. 125, which may, therefore, be the companion).

139. A LADY WITH HER HAND TO HER BREAST, SAID TO BE BARBARA VILLIERS, DUCHESS OF CLEVELAND, PROBABLY AFTER A PICTURE BY SIR PETER LELY. H.L., seated, with body turned to front, and head slightly to r., her eyes looking to front, her l. hand held to her breast. Wearing her hair partly falling on her l. shoulder, a pearl drop in her r. ear, a pearl necklet, and drapery.

Red chalk, strengthened with black lead and black chalk. 23·9 × 18·7 cm. (9¾ × 7¾ in.).

PROV.: As for No. 1.

G.g.4. W.5–83 (L.B., as attributed to Mary Beale, 140).

BIBL.: As for No. 1.

This drawing is catalogued by Mr. Binyon as a portrait of Barbara Villiers, Duchess of Cleveland, but it does not correspond with any of the authentic portraits of her.

140. HORTENSE MANCINI, DUCHESSE DE MAZARIN, PROBABLY AFTER A PICTURE BY SIR PETER LELY. Nearly H.L., seated, with body turned slightly to r., head half-l., and eyes looking to front, her l. arm resting on a ledge. Wearing her hair in curls, and a low-necked dress looped with strings of pearls.

Red chalk, strengthened with black lead and black chalk; the body lightly indicated; 23·9 × 18·1 cm. (9⅜ × 7⅜ in.).

INSCR.: Lettered on the mount, below the drawing, perhaps reproducing an inscription from the original album, *Hortense Mancini, Duchess of Mazarin.*

PROV.: As for No. 1.
G.g.4. W.5–84 (L.B., as attributed to Mary Beale, 139).

BIBL.: As for No. 1.

[Hortense Mancini (B. 1646: D. 1699),

favourite niece of Cardinal Mazarin and wife of Armand-Charles, Duc de Mazarin. Subsequently became the mistress of Charles II.]

The identification of the sitter in this drawing with the Duchesse de Mazarin is given on the mount, probably reproducing an earlier inscription in the album. Two portraits of her by Lely are recorded (*See Beckett*, p. 53, Nos. 337 & 338), both of which are known through engravings, one in mezzotint published by R. Tompson, the other in line by G. Valck, 1678 (*See B.M. Engraved Portraits*, III, p. 217, Nos. 4 & 5). The present drawing has some affinities with the latter.

141. A LADY, PERHAPS ANNE, DUCHESS OF MONMOUTH, AFTER A PICTURE BY SIR PETER LELY. Bust, with body nearly in profile to l., head turned half-l., and eyes looking to front. Wearing her hair in curls, a pearl necklet, and a low-necked dress.

Red chalk, strengthened with black lead and black chalk; the dress lightly indicated; 21·4 × 17·1 cm. (8⅜ × 6⅞ in.).

PROV.: As for No. 1.
G.g.4. W.5–91 (L.B., as attributed to Mary Beale, 101).

BIBL.: As for No. 1.

The sitter in this drawing has some affinity with the portrait by Lely of Anne Scott, Countess of Buccleuch (B. 1651: D. 1732), and wife of James, Duke of Monmouth, which is known through an anonymous mezzotint (*See B.M. Engraved Portraits*, III, p. 255, No. 5).

142. THE SAME LADY, PERHAPS ANNE, DUCHESS OF MONMOUTH, AS IN No. 141. Bust, with body nearly in profile to l., and eyes looking to front. Wearing her hair in curls, a pearl necklet, and a low-necked dress.

Red chalk, strengthened with black lead and black chalk; the dress lightly indicated; 20·2 × 17·2 cm. (7⅞ × 6⅝ in.).

PROV.: As for No. 1.
G.g.4. W.5–85 (L.B., as attributed to Mary Beale, 102).

BIBL.: As for No. 1.

(*See* note to No. 141, which is a larger version of the present drawing.)

143. A LADY, PROBABLY AFTER A PICTURE BY SIR PETER LELY. Bust, with body turned to front, head slightly to r., and eyes looking to front. Wearing her hair in curls, and a low-necked dress.

Red chalk, strengthened with black lead and black chalk; 24·4 × 18·8 cm. (9⅝ × 7⅜ in.).

PROV.: As for No. 1.

G.g.4. W.5–53 (L.B., as attributed to Mary Beale, 79).

BIBL.: As for No. 1.

144. A LADY, PROBABLY AFTER A PICTURE BY SIR PETER LELY. Bust, with body turned slightly to l., and head half-r. Wearing her hair in curls and her shoulders bare.

Red chalk, strengthened with black lead and black chalk; 21·2 × 17·4 cm. (8⅜ × 6⅞ in.).

PROV.: As for No. 1.

G.g.4. W.5–58 (L.B., as attributed to Charles Beale, 2).

BIBL.: As for No. 1.

145. A LADY WITH LIGHT-COLOURED HAIR, PROBABLY AFTER A PICTURE BY SIR PETER LELY. Bust, turned to front, with head slightly inclined to the l. Wearing the hair in curls, and a low-necked dress with a pearl pendant.

Red chalk, strengthened with black lead and black chalk; 21·6 × 18·4 cm. (8½ × 7¼ in.).

PROV.: As for No. 1.

G.g.4. W.5–78 (L.B., as attributed to Mary Beale, 78).

BIBL.: As for No. 1.

146. A LADY, PROBABLY AFTER A PICTURE BY SIR PETER LELY. Bust, with body turned to front and head half-l. Wearing her hair partly falling on her shoulder, and drapery.

Red chalk, strengthened with black lead and black chalk; 23·8 × 18·7 cm. (9⅜ × 7⅜ in.).

PROV.: As for No. 1.

G.g.4. W.5–92 (L.B., as attributed to Mary Beale, 100).

BIBL.: As for No. 1.

147. A LADY WITH LIGHT COLOURED HAIR, PROBABLY AFTER A PICTURE BY SIR PETER LELY. Bust, with body turned to front and head half-r. Wearing her hair partly loose and falling on her shoulder, a pearl drop in her r. ear, and low-necked dress.

Red chalk, strengthened with black lead and black chalk; 24·5 × 18 cm. (9⅝ × 7½ in.).

PROV.: As for No. 1.

G.g.4. W.5–95 (L.B., as attributed to Mary Beale, 98).

BIBL.: As for No. 1.

148. A LADY, PROBABLY AFTER A PICTURE BY SIR PETER LELY. Bust, turned half-r., with eyes looking to front. Wearing her hair in curls, and her shoulders bare.

Red chalk, strengthened with black lead and black chalk; 23·9 × 18·1 cm. (9⅝ × 7⅛ in.).

PROV.: As for No. 1.

G.g.4. W.5–114 (L.B., as attributed to Mary Beale, 107).

BIBL.: As for No. 1.

149. A LADY WITH LIGHT-COLOURED HAIR, PROBABLY AFTER A PICTURE BY SIR PETER LELY. Bust, turned half-r., with eyes looking to front. Wearing her hair partly in curls, and her shoulders bare.

Red chalk, strengthened with black lead and black chalk; 21·4 × 17·2 cm. (8⅜ × 6¾ in.).

PROV.: As for No. 1.

G.g.4. W.5–116 (L.B., as attributed to Mary Beale, 106).

BIBL.: As for No. 1.

150. A LADY, PROBABLY AFTER A PICTURE BY SIR PETER LELY. Bust, with body turned to front and head slightly to l. Wearing her hair in curls, and drapery.

Red chalk, strengthened with black lead and black chalk; 21·4 × 17·5 cm. (8⅜ × 6⅞ in.).

PROV.: As for No. 1.

G.g.4. W.5–118 (L.B., as attributed to Mary Beale, 103).

BIBL.: As for No. 1.

151. A LADY, PROBABLY AFTER A PICTURE BY SIR PETER LELY. Bust, turned slightly to l., with eyes looking to front. Wearing her hair in curls, and a low-necked dress, the folds of which are looped with strings of pearls and other jewels.

Red chalk, strengthened with black lead and black chalk, and perhaps touched with dark grey wash; 24 × 18·7 cm. (9⅝ × 7⅜ in.).

PROV.: As for No. 1.

G.g.4. W.5–119 (L.B., as attributed to Mary Beale, 104).

BIBL.: As for No. 1.

152. A LADY, PROBABLY AFTER A PICTURE BY SIR PETER LELY. Bust, turned half-l., with eyes looking to front. Wearing her hair in curls, and a low-necked dress.

Red chalk, strengthened with black lead and black chalk; 21·5 × 18·1 cm. (8½ × 7⅛ in.).

PROV.: As for No. 1.

G.g.4. W.5–120 (L.B., as attributed to Mary Beale, 118).

BIBL.: As for No. 1.

153. A LADY SEATED WITH HER HANDS CROSSED, PROBABLY AFTER A PICTURE BY SIR PETER LELY. T.Q.L., seated, with body turned to front and head to r., her hands crossed in her lap. Wearing her hair in curls falling on her neck, and drapery.

Red chalk, strengthened with black lead and black chalk; 24·2 × 18·1 cm. (9½ × 7⅛ in.).

PROV.: As for No. 1.

G.g.4. W.5–129 (L.B., as attributed to Mary Beale, 124).

BIBL.: As for No. 1.

154. A LADY, PROBABLY AFTER A PICTURE BY SIR PETER LELY. Bust, with body turned half-r., head slightly to r., and eyes looking to front. Wearing her hair in curls on her bare shoulders.

Red chalk, strengthened with black lead and black chalk; the dress lightly indicated; 21·8 × 17·5 cm. (8½ × 6⅞ in.).

PROV.: As for No. 1.

G.g.4. W.5–135 (L.B., as attributed to Mary Beale, 121).

BIBL.: As for No. 1.

155. A LADY, PROBABLY AFTER A PICTURE BY SIR PETER LELY. Bust, turned slightly to r., with eyes looking to front. Wearing her hair in curls, and drapery.

Red chalk; unfinished; 21·4 × 17·5 cm. (8⅜ × 6⅞ in.).

PROV.: As for No. 1.

G.g.4. W.5–166 (L.B., as attributed to Mary Beale, 45).

BIBL.: As for No. 1.

156. A SMALL GIRL, PROBABLY AFTER A PICTURE BY SIR PETER LELY. Bust, turned half-r., with eyes looking to front. Wearing her hair in curls, and drapery.

Red chalk, strengthened with black chalk; the drapery lightly indicated; 21·7 × 17·8 cm. (8½ × 7 in.).

PROV.: As for No. 1.

G.g.4. W.5–75 (L.B., as attributed to Mary Beale, 80).

BIBL.: As for No. 1.

157. A GIRL. Bust, turned slightly to r., with eyes looking to front. Wearing her hair in curls, and drapery.

Red chalk, strengthened with black chalk and black lead; the drapery lightly indicated; 21·3 × 16·6 cm. (8⅜ × 6⅛ in.).

PROV.: As for No. 1.
G.g.4. W.5–67 (L.B., as attributed to Mary Beale, 82).

BIBL.: As for No. 1.

[158–177]. STUDIES FROM SCULPTURE AND CASTS. This section includes perhaps the earliest extant academic drawings by an Englishman from sculpture. It is possible that Charles Beale may have made some of them from objects in Sir Peter Lely's collection, for in the latter's sale catalogue several pieces of sculpture, including 'A *Cupid*, big as the Life, of *Francisco Famingo*. White Marble', and 'Several Bronzes, being small figures' (*See Burl. Mag.*, LXXXII, p. 188).

158. STUDY FROM A CAST OF A STATUETTE OF 'ASTRONOMY', BY GIAMBOLOGNA. Seen from the front, the head broken off.

Red chalk, strengthened with black lead and black chalk; 23·9 × 16·9 cm. (9⅜ × 6⅝ in.).

INSCR.: *Recto*, on the base, in the centre, in red chalk, by the artist, *C B* (monogram).

PROV.: As for No. 1.
G.g.4. W.5–38 (L.B., as by Charles Beale, 8).

BIBL.: As for No. 1.

A version in gilded bronze of this statuette is in the Kunsthistorisches Museum at Vienna (*See Planiscig*, p. 148, No. 250).

159. STUDY FROM A CAST OF A STATUETTE OF 'GEOMETRY', BY GIAMBOLOGNA. Seen from the side. **Plate 81**

Red chalk, touched with black lead and black chalk; 24·3 × 17·2 cm. (9½ × 6¾ in.).

INSCR.: *Recto*, at the foot, in the centre, in red chalk, by the artist, *C B.* (monogram).

PROV.: As for No. 1.
G.g.4. W.5–31 (L.B., as by Charles Beale, 9).

BIBL.: As for No. 1.

Clearly belonging to the same series as the statuette of 'Astronomy', described above at No. 158.

160. STUDY FROM THE SAME CAST OF A STATUETTE OF 'GEOMETRY', BY GIAMBOLOGNA, AS IN No. 159. Seen from the back. **Plate 82**

Red chalk, strengthened with black lead and black chalk; 24·4 × 16·2 cm. (9⅝ × 6⅜ in.).

INSCR.: *Recto*, on the base, in the centre, in red chalk, by the artist, *C B* (monogram).

PROV.: As for No. 1.

G.g.4. W.5–35 (L.B., as by Charles Beale, 10).

BIBL.: As for No. 1.

See Note to No. 159.

161. STUDY FROM A VERSION OF THE BUST OF THE MADONNA, BY FRANÇOIS DU QUESNOY (FIAMMINGO) (?). Seen in profile to r.

Red chalk, touched with black lead; 23·2 × 17·4 cm. ($9\frac{1}{8} × 6\frac{7}{8}$ in.).

PROV.: As for No. 1.

G.g.4. W.5–8 (L.B., as attributed to Mary Beale, 165).

BIBL.: As for No. 1.

This bust has affinities with that in *Planiscig*, pp. 214 & 215, Pl. 343.

162. STUDY FROM A CAST OF A STATUETTE OF THE INFANT HERCULES SLAYING THE SERPENT, BY FRANÇOIS DUQUESNOY (FIAMMINGO) (?). Seen from the front and above.

Red chalk, strengthened with black lead; 19·7 × 16·7 cm. ($7\frac{3}{4} × 6\frac{5}{8}$ in.).

INSCR.: *Recto*, on the base of the statuette, to the l., in red chalk, by the artist, *C B* (monogram).

PROV.: As for No. 1.

G.g.4. W.5–25 (L.B., as by Charles Beale, 4).

BIBL.: As for No. 1.

This statuette seems to have affinities with those of sleeping *putti* reproduced in *Planiscig*, pp. 217–220, Pls. 347–352.

163. STUDY FROM THE SAME STATUETTE OF THE INFANT HERCULES, BY FRANÇOIS DUQUESNOY (FIAMMINGO) (?), AS IN No. 162. Seen from above.

Red chalk; 18·7 × 13·6 cm. ($7\frac{3}{8} × 5\frac{3}{8}$ in.).

INSCR.: *Recto*, on the base of the statuette, to the l., in red chalk, by the artist, *C B* (monogram).

PROV.: As for No. 1.

G.g.4. W.5–27 (L.B., as by Charles Beale, 3).

BIBL.: As for No. 1.

See note on No. 162.

164. STUDY FROM THE SAME STATUETTE OF THE INFANT HERCULES, BY FRANÇOIS DUQUESNOY (FIAMMINGO) (?), AS IN Nos. 162 & 163. Seen from the front.

Red chalk, strengthened with black lead; 14·8 × 17·6 cm. ($5\frac{3}{4} × 7$ in.).

INSCR.: *Recto*, on the base of the statuette, in the centre, in red chalk, by the artist, *C B* (monogram).

C.E.D.

PROV.: As for No. 1.

G.g.4. W.5–29 (L.B., as by Charles Beale, 2).

BIBL.: As for No. 1.

See note to No. 162.

165. STUDY FROM THE STATUETTE OF A *PUTTO* SKATING, WITH ARMS CROSSED. Seen from the front.

Red chalk, strengthened with black lead and black chalk; 22·3 × 16·1 cm. ($8\frac{3}{4} \times 6\frac{3}{8}$ in.).

INSCR.: *Recto*, at the foot, in the centre, in red chalk, by the artist, *C B* (monogram).

PROV.: As for No. 1.

G.g.4. W.5–20 (L.B., as by Charles Beale, 7).

BIBL.: As for No. 1.

166. STUDY FROM THE SAME STATUETTE OF A *PUTTO* SKATING AS IN No. 165. Seen from the side, turned to r.

Red chalk, strengthened with black lead and black chalk; 23·7 × 16 cm. ($9\frac{3}{8} \times 6\frac{1}{4}$ in.).

INSCR.: *Recto*, at the foot in the centre, in red chalk, by the artist, *C B.* (monogram).

PROV.: As for No. 1.

G.g.4. W.5–21 (L.B., as by Charles Beale, 5).

BIBL.: As for No. 1.

167. STUDY FROM THE SAME STATUETTE OF A *PUTTO* SKATING AS IN Nos. 165 & 166. Turned half-l. Plate 66

Red chalk, strengthened with black lead and black chalk; 24·1 × 16·1 cm. ($9\frac{1}{2} \times 6\frac{3}{8}$ in.).

INSCR.: *Recto*, at the foot, in the centre, in red chalk, by the artist, *C B.* (monogram).

PROV.: As for No. 1.

G.g.4. W.5–23 (L.B., as by Charles Beale, 6).

BIBL.: As for No. 1.

168. STUDY FROM A CAST OF THE HEAD OF A ROMAN EMPEROR (?). Turned slightly to r. and tilted over to the l. on the top of a wig-stand.

Red chalk, strengthened with black lead; 23·9 × 18 cm. ($9\frac{3}{8} \times 7\frac{1}{8}$ in.).

PROV.: As for No. 1.

G.g.4. W.5–11 (L.B., as attributed to Mary Beale, 159).

BIBL.: As for No. 1.

169. STUDY FROM THE SAME CAST OF THE HEAD OF A ROMAN EMPEROR (?), AS IN No. 168. Turned to l. and tilted over to the r. on the top of a wig-stand.

Red chalk; 22·6 × 16·3 cm. ($8\frac{7}{8} \times 6\frac{3}{8}$ in.).

BIBL.: As for No. 1.

PROV.: As for No. 1.

G.g.4. W.5–14 (L.B., as attributed to Mary Beale, 158).

170. STUDY FROM THE SAME CAST OF THE HEAD OF A ROMAN EMPEROR (?), AS IN Nos. 168 & 169. Turned to front, and tilted over to the r. on the top of a wig-stand.   **Plate 83**

Red chalk; 23·2 × 17·5 cm. (9⅛ × 6⅞ in.).   BIBL.: As for No. 1.

PROV.: As for No. 1.
  G.g.4. W.5–16 (L.B., as attributed to Mary Beale, 157).

171. STUDY FROM THE SAME CAST OF THE HEAD OF A ROMAN EMPEROR (?), AS IN Nos. 168 – 170. Almost in profile to l., tilted forward on the top of wig-stand.

Red chalk, touched with black lead and black chalk; 21·3 × 16 cm. (8⅜ × 6⅜ in.).

PROV.: As for No. 1.
  G.g.4. W.5–19 (L.B., as attributed to Mary Beale, 160).

BIBL.: As for No. 1.

172. STUDY FROM A CAST OF A CHILD'S HEAD. The r. side seen from below.

Red chalk, strengthened with black lead and black chalk; 19·4 × 18·6 cm. (7⅝ × 7¼ in.).

PROV.: As for No. 1.
  G.g.4. W.5–1 (L.B., as attributed to Mary Beale, 163).

BIBL.: As for No. 1.

173. STUDY FROM THE SAME CAST OF A CHILD'S HEAD AS IN No. 172. Turned nearly to front, and seen from below.

Red chalk, strengthened with black lead and black chalk; 19·7 × 16·5 cm. (7¾ × 6½ in.).

PROV.: As for No. 1.
  G.g.4. W.5–3 (L.B., as attributed to Mary Beale, 162).

BIBL.: As for No. 1.

174. STUDY FROM THE SAME CAST OF A CHILD'S HEAD AS IN Nos. 172 & 173. Turned nearly to front and looking downwards. Seen from above.

Red chalk, strengthened with black lead and black chalk; 19·6 × 16·4 cm. (7¾ × 6⅜ in.).

PROV.: As for No. 1.
  G.g.4. W.5–4 (L.B., as attributed to Mary Beale, 161).

BIBL.: As for No. 1.

175. STUDY FROM THE SAME CAST OF A CHILD'S HEAD AS IN Nos. 172–174. Lying on its side, towards the r. Seen from below.   **Plate 84**

Red chalk, strengthened with black lead; 14·8 × 17·4 cm. (5¾ × 6⅞ in.).

PROV.: As for No. 1.

G.g.4. W.5–9 (L.B., as attributed to Mary Beale, 164).

BIBL.: As for No. 1.

176. STUDIES OF A R. HAND AND WRIST, PERHAPS FROM A CAST.

Both with the fingers in the same position, thumb and index extended, the others bent, but seen from different points of view.

Red chalk, touched with black lead and black chalk; 16·7 × 18·7 cm. (6½ × 7⅜ in.).

PROV.: As for No. 1.
G.g.4. W.5–49 (L.B., as attributed to Mary Beale, 155).

Both studies show the hand cut off clean above the wrist, and this, coupled with the fact that in each the fingers are in the same position, suggests that they were made after a cast.

177. COPY OF FRANÇOIS PERRIER'S ETCHING OF A STATUE OF ATALANTA, THEN IN THE PALAZZO DELLA VALLE, ROME.

Red chalk; in outline; 24·5 × 16·9 cm. (9⅝ × 6⅝ in.).

PROV.: As for No. 1.
G.g.4. W.5–41 (L.B., as attributed to Mary Beale, 156).

Perrier's etching appears in his *SEGMENTA . . . statuarū . . . Vrbis æternæ*, 1638, Pl. 71.

DRAWINGS BY CHARLES BEALE II

Concordance of Registration Numbers and Numbers of Catalogue

[Single Drawing]
    G.g.1–455 = C.-M. & H.107
[Steevens-Cracherode Album]
    G.g.4. W.5– 1 C.-M. & H.172
    G.g.4. W.5– 2 = C.-M. & H. 33
    G.g.4. W.5– 3 = C.-M. & H.173
    G.g.4. W.5– 4 = C.-M. & H.174
    G.g.4. W.5– 5 = C.-M. & H. 12
    G.g.4. W.5– 6 = C.-M. & H. 43
    G.g.4. W.5– 7 = C.-M. & H. 34
    G.g.4. W.5– 8 = C.-M. & H.161
    G.g.4. W.5– 9 = C.-M. & H.175
    G.g.4. W.5– 10 = C.-M. & H. 44
    G.g.4. W.5– 11 = C.-M. & H.168
    G.g.4. W.5– 12 = C.-M. & H. 63
    G.g.4. W.5– 13 = C.-M. & H. 45

G.g.4. W.5– 14 = C.-M. & H.169
G.g.4. W.5– 15 = C.-M. & H. 48
G.g.4. W.5– 16 = C.-M. & H.170
G.g.4. W.5– 17 = C.-M. & H. 73
G.g.4. W.5– 18 = C.-M. & H. 64
G.g.4. W.5– 19 = C.-M. & H.171
G.g.4. W.5– 20 = C.-M. & H.165
G.g.4. W.5– 21 = C.-M. & H.166
G.g.4. W.5– 22 = C.-M. & H. 13
G.g.4. W.5– 23 = C.-M. & H.167
G.g.4. W.5– 24 = C.-M. & H. 65
G.g.4. W.5– 25 = C.-M. & H.162
G.g.4. W.5– 26 = C.-M. & H. 50
G.g.4. W.5– 27 = C.-M. & H.163
G.g.4. W.5– 28 = C.-M. & H.335
G.g.4. W.5– 29 = C.-M. & H.164

G.g.4. W.5– 30 = C.-M. & H. 86
G.g.4. W.5– 31 = C.-M. & H.159
G.g.4. W.5– 32 = C.-M. & H. 74
G.g.4. W.5– 33 = C.-M. & H. 7
G.g.4. W.5– 34 = C.-M. & H. 46
G.g.4. W.5– 35 = C.-M. & H.160
G.g.4. W.5– 36 = C.-M. & H. 66
G.g.4. W.5– 37 = C.-M. & H. 14
G.g.4. W.5– 38 = C.-M. & H.158
G.g.4. W.5– 39 = C.-M. & H. 51
G.g.4. W.5– 40 = C.-M. & H. 75
G.g.4. W.5– 41 = C.-M. & H.177
G.g.4. W.5– 42 = C.-M. & H. 52
G.g.4. W.5– 43 = C.-M. & H. 94
G.g.4. W.5– 44 = C.-M. & H.132
G.g.4. W.5– 45 = C.-M. & H.129
G.g.4. W.5– 46 = C.-M. & H. 10
G.g.4. W.5– 47 = C.-M. & H. 15
G.g.4. W.5– 48 = C.-M. & H. 36
G.g.4. W.5– 49 = C.-M. & H.176
G.g.4. W.5– 50 = C.-M. & H. 11
G.g.4. W.5– 51 = C.-M. & H. 67
G.g.4. W.5– 52 = C.-M. & H.128
G.g.4. W.5– 53 = C.-M. & H.143
G.g.4. W.5– 54 = C.-M. & H.106
G.g.4. W.5– 55 = C.-M. & H.114
G.g.4. W.5– 56 = C.-M. & H.122
G.g.4. W.5– 57 = C.-M. & H.115
G.g.4. W.5– 58 = C.-M. & H.144
G.g.4. W.5– 59 = C.-M. & H. 2
G.g.4. W.5– 60 = C.-M. & H.135
G.g.4. W.5– 61 = C.-M. & H.116
G.g.4. W.5– 62 = C.-M. & H.130
G.g.4. W.5– 63 = C.-M. & H.113
G.g.4. W.5– 64 = C.-M. & H. 1
G.g.4. W.5– 65 = C.-M. & H.127
G.g.4. W.5– 66 = C.-M. & H. 18
G.g.4. W.5– 67 = C.-M. & H.157
G.g.4. W.5– 68 = C.-M. & H. 3
G.g.4. W.5– 69 = C.-M. & H.112
G.g.4. W.5– 70 = C.-M. & H. 16
G.g.4. W.5– 71 = C.-M. & H.137
G.g.4. W.5– 72 = C.-M. & H. 87
G.g.4. W.5– 73 = C.-M. & H.111
G.g.4. W.5– 74 = C.-M. & H.119
G.g.4. W.5– 75 = C.-M. & H.156
G.g.4. W.5– 76 = C.-M. & H.123

G.g.4. W.5– 77 = C.-M. & H. 47
G.g.4. W.5– 78 = C.-M. & H.145
G.g.4. W.5– 79 = C.-M. & H. 53
G.g.4. W.5– 80 = C.-M. & H. 37
G.g.4. W.5– 81 = C.-M. & H. 88
G.g.4. W.5– 82 = C.-M. & H. 49
G.g.4. W.5– 83 = C.-M. & H.139
G.g.4. W.5– 84 = C.-M. & H.140
G.g.4. W.5– 85 = C.-M. & H.142
G.g.4. W.5– 86 = C.-M. & H. 21
G.g.4. W.5– 87 = C.-M. & H. 20
G.g.4. W.5– 88 = C.-M. & H.138
G.g.4. W.5– 89 = C.-M. & H.125
G.g.4. W.5– 90 = C.-M. & H.108
G.g.4. W.5– 91 = C.-M. & H.141
G.g.4. W.5– 92 = C.-M. & H.146
G.g.4. W.5– 93 = C.-M. & H. 38
G.g.4. W.5– 94 = C.-M. & H. 82
G.g.4. W.5– 95 = C.-M. & H.147
G.g.4. W.5– 96 = C.-M. & H. 83
G.g.4. W.5– 97 = C.-M. & H.136
G.g.4. W.5– 98 = C.-M. & H.133
G.g.4. W.5– 99 = C.-M. & H. 54
G.g.4. W.5–100 = C.-M. & H.110
G.g.4. W.5–101 = C.-M. & H.134
G.g.4. W.5–102 = C.-M. & H. 4
G.g.4. W.5–103 = C.-M. & H.109
G.g.4. W.5–104 = C.-M. & H.131
G.g.4. W.5–105 = C.-M. & H. 76
G.g.4. W.5–106 = C.-M. & H. 8
G.g.4. W.5–107 = C.-M. & H.104
G.g.4. W.5–108 = C.-M. & H.102
G.g.4. W.5–109 = C.-M. & H.100
G.g.4. W.5–110 = C.-M. & H.105
G.g.4. W.5–111 = C.-M. & H.103
G.g.4. W.5–112 = C.-M. & H.101
G.g.4. W.5–113 = C.-M. & H.124
G.g.4. W.5–114 = C.-M. & H.148
G.g.4. W.5–115 = C.-M. & H. 5
G.g.4. W.5–116 = C.-M. & H.149
G.g.4. W.5–117 = C.-M. & H. 95
G.g.4. W.5–118 = C.-M. & H.150
G.g.4. W.5–119 = C.-M. & H.151
G.g.4. W.5–120 = C.-M. & H.152
G.g.4. W.5–121 = C.-M. & H. 99
G.g.4. W.5–122 = C.-M. & H. 6
G.g.4. W.5–123 = C.-M. & H. 22

G.g.4. W.5–124 = C.-M. & H. 23

G.g.4. W.5–125 = C.-M. & H.117

G.g.4. W.5–126 = C.-M. & H. 57

G.g.4. W.5–127 = C.-M. & H. 77

G.g.4. W.5–128 = C.-M. & H. 78

G.g.4. W.5–129 = C.-M. & H.153

G.g.4. W.5–130 = C.-M. & H. 24

G.g.4. W.5–131 = C.-M. & H. 39

G.g.4. W.5–132 = C.-M. & H. 68

G.g.4. W.5–133 = C.-M. & H. 40

G.g.4. W.5–134 = C.-M. & H. 70

G.g.4. W.5–135 = C.-M. & H.154

G.g.4. W.5–136 = C.-M. & H. 84

G.g.4. W.5–137 = C.-M. & H. 85

G.g.4. W.5–138 = C.-M. & H. 126

G.g.4. W.5–139 = C.-M. & H. 93

G.g.4. W.5–140 = C.-M. & H. 89

G.g.4. W.5–141 = C.-M. & H. 90

G.g.4. W.5–142 = C.-M. & H.120

G.g.4. W.5–143 = C.-M. & H. 60

G.g.4. W.5–144 = C.-M. & H.118

G.g.4. W.5–145 = C.-M. & H. 61

G.g.4. W.5–146 = C.-M. & H. 69

G.g.4. W.5–147 = C.-M. & H. 41

G.g.4. W.5–148 = C.-M. & H. 55

G.g.4. W.5–149 = C.-M. & H. 58

G.g.4. W.5–150 = C.-M. & H. 56

G.g.4. W.5–151 = C.-M. & H. 91

G.g.4. W.5–152 = C.-M. & H. 9

G.g.4. W.5–153 = C.-M. & H. 79

G.g.4. W.5–154 = C.-M. & H. 59

G.g.4. W.5–155 = C.-M. & H. 92

G.g.4. W.5–156 = C.-M. & H. 96

G.g.4. W.5–157 = C.-M. & H. 97

G.g.4. W.5–158 = C.-M. & H. 80

G.g.4. W.5–159 = C.-M. & H.121

G.g.4. W.5–160 = C.-M. & H. 71

G.g.4. W.5–161 = C.-M. & H. 28

G.g.4. W.5–162 = C.-M. & H. 98

G.g.4. W.5–163 = C.-M. & H. 26

G.g.4. W.5–164 = C.-M. & H. 72

G.g.4. W.5–165 = C.-M. & H. 29

G.g.4. W.5–166 = C.-M. & H.155

G.g.4. W.5–167 = C.-M. & H. 19

G.g.4. W.5–168 = C.-M. & H. 27

G.g.4. W.5–169 = C.-M. & H. 62

G.g.4. W.5–170 = C.-M. & H. 81

G.g.4. W.5–171 = C.-M. & H. 25

G.g.4. W.5–172 = C.-M. & H.172

G.g.4. W.5–173 = C.-M. & H. 42

G.g.4. W.5–174 = C.-M. & H. 31

G.g.4. W.5–175 = C.-M. & H. 32

[Single Drawing]

1863–5–9–933 = C.-M. & H.17

BEALE, MARY

B. 1632/3: D. 1699

Portraitist

Born in March, 1632/3 and baptized on the 26th of that month at Barrow, Suffolk, the daughter of the Rev. John Cradock, B.D. (Rector of Redgrave, 1628–30, and Barrow, 1630–52), and Dorothy Cradock (maiden name unknown). Her grandfather, Richard Cradock, and her great-grandfather, John Cradock, were also divines, the former having been Vicar of Basingthorpe, Lincs., and Barrow, the latter Rector of Redgrave. May have inherited her artistic talent from her father who is perhaps identical with the Rev. John Cradock who 'presented a piece of painting of his owne makeing' to the Painter-Stainers' Company on July 7th, 1648. Received instruction from Lely (*q.v.*) and also perhaps from Lely's friend, a 'picture drawer' by name Bramwell of Bury St. Edmunds. Married, March 8th, 1651/2, Charles Beale I (*See* p. 153, No. 1) and soon after took up painting as a profession. Received lessons from her husband's friend, the poet-miniaturist Thomas Flatman and also perhaps from the Cromwellian portraitist Robert Walker. Lived in Hind Court, Fleet St., where her husband had official lodgings as a Deputy Clerk of the Patents. Was of sufficient eminence by 1658 to be commended by Sir William Sanderson with other English women painters, Mrs. Anne Carlisle, Mrs. Brooman and Mrs. Weimes but her name is misprinted as 'Mr. Beale'. Painted a portrait of Abraham Cowley (now in the possession of Mr. Hugh Beale) and counted a number of future distinguished divines among her sitters. Moved with her family in 1665 at the time of the Plague to Albrooke, near Otterbourne, Hants., remaining there till 1669. On returning to London settled first in Bow St., Clerkenwell, and then in a house 'next the Golden Ball, in Pall Mall' which soon became the centre of a distinguished circle of friends including Fellows of the Royal Society (who used it as an informal meeting-place), artists and men of letters (including Abraham Cowley) and prominent churchmen (including the future Bishops Stillingfleet and Tillotson). In 1665 her husband had lost his post as Deputy Clerk of the Patents, and Mary became the chief supporter of the family. From about 1672 onwards came again under the influence of Lely whose painting methods are noted down by Charles Beale in his notebook for that year. After Lely's death in 1680 was much employed in making replicas of his portraits. Occasionally painted miniatures, two cited by Long being dated respectively 1674 and 1677. The large group of characteristic drawings in red chalk, in the B.M. and elsewhere, formerly attributed to her, are now definitely established as the work of her son, Charles. At some time unknown wrote a *Discourse of Friendship*, the MS. of which is in the possession of Sir Charles Bunbury, Bart., at Bury, Suffolk. Continued painting up to at least a year before her death which took place in the autumn of 1699. Was buried in St. James's, Piccadilly, on Oct. 8th of that year.

BIBL.: *Painter-Stainers' Minutes*, I, p. 225. Sanderson, p. 20. Baker, *Lely*, II, pp. 34–42 & 162–9. Long, p. 21. Vertue, *Index*, p. 15. Walsh, *passim. Inf.* from Miss E. Walsh.

1. A YOUNG MAN, PERHAPS BARTHOLOMEW BEALE. Head, turned half-l., with eyes looking to front. Wearing long wavy hair.   Plate 107

Crayons on buff paper; $27 \cdot 5 \times 19 \cdot 3$ cm. ($10\frac{3}{4} \times 7\frac{5}{8}$ in.). Old mount; $39 \times 30 \cdot 5$ cm. ($15\frac{3}{8} \times 12$ in.).

INSCR.: *Recto*, on the old mount, at the foot in ink, *Mrs Mary Beale*, and in black lead, *portrait of her Son*.

Verso, also on the old mount, in the same hand, in ink, *v. H. Walpoles Annecdotes . . . Mrs Mary Beale, Portrait of her Son . . . JK/Z.*

PROV.: Richardson I or II (?), but not identifiable in any of their sales. Wellesley (Sale, Sotheby, 25:vi:1866, Lot 146 or 147). R. Buller Strode, from whom it was purchased, through Messrs. Christie, by the B.M., 1956.

1956–10–13–1.

[Bartholomew Beale (B. 1655/6: D. 1709). Elder son of Mary Beale. Born probably in Feb. 1655/6 in Hind Court, Fleet St., and was baptized on Feb. 12th at St. Paul's, Covent Garden. Like his brother, Charles (*q.v.*), intended to become a painter, and was taught by Thomas Flatman. Put in the draperies in his mother's portraits. Subsequently studied medicine at Cambridge, being admitted a pensioner at Clare, Jan. 22nd, 1679/80. Became M.B. in 1682. Was also a pupil of the well-known physician, Dr. Thomas Sydenham. Settled in Coventry about 1687 and practised there until his death. In 1697/8 complained that his fees were so small that he could not keep a horse. Published in 1706 his *Essay attempting a more certain and satisfactory discovery both of the true causes of diseases proceeding from vicious bloods, and the genuine operations of all remedies used internally in their cure*. Was buried in St. Michael's Church, Coventry].

The suggested identification of the present drawing cannot be established with any certainty; but comparison with the heads of the Beale boys in Mary's self-portrait at the N.P.G. (No. 1687) points to Bartholomew (on the l.) rather than to Charles as the possible sitter. Dr. Wellesley also owned a companion drawing, presumably of Charles Beale II, the present ownership of which is unknown. No other authentic drawings by Mary Beale have since come to light, with which the present example might be compared, so it is impossible to tell how far the inscription on the old mount, certainly of the XVIII c., can be relied on. The attribution is, however, consistent with the style of the drawing which is clearly of the Lely school, having noticeable affinities with a group of portrait-studies in the Department given to another pupil of Lely, Michael Dahl (pp. 294–295, Nos. 1–3).

BECKMAN, SIR MARTIN

Fl. from 1660: D. 1702

Military engineer and topographical draughtsman

Of Swedish origin. According to Vertue, in his mention of 'drawings done by Sir Marstin (*sic*) Beckman, views & shipping, this gentleman learnt of Mr Wyck to draw'. First heard of when he was in charge of the firework display on the Thames in honour of Charles II's Restoration. Soon after, petitioned the King for appointment as Royal Engineer, an office previously held by his brother under Charles I. In 1661 sailed as 'firemaster with and in his majesty's fleete' on an expedition under the 1st Earl of Sandwich against the Algerine pirates and subsequently to take possession of Tangier as part of Catherine of Braganza's dowry. Planned the fortifications there, and drew two maps of the place, both in the B.M. (*King's Topography*, CXVII, 77 & 78) one of which is inscribed *Made by the Schwediche Captain Martin Beckman fecit*. Was back in England by 1662, and was subsequently committed to the Tower apparently on a false charge. On his release went to Holland, but was recalled before 1670 when he was appointed 'third engineer of Great Britain'. In 1671 assisted in the capture of Colonel Thomas Blood when the latter attempted to steal the Crown Jewels. Was, at some time in the 1680's, commander of the fort at Hull when he executed oil paintings of river and shipping scenes now in the Trinity House, Hull. For the remainder of his life was much employed on inspecting coastal defences, and in this connexion drew several plans and views in grey wash and water-colour, which are characterized by neat execution, soft brush-work and a partiality for pale tints of greyish green and pinkish brown. Good examples are in *King's Topography* including views of Clifford's Fort at Tynemouth, 1672 (XXXIII, 23g), of Castle Cornet, Guernsey, 1694 (LV, 62), and a fair copy, made in 1701, of a prospect and plan of Gibraltar originally taken in 1684. Also took part in various expeditions, including that under Lord Dartmouth in 1683 to superintend the destruction of the defences of Tangier prior to its evacuation. Soon after James II's accession, in 1685, was knighted and became Chief Engineer of Great Britain. In 1688 was appointed 'comptroller of fireworkes, as well as for war as for triumph', and first head of the royal laboratory at Woolwich. At the Revolution was made chief engineer of the king's train of ordnance against William of Orange, but was not called upon to take action. Transferred his allegiance to William under whom he continued to give valuable service, especially in the development of coastal attack by means of bomb-ships. Some idea of his art as a master of pyrotechnics may be gathered from the effective mezzotint, probably by Bernard Lens II, of the firework display designed by Beckman in St. James's Square, Dec. 2nd, 1697, on the occasion of the Peace of Ryswyck. Died in London on June 24th, 1702.

BIBL.: *D.N.B., Suppl. I*, I, 1901, p. 160. *Vertue*, I, p. 160. *Inf.* from Dr. A. L. Binns.

1. MALAGA FROM THE N.W. Vicw over grassy and undulating ground towards the city, with the river Guadalmedina flowing by it. In the foreground, l., a church, probably that of La Trinidad, and in mid-distance, l., the Castill de Gibralfaro on its hill. Towards the centre, a lofty building not yet identified. In the background, the bay with shipping. **Plate 162 (a)**

Brush drawing in grcy wash; on two conjoined sheets; 15 × 69·8 cm. (5⅞ × 27½ in.).

INSCR.: *Recto*, in the lower margin, centre, *Malaga from the shore. 1661.*
   Verso, in the lower r.-hand corner, by the artist, *Malago from yᵉ Shoare | 1661 in | augusti | Monat.*

PROV.: Alfred Jowett, by whom it was presented to the B.M., 1935.
1935-5-16-1.

Drawn by Beckman when he accompanied the Earl of Sandwich on his expcdition against the Algerine pirates in 1661. The inscription in his hand on the *verso* is partly in English and partly in Swedish.

BOL, CORNELIS
B. 1589 (?). Working *c.* 1635–66 (?)
Topographical painter, draughtsman and etcher

Probably a member of a Flemish family of painters originally of Mechlin, and later of Antwerp. Thieme-Becker cites at least three Cornelis Bols: (1) B. 1535–6 at Mechlin, and living at Antwerp; (2) B. 1589 at Antwerp and living in London in 1640; (3) according to Immerzeel, working in London in 1666 at the time of the Great Fire, of which he painted a picture. Moens refers to 'Cornelis Bol, with his wife member of the Dutch Church London 1636 with attestation from Paris'. In the Gough collection at the Bodleian Library (*Miscellaneous Antiquities*, 17554, *ff.* 121–2) is an etching, signed *C.BOL FECIT.* and lettered: *A Representation in what manner the Spannisch fleet at this present lyeth in the downs and how the same is beset by the hollanders with thayr fleet 26 September, 1639.* The prospect is taken from the sea and shows the English coast in the background extending from Dover, l., to Sandwich, r., the ships and landmarks being identified by a key in English and French in the lower margin. According to Vertue, there were at Wotton, seat of the Evelyn family, 'three views of London from the River side. Arundel House Somersett House Tower Lond. painted before the fire of Lond. by Cornelius Bol. a good free Taste'. Walpole incorrectly states that these were at Sutton Place. They are still in the possession of the Evelyn family, and are now at Stonor Park, Henley-on-Thames. In the Dulwich College Gallery is a painting, signed *CB* and attributed to Cornelis Bol, representing London from the Thames with Somerset House in the foreground, looking towards Westminster Hall, the Savoy and Whitehall. A set of etchings by a Cornelis Bol after Abraham Casembrot, lettered *A. Kaesembrot invenit. Cornelius Bol fecit Ciatres execidit*, are probably by the same hand as that of the 'Spannisch

fleet' mentioned above. Four of them are fanciful Mediterranean coast scenes; but one (No. iii) is a view of Lambeth Palace, which, as Casembrot does not appear ever to have come to England, may be after Bol himself, and thus be incorrectly lettered. Colonel Grant suggests that the second and third on the list, as well as the Cornelis Bol cited by Moens, are all one and the same person, and this is very likely correct. To this artist may be attributed, therefore, all the above-mentioned works, together with the drawing described below.

BIBL.: *Immerzeel*, p. 71. *Walpole*, II, p. 432. *Moens*, p. 216. *Dulwich Cat.*, p. 99, No. 360–(112). *Wurzbach*, I, p. 127. *T.-B.*, IV, 1910, p. 238. *Grant*, I, p. 9. *Vertue, Index*, p. 22.

1. **THE BLOCKHOUSE AT GRAVESEND.** View looking W. up the Thames from the Kentish shore. In the l. foreground, a bank shaded by a tree, and at a little distance away, the blockhouse with a flag flying on the bastion and three cannon on the outer earthworks at the water's edge. A ship in mid-river, r. **Plate 46**

Pen and light brown ink with grey wash; 9.5×18.2 cm. ($3\frac{3}{4} \times 7\frac{1}{4}$ in.).

INSCR.: *Recto*, in the lower l.-hand corner, *S(?) CB*.

Verso, in an old hand, *Het Kasteel Te Schravesende door, Klots fg* (?).

PROV.: Mr. Crisp, from whom it was purchased by the B.M., 1859.
1859–12–10–919 (L.B.1).

When acquired by the Museum this drawing was attributed, on the strength of the inscription on the *verso*, to Valentin Klotz (*Fl.* 1667–91), a Dutch topographical draughtsman and military engineer. It is not by the same hand as the authentic examples of Klotz's work in the B.M. (*See* Hind, *Dutch & Flemish Drawings*, III, p. 126). Neither is

there any record of Klotz having come to England nor of his having had anything to do with the fortifications at Gravesend. The attribution to Cornelis Bol, suggested by Mr. Binyon, is more likely. It is probably based on the initials on the *recto* and on the close similitude, in the handling of the architecture, foliage and other details, with the etchings by Bol after Casembrot described above in the biographical note.

The blockhouse was one of two built by Henry VIII at Gravesend in 1539–43. It was visited by Pepys on June 10th, 1667. In 1778 it was considerably enlarged, along with other fortifications at Gravesend, under the superintendence of Sir Thomas Hyde Page. In 1834 it was sold to the Gravesend Corporation and the surrounding land made into public gardens (*See* Cruden, pp. 162–3 & 509).

BULFINCH, JOHN

Fl. c. 1680–1720 (?)

Draughtsman, and dealer in pictures, prints and drawings

Described by Granger as 'a print-seller in the latter end of the reign of Charles II', and as still living in that of Queen Anne. Was the author of thirty-six portrait-drawings of historical figures, apparently dated collectively *1680*, scattered through the volumes of the 'Sutherland *Clarendon*' in the Ashmolean Museum, Oxford. Mentioned by Vertue in connexion with Willem Van de Velde II's picture of the English and French fleets at the Nore, which Bulfinch acquired from the artist 'sometime after the Kings death' (i.e. after 1685). In collaboration with Thomas Rawlinson, the bibliophile, collected the original prints and drawings on which were based the engravings illustrating Isaac de Larrey's *Histoire d'Angleterre*, 1697–1713. After the death of Thomas Betterton, in 1710, bought up all that actor's pictures including 'a great many Crayon pictures of famous Playereses'. Must have been one of the first to extra-illustrate or 'grangerize' historical works with early prints and drawings, and according to this method, made up three sets of Clarendon's *History of the Rebellion*, one of which may have subsequently provided material, including Bulfinch's drawings already alluded to, for the 'Sutherland *Clarendon*'. Adopted the style of brush-drawing in grey wash generally associated with the type of record-drawing kept in the studios of Kneller (*q.v.*) and his contemporaries, but here used by Bulfinch to copy historical portraits. This method subsequently used also by Vertue. In this connexion it is interesting to note that Granger himself saw 'authentic drawings' by Bulfinch 'from original paintings'. Mentioned by Vertue on a number of occasions in his Notebook of 1713–21 as having provided him with information, so was evidently living still between those dates.

BIBL.: *Granger*, V, p. 347. *Vertue, Index*, p. 29. *Inf.* from Mr. John Woodward. *Sutherland Cat.*

1. SIR CHRISTOPHER MYNGS. T.Q.L., with body to front, head turned slightly to l. and eyes to front, his r. hand extended, his l. on the hilt of his sword. Wearing his light-coloured hair almost to his shoulders, a cravat with patterned ends, a loose dark coat and a broad sword-belt.

Brush drawing in grey wash; $27 \cdot 5 \times 21$ cm. ($10\frac{7}{8} \times 8\frac{1}{4}$ in.).

INSCR.: On a slip of paper, probably cut from the old mount, in ink, *Sir Christopher Mings | FROM | the Original Painting | in the Hands | of his son Cap: Mings | Super-Intendent | at | Portsmouth.*

PROV.: Henry Graves & Co., from whom it was purchased by the B.M., 1852.

1852–10–9–230 (L.B.1).

ENGR.: In mezzotint, by Robert Dunkarton, in Samuel Woodburn's *100 Portraits of Illustrious Characters*, 1810–15, No. 63 (See *C.S.*, I, p. 237, No. 63. *B.M. Engraved Portraits*, III, p. 304, No. 1).

[Vice-Admiral Sir Christopher Myngs (B. 1625: D. 1666). Born at Salthouse, Norfolk. Served in the Navy during the Commonwealth, and was one of the very few commanders not affected by the Restoration. Distinguished for his courage and honesty.

Was knighted for his services at the Battle of Lowestoft, 1665, and killed in that of the North Foreland, 1666.]

The whereabouts of the original painting, from which the present drawing is copied, is unknown. It does not correspond with the portrait of Myngs by Lely at the National Maritime Museum.

2. JOHN THURLOE. T.Q.L., with head and body turned half r. and eyes to front, holding in his r. hand a letter, his l. hand resting on a table on which is a standish. Wearing long curling and light-coloured hair, falling bands, and a dark cloak and doublet.

Brush drawing in dark grey wash, strengthened with gum: $27 \cdot 8 \times 22 \cdot 5$ cm. ($10\frac{7}{8} \times 8\frac{7}{8}$ in.).

PROV.: E. Daniell, from whom it was purchased by the B.M., 1871.
1871–8–12–1879 (L.B.2).

ENGR.: By R. Cooper in Caulfield's *Gallery of British Portraits*, 1814 (*See B.M. Engraved Portraits*, IV, p. 279, No. 3).

[John Thurloe (B. 1616: D. 1668). Secretary of State to Oliver Cromwell and to his son Richard, under whom he had charge of the Intelligence and Postal Services. Played a considerable part in elevating Cromwell to the Protectorate. At the Restoration was accused of high treason, but was later released.]

The original picture is now lost, but another copy of it by Vertue is also in the Department ((G.g. 1–465), and this suggests that it is probably identical with the only portrait of Thurloe mentioned by Vertue, that belonging (about 1736) to Dr. Samuel Knight (*See Vertue*, IV, p. 155).

BYNG, EDWARD

D: 1753

Portrait and drapery painter, and assistant to Sir Godfrey Kneller

Of a Wiltshire branch of the family. One of the nine sons of Thomas Byng (B. 1643 at Potterne, Devizes, described as 'some years Major of the Wiltshire Militia') and Anne Lowberry (said to have been of Gayton, Norfolk). Grandson of the Rev. Robert Byng (*Fl.* from 1625: D. 1658); Rector of All Cannings, Devizes, who married on Dec. 4th, 1639, Elizabeth Waller (a widow(?)), daughter of John St. Loe of Broadchalke and his wife Elizabeth, daughter of Laurence Hyde of East Hatch. Not known how or when he entered Kneller's employment, but is referred to in Kneller's Will (1723) as having 'for many years faithfully served me' and as then lodging in his master's house in Great Queen Street. A 'Mr. Byng' recorded by Vertue among the members of the Academy there in 1711, along with 'Mr. Weedman' (probably Wiedmann, but not identified) and 'Mr. Swartz' (probably Schwartz, also not identified), all three being described as 'painters to Sr. G. Kneller'. Uncertain whether this refers to Edward or Robert (a brother?, *See* below). Was bequeathed an annuity of £100 by Kneller, who also directed in his Will that those pictures left unfinished at his death should be finished by Byng or under his guidance, and for this trouble Byng was to receive the remaining sums due for those pictures already in part paid for, and that for those which had not been paid for at all, he was to receive half of what they fetched on disposal. In a codicil, Kneller further directed that 'in order to enforce and oblige the said Edward Byng to be assisting and subservient to my Wife as aforesaid', the annuity of £100 could be reduced at her instance to £80. In the possession of Mrs. E. M. Whiting, Lime Cottage, Thames Ditton, is a miniature of Byng by Bernard Lens III, signed and dated B L (monogram) 1724. Furnished Vertue with information about Kneller, Thomas Hawker, and Charles Jervas, and presumably was still living in London in 1726–7 when he spoke of the last-mentioned. Retired to Potterne, near Devizes, where his mother had died in 1726. Lived there with a brother Charles (D. 1745), and was later joined by his sister Elizabeth (D. 1759), widow of the Rev. William Wray (See No. 7, f. 92v.). Gave instruction to her son Robert Bateman Wray (B. 1715: D. 1779), later well-known as a gem-engraver in Salisbury. On his own, painted portraits, all in the Kneller manner, of members of his family, including a self-portrait (?) and one said to be of Elizabeth, his sister, now in the possession of Miss Catherine Clarkson of Penfold, Fernhill Road, New Milton, near Christchurch, Hants. Died at Potterne, and was buried there on Feb. 12th, 1753.

Another member of the family, Robert Byng (D: Aug. 1720) is also recorded as a painter. Can scarcely be identical with the Robert (B. 1642) shown in the family tree as the 2nd son of the Rev. Robert Byng (See above) and thus uncle to Edward, but is possibly one of Edward's seven brothers. Is said by Redgrave also to have been employed by Kneller, and to have worked in Salisbury. Was the author of three known portraits:

Josiah Pullen (B. 1631: D. 1714), Vice-Principal of Magdalen Hall (Oxford, Bodleian Library); Cave Underhill (B. 1634: D. 1710(?)), actor (Garrick Club); Timothy Rogers (B. 1658: D. 1728), Nonconformist divine (Dr. Williams's Library). Two other portraits (subjects not known) have been cited, both dated 1716. To Robert Byng may also perhaps be attributed two other pictures, both of sporting interest: one, signed Byng f/1706 (?), of a group of three foxhunters, their servant, and a pack of hounds (in the possession of Messrs. Leggatt, 1952); and the other, A Deer Hunter of the last Age, in Cap and Jack from an Original Picture Byng pinxit, known only through an engraving by C. R. Ryley of 1782.

The Byng relics appear to have descended to subsequent representatives of the family from two of Elizabeth Wray's children: R. B. Wray, the gem-engraver, and Mary Wray (B. 1719) who, according to the family tree, married Hugh Wilkins, an organist, and was the mother of the orientalist, Sir Charles Wilkins (B. 1749 (?): D. 1836), though the D.N.B. says that Sir Charles was the son of Walter Wilkins of Frome and Martha Wray, niece of the gem-engraver.

BIBL.: Administration of the Rev. Robert Byng (P.C.C., f. 97). Will of Sir Godfrey Kneller (Richmond, f. 261). Registers of All Cannings, Potterne, and Broadchalke (inf. from the Revs. C. W. St. Clair Risdall, C. W. Phillips and D. Bland). Tablet to Charles Wray (D. 1791), brother of R. B. Wray, in Potterne Church. Hoare, IV, Part 2, p. 153. Benson and Hatcher, pp. 643–4. Bull (?) Devizes, p. 274. N. and Q., Series III, XII, p. 285. Redgrave, p. 41. Byng Family Tree (Inf. from Mrs. E. N. Whiting). Vertue, Index, p. 31. Inf. from Mr. H. de S. Shortt and Capt. T. T. Barnard.

1. A GENTLEMAN, AFTER DAHL (?).

W.L. standing, turned half-r., his r. hand pointing across his body towards the r., his l. hand resting on his sword hilt. Wearing a dark-coloured coat, and carrying his hat under his l. arm. On the l., the base of a column carved with a military trophy, and in the background, r., statues of Minerva and Justice in niches.

Pen and brown ink, with grey wash, on blue-grey paper; 46·1 × 32·4 cm. (18⅛ × 12¾ in.).

PROV.: Richard Bull (Sale, Sotheby, 23:V:1831, Lot 39, as by Dahl). Purchased by the B.M. at the Bull Sale, through A. W. Thibaudeau, 1881.

1881–6–11–139 (L.B., as by Dahl, 2).

BIBL.: *Nisser*, p. 51, No. 173.

This drawing, like most of those in the sketchbooks described below, is clearly a copy from an oil-painting. Another version, fairly near to it in handling and size, is in one of these sketchbooks (No. 2, *f.* 11r.), and yet another smaller and rougher in execution is in the album (No. 8 (63)). In view of the old attribution to Dahl, it is possible that the original painting was by that artist. It should be compared with another drawing, also clearly after an oil-painting, the original of which may have been a portrait of the Duke of Marlborough by Dahl. This too was formerly in the Bull collection. It is now listed with the drawings by Dahl (No. 4).

[2–8.] SKETCHBOOKS AND ALBUM. These appear to have descended from Edward Byng, by way of his sister Elizabeth (*See* No. 7, *f.* 92v.), her son Charles Wray, and her grandson (?), Sir Charles Wilkins, to her great-great-grandson Cecil Wray Byng Wilkins Roberts, who owned them in 1877 (*See* No. 7, *ff.* 39r. & 93r.).

They have considerable interest as a commentary on the activities of Kneller's Studio in Great Queen Street, and Nos. 2–7, the sketchbooks, contain for the most part studies after portraits, all, or nearly all by him. They are in the familiar technique of black chalk and grey or brown wash, often strengthened with pen and ink and heightened with white, which one associates with this class of copying (*See* Introduction, p. xxxii), and may perhaps be looked on rather as models for poses than actual records of sitters. Unfortunately very few of the studies are named: if they had been, they would have presented a remarkable gallery of Kneller's clients and have been invaluable in helping to identify many unknown portraits by him; as it is, the finished paintings, or engravings after them, when found, have had to be used to identify these drawings.

The material at No. 8, originally loose in a portfolio and now mounted in an album, also includes drawings belonging to the same category of portrait-copy (Nos. (1)–(67)).

All these drawings have been attributed jointly to Edward and Robert Byng, and as such were catalogued by Mr. Binyon. Apart from the miscellaneous drawings in No. 8 (Nos. (68)–(86)), where certainly several hands are represented, there may be two distinct hands at work in the sketchbooks Nos. 2–7, one, the more competent, represented in Nos. 2, 3, 4 & 5, the other, characterized by heavy diagonal hatching, in No. 7.

These two possibly distinct hands are also found together apparently in the same book, No. 6. Unfortunately there is no clue as to which brother is responsible for which hand (that is assuming that the two brothers are really represented here), and their descendant, C. W. B. W. Roberts, in his MS. note in No. 4, *f.* 1v., only refers ambiguously to his 'Great Great Great Uncle while pupil to Sir Godfrey Kneller', without further specification. But that it was probably Edward whom Mr. Roberts associated with these drawings is, however, suggested by another note in No. 7, *f.* 43r., in which he asserts that Queen Anne was 'cousin thro the Hydes to Mr. Edward Byng'.

Other material relating to the Kneller portrait manufactory is to be found in No. 8 (Nos. (88)–(98)). In this are clearly studies for or after hands in portraits, and Nos. (99)–(114) are life-size tracings of heads and other details, in red chalk on varnished paper, direct from the finished oil-paintings, made no doubt for purposes of repetition.

Another side of the life in Kneller's studio, the academy founded there in 1711, is also represented in No. 8 (Nos. (68)–(86)). These drawings comprise nineteen academic studies by various hands, some of them very competent, notably Nos. (81)–(85) which recall certain drawings by Louis Chéron (*q.v.*), who was a member of the Kneller Academy until he broke with it in 1720. Two drawings from the series by other known assistants in the studio, John James Baker (Bakker) and the elder Marcellus Laroon, have been catalogued under those artists.

From the above it is obvious, as one might expect, that the Byngs, or rather Edward Byng, came into possession of much of the residue of Kneller's studio. Another and rather similar group of drawings, many of them actually signed by Kneller himself, to whom they have all been attributed, apparently descended from the same source, and were acquired in 1888 by the B.M. from a Mrs. E. A. Roberts, who was undoubtedly also a member of the family (*See* p. 390).

2. SKETCHBOOK. Containing 72 leaves, including insertions, filled with studies after portraits, most of which are presumably by Kneller, but some perhaps by Dahl.

Blue-grey paper; 54·7 × 32 cm. (21⅝ × 12⅝ in.).
BINDING: Original blue-grey paper boards with leather spine.

Outside the upper cover.
INSCR.: On a label, *Byng's drawings* | & | *Collections.*

Inside of upper cover.
INSCR.: In red chalk, *No. 1.*

f. 1. BLANK.

f. 2r. SIDNEY GODOLPHIN, 1st EARL OF GODOLPHIN, AFTER KNELLER. W.L., seated, with body half-r. and eyes to front, holding his white wand as Lord High Treasurer. Wearing Garter robes, his hat on a table beside him.

Pen and brown ink, with grey wash, heightened with white.

[Sidney Godolphin, 1st Earl of Godolphin (B. 1645: D. 1712). Lord High Treasurer, and Marlborough's political ally, 1702–10. At first a staunch Tory, but later veered towards the Whigs.]

The original picture is in the collection of the Duke of Marlborough at Blenheim (*See Scharf*, p. 198).

f. 3r. (*a*) A PAINTER. Nearly W.L., seated, painting at an easel, with body to l. and eyes to front. Wearing a cloak over his coat.

Pen and brown ink.

(b) SIR THOMAS ASTON, 3rd BART., AFTER KNELLER. W.L., standing, turned half-l., his l. hand resting on a fountain, his r. hand extended. In the distance l., a park, with a man holding a horse.

Pen and brown ink, with grey wash, heightened with white.

[Sir Thomas Aston, 3rd Bart. (B. 1665/6: D. 1724/5). Of Aston, Cheshire. Succeeded his father in 1702. Was Sheriff of Cheshire in 1723.]

Two versions of the picture are recorded, both formerly in the Aston collection, one with Messrs. Leggatt of 30 St. James's Street in 1928, the other, signed and dated 1711, in the collection of the Hon. Lady Ward (Sale, Christie, 17:v:1946, Lot 54). In the present drawing the head is tilted further back than in either painting.

f. 4r. A NAVAL OR MILITARY COM-MANDER. W.L. seated, with body half-r. and eyes to front, his l. arm resting on a table on which are his hat and a baton or telescope. On the floor, l., a helmet, breastplate and gauntlet.

Pen and brown ink, with grey wash, heightened with white.

f. 5r. HENRIETTA CAVENDISH (HESIGE), LADY HUNTINGTOWER, AFTER KNEL-LER. W.L., standing, with body nearly to front, her l. hand on her hip, her r. hand holding a whip with which she points down-wards. Wearing a three-cornered hat and riding-habit. In the background, r., a horse and groom.

Pen and brown ink, with grey wash, heightened with white.

[Henrietta Cavendish (Hesige), Lady Huntingtower (D. 1717/18). Illegitimate daughter of the 1st Duke of Devonshire. Married clandestinely in 1706 Lionel, Lord Huntingtower, son of the 3rd Earl of Dysart.]

The original picture is at Ham House. A rather similar portrait, also by Kneller,

signed and dated 1714, is that of Henrietta Cavendish Harley, Countess of Oxford, in the collection of the Duke of Portland (See Goulding, p. 24, No. 62, with notes on other versions).

f. 6r. EDWARD VILLIERS, 1st EARL OF JERSEY. W.L., standing, with body to front and head half-l., his l. arm resting on a pedestal carved with his shield of arms and supporting his coronet. Wearing a peer's robes, and a key suspended from his belt.

Pen and brown ink, with grey wash, touched with white.

[Edward Villiers, 1st Earl of Jersey (B. c. 1656: D. 1711). Son of Sir Edmund Villiers, of Richmond, Surrey, whom he succeeded as Knight Marshal in 1689. Created succes-sively Baron Villiers, Viscount Villiers, and finally, in 1697, Earl of Jersey. Minister at The Hague in 1697–8, and Paris in 1698–9. Lord Chamberlain to the Household of William III and Queen Anne in 1700–4.]

The original picture has not been traced, but the sitter has been identified through the shield of arms on the pedestal.

f. 7r. AN ELDERLY WIDOWED LADY. W.L., seated, with body half-r. and eyes to front. Wearing a dark-coloured dress. Beside her, r., an urn on a pedestal carved with a cherub contemplating an hour-glass.

Pen and brown ink, with grey wash, touched with white.

f. 8r. A MILITARY COMMANDER. W.L., standing, with body slightly to l., and holding a baton with both hands. Wearing armour. On the r., beneath a tree a helmet and gauntlet, and in the distance, l., a cavalry engagement near a fortress.

Pen and brown ink, with grey wash, touched with white.

f. 9r. A TREASURER OF THE NAVY. W.L., standing, with body half-l. and eyes to front, holding in his r. hand on a table a letter addressed *To the Treasurer | of her Maj* *Navy*. On the r., a pilaster carved with a naval trophy.

Pen and brown ink, with grey wash, touched with white.

f. 10*r.* A LADY. W.L., standing, with body nearly to front, head half-l. and eyes to front, her l. hand extended and pointing downwards. Wearing a white or light-coloured dress. On a table beside her, l., a bouquet of flowers.

Pen and brown ink, with grey wash, touched with white.

f. 11*r.* A GENTLEMAN, AFTER DAHL (?). W.L., standing, with body half-r. and eyes to front, his r. hand pointing across his body towards the r., his l. hand resting on his sword hilt. Wearing a dark-coloured coat, and carrying his hat under his l. arm. On the l., the base of a column carved with a military trophy, and in the background, r., statues of Minerva and Justice in niches.

Pen and brown ink, with grey wash, heightened with white. (*Cf.* other versions above at No. 1, and below at No. 8 (63).)

f. 12*r.* A LADY. W.L., standing, with body nearly to front, head half-l. and eyes to front, her l. hand resting on a fountain topped by a cupid holding a dolphin. Wearing a dark-coloured dress. At her feet, r., a small spaniel.

Pen and brown ink, with grey wash, heightened with white.

f. 13*r.* A GENTLEMAN. W.L., standing, with body half-r. and eyes to front, his r. hand on his hip, his l. hand by his side holding a glove. Wearing a dark-coloured coat, his hat on a table beside him, r. On the l., a column and curtain.

Pen and brown ink, with grey wash, touched with white.

f. 14*r.* A LADY. W.L., standing, with body nearly to front, head half-r. and eyes to front, her l. hand holding up a fold of her skirt, her r. hand pointing downwards. Wearing a light-coloured dress. On the l., a fountain with a cupid and a dolphin in a niche.

Pen and brown ink, with grey wash, touched with white.

f. 15*r.* A GENTLEMAN WITH A GREY-HOUND. W.L., standing, with body half-l. and eyes to front, his l. hand on his hip, his r. hand on the head of a hound. Wearing a light-coloured coat. Trees in the background, l.

Brush drawing in grey wash, touched with white.

f. 16*r.* A MILITARY COMMANDER, PER-HAPS JOHN CHURCHILL, 1st DUKE OF MARLBOROUGH, AFTER DAHL. W.L., standing, with body half-l. and head half-r., his l. hand on his hip, his r. on his plumed helmet. Wearing armour and the ribbon of an order over his r. shoulder. In the distance, r., a cavalry skirmish.

Pen and brown ink, with grey wash, touched with white.

A less accomplished version of the drawing listed as No. 4 under Michael Dahl.

f. 17*r.* DOROTHY WALPOLE, VISCOUN-TESS TOWNSHEND, AFTER KNELLER. W.L., standing, with body nearly to front, head half-l. and eyes to front, a parakeet perched on her l. hand, her r. hand pointing downwards across her body. Wearing a light-coloured dress. On the r., a dolphin fountain and basket of flowers.

Pen and brown ink, with grey-brown wash, touched with white.

[Dorothy Walpole, Viscountess Townshend (D. 1726). Daughter of Robert Walpole of Houghton, and sister to Sir Robert Walpole. Married Charles, 2nd Viscount Townshend *c.* 1713, as his second wife.]

The original picture, signed and dated

1715, was in the collection of Lady Townshend (Sale, Christie, 4:vii:1947, Lot 4).

f. 18r. A LADY WITH A SMALL DOG. W.L., seated, with body half-r., head half-l. and eyes to front, her l. hand pointing downwards, her r. hand held to her breast. Wearing a light-coloured dress. Beside her, r., a small dog.

Brush drawing in grey wash over black chalk.

f. 19r. A MILITARY COMMANDER. Standing, with body half-l. and eyes to front, his l. hand resting on his helmet, his r. hand outstretched and holding a baton. Wearing armour and the Ribbon of the Garter. In the distance, l., a cavalry skirmish below a fort.

Brush drawing in grey wash, heightened with white.

Cf. No. 4, *f.* 6r.

f. 20r. A GENTLEMAN. W.L., standing, with body half-r. and eyes to front, his l. hand on a stick, his r. hand on his hip holding a glove, his hat on a ledge beside him, r.

Brush drawing in grey wash, touched with pen and ink and heightened with white.

f. 21r. CHARLES SEYMOUR, 6th DUKE OF SOMERSET, AFTER KNELLER. W.L., standing, with body half-l. and eyes to front, his l. hand on his hip, his r. hand holding his plumed hat. Wearing Garter robes.

Brush drawing in grey wash, heightened with white.

[Charles Seymour, 6th Duke of Somerset (B. 1662: D. 1748). Succeeded his brother in 1678. Created Knight of the Garter in 1684. Supported William III in 1688, and later enjoyed the favour of Queen Anne. Was known as 'the Proud Duke'.]

A T.Q.L. version of the picture, signed and dated *1713*, is in the collection of Lord Leconfield at Petworth House (*See* Collins

Baker, *Petworth*, p. 68, No. 345.) Another T.Q.L. version, signed and dated *1720*, was in the collection of Miss J. M. Seymour (Sale, Christie, 19:i:1945, Lot 56), where it was wrongly described as Edward Seymour, 8th Duke.

f. 22r. A LADY. W.L., standing, with body to front and head half-l., her l. elbow leaning on a carved pedestal, r., her r. hand pointing downwards across her body. Wearing a light-coloured dress. In the background, l., a balustrade with trees beyond.

Brush drawing in grey wash, heightened with white.

f. 23r. A DUKE. W.L., standing, with body half-l. and eyes to front, his l. hand holding up a fold of his mantle, his r. hand touching his coronet on a table beside him. Wearing peer's robes.

Pen and brown ink, with grey wash, heightened with white.

f. 24r. HENRY GREY, 11th EARL AND 1st. DUKE OF KENT, AFTER KNELLER. W.L., standing, with body half-r. and eyes to front, his l. hand holding a glove, his r. hand tucked into a fold of his dark coat. Wearing the Star and Ribbon of the Garter, and a key suspended at his waist.

Pen and brown ink, with grey wash, heightened with white.

[Henry Grey, 11th Earl and 1st Duke of Kent (B. 1671: D. 1740). Succeeded his father as 11th Earl in 1702. Held various offices in the Royal Household, including that of Lord Chamberlain in 1704–10, and was Lord Lieutenant of the counties of Hereford, Bedford and Buckingham between 1704 and 1719. Was created Duke of Kent in 1710, Knight of the Garter in 1713, and in 1714 acted as one of the Lords Justices (Regents) at Queen Anne's death.]

The whereabouts of the original picture is not known, but the identification of the subject as the 1st Duke of Kent is suggested by his wearing the Star and Ribbon of the Garter and the key as Lord Chamberlain.

f. 25r. A LADY WITH HER INFANT SON, AND A NURSE. W.L., seated on a stone bench, with body half-r., head half-l. and eyes to front, holding in her lap her son. Behind the bench, r., a nurse leaning over and looking at the child to whom she offers a basket of flowers. In the background, r., an arcade.

Pen and brown ink, with grey wash, touched with white.

f. 26v. [inserted]. A YOUNG LADY WITH A HOUND. W.L., seated on a bench, with body half-r. and head to front, her l. hand resting on the bench, her r. hand in her lap. At her feet, l., a hound. Trees in the background, l.

Black chalk, heightened with white and strengthened with pen and ink.

Cf. No. *7, f. 60v.*

f. 27r. [inserted]. BLANK.

f. 28r. A LADY WITH HER CHILD. W.L., seated in a chair, with body slightly to r. and head half-l., holding in her l. arm an infant, her r. arm by her side.

Black lead outline.

f. 29r. A DUCHESS. W.L., seated, with body to front and head half-r., her l. hand resting in her lap, her r. hand touching a lock of her hair. Wearing an ermine-edged mantle over her dress, her coronet on a ledge beside her, l. An arcade in the background, r.

Pen and brown ink, with grey wash, heightened with white.

f. 30r. SIR GODFREY AND LADY KNELLER, AFTER KNELLER. Both W.L., he standing on the r., and holding by the hand his wife who is seated on the l. Beside each of them, a small spaniel. On the r., an orange

tree in a vase, and in the background, l., a grove of trees.

Pen and brown ink, with grey wash, heightened with white.

The whereabouts of the original picture is not known, but the identification of the subject with Kneller is suggested by the gold medal which he is shown wearing (that presented to him by William III), and by the resemblance to the self-portrait of him in the Bodleian Library (*See* Poole, *Oxford Portraits,* I, p. 89, No. 222, & Pl. XIV).   **Plate 85**

f. 31r. SARAH, DUCHESS OF MARLBOROUGH, AFTER KNELLER. W.L., seated, with body half-r., and head half-l. and eyes to front, her l. arm extended, her r. hand touching her breast. Wearing an ermine-edged mantle over her dress, and a key, as Mistress of the Robes, suspended from her waist, her coronet on a ledge beside her, l.

Pen and brown ink, with grey wash, heightened with white.

[Sarah (Jennings) Churchill, Duchess of Marlborough (B. 1660: D. 1744). Wife of John, 1st Duke of Marlborough, and the principal favourite of Queen Anne during the earlier part of her reign.]

The original picture, at Petworth, is signed and dated *1705* (*See* Collins Baker, *Petworth,* p. 67, No. 197). Another, signed alone, is at Woburn (*See* Scharf, *Woburn,* p. 136, No. 204), and T.Q.L. versions are at Althorp and in the National Portrait Gallery. The picture was engraved in mezzotint by John Faber the younger (*See B.M. Engraved Portraits,* III, p. 167).

f. 32r. MARGARET CECIL, COUNTESS OF RANELAGH, AFTER KNELLER. W.L., standing, with body slightly to l., head half-r. and eyes to front, her l. hand holding up a fold of her skirt, her r. hand extended. Wearing a light-coloured dress. On the r., a draped curtain, and on the l., a vase of flowers.

Pen and brown ink, with grey wash, heightened with white.

[Margaret Cecil, Countess of Ranelagh (B. 1673: D. 1727). Daughter of James, 3rd Earl of Salisbury. Married firstly John, 2nd Baron Stawell, and secondly Richard Jones, Earl of Ranelagh.]

The original picture is at Hampton Court (*See* Collins Baker, *Hampton Court*, p. 84, No. 37). It was engraved in mezzotint by John Faber the younger (*See B.M. Engraved Portraits*, III, p. 543, No. 1).

f. 33r. CAREY FRASER, COUNTESS OF PETERBOROUGH, AFTER KNELLER. W.L., standing, with body slightly to r., head slightly to l. and eyes to front, her l. hand resting on the base of a statue of Minerva, r., her r. hand held across her breast, wearing a light-coloured dress and drapery. A brocaded curtain in the background, l.

Pen and brown ink, with grey wash, touched with white.

[Carey Fraser, Countess of Peterborough (D. 1709). Daughter of Sir Alexander Fraser, Bart., Physician to the King. Married Charles Mordaunt, 3rd Earl of Peterborough, about 1678.]

The original picture is at Hampton Court (*See* Collins Baker, *Hampton Court*, p. 84, No. 33). It was engraved in mezzotint by John Faber the younger (*See B.M. Engraved Portraits*, III, p. 456, No. 1).

f. 34r. ISABELLA, DUCHESS OF GRAFTON, AFTER KNELLER. W.L., standing, with body slightly to r. and head half-l., her l. hand dipping a shell into the basin of a triton fountain beside her, r., her r. hand holding up drapery. On the l., an orange tree in a vase.

Pen and brown ink.

[Isabella (Bennet) Fitzroy, Duchess of Grafton (B. 1667: D. 1723). Daughter of Henry Bennet, 1st Earl of Arlington. Married Henry Fitzroy, 1st Duke of Grafton.]

The original picture is at Hampton Court (*See* Collins Baker, *Hampton Court*, p. 85, No. 46). It was engraved in mezzotint by Bernard Lens and by John Faber the younger (*See B.M. Engraved Portraits*, II, p. 362, Nos. 1 & 2).

f. 35r. A LADY, PERHAPS CATHARINE SEDLEY, COUNTESS OF DORCHESTER, AFTER KNELLER. W.L., standing, with body slightly to r. and head half-l., her l. arm resting on a large vase with an orange tree in it, r., her r. hand touching a fold of drapery. In the background, l., a fountain.

Pen and brown ink.

[Catharine Sedley, Countess of Dorchester (B. 1657: D. 1717). Daughter of Sir Charles Sedley. Became the mistress of James II, and was created Baroness Darlington and Countess of Dorchester in 1686. Married Sir David Colyear in 1696.]

This drawing corresponds exactly in details of drapery and accessories with a portrait of a lady by Kneller, called 'the Countess of Dorchester', formerly with Messrs. Knoedler and Messrs. Agnew, but the face seems to be different. Another rather similar portrait is that of the Duchess of St. Albans, also by Kneller, at Hampton Court (*See* Collins Baker, *Hampton Court*, p. 84, No. 26).

f. 35v. STUDY OF THE ROYAL MACE IN *f.* 36r.

Pen and brown ink, with brown wash, heightened with white.

f. 36r. WILLIAM COWPER, 1st EARL COWPER, AFTER KNELLER. W.L., standing, with body half-l. and eyes to front. holding in his r. hand a scroll. Wearing robes as Lord Chancellor. On a table beside him, l., the Mace.

Pen and brown ink, with brown wash, heightened with white.

[William Cowper, 1st Earl Cowper (B. c. 1665: D. 1723). Son of Sir William

Cowper, 2nd Bart. Supporter of William III and of the Whigs. Appointed Keeper of the Great Seal in 1705, Baron Cowper in 1706, Lord High Chancellor in 1707–10 and 1714–18, and finally Viscount Fordwich and Earl Cowper in 1717/18.]

The original picture may be at Panshanger. A bust-length portrait, corresponding with the upper part of the present drawing, was engraved in mezzotint by John Smith (*See B.M. Engraved Portraits*, I, p. 507, No. 1).

f. 37r. A DUCHESS, PERHAPS HARRIET, DUCHESS OF NEWCASTLE. W.L., standing, with body half-r. and head half-l., her l. hand holding a lock of her hair. Wearing an ermine-lined mantle over a light-coloured dress. On a ledge, r., a Duchess's coronet, and beyond, seen through an arch, a tower on a wooded hill, perhaps the White Tower on the Mount at Claremont.

Pen and brown ink, with grey wash, heightened with white.

[Harriet (Godolphin) Pelham-Hollis, Duchess of Newcastle (D. 1776). Daughter of Francis, 2nd Earl of Godolphin. Married Thomas Pelham-Hollis, 1st Duke of Newcastle, in 1717.]

The identification of the subject of this drawing with the Duchess of Newcastle is suggested by the tower in the background which resembles the White Tower at Claremont, the Duke's seat. The same building also occurs in the Kit Kat portrait group of the 1st Duke of Newcastle and Henry Clinton, 7th Earl of Lincoln in the N.P.G. (*See Killanin*, p. 51, Pl. 58).

f. 38r. A PEERESS IN CORONATION ROBES. W.L., standing, with body slightly to r., head slightly to l. and eyes to front, her l. hand resting on a ledge, her r. hand holding up a fold of her mantle. Beside her, r., her coronet indistinctly shown.

Pen and brown ink over black lead, with slight grey wash.

ff. 39–42. BLANK, except for occasional smudges of grey wash and offsets of white.

f. 43r. [inserted]. A LADY, PERHAPS ELIZABETH, VISCOUNTESS TOWNS-HEND, AFTER KNELLER. W.L., standing, with body slightly to r., head slightly to l. and eyes to front, her l. hand held to her breast, her r. hand on the arm (?) of a chair against which she leans. Wearing drapery.

Black chalk, with grey wash, heightened with white.

[Elizabeth, Viscountess Townshend (D. 1711). Daughter and heiress of Thomas, 1st Lord Pelham. Married Charles, 2nd Viscount Townshend in 1698, as his first wife.]

This drawing bears some resemblance to a portrait by Kneller of Viscountess Townshend formerly in the collection of Lady Townshend (Sale, Christie, 4:vii:1947, Lot 7).

f. 44. BLANK.

f. 45v. [inserted]. A PEERESS IN CORONATION ROBES. W.L., standing, with body nearly in profile to r., head half-r. and eyes to front, her hands clasped before her.

Black and red chalks, heightened with white.

A freer and more accomplished study than most of the others in this book, and perhaps by another hand.

f. 46. BLANK.

f. 47r. [inserted]. PART OF THE FIGURE OF A LADY, SEATED IN A CHAIR.
White chalk.

f. 47v. [inserted]. A GIRL BY A VASE. W.L., standing, with body in profile to l., head slightly to l. and eyes to front, her hands resting on the mouth of a large vase with a tree in it. On the r., the top of a balustraded stair.

Black chalk, heightened with white, and splashed with oil and red pigment.

Cf. No. 7, f. 44ᵛ.

f. 48. BLANK.

f. 49ᵛ. [inserted] A PEERESS. W.L., standing, with body half-l., head half-r. and eyes to front, her l. hand across her waist, her r. hand holding her coronet. Wearing Coronation robes. In the background, trees to the l., and a column to the r.

Black chalk, heightened with white.

INSCR.: *Recto*, on the column, *green pillar*. Perhaps by the same hand as the study on f. 45ᵛ.

f. 50r. OFFSET FROM f. 49ᵛ.

f. 51. BLANK.

f. 52ᵛ. [inserted] OFFSET FROM f. 53r.

f. 53r. [inserted] A YOUNG LADY WITH A BUNCH OF FLOWERS. W.L., standing, with body half-l. and head half-r., her l. hand holding a fold of drapery to her breast, her r. hand outstretched and holding a bunch of flowers. Behind her, a tall pier overgrown with foliage at the top.

Black chalk, with grey wash, heightened with white.

f. 54. BLANK.

f. 55ᵛ. [inserted] A YOUNG LADY. W.L., seated, with body half l., holding in her lap with her r. hand a bunch of flowers. Wearing drapery.

Black chalk, with grey wash, heightened with white.

ff. 56–9. BLANK, except for offsets from white chalk.

f. 60ᵛ. [inserted] A LADY. W.L., half-

seated, with body half-l., head slightly to r. and eyes to front, her l. hand holding up a fold of drapery, her r. arm resting on a ledge of rock.

Black chalk, with grey wash, heightened with white.

f. 61r. BLANK, except for slight offset from f. 60ᵛ.

ff. 62ᵛ. & 63r. [inserted] A LADY WITH A PARROT. T.Q.L., standing, with body half-l. and head half-r., holding a parrot, l. In the background, l., a wooded bank.

Black chalk, heightened with white, in an oval.

Cf. No. 7, f. 84ᵛ.

f. 64 BLANK.

f. 65r. [inserted] GEORGE, PRINCE OF DENMARK, AFTER KNELLER. W.L., standing, with body slightly to r. and head slightly to l., his l. arm crooked, his r. hand holding a baton and resting on an anchor. Wearing an ermine-trimmed mantle over armour, his helmet on the ground, r.

Black chalk, with grey wash, heightened with white.

[George, Prince of Denmark (B. 1653: D. 1708). 2nd son of Frederick III of Denmark, and Consort of Queen Anne.]

The original picture has not been traced. A bust-length version was engraved in mezzotint by John Smith (*See B.M. Engraved Portraits*, II, p. 319, No. 15).

ff. 66–7. BLANK.

ff. 68ᵛ.–69r. [inserted] QUEEN ANNE, AFTER KNELLER. W.L., standing, with body slightly to r., head slightly to l. and eyes to front, her l. hand holding the orb on a table beside her, her r. hand holding the sceptre. Wearing her crown and coronation robes. Behind her, l., her throne, supported by a cupid.

Pen and brown ink, with grey wash, heightened with white.

The original picture, commissioned in 1702, is in the Inner Temple. Another version, formerly at Wentworth Castle, is at Chelsea Hospital. Bust-length versions were engraved in mezzotint, in reverse, by John Smith and by W. Emmett (*See B.M. Engraved Portraits*, I, p. 58, Nos. 25 & 26).

Cf. No. 7, f. 42v.

f. 70r. [inserted] WILLIAM VILLIERS, 2nd EARL OF JERSEY, AFTER KNELLER. W.L., standing, with body turned half-l., and head half-r., his l. hand holding a spear, his r. hand resting on the parapet of a fountain. Wearing a tunic and drapery.

Pen and brown ink, with grey wash, heightened with white.

[William Villiers, 2nd Earl of Jersey (B. c. 1682: D. 1721). Tory M.P. for Kent in 1705–8. Succeeded his father (*See f. 6r.* above) in 1711. Supported the Jacobite cause, and was arrested on suspicion of having been concerned in the Rising of 1715.]

From the double portrait showing the Earl and his sister, Lady Mary Villiers. The original picture was in the collection of the Earl of Jersey at Osterley. It was engraved in mezzotint, in reverse, by John Smith (*See B.M. Engraved Portraits*, II, p. 641, No. 1).

Cf. No. 7, f. 109v.

ff. 71–2. BLANK.

Inside the lower cover. A SPANIEL JUMPING UP TOWARDS THE L.

Red chalk.

PROV.: Edward Byng. Elizabeth Wray (née Byng). Charles Wray. Sir Charles Wilkins. C. W. B. W. Roberts. G. R. Harding, from whom it was purchased by the B.M., 1897.

1897–8–13–3 (1–46) (L.B.1).

3. **SKETCHBOOK.** Containing 37 leaves, partly filled with studies after pictures mainly of family groups, all presumably by Kneller.

Brown-grey paper; 42 × 33 cm. (16½ × 13 in.).
BINDING: Original panelled calf.

Inside the upper cover.
INSCR.: In red chalk, *No. 2.*

f. 1r. A GENTLEMEN, HIS LADY, AND THEIR SON AND DAUGHTER. All T.Q.L. He standing, l., with his l. hand to his breast. His lady seated on a bench, r., her l. hand round her daughter's waist, her r. hand holding the hand of her son, who stands behind in the centre. Trees in the background, r. **Plate 86**

Pen and brown ink, with grey wash, touched with white.

Cf. No. 5, ff. 88r. & 89r.

f. 2r. A GENTLEMAN, HIS LADY, AND THEIR DAUGHTER. All T.Q.L. He stand-ing, l., with a hound beside him. His lady seated, r., with her small daughter leaning against her. On the r., an orange tree in a sculptured vase.

Pen and brown ink, with grey wash, touched with white.

Cf. No. 5, ff. 77r. & 90r., and No. 6, f. 4r.

f. 3r. A YOUTH AND HIS SISTERS. All W.L. He standing, l., with his r. hand on his hip. His elder sister seated, r., before a niche, a basket of flowers on her knee, the younger girl standing beside her. Trees in the background, l.

Pen and brown ink, with brown-grey wash, touched with white.

f. 4r. A GENTLEMAN AND HIS LADY. Both T.Q.L. He standing r., with his l. hand in the fold of his coat. She seated, l. On the r., a pier with a carved festoon, and in the centre, through a window, a view of a park.

Pen and brown ink, with brown-grey wash, touched with white.

f. 5r. A GENTLEMAN, HIS LADY, AND THEIR CHILD. All T.Q.L. He standing l., with his r. hand on his hip and holding up a fold of his cloak, and his l. hand resting on the base of a column. His lady seated, r., with her r. arm on the shoulder of their child, who leans against her. A parterre and trees in the background, r.

Brush drawing in grey wash, touched with white.

f. 6r. A GENTLEMAN, HIS LADY, AND THEIR TWO CHILDREN. All T.Q.L. He standing, l., with his l. hand to his breast, and a hound beside him. His lady seated, r., holding the younger child on her lap, the elder standing in the centre. Trees in the background, r.

Black chalk; in outline.

f. 7r. A GENTLEMAN AND HIS LADY OR DAUGHTER. Both T.Q.L. He seated, l., with his r. hand on his hip. She standing, r., with her l. hand holding a basket of flowers, her r. hand holding a fold of her drapery. Trees in the background, r.

Black chalk, with grey wash, touched with white.

f. 8r. THREE CHILDREN. All W.L. A boy in a tunic and cloak, standing, l., and holding by the hand his sister, centre, who points down at their infant brother, r., seated on a cushion and wearing a plumed cap. On the r., a vase, with trees beyond.

Pen and brown ink, with grey wash, touched with white.

f. 9r. A LADY. T.Q.L. Seated beside a fountain on the ledge of which she leans, with a basket of flowers at her elbow, l. On the r., a wooded prospect.

Pen and brown ink, with grey wash, touched with white, over preliminary red chalk.

f. 10r. A GENTLEMAN AND HIS LADY. Both T.Q.L. He standing, r., with his l. hand on his hip, and his r. in his waistcoat. She seated, l., with her l. hand in her lap and her r. touching a lock of her hair. On the l., an orange tree in a vase, and in the background, r., an arcade.

Pen and brown ink, with grey wash touched with white over preliminary red chalk.

f. 11r. FOUR OF THE SIX CHILDREN OF THOMAS, 1st LORD FOLEY, AFTER KNELLER. All W.L. The eldest son, Thomas, later 2nd Lord Foley, standing, l., with his l. arm on the shoulder of his sister, Mary or Elizabeth, who stands beside him, r. On the r., the 2nd son, Strode-Talbot, seated on a bench, behind which stands another son, Edward or Richard. In the lower r.-hand corner, a hound. Behind them, the balustrade of a terrace beyond which is a wooded prospect.

Pen and brown ink, with grey wash, touched with white over preliminary red chalk.

[Thomas, 2nd Lord Foley (B. 1703: D. 1766). Son of Thomas, 1st Lord, whom he succeeded in 1732/3. Became D.C.L. in 1733 and F.R.S. in 1740. Built the fine church of Witley Court, Worcs., which he fitted out with the painted ceiling by Bellucci and the stained glass by Joshua Price, acquired from the Duke of Chandos's Chapel at Canons. Of the other children represented, Strode-Talbot died at the age of 25, and the others even younger.]

The original picture, described as 'Lord Foley with two Brothers and a Sister', is mentioned as being in 1936 in the collection of Lord Foley at Ruxley Lodge, Esher (*See Goulding*, p. 455). The same picture, or another version, is said to have appeared in a

'Foley Sale, Wallrock, London, 30:iv:1923, Lot 332', and to have been bought in.

PROV.: As for No. 2.
1897-8-13-4 (L.B. 2).

4. SKETCHBOOK. Containing 42 leaves, partly filled with studies after portraits, presumably by Kneller. Those definitely known to be by him are indicated as such.

Blue-grey paper; 31·1 × 26·7 cm. (12¼ × 10½ in.).
BINDING: Original blue-grey paper boards.

Inside of upper cover.
INSCR.: In red chalk, *No. 3.*

f. 1*r.* BLANK.

INSCR.: At the top, in ink, *Cecil Wray Byng Wilkins Roberts | Portfolio of my Great Great Great Uncle | while pupil to Sir Godfrey Kneller.*

f. 2*r.* A LADY. T.Q.L., seated, with body half-r. and head half-l., her l. hand resting on the bench beside her, her r. hand holding a book in her lap. On the l., a column, and on the r., a dolphin fountain.
Pen and ink, with grey wash, heightened with white.

f. 2*v.* BLANK.

INSCR.: In the upper l.-hand corner, in black lead, *No. 1.*

f. 3*r.* A GENTLEMAN. T.Q.L., seated, with body half-l., his l. hand on his hip, his r. hand in the opening of his light-coloured coat. On the r., a curtain.
Pen and ink, with grey wash, heightened with white.

f. 3*v.* BLANK.

INSCR.: In the upper l.-hand corner, in black lead, *No. 2.*

f. 4*r.* A LADY. T.Q.L., seated, with body to front and head slightly to l., her l. hand holding drapery on her shoulder, her r. hand pointing downwards. Trees in the background.
Brush drawing in grey wash, heightened with white.

f. 4*v.* BLANK.

INSCR.: In the upper l.-hand corner, in black lead, *No. 3.*

f. 5*r.* A LADY. T.Q.L., seated, with body slightly to r. and head slightly to l., her l. hand resting on the bank beside her, her r. hand holding a basket of flowers in her lap. Trees in the background.
Brush drawing in grey wash, heightened with white.

f. 5*v.* BLANK.

INSCR.: In the upper l.-hand corner, in black lead, *No. 4.*

f. 6*r.* A MILITARY COMMANDER, PERHAPS JOHN CAMPBELL, 2nd DUKE OF ARGYLL. T.Q.L., standing, with body half-r. and head half-l., his l. hand on his hip, his r. hand on the top of a baton resting upright on a table. Wearing a cuirass under his coat and the Ribbon of the Garter (?), a plumed helmet beside him, l.
Brush drawing in grey wash, heightened with white.
This drawing should be compared with the portrait of the Duke by William Aikman, engraved in mezzotint by Jean Simon (*See B.M. Engraved Portraits*, I, p. 67, No. 1) and with the study in sketchbook No. 2, *f.* 19*r.*

f. 6*v.* BLANK.

INSCR.: In the upper l.-hand corner, in black lead, *No. 5.*

f. 7r. A MILITARY COMMANDER. T.Q.L., standing, with body half-l., his l. hand on his hip, his r. hand on a stick. Wearing a cuirass under his coat. Trees in the background, r.

Brush drawing in grey wash, heightened with white.

f. 7v. BLANK.

INSCR.: In the upper l.-hand corner, in black lead, *No. 6.*

f. 8r. A LADY. T.Q.L., seated, with body slightly to l. and head half-r., her l. hand holding a letter (?) in her lap, her r. hand resting on the seat. A wall in the background.

Brush drawing in grey wash; unfinished.

f. 8v. BLANK.

INSCR.: In the upper l.-hand corner, in black lead, *No. 7.*

f. 9r. A LAWYER. T.Q.L., seated, with body half-l. and head slightly to l., his l. hand holding a fold of his black robe, his r. holding a scroll. In the distance, l., a wooded prospect.

Brush drawing in grey wash, touched with white.

f. 9v. BLANK

INSCR.: In the upper l.-hand corner, in black lead, *No. 8.*

f. 10r. A LADY WITH LIGHT-COLOURED HAIR. T.Q.L., standing, with body half-l. and head half-r., her r. arm resting on a ledge, her l. arm held before her. A wall behind her, l., and trees in the distance, r.

Brush drawing in grey wash, heightened with white.

Mr. Binyon has suggested that this might represent Henrietta Churchill, Countess Godolphin (B. 1681: D. 1733), presumably on the strength of its resemblance to the portrait of her by Kneller, engraved in mezzotint by Francis Kyte (*See B.M. Engraved Portraits*, III, p. 167, No. 1), which, however, differs entirely in pose from the present drawing.

f. 10v. BLANK.

INSCR.: In the upper l.-hand corner, in black lead, *9.*

f. 11r. A LADY WITH A WREATH OF FLOWERS. T.Q.L., standing, with body half-l. and head half-r., holding before her, l., a wreath of flowers. On the r., a dolphin fountain.

Brush drawing in grey wash, heightened with white.

f. 11v. BLANK.

INSCR.: In the upper l.-hand corner, in black lead, *10.*

f. 12r. A YOUNG LADY. T.Q.L., standing, with body slightly to l. and head half-r., her l. hand in front of her holding drapery over her r. arm. Wearing a light-coloured dress and darker drapery over it.

Brush drawing in grey wash, heightened with white.

f. 12v. BLANK.

INSCR.: In the upper l.-hand corner, in black lead, *11.*

f. 13r. AN EARL. T.Q.L., standing, with body half-r., holding before him, r., his coronet. Wearing peer's robes. On the r., a column with part of an arcade beyond.

Pen and brown ink, with grey wash, heightened with white.

f. 13v. BLANK.

INSCR.: In the upper l.-hand corner, in black lead, *12.*

f. 14r. A LADY WITH DARK HAIR, AFTER KNELLER. T.Q.L., seated on a bank, with body slightly to l. and head to r., her l. hand resting in her lap, her r. hand beside her. Wearing a light-coloured dress. Trees in the background.

Pen and ink, with grey wash.

This portrait corresponds in pose with that of Mrs. Carter by Kneller, engraved in mezzotint by John Smith (*See B.M. Engraved Portraits*, I, p. 356, No. 1). The sitter is not the same, and the drapery different.

f. 14v. BLANK.

INSCR.: In the upper l.-hand corner, in black lead, *13*.

f. 15r. A WIDOWED LADY. T.Q.L., seated, with body half-l. and head half-r., with eyes looking down, her hands together in her lap. Wearing widow's weeds. On the l., a niche.

Pen and ink, with grey wash, touched with white.

In pose this may be compared with Kneller's portrait of the widowed Frances Bennet, Countess of Salisbury, at Hatfield House (*See* Holland, *Hatfield*, p. 77, No. 118), which was engraved in mezzotint by John Smith (*See B.M. Engraved Portraits*, IV, p. 16, No. 1).

f. 15v. BLANK.

INSCR.: In the upper l.-hand corner, in black lead, *14*.

f. 16r. A LADY. T.Q.L., standing, with body slight to l. and head half-r., her l. hand before her holding a fold of drapery, her r. hand pointing downwards. Wearing a light-coloured dress. Trees in the background.

Brush drawing in grey wash, heightened with white and touched with pen and ink.

f. 16v. BLANK.

INSCR.: In the upper l.-hand corner, in black lead, *15*.

f. 17r. A GENTLEMAN. T.Q.L., standing, with body half-l. and eyes to front, his l. hand on a table beside him, r., his r. hand in the opening of his light-coloured coat. On the l., a curtain.

Brush drawing in grey wash, touched with white.

The pose is a favourite one with Kneller. It occurs in the portrait of Edward Harrison, Governor of Fort St. George, signed and dated *1719*, formerly in the collection of Lady Townshend (Sale, Christie, 4:vii:1947, Lot 9), and in that of Joseph Addison, dated *1716*, at Northwick Park.

f. 17v. BLANK.

INSCR.: In the upper l.-hand corner, in black lead, *16*.

f. 18r. A GENTLEMAN. T.Q.L., seated, with body half-r., and head half-l., his l. hand on the arm of his chair, his r. hand held before him. Wearing a dark-coloured coat.

Brush drawing in grey wash, the chair indicated in black chalk.

f. 18v. BLANK.

INSCR.: In the upper l.-hand corner, in black lead, *17*.

f. 19r. A GENTLEMAN. T.Q.L., standing, with body turned half-r. and eyes looking to front, his l. hand on his hip, his r. hand on a console beside him, l. Wearing a light-coloured coat and brocaded waistcoat, his hat under his l. arm.

Brush drawing in grey wash touched with white.

f. 19v. BLANK.

INSCR.: In the upper l.-hand corner, in black lead, *18*.

f. 20r. (*a*) A GENTLEMAN. H.L., standing, with body in profile to r. and head half-r., with his r. hand pointing. Wearing a light-coloured coat.

Pen and ink, with grey wash, over red chalk.

(*b*) A LADY. H.L., with body turned to front, head slightly to r. and eyes looking to front. In an oval.

Pen and ink, with grey wash, touched with white, over red chalk.

f. 20v. BLANK.

INSCR.: In the upper l.-hand corner, in black lead, *19*.

f. 21r. A LADY. H.L., with body slightly to r., head half-l. and eyes looking to front, her r. hand holding a fold of drapery.

Pen and ink, with grey wash.

f. 21v. BLANK.

INSCR.: In the upper l.-hand corner, in black lead, *20*.

f. 22r. SIR ISAAC NEWTON, AFTER KNELLER. T.Q.L., seated, with body slightly to l. and head half-r., his l. elbow resting by his hat, on a pedestal carved with a celestial sphere, r., his r. hand holding a glove on his knee. On the l., a niche.

Pen and brown ink.

[Sir Isaac Newton (B. 1642: D. 1727). The famous mathematician and scientist.]

The original picture, signed and dated *1720*, is in the collection of Lord Leconfield at Petworth House (*See* Collins Baker, *Petworth*, p. 66, No. 153).

f. 22v. BLANK.

INSCR.: In the upper l.-hand corner, in black lead, *21*.

f. 23r. A BOY. W.L., standing, with body to front and head slightly to l., his l. hand on his hip, his r. hand pointing downwards. Wearing long curling hair, a light-coloured coat, and a sword. On the r., a wooded prospect.

Pen and ink, with grey wash, heightened with white, over red chalk.

f. 23v. BLANK.

INSCR.: In the upper l.-hand corner, in black lead, *22*.

f. 24r. A GIRL. W.L., standing, with body nearly to front and head slightly to l., her l. hand by her side, her r. hand holding a sprig of orange (?). On the l., a column, and on the r., trees beyond a balustrade.

Pen and ink over red chalk.

f. 24v. BLANK.

INSCR.: In the upper l.-hand corner, in black lead, *23*.

f. 25v. A GENTLEMAN. T.Q.L., standing, with body half r. and eyes to front, his r. hand before him holding a fold of the night gown in which he is draped, his r. arm crooked. Wearing a night cap.

Pen and ink, with grey wash, over red chalk.

f. 25v. BLANK.

INSCR.: In the upper l.-hand corner, *24*.

f. 26r. A LADY WITH DARK-COLOURED HAIR. T.Q.L., seated, with body slightly to r. and head slightly to l., her l. hand on the bank beside her, her r. hand holding a fold of drapery. Wearing a light-coloured dress. Behind her, l., a rock, and in the background, r., a wooded prospect.

Pen and ink, with grey wash, heightened with white.

f. 26v. BLANK.

INSCR.: In the upper l.-hand corner, in black lead, *25*.

f. 27r. A GENTLEMAN. T.Q.L., seated in a chair, with body nearly in profile to l., head half-l. and eyes to front, his l. hand on his hip, his r. hand holding a fold of his gown. Before him, l., a table with a letter on it.

Pen and ink, with grey wash, touched with white.

f. 27v. BLANK.

INSCR.: In the upper l.-hand corner, in black lead, *26*.

f. 28r. A LADY. T.Q.L., seated, with body slightly to r. and head half-l., her l. hand on the bench beside her, her r. hand to her breast. Wearing a light-coloured dress. On the l., a curtain, and in the background, r., an arch with a wooded prospect through it.

Pen and ink, with grey wash, touched with white.

f. 28v. BLANK.

INSCR.: In the upper l.-hand corner in black lead, *27*.

f. 29r. A LADY. T.Q.L., seated, with body slightly to r., and head slightly to l., her l. hand on her knee, her r. hand to her breast. Wearing a light-coloured dress. On the l., a curtain, and on the r., a festoon.

Pen and ink, with grey wash, heightened with white.

f. 29v. BLANK.

INSCR.: In the upper l.-hand corner, in black lead, *28*.

f. 30r. A PHYSICIAN. T.Q.L., seated, with body half-r. and eyes to front, his l. hand on the arm of his chair, his r. hand holding a fold of his night gown. Wearing a night cap. On the l. a column, and on the r. an emblematic statue of medicine, within a niche.

Pen and ink, with grey wash, heightened with white.

f. 30r. BLANK.

INSCR.: In the upper l.-hand corner, in black lead, *29*.

f. 31r. A WIDOWED LADY. H.L., with body half-r. and eyes to front. Wearing widow's weeds. In an oval.

Pen and ink, with grey wash, touched with white.

f. 31v. BLANK.

INSCR.: At the top, in black lead, *30*.

f. 32r. MATTHEW PRIOR, AFTER KNELLER. T.Q.L., standing, with body half-l. and eyes to front, his l. hand on a book resting on a ledge. Bare-headed, and wearing a cloak draped over his coat. In the background, a rock and foliage.

Pen and ink, with grey wash, heightened with white.

[Matthew Prior (B. 1664: D. 1721). Poet and diplomatist.]

The original, one of Kneller's best portraits, painted in 1700, is at Trinity College, Cambridge. It was engraved in mezzotint by John Faber the younger (*See B.M. Engraved Portraits*, III, p. 518, No. 4).

f. 32v. BLANK.

INSCR.: At the top, in black lead, *31*.

f. 33r. A GENTLEMAN SAID TO BE JOHN GUNNING, AFTER KNELLER. T.Q.L., standing, with body half-l. and eyes to front, his l. arm by his side and his r. hand in the opening of his light-coloured coat. Wearing a night cap.

Pen and ink, with grey wash, heightened with white.

[John Gunning, of Castle Coote, Co. Roscommon. Father of the celebrated beauties, Maria and Elizabeth Gunning, later respectively Countess of Coventry and Duchess of Hamilton and of Argyll.]

The original picture, signed and dated *1720*, is in the collection of the Earl of Coventry at Croome Court. Despite its provenance and traditional identification, it seems unlikely that it represents Gunning, who seems to have lived all his early life in Ireland, and could scarcely, therefore, have been painted by Kneller at this date.

f. 33ᵛ. BLANK.

INSCR.: In the upper l.-hand corner, in black lead, *32*.

f. 34ʳ. BLANK.

f. 34ᵛ. BLANK.

INSCR.: In the upper l.-hand corner, in black lead, *33*.

f. 35ʳ. A GENTLEMAN. T.Q.L., standing, with body half-r. and eyes to front, his r. hand pointing. Wearing a night cap and gown.

Pen and ink, with grey wash, heightened with white over red chalk.

f. 35ᵛ. BLANK.

INSCR.: In the upper l.-hand corner, in black lead, *34*.

f. 36ʳ. A LADY. T.Q.L., seated, with body half-l. Red chalk; unfinished outline only.

f. 36ᵛ. BLANK.

INSCR.: In the upper l.-hand corner, in black lead, *35 Blank*.

f. 37ʳ. A LADY WITH LIGHT-COLOURED HAIR. T.Q.L., seated, with body half-r. and head half-l., her l. elbow resting on a ledge, r., her r. hand in her lap. Wearing a light-coloured dress. Trees and a rock in the background.

Pen and ink, with grey wash, heightened with white.

In pose this corresponds with the portrait by Kneller of Anne Vaughan, Duchess of Bolton (D. 1751), in the collection of the Earl of Cawdor at Golden Grove, Llandillo, Carmarthen (*See* Howard & Campbell, *Golden Grove*). [Reproduction faces page (unnumbered) headed 'Picture in Dining Room, West Wall, over fireplace.']

f. 37ᵛ. BLANK.

INSCR.: In the upper l.-hand corner, in black lead, *36*.

f. 38ʳ. A LADY WITH A VEIL ON HER HEAD. T.Q.L., seated, with body half-l. and eyes to front, her l. hand in her lap, her r. arm resting on a ledge, l., with a bunch of flowers on it. On the r., a curtain.

Pen and ink, with brown wash, heightened with white.

f. 38ᵛ. BLANK.

INSCR.: At the top, in black lead, *37 the Last*.

f. 39ʳ. BLANK.

f. 39ᵛ. BLANK.

INSCR.: In the upper l.-hand corner, in black lead, *38*.

f. 40ʳ. BLANK.

f. 40ᵛ. BLANK.

INSCR.: In the upper l.-hand corner, in black lead, *39*.

ff. 41–42. BLANK.

PROV.: As for No. 2.
1897–8–13–5 (1–36) (L.B.3).

5. SKETCHBOOK. Containing 97 leaves, including insertions, filled with studies after portraits, many of which are by Kneller, including a number of the Kit-Cat series. Those definitely known to be by him are indicated as such.

Blue-grey paper, 28·6 × 22 cm. (11¼ × 8⅝ in.).
BINDING: Original panelled calf.

Inside the upper cover.

HENRY COMPTON, BISHOP OF LON-DON, AFTER KNELLER. Bust half-r., with eyes to front. Wearing a black skull-cap, long white hair, bands and rochet.
Pen and brown ink, with grey wash.

INSCR.- In the upper r.-hand corner, *X.*

[Henry Compton (B. 1632: D. 1713). Youngest son of Spencer Compton, 2nd Earl of Northampton. Followed a military career in early life. Entered the Church in 1662, becoming successively Rector of Cottenham (Cambs.), Canon of Christ Church in 1669, Bishop of Oxford in 1674, and Dean of the Chapel Royal and Bishop of London in 1675. Remained a staunch Protestant throughout his life, and played an important part in the Revolution of 1688.]
The original picture is in the N.P.G. (No. 2952).
Cf. No. 8 (3).

f. 1r. [inserted] BLANK.

INSCR.: In black lead, probably by the artist. *This Book of | Drawings is M.ͬ Byng's | at S.ͭ Godfrey Knellers | in Queen street Lincoln | 's In feilds,* and in a later hand (*an old Aquaintance | of M.ͬ Highmore's Father's*).

f. 2r. BLANK.

INSCR.: In red Chalk, *N⁰ 4.*

f. 2v. STUDY OF THE R. FOREARM OF LADY TORRINGTON on *f.* 3r.
Pen and brown ink, with brown wash.

f. 3r. ANNE, LADY TORRINGTON, AFTER KNELLER. T.Q.L., seated, with body slightly to r., head half l. and eyes to front, her l. hand to her breast, her r. hand pointing downwards. Trees in the background, r.
Pen and brown ink, with brown wash.

INSCR.: In the lower l.-hand corner, *No. 1.*

[Ann (Pierrepont) Newport, Lady Torrington (D. 1734/5). Daughter of Robert Pierrepont of Nottingham, and 3rd wife of Thomas Newport, 1st Baron Torrington.]
The original picture has not been traced. It was engraved in mezzotint, in reverse, by John Smith (*See B.M. Engraved Portraits,* IV, p. 293).

f. 4r. A LADY IN A LIGHT-COLOURED DRESS. T.Q.L., seated below a rock, with body slightly to l., and head slightly to r., her l. hand to her breast, her r. hand resting on the bank beside her. Trees in the distance, r.
Pen and brown ink, with brown wash.

INSCR.: In the lower l.-hand corner, in ink, *2.*

f. 5r. A LADY WITH A NOSEGAY. T.Q.L., seated, with body half-l., her l. hand in her lap, her r. hand resting on a ledge beside her and holding a nosegay. On the l., a niche with a basket of fruit or flowers in it, and on the r., a panel of scrolled ornament.
Pen and brown ink, with brown wash.

INSCR.: In the lower r.-hand corner, *3.*

f. 6r. A GENTLEMAN. T.Q.L., seated, with body half-r., head half-l., his l. hand on his hip, his r. elbow resting on a ledge beside him. Wearing a loose gown.
Pen and brown ink, with grey wash.

INSCR.: In the lower l.-hand corner, *4*, and in the upper r.-hand corner, *X*.

Cf. No. 8 (4).
Mr. Binyon suggested that this might represent Arthur Maynwaring (*Cf.* No. 7, *f.* 20*v*.).

f. 7*r*. A YOUNG LADY WITH LIGHT-COLOURED HAIR. T.Q.L., standing, with body slightly to r. and head slightly to l., her l. arm by her side, her r. hand holding up a fold of drapery. A wooded prospect in the background, r.
Pen and brown ink with grey wash.

INSCR.: In the lower l.-hand corner, *5*, and in the upper r.-hand corner, *X*.

f. 8*r*. WILLIAM CONGREVE, AFTER KNELLER. Nearly T.Q.L., standing, with body in profile to r., head half-r. and eyes to front, his r. hand pointing. Wearing a light-coloured coat. Behind him a rock, and in the distance, r., a wooded prospect.
Pen and brown ink, with grey wash, heightened with white.

INSCR.: At the foot, in the centre, *M*.ʳ *Congreve*, and in the lower l.-hand corner, *6*.

[William Congreve (B. 1670: D. 1729). The well-known dramatist.]
The original picture, one of the Kit-Cat portraits, is now in the N.P.G. (No. 3199).

f. 9*r*. JAMES STANHOPE, 1st EARL STAN-HOPE, AFTER KNELLER. Nearly T.Q.L., standing, with body nearly in profile to r., head half-r. and eyes looking to front, holding in his r. hand a baton. Wearing a velvet coat. In the background, r., a cavalry skirmish near a tower.
Pen and brown ink, with grey wash, heightened with white.

INSCR.: At the foot, in the centre, *Lord Stanhope*, and in the l.-hand lower corner, *7*.

[James Stanhope, 1st Earl Stanhope (B. 1673: D. 1721). Military commander and statesman. A supporter of the Hanoverian cause.]
The original picture, one of the Kit-Cat portraits, is in the N.P.G. (No. 3225).

f. 10*r*. A GENTLEMAN, PERHAPS A MEMBER OF THE MAINWARING FAMILY, AFTER KNELLER. T.Q.L., standing, with body half-r., head half-l. and eyes to front, his l. hand on his sword-hilt, his r. hand holding a fold of drapery. Wearing a light-coloured coat. Trees in the background.
Pen and brown ink, with grey wash.

INSCR.: In the lower l.-hand corner, *8*.

This corresponds with a picture, formerly in the collection of Mr. M. K. Mainwaring (Sale, Sotheby, 5:v:1946, Lot 107). It is described as being 'signed and dated 1680', which hardly fits the style of the sitter's dress.

f. 11*r*. A WIDOWED COUNTESS. T.Q.L., standing, with body slightly to r., head slightly to l., and eyes looking downwards, her l. elbow resting on a table beside her, on which is her coronet, her r. hand holding up a fold of drapery. Wearing widow's weeds.
Pen and brown ink, with grey wash, heightened with white.

INSCR.: In the lower l.-hand corner, *9*, and in the upper r.-hand corner, *X*.

f. 12*r*. A GENTLEMAN. T.Q.L., standing, with body half r. and eyes to front, his l. hand in the opening of his coat, his r. hand on his hip. Wearing a light-coloured coat.
Pen and ink, with grey wash, heightened with white.

INSCR.: In the lower r.-hand corner, *10*, and at the top, *X*.

f. 13*r.* A LADY WITH A BASKET OF FLOWERS. T.Q.L., seated, with body half-r. and head half-l., her l. hand holding a basket of flowers on a ledge beside her, her r. hand pointing to this. Trees in the background, r.

Pen and ink, with grey wash, heightened with white.

INSCR.: In the lower l.-hand corner, *11*, and in the upper r.-hand corner, *X*.

f. 14*r.* A BOY. T.Q.L., standing, with body half-l. and eyes to front, holding his hat under his l. arm, his r. arm extended. Trees in the background, l. In an oval.

Pen and ink with grey wash, heightened with white.

INSCR.: In the lower l.-hand corner, *12*, and in the upper r.-hand corner, *X*.

f. 15*r.* A YOUNG LADY WITH LIGHT-COLOURED HAIR. T.Q.L., standing, with body half-l. and eyes to front, her r. hand holding up drapery about her. Trees in the background, l. In an oval.

Pen and ink, with grey wash, heightened with white.

INSCR.: In the lower l.-hand corner, *13*, and in the upper r.-hand corner, *X*.

f. 16*r.* A GENTLEMAN. H.L., with body half-l. and eyes to front, his r. hand in the opening of his coat. Wearing a night cap, and light-coloured coat.

Pen and ink, with grey wash, heightened with white.

INSCR.: In the lower l.-hand corner, *14*.

Mr. Binyon has suggested that this drawing may represent Lt. General John Tidcomb (B. 1642: D. 1713), on account of a likeness to the portrait of him in the Kit-Cat series at the N.P.G. (No. 3229).

f. 17*r.* JOHN SOMERS, 1st LORD SOMERS, AFTER KNELLER. Nearly T.Q.L., standing, with body half-r. and head half-l., his l. hand on his hip, his r. hand on a book. In the background, a rock.

Pen and ink, with grey wash, heightened with white.

INSCR.: In the lower l.-hand corner, *15*.

[John Somers, 1st Lord Somers (B. 1651: D. 1716), Lord Chancellor, and patron of Addison, Congreve, Steel, and other men of letters.]

The original picture, one of the Kit-Cat portraits, is in the N.P.G. (No. 3223).

f. 18*r.* A GENTLEMAN. Nearly T.Q.L., standing, with body half-l. and eyes to front, his r. hand in the opening of his coat. Wearing long curling hair or periwig. Trees in the background, l.

Pen and ink, with grey wash, heightened with white.

INSCR.: In the lower l.-hand corner, *16*, and in the upper r.-hand corner, *X*.

Cf. No. 8 (*5*).

f. 19*r.* GEORGE STEPNEY, AFTER KNELLER. Nearly T.Q.L., with body in profile to l., head half-l. and eyes to front, his r. hand holding a fold of drapery.

Pen and ink over black chalk.

INSCR.: In the lower l.-hand corner, *17*.

[George Stepney (B. 1663: D. 1707), diplomatist (principally in Germany and Austria), and poet.]

The original picture, one of the Kit-Cat portraits, is in the N.P.G. (No. 3228).

f. 20*r.* ADMIRAL SIR CHARLES WAGER, AFTER KNELLER. T.Q.L., standing, with body half-r., head half-l. and eyes to front, his l. hand on his hip, his r. hand on the top of his baton. Wearing a light-coloured coat.

Pen and ink, with grey wash, heightened with white.

INSCR.: In the lower l.-hand corner, *18*.

[Admiral Sir Charles Wager (B. 1666: D. 1743) saw service in the Mediterranean between 1690 and 1706. Appointed Rear-Admiral in 1707, and given the command at Jamaica, defeating a Spanish treasure-fleet off Cartagena in 1708. Was knighted in 1709. Blockaded Cadiz in 1727–8. Became Admiral in 1731, and served as First Lord of the Admiralty in 1733–42.]

The original picture is at the National Maritime Museum, Greenwich.

f. 21r. A LADY WITH A WREATH OF FLOWERS. T.Q.L., seated, with body half-r. and eyes to front, holding in her lap a wreath of flowers. On the r., an orange tree in a vase.

Pen and brown ink, with grey wash, heightened with white.

INSCR.: In the lower l.-hand corner, *19*, and in the upper r.-hand corner, *X*.

f. 22r. A LADY. T.Q.L., standing, with body to front and head half-l., her l. hand by her side, her r. elbow resting on a ledge beside her, her r. hand holding up drapery. On the r., a group of trees, and in the background, a portico.

Pen and brown ink, with grey wash, heightened with white.

INSCR.: In the lower l.-hand corner, *20*, and in the upper r.-hand corner, *X*.

f. 23r. A LADY. H.L., with body slightly to r., head slightly to l. and eyes to front. In an oval.

Pen and ink, with grey wash, heightened with white.

INSCR.: In the lower l.-hand corner, *21*, and in the upper r.-hand corner, *X*.

f. 24r. A LADY SEATED AMIDST TREES. T.Q.L., seated, leaning against a pedestal, with body half-r., head slightly to l. and eyes to front, her l. hand on her knee, her r. hand to her breast. Wearing a light-coloured dress.

Pen and brown ink, with grey wash, heightened with white.

INSCR.: In the lower l.-hand corner, *22* and *X*.

f. 25r. A LADY WITH DRAPERY OVER HER HEAD. H.L., with body slightly to r. and head slightly to l. In an oval.

Pen and brown ink, with grey wash, heightened with white.

INSCR.: In the lower l.-hand corner, *23*, and in the upper r.-hand corner, *X*.

Cf. No. 8 (6).

f. 26r. A LADY WITH A BUNCH OF FLOWERS. T.Q.L., seated, with body half-r., head slightly to l. and eyes to front, her l. hand resting on the bank beside her, her r. hand holding a bunch of flowers. Wearing a light-coloured dress. Trees in the background.

Pen and brown ink, with grey wash, heightened with white.

INSCR.: In the lower r.-hand corner, *24*, and in the upper r.-hand corner, *X*.

Cf. No. 8 (7).

f. 27r. A GENTLEMAN WITH A HOUND. T.Q.L., standing, with body nearly in profile to l., head half-l. and eyes to front, his l. hand on the base of a column, his r. hand outstretched. A hound beside him in the foreground.

Pen and brown ink, with grey wash.

INSCR.: In the lower r.-hand corner, *25*, and in the upper r.-hand corner, *X*.

Cf. No. 8 (8).

f. 28r. A LADY WITH A BASKET OF FLOWERS. T.Q.L., standing, with body slightly to l. and head slightly to r., her l. hand supporting a basket of flowers on a ledge beside her. Wearing a light-coloured dress. Trees in the distance, r.

Pen and brown ink, with grey wash, heightened with white.

INSCR.: In the lower r.-hand corner, *26*. and in the upper l.-hand corner, *X*.

f. 29r. A GENTLEMAN. T.Q.L., standing, with body half-l. and eyes to front, holding his hat under his l. arm, his r. hand pointing. Wearing a light-coloured coat. A tree behind him, r.

Pen and brown ink, with grey wash, heightened with white.

INSCR.: In the lower l.-hand corner, *27*, and in the upper r.-hand corner, *X*.

Cf. No. 8 (9).

f. 30r. A GENTLEMAN. T.Q.L., standing, with body half-r., head half-l. and eyes to front, holding his hat under his l. arm, his r. hand on his hip. Trees in the background.

Pen and brown ink, with grey wash, heightened with white.

INSCR.: In the lower r.-hand corner, *28*, and in the upper r.-hand corner, *X*.

f. 31r. A NAVAL COMMANDER. T.Q.L., standing, with body half-l. and eyes to front, his l. hand on his hip, his r. hand on his baton. Trees on the r., and in the distance, l., a naval engagement.

Pen and ink, with brown-grey wash, heightened with white.

INSCR.: In the lower r.-hand corner, *29*, and in the upper r.-hand corner, *X*.

Cf. No. 8 (10).

f. 32r. A LADY. H.L., with body half r., head half-l. and eyes to front. Wearing loose drapery. In an oval.

Pen and brown ink, with brown-grey wash, heightened with white.

INSCR.: In the lower l.-hand corner, *30*, and in the upper r.-hand corner, *X*.

f. 33r. A YOUNG MAN. H.L., with body half-l. and eyes to front. Wearing long curling hair. In an oval.

Pen and brown ink, with grey wash, heightened with white.

INSCR.: In the lower l.-hand corner, *31*, and in the upper r.-hand corner, *X*.

Cf. No. 8 (11) & (12).

f. 34r. THOMAS PARKER, 1st EARL OF MACCLESFIELD. T.Q.L., standing, with body half-r. and eyes to front, his l. hand touching his girdle, his r. hand holding his cap. Wearing robes as Lord Chief Justice. On a table, r., a letter addressed to him.

Pen and brown ink, with grey wash, heightened with white.

INSCR.: In the lower l.-hand corner, *1711* and *32*, and in the lower r.-hand corner, *X*.

[Thomas Parker, 1st Earl of Macclesfield (B. 1666 (?): D. 1732). Early in his career was noted for his activity against Dr. Sacheverell, and later against the Jacobites, becoming a great favourite with George I. Was knighted in 1705, and appointed Lord Chief Justice in 1710 and Earl of Macclesfield in 1721.]

The original picture has not been traced.

Cf. No. 6, *f.* 1r.

f. 35*r.* A LADY WITH LIGHT-COLOURED HAIR. T.Q.L., standing, with body half-l. and eyes to front, her l. hand holding up a fold of drapery. Wearing a light-coloured dress. Trees in the background, l.

Pen and ink, with brown-grey wash, heightened with white.

INSCR.: In the lower l.-hand corner, *33*, and in the upper r.-hand corner, *X.*

f. 36*r.* A NAVAL COMMANDER. T.Q.L., standing, with body turned half-r. and eyes to front, his l. hand on his hip, his r. hand holding a baton. Ships in the background, r.

Pen and brown ink, with brown-grey wash, heightened with white.

INSCR.: In the lower l.-hand corner, *34*, and in the lower r.-hand corner, *X.*

Cf. No. 8 (13).

f. 37*r.* SIR RICHARD STEELE, AFTER KNELLER. Nearly T.Q.L., standing, with body half-r., head half-l. and eyes to front, his r. elbow resting on a ledge beside him. Wearing his coat open in front. Trees on the r.

Pen and brown ink, with brown-grey wash.

INSCR.: In the lower l.-hand corner, *35*, and in the centre, *Sir Rich*ᵈ *Steele.*

[Sir Richard Steele (B. 1672: D. 1729). Essayist and founder of *The Tatler* and *The Spectator.*]

The original picture, one of the Kit-Cat portraits, is in the N.P.G. (No. 3227).

f. 38*r.* LOUISA, COUNTESS OF BERKELEY, AFTER KNELLER. Bust in profile to l., looking upwards.

Pen and ink, with grey wash, heightened with white.

INSCR.: In the lower l.-hand corner, *36.*

[Louisa Lennox, Countess of Berkeley (B. 1694: D. 1716/7). Daughter of Charles, 1st Duke of Richmond and wife of James, 3rd Earl of Berkeley, whom she married in 1710/1. Was appointed Lady of the Bedchamber to Caroline, Princess of Wales in 1714.]

The original picture has not been traced. It was engraved in mezzotint by John Faber the younger (*See B.M. Engraved Portraits,* I, p. 175, No. 1).

Cf. No. 8 (49).

f. 39*r.* A LADY WITH A SMALL SPANIEL. W.L., standing, with body slightly to r., head half-l. and eyes to front. Her l. hand resting on a parapet behind her, her r. hand holding up a fold of drapery. Wearing a light-coloured dress. At her feet, r., a small spaniel. On the l., a vase of flowers, and trees in the background, r.

Pen and ink, with grey wash, heightened with white.

INSCR.: In the lower l.-hand corner, *37*, and in the lower r.-hand corner, *X.*

Cf. No. 6, *f.* 3*r.*

f. 40*r.* A LADY WITH LIGHT-COLOURED HAIR. H.L., with body half-l., head half-r. and eyes to front. Wearing loose drapery. In an oval.

Pen and ink, with grey wash heightened with white.

INSCR.: In the lower l.-hand corner, *38*, and in the lower r.-hand corner, *X.*

f. 41*r.* A GENTLEMAN. H.L., with body slightly to r., head slightly to l. and eyes to front. His coat open in front. In an oval.

Pen and ink, with grey wash, heightened with white.

INSCR.: In the lower l.-hand corner, *39*, and in the lower r.-hand corner, *X.*

Cf. No. 8 (14).

f. 42r. A LADY SEATED AMIDST TREES, AFTER KNELLER. T.Q.L., seated, with body half-l., head half-r. and eyes to front, her l. hand in her lap, her r. hand on the bank beside her. Wearing a light-coloured dress. Trees in the background.

Pen and ink, with grey wash, heightened with white.

INSCR.: In the lower l.-hand corner, *40*.

In pose this corresponds with a portrait by Kneller of Mrs. Henry Portman, sold at Sotheby's, 7:vii:1948, Lot *5*, but the sitter is different.

f. 43r. CHARLES SEYMOUR, 6th DUKE OF SOMERSET. Nearly T.Q.L., with body half-l. and eyes to front, his r. hand holding a fold of drapery.

Pen and ink, with grey wash, heightened with white.

INSCR.: At the foot, *Cha^n | Duke of Somerset*, on the r., *41*, and in the upper r.-hand corner, *X*.

For the sitter's biography *See* No. 2, *f.* 21r. The original picture has not been traced.

f. 44r. SIR ROBERT COTTON, 5th BART., AFTER KNELLER. H.L., with body in profile to r., head half-r. and eyes to front. Wearing drapery. In an oval.

Pen and brown ink, with brown wash, heightened with white.

INSCR.: In the lower l.-hand corner, *42*, and in the upper r.-hand corner, *X*.

[Sir Robert Cotton, 5th Bart. (B. 1669: D. 1749). Son of Sir John Cotton, 3rd Bart., and great-grandson of Sir Robert Bruce Cotton, 1st Bart. and founder of the Cottonian Library.]

The original picture, signed, was in the collection of Viscount Feilding at Newnham Paddox.

f. 45r. THOMAS COVENTRY, 3rd EARL OF COVENTRY, AFTER KNELLER. H.L., with body half-l., head half-r. and eyes to front, his l. arm bent, his r. hand in the opening of his coat.

Pen and ink, with brown-grey wash, heightened with white. In an oval.

INSCR.: In the lower l.-hand corner, *43*, and in the upper r.-hand corner, *X*.

[Thomas Coventry, 3rd Earl of Coventry (D. 1711/12). Son of Thomas, 2nd Earl, whom he succeeded in 1710. Died at Eton.]

The original picture has not been traced. It was engraved in mezzotint by Jean Simon (*See B.M. Engraved Portraits*, I, p. 503, No. 1).

f. 46r. A LADY WITH LIGHT-COLOURED HAIR. H.L., standing, with body to front, head slightly to r. and tilted, and eyes to front, her l. hand holding drapery, her r. arm by her side.

Pen and ink, with brown-grey wash, heightened with white.

INSCR.: In the lower l.-hand corner, *44*, and in the upper r.-hand corner, *X*.

f. 47r. A LADY AS A SHEPHERDESS. T.Q.L., seated, with body slightly to r., head slightly to l. and eyes to front, her l. hand pointing, her r. hand holding a shepherdess's staff. Behind her, a rock, and in the distance, r., a clump of trees.

Pen and ink, with grey wash, heightened with white.

INSCR.: In the lower l.-hand corner, *45*, and in the upper r.-hand corner, *X*.

f. 48r. A LADY. H.L., with body half-r. and eyes to front. Wearing a light-coloured dress. Behind her, a rock, and trees in the distance, r. In an oval.

Pen and brown ink, with grey wash, heightened with white.

INSCR.: In the lower l.-hand corner, *46*, and in the upper r.-hand corner, *X*.

Probably the companion portrait to that on *f*. *49r*.

f. *49r*. A GENTLEMAN. H.L., with body to l. and eyes to front. In an oval.

Pen and brown ink, with grey wash, heightened with white.

INSCR.: In the lower l.-hand corner, *47*, and in the lower r.-hand corner, *X*.

Probably the companion portrait to that on *f*. *48r*.

f. *50r*. A LADY WITH A BASKET OF FLOWERS. T.Q.L., seated, with body half-r. and eyes to front, holding in her lap a basket of flowers. Wearing a light-coloured dress. On the l., a tall plinth carved with a cupid and scrollwork, and behind her, r., an orange tree in a vase.

Pen and ink, with grey wash, heightened with white.

INSCR.: In the lower r.-hand corner, *48* and *X*.

The l.-hand half of a double-portrait group, of which the other half is on *f*. *51r*.

f. *51r*. A LADY WITH DARK HAIR. T.Q.L., standing, with body slightly to l. and eyes to front, her l. hand holding up a fold of drapery, her r. hand resting on a vase with an orange tree in it. Wearing a light-coloured dress. Behind her r., a balustrade, and beyond, a tall clipped hedge.

Pen and ink, with grey wash, heightened with white.

INSCR.: In the lower l.-hand corner, *49*, and in the lower r.-hand corner, *X*.

The r.-hand half of a double-portrait group of which the other half is on *f*. *50r*.

f. *52r*. A GENTLEMAN. W.L., standing, with body slightly to l., head half-r. and eyes to front, holding his hat under his l. arm, his r. hand pointing downwards. Wearing a light-coloured coat. On the r., a fluted column, and on the l., a garden prospect seen through a window.

Pen and brown ink, with grey wash, heightened with white.

INSCR.: In the lower l.-hand corner, *50*, and in the lower r.-hand corner, *X*.

Cf. No. 6, *f*. *2r*.

f. *53r*. A LADY WITH A BOOK. T.Q.L., seated, with body half-r., and head half-l., holding a book open on a table beside her, r. Wearing drapery on her head.

Pen and ink, with grey wash, heightened with white.

INSCR.: In the lower l.-hand corner, *51* and *X*.

f. *54r*. A LADY. H.L., with body slightly to r. and head slightly to l. Wearing a light-coloured dress. In an oval.

Pen and ink, with grey wash, heightened with white.

INSCR.: In the lower l.-hand corner, *52*, and in the lower r.-hand corner, *X*.

Cf. No. 7, *f*. *28r*.

f. *55r*. SUSANNAH, LADY KNELLER, AFTER KNELLER. H.L., with body slightly to l., head half-r. and eyes to front. Wearing a light-coloured dress. In an oval.

Pen and ink, with grey wash, heightened with white.

INSCR.: At the foot, in the centre, *Lady Kneller*, in the lower l.-hand corner, *53*, and in the lower r.-hand corner, *X*.

[Susannah, Lady Kneller (D. 1729). Daughter of the Rev. John Cawley, Archdeacon of Lincoln, and granddaughter of William Cawley, the Regicide. Married firstly Mr. Grave, and secondly, in 1703/4, Sir Godfrey Kneller.]

The original picture has not been traced.

Cf. No. 7, *f*. 17*v*.

f. 56*r*. A LADY. H.L., with body half-l. and eyes to front, a long lock of hair falling on her r. shoulder. Wearing drapery. Trees in the distance, l. In an oval.

Pen and ink, with grey wash, heightened with white.

INSCR.: In the lower l.-hand corner, *54*, and in the upper l.-hand corner, *X*.

Cf. No. 7, *f*. 5*v*.

f. 57*r*. A LADY. H.L., with body half-l., head half-r. and eyes to front, a long lock of hair falling over her l. shoulder. Wearing a low-necked dress. In an oval.

Pen and ink, with grey wash, heightened with white.

INSCR.: In the lower l.-hand corner, *55*, and in the upper r.-hand corner, *X*.

f. 58*r*. A LADY. H.L., with body nearly to front, head half-l. and eyes to front. Wearing a low-necked dress and drapery. Trees in the background. In an oval.

Pen and ink, with grey wash, heightened with white.

INSCR.: In the lower l.-hand corner, *56*, and in the upper r.-hand corner, *X*.

f. 59*r*. A LADY. H.L., with body slightly to r. and head half-l. Wearing drapery falling behind from her hair. In an oval.

Pen and ink, with grey wash, heightened with white.

INSCR.: In the lower l.-hand corner, *57*, and in the upper r.-hand corner, *X*.

f. 60*r*. A LADY. H.L., with body half-r. and eyes to front. Wearing a low-necked dress.

Pen and ink, with grey wash, heightened with white.

INSCR.: In the lower l.-hand corner, *58*, and in the upper r.-hand corner, *X*.

Cf. No. 7, *f*. 74*r*.

f. 61*r*. A LADY. H.L., with body half-l., head half-r. and eyes looking downwards. Wearing a low-necked dress.

Pen and ink, with grey wash, heightened with white.

INSCR.: In the lower l.-hand corner, *59*, and in the upper r.-hand corner, *X*.

f. 62*r*. A GENTLEMAN. T.Q.L., standing, with body half-l. and eyes to front, his hat under his l. arm, his l. hand holding a glove, and his r. hand resting on his cane. Wearing a dark coat.

Pen and ink, with grey wash, heightened with white.

INSCR.: In the lower l.-hand corner, *60*, and in the lower r.-hand corner, *X*.

Cf. No. 6, *f*. 12*v*.

f. 63*r*. A WIDOWED LADY. T.Q.L., standing, with body nearly to front and eyes looking slightly downwards, leaning with her l. elbow on a table, r., on which is a flower, her r. arm by her side. Wearing widow's weeds.

Pen and ink, with grey wash, heightened with white.

INSCR.: In the lower l.-hand corner, *61*, and in the upper r.-hand corner, *X*.

f. 64r. AN EARL. T.Q.L., standing, with body half-l. and eyes to front, his l. hand on his hip, his r. hand on a scroll which lies on a table beside his coronet. Wearing peer's robes over ordinary dress. In the background, l., an alcove, and r., a curtain.

Pen and ink, with grey wash.

INSCR.: In the lower l.-hand corner, *62*.

f. 65r. A GENTLEMAN, PERHAPS A NAVAL OR MILITARY COMMANDER. T.Q.L., standing, with body half-r. and eyes to front, his hat under his l. arm, his r. hand resting on his cane. Wearing a dark coat. Behind him, l., a tree, and in the distance, r., a fort on the shore of an estuary.

Pen and ink, with grey wash, heightened with white.

INSCR.: In the lower r.-hand corner, *63*, and in the upper r.-hand corner, *X*.

f. 66r. A NAVAL COMMANDER, PERHAPS ADMIRAL SIR JOHN NORRIS, AFTER KNELLER. T.Q.L., standing, with body half-l. and eyes to front, his l. hand on the hilt of his hanger, his r. hand on a cannon. Wearing a dark-coloured coat. Ships in the distance, l.

Pen and ink, with grey wash, heightened with white and touched with red chalk.

INSCR.: In the lower l.-hand corner, *64X*.

[Admiral Sir John Norris (B. 1660: D. 1749). After a career in which his promotion apparently owed not a little to the influence of powerful friends, was knighted in 1705, and in the following year, became Rear-Admiral of the Blue. Later, played an important part in bringing to an end the struggle between Russia and Sweden (1716–27).]

The original picture, signed and dated *1711*, is in the National Maritime Museum. Doubts have been expressed, however, as to whether it actually represents Norris.

f. 67r. MR. FERHILL (?), AFTER KNELLER. T.Q.L., standing, with body half-r., and eyes to front, his l. hand in the opening of his coat, his r. hand on the head of his hound. Wearing a cap. Trees in the background.

Pen and ink, with grey wash, heightened with white.

INSCR.: On the hound's collar, Mr *Ferhil*, and in the lower l.-hand corner, *65*.

The sitter has not been identified, but the picture corresponds in pose, costume and background with the portrait of William Bulwer (B. 1695: D. 1755) in 1909 in the collection of Mr. W. E. E. L. Bulwer, at Heydon Hall, Norfolk (*See Duleep Singh*, I, p. 230, No. 4 & Pl. at p. 240).

f. 68r. A LADY WITH A BASKET OF FLOWERS. T.Q.L., seated, with body half-r. and head half l., her l. hand beside her resting on the bench, her r. hand holding a basket of flowers in her lap. Wearing a light-coloured dress. In the background, r., a garden prospect.

Pen and ink, with grey wash, heightened with white.

INSCR.: In the lower r.-hand corner, *66* (*67* crossed out), *X*.

f. 69r. A SMALL BOY OR GIRL WITH A SPANIEL. T.Q.L., standing, with body half-r., head half-l. and eyes to front, his (or her) l. hand touching the head of a spaniel, r. his (or her) l. hand pointing towards the r. Trees in the background, l. In an oval.

Pen and ink, with grey wash.

f. 69v. ANOTHER VERSION OF *f. 69r.*

Pen and ink, with grey wash, heightened with white.

INSCR.: In the lower l.-hand corner, $\frac{68}{67}$.

f. 70r. BLANK.

f. 70v. A BOY. Nearly T.Q.L., standing, with body to r. and eyes to front, his hat under his l. arm, his r. hand outstretched. Wearing long curling hair.

Pen and ink, with grey wash, heightened with white.

INSCR.: In the lower l.-hand corner, *69.*

f. 71r. A BOY. W.L., standing, with body half-r. and eyes to front, his l. hand on the pommel of his sword, his r. hand on his hip. Wearing long curling hair and a cloak draped over his l. arm. Trees in the background.

Pen and ink with grey wash, over red chalk.

INSCR.: In the lower r.-hand corner, *69* (*70* crossed out).

Probably the l.-hand half of a portrait-group, of which the other half is on *f. 72r.*

f. 71v. STUDIES OF THE HANDS OF THE BOY ON *f. 71r.*
Pen and ink, with grey wash.

f. 72r. TWO GIRLS. W.L. The elder seated on the r. with body half-l., head half-r. and eyes to front, her l. hand on drapery beside her, her r. hand holding a basket of flowers on her lap. The younger standing on the l. Behind them a shell-topped alcove.

Pen and ink, with grey wash, heightened with white.

INSCR.: In the lower r.-hand corner, *70.*

Probably the r.-hand half of a portrait-group, of which the other half is on *f. 71r.*

f. 72v. A MILITARY COMMANDER. H.L.,

with body half-r. Wearing armour. In an oval.

Black chalk; outline only.

f. 73r. [inserted] A GENTLEMAN. H.L., with body half-r. and eyes to front. Wearing drapery.

Pen and brown ink, with grey wash, heightened with white.

INSCR.: In the lower r.-hand corner, *71,* and in the upper r.-hand corner, *X.*

f. 74r. A GENTLEMAN. T.Q.L., standing, with body half-l. and eyes to front, his cocked hat under his l. arm, his r. hand in the opening of his coat. Wearing a powdered or light-coloured wig. On the r., a curtain.

Pen and ink, with grey wash.

f. 74v. A GENTLEMAN. Nearly H.L., with body in profile to l., head half-l. and eyes to front. Wearing a long curling wig.

Pen and ink, with grey wash, heightened with white.

f. 75r. A LADY. T.Q.L., standing, with body to front and head half-r., her l. hand holding up a fold of drapery, her r. hand by her side. On the r., a column, and in the background, l., a line of cypresses.

Pen and ink, with grey wash, heightened with white.

INSCR.: In the lower r.-hand corner, *72.*

f. 76r. [inserted] MARGARET, COUNTESS OF HARDWICKE, AFTER KNELLER. T.Q.L., seated, with body half-r. and head half-l., her eyes to front, holding a chaplet. On the l., two lambs, and in the background, a rock and trees.

Pen and brown ink, with grey wash, heightened with white.

INSCR.: In the lower r.-hand corner, *73/X.*

[Margaret (Cocks) Lygon, Countess of Hardwicke (D. 1761). Daughter of Charles Cocks of Worcester, and widow of John Lygon. Married Philip Yorke, 1st Earl of Hardwicke, in 1719.]

The original picture has not been traced. It was engraved in mezzotint by John Faber the younger (*See B.M. Engraved Portraits*, II, p. 441, No. 1).

Cf. No. 6, 5r.

f. 77r. A LADY AND CHILD. Another version of the r. hand half of No. 3, *f.* 2r.
Pen and ink, with grey wash.

f. 78r. A YOUNG MAN. Nearly T.Q.L., standing, with body half-r. and eyes to front, his hat under his l. arm, his r. hand outstretched holding his cane. In the background, a wooded prospect.
Pen and ink, with grey wash, heightened with white.

INSCR.: In the lower r.-hand corner, 74, and in the lower l.-hand corner, X.

f. 79r. [inserted] DR. JOHN RADCLIFFE, AFTER KNELLER. T.Q.L., seated, with body slightly to r., head slightly to l. and eyes to front, his l. hand, gloved, on his thigh, his r. hand to his chest. On the table beside him, l., his hat and a letter.
Pen and ink, with grey wash, heightened with white.

INSCR.: In the lower l.-hand corner, D.r Radcliffe and 75.

[Dr. John Radcliffe (B. 1650: D. 1714). The well-known physician, and benefactor to the University of Oxford.]

The original picture is in the Radcliffe Camera, Oxford. There are several other versions, including two also at Oxford, one in the Bodleian Library (by Dahl), the other at University College (*See* Poole, *Oxford Portraits*, I, p. 81, No. 204, p. 225, No. 682, and II, p. 6, No. 15).

f. 80r. A GENTLEMAN. T.Q.L., standing, with body half-l. and eyes to front, his hat under his l. arm, his l. hand holding a glove and his r. hand in the opening of his coat. Trees in the background.
Pen and brown ink, with grey wash.

INSCR.: In the lower r.-hand corner, X.

f. 81r. ANOTHER VERSION OF *f.* 80r.
Pen and ink, with grey wash, heightened with white.

INSCR.: In the lower r.-hand corner, 76.

f. 82r. [inserted] SARAH, DUCHESS OF MARLBOROUGH. T.Q.L., seated, with body slightly to r. and head half-l., her l. elbow resting on a table, r., her r. hand in her lap. Wearing peeress's robes, her key as Mistress of the Robes at her waist, and her coronet beside her, r.
Pen and brown ink, with brown wash, heightened with white.

INSCR.: In the upper r.-hand corner, 77.

The original picture has not been traced, but there seems to be no doubt about the identity of the sitter.

f. 83r. ANOTHER VERSION OF *f.* 82r.
Pen and brown ink, with grey wash.

f. 84r. A LADY WITH A PARROT. T.Q.L., seated, with body half-r., head half-l., her l. elbow resting on a pedestal, a parrot perched on her l. hand, her r. hand in her lap. In the background, l., a tree.
Pen and brown ink, with grey wash, heightened with white.

INSCR.: In the lower r.-hand corner, 78.

f. 85r. A GENTLEMAN. T.Q.L., standing, with body slightly to r., head half-l. and eyes to front, his l. hand on his hip, his r.

hand on the corner of a ledge. Wearing a gown. In an oval.

Pen and ink, with grey wash, heightened with white.

INSCR.: In the lower r.-hand corner, 79.

f. 86r. AN ELDERLY LADY. T.Q.L., standing, with body half-l. and eyes to front, her l. hand holding up a fold of drapery. In an oval.

Pen and ink, with grey wash, heightened with white.

INSCR.: In the lower r.-hand corner, 8.

f. 87r. A YOUNG MAN. H.L., standing, with body half-l. and eyes half-r., his r. hand in the opening of his coat. In an oval.

Pen and ink, with grey wash, heightened with white.

INSCR.: In the lower r.-hand corner, 81.

f. 88r. A GENTLEMAN AND HIS SON. The l.-hand half of the group in No. 3, *f.* 1r.

Pen and ink, over black chalk.

INSCR.: In the lower r.-hand corner, 82.

f. 89r. A LADY AND CHILD. The r.-hand half of the group in No. 3, *f.* 1r.

Pen and ink, over black chalk.

INSCR.: In the lower r.-hand corner, 83.

f. 90r. [inserted] A LADY AND CHILD. Another version of the r.-hand half of No. 3, *f.* 2r.

Pen and ink, with grey wash, heightened with white.

INSCR.: In the lower r.-hand corner, X and 84.

f. 91r. [inserted] A NAVAL COMMANDER, PROBABLY JAMES BERKELEY, 3rd

EARL OF BERKELEY, AFTER KNELLER. T.Q.L., standing, with body half-r. and eyes to front, his l. hand on his hip, his r. hand pointing with a baton. Wearing a breastplate over his coat. Behind him, l., a wall, and in the distance, r., two ships.

Pen and brown ink, with grey wash, heightened with white.

INSCR.: In the upper r.-hand corner, 85.

[James Berkeley, 3rd Earl of Berkeley (B. 1680: D. 1736). Son of Charles, 2nd Earl, whom he succeeded in 1710. Had a distinguished career in the Navy, becoming Vice-Admiral in 1707/8 and First Lord Commissioner of the Admiralty in 1717.]

The present drawing corresponds with two portraits of the Earl, one of which was sold at Christie's, 7:xii:1934, Lot 101, the other formerly in the collection of Mrs. J. H. Wilson (Sale, Sotheby, 27:vii:1938, Lot 131).

Cf. No. 6, *f.* 48v.

f. 92r. [inserted] A LADY. T.Q.L., standing, with body to front, head half-l., her l. hand touching a lock of her hair, her r. hand pointing downwards. Wearing a low-necked dress and drapery. Trees and a rock in the background.

Pen and brown ink, with grey wash, heightened with white.

INSCR.: In the lower r.-hand corner, 86.

f. 93r. [inserted] A GENTLEMAN. Another version of *f.* 74r., though perhaps a different sitter.

Pen and ink, with grey wash, heightened with white.

INSCR.: In the lower r.-hand corner, 87.

f. 94r. [inserted] A GENTLEMAN. T.Q.L., standing, with body slightly to r. and head slightly to l., his gloved l. hand on

235

his hip, his r. hand on a table, l. A curtain on the r.

Pen and ink, with grey wash, heightened with white.

INSCR.: In the lower l.-hand corner, *88*.

f. 95r. [inserted] A LADY. T.Q.L., standing, with body slightly to r., head slightly to l. and eyes to front, her l. arm by her side, her r. hand touching a lock of her hair. Wearing a low-necked dress and drapery. Trees in the background. In an oval.

Pen and ink, with grey wash, heightened with white.

INSCR.: In the lower r.-hand corner, *89*.

f. 96r. [inserted] A LADY. H.L., with body turned slightly to r., and head half-l., a lock

of hair falling on her r. shoulder. Wearing a low-necked dress.

Pen and brown ink, with grey wash, heightened with white.

INSCR.: In the lower r.-hand corner, *90*.

Cf. No. 8 (47).

f. 97r. [inserted] A CHILD. H.L., with body slightly to l. and head half-r. Wearing drapery over its dress. In an oval.

Pen and brown ink, with grey wash, heightened with white.

INSCR.: In the lower r.-hand corner, *91*.

PROV.: As for No. 2.
1897–8–13–6 (L.B.4).

6. SKETCH BOOK. Containing 59 leaves, including insertions, filled with studies after portraits, most of which are presumably by Kneller. Those definitely known to be by him are indicated as such.

Blue-grey paper; 27·9 × 22·2 cm. (11 × 8¾ in.).

BINDING: Original panelled calf.

Inside the upper cover.

INSCR.: In red chalk, *No. 5*.

f. 1r. THOMAS PARKER, 1st EARL OF MACCLESFIELD. Another version of No. 5, *f. 34r*.

Pen and ink, with grey wash, heightened with white.

f. 2r. A GENTLEMAN. Another version of No. 5, *f. 52r*.

Pen and brown ink, with grey wash, heightened with white.

f. 3r. A LADY WITH A SMALL SPANIEL. Another version of No. 5, *f. 39r*.

Pen and brown ink, with grey wash, heightened with white.

f. 4r. A LADY AND CHILD. Another version of the r.-hand half of No. 3, *f. 2r*.

Pen and brown ink, with brown-grey wash, heightened with white.

f. 5r. MARGARET, COUNTESS OF HARDWICKE, AFTER KNELLER. Another version of No. 5, *f. 76r*.

Pen and brown ink, with grey wash, heightened with white.

f. 6r. [inserted] A YOUNG MAN. T.Q.L., standing, with body half-r. and eyes to front, his hat under his l. arm, his r. hand outstretched and holding a cane. Wearing his own hair. Trees in the background.

Pen and brown ink, with grey wash, heightened with white.

f. 7v. A LADY. T.Q.L., seated, with body slightly to l., head slightly to r. and eyes to front, her l. hand in her lap, her r. hand touching a lock of hair. On the r., a column, and in the background, l., trees.

Pen and brown ink, with grey wash, heightened with white.

f. 8*v.* AN ELDERLY GENTLEMAN. H.L., with body half-r. and eyes to front. Wearing a braided coat. In an oval.

Pen and brown ink, with grey wash, heightened with white.

f. 9*v.* JOHN MONTAGUE, 2nd DUKE OF MONTAGUE, AFTER KNELLER. Nearly T.Q.L., standing, with body slightly to r., head half-l. and eyes to front, his hat under his l. arm, his r. hand holding a cane towards the r.

Pen and brown ink, with grey wash, heightened with white.

[John Montague, 2nd Duke of Montague (B. 1690: D. 1749), son of Ralph, 1st Duke, whom he succeeded in 1709. Attempted the colonizing of St. Lucia and St. Vincent in 1722. Was created K.G. and elected F.R.S. Corresponded with Stukeley, the antiquary. Was noted in his day as a practical joker.]

The original picture, one of the Kit-Cat portraits, is in the N.P.G. (No. 3219).

f. 10*v.* JAMES CRAGGS THE YOUNGER, AFTER KNELLER. T.Q.L., standing, with body half-l. and eyes to front, his hat under his l. arm, his r. hand by his side holding a paper. On the r., a decorated pilaster.

Black chalk, with brown wash, heightened with white.

[James Craggs the younger (B. 1686: D. 1721), Secretary of State, opponent of Walpole, and friend of Pope and Addison.]

A version of the original picture is in the N.P.G. (No. 1134).

f. 11*v.* A GENTLEMAN. H.L., standing with body slightly to r., and head half-l.

Black chalk; faint outline only.

f. 12*v.* [inserted] A GENTLEMAN. Another version of No. 5, *f.* 62*r.*

Pen and brown ink, with grey wash, heightened with white.

f. 13*v.* FRANCIS GODOLPHIN, 2nd EARL OF GODOLPHIN, AFTER KNELLER. Nearly T.Q.L., standing, with body half-r. and head half-l., his l. hand on his hip, his r. arm resting on a ledge. Wearing a patterned coat. Trees in the background, r.

Pen and brown ink, with grey wash, heightened with white.

[Francis Godolphin, 2nd Earl of Godolphin (B. 1678: D. 1766). Son of Sidney, 1st Earl, whom he succeeded in 1712. Held various appointments under the Crown, and was M.P. successively for Oxfordshire and Tregony. Married Henrietta, eldest daughter of the 1st Duke of Marlborough.]

The original picture, one of the Kit-Cat portraits, is in the N.P.G. (No. 3209).

f. 14*v.* AN EARL. T.Q.L., seated, with body half-l., his l. hand on his hip, his r. arm resting on the edge of a table, on which is also his coronet. Wearing peer's robes. Trees in the background, l.

Pen and brown ink, with grey wash, heightened with white.

f. 15*v.* A LADY. T.Q.L., seated, with body slightly to r., and head slightly to l., her l. arm resting on a table or ledge, her r. hand in her lap.

Black chalk; faint outline only.

f. 16*v.* A SMALL BOY. W.L., seated on a step, with body half l. and eyes to front, holding in both hands a sprig of orange. Wearing a plumed cap and petticoat with leading-strings.

Pen and brown ink, with grey wash, heightened with white.

f. 17*v.* [inserted] A GENTLEMAN. T.Q.L., standing, with body half-l. and eyes to front, his l. hand resting on a plinth, his r. hand outstretched.

Pen and brown ink, with grey wash, heightened with white.

f. 18*v*. [inserted] EDMUND DUNCH, AFTER KNELLER. Nearly T.Q.L., with body half-l. and eyes to front, his l. hand held in front of him. In the background, a wall, with an arch and a leafy branch on the l.

Pen and brown ink, with grey wash, heightened with white.

[Edmund Dunch (B. 1657: D. 1719). M.P. successively for Cricklade, Borough-bridge and Wallingford, 1701–19. Master of the Household to Queen Anne and George I. Was noted as a bon vivant and gamester.]

The original picture, one of the Kit-Cat portraits, is in the N.P.G. (No. 3206).

f. 19*v*. [inserted] A LADY WITH LIGHT-COLOURED HAIR. H.L., with body slightly to r., head half-l. and eyes to front. Wearing her hair in two locks on her l. shoulder, and a bow on her gown. In an oval.

Pen and brown ink, with grey wash, heightened with white.

f. 20*v*. [inserted] A GENTLEMAN. T.Q.L., standing, with body half-r., head half-l. and eyes to front, his l. hand on his hip, his r. arm resting on a plinth.

Pen and ink, with grey wash, heightened with white.

f. 21*v*. [inserted] A GENTLEMAN. Bust, with body half-l. and eyes to front. Wearing drapery over his shoulder. In an oval.

Pen and brown ink, with grey wash, heightened with white.

Mr. Binyon suggested that this might represent John Somers, 1st Baron Somers.

f. 22*v*. [inserted] JOSEPH ADDISON, AFTER KNELLER. Nearly T.Q.L., standing, with body half-r., head half-l. and eyes to front, his l. arm by his side, his r. hand resting on a rock. Trees in the background, r.

Pen and brown ink, with grey wash, heightened with white.

[Joseph Addison (B. 1672: D. 1719). Essayist, and joint-founder, with Steele, of *The Spectator*.]

The original picture, one of the Kit-Cat portraits, is in the N.P.G. (No. 3193).

f. 23*v*. [inserted] A LADY HOLDING A BOOK. Nearly T.Q.L., standing, with body slightly to r., head slightly to l. and eyes to front, her l. arm by her side, her r. elbow resting on a plinth, and her r. hand holding a book. Wearing a veil on her head. A rock and trees in the background.

Pen and ink, with grey wash, heightened with white.

f. 24*v*. [inserted] A GENTLEMAN. T.Q.L., standing, with body half-l. and eyes to front, his l. hand resting on a plinth, his r. hand outstretched.

Pen and ink, with grey wash, heightened with white.

f. 25*v*. [inserted] A LADY. T.Q.L., seated, with body slightly to r. and head half-l., her l. hand holding a fold of drapery, her r. hand in her lap. Behind her, a steep bank with trees.

Pen and ink, with grey wash, heightened with white.

f. 26*v*. A LADY WITH LIGHT-COLOURED HAIR. H.L., with body slightly to r., head half-l., and eyes to front. Wearing drapery. In an oval.

Pen and ink, with grey wash, heightened with white.

f. 27*v*. A GENTLEMAN. H.L., with body half-r., head half-l. and eyes to front. Wearing drapery over his shoulder. In an oval.

Pen and brown ink, with grey wash, heightened with white.

f. 28*v*. A GENTLEMAN HOLDING A PAPER. T.Q.L., standing, with body half-l. and eyes to front, his l. hand resting on a plinth, his r. hand holding up a paper.

Pen and brown ink, with grey wash, heightened with white.

f. 29*v.* A GENTLEMAN HOLDING A PAPER. Another version of *f.* 28*v.*
 Brush drawing in grey wash.

f. 30*v.* [inserted] THE HON. ELIZABETH MOHUN, AFTER KNELLER. T.Q.L., seated, with body slightly to r., head slightly to l. and eyes to front, her l. hand on the back of a lamb, r., her r. hand holding a cocked hat. Trees in the background, l.
 Pen and brown ink, with grey wash, heightened with white.
 [The Hon. Elizabeth Mohun (D. 1710). Daughter of Charles, 3rd Lord Mohun, and sister of Charles, 4th Lord, the notorious rake and duellist. Was Maid of Honour to Queen Mary and Queen Anne. Her recovery from smallpox in 1694 occasioned three sets of verses, one by Charles Hopkins.]
 The original picture is said to have been at one time in the possession of Messrs. Tooth.

f. 31*v.* A LADY WITH LIGHT-COLOURED HAIR. T.Q.L., seated, with body half-l., head half-r. and eyes to front, her l. hand on a fold of drapery in her lap, her r. hand pointing. A tree behind her, r., and a wooded prospect in the distance, l.
 Pen and brown ink, with grey wash, heightened with white.

f. 32*v.* A LADY. T.Q.L., standing, with body slightly to r., head slightly to l. and eyes to front, her l. elbow resting on a plinth, her r. arm across her body. Trees in the background.
 Pen and ink, with grey wash, heightened with white.

f. 33*v.* A LADY WITH A BASKET OF FLOWERS, AND FLOWERS IN HER HAIR. T.Q.L., seated, with body slightly to r., head slightly to l. and eyes to front, her l. hand to her breast, her r. hand touching a basket of flowers in the lower l.-hand corner. On the l., a pilaster of foliated scrollwork, and in the distance, r., a garden prospect.

Pen and ink, with grey wash, heightened with white.

f. 34*v.* A LADY WITH A BASKET OF FLOWERS. T.Q.L., standing, with body slightly to r. and head slightly to l., holding in her l. hand a basket of flowers, her r. hand pointing downwards. Trees in the background, r.
 Pen and ink, with grey wash, heightened with white.

f. 35*v.* A GENTLEMAN. T.Q.L., standing, with body half-r. and eyes to front, his l. hand holding a glove by his side, his r. hand in the opening of his coat. His hat on a table, r.
 Pen and ink, with grey wash, heightened with white.

f. 36*v.* JOHN CUTTS, 1st LORD CUTTS, AFTER KNELLER. T.Q.L., standing, with body slightly to r. and head half-l., his l. hand on his helmet, his r. hand holding a baton. Wearing armour. A rock behind him, r., and a cavalry skirmish in the distance, l.
 Pen and ink, with grey wash, heightened with white.
 [John Cutts, 1st Lord Cutts (B. 1661: D. 1707). Saw service against the Turks. Later served at the Boyne under William III, who created him Baron Cutts in 1690, and at the siege of Namur, where he first gained his reputation for romantic courage and his nickname of the 'Salamander'. Was third in command at Blenheim. Had literary pretensions and published some of his verses.]
 The original picture has not been traced. It was engraved in mezzotint by Jean Simon (*See B.M. Engraved Portraits,* I, p. 546, No. 3).

f. 37*v.* A LADY. T.Q.L., standing, with body slightly to r., head slightly to l. and eyes to front, her l. arm by her side, her r. hand holding up a fold of drapery. On the l., the corner of a window, and trees in the distance, r. In an oval.

Pen and brown ink, with grey wash, heightened with white.

f. 38*v.* SARAH, DUCHESS OF MARL-BOROUGH. T.Q.L., seated, with body slightly to r., and head half-l., her l. hand holding up a fold of drapery in her lap, her r. hand supporting her head. Wearing loose drapery, her coronet on a ledge, r. Behind her, l., a curtain, and trees in the distance, r.

Pen and brown ink, with grey wash, heightened with white.

The original picture is in the collection of Earl Spencer at Althorp. It was engraved in mezzotint, in reverse, by Jean Simon (*See B.M. Engraved Portraits*, III, p. 167, No. 8).

f. 39*v.* A BOY WITH A LAMB. W.L., seated, with body slightly to r., head slightly to l. and eyes to front, his l. hand resting on the back of a lamb, his r. elbow on a plinth, l. Wearing a tunic and cloak. Behind him, l., a tree, and in the distance, r., a wooded prospect.

Pen and brown ink, with grey wash, heightened with white.

f. 40*v.* A SMALL GIRL. Nearly T.Q.L., standing, with body half-r. and eyes to front, her r. elbow resting on a ledge. Wearing loose drapery. Behind her, l., a tree and a rock, and other trees in the distance, r. In an oval.

Pen and brown ink, with grey wash, heightened with white.

f. 41*v.* A GENTLEMAN. T.Q.L., standing, with body half-r. and eyes to front, his l. hand on his hip, his r. hand in the opening of his coat. Behind him, l., a fluted column, and trees in the distance, r.

Pen and brown ink, with grey wash, heightened with white.

f. 42*v.* JOHN DORMER. H.L., standing, with body half-r. and eyes to front, his l.

hand on his hip, his r. forearm resting on a ledge, with finger pointing. Wearing a night gown.

Pen and brown ink, with grey wash, heightened with white.

[John Dormer (B. 1669: D. 1719). Grandson of Sir Charles Cotterell (*see* Lely, No. 28). Was Deputy Lieutenant of Oxfordshire in 1701.]

The original picture, one of the Kit-Cat portraits, is in the N.P.G. (No. 3203).

f. 43*v.* LIONEL CRANFIELD SACKVILLE, 1st DUKE AND 7th EARL OF DORSET. Nearly T.Q.L., standing, with body slightly to r. and eyes to front, holding in his l. hand his wand as First Lord of the Bedchamber, his r. arm by his side. Wearing the Ribbon and Star of the Garter.

Pen and brown ink, with grey wash, heightened with white.

[Lionel Cranfield Sackville, 1st Duke and 7th Earl of Dorset (B. 1688: D. 1765). Succeeded his father as 7th Earl in 1706. Held several appointments under the Crown. Was created K.G. in 1714, and Duke of Dorset in 1720.]

The original picture, one of the Kit-Cat portraits, is in the N.P.G. (No. 3205).

f. 44*v.* ALGERNON CAPEL, 2nd EARL OF ESSEX. Nearly T.Q.L., standing, with body in profile to l., head half-l. and eyes to front, his l. forearm hidden by drapery held up by his r. hand. Trees in the background, l.

Pen and brown ink, with grey wash, heightened with white.

[Algernon Capel, 2nd Earl of Essex (B. 1670: D. 1710). Son of Arthur, 1st Earl, whom he succeeded in 1683. Was Gentleman of the Bedchamber to William III, and had a distinguished career in the Army, rising to the rank of Lieut.-General in 1708.]

The original picture, one of the Kit-Cat portraits, is in the N.P.G. (No. 3207).

Cf. Nos. 7, *f.* 23*v* & 8 (22).

f. 45v. CHARLES MONTAGU, 1st EARL OF HALIFAX. Nearly T.Q.L., standing, with body slightly to r., head slightly to l. and eyes to front, his r. arm by his side, his l. hand holding a fold of drapery in front of him.

Pen and brown ink, with grey wash, heightened with white.

[Charles Montagu, 1st Earl of Halifax (B. 1661: D. 1715). During his parliamentary career played an important part in connexion with the country's finances, and was the founder of the National Debt. Was created K.G. and Earl of Halifax in 1714.]

The original picture, one of the Kit-Cat portraits, is in the N.P.G. (No. 3211).

f. 46v. SIR JOHN VANBRUGH. H.L., seated behind a table, with body slightly to r. and head slightly to l., his l. arm crooked, his r. forearm resting on a table in front of him, his r. hand holding a compass. Wearing a medallion suspended from his neck.

Pen and brown ink, with grey wash, heightened with white.

[Sir John Vanbrugh (B. 1664: D. 1726). Architect and dramatist.]

The original picture, one of the Kit-Cat portraits, is in the N.P.G. (No. 3231).

Cf. No. 7, *f*. 18v.

f. 47v. SIR SAMUEL GARTH. Nearly T.Q.L., standing, with body in profile to l., leaning slightly backwards, head half-l., and eyes to front, his r. hand resting on his l. arm.

Pen and brown ink, with grey wash, heightened with white.

[Sir Samuel Garth (B. 1661: D. 1719). Physician-in-Ordinary to George I, and the author of much occasional and satirical verse.]

The original picture, one of the Kit-Cat portraits, is in the N.P.G. (No. 3208).

f. 48v. JAMES BERKELEY, 3rd EARL OF BERKELEY. Nearly T.Q.L., standing, with body half-r. and eyes to front, his l. arm by his side, his r. hand holding up a baton. Ships in the background, r.

Pen and brown ink, with grey wash, heightened with white.

Cf. No. 5, *f*. 91r.

The original picture, one of the Kit-Cat portraits, is in the N.P.G. (No. 3195).

f. 49v. A GENTLEMAN, PROBABLY A WRITER. H.L., seated behind a table, with body slightly to l., head slightly to r. and eyes to front, holding up before him, with both hands, a scroll lettered, *The Little Whig^e* | *-ab uno* | *Disce omnes*.

Pen and brown ink, with grey wash, heightened with white.

The sitter has not been identified, nor is there apparently any record of a pamphlet entitled *The Little Whig*. The inscription on the scroll which he holds refers to Lady Anne (Churchill), wife of Charles Spencer, 3rd Earl of Sunderland and 3rd daughter of the Duke of Marlborough. According to Colley Cibber she was 'the toast and pride' of the Whig party and the first stone of the Haymarket Opera House was inscribed 'The Little Whig' in her honour.

f. 50v. RICHARD TEMPLE, 1st VISCOUNT COBHAM. Nearly T.Q.L., standing, with body slightly to r., head half-l. and eyes to front, his l. arm by his side, his r. hand on his hip.

Pen and brown ink, with grey wash, heightened with white.

[Richard Temple, 1st Viscount Cobham (B. 1675: D. 1749). Served with distinction in the army under Marlborough. Was later an opponent of Walpole and the Hanoverian policy. Created the splendid house and gardens of Stowe, and was a patron of letters.]

The original picture, one of the Kit-Cat portraits, is in the N.P.G. (No. 3198).

[One leaf cut out.]

f. 51v. CHARLES LENNOX, 1st DUKE OF RICHMOND. Nearly T.Q.L., standing, with body turned slightly to r. and eyes looking to front, his l. forearm resting on a ledge, his r. hand behind his hip. Wearing the Ribbon and Star of the Garter.

Pen and brown ink, with grey wash, heightened with white, over black chalk.

[Charles Lennox, 1st Duke of Richmond (B. 1672: D. 1723). Natural son of Charles II and Louise de Kéroualle, Duchess of Portsmouth.]

The original picture, one of the Kit-Cat portraits, is in the N.P.G. (No. 3221).

f. 52v. A YOUTH. Nearly T.Q.L., standing, with body turned half-l. and eyes looking to front, his hat under his l. arm, his l. hand on the hilt of his sword, his r. arm held slightly in front of him. In an oval.

Pen and brown ink, with grey wash, heightened with white.

f. 53v. A LADY. H.L., with body half-l. and head half-r. Wearing low-necked dress and drapery. In an oval.

Brush drawing in grey wash, heightened with white, over black chalk.

f. 54v. A PLUMP LADY. Nearly T.Q.L., standing with body slightly to l. and head half-r., her l. elbow resting on a ledge, her r. arm by her side. Wearing a low-necked dress and drapery. In the background, a wooded bank.

Black chalk, with grey wash, heightened with white.

f. 55v. A LADY IN MOURNING. Nearly T.Q.L., kneeling at a praying-desk, with body half-l. and head half-r., her hands clasped before her over a prayer-book. Wearing drapery over her head, and at her breast a brooch in the shape of a cherub.

Brush drawing in grey wash, heightened with white, over black chalk.

f. 56v. A LADY. T.Q.L., seated on a bank, with body slightly to r., head slightly to l. and eyes to front, her l. arm beside her, her r. hand holding up a fold of drapery. Trees in the background.

Pen and brown ink, with grey wash, heightened with white.

f. 57v. A LADY. T.Q.L., seated on a bank, with body half-l., head half-r. and eyes to front, her l. arm across her lap, her r. arm resting on the top of a fountain. Behind her, l., a wooded cliff, and trees in the distance, r.

Pen and brown ink, with grey wash, heightened with white.

f. 58v. A GENTLEMAN. T.Q.L., standing, with body half-l. and eyes to front, his l. hand in the opening of his coat, his r. hand pointing downwards. Behind him, a plinth, and in the distance, l., trees.

Pen and brown ink, with grey wash, heightened with white.

f. 59v. A GENTLEMAN. T.Q.L., standing, with body half-r. and eyes to front, his hat under his l. arm, his r. hand on his hip. Behind him a tall pedestal, and in the distance, r., a wooded prospect.

Pen and brown ink, with grey wash, heightened with white.

PROV.: As for No. 2.
1897–8–13–7 (L.B.5).

7. SKETCHBOOK. Containing 114 leaves, including insertions, filled with studies after Roman coins (*ff.* 1r.–4r.), animals, etc. (*ff.* 6r.–7v.), Turkish and other costumes (*ff.* 8r.–16r.), and portraits (*ff.* 17v.–114v.) many of which are by Kneller, including a number of the Kit-Cat series. Those definitely known to be after Kneller are indicated as such.

The book has been used for two purposes: the collection of numismatic, ethnographic and other material (*ff.* 1r.–16r.), and, like Nos. 2–6, as a portrait-record (*ff.* 17v.–114v.). Though the drawings on *ff.* 1r.–16r. appear superficially to be by a different hand from those in the remainder of the book, this in reality is probably not the case, for certainly those on *ff.* 1r., 2v. and 6r.–16r. are, for example, by the same hand as *ff.* 89v. and 90v.; and *f.* 1v. by the same hand as *f.* 76v.

White paper (some leaves washed with blue, grey or buff) and blue-grey paper; 23·5 × 17·7 cm. (9¼ × 6⅞ in.).

BINDING: Original vellum.

Inside the upper cover.
INSCR.: At the top, *Mr. Vareys at Mr. Guys house in St. Jamese's Street*, and in the centre, in red chalk, *No. 6*.

[*ff.* 1r.–4r.] **Studies of Roman Coins,** probably after engravings in a work not yet identified.

f. 1r. OBVERSES AND REVERSES OF COINS OF THE ROMAN EMPERORS AURELIAN, NUMERIANUS AND HADRIAN.
Brush drawings in grey wash over black chalk.

INSCR.: Biographical notes on the Emperors, and a reference to Balthasar de Monconys' *Journal des Voyages*, 1665, Part I, p. 431, where the author speaks of having been given a silver coin of Domitian by the French Vice-Consul at Ephesus.

f. 1v. TWO SILVER PHEASANTS, AFTER A CHINESE ORIGINAL.
Pen and brown ink, with grey wash.
Copied perhaps from a painting on porcelain, of the type to be seen on a late K'ang Hsi dish in the B.M. (R. L. Hobson, *Handbook of the Pottery and Porcelain of the Far East*, 1937, Pl. XIV).

f. 2r. OBVERSES AND REVERSES OF COINS OF CLAUDIUS II, TETRICUS, AND CLAUDIUS I.

Pen and ink, with grey wash, over black lead.

INSCR.: Biographical notes on the Emperors concerned.

f. 3r. OBVERSES AND REVERSES OF COINS OF SALOMINUS, AUGUSTUS AND PROBUS.
Pen and brown ink over black lead.

INSCR.: Biographical note on Probus.

f. 3v. OBVERSE AND REVERSE OF A COIN OF JULIA SOÆMIAS.

INSCR.: Biographical note on Julia Soæmias, and *This medal was silver and found in Alchester field near Graven hill Wood by Bister in | Oxfordshire.*

f. 4r. OBVERSES AND REVERSES OF COINS OF DIOCLETIAN, MAXIMIANUS AND PROBUS.
Pen and brown ink over black lead.

INSCR.: Biographical notes on the Emperors concerned.

f. 5v. [inserted] A LADY. Another version of No. 5, *f.* 56r.
Pen and brown ink, with grey wash, heightened with white, on blue-grey paper.

[*ff.* 6r.–7v.] **Studies from Animals** and other details from portraits probably by Kneller.

f. 6r. STUDIES OF A KING CHARLES SPANIEL AND SHEEP.
Brush drawings in grey wash.

f. 6v. STUDIES OF SHEEP.
Brush drawings in grey wash.

f. 7r. STUDIES OF SHEEP.
Brush drawings in grey wash.

f. 7v. STUDIES OF HANDS, FEET AND A SHEEP.
Brush drawings in grey wash.

[One leaf missing (?)]

[*ff. 8r.–16r.*] **Costume.** Copies of Turkish, Greek and Cypriot costumes in Cornelis de Bruyn's *Reizen . . . Door de vermaardste Deelen van Klein Asia*, 1698 (French edn., 1700) accompanied by English translations of extracts from the printed text referring to them.

f. 8r. A WOMAN OF THE GREEK ARCHIPELAGO, AND A WOMAN OF SMYRNA (*De Bruyn*, Pls. 17 & 18).
Brush drawings in grey wash over black chalk.

INSCR.: Extract from *De Bruyn*, p. 35, relating to the wearing of the face-veil.

f. 9r. A JEWESS OF SMYRNA, AND A WOMAN WITH THE VEIL COVERING HER FACE (*De Bruyn*, Pls. 19 and 20).
Brush drawings in grey wash over black chalk.

INSCR.: Extract from *De Bruyn*, p. 35, relating to types of footwear.

f. 10r. EXTRACTS FROM *DE BRUYN*, pp. 58–9 (French edn. pp. 56–8), RELATING TO THE COSTUMES OF THE LADIES OF CONSTANTINOPLE AND OF THE JANISSARIES, WITH REFERENCE TO *ff.* 11r, 12r, 13r and 14r.

f. 11r. TWO LADIES OF CONSTANTINOPLE (*De Bruyn*, Pls. 34 and 35).

Brush drawings in grey wash over black chalk.

INSCR.: At the top, respectively, 5 and 6.

f. 12r. A LADY OF CONSTANTINOPLE (*De Bruyn*, Pl. 36).
Brush drawing in grey wash over black chalk.

INSCR.: In the upper l.-hand corner, 7.

f. 13r. FOUR LADIES OF THE 'GRAND SEIGNIORS' SERAGLIO' (*De Bruyn*, Pl. 37).
Brush drawings in grey wash over black chalk.

INSCR.: At the top, 8.

f. 14r. A TURK IN A TURBAN, AND A JANISSARY (*De Bruyn*, Pls. 38 & 39).
Brush drawings in grey wash over black chalk.

INSCR.: Respectively, 9 and 10.

f. 15r. A WOMAN OF SCIO (*De Bruyn*, Pl. 62).
Brush drawing in grey wash over black chalk.

INSCR.: Extract from *De Bruyn*, p. 169, relating to the women of Scio.

f. 15v. CONTINUATION OF THE EXTRACT RELATING TO THE WOMEN OF SCIO. Refers also to Monconys's *Journal des Voyages*, Part I (*Cf. f.* 1r.), p. 433, and to Jean Dumont's *A New Voyage to the Levant*, 1696, p. 192.

f. 16r. A CYPRIOT WOMAN (*De Bruyn*, Pl. 202).
Brush drawing in grey wash over black chalk.

INSCR.: Extract from *De Bruyn*, pp. 377–8

(French edn. pp. 385–6), relating to the habits of the women of Cyprus.

[*ff.* 17*v.*–114*v.*] **Studies after portraits.**

f. 17*v.* [inserted] LADY KNELLER. Another version of No. 5, *f.* 55.

Pen and brown ink, with grey wash, heightened with white, on blue-grey paper.

f. 18*v.* SIR JOHN VANBRUGH. Another version of No. 6, *f.* 46*v.*

Brush drawing in grey wash, strengthened with pen and ink and touched with white, on buff-washed paper.

INSCR.: In the upper l.-hand corner, *123*.

f. 19*v.* A GENTLEMAN. Nearly T.Q.L., with body slightly to r. and head half-l., his r. forearm resting on a table before him and his r. hand pointing.

Brush drawing, in grey wash, strengthened with pen and ink, and heightened with white, on buff-washed paper.

INSCR.: In the upper l.-hand corner, *122*.

Study from a portrait of the Kit-Cat type, though it does not belong to the original series.

f. 20*v.* ARTHUR MAYNWARING. Nearly T.Q.L., standing, with body half-l., and head half-r., his l. hand in the opening of his coat, his r. arm outstretched.

Pen and brown ink, with grey wash, heightened with white, on buff-washed paper.

INSCR.: In the upper l.-hand corner, *121*.

[Arthur Maynwaring (B. 1668: D. 1712). Auditor of imprests and successively M.P. for Preston and West Looe, 1705–12. As a political writer was the opponent of Sacheverell and a supporter of Marlborough.

Wrote prologues for the actress Anne Old-field, who was his mistress.]

The original picture, one of the Kit-Cat portraits, is in the N.P.G. (No. 3217).

f. 21*v.* SPENCER COMPTON, 1st EARL OF WILMINGTON. Nearly T.Q.L., with body in profile to l., head half-l. and eyes looking to front, his l. forearm resting on a ledge.

Brush drawing in grey wash, touched with white, on buff-washed paper.

INSCR.: In the upper l.-hand corner, *120*.

[Spencer Compton, 1st Earl of Wilmington (B. 1674 (?): D. 1743). Son of the 3rd Earl of Northampton. As a Whig enjoyed a long political career, during which he was Speaker (1715–27) and Paymaster General (1722–30). Was created Earl of Wilmington in 1730. Subsequently turned against Walpole.]

The present drawing corresponds with the portrait in the Kit-Cat series in the N.P.G. (No. 3234), but the Ribbon and Star of the Garter are omitted.

Cf. f. 41*v* and 8 (28).

f. 22*v.* CHARLES FITZROY, 2nd DUKE OF GRAFTON. Nearly T.Q.L., standing, with body slightly to r., head slightly to l. and eyes to front, his l. arm crooked, his r. hand at the opening of his coat. Wearing a night cap.

Brush drawing in grey wash, heightened with white, on buff-washed paper.

INSCR.: In the upper l.-hand corner, *119*.

Another copy of this portrait, also from the Kneller studio, is described on p. 392, No. 16. Appended to it are notes on the sitter and the original picture.

f. 23*v.* ALGERNON CAPEL, 2nd EARL OF ESSEX. Another version of No. 6, *f.* 44*v.*

Brush drawing in grey wash, touched with white, on buff-washed paper.

INSCR.: In the upper l.-hand corner, *118*.

f. 24v. A LADY. H.L., with body slightly to r., head half-l. and eyes to front. Wearing loose drapery. In an oval.
Brush drawing in brown wash, strengthened with pen and ink and touched with white, on buff-washed paper.

INSCR.: In the upper l.-hand corner, *117*.

[One leaf torn out.]

f. 25v. A LADY WEARING A CROSS. H.L., with body slightly to r., head slightly to l. and eyes to front. Wearing a necklace of pearls with a cross, a bunch of flowers at her breast, and dark drapery. In an oval.
Pen and brown ink, with grey wash, touched with white, on buff-washed paper.

INSCR.: In the upper l.-hand corner, *115*.

f. 26r. [inserted] A GENTLEMAN. H.L., with body half-l. and eyes to front. In an oval.
Pen and brown ink, with grey wash, heightened with white, on blue-grey paper.

f. 27v. A LADY WITH A SPANIEL. H.L., with body slightly to l., head slightly to r. and eyes to front, her l. hand resting on the side of the spaniel who sits on a ledge in front of her. In the background, a tree-trunk, l., and another tree, r. In an oval.
Pen and ink, with grey wash, touched with white, on buff-washed paper.

INSCR.: In the upper l.-hand corner, *114*.

f. 28r. [inserted] A LADY. Another version of No. *5, f. 54r.*
Pen and brown ink, with grey wash, heightened with white, on blue-grey paper.

f. 29 v. SIR JOHN LEAKE, AFTER KNEL-LER. T.Q.L., standing with body half-r. and eyes to front, his l. hand on his hip, his r. hand before him holding a baton towards the r. A rock behind him, l.
Pen and brown ink, with grey wash, heightened with white, on buff-washed paper.

INSCR.: In the upper l.-hand corner, *113*.

[Sir John Leake (B. 1656: D. 1720). Admiral of the Fleet. In operation off the coast of Spain, 1704–6. Captured Minorca in 1708 when Commander-in-Chief, Mediterranean.]

f. 30v. JOHN GRAYDON, AFTER KNEL-LER. T.Q.L., standing, with body turned half-l. and eyes to front, his l. hand on his sword-hilt, his r. arm resting on a rock, and his r. hand holding a baton.
Pen and brown ink, with grey wash, heightened with white, on buff-washed paper.

INSCR.: In the upper l.-hand corner, *112*.

[John Graydon (D. 1726). Vice-Admiral of the Red. Commander-in-Chief W. Indies, 1703. Cashiered in same year for failing to attack Placentia in Newfoundland, in spite of sickness and foul weather.]

f. 31v. SIR THOMAS DILKES, AFTER KNELLER. T.Q.L., standing, with body slightly to r., head half-l. and eyes to front, his l. hand in his sword belt, his r. hand on the top of a baton resting upright on a ledge, l. A rock behind him, l.
Pen and brown ink, with grey wash, heightened with white, on buff-washed paper.

INSCR.: In the upper l.-hand corner, *111*.

[Sir Thomas Dilkes (B. 1667 (?): D. 1707). Rear-Admiral of the Red. Captured

French convoy, 1702. Succeeded Sir Cloud-isley Shovell in the Mediterranean Command in 1707.]

f. 32ᵛ. A GENTLEMAN. Nearly T.Q.L., standing, with body half-r., head half-l. and eyes to front, his l. hand on his hip, his r. hand in front of him.

Pen and brown ink, with grey wash, heightened with white, on buff-washed paper.

INSCR.: In the lower l.-hand corner, *110.*

Study from a portrait of the Kit-Cat type, based on that of John Somers, 1st Baron Somers, in the N.P.G. (No. 3223).

f. 33ᵛ. A LADY AS DIANA OR A SHEP-HERDESS. T.Q.L., walking, with body to r. and head half-l., holding in her l. hand a spear or crook (the hand not shown), her r. arm pointing across her body. Behind her, a wooded bank.

Pen and brown ink, with grey wash, touched with white, on buff-washed paper.

INSCR.: In the upper l.-hand corner, *109.*

Cf. No. 8 (24).

f. 34ᵛ. A LADY WITH A BASKET OF FRUIT. T.Q.L., standing with body half-r., head half-l. and eyes to front, holding on her l. hip a basket of fruit, her r. hand pointing downwards. Trees in the background.

Pen and ink, with grey wash, touched with white, on buff-washed paper.

INSCR.: In the upper l.-hand corner, *108.*

The l.-hand part of a portrait-group, of which the centre is on *f.* 35ᵛ. and the r.-hand part on *f.* 36ᵛ.

f. 35ᵛ. A LADY AND CHILD. T.Q.L., seated with body slightly to l. and head half-r., holding the child in her lap with her

l. hand, her r. hand taking a fruit from the basket held by the lady on *f.* 34ᵛ. Trees in the distance.

Pen and brown ink, with grey wash, heightened with white, on buff-washed paper.

INSCR.: In the upper l.-hand corner, *107.*

The centre of a portrait group, of which the l.-hand part is on *f.* 34ᵛ. and the r.-hand part on *f.* 36ᵛ.

f. 36ᵛ. A GENTLEMAN WITH HIS SON AND A HOUND. T.Q.L., standing with body half-l. and eyes to front, his l. arm crooked, his r. hand holding a fold of his cloak, his small son beside him, r., touching the hound's head. Behind them, the corner of a building.

Pen and brown ink, with grey wash, touched with white, on buff-washed paper.

INSCR.: In the upper l.-hand corner, *106.*

The r.-hand part of a portrait group, of which the l.-hand part is on *f.* 34ᵛ. and the centre on *f.* 35ᵛ.

f. 37ᵛ. A BOY WITH A HOUND. W.L., standing, with body slightly to l., head half r. and eyes to front, his l. hand resting on the head of a hound r., to which he points out with his r. hand a squirrel on the branch of a tree, l. Wearing a lorica and cloak.

Pen and ink, with grey wash, touched with white, on buff-washed paper.

INSCR.: In the upper l.-hand corner, *105.*

f. 38ᵛ. AGNES VOSS, AS ST. AGNES, AFTER KNELLER. H.L., standing behind a ledge, with body turned slightly to r., head slightly to l. and eyes looking downwards, her l. hand resting on the ledge, her r. on the back of a lamb. Trees in the background.

Red chalk, strengthened with pen and ink

and grey wash, and heightened with white, on buff-washed paper.

INSCR.: In the upper l.-hand corner, *104*.

[Agnes Voss (*Fl.* 1685–1710), Kneller's daughter by Mrs. Voss (proprietress of a coffee-house in St. James's Market). Was painted with her mother by Kneller about 1685–90. Later married a Mr. Huckle by whom she had a son, Godfrey Huckle Kneller, ancestor of the present members of the Kneller family.]

The original picture was once in the collection of Godfrey Huckle Kneller at Donhead Hall, Wilts. (*See* Hoare, *Modern Wiltshire*, IV, Part I, p. 33), but has since disappeared. A small version of it was formerly in the possession of the Byng-Wray family (see *f.* 39r.) and now belongs to Miss Catherine Clarkson, of Penfold, Fern-Hill Road, New Milton, Hants. It was engraved in mezzotint by John Smith in 1705 (*See B.M. Engraved Portraits*, II, p. 579, No. 2).

Cf. No. 8 (25).

f. 39r. BLANK.

INSCR.: At the top, referring to the portrait of Agnes Voss on *f.* 38v., *This was among the Family pictures | bequeathed by Mr. Charles Wray of Bath | to his Nephew Sir Charles Wilkins | now in the possession of George Stratton | CR.* [*i.e.* C. W. B. W. Roberts].

f. 39v. A LADY WITH A SPRIG OF ORANGE (?). T.Q.L., seated, with body half-l. and eyes to front, her l. hand in her lap, her r. hand holding a sprig of orange (?). On the r., a patterened curtain, and through a window, l., a clump of trees.

Pen and brown ink, with grey wash, heightened with white, on blue-washed paper.

INSCR.: In the upper l.-hand corner, *103*.

f. 40v. A GENTLEMAN. H.L., with body half-r. and eyes to front. Wearing his shirt open at the neck and drapery over his shoulders. In an oval.

Pen and brown ink, with grey wash, heightened with white, on blue-washed paper.

INSCR.: In the upper l.-hand corner, *102*.

Cf. No. 8 (27).

f. 41v. SPENCER COMPTON, 1st EARL OF WILMINGTON, AFTER KNELLER. Another version of *f.* 21v., but reduced and in an oval.

Pen and brown ink, with grey wash, heightened with white, on blue-washed paper.

INSCR.: In the upper l.-hand corner, *101*.

f. 42v. QUEEN ANNE, AFTER KNELLER. Another version of No. 2, *ff.* 68v.–69r.

Pen and brown ink, with grey wash, touched with white, on blue-washed paper.

INSCR.: In the upper r.-hand corner, *100*.

f. 43r. BLANK.

INSCR.: At the top, by Mr. C. W. B. W. Roberts, *Queen Anne | Cousin thro the Hyde's to Mr | Edward Byng*.

The inscription refers to Edward Byng's great-great grandfather, Lawrence Hyde of Broadchalke, who was a first cousin of Edward Hyde, 1st Earl of Clarendon, grandfather of Queen Anne.

f. 43v. A GENTLEMAN. T.Q.L., standing, with body half-l. and eyes to front, his l. hand on his hip, his r. hand on the ledge of a window. On the r., a pilaster decorated with a festoon, and on the l., through the window, a wooded prospect.

Pen and brown ink, with grey wash, heightened with white, on blue-washed paper.

INSCR.: In the upper l.-hand corner, *99*.

f. 44ᵛ. A GIRL BY A VASE. Another version of No. 2, *f. 47ᵛ.*
Pen and brown ink, with grey wash, touched with white, on blue-washed paper.

INSCR.: In the upper l.-hand corner, *98*.

f. 45ᵛ. A COMMANDER, *c.* 1665. T.Q.L., standing, with body half-r. and eyes to front, his l. hand holding a glove by his side, his r. hand on his hip. Wearing long white or light-coloured hair, and a breastplate over a coat with short sleeves. Mountains in the distance, r.
Pen and brown ink, with grey wash, touched with white, on blue-washed paper.

INSCR.: In the upper l.-hand corner, *97*.

Probably after an original picture by Lely or one of his contemporaries.

f. 46ᵛ. LEBECK, AFTER KNELLER. H.L., with body half-r. and eyes looking to front, holding in his l. hand a wine glass. Wearing a night cap.
Pen and brown ink, with grey wash, on blue-washed paper.

INSCR.: In the upper l.-hand corner, *96*.

[Lebeck (*Fl.* 1710). Proprietor of a tavern in Half Moon St. or Chandos St.
Cf. Sir Godfrey Kneller, No. 12, for what is perhaps an original sketch for this portrait.

f. 47ᵛ. A LADY HOLDING A SPRAY OF BLOSSOM. T.Q.L., seated, with body half-l. and head half-r., her l. hand holding the spray in her lap, her right hand supporting

her head. On the r., a column, and behind her, l., a curtain and hanging foliage.
Pen and brown ink, with brown wash, on blue-washed paper; indented.

INSCR.: In the upper r.-hand corner, *95*.

f. 48ᵛ. A GENTLEMAN. T.Q.L., standing, with body half-l. and eyes to front, his l. hand on his hip, his r. elbow resting on the ledge of a window. Wearing a cloak draped over his arm and side. Behind him, r., a border of tapestry, and through the window, l., a clump of trees.
Pen and brown ink, with grey wash, touched with white, on blue-washed paper.

INSCR.: In the upper l.-hand corner, *94*.

f. 49ᵛ. A LADY IN MOURNING (?). T.Q.L., standing with body half-l. and head half-r., her hands clasped and resting on a rock, l. Wearing drapery over her head. Behind her, a cliff.
Pen and brown ink, with grey wash touched with white, on blue-washed paper.

INSCR.: In the upper l.-hand corner, *93*.

f. 50ᵛ. A GENTLEMAN. T.Q.L., seated, with body half-l. and eyes to front, his l. hand on his hip, his r. hand in his lap. Wearing a cloak draped over his l. shoulder. Behind him a curtain, r., and a cypress in the distance, l.
Pen and brown ink, with grey wash, touched with white, on blue-washed paper.

INSCR.: In the upper l.-hand corner, *92*.

f. 51ᵛ. A LADY AND CHILD. Both T.Q.L., the mother seated with body turned slightly to r. and head half-l., her arms round her child who stands leaning against her, r. Wearing an ermine-lined cloak. Behind her, l., a border of tapestry, and through the window, r., a tree.

Pen and brown ink, with grey wash, touched with white, on blue-washed paper.

INSCR.: In the upper l.-hand corner, *91*.

f. 52v. A LADY. T.Q.L., seated, with body half-l. and head half-r., her l. hand on her knee, her r. hand holding up a small unidentified object. Behind her, a rock.

Pen and brown ink, with grey wash, touched with white, on blue-washed paper.

INSCR.: In the upper l.-hand corner, *90*.

f. 53v. A LADY WITH A WREATH OF FLOWERS AND A LAMB. T.Q.L., seated with body half-r. and head slightly to l., her l. hand resting on a bank beside her, her r. hand holding the wreath of flowers in her lap. On the r., a lamb, and behind her, a wooded bank.

Pen and brown ink, with grey wash, touched with white, on blue-washed paper.

INSCR.: In the upper l.-hand corner, *89*.

f. 54v. TWO SMALL BOYS WITH A GREYHOUND. Both W.L., one standing, r., with body to front and head half-r., his l. arm across his breast, his r. hand pointing to the other child who is sitting, l., with body half-r., his l. hand with a bird perched on it. The former wearing a tunic and cloak, the latter, drapery. On the r., a greyhound. In the background, r., a pedestal.

Pen and brown ink, with grey wash touched with white, on blue-washed paper.

INSCR.: In the upper l.-hand corner, *88*.

f. 55v. A GENTLEMAN. H.L., with body slightly to r., head half-l. and eyes to front. In an oval.

Pen and brown ink, with grey wash, touched with white, on blue-washed paper.

INSCR.: In the upper l.-hand corner, *87*.

Cf. No. 8 (29).

f. 56v. EDWARD MONTAGU, VISCOUNT HINCHINGBROKE, AFTER KNELLER. Nearly T.Q.L., standing, with body half-l., head half-r. and eyes to front, his l. hand on his hip, his r. arm outstretched. Wearing a night cap. In an oval. In the lower margin, studies of foliage.

Pen and brown ink, with grey wash, touched with white, on blue-washed paper.

INSCR.: In the upper l.-hand corner, *86*.

[Edward Montagu, Viscount Hinchingbroke (B. 1692: D. 1722). Son of Edward, 3rd Earl of Sandwich. Between 1712 and 1722 served as an officer in the army, as M.P. for Huntingdon and Lord Lieutenant for Hunts.]

The original picture is presumably in the collection of the Earl of Sandwich at Hinchingbroke.

f. 57v. WILLIAM, DUKE OF GLOUCESTER, AFTER KNELLER. Nearly T.Q.L., standing, with body slightly to l., head half-r. and eyes to front, his l. hand on his hip, his r. arm outstretched. Wearing the Star and Ribbon of the Garter. In an oval.

Pen and brown ink, with grey wash, touched with white, on blue-washed paper.

INSCR.: In the upper l.-hand corner, *85*.

[William, Duke of Gloucester (B. 1689: D. 1700). Son of Queen Anne. (For a fuller biographical note *see* under *Robert White*, No. 6.)]

f. 58v. A GENTLEMAN. T.Q.L., standing with body in profile to r., head turned half-r. and eyes to front, his l. hand on his breast, his r. hand pointing. Wearing a cloak draped over his l. shoulder and forearm. A tree in the background, r.

Pen and brown ink, with grey wash, touched with white, on blue-washed paper.

INSCR.: In the upper l.-hand corner, *84*.

The l.-hand half of a portrait group, of which the other half is on *f. 59v*.

f. 59v. A GENTLEMAN. T.Q.L., standing, with body slightly to l., his l. hand by his side holding drapery, his r. forearm resting on a plinth at the foot of a tree.

Pen and brown ink, with grey wash, touched with white, on blue-washed paper.

INSCR.: In the upper l.-hand corner, *83*.

The r.-hand half of a portrait group, of which the other half is on *f. 58v*.

f. 60v. A LADY WITH A HOUND. Another version of No. 2, *f. 26v*.

Pen and brown ink, with grey wash, heightened with white, on blue-washed paper.

INSCR.: In the upper l.-hand corner, *82*.

The hand, belonging to another figure, which touches the sitter's l. arm suggests that this is the l.-hand half of a portrait group, of which the other half may be on *f. 61v*.

f. 61v. A LADY. W.L., standing, with body half-l. and head half-r., her l. hand holding drapery to her breast, her r. hand holding a bunch of flowers. Behind her, a tall pedestal.

Pen and brown ink, with grey wash, heightened with white, on blue-washed paper.

INSCR.: In the upper l.-hand corner, *81*.

Probably the r.-hand half of a portrait group, of which the other half is on *f. 60v*.

f. 62v. A GENTLEMAN WITH A GREY-HOUND. T.Q.L., standing, with body slightly to l. and eyes to front, his l. hand on his hip, his r. hand pointing downwards. Wearing drapery over his shoulder. A greyhound looking up at him from the l. Trees in the background.

Pen and brown ink, with grey wash, heightened with white, on blue-washed paper.

INSCR.: In the upper l.-hand corner, *80*.

f. 63v. A GENTLEMAN. T.Q.L., standing, with body half-l. and head half-r., his l. hand on his hip, his r. hand resting on a ledge. Wearing a cloak draped over his shoulder and side. Behind him, a wall, and in the distance, l., trees.

Pen and brown ink, with grey wash, on blue-washed paper.

INSCR.: In the upper l.-hand corner, *79*.

f. 64v. SIR JOHN PERCEVAL, LATER 1st EARL OF EGMONT, AFTER KNELLER. T.Q.L., standing, with body slightly to r., head half-l. and eyes to front, his l. hand on his hip, his r. on a table or ledge beside him. Wearing a cloak draped over his l. forearm.

Pen and brown ink, with grey wash, heightened with white, on blue-washed paper.

INSCR.: In the upper l.-hand corner, *78*.

[Sir John Perceval, 5th Bart., later 1st Earl of Egmont (B. 1683: D. 1748). One of the founders of the American colony of Georgia. Was noted for his genealogical and antiquarian interests.]

The present drawing corresponds, but in reverse, with the W.L. portrait of Perceval by Kneller engraved by John Smith (See *B.M. Engraved British Portraits*, II, p. 139, No. 3).

f. 65v. A LADY. H.L., with body half-l. and head half-r. Wearing a cloak draped over her r. shoulder. In an oval.

Pen and brown ink, with grey wash, touched with white, on blue-washed paper.

INSCR.: In the upper l.-hand corner, 77.

Cf. No. 8 (30).

f. 66v. A GENTLEMAN. H.L., with body slightly to r., head half-l. and eyes to front. In an oval.

Pen and brown ink, with grey wash, heightened with white, on blue-washed paper.

INSCR.: In the upper l.-hand corner, 76.

f. 67v. A LADY. T.Q.L., standing, with body half-l. and head half-r., her l. hand holding drapery in front of her, her r. hand resting on a window ledge. Behind her, r., a border of tapestry, and a tree in the distance, l.

Pen and brown ink, with grey wash, heightened with white, on blue-washed paper.

INSCR.: In the upper l.-hand corner, 75.

f. 68v. A LADY WITH A WREATH, AFTER KNELLER. T.Q.L., seated, with body half-r., head half-l. and eyes to front, holding with both hands a wreath in her lap. Behind her, a tree and a cliff.

Pen and brown ink, with grey wash, heightened with white, on blue-washed paper.

INSCR.: In the upper l.-hand corner, 74.

The general pose is not unlike that of Kneller's portrait of Lady Jane Smyth, dated 1713, in the Nottingham City Art Gallery (See Killanin, Pl. 56).

f. 69v. A LADY. H.L., with body slightly to r., head half-l. and eyes to front. In an oval.

Pen and brown ink, with grey wash, on grey-washed paper.

INSCR.: In the upper l.-hand corner, 73.

f.70v. A GENTLEMAN. T.Q.L., standing, with body slightly to r., head half-l. and eyes to front, his l. hand on his hip, his r. hand on a ledge. Behind him, a curtain, l., and a rock. Trees in the distance, r.

Pen and brown ink, with grey wash, touched with white, on grey-washed paper.

INSCR.: In the upper l.-hand corner, 72.

f. 71v. SIR JOHN COTTON, 2nd BART. AFTER KNELLER. T.Q.L., standing, with body half-l. and eyes to front, his l. hand on his hip, his r. forearm resting on a window ledge. Wearing drapery. Trees in the distance, l.

Pen and brown ink, with grey wash, heightened with white, on grey-washed paper.

INSCR.: In the upper l.-hand corner, 71.

[Sir John Cotton, 2nd Bart. (D. 1712/13). Of Landwade and Madingley Hall, Cambs. Succeeded his father in 1689. Was Recorder and M.P. for Cambridge from 1689 to 1708.]

The original picture, signed and dated 1692, was formerly at Madingley, subsequently in the Antrobus collection (?).

f. 72v. A GENTLEMAN. T.Q.L., standing, with body half-r. and head half-l., his l. hand resting on a table, his r. hand in the opening of his coat. Wearing a draped cloak. Behind him, a curtain, and on the r., a border of tapestry.

Pen and brown ink, with grey wash, touched with white, on grey-washed paper.

INSCR.: In the upper l.-hand corner, 70.

f. 73v. A PUG AND A KING CHARLES SPANIEL.

Pen and brown ink, with grey wash, touched with white, on grey-washed paper.

INSCR.: In the upper l.-hand corner, *69.*

74r. [inserted] A LADY. Another version of No. *5, f. 60r.*

Pen and ink, with grey wash, heightened with white, on blue-grey paper.

f. 75v. A YOUTH. H.L., with body half-r. and head half-l. Wearing a cloak buckled on his r. shoulder. In an oval.

Pen and brown ink, with grey wash.

INSCR.: In the upper l.-hand corner, *68.*

f. 76v. RACHEL HOW, AFTER KNELLER. A little girl, T.Q.L., standing, with body to front and head slightly to l., a dove perched on her l. hand, her r. hand to her breast. Trees in the distance, l.

Pen and brown ink, with grey wash.

INSCR.: In the upper l.-hand corner, *67.*

[Rachel How (*Fl.* 1702 (?)). Perhaps daughter of John Grubham Howe, 1st Baron Chedworth, or of his younger brother, Emmanuel Scrope Howe.]

The original picture has not been traced. It was engraved in mezzotint, in reverse, by John Smith (*See B.M. Engraved Portraits,* II, p. 570, No. 1).

f. 77v. A LADY. H.L., with body slightly to l. and head slightly to r., her l. hand holding drapery across her. In an oval.

Pen and brown ink, with grey wash.

INSCR.: In the upper l.-hand corner, *66.*

f. 78v. A BOY. H.L., with body slightly to l. and head slightly to r., a cloak over his r. shoulder. In an oval.

Pen and brown ink, with grey wash, heightened with white, on grey-washed paper.

INSCR.: In the upper l.-hand corner, *65.*

Cf. No. 8 (31).

f. 79v. A BOY. T.Q.L., standing, with body to front, his l. hand on his hip. Wearing an open coat, showing a striped waistcoat. In an oval.

Pen and brown ink, with grey wash, heightened with white, on grey-washed paper.

INSCR.: In the upper l.-hand corner, *64.*

Cf. No. 8 (33).

f. 80v. A LADY. H.L., with body slightly to r., head slightly to l. and eyes to front. Wearing drapery. In an oval.

Pen and brown ink, with grey wash, heightened with white, on grey-washed paper.

INSCR.: In the upper l.-hand corner, *63.*

Cf. No. 8 (48).

f. 81v. A YOUTH. H.L., with body slightly to r., head slightly to l. and eyes to front, his r. hand holding in front of him a fold of his nightgown. In an oval.

Pen and brown ink, with grey wash, heightened with white on grey-washed paper.

INSCR.: In the upper l.-hand corner, *62.*

f. 82v. A BOY IN HUNGARIAN OR POLISH DRESS. T.Q.L., with body slightly to r., head slightly to l. and eyes to front, his l. hand on his hip, his r. hand holding a bow. Wearing a frogged coat.

Pen and brown ink, with grey wash,

heightened with white, on grey-washed paper.

INSCR.: In the upper l.-hand corner, *61.*

f. 83*v.* A LADY. T.Q.L., standing, with body slightly to l. and head half-r., her l. hand holding drapery to her breast. In the lower r.-hand corner, a relief of two cupids. Behind her, a square pillar, and trees in the background, l.
Pen and brown ink, with grey wash, heightened with white, on grey-washed paper.

INSCR.: In the upper l.-hand corner, *60.*

f. 84*v.* A LADY WITH A PARROT. Another version of No. 2, *ff.* 62*v.* and 63*r.* In an oval.
Pen and brown ink, with grey wash, touched with white, on grey-washed paper.

INSCR.: In the upper l.-hand corner, *59.*

f. 85*v.* A LADY AS A SHEPHERDESS. T.Q.L., standing, with body slightly to r., head slightly to l. and eyes to front, holding in her r. hand a crook.
Pen and brown ink, with grey wash, touched with white, on grey-washed paper.

INSCR.: In the upper l.-hand corner, *58.*

Cf. No. 8 (*35*).

f. 86*v.* A LADY WITH A BUNCH OF FLOWERS. T.Q.L., standing, with body half-r. and head half-l., holding with her l. hand a bunch of flowers which she also touches with her r. hand. Behind her, a rock.
Pen and brown ink, with grey wash, touched with white, on grey-washed paper.

INSCR.: In the upper l.-hand corner, *57.*

f. 87*v.* A GENTLEMAN. H.L., with body half-r., head slightly to l. and eyes to front. Wearing a cloak. In an oval.
Pen and brown ink, with grey wash, touched with white, on grey-washed paper.

INSCR.: In the upper l.-hand corner, *54.*

f. 88*v.* A GENTLEMAN. H.L., with body half-r., head half-l. and eyes to front. In an oval.
Pen and brown ink, with grey wash, touched with white, on grey-washed paper.

INSCR.: In the upper l.-hand corner, *53.*

f. 89*v.* A YOUNG MAN IN AN EM-BROIDERBD COAT. T.Q.L., with body half-r. and eyes to front. In an oval.
Brush drawing in grey wash.

INSCR.: In the upper l.-hand corner, *52.*

f. 90*v.* MARY, COUNTESS OF ESSEX, AFTER KNELLER. T.Q.L., standing, with body slightly to l., head half-r. and eyes to front, her r. hand holding up drapery to her breast. Behind her, a rock, and trees in the distance, l.
Brush drawing in grey wash, strengthened with pen and ink.

INSCR.: In the upper l.-hand corner, *51.*

[Mary Bentinck, Countess of Essex (D. 1726). Daughter of William, 1st Earl of Portland, and wife of Algernon, 2nd Earl of Essex, whom she married in 1691/2. Married secondly, 1714, Sir Conyers Darcy, K.B.]
The original picture has not been traced. It was engraved in mezzotint in reverse by John Smith (*See B.M. Engraved Portraits*, II, p. 175, No. 2).

f. 91*v.* MRS. CROSS AS ST. CATHERINE, AFTER KNELLER. W.L., kneeling, her l.

hand holding a palm branch, her r. hand on the broken wheel.

Pen and brown ink, with grey wash.

INSCR.: In the upper l.-hand corner, *48.*

[Mrs. Catherine (?) Cross (*Fl.* early XVIII c.), singer and actress.]

The original picture has not been traced, but it is known through a mezzotint after it by John Smith (*See B.M. Engraved Portraits*, I, p. 534, No. 2).

f. 92v. ELIZABETH WRAY (?) AS THE MAGDALEN. W.L., kneeling towards the r.

Pen and brown ink, with grey wash.

INSCR.: In the upper l.-hand corner, *47.*

[Elizabeth Wray (D. 1759). Daughter of Thomas and Anne Byng, sister of Edward Byng (*See* biographical note above), and wife of the Reverend William Wray (D. 1730; successively Rector of Newton Tony, and Vicar of Broadchalke and Stour Provost). Mother of Robert Bateman Wray (B. 1715: D.1779), gem engraver of Salisbury. Died at Potterne, where she was buried, Jan. 17th, 1759.

f. 93r. BLANK.

INSCR.: At the top, referring to the portrait of Elizabeth Byng on *f.* 92v., *This picture in the original hung | over the dining room mantelpiece | in my great Uncle's House (Sir | Charles Wilkins) at 40 Baker Street | and was said to be Elizabeth Byng | the sister of Edward Byng—and afterwards | wife of the Rev. William Wray | Rector of Broadchalke in Wilts | my great great Grandmother | [signed] Cecil Wray Byng Wilkins Roberts | March 18. 1877. | This picture is now in the possession | of my cousin George Locke Stratton.*

f. 93v. A LADY. H.L., with body slightly to r., head slightly to l. and eyes to front. In an oval.

Pen and brown ink, with grey wash, heightened with white, on blue-grey paper.

INSCR.: In the upper l.-hand corner, *46.*

Cf. No. 8 (36).

f. 94v. A LADY. H.L., with body to front, head slightly to l. and eyes to front. In an oval.

Pen and brown ink, with grey wash, heightened with white, on blue-grey paper.

INSCR.: In the upper l.-hand corner, *45.*

f. 95v. A GENTLEMAN. H.L., with body in profile to l., head half-l. and eyes to front. Wearing a cloak draped over his l. shoulder. In an oval.

Pen and brown ink, with grey wash, heightened with white, on blue-grey paper.

INSCR.: In the upper l.-hand corner, *44.*

f. 96v. A LADY. H.L., with body slightly to l. and head half-r. In an oval.

Pen and brown ink, with grey wash, heightened with white, on blue-grey paper.

INSCR.: In the upper l.-hand corner, *43.*

f. 97v. A LADY. H.L. with body slightly to r. and head half-l. In an oval.

Pen and brown ink, with grey wash, heightened with white, on blue-grey paper.

INSCR.: In the upper l.-hand corner, *42.*

f. 98v. JOHN DRYDEN, AFTER KNELLER. T.Q.L., standing, with body in profile to l., head half-l. and eyes to front, holding in his r. hand a laurel wreath. Wearing a night gown.

Pen and brown ink, with grey wash, touched with white, on blue-grey paper.

INSCR.: In the upper l.-hand corner, *41.*

[John Dryden (B. 1631: D. 1700), poet and dramatist.]

The original picture is at Trinity College, Cambridge.

f. 99*v*. LADY ANNE CHURCHILL, LATER COUNTESS OF SUNDERLAND, AS A CHILD, AFTER KNELLER. W.L., with body leaning to l. and eyes looking upwards to r., resting on her r. hand. Behind her, l., a tree.

Pen and brown ink, with grey wash, heightened with white, on blue-grey paper.

INSCR.: In the upper l.-hand corner, *40*.

[Lady Anne Churchill, later Countess of Sunderland (D. 1716). Second daughter of the 1st Duke of Marlborough. Married in January, 1699/1700 Charles, 3rd Earl of Sunderland, her second son succeeding his grandfather as 2nd Duke of Marlborough.]

The original picture, signed and dated *1688*, in which Lady Anne appears with her sister, Lady Henrietta, was formerly at Holywell House, St. Albans, and is now in the collection of Earl Spencer at Althorp.

f. 100*v*. A SMALL BOY IN HEROIC DRESS. W.L., seated, with body leaning to l. and head half-r., his l. hand fondling a spaniel in his lap, his feet resting on a cushion. Wearing a plumed cap and drapery. In the distance, r., a wooded prospect.

Pen and brown ink, with grey wash, touched with white, on blue-grey paper.

INSCR.: In the lower l.-hand corner, *39*.

f. 101*v*. A GENTLEMAN. H.L., with body half-l. and eyes to front. Wearing a cloak. In an oval.

Pen and brown ink, with grey wash, heightened with white, on blue-grey paper.

INSCR.: In the upper l.-hand corner, *38*.

f. 102*v*. A LADY WITH FAIR HAIR AND A NECKLACE OF PEARLS. H.L., with body slightly to l., head slightly to r. and eyes to front, her l. hand supporting her head. In an oval.

Pen and ink, with grey wash, heightened with white.

INSCR.: In the upper l.-hand corner, *37*.

f. 103*v*. (*a*) A LADY. H.L., with body to l. and head to r.
(*b*) A MONSTROUS MASK SPEWING WATER.

Pen and ink, with grey wash, touched with white, on blue-grey paper.

INSCR.: In the upper l.-hand corner, *36*.

f. 104*r*. A CHANCELLOR OF THE ORDER OF THE GARTER, PROBABLY GILBERT BURNET. H.L., with body to l. and eyes to front. Wearing his mantle as Chancellor of the Order of the Garter.

Pen and ink, touched with white, on blue-grey paper.

[Gilbert Burnet (B. 1643: D. 1715). Brought up in the Scottish Presbyterian Church, and throughout his life held Protestant views, though he showed some toleration towards the Catholics. Disliked by Charles II (whom he reproved for his profligacy) and James II, but found favour with William III. Became Bishop of Salisbury and Chancellor of the Order of the Garter in 1689. Was the author of *The History of the Reformation in England* and a *History of his own Times*.]

The present drawing seems to be after a reduced version of the two T.Q.L. portraits of Burnet, one attributed to Riley, in (or formerly in) the collection of Mr. David Minlore, the other, attributed to Kneller, in

1832 in the collection of the Earl of Hard-wicke, when it was engraved by H. Robinson.

f. 104v. A LADY. T.Q.L., seated, with body half-l., head half-r. and eyes to front, her l. hand in her lap, her r. elbow resting on a ledge. Behind her, a rock.

Pen and ink, with grey wash, touched with white, on blue-grey paper.

INSCR.: In the upper l.-hand corner, *35*.

f. 105r. A LADY. Another version in faint outline of *f.* 104v.

White chalk on grey-blue paper.

f. 105v. A LADY AND HER DAUGHTER. Both W.L., the lady seated, with body half-r., her l. arm round her daughter who holds a pug. In the background, l., a curtain.

Pen and brown ink, with grey wash, touched with white, on blue-grey paper.

INSCR.: In the upper l.-hand corner, *34*.

Cf. No. 8 (*37*).

f. 106v. A LADY AND HER CHILD. Both W.L., the lady standing, with body slightly to r. and head slightly to l., her arms round her child who is seated, r., on a ledge. Trees in the background.

Pen and ink, with grey wash, touched with white, on blue-grey paper.

INSCR.: In the upper l.-hand corner, *33*.

Cf. No. 8 (*38*).

f. 107v. MARY SOMERSET, DUCHESS OF ORMONDE, AFTER KNELLER. W.L., standing, with body slightly to r., head slightly to l. and eyes to front, her l. hand pointing downwards, her r. hand holding drapery to her breast. On the l., a negro page holding her train. In the background, a curtain, and r., an arcade.

Pen and brown ink, with grey wash, heightened with white, on blue-grey paper.

[Mary Somerset, Duchess of Ormonde (B. *c.* 1665: D. 1733). Daughter of Henry, 1st Duke of Beaufort, and second wife of James, 2nd Duke of Ormonde, whom she married in 1685. Was Lady of the Bed-chamber to Queen Anne.]

The original picture has not been traced. It was engraved in mezzotint by John Smith (*See B.M. Engraved Portraits*, III, p. 381, No. 1).

f. 108v. A LADY. W.L., half-seated, with body slightly to r., head half-l., her l. hand pointing, her r. hand resting on drapery. Behind her, a rock.

Pen and brown ink, with grey wash, heightened with white, on blue-grey paper.

INSCR.: In the upper l.-hand corner, *31*.

f. 109v. WILLIAM VILLIERS, 2nd EARL OF JERSEY, AFTER KNELLER. Another version of No. 2, *f.* 70r.

Pen and brown ink, with grey wash, heightened with white, on blue-grey paper.

INSCR.: In the upper l.-hand corner, *30*.

f. 110v. A LADY. T.Q.L., standing, with body half-l., head half-r. and eyes to front, her l. hand touching a basin, r., her r. hand holding up a fold of the curtain draped behind her.

Pen and brown ink, with grey wash, touched with white, on blue-grey paper.

INSCR.: In the upper l.-hand corner, *29*.

f. 111v. A LADY. T.Q.L., seated, with body slightly to r., head slightly to l. and eyes to front, her l. hand to her breast, her r. hand in her lap. A tree in the background, l.

Pen and brown ink, with grey wash, touched with white, on blue-grey paper.

INSCR.: In the upper l.-hand corner, *28*.

f. 112*v*. A LADY. T.Q.L., seated, with body half-l., head half-r. and eyes looking slightly upwards, her l. hand in her lap, her r. hand resting on drapery. A tree behind her, r.

Pen and brown ink, with grey wash (the tree in black chalk), heightened with white, on blue-grey paper.

INSCR.: In the upper l.-hand corner, 27.

f. 113*v*. A DUKE IN ANTIQUE ROMAN DRESS. T.Q.L., standing, with body slightly to r. and head half-l., his l. arm crooked, his r. hand on a ledge. Wearing a cloak draped over a Roman *lorica* and kilt. On the r., his coronet.

Pen and brown ink, with grey wash, touched with white, on blue-grey paper.

INSCR.: In the upper l.-hand corner, 26.

f. 114*v*. A YOUNG MAN. T.Q.L., standing, with body half-l. and eyes to front, his l. hand on a fold of his cloak, his r. hand on his hip. Wearing a sword belt. In the background, l., a curved arcade.

Pen and brown ink, with grey wash, touched with white, on blue-grey paper.

INSCR.: In the upper l.-hand corner, 25.

Cf. No. 8 (39).

PROV.: As for No. 2.

1897–8–13–8 (L.B.6).

8. ALBUM. Containing the following material, originally loose in a portfolio: (1)–(67) studies after portraits; (68)–(86) academic figure-studies; (87)–(98) miscellaneous studies, mostly of hands for and after portraits; (99)–(113) tracings from portrait heads, hands, etc.: and (114)–(115) other studies not related to any of the foregoing.

Two drawings from this series, one by John James Baker (Bakker) (**1897–8–13–9** (95)), the other by Marcellus Laroon II (**1897–8–13–9** (113)), have been placed separately with, and catalogued under, their respective artists.

Inside of the upper fly-leaf.

INSCR.: On a label from the old portfolio, *These belong to Cecil Wray | Byng Wilkins Roberts*, and *Byng's drawings | and Collections.*

[(1)–(67)]. **Studies after portraits,** in the manner of those of the preceding sketchbooks, Numbers 2–7.

(1) RICHARD WILLIS, BISHOP OF WINCHESTER. T.Q.L., seated, with body half-l. and eyes half-r., his l. elbow resting on the arm of his chair, his r. hand holding his academic cap on his knee. Wearing a rochet and bands. On the l., a book on the ledge of a shell-topped niche.

Pen and ink, with grey wash, heightened with white, on blue-grey paper; 28·6 × 22·6 cm. ($11\frac{1}{4} \times 8\frac{7}{8}$ in.).

[Richard Willis (B. 1664: D. 1734). Was Chaplain to William III in Holland, 1694–5, a promoter of the S.P.C.K., 1699, and successively Bishop of Gloucester, Salisbury and Winchester, 1714–34.]

This drawing bears some resemblance to the portrait of Willis by Dahl, engraved in mezzotint by Jean Simon (*See B.M. Engraved Portraits*, IV, p. 504, No. 1).

(2) *Recto*. A LADY. Nearly H.L., with body to front and head half-r. Wearing a low-necked dress. In an oval.

Black and white chalk, on blue-grey paper; unfinished; 29·2 × 21·8 cm. ($11\frac{1}{2} \times 8\frac{5}{8}$ in.).

INSCR.: In the upper r.-hand corner, 35.

Verso. A HELMET.
Black chalk, touched with white.

INSCR.: On the r., *J.B.*

(3) HENRY COMPTON, BISHOP OF LONDON. Another version of the drawing in No. 5, inside the upper cover.

Pen and brown ink, with grey wash, touched with white, on buff paper; 25 × 21 cm. (9¾ × 8¼ in.).

INSCR.: *Recto*, in the lower r.-hand corner, *1*.

(4) A GENTLEMAN. Another version of No. 5, *f*. 6r.

Pen and ink, with grey wash, touched with white, on blue-grey paper; 28·6 × 23·5 cm. (11¼ × 9¼ in.).

(5) A GENTLEMAN. Another version of No. 5, *f*. 18r.

Pen and brown ink, with grey wash, touched with white, on buff paper; 24·3 × 19·7 cm. (9½ × 7⅞ in.).

INSCR.: *Recto*, in the lower r.-hand corner, *2*.

(6) A LADY WITH DRAPERY OVER HER HEAD. Another version of No. 5, *f*. 25r.

Pen and brown ink, with grey wash, touched with white, on buff paper; 25·8 × 20·6 cm. (10⅛ × 8⅛ in.).

INSCR.: *Recto*, in the lower r.-hand corner, 5.

(7) A LADY WITH A BUNCH OF FLOWERS. Another version of No. 5, *f*. 26r., but with a hound in the lower r.-hand corner.

Pen and ink, with grey wash, touched with white, on blue-grey paper; 29·6 × 23·9 cm. (11⅝ × 9⅜ in.).

(8) A GENTLEMAN WITH A HOUND. Another version of No. 5, *f*. 27r.

Pen and ink, with grey wash, on blue-grey paper; 28 × 22·3 cm. (11 × 8¾ in.).

(9) A GENTLEMAN. Another version of No. 5, *f*. 29r.

Pen and ink, with grey wash, touched with white, on blue-grey paper; 29·7 × 23·4 cm. (11⅝ × 9¼ in.).

(10) A NAVAL COMMANDER. Another version of No. 5, *f*. 31r.

Pen and ink, with grey wash, heightened with white, on blue-grey paper; 28 × 21·7 cm. (11 × 8⅝ in.).

(11) A YOUNG MAN. Another version of No. 5, *f*. 33r.

Pen and brown ink, with grey wash, heightened with white, on buff paper; 25·8 × 21·1 cm. (10⅛ × 8⅜ in.).

INSCR.: *Recto*, in the lower r.-hand corner, 4.

(12) A YOUNG MAN. Yet another version of No. 5, *f*. 33r.

Brush drawing in brown wash, heightened with white, over a black lead outline, on oiled paper; 22·5 × 18·2 cm. (8⅞ × 7⅛ in.).

INSCR.: *Recto*, in the lower l.-hand corner, *31*.

(13) A NAVAL COMMANDER. Another version of No. 5, *f*. 36r.

Pen and brown ink, with grey wash, touched with white, on blue-grey paper; 27·7 × 21·5 cm. (10⅞ × 8½ in.).

(14) A GENTLEMAN. Another version of No. 5, *f*. 41r.

Pen and ink, with grey wash, heightened with white, on blue-grey paper; 24·6 × 20·1 cm. (9⅝ × 7⅞ in.).

INSCR.: *Recto*, in the lower r.-hand corner, *10*.

(15) CHARLES SEYMOUR, 6th DUKE OF SOMERSET. Another version of No. 5, *f*. 43r.

Pen and ink, with grey wash, heightened with white, on blue-grey paper; 25·9 × 20·9 cm. (10¼ × 8¼ in.).

(16) SIR ROBERT COTTON, 5th BART., AFTER KNELLER. Another version of No. 5, *f*. 44*r*.

Pen and ink, with grey wash, heightened with white, on blue-grey paper; 25·3 × 20 cm. (9⅞ × 7⅞ in.).

INSCR.: In the lower r.-hand corner, *14*.

(17) A LADY WITH A BOOK. Another version of No. 5, *f*. 53*r*.

Brush drawing in brown wash, over black lead, heightened with white, on oiled paper; 29·2 × 21·7 cm. (11½ × 8½ in.).

INSCR.: In the upper r.-hand corner, *8*, and in the lower l.-hand corner, *51*.

(18) A LADY. Another version of No. 5, *f*. 57*r*.

Pen and ink, with grey wash, heightened with white, on blue-grey paper; 18·5 × 15·3 cm. (7¼ × 6⅛ in.).

(19) A WIDOWED LADY. Another version of No. 5, *f*. 63*r*.

Pen and ink, with grey wash, heightened with white, on blue-grey paper; 24·6 × 19·6 cm. (9⅝ × 7¾ in.).

(20) A NAVAL COMMANDER, PERHAPS ADMIRAL SIR JOHN NORRIS, AFTER KNELLER. Another version of No. 5, *f*. 66*r*.

Pen and ink, with grey wash, heightened with white, on blue-grey paper; 27·2 × 23·5 cm. (10⅞ × 9¼ in.).

(21) A SMALL BOY OR GIRL WITH A SPANIEL. Another version of No. 5, *f*. 69*r*.

Pen and ink, with grey wash, heightened with white, on blue-grey paper; 23·2 × 20·1 cm. (9¼ × 8 in.).

INSCR.: In the lower l.-hand corner, *67*.

(22) ALGERNON CAPEL, 2nd EARL OF ESSEX. Another version of No. 6, *f*. 44*v*.

Black chalk, with grey wash, heightened with white, on blue-grey paper; 26·3 × 19·9 cm. (10¼ × 7⅞ in.).

(23) A LADY. Another version of No. 7, *f*. 24*v*.

Black chalk, with grey wash, heightened with white, on blue-grey paper; 27 × 20·5 cm. (10⅝ × 8 in.).

(24) A LADY AS DIANA OR A SHEP-HERDESS. Another version of No. 7, *f*. 33*v*.

Black chalk, with grey wash, heightened with white, on blue-grey paper; 31·6 × 25·5 cm. (12⅜ × 10⅛ in.).

(25) AGNES VOSS AS ST. AGNES, AFTER KNELLER. Another version of No. 7, *f*. 38*v*.

Black chalk, with grey wash, heightened with white, on blue-grey paper; 27·8 × 22·2 cm. (10⅞ × 8¾ in.).

(26) OFFSET FROM (25).

Blue-grey paper; 28·2 × 22·3 cm. (11⅛ × 8¾ in.).

INSCR.: At the top, by Mr. Roberts, *This family picture in the | original was in the possession | of Sir Charles Wilkins.*

(27) A GENTLEMAN. Another version of No. 7, *f*. 40*v*.

Black chalk, with grey wash, heightened with white, on blue-grey paper; 26·3 × 20·3 cm. (10¼ × 8 in.).

(28) SPENCER COMPTON, 1st EARL OF WILMINGTON, AFTER KNELLER. Another version of No. 7, *ff*. 21*v*. & 41*v*.

Black chalk, with grey wash, heightened with white, on blue-grey paper; 28·4 × 21 cm. (11⅛ × 8¼ in.).

(29) A GENTLEMAN. Another version of No. 7, *f*. 55*v*.

Black chalk, with grey wash, heightened with white, on blue-grey paper; 23·2 × 19 cm. (9¼ × 7½ in.).

(30) A LADY. Another version of No. 7, *f.* 65*v.*
Black chalk, with grey wash, heightened with white, on buff paper; 27·6 × 21·3 cm. (10⅞ × 8⅜ in.).

(31) A BOY. Another version of No. 7, *f.* 78*v.*
Black chalk, with grey wash, heightened with white, on blue-grey paper; 25 × 20·7 cm. (9⅞ × 8⅛ in.).

(32) OFFSET FROM (31).
Blue-grey paper; 24·4 × 20·7 cm. (9⅝ × 8⅛ in.).

(33) A BOY. Another version of No. 7, *f.* 79*v.*
Black chalk, with grey wash, heightened with white, on blue-grey paper; 27 × 21·3 cm. (10⅝ × 8⅜ in.).

(34) OFFSET FROM (33).
Blue-grey paper; 26·2 × 21·3 cm. (10¼ × 8⅜ in.).

(35) A LADY AS A SHEPHERDESS. Another version of No. 7, *f.* 85*v.*
Black chalk, with grey wash, heightened with white, on blue-grey paper; 29·2 × 23·2 cm. (11½ × 9¼ in.).

(36) A LADY. Another version of No. 7, *f.* 93*v.*
Pen and ink over black chalk, with grey wash, heightened with white, on blue-grey paper; 29·9 × 21·9 cm. (11¾ × 8⅝ in.).

(37) A LADY AND HER DAUGHTER. Another version of No. 7, *f.* 105*v.* A study of the daughter's hand in the upper r.-hand corner.
Black chalk, with grey wash, touched with pen and ink and heightened with white, on blue-grey paper; 45 × 28·5 cm. (17⅝ × 11¼ in.).

(38) A LADY AND HER CHILD. Another version of No. 7, *f.* 106*v.*
Black chalk, with grey wash, heightened with white, on blue-grey paper; 45·9 × 29·3 cm. (18 × 11½ in.).

(39) A YOUNG MAN. Another version of No. 7, *f.* 114*v.*
Brush drawing in grey wash, over black chalk, heightened with white, on blue-grey paper; 29·9 × 23·7 cm. (11¾ × 9⅜ in.).

(40) *Recto.* A GENTLEMAN. T.Q.L., seated, with body half-r. and head half-l., his r. forearm resting on a table, l. Wearing a cloak draped over his r. shoulder.
Black chalk, with grey wash, heightened with white, on blue-grey paper; 29 × 23·5 cm. (11⅜ × 9¼ in.).
Verso. A COMMANDER. T.Q.L., standing, with body half-l. and eyes to front, his l. hand on his hip, his r. hand resting on a table, l. Wearing armour and a sash round his waist.
Black chalk, heightened with white; outline only.

INSCR.: In the upper r.-hand corner, *34*.

(41) A LADY. T.Q.L., standing, with body slightly to r., head slightly to l. and eyes to front, her l. hand resting on a ledge, r., her r. hand holding up drapery to her breast. A rock and trees in the background.
Black chalk, with grey wash, heightened with white, on blue-grey paper; 26·9 × 21·1 cm. (10⅝ × 8¼ in.).

(42) A LADY. T.Q.L., seated, with body half-l., head slightly to r. and eyes to front, her l. hand in her lap touching a fold of drapery, her r. hand pointing. Behind her, a

bank with a tree, and other trees in the distance, l.

Black chalk, with grey wash, heightened with white, on blue-grey paper; 26·5 × 19·4 cm. ($10\frac{1}{2}$ × $7\frac{5}{8}$ in.).

(43) A LADY. T.Q.L., seated, with body slightly to r., head slightly to l. and eyes to front, her l. hand resting on her knee, her r. hand holding a fold of drapery over her l. arm. Behind her, a wooded bank, and trees in the distance, r.

Black chalk, with grey wash, heightened with white, on blue-grey paper; 26·5 × 20·5 cm. ($10\frac{3}{8}$ × 8 in.).

(44) A LADY. H.L., with body half-l. and eyes to front. Wearing a lock of hair on her r. shoulder, and loose drapery. In an oval.

Black chalk, with grey wash, heightened with white, on blue-grey paper; 24·9 × 18·7 cm. ($9\frac{3}{4}$ × $7\frac{3}{8}$ in.).

(45) *Recto*. A LADY. H.L., with body slightly to l., head slightly to r. and eyes to front. Wearing a lock of hair on her r. shoulder and drapery fastened on her l. In an oval.

Black chalk, with grey wash, touched with white, on blue-grey paper; 27·4 × 21·3 cm. ($10\frac{3}{4}$ × $8\frac{3}{8}$ in.).

Verso. ST. MARY MAGDALEN. Nearly T.Q.L., standing, with body slightly to l. and head half-r., leaning back on a ledge, r., above which is a crucifix, her l. hand holding a book, her r. hand to her breast.

Black chalk, heightened with white.

INSCR.: In the upper l.-hand corner, 29.

A completely different figure from that in No. 7, f. 92v.

(46) A YOUNG LADY. H.L., with body to front, head slightly to l. and eyes to front, her r. hand holding drapery to her breast. Wearing pearls in her hair. In an oval.

Black chalk, with grey wash, heightened with white, on blue-grey paper; 27·3 × 21·8 cm. ($10\frac{3}{4}$ × $8\frac{1}{2}$ in.).

(47) A LADY. Another version of No. 5, f. 96r. In an oval.

Brush drawing in brown wash, over black lead, heightened with white, on oiled paper; 23·3 × 18·5 cm. ($9\frac{1}{4}$ × $7\frac{3}{8}$ in.).

INSCR.: In the lower r.-hand corner, 90, and in the upper r.-hand corner, in a later hand, 7.

(48) A LADY. Another version of No. 7, f. 80v.

Black chalk, with greenish wash, touched with white, on blue-grey paper; 27·6 × 21·1 cm. ($10\frac{3}{4}$ × $8\frac{1}{4}$ in.).

(49) LOUISA, COUNTESS OF BERKELEY, AFTER KNELLER. Another version of No. 5, f. 38r.

Red chalk, touched with white, on blue-grey paper; 28·6 × 22·7 cm. ($11\frac{1}{4}$ × $8\frac{7}{8}$ in.).

(50) A GIRL AND HER SMALL BROTHER. Both W.L., she standing, l., holding a wreath in her outstretched r. hand, he half-naked, seated and playing with a spaniel. Trees in the background.

Pen and ink, with grey wash, heightened with white, on blue-grey paper; 31·9 × 26·2 cm. ($12\frac{1}{2}$ × $10\frac{1}{4}$ in.).

(51) A BOY. W.L., standing, with body half-r. and eyes to front, his l. arm upraised with drapery over it, his r. hand resting on a bank. Behind him, l., a tree, and other trees in the distance, r.

Black chalk, with grey wash, heightened with white, on blue-grey paper; 43 × 26·9 cm. (17 × $10\frac{1}{2}$ in.).

(52) A GIRL WITH A WREATH OF FLOWERS. Nearly T.Q.L., with body half-l. and head half-r., her l. hand pointing towards

the l., her r. hand holding a wreath of flowers. Wearing a low-necked dress and drapery.

Black chalk, with grey wash, heightened with white and coloured crayons, on blue-grey paper; 31 × 25·5 cm. (12⅛ × 10 in.).

(53) A SMALL GIRL. H.L., with body half-r. and eyes to front. Wearing drapery. In an oval.

Black chalk, with grey wash, heightened with white; 28·5 × 22 cm. (11¼ × 8⅝ in.).

(54) A YOUNG LADY. H.L., with body half-l., head half-r. and eyes to l. Wearing a low-necked dress and drapery. In an oval.

Black chalk, outline only, on blue-grey paper; 23·8 × 17·5 cm. (9⅜ × 6⅞ in.).

(55) A LADY. T.Q.L., seated, with body to front and head half-r., her l. hand in her lap, her r. hand resting on the bank beside her, l. Wearing a long-sleeved dress. Behind her, a tree, and other trees in the distance, l.

Pen and ink, with grey wash, heightened with white, on blue-grey paper; 31·7 × 26·5 cm. (12½ × 10⅜ in.).

(56) A LADY. T.Q.L., moving towards the l., with eyes to front, her l. hand holding drapery before her, her r. hand pointing. In the background, l., a colonnade.

Brush drawing in brown wash, heightened with white, on blue-grey paper; 31·6 × 26·8 cm. (12½ × 10½ in.).

(57) A LADY. T.Q.L., moving towards the r., with eyes to front, holding in her l. hand a basket of flowers, and in her r. hand, a sprig. Wearing a low-necked dress and drapery. Behind her, through a window, a wooded prospect.

Pen and ink, with grey wash, heightened with white, on blue-grey paper; 30·7 × 23·6 cm. (12⅛ × 9¼ in.).

(58) A LADY. T.Q.L., standing, with body nearly to front and head slightly to l., her l. elbow resting on a fountain, r., her l. hand holding up drapery, her r. hand pointing. Wearing a low-necked dress. Behind her, trees and a tall pedestal.

Pen and ink, with grey wash, heightened with white, on blue-grey paper; 31 × 26·3 cm. (12¼ × 10¼ in.).

(59) A YOUNG LADY. H.L., with body slightly to l. and head half-r. Wearing a lock of hair on her r. shoulder, and a low-necked dress. In an oval.

Black chalk, touched with white, on blue-grey paper; the lower margin made up; 33·5 × 27·2 cm. (13⅛ × 10¾ in.).

(60) A GENTLEMAN. T.Q.L., standing, with body half-r. and eyes to front, his l. hand beside him, his r. hand holding drapery to his hip. A tree behind him, l., and in the distance, r., an avenue.

Black chalk, with grey wash, heightened with white, on blue-grey paper; 27·2 × 19·4 cm. (10⅝ × 7⅝ in.).

(61) A GENTLEMAN. T.Q.L., standing, with body nearly to front, head slightly to l. and eyes to front, his l. arm, draped in a cloak, crooked, his r. hand in the opening of his coat. Trees in the background.

Black chalk, with grey wash, heightened with white, on blue-grey paper; 26·9 × 19·5 cm. (10⅝ × 7⅝ in.).

(62) A LADY. W.L., standing, with body slightly to l. and head half-r., her l. hand holding up drapery, her r. hand resting on a ledge, l. Behind her, r., the corner of a wall and in the distance, l., an avenue of trees.

Pen and ink, with grey wash, heightened with white, on blue-grey paper; 31·7 × 26·2 cm. (12½ × 10¼ in.).

(63) A GENTLEMAN. Another version of No. 1, and No. 2, f. 11r.

Pen and ink, with grey wash, on blue-grey paper; 31·6 × 26·3 cm. (12½ × 10⅜ in.).

263

(64) *Recto*. A GENTLEMAN. H.L., seated, with body in profile to l., head half-l. and eyes to front. Wearing long curling hair, and a cloak draped over his l. forearm.

Black chalk, heightened with white, on blue-grey paper; 21·7 × 18·1 cm. (8½ × 7⅛ in.).

Verso. A HEAD IN TWO POSITIONS. Black chalk, outline only.

INSCR.: In the upper r.-hand corner, *50*.

(65) A LADY. T.Q.L., standing, with body slightly to r., head half-l. and eyes to front, her l. arm by her side, her r. hand holding up drapery to her breast. Wearing a low-necked dress. Behind her, l., the angle of a wall, and in the distance, r., a view of a park.

Pen and brown ink, with grey wash, touched with white, on buff paper; 26·2 × 20·7 cm. (10¼ × 8⅛ in.).

INSCR.: *Recto*, in the lower r.-hand corner, *8*.

(66) A LADY. H.L., with body slightly to r., head slightly to l. and eyes to front. Wearing a low-necked dress and drapery. In an oval.

Pen and ink, with grey wash, heightened with white, on blue-grey paper; 24·5 × 20·2 cm. (9⅝ × 8 in.).

INSCR.: *Recto*, in the lower r.-hand corner, *9*.

(67) LADY'S HANDS HOLDING A SPANIEL, AND A HAND HOLDING A GLASS FROM THE PORTRAIT OF LEBECK, AFTER KNELLER (*Cf.* No. 7, *f.* 46*v.*).

Offset from black and white chalks, on blue-grey paper; 29·3 × 23 cm. (11½ × 9⅛ in.).

[(68)–(71)]. **The following four studies are by the same hand.**

(68) A NUDE MAN KNEELING, SEEN FROM BEHIND.

Black chalk, heightened with white, on blue-grey paper; 29·1 × 36·5 cm. (11½ × 14⅜ in.).

(69) A NUDE MAN RECLINING TO-WARDS THE L., SEEN FROM BEHIND.

Black chalk, heightened with white, on blue-grey paper; 26·8 × 34·8 cm. (10½ × 13¾ in.).

(70) A NUDE MAN SEATED, WITH DRAPERY ABOUT HIS LOINS AND FOREARM.

Black chalk, heightened with white, on blue-grey paper; 42 × 28 cm. (16½ × 11 in.).

(71) A NUDE MAN RUNNING TO THE R., WITH R. ARM UPRAISED IN THE ACT OF THROWING.

Black chalk, heightened with white; 44·4 × 23·8 cm. (17½ × 9⅜ in.).

[(72)–(73)]. **The following two studies by the same hand are probably by Chéron.**

(72) A NUDE MAN SEATED, LOOKING DOWN, HIS L. ELBOW RESTING ON A LEDGE, HIS R. ARM EXTENDED ACROSS HIS LAP. **Plate 97**

Black chalk, heightened with white, on blue-grey paper; 44·3 × 29·1 cm. (17⅜ × 11½ in.).

(73) A NUDE MAN SEEN FROM BEHIND, HIS R. ARM RAISED, HIS HAIR BOUND WITH A FILET.

Black chalk, heightened with white, on blue-grey paper; 45 × 28·1 cm. (17¾ × 11⅛ in.).

(74) A NUDE MAN SEEN FROM BEHIND, LEANING WITH HIS R. ELBOW ON DRAPERY.

Black chalk, heightened with white, on blue-grey paper; 29 × 31·5 cm. (11⅜ × 12¼ in.).

Perhaps by the same hand as Nos. (68)–(71).

[(75)–(80)]. **Six Studies,** all probably for a composition connected with the story of Argus, are by the same hand. The heavy cross-hatching is near to that used in Nos. (81)–(85) which have affinities to known drawings by Louis Chéron.

(75) ARGUS SEATED TO R., HIS LOINS GIRT WITH A FLORAL CHAIN.
Black chalk, heightened with white, on blue-grey paper; 36 × 22·8 cm. ($14\frac{1}{8}$ × 9 in.).

(76) ARGUS SEEN FROM BEHIND, SEATED WITH LEGS CROSSED, HOLDING HIS STAFF.
Black chalk, heightened with white, on blue-grey paper; 37·3 × 23·5 cm. ($14\frac{3}{4}$ × $9\frac{1}{8}$ in.).

(77) ARGUS SEEN FROM BEHIND, SEATED, HIS L. ARM OUTSTRETCHED.
Black chalk, heightened with white, on blue-grey paper; 22 × 29 cm. ($8\frac{5}{8}$ × $11\frac{3}{8}$ in.).

(78) A NUDE MAN (MERCURY (?)) SEEN FROM BEHIND, KNEELING, WITH HIS R. ARM RAISED AS IF TO STRIKE.
Black chalk, heightened with white, on blue-grey paper; 37·7 × 22 cm. ($14\frac{7}{8}$ × $8\frac{5}{8}$ in.).

(79) ARGUS SEATED, LEANING ON HIS L. ELBOW, ASLEEP, IO AS A COW BEHIND, L.
Black chalk, heightened with white, on blue-grey paper; 28·9 × 23 cm. ($11\frac{3}{4}$ × $9\frac{1}{8}$ in.).

(80) ARGUS, SEEN FROM BEHIND, SEATED TO L. ON A BLOCK OF STONE.
Black chalk, heightened with white, on blue-grey paper; 38·2 × 23·7 cm. (15 × $9\frac{1}{4}$ in.).

[(81)–(85)]. **Five Studies.** These recall certain authentic drawings by Louis Chéron, Nos. (60)–(72) in an album of his work formerly in the collection of the Earl of Derby at Knowsley Hall and now in the B.M. (*See* under that artist, No. 5 (60)–(91).

(81) A NUDE MAN SEEN FROM BEHIND, BENDING DOWN TOWARDS THE L.
Plate 98
Black chalk, touched with white, on buff paper; 46·4 × 31·4 cm. ($18\frac{1}{4}$ × $12\frac{3}{8}$ in.).

(82) A RIGHT LEG.
Black chalk, heightened with white, on buff paper; 48·2 × 31 cm. (19 × $12\frac{1}{4}$ in.).

(83) A RIGHT LEG.
Black chalk, heightened with white, on buff paper; 48·8 × 30·2 cm. ($19\frac{1}{8}$ × $11\frac{7}{8}$ in.).

(84) A LEFT LEG BENT, THE THIGH DRAPED.
Black chalk, heightened with white, on buff paper; 31 × 40·7 cm. ($12\frac{1}{4}$ × 16 in.).

(85) A RIGHT LEG BENT, THE THIGH DRAPED.
Black chalk, heightened with white, on buff paper; 46·7 × 31 cm. ($18\frac{3}{8}$ × $12\frac{1}{4}$ in.).

(86) *Recto.* A NUDE MAN SEATED, IN PROFILE TO R., HIS HEAD BOWED, HIS HANDS CLASPED BEHIND HIS NECK, HIS L. KNEE UP.
Red chalk, heightened with white, on buff paper; 31·5 × 19 cm. ($12\frac{3}{8}$ × $7\frac{1}{2}$ in.).
Verso. THE SAME FIGURE IN PROFILE TO L., WITH HEAD ERECT.
Black chalk outlines.

INSCR.: *Recto*, at the top, *N⁰ 3*.

[(87)–(98)]. **Miscellaneous Studies,** mostly of hands, for or after portraits.

(87) A PAIR OF HANDS WRITING WITH A QUILL PEN.
Offset from black and white chalks, on

blue-grey paper; 22·9 × 29·5 cm. (9 × 11⅝ in.).

(88) *Recto*. STUDIES OF HANDS.
Black chalk, heightened with white, on blue-grey paper; 21·7 × 37 cm. (8½ × 14½ in.).
Verso. A MAN'S RIGHT ARM BENT AND DRAPED.
Black chalk, heightened with white.

(89) *Recto*. A WOMAN'S LEFT HAND.
Black chalk, heightened with white, on blue-grey paper; 25·5 × 19·5 cm. (10 × 7⅝ in.).
Verso. A MAN STANDING, IN A BROAD-BRIMMED HAT.
Black chalk.

INSCR.: At the top, *nosco 7 . . . ing* (?) (partly cut away).

This figure is rather like some of those in the elder Marcellus Laroon's *The Cryes of the City of London*, 1711.

(90) FOUR STUDIES OF A MAN'S LEFT HAND.
Black and red chalks, touched with white, on blue-grey paper; 29 × 21·4 cm. (11⅜ × 8⅜ in.).

INSCR.: In the upper r.-hand corner, 69.

(91) A MAN'S LEFT HAND, WITH THE WRIST DRAPED.
Black chalk, heightened with white, on blue-grey paper; 28·5 × 36 cm. (11¼ × 14⅛ in.).

(92) A WOMAN'S RIGHT HAND AND FOREARM.
Black chalk, heightened with white, on blue-grey paper; 28·5 × 38·3 cm. (11⅛ × 15 in.).

(93) *Recto*. A RIGHT LEG, FROM THE FRONT.

Pen and brown ink, with brown wash, over black chalk; 41·9 × 20·4 cm. (16½ × 8 in.).
Verso. A RIGHT LEG, FROM THE BACK.
Pen and brown ink.

(94) A LEFT HAND AND FOREARM, AND A RIGHT HAND AND FOREARM.
Black chalk, heightened with white, on blue-grey paper; 26·4 × 21·1 cm. (10½ × 8⅜ in.).

(95) A RIGHT HAND, A LEFT HAND, AND A PAIR OF FEET.
Black chalk, heightened with white, on blue-grey paper; 19·4 × 26·6 cm. (7⅝ × 10½ in.).

(96) A WOMAN'S LEFT HAND AND FOREARM HOLDING A STAFF.
Red chalk, on buff paper; 39·8 × 31·1 cm. (15⅝ × 12¼ in.).

(97) A WOMAN'S RIGHT HAND AND FOREARM, HOLDING UP DRAPERY.
Red chalk, on buff paper; 40·5 × 29·9 cm. (15⅞ × 11¾ in.).

(98) *Recto*. LADY DIANA HOWARD. Head in profile to r.
Black chalk on blue-grey paper; 32·1 × 22 cm. (12⅝ × 8⅝ in.).
Verso. STUDIES OF LEFT HANDS AND FOREARMS.
Black chalk, touched with white.

INSCR.: *Recto*, in the lower r.-hand corner, *Mr. Thomas Howerds | Lady. A° 1690 | at Aschsted | near Ipsum* [Epsom], and in the lower l.-hand corner, *12*.

[Lady Diana Howard (D. 1731/2). Daughter of Francis Newport, 1st Earl of Bradford. Married firstly Thomas Howard of Ashstead (D. 1701), a teller of the Exchequer, and secondly The Hon. William

Fielding (D. 1723), son of William, 3rd Earl of Denbigh.]

[(99)–(114)]. **Tracings of heads, hands, etc.,** from finished oil-paintings.

(99) HEAD OF A MAN. Half-l., with eyes to front. Wearing long flowing hair.

Tracing in red chalk, heightened with white, on oiled paper; 34 × 25·6 cm. ($13\frac{3}{8}$ × 10 in.).

(100) HEAD OF AN ELDERLY MAN. Slightly to r., with eyes to front. Wearing long hair.

Tracing in red chalk on oiled paper; 36·2 × 24·5 cm. ($14\frac{1}{4}$ × $9\frac{5}{8}$ in.).

(101) HEAD OF A MAN. Slightly to l., with eyes to front.

Tracing in red chalk on oiled paper; 37·9 × 24·3 cm. (15 × $9\frac{1}{2}$ in.).

(102) HEAD OF A MAN. Slightly to l., with eyes to front.

Tracing in red chalk on oiled paper; 37·2 × 24 cm. ($14\frac{1}{10}$ × $9\frac{1}{2}$ in.).

(103) HEAD OF A LADY. Slightly to l., with eyes to front.

Tracing in red chalk on oiled paper; 37·1 × 23·5 cm. ($14\frac{5}{8}$ × $9\frac{1}{4}$ in.).

(104) HEAD OF A LADY. Slightly to l., with eyes to front.

Tracing in red chalk on oiled paper; 38 × 24·3 cm. (15 × $9\frac{1}{2}$ in.).

(105) HEAD OF A LADY. Slightly to r., with eyes to front.

Tracing in red chalk on oiled paper; 36 × 23·3 cm. ($14\frac{1}{8}$ × $9\frac{1}{8}$ in.).

(106) HEAD OF A LADY. Slightly to l., with eyes to front.

Tracing in red chalk, heightened with white, on oiled paper; 37 × 25·5 cm. ($14\frac{1}{2}$ × 10 in.).

(107) HEAD OF A LADY. Half-l., with eyes to front.

Tracing in red chalk on oiled paper; 36·7 × 24·3 cm. ($14\frac{3}{8}$ × $9\frac{1}{2}$ in.).

(108) A CHILD. H.L., with body to front, head slightly to l. and eyes to front, its r. hand to its breast.

Tracing in red chalk on oiled paper; 36·7 × 24·1 cm. ($14\frac{3}{8}$ × $9\frac{1}{2}$ in.).

(109) A RIGHT HAND.

Tracing in red chalk on oiled paper; 16 × 24·4 cm. ($6\frac{3}{8}$ × $9\frac{5}{8}$ in.).

(110) A WOMAN'S LEFT HAND AND FOREARM, HOLDING A LOCK OF HAIR. **Plate 87**

Tracing in red chalk on oiled paper; 24·2 × 37·7 cm. ($9\frac{3}{4}$ × $14\frac{5}{8}$ in.).

(111) A WOMAN'S RIGHT HAND AND FOREARM, POINTING DOWNWARDS.

Tracing in red chalk on oiled paper; 21 × 35·6 cm. ($8\frac{1}{4}$ × 14 in.).

(112) A WOMAN'S LEFT HAND AND FOREARM.

Tracing in red chalk, heightened with white, on oiled paper; 21 × 35·7 cm. ($8\frac{1}{4}$ × 14 in.).

(113) A MAN'S HANDS, ONE HOLDING A CANE.

Tracing in red chalk on oiled paper; 21 × 37 cm. ($8\frac{1}{4}$ × $14\frac{1}{2}$ in.).

[(114)–(115)]. **Miscellaneous studies.**

(114) HEAD OF A YOUNG MAN. In profile to l., with curling hair.

Candle smudge, the lips tinted in colour, 37 × 29 cm. ($14\frac{1}{2}$ × $11\frac{1}{2}$ in.).

Stylistically this drawing seems to belong to a much later date than the bulk of those here described.

(115) STUDY OF AN OLD TREE.

Black chalk, touched with white, on blue-grey paper; 32·5 × 26 cm. (12¾ × 10¼ in.).

PROV.: As for No. 2.

1879–8–13–9 (1)–(114), excluding Nos. (95) & (113), L.B.7.

CARTER, GEORGE

B. c. 1654 (?) D. 1727

Perhaps an amateur draughtsman

Born probably at Beoley on the Worcester-Warwickshire border. Eldest son of Robert Carter (son of Ralph Carter of Moseley Hall, Worcs.) and Anne Whitmore (daughter of the steward to Ralph Sheldon of Beoley). As his family was Roman Catholic, was sent to the Jesuit college at Douai in 1668, where he remained till about 1684/5 when he returned to England. Nothing known of his later life. Was uncle and godfather to George Vertue (*See* below), according to whom Carter died at the age of 73 or 74 in 1727.

BIBL.: *Vertue*, I, p. 162 & VI, p. 108.

1. GEORGE VERTUE AS A BOY. H.L., turned slightly to l., with eyes looking to front, and l. arm crooked. Long curling hair falling on the shoulders.　　**Plate 101**

Black chalk, the face touched with red chalk; 21·3 × 16·6 cm. (8⅜ × 6½ in.).

INSCR.: *Verso*, at the top, in brown ink, *Geo Virtue done by his Uncle George was born in the parish of | S.t Martins in the fields in the year 1684.*

PROV.: Purchased by the B.M. through the H. L. Florence Fund, from P. & D. Colnaghi, 1941.

1941–11–8–10.

George Vertue (B. 1684: D. 1756). Engraver and historian of the Fine Arts in England. For a list of subsequent portraits of him *see B.M. Engraved Portraits*, IV, p. 345.

CHÉRON, LOUIS

B. 1660: D. 1725

History and decorative painter, and book illustrator

Born in Paris, the son of Henri Chéron (enamel painter and etcher) and brother of Elisabeth-Sophie Chéron (painter, gem-engraver, and poetess). Studied at the Academie de Peinture et de Sculpture. On Nov. 20th, 1676, was placed first in the Grand Prix de Rome, with his *Bannissement du* *Paradis terrestre*, and became *Pensionnaire de l'Académie* in Rome. During his stay there, is said to have studied especially Raphael and Giulio Romano. On Jan. 29th, 1678, was again placed first with his *Punition d'Adam et d'Eve*, though there is no record that he actually went to Rome on this second

268

occasion. In 1687 and 1690 painted two of the pictures (now in the Louvre), presented annually by the Goldsmiths' Guild to the Cathedral of Notre Dame, respectively *Habakkuk prophesying the captivity of St. Paul*, and *Herodias with the head of John the Baptist*. About the same time painted a *Visitation* for the Cloître des Jacobins in the Rue St. Jacques. Also decorated his sister Elisabeth-Sophie's salon with an *Apotheosis of Hercules*, a *Moses striking the Rock*, and an *Angelica and Medoro*. Encouraged to come to England in 1695 by Verrio's patron, Ralph, 1st Duke of Montague and, being a Protestant, decided to stay here. May be considered as one of the last of the Italo-French school of decorative painters, emanating from Le Brun and founded in England by Verrio and Laguerre. In this capacity was employed at the second Montague House (*See* p. 328) where he painted two ceilings of '2 rooms below stairs', but his work is said to have suffered by comparison with that of his fellow-countrymen Charles de la Fosse and Jacques Parmentier. Also worked for Montague at his country seats of Boughton (Northants) and Ditton Park (Bucks), for John, 5th Earl of Exeter at Burghley House (Northants), and for William, 1st Duke of Devonshire at Chatsworth. His most important decorations extant at Boughton, consisting of seven ceilings, including a vast composition of the *Marriage of Hercules and Hebe* in the Great Hall (showing strongly the influence of Le Brun) and a spirited group of Zodiacal figures, among them *Arcas taking aim at the Bear Callisto*. At Chatsworth painted, about 1700, in the Gallery, the Little Dining Room, and the Bowling House. Five scenes by him from Guarini's *Il Pastor Fido*, formerly in the first two rooms, are now in the ceiling of the Theatre. On April 5th, 1709, submitted, with Pierre Berchet, Giovanni Battista Catenaro, Giovanni Antonio Pellegrini, and Thornhill, designs for painting the dome of St. Paul's. According to Vertue, also took to painting 'Easel pictures in which he had

implyment', among them *The Marriage by proxy of Henrietta to Charles I*, engraved by Nicholas Gabriel Dupuis, which is interesting as an early attempt to depict the costumes correctly from a historical point of view. Though the same authority definitely states that Chéron taught and had a great following at the Kneller Academy of 1711, there is no mention of his name in the list of original members as given in *Vertue*. Broke with the Kneller establishment, and joined with the history and portrait painter John Vanderbank to found in 1720 another academy in St. Martin's Lane, where Hogarth was a student. Other engravings after his work include some curious mezzotints, heightened with white, by Elisha Kirkall, and a number of book illustrations, included those to Jacob Tonson's edition of *The Poetical Works of Mr. John Milton*, 1720 and some of those to the 'Vinegar Bible', 1717. Etched on his own account the title and plates of his sister Sophie's *Pseaumes Nouvellement Mis en Vers*. Was unmarried, and lived in the Piazza, Covent Garden, where he eventually died of apoplexy in May, 1725. Was buried in the porch of the neighbouring church of St. Paul's, on the 29th of that month. In his Will, original in French dated Jan. 25th, 1723/4, and in a codicil, dated Jan. 14th, 1724/5, made the following bequests: to six poor young boys and six poor young girls £20 'to put them out to apprenticeshipp'; to his maid Appolonia Yates, £400, a quarterly payment of £30, and his household furniture, plate, clothes, periwigs, and one of his portraits; to Isaac Grassineau, £300, all his pictures (except three), and all his drawings which included 'a portfolio with green Ribbons' containing studies from 'the Galatea of Raphael, a Bacchanalia after Pousin, and Jupiter after Carachio'; to Mr. Justerman, his picture of the *Brazen Serpent*; to Louis Smartre, his godson, £50 and his pictures of *Ecce Homo* and *Charity*; to Louis Paul Bauvois, another godson, £50; to Mary Borton, £50 and his 'grinding stones and grinders'; to his sisters in Paris, £200 each, if still living, and, if not, to 'the poor of the ffrench hospitall'; to René Pettier, £100, and all his prints, books and 'ffigures done in plaister'; to Mr. Atkins, £50; also mention of his 'two Golden Medalls' presumably those he won in the *Prix de Rome*. The witnesses were Alexandre Marchegay and John Julliot, and executors, Moses Pujolas and Andrew Juliot. The charitable nature of some of these bequests bears out Vertue's statement that he was 'of an affable good natur'd temper, very communicative of his Art with a plain open sincerity that made him agreable and belov'd'. Was much admired for his drawings, the best of which were acquired by the 10th Earl of Derby (*See* No. 5 below). Besides those listed here other drawings in the B.M., which can probably be ascribed to him on stylistic grounds, are described on p. 264 amongst the material from Kneller's studio later in the possession of Edward Byng. Two sales of his works held after his death, one, according to Vertue, about 1726,

the other advertised in *The London Daily Post* for Nov. 21st, 1740 ('The Pictures, Prints, Drawings, Mathematical Instruments, and Books, in French and Italian, late of Mons. Louis Cherone, History Painter, deceased; at Mr. HEATH'S *Great Room* in Hart-Street, Covent Garden'). No catalogue of either recorded.

BIBL.: *Will, P.C.C. (Romney, f.* 130). Stukeley, *Memoirs*, III, p. 64. *D.N.B.*, X, 1887, p. 188 (with *Bibl.*). *St. Paul's, Covent Garden, Registers*, IV, p. 290. *Guiffrey & Barthelemy*, pp. 13, 14. *T.-B.*, VI, 1912, p. 466. *Wren Soc.*, XVI, p. 108. Vertue, *Index*, p. 43. Thompson, *Chatsworth*, pp. 163: (Pl. 76), 165, 168–9, 196: (Pl. 91), 200 (*Footnote*). Vertue, VI, p. 219.

DRAWINGS IN OTHER COLLECTIONS: *See* Biography above. Also Mrs. E. E. Dakeyne, Granit Field, Dun Loaghaire, Dublin (four highly finished roundels of subjects connected with the *Pastor Fido* subjects at Chatsworth (?)).

1. HERCULES SLAYING THE NEMEAN LION. Hercules, r., bending over the lion, l., whose mane he seizes with his r. hand, while he plants his knee on the animal's back and raises his club with his l. hand. Wooded background.

Pen and brown ink with brown wash over black chalk, heightened with white, on blue-grey paper; on two sheets, the one stuck over the other, to enlarge the composition; 26·7 × 21·8 cm. (10½ × 8⅝ in.).

PROV.: Sir Hans Sloane, Bart., by whom it was bequeathed to the B.M., 1753.
Sloane 5223. A.20–21 (L.B.1).

ETCH.: Study for the etching by Chéron completed by G. Van de Gucht. The general composition of the etching is in reverse to

the drawing and differs considerably from it: Hercules, in the act of strangling the lion over his knee, seizes the animal by its mane and round its neck, while his club lies abandoned on the ground.

BIBL.: *Sloane Cat.*, p. 172, No. 21.

Other drawings from this same series were evidently in the collection of Dr. Edward Peart, and appeared in his sale (Christie, 29:iv:1822, Lot 148) 'Six of the Labours of Hercules, by Cherot (*sic*) *fine*'.

2. HERCULES SLAYING THE STYMPHALIAN BIRDS. Hercules, turned to l., planting his r. foot on the body of one of the monsters (represented as winged dragons with women's heads), and warding off the attacks of two others with the

lion's skin over his r. arm, while he holds his club (not wholly included in the design) in his outstretched l. hand.

Pen and brown ink with brown wash over black chalk, heightened with white, on blue-grey paper; 24·7 × 18 cm. (9¾ × 7 in.).

PROV.: As for No. 1.
Sloane 5223. A.20–22 (L.B.2).

ETCH.: Study for the etching by Chéron completed by G. Van de Gucht. The general composition corresponds with the drawing, but is in reverse to it and differs in certain details, one of the attacking monsters appearing at the hero's side round the lion's skin instead of over his shoulder as in the drawing, and the whole of the club shown in his hand and held downwards.

BIBL. & REPR.: *Sloane Cat.*, p. 173, No. 22. Braun, *Reproductions*, p. 93, No. 73155.

2(a). JUPITER AND ANTIOPE (?). A man, assisted by Cupid, unveiling a nude woman lying on the ground beneath a tree. At the foot, a small study of the woman alone.

Pen and brown ink; 13·9 × 16·9 cm. (5½ × 6⅝ in.).

INSCR.: Verso, in the lower l.-hand corner, *To/Mr. Louis Chéron/in Covent Garden/London*.

PROV.: As for No. 1.
SLOANE **5224–64**.

BIBL.: *Sloane Cat.*, p. 187, No. 64 (As anon. Italian).

3. ST. PHILIP BAPTIZING THE EUNUCH (*Acts*, VIII, 38). The Eunuch kneeling, l., beside a stream, while the Apostle, standing before him, pours water over his head from a shell. On the r., one of the Eunuch's slaves holding his cloak, and in the background, the other curbing the two spirited horses harnessed to his magnificent chariot.

Pen and brown ink with brown wash, heightened with white, on blue-grey paper; 34·6 × 27 cm. (13⅝ × 10⅝ in.).

PROV.: William Fawkener, by whom it was bequeathed to the B.M., 1799.
Fawkener 5213–17 (L.B.3).

ETCH.: By the artist, in reverse.

BIBL.: *Fawkener Cat.*, p. 56, No. 17.

4. ANGELICA AND MEDORO (*Orlando Furioso*, Canto xxiii, Stanza 103). Angelica naked, seated on a bank, writing with her r. hand the monogram *M A* with stylus on the trunk of a tree, her l. hand on the shoulder of Medoro who, wearing classical armour, is seated below her. On the r., three *amorini*, one holding Medoro's helmet, and a fourth, above, winding drapery over the branch of a tree.

Pen and brown ink, with brown wash, heightened with white, on brown-toned paper; 39·1 × 27·8 cm. (15⅜ × 11 in.). Old mount; 47·9 × 34·9 cm. (18⅞ × 13¾ in.).

271

INSCR.: *Recto*, on the old mount, in pencil and in a later hand, *Angelique et Medor*.

PROV.: Van Haecken (*Lugt*, No. 2516. Sale, Langford, 12:ii:1750/1, Lot 25 or 37, or 13:ii:1750/1, Lot 44 (?)). William Fawkener, by whom it was bequeathed to the B.M., 1799.
Fawkener 5212–59.

This drawing was attributed to an anonymous Italian artist in the *Fawkener Cat.* (p. 46, No. 59), but there is no doubt that it is in reality by Chéron, working in his finished manner, as in Nos. 1–3 above.

The subject was a favourite one with history and decorative painters of the late XVII and XVIII c.

5. ALBUM. Containing the following material now bound in two volumes: (1)–(59) subjects mainly from classical mythology in various media, some being preliminary studies in chalk and wash for ceilings at Boughton House, others being elaborately finished drawings in pen and wash, heightened with white, of the type listed above at Nos. 1–4; (60)–(99) academic studies in black and white chalks and red and white chalks; and (100)–(126) studies of details from well-known Roman frescoes, mainly after Raphael.

This album no doubt contains most of the large collection of drawings by Chéron which, according to Vertue, were purchased by the 10th Earl of Derby on two separate occasions, the first being a few years before the artist's death ('most of his fine drawings he did in Italy after Raphael'), the second at the artist's sale of c. 1726 ('72 drawings mostly Ink drawn on Blew paper, hightened with white . . . 265 guineas'). It remained in the library at Knowsley until purchased by the B.M. at the sale of the Earl of Derby's library, Oct. 19th, 1953.

BINDING: XVIII c. brown calf, with bookplate of the 13th (?) Earl of Derby.

[(1)–(59)]. **Subjects mainly from mythology** (Homer, *Iliad*; and Ovid, *Metamorphoses*).

(1) CUPID AND PSYCHE BEFORE THE ASSEMBLED GODS. **Plate 90**
Grey wash over black chalk, on grey paper; 45·2 × 61·7 cm. ($17\frac{3}{4} \times 24\frac{1}{4}$ in.).
Perhaps a study for the ceiling either of the Little Hall or the First State Room at Boughton.

(2) DISCORD THROWING THE APPLE AMONGST THE GODS ASSEMBLED FOR THEIR FEAST. **Plate 89**
Grey wash over black chalk, touched with white, on grey paper; 50·2 × 56·5 cm. ($19\frac{3}{4} \times 22\frac{1}{4}$ in.).
Study for the staircase ceiling at Boughton.

(3) JUPITER RESTRAINING ARCAS FROM SHOOTING AT HIS MOTHER THE BEAR CALLISTO, THE FOUR ELEMENTS IN THE CORNERS (*Met.*, II, 496–505). **Plate 92**
Grey wash over black chalk, touched with white, on grey paper; 45·5 × 48·5 cm. ($17\frac{7}{8} \times 19\frac{1}{8}$ in.).
Study for the ceiling of the Fourth State Room at Boughton.

(4) *Recto.* VULCAN CATCHING MARS AND VENUS IN HIS NET, THE ASSEMBLED GODS WATCHING THE SCENE (*Met.*, IV, 176–89). **Plate 91**
Grey wash over black chalk, touched with

white, on grey paper; 48·6 × 54·3 cm. (19⅛ × 21⅜ in.).

Study for the ceiling of the Third State Room at Boughton. An oil sketch for this same subject in the possession of the Old Master Galleries, 1950.

Verso. STUDIES FOR JUPITER'S EAGLE.
Grey wash over black chalk.

(5) THE ALMIGHTY APPEARING TO MOSES OUT OF THE BURNING BUSH. In a fan-shaped panel.
Pen and brown ink, with brown wash, heightened with white, on brown paper; highly finished; 45·8 × 66 cm. (18 × 26 in.).

(6) DEUCALION AND PYRRHA (*Met.*, I, 395–400). Deucalion and Pyrrha throwing stones behind them in order to re-populate the world after the flood, as instructed by the Goddess Themis, whose statue in a portico appears in the background. **Plate 94**
Pen and brown ink, with brown wash, heightened with white, on brown paper; highly finished; indented; 41·3 × 55·6 cm. (16¼ × 21⅞ in.).

(7) ST. PETER AND ST. JOHN PREACH-ING TO THE PRIESTS AFTER HEALING THE LAME MAN (*Acts*, III–IV).
Pen and grey wash, heightened with white, on grey-blue paper; highly finished; 29·3 × 41 cm. (11½ × 16⅛ in.).

(8) UNIDENTIFIED SUBJECT: A BATTLE BETWEEN NUDE MEN.
Pen and brown ink, with brown wash, heightened with white, on brown paper; indented; 43·8 × 57·2 cm. (17¼ × 22½ in.).

(9) THE GIANTS PILING UP ROCKS TO REACH THE HEAVENS (*Met.*, I, 151).
Pen and brown ink, with brown wash, heightened with white, on brown paper; highly finished; 43 × 57·2 cm. (16⅞ × 22½ in.).

(10) APOLLO ALLOWING PHAETON TO DRIVE THE CHARIOT OF THE SUN (*Met.*, II, 151–3).
Pen and brown ink, with brown wash, heightened with white, on brown paper; highly finished; 43 × 54·6 cm. (16⅞ × 21½ in.).

(11) JUPITER RESTRAINING ARCAS FROM SHOOTING AT HIS MOTHER THE BEAR CALLISTO, WITH CHIRON, AQUARIUS AND SCORPIO ON THE R. (*Met.*, II, 496–505).
Pen and brown ink, with brown wash, heightened with white, on brown paper; highly finished; 41·9 × 55·9 cm. (16½ × 22 in.).
The composition resembles that of the ceiling in the Fourth State Room at Bough-ton (*Cf.* No. (3)).

(12) NARCISSUS CATCHING SIGHT OF HIS REFLECTION IN THE WATER, AND WATCHED BY THE NYMPH OF THE POOL AND NEMESIS, WHILE CUPID SHOOTS AN ARROW AT HIM (*Met.*, III, 407–18).
Pen and brown ink, with grey wash, heightened with white, on grey paper; highly finished; 43·8 × 57·5 cm. (17¼ × 22⅝ in.).

(13) APOLLO, AIDED BY THE WINDS, SLAYING PYTHON (*Met.*, I, 441–4).
Pen and brown ink, with brown wash, heightened with white, on brown paper; indented; 42·9 × 56·5 cm. (16⅞ × 22¼ in.).

(14) OCYRHOE CHANGED INTO A MARE, AS CHIRON INTERCEDES FOR HER WITH JUPITER (*Met.*, II, 661–3).
Pen and brown ink, with brown wash, heightened with white, on brown paper; highly finished; indented; 43·2 × 57·2 cm. (17 × 22½ in.).

(15) JASON AND THE WARRIORS WHO SPRANG FROM THE DRAGON'S TEETH,

WATCHED BY MINERVA (*Met.*, VII, 141–2).

Pen and brown ink, with grey wash, heightened with white, on brown paper; highly finished; 43·2 × 57·5 cm. (17 × 22$\frac{5}{8}$ in.).

(16) APOLLO AND CORONIS (*Met.*, II, 606–18). Apollo, alighted from his chariot, looking down at Coronis, whom he has killed with his arrow, and who lies dying in the arms of the First Hour. On the l., the Raven flying away.

Pen and brown ink, with brown wash, heightened with white, on brown paper; highly finished; 41·7 × 54·3 cm. (16$\frac{3}{8}$ × 21$\frac{3}{8}$ in.).

(17) JUPITER APPEARING IN MAJESTY TO SEMELE (*Met.*, III, 307–8).

Pen and brown ink, with grey wash, heightened with white; on brown paper; highly finished; 42·6 × 56·5 cm. (16$\frac{3}{4}$ × 22$\frac{1}{4}$ in.).

(18) TIRESIAS STRUCK BLIND BY JUNO, THE SCENE WATCHED BY JUPITER, WHILE FLORA SCATTERS FLOWERS FROM ABOVE (*Met.*, III, 335).

Pen and brown ink, with grey wash, heightened with white, on brown paper; highly finished; 42·8 × 56·5 cm. (16$\frac{7}{8}$ × 22$\frac{1}{4}$ in.).

(19) THE CENTAUR NESSUS CARRYING OFF DEJANIRA FROM HERCULES, THE SCENE WATCHED BY THE RIVER GOD EVENUS AND HIS NYMPHS (*Met.*, IX, 111).

Pen and brown ink, with brown wash, heightened with white, on brown paper; highly finished; indented; 46·3 × 59·3 cm. (18$\frac{1}{4}$ × 23$\frac{3}{8}$ in.).

(20) NESSUS, SHOT BY HERCULES (WHO APPEARS IN THE BACKGROUND, L.), GIVING DEJANIRA HIS POISONED SHIRT (*Met.*, IX, 131–3).

Pen and brown ink, with brown wash, heightened with white, on brown paper; highly finished; 50·8 × 62 cm. (20 × 24$\frac{3}{8}$ in.).

(21) CORONE, FLEEING FROM NEPTUNE, CHANGED INTO A CROW BY MINERVA (*Met.*, II, 579–88).

Pen and brown ink, with brown wash, heightened with white, on brown paper; highly finished; indented; 43·5 × 57·8 cm. (17$\frac{1}{8}$ × 22$\frac{3}{4}$ in.).

(22) JUNO VISITING HADES (*Met.*, IV, 447–73). Juno calling upon the Furies to drive Athamas mad. On the l., Cerberus, and on the r., the Belides filling a vat with water.

Pen and brown ink, with grey wash, heightened with white, on brown-grey paper; indented; 41·9 × 56·8 cm. (16$\frac{1}{2}$ × 22$\frac{3}{8}$ in.).

(23) THE YOUTH HERMAPHRODITE SEIZED BY THE NYMPH SALMACIS AS HE IS ABOUT TO ENTER THE STREAM (*Met.*, IV, 356–60).

Pen and brown ink, with grey wash, heightened with white, on brown-grey paper; highly finished; indented; 39·3 × 52·5 cm. (15$\frac{1}{2}$ × 20$\frac{5}{8}$ in.).

INSCR.: In the lower l.-hand corner, by the artist, *Lodovicus Chéron invenit et delineavit.*

(24) THE DELUGE (*Met.*, I, 262–73). Jupiter commanding Notus, the S. Wind, to flood the World.

Pen and brown ink, with brown wash, heightened with white, on brown paper; highly finished; indented; 43·2 × 57·5 cm. (17 × 22$\frac{5}{8}$ in.).

(25) THE SAME (*Met.*, I, 262–92). Jupiter commanding Notus to flood the World, whilst Iris draws up water to the clouds, and Neptune stirs up the waves.

Pen and brown ink, with brown wash, heightened with white, on brown paper; highly finished; indented; 42·3 × 54·9 cm. ($16\frac{5}{8} \times 21\frac{5}{8}$ in.).

(26) PERSEUS, WATCHED BY MINERVA, TURNING HIS RIVALS TO STONE WITH THE GORGON'S HEAD (*Met.*, V, 177–235).

Pen and brown ink, with grey wash, heightened with white, on blue-grey paper; highly finished; 43·2 × 57·8 cm. ($17 \times 22\frac{3}{4}$ in.).

(27) MINERVA VISITING THE MUSES ON MT. HELICON IN ORDER TO SEE PEGASUS (*Met.*, V, 254–9).

Pen and brown ink, with grey wash, heightened with white, on blue-grey paper; highly finished; indented; 43·8 × 57·1 cm. ($17\frac{1}{4} \times 22\frac{1}{2}$ in.).

(28) CERES, ACCOMPANIED BY TRIPTOLEMUS, TEACHING MEN THE ART OF AGRICULTURE (*Met.*, V, 645–7).

Pen and ink, with grey wash, heightened with white, on brown-grey paper; highly finished; indented; 42·8 × 55·9 cm. ($16\frac{7}{8} \times 22$ in.).

(29) PENTHEUS, TORN TO PIECES BY HIS MOTHER AGAVE AND HER FELLOW BACCHANALS FOR SPYING ON THEIR RITES (*Met.*, III, 711–28).

Pen and brown ink, with grey wash, heightened with white, on brown-grey paper; highly finished; 42·9 × 56·5 cm. ($16\frac{7}{8} \times 22\frac{1}{4}$ in.).

(30) CERES CHANGING STELLIO INTO A LIZARD (*Met.*, V, 451–61). Ceres, outside the old woman's cottage, throwing the barley-water over Stellio, who thereby becomes a lizard. Above, two cupids with torches to light the Goddess through the world, and in the background, her dragon-drawn chariot.

Pen and ink, with grey wash, heightened with white, on blue-grey paper; highly finished; 46·1 × 60·5 cm. ($18\frac{1}{8} \times 23\frac{3}{4}$ in.).

(31) ASCALAPHUS CHANGED BY PROSERPINA INTO AN OWL (*Met.*, V, 511–550). Ceres and Proserpina standing before the assembled Gods, and Ascalaphus flying off to the r., having been changed into an owl by Proserpina for having prevented her return to earth.

Pen and ink, with grey wash, heightened with white, on blue-grey paper; highly finished; 47 × 57·1 cm. ($18\frac{1}{2} \times 22\frac{1}{2}$ in.).

(32) THE DEATH OF THISBE (*Met.*, IV, 162–3). Thisbe falling on Pyramus's sword over her dead lover. Ninus's tomb in the background.

Pen and brown ink, with grey wash, heightened with white, on brown-grey paper; highly finished; indented; 43·2 × 56·5 cm. ($17 \times 22\frac{1}{4}$ in.).

(33) PERSEUS CUTTING OFF MEDUSA'S HEAD, WHILE, AT MINERVA'S DIRECTION, HE LOOKS INTO HIS SHIELD. PEGASUS L., SPRINGING TO LIFE (*Met.*, IV, 782–5).

Pen and brown ink, with grey wash, heightened with white, on brown-grey paper; highly finished; indented; 43·5 × 57·5 cm. ($17\frac{1}{8} \times 22\frac{5}{8}$ in.).

(34) APOLLO AND CORONIS (*Met.*, II, 606–18). The dead Coronis, pierced by Apollo's arrow, lying amidst rocks on the r. In the centre, Apollo turning round to curse the Raven which flies away towards the l.

Pen and brown ink, with brown wash, heightened with white, on brown paper; highly finished; indented; 40 × 54·3 cm. ($15\frac{3}{4} \times 21\frac{3}{8}$ in.).

(35) THE RAPE OF PROSERPINA (*Met.*, V, 391–424). Pluto carrying off Proserpina in his chariot into the abyss, watched by

Venus above, r., and by the nymph Cyane, below, l., who lifts her hand in protest.

Pen and ink, with grey wash, heightened with white, on blue-grey paper; highly finished; indented; 46·1 × 60·5 cm. (18⅛ × 23¾ in.).

(36) BACCHUS RESTORING MIDAS TO HIS FORMER CONDITION (*Met.*, XI, 127–43). Midas imploring Bacchus to relieve him of his fatal gift of turning everything he touched to gold, and the god instructing him to bathe in the river which flows beside Sardis.

Pen and brown ink, with brown wash, heightened with white, on brown paper; highly finished; indented; 41·6 × 56·3 cm. (16⅜ × 22⅛ in.).

(37) *Recto*. A BACCHIC ORGY.

Grey wash over black chalk, on grey paper; 46·3 × 59 cm. (18¼ × 23¼ in.).

Perhaps a study for the ceiling of the Egyptian Hall at Boughton.

Verso. ANOTHER VERSION OF THE SAME SUBJECT.

Grey wash over black chalk.

(38) A BACCHIC ORGY.

Grey wash over black chalk, on grey paper; 46·3 × 59 cm. (18¼ × 23¼ in.).

Perhaps a study for the ceiling of the Egyptian Hall at Boughton.

(39) VENUS ASKING VULCAN TO FORGE ARMOUR FOR AENEAS.

Grey wash over black chalk; indented; 42 × 61·3 cm. (16½ × 24⅛ in.).

(40) JUNO VISITING AEOLUS, WHO IS SURROUNDED BY THE WINDS.

Grey wash over black chalk, heightened with white, on grey paper; indented; 46·7 × 59·4 cm. (18⅜ × 23⅜ in.).

[(41)–(44)]. The following four designs are probably for some decorative scheme.

(41) APOLLO PURSUING DAPHNE TO THE EDGE OF HER FATHER PENEUS'S RIVER (*Met.*, I, 543–7).

Brush drawing in brown ink, with red chalk, on blue-grey paper; within an oval; 42·6 × 29 cm. (16¾ × 11⅜ in.).

INSCR.: At the foot, *1*.

(42) MINERVA VISITING THE MUSES ON MT. HELICON, IN ORDER TO SEE PEGASUS (*Met.*, V, 254–9).

Brush drawing in brown ink, with red chalk, on blue-grey paper; within an oval; 40·7 × 28·9 cm. (16 × 11⅜ in.).

INSCR.: At the foot, *2*.

A different composition from that listed at No. (27).

(43) NARCISSUS CATCHING SIGHT OF HIS REFLECTION IN THE WATER, AND WATCHED BY THE NYMPH OF THE POOL, AND NEMESIS (*Met.*, III, 407–18).

Brush drawing in brown ink, with red chalk, on blue-grey paper; within an oval; 41·3 × 28·5 cm. (16¼ × 11¼ in.).

INSCR.: At the foot, *3*.

(44) ACTÆON CHANGED INTO A STAG FOR HAVING SPIED DIANA AND HER NYMPHS BATHING (*Met.*, III, 189–97).

Brush drawing in brown ink, with red chalk, on blue-grey paper, within an oval; 43 × 30·1 cm. (16⅞ × 11⅞ in.).

INSCR.: At the foot, *4*.

(45) *Recto*. AENEAS RETURNED FROM HUNTING DIRECTING THE LAYING OUT OF HIS SPOILS, WHILE DIDO WATCHES FROM THE R.

Grey wash over black chalk, on grey paper; 46·4 × 59·4 cm. (18¼ × 23⅜ in.).

Verso. ANOTHER VERSION OF THE SAME SUBJECT (?)
Black chalk.

(46) THE CENTAUR NESSUS OFFERING TO CARRY DEJANIRA, THE SCENE WATCHED BY THE RIVER GOD EVENUS AND HIS NYMPHS (*Met.*, IX, 109–11).
Red chalk and light brown wash; 42·2 × 60·8 cm. (16⅝ × 23⅞ in.).

(47) BACCHUS RESTORING MIDAS TO HIS FORMER CONDITION (*Met.*, XI, 127–43).
Brush drawing in grey wash over black chalk, heightened with white, on grey paper; 46·4 × 59·1 cm. (18¼ × 23¼ in.).
A different composition from that listed at No. (36).

(48) NEPTUNE REBUKING THE WINDS RAISED BY AEOLUS.
Grey wash over black chalk, heightened with white, on grey paper; 46·4 × 59 cm. (18¼ × 23¼ in.)

(49) THE CENTAUR NESSUS OFFERING TO CARRY DEJANIRA (*Met.*, IX, 109).
Red chalk with light brown wash; 44·7 × 60·9 cm. (17⅝ × 24 in.).
A different composition from that listed at No. (46).

(50) THETIS SUPPLICATING JUPITER TO AVENGE THE GREEKS AND HER SON ACHILLES (*Iliad.*, I, 495–510).
Grey wash over black chalk; 41·6 × 60·9 cm. (16⅜ × 24 in.).

(51) HECTOR'S BODY DRAGGED ROUND THE WALLS OF TROY (*Iliad*, XXII, 395–404).
Grey wash over black chalk; 42·6 × 61·1 cm. (16¾ × 24⅛ in.).

(52) VENUS SENDING A CLOUD TO SHIELD AENEAS FROM DIOMEDE (*Iliad*, V, 311–18).

Grey wash over black chalk; 41·4 × 62·9 cm. (16¼ × 24¾ in.).

(53) THE SACRIFICE OF POLYXENA AT THE TOMB OF ACHILLES (*Met.*, XIII, 475–80). **Plate 93**
Red chalk with light brown wash; indented; 41·5 × 62·3 cm. (16¼ × 24½ in.).

(54) MINERVA VISITING THE MUSES ON MT. HELICON, IN ORDER TO SEE PEGASUS (*Met.*, V, 254–9).
Grey wash over black chalk; 40·6 × 61·5 cm. (16 × 24¼ in.).
A different composition from that listed at No. (27).

(55) *Recto.* BACCHUS RESTORING MIDAS TO HIS FORMER CONDITION (*Met.*, XI 127–43). In the centre, Midas kneeling before Bacchus, who points to the river. the background, l., the drunken Silenus. In
Red chalk over light brown wash; 40·7 × 60 cm. (16 × 23⅝ in.).
A different composition from those listed at Nos. (36) and (47).
Verso. ANOTHER VERSION OF THE SAME SUBJECT.
Red chalk.

(56) THE JUDGMENT OF PARIS. Paris seated in the centre beneath a tree, giving the apple to Venus, while Mercury flies off. On the r., Juno departing and Minerva picking up her helmet.
Grey wash over black chalk; 43·5 × 59·4 cm. (17⅛ × 23⅜ in.).

(57) UNIDENTIFIED SUBJECT. A maiden carried off by a king and his warriors. On the l., a sea-goddess (Galatea (?)), and in the background, Polyphemus on his mountain.
Grey wash over black chalk; 40·7 × 62 cm. (16 × 24⅜ in.).

(58) CHRYSES SUPPLICATING APOLLO TO AVENGE HIM FOR THE CAPTURE

CHÉRON

OF HIS DAUGHTER BY AGAMEMNON (*Iliad*, I, 35–43).

Grey wash over black chalk; 41·9 × 62 cm. (16½ × 24⅜ in.).

(59) VENUS ENVELOPING PARIS IN A CLOUD TO SAVE HIM FROM MENELAUS (*Iliad*, III, 379–82).

Grey wash over black chalk; 42·9 × 60 cm. (16⅞ × 23⅝ in.).

[(60)–(91)]. **Academic studies,** mainly in black chalk.

(60) A NUDE AND BEARDED MAN DRAWING A SWORD.

Black chalk, heightened with white, on grey paper; 61·3 × 45·1 cm. (24⅛ × 17¾ in.).

(61) A NUDE MAN, IN A SPHERICAL HELMET, DRAWING A SWORD.

Black chalk, heightened with white, on grey paper; 59·7 × 43·5 cm. (23½ × 17⅛ in.).

The sword seems to be of late XVII or early XVIII c. pattern, which suggests that the drawing was made from the life. The helmet, on the other hand, is 'antique' and may be a studio property.

(62) A NUDE MAN (A FAUN(?)) SEATED TO R., LOOKING AWAY AND UPWARDS.

Black chalk, heightened with white, on grey paper; 60·5 × 44·5 cm. (23⅞ × 17½ in.).

(63) A NUDE MAN, SEEN FROM BEHIND, HOLDING A STAFF.

Black chalk, heightened with white, on grey paper; 60·5 × 44·5 cm. (23⅞ × 17½ in.).

(64) HERCULES SEATED TO L.

Black chalk, heightened with white, on grey paper; 55·2 × 44·2 cm. (21¾ × 17⅜ in.).

(65) *Recto*. PERSEUS STANDING TO R., HOLDING THE GORGON'S HEAD.

Black chalk, heightened with white, on grey paper; 59·8 × 43·7 cm. (23½ × 17¼ in.).

Verso. A FAUN DANCING TO R.

Black chalk.

(66) A NUDE WOMAN SEATED TO FRONT.

Black chalk, heightened with white, on grey paper; 60·5 × 43·7 cm. (23⅞ × 17¼ in.).

(67) A NUDE WOMAN SEATED TO FRONT.

Black chalk, heightened with white, on grey paper; 60 × 45 cm. (23⅝ × 17¾ in.).

(68) A NUDE WOMAN SEATED, SEEN FROM BEHIND.

Black chalk, heightened with white, on grey paper; 60 × 43·8 cm. (23⅝ × 17¼ in.).

(69) A RIVER NYMPH.

Black chalk, heightened with white, on grey paper; 60·5 × 44·6 cm. (23¾ × 17½ in.).

(70) A NUDE WOMAN HOLDING A SCROLL. In the lower r.-hand corner, a slight sketch of a man in a broad-brimmed hat.

Black chalk, heightened with white, on grey paper; 61 × 44·6 cm. (24 × 17½ in.).

(71) A NUDE WOMAN LEANING TO R., HER L. ELBOW ON A LEDGE.

Black chalk, heightened with white, on grey paper; 61·1 × 44·6 cm. (24 × 17½ in.).

(72) A NUDE WOMAN SEATED TO L.

Black chalk, heightened with white, on grey paper; 60·7 × 44·6 cm. (23⅞ × 17½ in.).

(73) A NUDE WOMAN STANDING TO R.

Black and red chalk, heightened with white, on grey paper; 59 × 41·3 cm. (23¼ × 16¼ in.).

(74) A NUDE MAN SEATED, WITH A SCULPTURED SLAB.

Black chalk and stump, on grey paper; 60·1 × 43·5 cm. (23⅝ × 17⅛ in.).

(75) A NUDE AND BEARDED MAN (HERCULES (?)) SEATED.

Black chalk, heightened with white, on grey paper; $56 \cdot 5 \times 42 \cdot 8$ cm. ($22\frac{1}{4} \times 16\frac{7}{8}$ in.).

(76) A NUDE MAN SEEN FROM BEHIND.

Black chalk on grey paper; $60 \cdot 5 \times 44 \cdot 5$ cm. ($23\frac{3}{4} \times 17\frac{1}{2}$ in.).

(77) A NUDE AND BALD-HEADED MAN SEATED TO L.

Black chalk, heightened with white, on grey paper; $65 \cdot 6 \times 56 \cdot 3$ cm. ($25\frac{3}{4} \times 22\frac{1}{4}$ in.).

INSCR.: *Recto*, in the lower r.-hand corner, 5.

(78) A NUDE AND BALD-HEADED MAN STANDING, HIS L. ARM OUTSTRETCHED, HIS R. HAND HOLDING A STAFF. **Plate 95**

Black chalk, heightened with white, on grey paper; $65 \cdot 5 \times 55 \cdot 9$ cm. ($25\frac{3}{4} \times 22$ in.).

INSCR.: *Recto*, in the lower r.-hand corner, 7.

(79) A NUDE AND BALD-HEADED MAN SEATED TO R., HIS R. ARM OUTSTRETCHED.

Black chalk, heightened with white, on grey paper; $65 \cdot 8 \times 56 \cdot 2$ cm. ($25\frac{7}{8} \times 22\frac{1}{8}$ in.).

INSCR.: *Recto*, in the lower r.-hand corner, 8.

(80) A NUDE MAN SEEN FROM BEHIND, SEATED TO L. AND HOLDING A STAFF.

Black chalk, heightened with white, on grey paper; $65 \cdot 3 \times 56 \cdot 2$ cm. ($25\frac{3}{4} \times 22\frac{1}{8}$ in.).

INSCR.: *Recto*, in the lower r.-hand corner, 9.

(81) A NUDE AND BALD-HEADED MAN SEATED TO L. AND LOOKING UPWARDS.

Black chalk, heightened with white, on grey paper; $65 \cdot 5 \times 56 \cdot 2$ cm. ($25\frac{3}{4} \times 22\frac{1}{8}$ in.).

INSCR.: *Recto*, in the lower r.-hand corner, 10.

(82) A NUDE AND BALD-HEADED MAN, SEATED AND HOLDING A STAFF.
Plate 96

Black chalk, heightened with white, on grey paper; $64 \cdot 8 \times 56 \cdot 2$ cm. ($25\frac{1}{2} \times 22\frac{1}{8}$ in.).

INSCR.: *Recto*, in the lower r.-hand corner, 13.

(83) A NUDE MAN SEEN FROM BEHIND, KNEELING WITH ARMS RAISED.

Black chalk, heightened with white, on grey paper; $65 \cdot 4 \times 56 \cdot 5$ cm. ($25\frac{3}{4} \times 22\frac{1}{4}$ in.).

(84) A NUDE MAN SEATED, LEANING TO R. AND LOOKING UP, HIS R. ARM RAISED.

Black chalk, heightened with white, on grey paper; $65 \times 55 \cdot 6$ cm. ($25\frac{5}{8} \times 21\frac{7}{8}$ in.).

(85) A NUDE MAN HALF KNEELING, HIS R. HAND TO HIS HEAD.

Black chalk, heightened with white, on grey paper; $64 \cdot 8 \times 55 \cdot 9$ cm. ($25\frac{1}{2} \times 22$ in.).

(86) A NUDE MAN SEATED IN PROFILE TO R., DRAWING ON A BOARD.

Black chalk, heightened with white, on grey paper; $64 \cdot 8 \times 56 \cdot 2$ cm. ($25\frac{1}{2} \times 22\frac{1}{8}$ in.).

(87) THE SAME NUDE MAN AS IN NO. 86, SEATED IN PROFILE TO R., WITH LEGS CROSSED, POINTING TO HIS BOARD.

Black chalk, heightened with white, on grey paper; $55 \cdot 9 \times 65$ cm. ($22 \times 25\frac{5}{8}$ in.).

(88) THE SAME NUDE MAN SEATED IN PROFILE TO R., RESTING HIS CHIN ON HIS L. HAND, A STAFF IN HIS R.

Black chalk, heightened with white, on grey paper; 64·8 × 55·9 cm. (25½ × 22 in.).

(89) A RIVER GOD, SEEN FROM BEHIND, RECLINING WITH HIS R. HAND RAISED.
Black chalk, heightened with white, on grey paper; 56·5 × 65·8 cm. (22¼ × 25⅞ in.).

(90) A NUDE WOMAN SEATED, HER L. ARM OUTSTRETCHED.
Black chalk, heightened with white, on grey paper; 65·8 × 56·2 cm. (25⅞ × 22⅛ in.).

(91) A NUDE WOMAN WITH DRAPERY, FLEEING TO L.
Black chalk, heightened with white, on grey paper; 65·4 × 55·3 cm. (25¾ × 21¾ in.).

[(92)–(99)]. **Academic studies in red chalk.**

(92) *Recto*. A YOUTH RECLINING TO L., WITH A STAFF.
Red chalk, touched with white, on buff paper; 43 × 57·2 cm. (16⅞ × 2½ in.).
Verso. THE SAME YOUTH RECLINING TO R. WITH A STAFF.
Red chalk.

INSCR.: *Recto*, in the lower r.-hand corner, = 58.

(93) THE SAME YOUTH STANDING, WITH A STAFF.
Red chalk, touched with white, on buff paper; 57·2 × 43·8 cm. (22½ × 17¼ in.).

(94) THE SAME YOUTH STANDING, POINTING WITH HIS L. HAND ACROSS HIS BODY.
Red chalk, touched with white, on buff paper; 57·2 × 42·3 cm. (22½ × 16⅝ in.).

(95) *Recto*. THE SAME YOUTH SEATED ON A ROCK, HOLDING WITH HIS L. HAND A STAFF, HIS R. LEG OUTSTRETCHED.

Red chalk, heightened with white, on buff paper; 57·2 × 42·9 cm. (22½ × 16⅞ in.).
Verso. SLIGHT STUDY OF THE SAME SUBJECT.
Red chalk, touched with white.

(96) THE SAME YOUTH SEATED ON A ROCK, TURNED TO R.
Red chalk, heightened with white, on buff paper; 56·5 × 42·9 cm. (22¼ × 16⅞ in.).

(97) A YOUNG SHEPHERD SEATED ON A ROCK, ASLEEP.
Red chalk, heightened with white, on buff paper; 56·6 × 43·8 cm. (22¼ × 17¼ in.).

(98) A NUDE MAN, SEEN FROM BEHIND, SEATED AMIDST ROCKS.
Red chalk, heightened with white, on buff paper; 56·2 × 42·4 cm. (22⅛ × 16⅝ in.).

(99) A NUDE MAN THRUSTING HIS SPEAR DOWN THE THROAT OF A DRAGON.
Red chalk, heightened with white, on buff paper; 62·9 × 47·5 cm. (24¾ × 18⅝ in.).

[(100)–(105)] **Details from Raphael's frescoes** in the Stanze at the Vatican.

(100) FIGURES KNEELING ON THE L. IN THE 'DISPUTA' (STANZA DELLA SEGNATURA).
Red chalk, heightened with white, on buff paper; 56·5 × 43·2 cm. (22¼ × 17 in.).

(101) HEAD OF ONE OF THE SAME FIGURES.
Red chalk, heightened with white, on buff paper; 43·8 × 27·9 cm. (17¼ × 11 in.).

(102) HEAD OF MICHELANGELO IN THE 'SCHOOL OF ATHENS' (STANZA DELLA SEGNATURA).
Red chalk, on pink prepared paper; 43 × 28·2 cm. (16⅞ × 11⅛ in.).

(103) HEAD OF THE BEARDED PHILO-
SOPHER READING IN THE L. FORE-
GROUND OF THE 'SCHOOL OF ATHENS'
(STANZA DELLA SEGNATURA).

Red chalk, on pink prepared paper;
$57 \cdot 2 \times 43 \cdot 7$ cm. ($22\frac{1}{2} \times 17\frac{1}{4}$ in.).

(104) HEAD OF ONE OF ATTILA'S
WARRIORS, IN 'THE MEETING OF LEO I
AND ATTILA' (STANZA D'ELIODORO).

Red chalk, heightened with white, on
buff paper; $43 \cdot 2 \times 28 \cdot 2$ cm. ($17 \times 11\frac{1}{8}$ in.).

(105) HEAD OF ONE OF ATTILA'S WAR-
RIORS IN A JANISSARY'S CAP, IN 'THE
MEETING OF LEO I AND ATTILA'
(STANZA D'ELIODORO).

Red chalk, heightened with white, on
buff paper; $43 \cdot 1 \times 27 \cdot 3$ cm. ($17 \times 10\frac{3}{4}$ in.).

[(106)–(114)]. **Details from Raphael's
ceilings** in the Loggia of the Farnesina,
Rome.

(106) JANUS AND VULCAN, AT
PSYCHE'S RECEPTION IN OLYMPUS.

Red chalk, on buff paper; $55 \cdot 6 \times 43$ cm.
($21\frac{7}{8} \times 16\frac{7}{8}$ in.).

(107) PSYCHE RECEIVED IN OLYMPUS.

Red chalk, on buff paper; $56 \cdot 2 \times 42 \cdot 9$ cm.
($22\frac{1}{8} \times 16\frac{7}{8}$ in.).

(108) DIANA, JUNO AND MINERVA, AT
PSYCHE'S RECEPTION IN OLYMPUS.

Red chalk, on buff paper; $55 \cdot 3 \times 43$ cm.
($21\frac{3}{4} \times 16\frac{7}{8}$ in.).

INSCR.: *Recto*, in the lower r.-hand corner,
in black chalk, *Plaidoyer de l'amour 10 F.*

(109) PAN AND OTHER DEITIES AT
THE MARRIAGE FEAST OF CUPID AND
PSYCHE.

Red chalk, on buff paper; $56 \cdot 2 \times 43$ cm.
($22\frac{1}{8} \times 16\frac{7}{8}$ in.).

(110) VULCAN AND HERCULES AT THE

MARRIAGE FEAST OF CUPID AND
PSYCHE.

Red chalk, on buff paper; $56 \cdot 2 \times 43$ cm.
($22\frac{1}{8} \times 16\frac{7}{8}$ in.).

(111) WINGED MAIDENS STREWING
FLOWERS AT THE MARRIAGE FEAST OF
CUPID AND PSYCHE.

Red chalk, on buff paper; $56 \cdot 2 \times 43 \cdot 2$ cm.
($22\frac{1}{8} \times 17$ in.).

(112) GANYMEDE OFFERING UP THE
CUP AT THE MARRIAGE FEAST OF
CUPID AND PSYCHE.

Red chalk, on buff paper; $56 \cdot 2 \times 43 \cdot 4$ cm.
($22\frac{1}{8} \times 17\frac{1}{8}$ in.).

(113) JUPITER AND JUNO AT THE
MARRIAGE FEAST OF CUPID AND
PSYCHE.

Red chalk, on buff paper; $55 \cdot 9 \times 43 \cdot 2$ cm.
(22×17 in.).

(114) THE THREE MAIDENS ATTEND-
ING ON CUPID AND PSYCHE AT THEIR
MARRIAGE FEAST.

Red chalk, on buff paper; $55 \cdot 3 \times 42 \cdot 7$ cm.
($21\frac{3}{4} \times 16\frac{7}{8}$ in.).

INSCR.: *Recto*, in the lower l.-hand corner,
in black chalk, *Festin des Dieux 14 Feuilles |
Manquent . . .* (illegible and struck out).

[(115)–(119)]. **Details from Raphael's
ceilings** in the Loggie at the Vatican.

(115) TWO MEN WITH A RAM, FROM
'NOAH'S SACRIFICE'.

Red chalk, heightened with white, on
buff paper; $57 \cdot 2 \times 43$ cm. ($22\frac{1}{2} \times 16\frac{7}{8}$ in.).

(116) JACOB AND RACHEL.

Red chalk, heightened with white, on
buff paper; $57 \times 42 \cdot 9$ cm. ($22\frac{1}{2} \times 16\frac{7}{8}$ in.).

(117) MOSES WITH THE TABLES OF THE
LAW.

Red chalk, heightened with white, on buff paper; 57·2 × 43·5 cm. (22½ × 17⅛ in.).

(118) FIGURES FROM 'MOSES WITH THE TABLES OF THE LAW'.
Red chalk, heightened with white, on buff paper; 56·9 × 43·2 cm. (22⅜ × 17 in.).

(119) THREE WARRIORS CROUCHING BENEATH SHIELDS, FROM 'JOSHUA STAYING THE SUN'.
Red chalk, heightened with white, on buff paper; 43·2 × 57·2 cm. (17 × 22½ in.).

[(120)–(124)]. **Details from Annibale Carracci's ceiling** in the Gallery of the Palazzo Farnese in Rome.

(120) PAN OFFERING THE FLEECE TO SELENE.
Red chalk, heightened with white, on buff paper; 55·6 × 41·3 cm. (21⅞ × 16¼ in.).

(121) *Recto.* A RECLINING SATYR WITH A GOAT, FROM THE 'TRIUMPH OF BACCHUS AND ARIADNE'.
Red chalk, heightened with white, on buff paper; 40·3 × 55 cm. (15⅞ × 21⅝ in.).
Verso. PERSEUS.
Red chalk.

(122) A SLAVE CROUCHING TO L., HIS HANDS CLASPED BEHIND HIS HEAD.

Red chalk, touched with white, on buff paper; 56·2 × 43 cm. (22⅛ × 16⅞ in.).

(123) A SLAVE SEATED TO L.
Red chalk, heightened with white, on buff paper; 55·9 × 42·5 cm. (22 × 16¾ in.).

(124) A SLAVE SEATED TO R., AND LOOKING OVER HIS L. SHOULDER.
Red chalk, heightened with white, on buff paper; 42 × 55·7 cm. (16½ × 21⅞ in.).

[(125)–(126)]. **Studies of details from unidentified works.**

(125) HEADS OF A BEARDED MAN AND A YOUTH LOOKING TO L.
Red chalk, heightened with white, on buff paper; 43 × 28·5 cm. (16⅞ × 11¼ in.).

(126) *Recto.* HEAD OF A WOMAN IN PROFILE TO L.
Red chalk, heightened with white, on buff paper; 47 × 27·3 cm. (18½ × 10¾ in.).
Verso. A NUDE MAN.
Red chalk.

PROV.: The Artist. James Stanley, 10th Earl of Derby. Descended to the 18th Earl of Derby (Sale, Christie, 19:x:1953, Lot 1). Purchased by the B.M., at Lord Derby's Sale, 1953.
1953–10–21–11 (1–126).

BIBL.: *Vertue*, III, pp. 22 & 28.

6. AARON'S ROD CHANGED INTO A SERPENT BEFORE PHARAOH.

(Exodus, VII, 10–13). In the centre, Moses pointing to the ground where his rod has changed into a serpent which devours the serpent-rods of the Egyptian wise men and sorcerers, who look down in wonder at the miracle. On the l., Pharaoh enthroned. In the background, a colonnade and distant palm trees near a pyramid.

Red chalk, with brown-grey wash; 14 × 26 cm. (5½ × 10¼ in.). Old mount, 21 × 32·3 cm. (8¼ × 12¾ in.).

INSCR.: *Recto*, in the lower l.-hand corner, *Chéron.*

PROV.: The Pulitzer Gallery, from whom it was purchased by the B.M., 1957.
1957–12–14–4.

Designed, but not engraved, as a headpiece to the *Book of Exodus* in the so-called

'Vinegar Bible', published by John Baskett at Oxford in 1717. Another subject, the *Finding of Moses*, also designed by Chéron, was used instead and was engraved by Gerard Vandergucht. With the present drawing was purchased a drawing by Sir James Thornhill, also for a head-piece to the 'Vinegar Bible', representing *Moses anointing Aaron* (Leviticus, VIII, 12).

CLEYN, FRANCIS

[CLEIN]

B. 1582 (?): D. 1658

Decorative painter, tapestry designer, and book illustrator

Said to have been born at Rostock in the Baltic provinces, the son of a goldsmith Hans Cleyn. No information extant about his early training, but perhaps, on the evidence of the drawing described below at No. 2, and of other drawings in the Print Room of the National Museum, Copenhagen, may have studied in the Low Countries in the early years of the XVII c. Apparently in Denmark by 1611, the date inscribed on a portrait, attributed to him, of Christian IV (now in the Royal Gallery at Copenhagen) which is said to have been copied from an original by the then court painter, Jacob van der Doordt. Went to Italy, probably between 1611 and 1617, staying there four years and visiting Venice, where he met the English ambassador, Sir Henry Wotton, either at the end of the latter's first tour of duty there in 1612, or at the beginning of his second tour in 1616. Was certainly back in Denmark by 1617, in which year he is known to have been living in Copenhagen and to have inscribed a drawing there of *Apollo and Marsyas* now in the National Museum. Between 1618 and 1623 was employed extensively by Christian IV at the recently built castle of Rosenborg, where he first decorated the panels of the king's writing-closet with pastoral and *genre* scenes, Venetian views, and thoroughly Italianate grotesques, and later was en-trusted with figure-subjects on a larger scale which show strong Venetian influence. Similarly employed at the castles of Frederiksborg, Christiansborg and Kronborg. In 1623 visited England with a recommendation from the English envoy at Copenhagen, Sir Robert Anstruther, to Prince Charles, who, however, was absent in Spain at the time. Was well received by James I, who, much impressed with his ability, wished to retain him, and sent him back to Christian with a letter, dated July 12th, 1623, asking leave for the painter to return. Dutifully stayed at the Danish court to finish his commissions, and did not finally settle in England till late in 1625, but was here before then, however, as testified by a remarkable document in the P.R.O. giving a list of works executed by him for Charles I in 1625, including 'all manner of drawings for ye Arch Triumphall' (probably for the arrival of Henrietta Maria) made under the supervision of 'Mr. Survaior' (Inigo Jones) (£11); 'divers patternes one on both Sides for the greate seale' (£5); copies of *The Death of Ananias* (£70) and *The Blinding of Elymas* (£60) from the Raphael Cartoons; 'the Crucifix for St. James Chappel' and the Queen's Cabinet at Somerset House. Was denizenized after his arrival and granted an annuity of £100. Appointed as principal designer to the Mortlake tapestry works originally founded in 1619. A memorandum, drawn up on April 13th, 1637, on the occasion of the King's buying the manufactory, specifies that 'Mr. Clayne' the painter, was to receive £250 a year and to choose an assistant. Drew for Mortlake the original designs for the *Hero and Leander* set (completed in 1636), the working cartoons (in distemper) after Raphael and the borders (once attributed to Van Dyck) for *The Acts of the Apostles*, the original designs for the so-called *Horses* set, and the *Five Senses* (a set of which is at Haddon Hall). Continued his association with Mortlake under the Commonwealth, and was consulted by the Council of State on the choice of designs in 1657, the year before his death. His 'excellent designes for those rare *Tapestry* work (*sic*), wrought at *Moretlake*, and otherwise, which will eternize his aged body', thus commended, under the incorrectly spelt name *Cleve*, by Sir William Sanderson. Was also much employed on the decoration of country houses, including Carew House at Parsons Green (external painting 'large and bold'), Ham House, Somerset House (The Queen's Closet), Stoke Bruerne (seat of Sir Francis Crane, manager of the Mortlake works), and Wimbledon House ('with large and ample figures without doors'). Of these only Ham House has survived, with the Miniature Room, an overmantel and a number of overdoors painted by Cleyn with playing *putti* after Polidoro da Caravaggio. Vertue also attributes to Cleyn, but without documentary evidence, 'the open gallery all painted by the hand of a second Titian' at Hanworth, the former Gilt Room at Holland House (for which Cleyn is also said to have designed a set of Italianate shell-backed chairs, some of which are now in the V. & A. Museum), and (certainly erroneous) some of the rooms at Bolsover Castle. The picture of *Christ and Mary*, which Walpole saw at Kensington Palace and wrongly ascribed to Cleyn, can be identified as that by Hans Vredeman de Vries now at Hampton Court

(*See* Collins Baker, *Hampton Court*, p. 158, No. 648). Was renowned for his painting in grotesque, of which examples by him were formerly in the Queen's Closet at Somerset House and are still in the Miniature Room at Ham House. In this vein designed three sets of decorative panels, respectively entitled *varii Zophorii Animalium* (according to Vertue published in 1645), *Quinque | sensum descriptio, In co picturæ | genere. Quod (Grottesche) vocant | Itali* (published by Thomas Hinde, 1646), and *PÆOPÆGNION | sive | PVERORVM LVDENTIVM SCHEMATA VARIA* (etched by William Carter, and published by Peter Stent, 1650 or 1658), with *VARIAE | DEORVM | ETHNICORVM | EFFIGIES* (etched by Josias English, 1654). Also essayed *genre* with his picture of a *Toper* etched by Josias English. (English was evidently a neighbour and friend of Cleyn's at Mortlake). Etched, on his own account, a series of seven plates with an emblematic title, *Septem Liberales Artes*, 1645 (which Vertue attributes, apparently without foundation, to one of Cleyn's sons, also a Francis), and two separate plates, *The Woman taken in Adultery* (an impression of which on vellum is in the Department), and an emblematic plate connected with rainfall, lettered *Guave* (*sic* for *gare*) *l'Eau la bas*. His several book illustrations include plates (several of them etched by Hollar) to a number of noble editions of the Classics, among them George Sandys' *Ovid's Metamorphosis* (1632), and John Ogilby's *Virgil* (1658) and *Iliad* (1660), together with title-pages to Richard Brome's *Lachrymae Musarum* (1649), and Thomas Fuller's *A Pisgahsight of Palestine* (1650). Designed Charles I's first Great Seal for which he drew 'divers patterns one on both sides' and received £5 in 1625. Four of the drawings, executed on blue paper, said by Walpole to have been in Charles I's own collection and later to have belonged to the Earl of Moray. With these drawings were two other designs for another Great Seal by the royal limner, John Hoskins. Was the master of the portraitist

William Dobson, whose work shows Cleyn's influence in the decorative accessories of some of his backgrounds and notably in the curious allegorical picture of the Civil Wars of France (in the collection of Mr. T. Cottrell-Dormer). Three of Cleyn's own family, his sons Francis (B. 1625) and John (B. 1629), and his daughter Penelope, practised painting, notably as miniaturists. Francis II and John also made reduced copies in pen and ink of the Raphael Cartoons, dating from 1640–6, which now belong to Wadham College and have been deposited in the Ashmolean Museum. Vertue was told that the Solebay tapestries, woven at Mortlake about 1674–8, may have been 'after designs of Kleyn'. The main incidents were of course drawn by the elder Van de Velde (q.v.) but it is possible that the decorative borders may have been by one of the younger Cleyns. Vertue also notes five portraits of the elder Cleyn, including one with his wife, another with his family by candle-light, and a third, with his friend the dwarf limner Richard Gibson, dressed as archers. In 1653 was living in Covent Garden, when he was working on the illustrations to Ogilby's *Virgil*. According to Buckeridge, died at Mortlake, but was certainly buried at St. Paul's, Covent Garden, on Mar. 23rd, 1657/8. Does not appear to have left a Will.

BIBL.: *Norgate*, pp. 62–4. *Sanderson*, pp. 20 & 24. *Evelyn, Sculptura*, p. 111. *Buckeridge*, p. 362. *Walpole II*, pp. 375–9. *C.S.P. Dom. James I, 1623–5*, p. 14. *C.S.P. Dom. Charles I, 1637*, p. 567. *T.-B., VII, 1912*, p. 104. *Long* (with *Bibl.*), pp. 72–3. *Johnson*, p. 6. *Thomson, passim. Beckett. Watson*, pp. 226–7. *Vertue, Index*, p. 48. *Weilbach I*, p. 212. *Ham House*, pp. 16, 30, 31, 42, 43, 45 & Pl. 18. *Millar, Dobson*, pp. 2 & 3. *Woodward*, p. 22.

DRAWINGS IN OTHER COLLECTIONS: Formerly the Earl of Moray (*See* Walpole, *Anecdotes*, II, p. 377). *See* also Biography above and No. 2 below.

1. DESIGN FOR AN ALLEGORICAL COMPOSITION. On the r., Hercules, clad in a lion's skin, and Minerva, who points towards the figure of Justice enthroned on clouds, l., poising the balance in her r. hand, and holding out money-bags (?) and a laurel-wreath (?) in her l. Above, a winged *putto* descending to crown Hercules with a wreath, and in the centre foreground, two other *putti* emptying a cornucopia. Behind Hercules, on the ground, a globe, compasses and other symbols of Learning.

Plate 99

Brush drawing in grey wash over black chalk, heightened with white, on blue-grey paper; 19·7 × 28·7 cm. (7¾ × 11⅜ in.).

INSCR.: *Recto*, in the lower l.-hand corner, in black lead, *F Cleine* (probably not a signature); at the top of the margin on the r., in ink, in an Italianate hand, *Il frutto della Gloria | Nasce Sopra l'Albora | della Virtù.*

PROV.: Hugh Howard. Dr. Robert Howard (Bishop of Elphin). The Earls of Wicklow. Charles Howard, 5th Earl, from whom it was purchased by the B.M., 1874. **1874–8–8–21** (L.B.1).

2. STUDY OF OR FOR THE R.-HAND WING OF A TRIPTYCH. A lady kneeling to l., holding a prayer-book, with her seven daughters kneeling before and behind her. In the background, under a draped canopy, St. Catherine, the lady's patron saint, on a larger scale than the other figures, with a sword and toothed wheel

at her r. side, and a circular tower, presumably representing a votive building, in the crook of her l. arm.

Plate 100

Pen and brown ink; 24·3 × 13·6 cm. (9½ × 5⅜ in.).

INSCR.: *Recto.* in the upper l.-hand corner, in a German hand, *Frantz Klein.*

Verso, a series of accounts, reckoned in Netherlandish currency (gulden, shillings and styvers), the few legible words, including *untfangen* (received), suggesting a variety of low German.

PROV.: Randall Davies (Sale, Sotheby, 12:ii:1947, Lot 352). P. & D. Colnaghi, from whom it was purchased by the B.M., 1947.

1947–4–12–155.

This drawing is connected in style with a group of eighteen studies in pen and ink, attributed to Cleyn, in the Print Room of the National Museum, Copenhagen. These are variously inscribed *F: Klein, Fr: Klein, f: Klein, fr: Klein, Fr: Klein fe, Francesco Clein,* and *F Kleyen,* and three of them, representing an Assumption, a sculptor or connoisseur (?), and a coat of arms, have on them accounts in Netherlandish currency similar to those on the present drawing. The drawing with the sculptor also bears the date 1608, and another, representing one of the Malefactors in a Crucifixion, is inscribed *Amsterdam.* All this suggests that the artist was in the Low Countries in the early years of the XVII c.

CLOSTERMAN, JOHN BAPTIST

[CLOOSTERMAN, KLOSTERMAN]

B. *c.* 1660: D. 1711

Portrait painter and picture dealer

Born at Osnabrück where he first studied under his father, also a painter. Went to Paris with another German or Dutch artist, Henry Tiburen or Tiburing (who later gave Vertue information about Closterman) and in 1679 worked as a pupil of François de Troy. Came to London in 1681 where he painted draperies for John Riley (*q.v.*), with whom he later entered into partnership, probably in 1688. Also seems to have associated about this time with the history and decorative painter, Jacques Parmentier. Shared with Riley the profits from whole and half-length portraits but received only 30s. of the £10 asked for 'heads' and is said in consequence to have fallen into debt. Nevertheless, continued with Riley until the latter's death in 1691 and afterwards completed his partner's unfinished portraits.

Inherited the patronage extended to Riley of Charles, 6th Duke of Somerset, for whom he acted both as painter and agent for buying pictures. Painted the group of the Duke's seven children (Syon House). Is said to have parted from his patron as the result of a quarrel over the purchase of a painting by Guercino. Also worked for the 1st Duke of Marlborough and painted the vast group of the Duke and Duchess and their children (Blenheim; *See* Scharf, *Blenheim,* pp. 13–14). Visited Spain in 1696, and in Madrid painted portraits of the reigning monarch Charles II and of the English envoy, the Hon. Alexander Stanhope (1698, Chevening). According to Vertue, provided Richard Graham with information about Spanish collections, but if so, this was not included in Graham's additions to Du Fresnoy's *Art of Painting* (1716).

Moved to Rome in 1699 and while there painted Carlo Maratta's portrait, besides collecting a quantity of pictures which he was prevented from bringing to England by Pope Clement XI who exhibited them instead at the Vatican. Also acted as an intermediary for Anthony Ashley, 3rd Earl of Shaftesbury, in his attempt to secure the collaboration of Domenico Guidi (B. 1625: D. 1701) for the execution of statues representing the Virtues expressive of Shaftesbury's philosophical ideas. Closterman's letter to his patron suggests that Shaftesbury would get more satisfaction by employing an English carver to work under his own supervision, Closterman himself assisting with the designs. Returned to England, perhaps in 1701, when he was paid £25 by the Mercers' Company 'for drawing a Coppy of the Picture by Thomas

Papillon Esqr'. Lived in Covent Garden and continued to practise as a portraitist. His later work much in the style of Kneller, as, for instance, the portrait of the composer, Henry Purcell (N.P.G., No. 1352). Towards the end of his life turned to dealing. Was married twice, his first wife, Hannah, being buried at St. Paul's, Covent Garden, on Jan. 27th, 1702. His second wife, Margaret, gave birth to a daughter, Catherine, six months after the artist's death, which took place in May, 1711. Was buried at St. Paul's, Covent Garden, on the 24th of that month.

BIBL.: *Mercers' Accts.*, 1701. Houbraken, pp. 278–9,425. *T.-B.*, VII, 1912, p. 115 with *Bibl.* Vertue, *Index*, pp. 48–9. Wind, *Shaftesbury*, *passim*. Waterhouse, pp. 100–101.

1. ANTHONY ASHLEY COOPER, 2nd EARL OF SHAFTESBURY (?). T.Q.L., standing, with body turned half-l. and eyes looking to front, his l. hand on his hip, his r. arm resting on a rock. Wearing a full-bottom wig, cravat, breastplate over his coat, and drapery over his r. arm.

Plate 102

Brush drawing in grey wash; 31·3 × 22 cm. (12¼ × 8¾ in.).

INSCR.: Apparently on the old mount, identifying the artist as Closterman and the sitter as 'the Earl of Shaftesbury', but the original unfortunately destroyed and the exact lettering not preserved.

PROV.: F. R. Meatyard, from whom it was purchased by the B.M., 1929.

1929–2–11–2.

BIBL.: *B.M. P.R. Purchases*, 11:ii:1929.

[Anthony Ashley Cooper, 2nd Earl of Shaftesbury (B. 1651/2: D. 1699). Born at Wimborne St. Giles. Educated at Trinity College, Oxford. M.P. for Weymouth and

Melcombe Regis, 1670–9 and 1680–3. Vice-Admiral of Dorset, 1679 and 1685–99. Succeeded his father as 2nd Earl, 1683. Died at Wimborne St. Giles, Nov. 2nd, 1699.]

The attribution to Closterman rests solely on the former inscription on the old mount; it cannot be substantiated as no authentic drawings by the artist are known with which it could be compared. Closterman painted the more famous 3rd Earl, but his portrait of that nobleman does not in any way correspond with the present drawing, the sitter of which looks more like the 2nd Earl (*Cf.* Lely's portrait of the 2nd Earl, published as a mezzotint by R. Tompson. *B.M. Engraved Portraits*, IV, p. 59, No. 1). In style the present drawing has much in common with the 'pose-drawings' of the Kneller studio (*See* p. 206).

COLONIA, ADAM

B. 1634: D. 1685

Landscape painter

Born in Rotterdam on Aug. 12th, 1634, the son of the painter, Isaac Colonia (B. 1611: D. 1663), and grandson of another painter, Adam Louisz Colonia (B. 1574: D. 1651). Probably received his artistic training from father and grandfather. Married Cornelia Kerchoven on Jan. 14th, 1665. Shortly after 1670 settled in London. He and his wife recorded as members of the Dutch church of Austin Friars in 1675. Died in 1685 and was buried in St. Martin-in-the-Fields on Sept. 10th of that year. Of his four children one, Adrian (B. 1668: D. 1701), became a painter and another, Huberta, married Adriaen van Diest (*q.v.*). Buckeridge says that he 'became especially eminent for his small figures in rural pieces, for his cattle, country-wakes, fire-pieces &c. He also copied many pictures of beasts after Bassan, particularly those of the Royal collections which are esteemed his best performances'. A painting, *The Angels appearing to the Shepherds*, formerly in the Painter-Stainers' Hall and another of the same subject at Lille, show the influence of Giacomo Bassano.

BIBL.: *Buckeridge*, p. 362. *D.N.B.*, XI, 1887, p. 399. *Lille Catalogue*, p. 64. *Crace, Painter-Stainers' Pictures*, p. 10, No. 38. *St. Martin-in-the-Fields Register. Ogden*, p. 220 (*Index*).

1. A WOODLAND GLADE. View along a path leading into the background, with oaks upon a bank, l.
Plate 103

Brush drawing in light brown wash, touched with red chalk at the top; 18·9 × 30 cm. (7½ × 11¾ in.).

PROV.: Richard Payne Knight, by whom it was bequeathed to the B.M., 1824.
O.o.10–238 (L.B.1).

BIBL.: *Payne-Knight Cat.*, p. 154, No. 238.

2. *Recto.* **STUDY OF AN OAK, WITH TWO ASHES ON THE L. OF IT.**

Brush drawing in light brown wash; 19 × 23·8 cm. (7½ × 9⅜ in.).

Verso. **JUPITER AND ANTIOPE (?).**

Pen and brown ink.

PROV.: As for No. 1.
O.o.10–239 (L.B.2).

BIBL.: *Payne-Knight Cat.*, p. 154, No. 239.

COOKE, HENRY

B. 1642 (?): D. 1700
History and decorative painter

Said by Redgrave to have been born in 1642, but no authority given for this. Redgrave's other statement that he was the son of 'Henry Cook' a portraitist employed in 1640 by the Ironmongers' Company is incorrect, as this painter is shown in the Company's records to have been named 'Edward Cocke'. Cooke's earliest biographer, Buckeridge, says that he came of a good family and was educated at Cambridge, though he cannot be identified in J. and J. A. Venn's *Alumni Cantabrigienses*. Lived five years with Theodore Russel (nephew of Cornelius Johnson and copyist of Van Dyck), during which time he killed a man in a brawl over a woman whom he is said eventually to have married. Fled abroad and resided in Italy for two periods of seven years each, studying 'the great Antique Masters', and becoming, according to Marshall Smith, a pupil of Salvator Rosa. On his return to England lived in obscurity until the trouble blew over, and then went into partnership with a house-painter in Knaves Acre off Wardour St. Painted a staircase ceiling 'in the Corner house in Soho Square, next the Duke of Monmouth's', probably that at the N.W. corner of Greek St. and the Square, when in the occupation of Charles Howard, 3rd Earl of Carlisle, 1692–4. According to Walpole would also have painted the staircase of the main and more famous Carlisle House in Soho Square (this, however, being perhaps a confusion with the formerly mentioned 'Corner house'). Was employed, on the strength of his Soho Square commission, by Sir Godfrey Copley, 2nd Bart., to work at Sprotborough Hall near Doncaster (built about 1685–90), and received £150 for this. Only one of his ceilings remained in the house at the time of its demolition in the 1920's. Worked at Chelsea under the patronage of Richard Jones, 1st Earl of Ranelagh, for whom he painted a staircase and overdoors at Ranelagh House. Also completed and signed the large equestrian wall-painting of Charles II (a presentation from Lord Ranelagh) begun by Verrio in the hall of Chelsea Hospital. Between 1688 and 1697 painted the allegorical portrait of William III in the ceiling of the Oak Room of the New River Company (now reconstructed in the offices of the Metropolitan Water Board, Islington), and about 1695 decorated the E. end of New College Chapel, Oxford, with an architectural deception of 'a semi-rotunda' in which appeared the Salutation. Was employed by William III to repair and piece together again the Raphael Cartoons, and to restore other pictures in the Royal Collection. His picture of a 'Listning Fawn' commemorated in an epigram by John Elsum. Another easel picture by him, 'a history representing charity a woman & several children . . . as big as life' mentioned by Vertue as being in the collection of Lord Leicester. In the State Bedroom at Drayton House, Northants., are three overdoors by him said to be of Druidical ceremonies. A number of landscapes by him recorded in early sale catalogues. Painted a few portraits, among them that of Thomas Mace, the lutenist, which was engraved by Faithorne as the frontispiece to Mace's *Musick's Monument*, 1676. Designed the emblematic title, engraved by Gribelin, to Dryden's translation of Du Fresnoy's *The Art of Painting*, 1695. Died on Nov. 18th, 1700, at his house in Bloomsbury Square, near King St., and was buried on Nov. 22nd at St. Giles-in-the-Fields. In his Will appointed as his executors, John Closterman the portraitist (*q.v.*) and James Seamer (or Seymour), goldsmith and banker of Fleet St., who were to take charge of Cooke's son, also a Henry, until he reached the age of twenty-one. The sale of his library of 'Books of Architecture, Painting, Statuary, Views and Prospects, Lives, &c. in Latin, French, Italian, and English, in all Volumes, most of them gilt on the Back' advertised in the *London Gazette*, No. 3663, Dec. 16th–19th, 1700, to take place at his house in Blooms-bury Square on Dec. 30th. Buckeridge also refers to his excellent collection of pictures having been sold after his death, among which 'were many fine copies of the cartoons of Raphael . . . drawn in turpentine oil, after the manner of distemper'. One of these copies of the Cartoons, together with other pictures by Cooke (including one of ships, three of flowers, two of dogs, one of birds, and a battle-piece) were in the collection of Sir Hans Sloane. Cooke's small oval self-portrait, formerly in the possession of his executor James Seamer, passed through

Vertue to Horace Walpole, and appeared in the Strawberry Hill Sale, 18:v:1842, Lot 105.

His son, Henry, also probably a painter and identical with the 'M.ʳ H. Cooke' who was a Director of Kneller's Academy in Queen's St. in 1711, and with the *H.C.* who signed some of the etched plates in the English edition of Cesare Ripa's *Iconologia*, 1709.

BIBL.: *Will* (*Noel, f.* 176). Smith, *Painting*, p. 24. Buckeridge, pp. 363–4. *Sloane Antiquities etc.*, Nos. 135, 138, 153, 154, 162, 163, 165, 167 & 223. *Walpole*, II, pp. 602–3. *Redgrave*, p. 95. *D.N.B.*, XII, 1887, p. 66. *B.M. Engraved Portraits*, III, p. 123, 1 & 2. *Hussey*, pp. 174–80. *B.F.A.C.*, *British born Artists*, p. 29, No. 57. *Vertue*, Index, p. 51. *Vertue*, VI, p. 168. *Ogden*, p. 220 (*Index*).

DRAWINGS IN OTHER COLLEC-TIONS: Mr. Iolo Williams. Whitworth Art Gallery, Manchester.

---

1. DESIGN FOR A FRIEZE. In the centre, a horse's skull hung with a leafy swag, and on either side, a medallion with the profile of a Roman Emperor. **Plate 104**

Brush drawing in brown, heightened with white, on brown-washed paper; $6 \times 24 \cdot 2$ cm. ($2\frac{3}{8} \times 9\frac{1}{2}$ in.).

PROV.: Hugh Howard. Dr. Robert Howard (Bishop of Elphin), and The Earls of Wicklow. Charles Howard, 5th Earl, from whom it was purchased by the B.M., 1874.
1874–8–8–100 (L.B.1a).

The attribution to Cooke of this and the following two drawings is presumably a traditional one, dating from the time when they were in the Wicklow collection.

The type of ornament depicted may be that which would have been used to decorate the characteristic 'proscenia' used by Verrio and his followers to frame their wall-paintings.

---

2. DESIGN FOR A FRIEZE. In the centre, a trophy of a helmet and two crossed maces. On either side, a circular shield, that on the l. with a spiked boss, that on the r. with the Gorgon's head. **Plate 104**

Brush drawing in brown, heightened with white, on brown-washed paper; $6 \cdot 1 \times 24 \cdot 2$ cm. ($2\frac{3}{8} \times 9\frac{1}{2}$ in.).

PROV.: As for No. 1.
1874–8–8–101 (L.B.1b).

3. DESIGN FOR A FRIEZE. In the centre, a horse's skull hung with a leafy swag. On either side, a circular shield with a spiked boss.　　　　**Plate 104**

Brush drawing in brown, heightened with white, on brown-washed paper; 6·2 × 23·3 cm. (2½ × 9¼ in.).

PROV.: As for No. 1.
1874–8–8–102 (L.B.1c).

CRADOCK, MARMADUKE

B. 1660 (?): D. 1716
Animal and bird painter

According to Vertue, who consistently and incorrectly calls him 'Luke Craddock', was born at Somerton in Somerset, though there is no record of his birth in the Parish Register there. His Will mentions four brothers, Edward, John, Oliver, and William Overton Cradock, a sister Grace Gaite, and a cousin Andrews Overton, the last named suggesting a connexion with the family of Overton of Babcary, a parish adjacent to that of Somerton. Was sent to London where he was apprenticed to a house-painter, and later taught himself. Though he contributed a panel of dead game to the Painted Chamber of the Painter-Stainers' Company, of which he was presumably a member, is not recorded in the Company's minutes. Nor apparently is he connected with the amateur still life painter, the Rev. John Cradock (father of the 'paintress' Mary Beale, *q.v.*), who in 1648 presented to the Company a picture of fruit. Became one of the foremost painters of animals and birds of his day, in the same style as that of his fellow-countryman Francis Barlow, and of his foreign predecessor and contemporaries, Melchior d'Hondecoeter, James Bogdany and Peter Casteels. Worked principally 'for persons that pay'd him *p diem*, or that dealt in pictures', and is said to have shunned the patronage of the 'Nobility and Quality, always supposing they wou'd confine his genius to their fancy or make him

Wait their pleasures'. Painted rapidly and left many works behind him, which are said to have increased three or four times in value after his death. Another bird painter, Coniers (not otherwise recorded), is said to have received instruction from him. Vertue noted several of Cradock's best works in a sale of Mr. Halstead's pictures, May, 1726, and in 1739, at Sir Robert Walpole's in Whitehall, 'in the bed chamber red Damask . . . over three doors, fowles dead game &c.— Boedani [Bogdany] Craddock'. Four engravings by Joseph Sympson after pictures by Cradock (one in the *Collection of John Kettle Esq! Windsor Herald*) were published 1740–3. In the Witt Library are about 11 reproductions of paintings attributed to Cradock, including one of a fighting cock, dated *1696*, in the collection of the Hon. Mrs. Tennant. The only recorded drawings by him are the three described below, and one formerly in the collection of Dr. Barry Delany, M.D. (Sale, Sotheby, 5:vi:1872, Lot 54, 'Luke Cradock (*sic*). Study of the figure of a Bear, *black chalk*'). Died in the parish of St. Mary, Whitechapel, where he was buried on March 24th, 1716. His Will, proved on April 1st, 1717, includes the following bequests: to his brother, Oliver Cradock, all his 'real Estate in the County of Somerset'; to Hannah Dale, 'wife of Humphrey Dale, painter £46'; to Robert and Humphrey, sons of Hannah Dale, all his prints. This painter, Humphrey Dale, does not appear to have been previously recorded.

BIBL.: *Will (P. C. C. Whitfield, f. 75). Colby*, p. 82. *T.-B.*, VIII, 1913, p. 44 (with *Bibl.*). *Vertue, Index*, p. 55.

1. STUDIES OF POULTRY. Among those represented, in the upper l.-hand corner, three white-crested 'Polish' fowls, and at the foot, three brown-crested fowls of the type now known as 'Orloff'.

Plate 105

Water-colours, touched with body-colours, over black lead; 25·6 × 22 cm. (10⅛ × 8⅝ in.).

PROV.: John Henderson, by whom it was presented to the B.M., 1863.

1863–1–10–232 (L.B.1).

BIBL.: *T.-B.*, VIII, 1913, p. 44. *Inf.* from Mr. Michael Pease.

Neither the white 'Polish' nor the brown 'Orloff' would probably have been found in England in the XVII c., but certainly the former fowl was well known to Hondecoeter and his followers, and it may well be that Cradock copied these two groups from paintings by one of his continental contemporaries.

2. STUDIES OF WATERFOWL. From l. to r.: 1st row, three Teal; 2nd row, a Gadwall (?) and a Mallard; 3rd row, a Brent Goose (?) and a Shell-duck; 4th row, an adult Cormorant (?) and a young Cormorant (?); 5th row, two Shell-ducks and a Pochard.

Plate 106

Water-colours, touched with body-colours, over black lead; 18·8 × 24 cm. (7⅜ × 9½ in.).

INSCR.: *Verso, J H* ((?) for John Henderson, but not recorded as a mark), and in a more recent hand, *Luke Cradock*.

PROV.: As for No. 1.

1863–1–10–233 (L.B.2).

BIBL.: As for No. 1.

3. *Recto.* STUDY OF A GROUP OF BIRDS. A peacock perched on a low wall in the centre, and a parrot on a branch, l. Below, l., a turkey, another peacock, and a hen. On the r., a cock crowing on a mound, and chickens feeding.

Black lead; 21·3 × 27·1 cm. (8⅜ × 10⅝ in.).

Verso. SLIGHT SKETCH OF A MAN'S HEAD.

Black lead.

INSCR.: *Verso, J H* ((?) for John Henderson, but not recorded as a mark), and in a more recent hand, *Luke Cradock*.

PROV.: As for No. 1.

1863–1–10–234 (L.B.3).

BIBL.: As for No. 1.

Study for a decorative picture of birds, of the type mentioned in the biographical note above.

DACKETT, T.

Fl. 1684

Portrait draughtsman

Only known through the drawing listed below, which has affinities with the work of David Loggan (*q.v.*) and Robert White (*q.v.*). The only other record of this name is of a certain Francis Dackett, the notice of whose marriage on Jan. 17th, 1682, appears in the register of St. Nicholas, Cole Abbey. It is possible that 'Daggett' is an alternative form of the name.

1. A GENTLEMAN. Bust turned half-r., with eyes to front. Wearing a long curling wig, a lace cravat, and a cloak with a patterned border. **Plate 127**

Black lead on vellum; oval; 12 × 9·6 cm. (4¾ × 3¾ in.).

INSCR.: *Recto*, in the lower r.-hand corner, *T Dackett* (*T D* in monogram) | *fe : ad : vi :* | *vm. 1684.*

PROV.: Mrs. Pritchard, from whom it was purchased by Sir Hans Sloane, by whom it was bequeathed to the B.M., 1753. **Sloane—8** and **G.g.1–494** (L.B.1).

BIBL.: *Sloane Antiquities, Pictures & Drawings*, No. 8 ('A *busto* of a man in black lead Dackett a viv.—delin. 1684 bought of Mrs Pritchard'). *Long*, p. 113.

DAHL, MICHAEL

B. 1659 (?): D. 1743

Portrait painter

Born in Stockholm, probably on Michaelmas Day, 1659, the son of Catarina Dahl. His father's name not known. Studied first under Martin Hannibal, portrait and decorative painter, and subsequently under the court-painter, David Klöker Ehrenstrahl, leader of Italo-French academism in Sweden, under whose influence he was trained both in portraiture and history painting. Was himself appointed assistant court painter. In 1682 came to London where he became acquainted with Kneller and Henry Tilson. Travelled on the Continent with Tilson, visiting Paris in 1685, and subsequently Venice, Rome and Naples. In Rome was converted to Roman Catholicism in order to gain the favour of the exiled Queen Christina of Sweden, whose portrait he painted. Started back for England in 1687, always in company with Tilson, and arrived here *via* Germany in 1688/9. Built up a good reputation as a portrait painter, becoming the principal rival to Kneller, though not possessing the latter's power of self-advertisement. Counted among his patrons Princess, later Queen Anne, and her husband, Prince George of Denmark, and members of their circle, and Charles Seymour, 6th Duke of Somerset. Kept in touch with his native country, and was offered the post of principal court painter on the death of his old master, Ehrenstrahl, in 1698, but did not accept. Was also considered for the post of principal painter to the King of England left vacant by Kneller's death in 1723 but as a Tory fell out of favour with the Hanoverians. Died on Oct. 20th, 1743, and was buried at St. James's, Piccadilly.

BIBL.: *T.-B.*, VII, 1913, pp. 272–4 (with *Bibl.*). Nisser. *Vertue, Index*, p. 58.

1. A YOUNG LADY. Nearly H.L., looking half-r., with hair dressed rather high, under a draped head-dress. Plate 109

Black, red and white crayons, on buff paper; 29·3 × 19·7 cm. ($11\frac{1}{2} × 7\frac{3}{4}$ in.). Mount (not old); 36·5 × 27·1 cm. ($14\frac{3}{8} × 10\frac{5}{8}$ in.).

PROV.: Jonathan Richardson II (*Lugt*, 2170 (?). Sale, Langford, as by Lely, 7:ii:1772, Lots 24 or 68; or 12:ii:1772, Lot 12). Richard Payne Knight, by whom it was bequeathed to the B.M., 1824.
O.o.10–178.

BIBL. & REPR.: *Payne Knight Cat.*, p. 146, No. 178. Binyon, *Drawings of English Women*, p. 80 and Pl. oppos. p. 71. B.M. P.R. *Purchases*, 6, VI, 1914.

This drawing is attributed to Lely in the *Payne Knight Catalogue*, and certainly shows affinity with his manner of working in crayons, though the style of costume and *coiffure, c.* 1690, indicates a later period than his. Mr. Binyon subsequently suggested that it has something in common with the work of Richard Gibson, the dwarf, whose drawings in the B.M. are, however, again of earlier date. The attribution to Dahl was first put forward on the occasion of the purchase of the portrait of the young man, listed below at No. 3, which bears an old inscription giving it to that artist. Though in the present drawing the handling of the crayons is broader, there are certain points in common between the two works, notably the placing of the subject on the paper and the heavy shadow on the jaw. The present drawing and No. 2 below should also be compared with the portrait of *Lady Warner* in the V. & A. Museum (510–1892) which is described as 'Style of Michael Dahl' and reproduced in *V. & A. M. Portrait Drawings*, No. 6.

2. A YOUNG LADY. Nearly H.L. and nearly full face, with head slightly inclined to the l. and curling hair dressed rather high, with one lock falling on her r. shoulder. Wearing a low-necked dress. Plate 110

Black, red and white crayons, on buff paper; 29·5 × 18·9 cm. ($11\frac{5}{8} × 7\frac{3}{8}$ in.). Old mount; 36·6 × 26·1 cm. ($14\frac{3}{8} × 10\frac{1}{4}$ in.).

PROV.: Charles Rogers (*Lugt*, No. 625 (?), Sale, Philipe, as by Lely, 18:iv:1799, Lot 371). P. & D. Colnaghi, from whom it was purchased by the B.M., 1906.
1906–7–19–2.

BIBL. & REPR.: Binyon, *Drawings of Englishwomen*, p. 80 and Pl. III. B.M. P.R. *Purchases*, 19, VII, 1916.

Like No. 1 this drawing too had a long-standing attribution to Lely, and again like No. 1 a new attribution to Dahl was put forward at the time the portrait of a young man (No. 3) was acquired. It has characteristics in common with the other two drawings in the placing of the subject on the paper and the heavy shadow on the jaw, but the handling of the crayon is lighter than in No. 1, and in this it comes nearer to No. 3. The actual pose of the figure, though a conventional one of the time, was certainly a favourite with Dahl, as seen in the portraits of Rachael Russell, Duchess of Devonshire, Mary Somerset, Duchess of Ormonde, Margaret Sawyer, Countess of Pembroke, Sarah Jennings, Duchess of Marlborough, and Countess Maya Gustave Bonde (*See Nisser*, Pls. I, XIV, XVII, XX & XXIV).

3. A YOUNG MAN. Nearly H.L., looking half-l., his l. hand tucked into the front of his coat. Wearing curled hair falling on the shoulders, and a long cravat. **Plate 108**

Black, red and white crayons, on buff paper; 26·9 × 18·7 cm. (10½ × 7⅜ in.). Old mount; 33·8 × 26 cm. (13¼ × 10¼ in.).

INSCR.: *Recto*, on the old mount, in the lower r.-hand corner, *M. Dahl*.

PROV.: Ernest Brown and Phillips, from whom it was purchased by the B.M., 1914. **1914–6–15–1.**

BIBL.: *B.M. P.R. Purchases*, 6:vi:1914. *Nisser*, p. 51, No. 175.

This drawing, like Nos. 1 and 2 above, follows the tradition of Lely's manner of working in crayons. The attribution to Dahl rests on the old inscription on the mount and has also suggested the authorship of these other two (*See* notes to Nos. 1 & 2). No other drawings by Dahl, however, are known which might help to confirm the attributions.

4. A MILITARY COMMANDER, SAID TO BE JOHN CHURCHILL, 1st DUKE OF MARLBOROUGH, AFTER DAHL (?). W.L., standing, with body turned half-l. and head half-r., his l. hand on his hip, his r. on his plumed helmet. Wearing armour and the ribbon of an order over his r. shoulder. In the distance, r., a cavalry skirmish.

Pen and brown ink, with grey wash, on buff paper; 48·5 × 29·5 cm. (19⅛ × 11⅝ in.).

INSCR.: *Recto*, in the lower r.-hand corner, *John Duke of Marlborough* drawn *by Dahl | Lord Portmore has the picture at Weybridge* [Ham Farm, Weybridge].

PROV.: Richard Bull (Sale, Sotheby, 23:v:1881, Lot 38, as by Dahl). Purchased by the B.M. at the Bull Sale, through A. W. Thibaudeau, 1881. **1881–6–11–138** (L.B.3).

BIBL.: *Nisser*, p. 29, No. 95.

[John Churchill, 1st Duke of Marlborough (B. 1650: D. 1722). The celebrated military commander of the age of Queen Anne.]

This drawing does not seem to be an original study for a picture. Rather does it suggest, in style, the type of copy made from a finished portrait in oils, for record purposes, such as appears to have been the practice in the studios of Kneller and his contemporaries. Another version, in much the same vein, but by a less accomplished hand, does in fact occur in one of Edward or Robert Byng's sketchbooks (No. 2, *f.* 16r.). In handling it has nothing to do with the drawings described above (Nos. 1–3), and the attribution to Dahl rests solely on the inscription. Unfortunately the relevant picture, which might have helped to substantiate this has not been traced. The inscription is said by Mr. Binyon to be in Horace Walpole's handwriting, but this does not seem to be the case.

DANCKERTS, HENDRIK

B. *c.* 1630: D. after 1679

Landscape painter and engraver

Born at the Hague, the son of Johan Danckerts. Worked from 1645 to 1653 in his native city where he is said to have been trained first as an engraver, and later to have taken up landscape painting on the advice of his brother, Johan (B. *c.* 1615: D. *c.* 1661) who was Dean of the Guild of St. Luke there. Became himself a member of the guild in 1651. Probably visited England in 1650, but did not settle here until 1666. Later employed to paint a prospect of Rome and views of Roman *vigne* in Clarendon House, Piccadilly. Subsequently won favour as a painter of the decorative topographical landscapes then in fashion for overmantels and overdoors in English houses. Pepys noted in his diary on Jan. 22nd, 1668/9 'At the 'Change I met with Mr. Dancre, the famous landscape painter, . . . and he took measure of my panels in my dining room, where . . . I intend to have the four houses of the King, Whitehall, Hampton Court, Greenwich and Windsor'. Later he chose a view of Rome instead of that of Windsor. Buckeridge remarks that he was 'employed by Charles II to paint all the sea-ports in England and Wales; as also all the Royal Palaces; which he performed admirably well'. Also painted the picture of the presentation of the first pineapple grown in England to Charles II by his gardener, Rose. On Jan. 30th, 1675, in the Treasury Books a payment is recorded of '£73-18-0 to Henry Dankert, a picture drawer, for several prospect pictures by him furnished for the King's service', and in a list of bills dated 1678/9, £34-5-6 was 'paid to Henry Dankart for several prospect pictures and landscapes'. Was forced to leave England during the disturbances over the Popish Plot and returned presumably to Holland where he died. Buckeridge states that 'he worked for great numbers of our nobility and gentry, and had good rates for what he did, being esteemed the neatest and best painter, in his way, of that time'. Works by him are at St. James's Palace, Hampton Court, the National Maritime Museum, the Brighton Art Gallery, and in the collections of the Earl of Sandwich (views of Plymouth and Tangier), Lord Fairhaven, Lord Berkeley and Sir Bruce Ingram. Engraved portraits after Titian and of Charles I, Henrietta Maria and Princess Mary. His brother, Johan, provided seven illustrations, engraved by Hollar, to the 1660 edition of Stapleton's *Juvenal*. His two styles of draughtsmanship are exemplified by the rocky landscape, much like those of Griffier and Van der Vaart, and the country house portrait.

BIBL.: *Buckeridge*, p. 367. *D.N.B.*, XIV, 1888, pp. 14–15 (with *Bibl.*). *C.T.B.*, IV, 1672–5, p. 769 & V (2), 1676–9, p. 1278. *T.-B.*, VIII, 1913, pp. 342–3 (with *Bibl.*). *Grant*, p. 17. *Gunther*, p. 153. *Wren Soc.*, VII, p. 253. *Vertue, Index*, p. 59. *Ogden*, p. 220 (*Index*). *Inf.* from Mr. Clifford Musgrave.

1. WHITEHALL AND WESTMINSTER FROM ST. JAMES'S PARK. View looking E. along the Park with the Mall, l., and the canal, r. In the distance, from l. to r., Northumberland House, the houses bordering on Whitehall, Wallingford House (site of the present Admiralty), the Banqueting House, Holbein's Gate, the Cockpit, the Clock Tower, the W. gate of New Palace Yard, Westminster Hall, St. Margaret's,

Westminster and the Abbey. In the middle distance, towards the l., a tall post or maypole with a group of figures to the l.   **Plate 111**

Pen and brown ink, with grey wash, tinted in water-colours; on three conjoined sheets with two strips interpolated; 26·5 × 104·8 cm. (10⅜ × 41¼ in.).

INSCR.: *Recto*, in brown ink, by the artist, above the buildings, a number of abbreviated colour notes (?).

          Verso, in brown ink, *Het Paerck* and *2592 | Hampton Koert | 16 gulder | Reygaet (?) | Kinston*.

PROV.: Jonathan Richardson I (*Lugt*, 2184). William Stevenson. P. & D. Colnaghi, from whom it was purchased by the B.M., 1853.

1853-4-9-78.

ENGR.: By S. Rawle in Smith, *Westminster*, p. 24 (Pl. IV).

BIBL. & REPR.: *Smith, Westminster*, pp. 24–6. Hind, *Dutch and Flemish Drawings*, IV, p. 132, Pl. LXXIX.

2. VIEW OF ST. JAMES'S PARK FROM THE N.E. View of the open park as seen from the eastern end of the canal and looking directly along it towards a distant building, probably Tart Hall. In the immediate foreground, along the near end of the canal, three statues of classical figures, the central and largest representing a gladiator. Along both sides of the canal, rows of young trees turning off from the foreground to form two avenues running outwards diagonally towards the middle distance. On the extreme l., beyond a wall with a gateway, a double-gabled house with small pilastered balcony, and to its r., other buildings, one, the most distant, with a tower (New Chapel, Westminster (?)). To the r., in the middle distance, a tall post, probably a maypole and beyond it the Mall, visible through an avenue of taller trees.   **Plate 111**

Pen and brown ink over black lead, with washes of light and dark grey, brown and blue-green; on two conjoined sheets; 28·2 × 90 cm. (11 × 33¾ in.).

PROV.: Hugh Howard. Robert Howard, Bishop of Elphin. The Earls of Wicklow. Charles Howard, 5th Earl, from whom it was purchased by the B.M., 1874.

1874-8-8-106 (L.B., as by Hugh Howard, 7).

The statue of the gladiator by Le Sueur, probably erected in 1661 (*See Wheatley & Cunningham*, II, p. 291 and note). The appearance of the newly-planted avenues of young trees suggests a date not many years after the Restoration when these improvements in St. James's Park were carried out.

3. LANDSCAPE WITH A ROCKY BANK. View from the side of a roadway at the foot of a high rocky bank rising in the foreground, r., and crowned with trees. In the distance, l., undulating country broken by trees and hedgerows.   **Plate 114**

Brush drawing in grey wash over black chalk on blue-grey paper; 27·3 × 21·5 cm. (10¾ × 8½ in.).

INSCR.: *Recto*, in the upper l.-hand corner, in red chalk, *76 (?) By Mr Dankerts*.

PROV.: Sir Walter Trevelyan, Bart., by whom it was presented to the B.M., 1871. **1871-12-9-6290** (L.B.1).

BIBL. & REPR.: *Ogden*, p. 154, Fig. 72.

4. BADMINTON HOUSE FROM THE E. An open landscape with a double avenue of young trees leading up to a large country house crowned with an oval cupola. To the l. of the house a church with a pinnacled Perpendicular tower. To the r. of the avenue, in the foreground, the front quarters of a stag sketched in.

Plate 112

Pen and brown ink with grey and blue-grey wash; on three conjoined pieces of paper; 28·5 × 32·3 cm. (11¼ × 12¾ in.).

INSCR.: *Recto*, on the horizon, in ink, in the artist's hand, colour notes; in the upper r.-hand corner, in black lead, in a later hand, *42* and across the centre, *Country House / 72.*

    Verso, in brown ink, *No. 10, No. 61* and *No. 41 / Prospect of / two Country houses / by Dankers.*

PROV.: Lieut. General William Skinner, R.E. J. Skinner. Lieut. Monier Skinner,

R.E. War Office, whence it was transferred to B.M., Dept. of MSS., 1887. Transferred to the Dept. of P. & D., 1948.
    1948–11–26–11.

Badminton House, the seat of the Dukes of Beaufort, was rebuilt largely in its present form during the second half of the XVII c., by Henry Somerset, 1st Duke of Beaufort. The name of the architect is not known. This prospect should be compared with Kip's engraved view of 1715 showing an elaborate formal garden which was probably never realized.

5. BADMINTON HOUSE FROM THE N. Prospect of a large country house, with a classical central block crowned by an oval cupola, in an open landscape planted with young trees. A church tower on distant horizon to r.

Plate 112

Pen and brown ink with grey and bluish wash; on three conjoined pieces of paper; 28·8 × 86·3 cm. (11⅜ × 34 in.).

INSCR.: *Recto*, above the house, in ink, in the artist's hand, abbreviated colour notes. In black lead, in a later hand, in sky, to the l., *No. 19*, and in upper r.-hand corner, *43.*

    Verso, in ink, *No. 30 / No. 11*, and *prospect of / a Country House.* In black lead, in a later hand, *Badminton.*

PROV.: As for No. 4.
    1948–11–26–12.

The central block of the house is clearly inspired by Inigo Jones's gallery at Old Somerset House. This view should be compared with an engraving by Robert White, taken from the same point. The distant church tower seems to be that of Tormarton.

6. VIEW ON THE RIVER TAF. In the foreground the river running over a rocky bed towards the middle distance, l. Beyond, on the r., a steep hill surmounted by rocks and on the l., a more distant hill with farm buildings partly visible on the crest.

Pen and grey ink, with grey washes heightened with black; folded in the centre and with a black ink border; 42 × 56 cm. (16½ × 22⅛ in.).

INSCR.: *Recto*, in the upper l.-hand corner, *The river Taff. in Glamorganshire.*

PROV.: William James Harris, 6th Earl of Malmesbury (Sale, Christie, 21:iv:1950, Lot 100). P. & D. Colnaghi, from whom it was purchased by the B.M., 1957.
    1957–7–13–1   Plate 113

DU BOIS, EDWARD

B. 1619: D. 1696

History, landscape and portrait painter

Born in Antwerp and baptized on Dec. 9th, 1619, the son of Hendrik Du Bois, a portrait painter, and elder brother of Simon Du Bois (*q.v.*). With his father moved from Antwerp to Rotterdam in 1638. Said to have been the pupil of the landscape painter Pieter Anthonisz van Groenewegen. Spent some eight years in Italy where, according to Buckeridge, 'he study'd the *Antiquities*, and Painted after the *Italian gusto*, jointly with his Brother . . .', and was employed at Turin by Charles Emmanuel, Duke of Savoy. Also worked in Paris for a short time. Soon after his return to Holland he left for England where he spent the rest of his life. Vertue considered his work much inferior to that of his brother, but the paintings of one have frequently been attributed to the other. Among his portraits is that of John Wilmot, Earl of Rochester (Knole Park). Buckeridge states that he and his brother 'by their extraordinary industry, have made one of the finest collections of closet pieces especially of any in *England*'. Died in London in 1696, not 1697 as is usually stated, and was buried at St. Giles-in-the-Fields on Sept. 6th.

BIBL.: *St. Giles-in-the-Fields Registers. Buckeridge*, p. 359. *D.N.B.*, XVI, 1888, p. 78. *Van Rÿsewijk, Schilders du Bois*, pp. 176–85. *T.-B.*, IX, 1913, p. 603. *Vertue, Index*, p. 67.

1. FOUR STUDIES OF A HORNED SHEEP AND THREE OF A DONKEY'S HEAD. Arranged, in three rows, the upper two of the sheep, the lower of the donkey.   **Plate 116**

Oil-colours on a dark red-brown ground; $29 \cdot 3 \times 20 \cdot 1$ cm. ($11\frac{1}{2} \times 7\frac{7}{8}$ in.). Old mount; $36 \cdot 6 \times 27 \cdot 5$ cm. ($14\frac{3}{8} \times 10\frac{7}{8}$ in.).

INSCR.: *Recto*, in the upper r.-hand corner, . . . *R K* (monogram (?)) *V* . . . (perhaps a collector's mark but not identified and partly indecipherable as the corner is damaged).

PROV.: A. M. Champernowne (*Lugt*, No. 153), from whom it was purchased by the B.M., 1910.

1910–10–13–8.

DU BOIS, SIMON

B. 1632: D. 1708

Portrait, history and landscape painter

Born in Antwerp and baptized on July 26th, 1632, son of Hendrik Du Bois (B. 1589: D. 1646) and younger brother of Edward Du Bois (*q.v.*). A pupil of Philip Wouverman from April 1652 to Oct. 1653. Visited Italy with his brother and is recorded to have been in Venice in 1657 but had returned to Haarlem by 1661. Usually said to have come to England in 1685 but his portraits of Sir William and Lady Jones at Dulwich are dated 1682. Patronized by Lord Chancellor Somers, whose portrait he painted. Lived with his brother in Covent Garden. On Sept. 16th, 1706, married Sarah Atkins in St. Paul's, Covent Garden; she was his junior by 39 years, the daughter of William Van de Velde the younger (*q.v.*); he is said to have become acquainted with her while painting her portrait. After two years of married life, died and was buried in St. Paul's, Covent Garden, on May 26th, 1708. Vertue states that he was at his best as a painter of 'battles and horses', that he was 'a great mimick of Italien Masters, especialy their small easel pictures, abundance of which were sold by him during his Life for capital Italian paintings' but 'he Painted Portraits Curiously tho' not very successfull that way being indeed rather a mannerist than a true imitator of flesh and blood'. Among his recorded sitters were Archbishop Tenison, John Wilmot, 2nd Earl of Rochester, William Bentinck, 1st Earl of Portland, and Adrian Beverland (B. 1654: D. 1712), licentious writer, virtuoso, and correspondent of Sir Hans Sloane. The last mentioned portrait, for which the artist received £10-15-0, is known through Isaac Beckett's mezzotint of it and shows Beverland seated with a drawing board before an elaborate architectural background composed of a statue of Venus, sphinxes and obelisks. This picture is perhaps identical with a 'Vertuoso deseigning' listed as by Du Bois and dated 1687 in a *Catalogue of Curious picturs collected out of Mr. Du Bois and Mr. Van de Velde Collections by Mr. H. Beverland J.U.D. to be sold by auction on . . . the . . . .* (Sloane MS., 1985, *f.* 7).

BIBL.: *D.N.B.*, XVI, 1888, pp. 79–80. *T.-B.*, IX, 1913, pp. 615–16. *Vertue, Index,* 67–8. *Sloane MS.*, 1985, *ff.* 2, 7. St. Paul's, Covent Garden, Registers, III, Marriages, p. 82. *Van Rijsewijk, Schilders du Bois*, pp. 176–85, 240.

1. STUDIES OF FIGURES FROM A PICTURE, PERHAPS OF JACOB AND RACHEL AT THE WELL.

From l. to r.: a youth advancing towards the l. with a spear or staff on his r. shoulder. A man partially draped standing to l., his r. hand outstretched, his l. hand holding a staff. A woman in a turban and loose tunic standing by a ledge on which she rests a pitcher. A woman walking away, r., with a basket on her back. Below, the head, shoulders and r. arm of a nude man, seen from behind.

Plate 115

Brush drawing in brown, heightened with white (oil-colour), on oiled brown-toned paper; 11·1 × 14·2 cm. (4⅜ × 5⅝ in.).

PROV.: Hugh Howard. Dr. Robert Howard (Bishop of Elphin). The Earls of Wicklow. Charles Howard, 5th Earl, from whom it was purchased by the B.M., 1874. **1874–8–8–28** (L.B.1b).

Perhaps a sheet of studies after a XVII c. Italian composition.

2. ST. CATHERINE OF SIENA.

Study of the Saint's head and shoulders, her head, covered with the hood and coif of her Order, inclined to l., her eyes half closed, her hands raised and open to show the stigmata.

Plate 115

Brush drawing in brown, heightened with white (oil-colour), on oiled brown-toned paper; 14·5 × 10·8 cm. (5¾ × 4¼ in.).

PROV.: As for No. 1.
1874–8–8–136 (L.B.1a).

Probably a study after a late XVI c. Sienese master, and thus dating from Du Bois' visit to Italy in the late 1650's.

3. THE MARRIAGE OF ALEXANDER AND ROXANA (AFTER GIOVANNI JACOPO CARAGLIO).

Pen and light brown ink; 4·7 × 5·6 cm. ($1\frac{7}{8} \times 2\frac{1}{4}$ in.).

Copy of an engraving by G. J. Caraglio (*Bartsch*, XV, p. 95, No. 62), after a drawing by Raphael in the Albertina.

Prov.: Unidentified coll. (*Lugt*, 2883A). W. A. Marsden, by whom it was presented to the B.M., 1932.
1932–6–23–1.

4. PROSERPINA GIVES PSYCHE THE CASKET OF BEAUTY (AFTER AGOSTINO VENEZIANO); WITH AN UNIDENTIFIED SUBJECT ON THE R. The unidentified subject showing a seated woman, her r. arm raised as if pointing out some object to a man who kneels behind her, r.

Pen and light brown ink; 3·8 × 6·7 cm. ($1\frac{1}{2} \times 2\frac{5}{8}$ in.).

Copy of an engraving by Agostino Veneziano (*Bartsch*, XV, p. 222, No. 65, as by the Master of the Die), according to Vasari after a design by Michel Coxcie.

Prov.: As for No. 3.
1932–6–23–2.

5. VENUS AND CUPID BEFORE THE ASSEMBLY OF THE GODS (AFTER AGOSTINO VENEZIANO).

Pen and light brown ink; 4·7 × 8·5 cm. ($1\frac{7}{8} \times 3\frac{3}{8}$ in.).

Copy of an engraving by Agostino Veneziano (*Bartsch*, XV, p. 223, No. 68, as by the Master of the Die), according to Vasari after a design by Michel Coxcie.

Prov.: As for No. 3.
1932–6–23–3.

6. THE TWO MARIES ON THE STEPS OF THE TEMPLE (AFTER MARCANTONIO).

Pen and light brown ink; 5·2 × 7·4 cm. (2 × $2\frac{7}{8}$ in.).

Prov.: As for No. 3.
1932–6–23–4.

Inscr.: On the old mount, at the foot, in gold, *Symon Du Bois*.

Copy of an engraving by Marcantonio (*Bartsch*, XIV, p. 51, No. 45), after Raphael.

DUNSTALL, JOHN

D. 1693

Topographical and natural history draughtsman and etcher

Probably a native of W. Sussex. A family of that name recorded at Cowfold from the XVI c. onwards, members of it appearing in the Parish Register from 1564, including several Johns, though none can be identified with the present artist. Other Dunstalls appear in the Register of All Saints, Chichester, in 1564–1623. Was no doubt connected with an earlier John Dunstall, author of a bird's-eye view of Carrickfergus in Ireland, in pen and ink tinted in water-colour, signed and dated *John Dunstall pinxit 1612* (*B.M., Cotton MS.*, Aug. I, ii, 41). Five conjoined leaves from a sketchbook, formerly in the collection of Mr. Norman Lupton, with views of Pevensey Castle, dated *August ye 18 1635*, and of Bramber Castle, Chanctonbury Hill, and Wiston Place, dated between Feb. 12th and 22nd, *1635* (*i.e.* 1635/6), may perhaps, on the strength of their W. Sussex connexion and of the affinities between the formal scripts on them and the script on the Carrickfergus drawing, be tentatively attributed to this elder Dunstall. Mr. Lupton's drawings, too, have some interest in their relation to Hollar, as they were used by him, ten years later, as the bases for five of his small Sussex etchings (*Parthey*, Nos. 931, 944, 946, 949 & 951). The younger Dunstall also worked in W. Sussex, etching five views of Chichester, probably before the Civil War (*See* the drawing at No. 2 below). In 1661 published his earliest known dated work, the etched designs of the *second* and *third booke of Flowers Fruicts Beastes Birds and Flies* (sequels to a first *Booke* which had appeared without Dunstall's name or the year, but with the monogram *FD* on Pl. 1). A copy of Pl. 14 of the *Third Booke of Flowers* appears in a volume of drawings of natural history subjects, dated between 1633 and 1674, by the Persian miniaturist Shafi Abbasi which is in the collection of Mr. Gerald Cobb of the College of Arms. Was probably in London by the early 1660's, Vertue recording him as living 'in the Strand a small professor & teacher of drawing as by a title in a book of flowers drawn & etched by him 1662' (this publication not yet identified). Etched a single plate after Hollar in *Animalium*

Ferarum & Bestiarum, Florum, Fructuum . . . 1674 (*Parthey*, No. 2068), and in 1675 six plates of *Festoons*, and an undated series of six swags of musical instruments, shells, fruit and flowers, all presumably after his own designs. Was the author of several small sets of plates intended as drawing copy-books, none of them dated, but nearly all bearing characteristic Greek titles such as $\beta\iota\beta\lambda\circ\varsigma$ $\Delta\epsilon\nu\delta\rho\omega\nu$ . . . *A Book of Trees*, $\beta\iota\beta\lambda\circ\varsigma$ $\dot{\circ}\iota\kappa\omega\nu$ . . . *A Book of Houses*, $\beta\iota\beta\lambda\circ\varsigma$ $A\nu\theta\omega\nu$ . . . . *A Book of Flowers*, and $\beta\iota\beta\lambda\circ\varsigma$ $K\alpha\rho\pi\omega\nu$ . . . . *A Book of Fruits*, together with his addresses, which alternate between Blackfriars and London House Yard, Ludgate St., most of these plates also being used to illustrate his autograph treatise *The Art of Delineation* (*B.M., Add. MS.*, 5244), which is mainly concerned with drawing in black and white. This MS. also contains three sets of etchings of flowers (*ff.* 51–82) which may be considered among his best works in this field. Etched a number of portraits, mainly as frontispieces or illustrations to books, including those of Lancelot Colson (in his *Poor Man's Physician*, 1663), Samuel Clarke (in his *Marrow of Ecclesiastical history*, 1675), John Carter, William Gouge and James Ussher (in Samuel Clarke's *The lives of sundry eminent persons*, 1683), and of William III and Queen Mary (not dated). Besides the views of Chichester noted above, etched a number of small topographical plates, all undated, including elevations of Basing House and St. Mary's Church, Nottingham, and, in London, of Clarendon House, the Custom House, Southampton House, Tennet (Thanet) House, St. Mary Overy (after Hollar) and a distant prospect of old St. Paul's with a coach in the foreground, together with *A Representation of the two Malefactors* [George Allen and Francis Jackson] *Hanging in Chains. The one at Hampsted, the other at Ring-cross near Islington* (Bodleian Library, *Gough Topography*, 17555, No. 316). The two drawings listed below, the only ones by him known, show a traditional technique of opaque water-colour on vellum, which goes back to the Middle Ages and was much used in the XVI c. for making maps and semi-cartographical bird's-eye views. Dunstall's use of it corresponds exactly with that described in Sir William Sanderson's *Graphice*, 1658, p. 70, in the section devoted to limning a landscape. Died in Warwick Court, Warwick Lane, to which he had removed from the parish of St. Anne, Black-friars, shortly before his death. In his Will, proved on June 20th, 1693, in which he describes himself as a 'schoolmaster' (this designation appearing also on the titles of some of his publications), bequests are made to his wife Margaret, and to other relatives, Daniell and Mary Duffell, and Mary Borne 'of St. Andrews Holburne'. Is probably identical with the 'John Dunstar' who was buried on June 12th, 1693, at Christchurch, Newgate, in which parish is situated Warwick Court. In *The London Gazette*, No. 2902, Aug. 31st–Sept. 4th, 1693, was advertised the sale at Tom's Coffee-house, Ludgate, of Dunstall's library 'consisting of choice Books in Divinity, History, Architecture, Perspective, Eng. & Lat., in all Volumes; Also his Curious Collection of Prints and Drawings, by the best Masters, with his Mathematical Instruments, Graving and Etching Tools, &c.'

BIBL.: *Will, London, Reg.: 45, f. 160. Wellesley, Dunstall. Freeman, Dunstall. Blaauw. Christchurch, Newgate Registers*, p. 309. *T.-B.*, X, 1914, p. 148 (with *Bibl.*). *Cowfold Register*, p. 3. *Johnson*, p. 14 f. *Vertue, Index*, p. 68. *Peckham, St. Bartholomew, Chichester*, XI, 1947, p. 112. *Woodward*, p. 26.

1. N. FACADE OF BETHLEHEM HOSPITAL. N. elevation of the stone-faced central pavilion of the building, the principal feature of which is a lunette-shaped tympanum containing the Royal Arms, supported on four Corinthian pilasters and topped by a clock-turret. On either side, wings of red brick with high-pitched slate roofs. In front of the pavilion, the main gateway on the piers of which are the recumbent figures of *Raving Madness* and *Melancholy Madness* by Caius Gabriel Cibber.

Plate 118

Brush drawing in grey wash and water-colours, over black lead, the sky in body-colour and the windows outlined in white; on vellum; 13 × 15·8 cm. (5 × 6¼ in.).

INSCR.: *Recto*, in the lower l.-hand corner, by the artist, *John. Dunstall delineavit.*
Verso, in a later hand, *Bedlam.*

PROV.: P. & D. Colnaghi, from whom it was purchased by the B.M., 1870.
1870–10–8–2954 (L.B.1).

The building represented in the present drawing was the second Bethlehem (or Bedlam) Hospital, which was erected in Moorfields between April, 1675, and July, 1676, from the designs of Robert Hooke, F.R.S. (B. 1635: D. 1703), the forerunner of Sir Isaac Newton. It was demolished when the third Hospital was built in Lambeth in 1812–15. Cibber's two figures surmounting the gateway are now in the Guildhall Museum (*See Wheatley & Cunningham*, I, p. 173). Dunstall's drawing should be compared with two early engravings of the second Hospital, one by John Nutting (1689), the other by Robert White (Crace Coll., XXVI, Sheets 1, 3). In style it has much in common with Dunstall's own etched elevations of houses, βιβλος ὀικων.

2. A POLLARD OAK NEAR WEST HAMPNETT PLACE, CHICHESTER.
View looking S.W. In the foreground, a large oak tree on a grassy bank, with a thick cluster of bare branches sprouting from its top. Beyond it, r., the half-timbered mill

over the Lavant, and l., on the far side of the water, West Hampnett Place, a red-brick gabled house of the XVI c. On the r. of the tree, a lady and gentleman in the dress of about 1660, standing on a road which leads back to the mill. In the distance, the city of Chichester, a prominent feature of which is the cathedral with its spire and detached belfry. **Plate 117**

Brush drawing in water-colours over black lead, touched with white on the figures; on vellum; 13·4 × 16 cm. (5¼ × 6¼ in.).

INSCR.: *Recto*, in the lower l.-hand corner, by the artist, *John Dunstall fecit*. On either side of the old wrapper, which originally enclosed the drawing, *No. 90*.

PROV.: Sir Erasmus Philipps, 5th Bart. Richard Philipps, 1st Baron Milford. Richard Grant Philipps, 1st Baron Milford of the 2nd creation (with his armorial seal bookplate on the wrapper). H. M. Calmann, from whom it was acquired by the B.M., in exchange for duplicate prints, 1943.

1943–4–10–1.

The topography of the drawing is established by an etching by Dunstall, *Hampnett House* (West Hampnett Place), one of a series of five views in the neighbourhood of Chichester, the others being *Chichester* (the city from the N.W.), *A temple by Chichester* (a small circular chapel on a mound now occupied by St. Bartholomew's Church), *by Chichester* (a different view of the same chapel), and *A Ruine neere Chichester* (a ruined building on rising ground, not identified).

Impressions of all five are in the Bodleian Library (*Gough Topography*, 17528, *f.* 1b) and of four in the B.M. (*King's Topography*, XLII, 19.a). Though less skilful than the present drawing, these etchings resemble it both in general treatment of the subject, and in certain details in the foregrounds, like the prominent single trees and the little figures in contemporary costume. The pollard oak itself should also be compared with the studies of trees in βιβλος Δενδρων.

Further identification of the subject is provided by a comparison with an anonymous XVIII c. engraved map of W. Sussex, in the possession of Mr. G. Howard Tripp, of 55 West St., Chichester (photostat in the Map Room, Maps 183.0.1). From this, West Hampnett Place is correctly sited in the present drawing in relation to the distant Chichester, but the draughtsman, obviously to obtain a more picturesque foreground, has shifted the position of the mill and the stream.

West Hampnett Place was built by Richard Sackville in the XVI c., but was considerably modified in later times. It subsequently became a hospital, and was destroyed by fire about 1930 (*See* Horsfield, *Sussex*, II, p. 57).

EMMETT, WILLIAM

B.1671: D. 1736

Amateur engraver and architectural draughtsman

Baptized on Dec. 14th, 1671, in St. Margaret's, Westminster. Son of Morris Emmett (B. 1646: D. 1694; from 1677 master bricklayer of all the King's buildings in England,

in which office he worked under Wren at Hampton Court). Nephew to the following: William Emmett (B. 1641, described in the Calendar of Treasury Books as 'Carver to the

Works'), George Emmett (B. 1655, worked as bricklayer at the Horse Guards), and Henry Emmett (B. 1657 and styled himself 'Citizen and Painter Stainer of London' in the Heralds' Visitation of 1687, when he made an unsuccessful claim to arms and registered an inaccurate pedigree). Nothing known of his upbringing though his younger brother, Maurice, was educated at Merton College, Oxford. In 1694 appointed to be Registry Clerk to the Exchequer Court at £200 a year with an annuity, a place he sold to a Mr. Elers for £500 in 1698 and went to live in Bromley. Married Eleanor Thornhill of Lincolnshire. Engraved a series of views of St. Paul's Cathedral (1702–3) and mezzotint portraits of Queene Anne, Prince George of Denmark (both after Kneller) and Princess Sophia, which were published from a house in New Street where property had been inherited by his brother, Maurice, from their father. Lived in Bromley on an income of about £400 a year derived from an annuity and the farming of glebe lands, and was a church warden. In 1704, helped with the prosecution of certain tax collectors for fraud. Owned, in addition to the architectural drawings in the B.M. (See under Inigo Jones), a collection of paintings ascribed to Cornelius Johnson (q.v.), Rubens, Rembrandt, Dobson, Barlow (q.v.), and Balthazar Lemens, who painted Emmett's and his wife's portraits, a number of religious subjects and a ceiling panel of Apollo and the Nine Muses, for the hall of Emmett's house. Compiled a glossary of architectural terms which, with a MS. comparison of the Orders is in the Kent County Record Office at Maidstone. In 1731 designed a workhouse, his only recorded building, in Bromley (demolished). Died on May 11th, 1736, and was buried in his parish church. His wife died a year later leaving £100 to Bromley College.

BIBL.: *Norman Papers. C.T.B.*, 1685/9, p. 1847. C.S., I, pp. 263–4. *Foster, Alumni*, II (E–K), p.462. *T.-B.*, X, 1914, p. 505. *Wren Soc., Index*, p. 65. *Colvin*, p. 196.

1. DESIGN FOR WHITEHALL PALACE, NORTH FRONT. A long two-storey building terminated at either end by a pavilion supporting a high drum crowned with a cupola. Plate 119 (b)

Pen and brown ink, with grey wash; 27·4 × 100·8 cm. (10¾ × 39⅝ in.).

INSCR.: *Recto*, Along the lower edge in brown ink by the artist, *That Incomparable Architect Inigo Jones, having in yᵉ Year. 1639 presented these his Designes for yᵉ Building of White Hall, to King Charles yᵉ First: which through yᵉ Iniquity of yᵉ Times, could not be put in Execution. It has unfortunately happened yᵗ (as one Evil is often yᵉ Cause of more) that yᵉ North Front of this Designe having been lost—I have to yᵉ best of my | Judgment Erected this Front, from yᵉ Original Plan of Mr. Jone's, in his Stile, to make yᵉ Designe Compleat. Wm. Emmett of Bromley in yᵉ County of Kent: Anº: 1717.* At the top in black lead, in a later hand, *Charles I's palace at Whitehall | North Front by Emmett | That by Jones being lost.*

PROV.: William Emmett. G. W. de Norman, by whom it was presented to the B.M., 1848.

1848–8–5–9 (L.B.9, as by Inigo Jones).

This elevation fits the plan (Jones, E. C. M., 11) which seems to have emanated from Inigo Jones's office. Campbell did not make use of it in *Vitruvius Britannicus*.

2. DESIGN FOR THE ELEVATION OF A PALACE FOR QUEEN ANNE. A long building of three stories above a basement, decorated with Corinthian pilasters and statues. In the pediments royal coats of arms, trophies and the monogram *A R*.

The skyline broken by statues and urns on a balustrade. At the r.-hand end an Ionic doorway is pasted over another as an alternative. The first, second and fifth doorways pasted over the original design.   **Plate 119 (a)**

Pen and brown ink with grey wash; r.-hand portion damaged; in four separate sections: (1) 33·2 × 50·3 cm. (13 × 19¾ in.); (2) 33·2 × 52 cm. (13 × 20½ in.); (3) 33·2 × 65·5 cm. (13 × 25¾ in.); (4) 33·2 × 30·2 cm. (13 × 12 in.).

INSCR.: *Recto*, at the l.-hand end of façade, in ink, by the artist, a scale of modules; and in the lower l.-hand corner, by another hand, *E.J.* At the r.-hand end, along the base of the building, *William Emmett de Bromley in Com̄ Kent Esqr. Ano. Dom. 171.* Above the centre in black lead, in a later hand, *This is no part of Inigo* [Jones's Pa]*lace* / *It appears to be a*

Design by Em[mett for] *a Palace* / *for Queen* [Anne] / *vide Pedi* (?).

PROV.: As for No. 1.

1848–8–5–1–4 (L.B. 21–4, as Inigo Jones).

From the monogram it may be assumed that the design was of a projected palace for Queen Anne and can be dated between 1710 and 1714. In an inventory of William Emmett's property among the Norman papers in the County Record Office at Maidstone, is a note of 'three very neat and large drawings of Architecture drawn by Wm. Emmett of Bromley' almost certainly identical with this design.

EVELYN, JOHN

B. 1620: D. 1706

Diarist, author, virtuoso, amateur draughtsman and etcher

Born at Wotton, Surrey, second son of Richard Evelyn, Sheriff of Sussex and Surrey in 1633/4, and of Eleanor (or Ellen) Stansfield. After studying at Balliol College, Oxford, as a fellow-commoner from 1637 to 1640, spent a large part of the next twelve years abroad travelling in the Low Countries, France and Italy, and cultivating an extensive interest in the arts and natural sciences. In 1647 married Mary, daughter of Sir Richard Browne, Charles I's agent in Paris. On his return, settled at Sayes Court, Deptford, an estate belonging to his wife's family which became notable for its gardens and trees. Established himself by the publication of *Sylva* (1664, with many subsequent edns.) as the most eminent authority in England on the cultivation of timber. His many publications included several on the fine arts, among them the *Parallel of Architecture* (1664), a

translation from the French of Roland Fréart, to which he appended an original *Account of Architects and Architecture*; the *Perfection of Painting* (1668); *Numismata* (1697), which contains incidental information on portraiture; and best known, *Sculptura* (1662), mentioned below. After the Restoration, held office on various government committees. Was consulted on the requirements for Chelsea Hospital and became treasurer of the foundation fund for Greenwich Hospital (he had formerly discussed the rebuilding of the Palace with Charles II). Was interested in the architectural improvement of London and was commissioned with Wren and others to report on proposals for repairing old St. Paul's just before the Fire. After the Fire submitted suggestions to the King for the rebuilding of the City. Was an original Fellow of the Royal

Society and frequently a member of its Council. Inherited Wotton on the death of his brother George in 1699. Died at his London house in 1706 and was buried at Wotton, his wife living until 1709. Susanna, the only one of nine children to survive him, was an amateur painter and draughtsman of some ability.

Probably owed his training in the visual arts to Thomas, 1st Earl of Arundel, who owned Albury near Wotton and who was with him in the Low Countries in 1641, and at Padua in 1645–6. May through him have become acquainted with Hollar (q.v.) who etched designs by Evelyn or his wife for frontispieces to Evelyn's *Lucretius* (1656) and to Thomas Sprat's *History of the Royal Society* (1667) and also dedicated to Evelyn an etching of a self-portrait by Van Dyck. Mentions in the *Diary* or in his correspondence many artists then working in England, among them: Francis Barlow (q.v.), who dedicated an engraving of Titian's *Venus* to Evelyn; Francis Cleyn (q.v.); Samuel Cooper; Faithorne (q.v.); Grinling Gibbons (q.v.), whom he introduced to Charles II; Kneller (q.v.), who painted portraits of him in 1685 and 1689; Lely (q.v.); Pierre Lombart; Prince Rupert (q.v.); Robert Streeter; Hendrik van der Borcht the younger who painted his portrait in 1641; Antonio Verrio (q.v.), of whose work as a decorative painter at Windsor and as superintendent of the gardens at St. James's Evelyn writes with admiration; Robert Walker, who painted his portrait in 1648; and John Michael Wright. Whilst abroad, met among others: Stefano della Bella (the *Diary* for April 30th, 1650, reads 'I went to see the Collection of the famous Sculptor Steffano de la Bella, returning now into Italy, & bought some prints'); Abraham Bosse whom he commissioned to design a bookplate for him in 1652; L. de Lincler, the French artist and collector; Carlo Maratta, who among other commissions drew for him at Rome the Arch of Titus in 1645; and Nanteuil who drew his portrait

and that of his wife in Paris in 1650. Was particularly interested in engraving and its processes. Evelyn's *Sculptura*, intended only as a part of an ambitious *History of Arts Illiberal and Mechanical*, is famous as the first account of engraving to appear in England and also for its announcement of the discovery of the new process of mezzotint (a term probably invented by Evelyn) by Prince Rupert. According to the *Diary*, Rupert first showed the process to Evelyn on Feb. 21st, 1660/1. Later in *Numismata* (1697), ascribed the invention to Ludwig von Siegen. Composed a full account of the process for the Royal Society. The manuscript remained substantially unpublished and was long thought to have been lost, but is now known to be among the Evelyn MSS. (Christ Church, Oxford). Vertue notes that in his collection was a volume of engraved English portraits and another of engravings of works in the Arundel collection. His ability as an etcher and draughtsman was mediocre and directed mainly to topographical and antiquarian subjects. Fourteen of his plates are known: a set of larger landscapes apparently taken from works by old masters; views of Wotton House, for which the drawings (of about 1646) still exist, and of the Thames at Putney. One of the first English amateurs known to have drawn landscape, recording in the *Diary* (Sept. 30th, 1644), 'the Prospect was so tempting, that I could not forbeare to designe it with my Crayon.' The present collection of Mr. John Evelyn, his descendant, now at Stonor Park, is composed of a wide range of works mainly by earlier XVII c. artists, many of which no doubt originally belonged to the diarist. Among them, in addition to those by artists already named, are *genre* paintings by Jan Lievens and J. M. Molenaer, views of London by Cornelis Bol (q.v.), and engravings or etchings by Theodor de Bry, Callot, Cornelis Cort, Goltzius, Jean Morin, Francis Place (q.v.), Rembrandt and Waterlo. Vertue also mentions as belonging to Evelyn a drawing by Peter Oliver (*q.v.*) after Raphael, and his own head carved in wood by Grinling Gibbons (*q.v.*), a gift of the sculptor.

In his designs for the gardens at Albury, Sayes Court and Wotton, anticipated the more naturalistic effects cultivated by English landscape gardeners of the XVIII c.

Was a collector of fine books and commissioned Thomas Simon, graver at the Mint, to design and cut dies of his crest for impressing on the covers of his library volumes. Among his manuscripts was a prayer-book (still in the Evelyn collection) with a frontispiece drawn by Nanteuil, the calligraphy being the work of Evelyn's amanuensis, Richard Hoare, the engraver (*See Diary*, July 12th, 1649).

BIBL.: Evelyn, *Sculptura*. T.-B., XI, 1915, pp. 103–4 (with *Bibl.*). Evelyn, *Diary*. Vertue, *Index*, p. 76. Keynes. Oswald, pp. 598–602. *Inf.* from Mr. E. S. de Beer.

1. **EZEKIEL RECEIVING THE WORD OF GOD, AFTER A MINIATURE.** Standing figure of the Prophet turned half-r., wearing a loose robe and holding a book, a nimbus about his head. In the upper r.-hand corner, appearing from a cloud, the hand of the Almighty holding a scroll. On the l. *ΠΡΦ* in monogram, and on the r., *ΙΕΣΕ / ΚΙΗΛ*.

Pen and brown ink; 16·9 × 10·2 cm. (6⅝ × 4 in.).

INSCR.: *Recto*, by the artist, at the foot, *Ezechielis prophetæ Effigies ex / Pervetusto Manuscripto— / Vaticana codice / deprompta.*, and in the upper l.-hand corner, *Put this in / Bundle XI*, and to the r. (55). Along the l.-hand edge, in pencil, by William Upcott, *Sketched by the celebrated John Evelyn.*

PROV.: William Upcott (when it was mounted in an album containing etchings by Evelyn and other material relating to the artist) from whom it was purchased by the B.M., 1838.

1838–5–30–12.

BIBL.: *T.-B.*, XI, 1915, p. 104.

The miniature after which the above was drawn is in a XII c. MS. on the Prophets, in the Vatican Library (Vat. Gr. 1153, *f.*236*v.*).

In one of the volumes of the Evelyn papers, formerly owned by William Upcott, the antiquary and collector, and now in the Dept. of MSS. (Add. MS. 1590, *f.* 80) is a list in Evelyn's hand of the contents of the 'Bundle' or roll of, 'Excerpts & Collections, casually gathered out of several Authors &c., and intended to have been transcribed into Adversaria, . . .' The headings include, 'P.— Notes for the History, & Art of painting Sculpture &c. . . .' and 'MSS.: A Discourse of Manuscripts, Begun, but Imperfect'. The present drawing, therefore, having also come from Upcott's collection, may have originally belonged to this bundle of notes. In the opinion of Mr. E. S. de Beer, Evelyn's visit to the Vatican was probably too hurried to have allowed him to make a copy directly from the miniature in question. He is more likely to have used some facsimile which has not however been identified.

2. **NAPLES FROM MOUNT VESUVIUS.** View from the N.W. side of the volcano looking over the Bay in which are a galley firing a salute and other craft. In the foreground, a horseman viewing the prospect through a telescope, and, further down the slope, two men carrying staves on their shoulders. Below, on the l., a small

church, and, on the r., the city of Naples with the Castello S. Elmo rising in its midst.   **Plate 128**

Pencil, partly strengthened with red chalk; 10·4 × 14·1 cm. (4⅛ × 5½ in.).

INSCR.: *Recto*, in the margin at the foot, *Prospect from* . . . (partly obliterated and cut away).

PROV.: H. J. Hosper, from whom it was purchased by the B.M., 1911.

1911–10–18–2.

ETCH.: By the artist with the title, *Prospectus versus Neapolin a Mont Vesuv:* in the series *Locorū aliquot Insignium et celeberrimorum inter ROMAM et NEAPOLIN* . . . (*See* biography above). In the etching the further of the two figures carrying staves has been omitted.

The view is described in the *Diary*, 7:ii:1645.

FABER, JOHN, I

B. *c.* 1650 — 1660: D. 1721

Portrait draughtsman, engraver in mezzotint, and calligrapher

Said to have been born at the Hague. Not known under whom he studied. His earlier portrait-drawings in fine pen and ink on vellum, however, reflect a tradition already long established in the Low Countries (as can be studied in the Dept. in the work of Sir Balthazar Gerbier (*q.v.*), M. J. Mierevelt (Hind, *Dutch & Flemish Drawings*, III, p. 143, No. 1), and Crispin van Queborn (Hind, *Dutch & Flemish Drawings*, IV, p. 32, Nos. 1 & 2)) and thereby represent a rather older technique in monochrome portraiture than that of black lead on vellum. Both drew from the life and copied earlier portraits. His practice of inscribing his works with specimens of his calligraphy should be compared with that of Ludolf Backhuysen (Hind, *Dutch & Flemish Drawings*, III, p. 11, No. 1, p. 12, Nos. 3 & 32). His earliest recorded drawing, that of Johann Georg III, Elector of Saxony, formerly in the Wellesley collection, dated *1688*. According to Chaloner Smith, quoting different but unspecified authorities, may have come to England in 1687 or 1695. Inscriptions on other drawings in the Wellesley collection, however,—

all portraits of well-known Dutch naval commanders—show him to have been working at the Hague in 1692 and at Amsterdam in 1693 and 1696, and thus suggest that he either returned to Holland at this time, or that he did not actually pay his first visit to England till after 1696. Not certain whether the drawings listed below at Nos. 6–10, all dated *1697*, were executed in Holland or England, but No. 2, inscribed *I faber Londini fecit 1698*, shows that the artist was definitely established here by the latter year. Other recorded portrait-drawings by him, mainly of English sitters, dated between 1699 and 1712. Several of these in the Wellesley collection, being in black lead on vellum, point to his having adopted this alternative method, after coming to this country, in emulation of such masters as Loggan and White. Subsequently took to engraving in mezzotint, occasionally after drawings by himself. His plates, some of which are dated between 1707 and 1719, include portraits of divines, 'Remarkable Persons' (such as James Bick the ventriloquist, and Nicholas Hart 'the sleepy man'), the Red Indian Kings who came to England in 1710, and sets of the Founders of Oxford and Cambridge colleges and the Reformers. From the lettering on these, appears to have carried on his business in the Strand, first at 'a Picture Shop' near the Savoy, and later, in 1716, 'att ye Golden Eagle near ye Fountain Tavern', and, about 1718, 'at the Picture Shop near Essex Street'. Was working at Oxford before 1711, and in Cambridge before 1714, when making the preliminary drawings for his two series of Founders. Died at Bristol in May, 1721. Is described as of the parish of St. Clement Danes, in the Act of Administration granted, on May 29th of that year, to his son, John Faber II (*See* below). In this document is mentioned too his widow, Elizabeth Faber.

Was the father of John Faber II, who is said to have been brought to England at the age of three, and who became one of the most prolific engravers in mezzotint in the first half of the XVIII c. According to the *D.N.B.*, there should be in the 'print room of the British Museum . . . a small portrait of the younger Faber, as a child of under ten years of age, executed by his father in December 1704', but no trace of this has been found in any official inventory.

DRAWINGS IN OTHER COLLECTIONS: Ashmolean Museum.

BIBL.: *Admin. P.C.C. Middlesex*, May 29th, 1721. *Redgrave*, p. 147. *Chaloner Smith*, Pt. I, pp. 266–99. *D.N.B.*, XVIII, 1899, p. 112. *T.-B.*, XI, 1915, p. 154 (with *Bibl.*). *Wellesley Catalogue*, pp. 20–22, 60. *Long*, p. 146. *Vertue, Index*, p. 77.

1. AEMILIUS VAN CUYLENBURGH. Bust turned half-r., with eyes looking to front, wearing long curling hair, a gown and falling bands. **Plate 122**

Pen and black ink, highly finished, on vellum; oval; 13·9 × 12·3 cm. (5½ × 4⅞ in.).

INSCR.: *Recto*, in the surrounding border, by the artist, *ÆMILIUS van CUILEMBORGH Gelrûs. olim Batobûrgi per 4 Heûsdæ per 14, et nûnc per 9 Annos* LONDINI *in Anglia Belgicûs Sancti Euangel: Minis^tr*, and at the foot, *I: faber Delineavit 1701.*

PROV.: The Rev. C. M. Cracherode, by whom it was bequeathed to the B.M., 1799.
G.g.1.–514 (L.B.1).

BIBL.: *Cracherode Cat.*, p. 108, No. 514.

[Aemilius van Cuylenburgh (B. 1650: D. 1704), Minister in the Reformed Church of Holland. Born at Wageningen. Studied Theology at Utrecht. Was pastor at Batenburg, and subsequently, in 1692, pastor to the Dutch Evangelical Church in London, a post which he held till 1703, when he removed to Canvey Island, Essex, where he died in the following year. Was the author of a number of orations in praise of William III, published between 1688 and 1691.]

2. SIMON EPISCOPIUS. Bust turned half-l., with eyes looking to front, curling hair, moustache and beard. Wearing a fur-trimmed gown over his doublet, and a falling ruff. Within a circular border.

Pen and black ink, highly finished, on vellum; 17·7 × 12·3 cm. (7 × 4⅞ in.).

INSCR.: *Recto*, below the portrait, by the artist, in brown ink, *I faber Londini fecit 1698;* within the circular border, in light brown ink, *Mr SIMON EPISCOPIUS. S.S. Theologiæ*

Professor Aetatis Suae LX A? D? 1643; at the foot, the following verses in Dutch:

Hier sietge afgebeeld, den Tolck van Goodes woort.
Die't Hemels Vaderlant aanwees, door Leer, en Leven

Wiens Wÿse pen getüÿght (al hebt g' Hem noit
    gehoort
Wat Goddelÿk verstant Hem was van Godt
    gegeven
Dus heeft hÿ d'aard betreen: tot eer van Syne
    Stam:
Tot Heÿl van Goods gemeent: tot Roem van
    Amsterdam
I: faber Script   C: P: Wittenoom Comp.

PROV.: E. Daniell, from whom it was purchased by the B.M., 1872.
    1872–10–12–3979* (L.B.2).

[Simon Episcopius (Bischop) (B. 1583: D. 1643). Dutch Theologian and follower of Arminius. The present drawing is adapted from one of several engravings after the portrait of Episcopius by H. M. Sorg.]

3. QUEEN ANNE. Bust with head turned slightly to l., body slightly to r. and eyes looking to front. Wearing a crown set in her long curling hair, pearls at her throat and in her dress, and the George suspended on a ribbon.

Pen and black ink, highly finished, on vellum; oval; 11 × 8·7 cm. (4⅜ × 3⅜ in.).

INSCR.: *Recto*, at the foot, by the artist, *I. Faber 1711.*

PROV.: Robert Jackson. Dr. John Percy, who purchased it from Jackson, 1882 (Sale,

Christie, 16:iv:1890, Lot 423). Purchased at the Percy Sale by the B.M., 1890.
    1890–5–12–75 (L.B.3).

BIBL.: *Percy Cat.*, pp. 40–2.

Probably adapted from a portrait of Queen Anne by Sir Godfrey Kneller.

4. JEAN CALVIN. Bust turned half-r., with long pointed white beard. Wearing a flat dark cap, and a fur-trimmed gown.

Pen and black ink, highly finished, on vellum; 13·5 × 11·1 cm. (5¼ × 4⅜ in.).

INSCR.: *Recto*, on the r., by the artist, *Faber | Delint.*, and round the top, *Mr JOHANNES CALVINUS. Natus X Jul. Aº 1509. Denatus xxvii May Aº 1564.*

PROV.: J. Nilsen. Capt. E. G. Spencer-Churchill, from whom it was purchased by the B.M., 1928.
    1928–3–13–459.

Based on an engraving after the so-called 'Basle portrait' of Calvin (*See* E. Doumergue, *Iconographie Calvinienne*, 1909, p. 25).

5. A MAN WITH A POINTED CHIN. H.L., turned half-r., with white or light-coloured hair and pointed chin. Wearing a dark conical hat on one side of his head, white cravat about his neck, dark coat, and a sash with a pipe stuck in it.   **Plate 122**

Pen and black ink, highly finished, on vellum; oval; 12·5 × 9·8 cm. (4⅞ × 3⅞ in.).

INSCR.: *Recto*, on the r., by the artist, *I Faber* (the *I F* in monogram) *fecit/ad/vivúm Aº 1702.*

PROV.: John Grimston. Lady Waechter de Grimston, by whom it was presented to the B.M., 1937.
    1937–2–15–1.

6. KING WILLIAM III. Bust turned half-r., with eyes looking to front. Wearing a long curling wig, lace cravat, armour, cloak edged with ermine, and the collar of the Order of the Garter. Within a circular border.   **Plate 120**

Pen and brown-black ink, highly finished; on vellum; 24·9 × 19·9 cm. (9¾ × 7⅞ in.).

INSCR.: *Recto*, within the inner circle of the border, by the artist, *WILLIAM. III. by the Grace of God King of England. Scotland. France and Yrland. Defender of the faith Ætatis Suæ XXXXVI A⁰ MDCXCVI* and in the outer circle, at the foot, *I. faber 1697*. Below the drawing, the following verses in Dutch:

De Koning Wilhem, 't grootst dat oit de zonnezag,
Om Gods dienst, wysheit en om dapperheit geprezen,
Vervůld dit parkement met zÿn doorlůgtig wezen,
Zÿn met Rÿk deůgden, en het aardryk met ontzag.

Sÿlvius
Faber | Scripsit |, 1697.

PROV.: K. J. Lander, from whom it was purchased by the B.M., 1950.

1950–7–22–1.

Probably adapted from an oil-painting not yet identified.

The author of the verses below the present drawing, and Nos. 7, 9 and 10, is perhaps Sir Gabriel de Sylvius (D. 1697), courtier and diplomatist in the service of William III, and an acquaintance of John Evelyn. From their wording it would seem that they had been specially composed to accompany the drawings.

7. QUEEN MARY II.

Bust turned to front, with head turned slightly to l. Wearing her hair curled, and a lock on her r. shoulder, an ermine-edged gown, and pearls. Within a circular border.
Plate 121

Pen and brown-grey ink, highly finished, on vellum; 25·3 × 19·8 cm. (10 × 7¾ in.).

INSCR.: *Recto*, in the inner circle of the border, by the artist, *MARIA. II. by the Grace of God Queen of England. Scotland. France and Yrland, Defens. of the faith Obÿt A⁰ MDCXCV A⁰ Ætatis suæ XXX* and at the foot, *I. faber delin:*. Below the drawing, the following verses in Dutch:

Al poogt de konst vol vůir haar pen in inkt telaven
Om af te malen't beeld van koningin Marÿ
Weergade loose in deugd in Schoonheid en in gaven

't Is maar een Schaduw van haar Majesteits waardij.

Sÿlvius
I: faber Scripsit | 1697.

PROV.: As for No. 6.

1950–7–22–2.

Probably adapted from an oil-painting not yet identified.

Another portrait drawing in pen and ink of Queen Mary at a more advanced age was in the collection of Mr. Francis Wellesley. A reproduction of this is in the Department (**1911–4–21–2**).

8. MARTIN LUTHER, AFTER LUCAS CRANACH.

Bust turned half-l., wearing a dark gown with a high collar. Within a circular border.

Pen and brown-grey ink, highly finished, on vellum; 27·8 × 22·2 cm. (11 × 8¾ in.).

INSCR.: *Recto*, below the portrait, by the artist, *I: faber 1697*, and in the inner circle of the border, above, D.* MARTINUS LUTHERUS, and below, Natus MCCCCLXXXIII Obijt A° MDXLVI. Below the drawing, the following verses in Dutch:

Als't Christenrijk wel eer was onderdrukt van romen
Met. leugens en bedrog, verbÿsterd en vermomd,
Is Lúther als een held des Heeren voortgekomen

En heeft met pen en tong den antichrist verstomd.

I faber scripsit | 1697.

PROV.: As for No. 6.
1950–7–22–3.

Probably based on one of the several engravings of the Cranach portrait of Luther, showing him in late middle life.

9. DESIDERIUS ERASMUS, AFTER HOLBEIN. Bust turned half-l. Wearing a dark furred gown. Within a circular border.

Pen and brown-grey ink, highly finished, on vellum; 24·6 × 19·6 cm. (9⅝ × 7¾ in.).

INSCR.: Recto, below the portrait, by the artist, I: faber 1697 cum penna fecit, and above, in the inner circle of the border, DESIDERIUS ERASMUS ROTTERODAMUS. Below the drawing, the following verses in Dutch:

Dùs blonk in Rotterdam Erasmùs, groot van naam,
De waerelt door vermaart voor't hooft der Letterhelden.

Hÿ heeft met lof vervúld den horen van de faam,
Gelÿk d'orakels van zÿn hoog Latÿn vermelden.

Faber Scripsit, | 1697   Sylviùs.

PROV.: As for No. 6.
1950–7–32–4.

Probably adapted from the engraving by C. Koning after Holbein, published at Haarlem.

10. HUGO GROTIUS, AFTER MIEREVELT. Bust turned half-r., with eyes looking to front, curling hair, moustache and beard. Wearing a falling ruff and dark gown. Within a circular border.

Pen and brown-grey ink, highly finished, on vellum; 26·2 × 22·1 cm. (10¼ × 8¾ in.).

INSCR.: Recto, at the top, in the inner circle of the border, by the artist, HUGO GROTIUS, and at the foot, I: faber 1697. Below the drawing, the following verses in Dutch:

De fenix Huig de Groot, die Latium en grieken

Konde overzweven met den luister van zÿn' wieken
Bataafsche wonder in der wÿzen oog en oor,
Dit Delfsche Orakel klonk de wÿde werelt door.
I: faber | Scripsit   Sylviùs.

PROV.: As for No. 6.
1950–7–22–5.

Probably adapted from the engraving by W. Delff after Mierevelt.

FAITHORNE, WILLIAM

B. 1616 (?): D. 1691

Engraver and portrait draughtsman in crayons

The main source for Faithorne's life derived from a MS. biography by John Bagford (D. 1716), the collector, from information given to him by a certain 'Will Hill: Charke'. Born in London, the date usually given, 1616 (but possibly several years later), being inferred from Buckeridge who supposed that he was seventy-five when he died in 1691. According to the records of the Goldsmiths' Company 'son of Daniell Faithorne of London, lorimer [i.e. bit-maker]'. Apprenticed to William Veale, 'citizen and goldsmith', on Oct. 23rd, 1635, but no record of his having become a freeman of the Goldsmiths' Company. Encouraged to take up engraving by his first master, the elder Robert Peake (Sergeant-Painter), and continued working under the engraver John Payne (B. 1607 (?): D. 1647), probably from 1636–9. Later attached himself to Sir Robert Peake (B. 1592 (?): D. 1667), printseller and son of the elder Peake, under whose command he served at the Siege of Basing House. On the surrender of the garrison (1645) was sent as a prisoner to Aldersgate where he was allowed to engrave portraits such as that of the 'great Duke of Buckingham after the manner of Mellan [Claude Mellan (B. 1598 (?): D. 1688)] in little'. Was banished to France (probably for refusing to take the oath of loyalty to Cromwell), where he secured the patronage of the famous collector, Abbé Michel de Marolles. Is said to have been instructed by Philippe de Champaigne (B. 1602: D. 1672) and probably worked with Robert Nanteuil (B. 1632 (?): D. 1678). Returned to London about 1650 where he settled 'next ye sign of the Drake, against the Palsgrave's Head without Temple Barr', and set up as an engraver, publisher and printseller. Re-

ceived the patronage of some of the Commonwealth leaders, and was himself painted by Robert Walker (D. 1658), holding his engraving of Sir Robert Fairfax (*N.P.G.*, No. 618). After the Restoration equally enjoyed the favour of the Court, and styled himself 'painter to Prince Rupert'. Was visited a number of times between 1660 and 1669 by Pepys who bought several of his 'cuts'. In 1673 published Barlow's *Multae et Diversae Avium Species*, with etchings by Hollar. Moved to Printing House Yard in the parish of St. Anne's, Blackfriars, about 1680, when he gave up his printselling business to devote himself to engraving and 'to painting in Craions from ye life with good Success'. In Vertue's opinion was 'the first Englishman that arivd to any perfection' [in engraving] 'especially in heads & in his time prefferable to any other of his proffession in this Land'. His numerous portrait engravings include works after his own drawings as well as others after William Dobson (B. 1610: D. 1646), William Sheppard (*Fl. c.* 1670) and other portrait painters of the day. Also engraved a large number of frontispieces, book illustrations, etc., notably plates for: Jeremy Taylor's *Life of Christ*, 1663; Samuel Wesley's *Life of Our Blessed Lord . . . An Heroic Poem*, 1693; and two large maps, one of London and Westminster (1658), the other of Virginia and Maryland (1673), both issued by himself. His *art of graveing and etching*, 1662 (a translation of Abraham Bosse's *Traicté des manières de Graver en taille douce*), was the first technical account of its kind to be published in England and caused Evelyn (*q.v.*) to forego the treatise on the same subject which was to have formed an appendix to his *Sculptura* (pp. 149–50). The miniaturist,

Thomas Flatman (B. 1637: D. 1688) eulogized Faithorne's treatise in verse.

As a draughtsman worked both in crayons (often in conjunction with body-colours) and in a mixture of black lead and wash (Indian ink). His work in the latter medium shows a certain resemblance to Nanteuil's manner, though it is doubtful whether the French artist was ever his master as Vertue states, being the younger man. Nanteuil's influence less marked in Faithorne's crayon drawing than in those of some other contemporaries (Cf. Edmund Ashfield). Also evolved a method of crayon drawing on copper, employed later by Edward Lutterell (q.v.) by which the plate was roughened with a mezzotint rocker to hold the chalks. According to Buckeridge was known for his speed in drawing, a gift shared by Francis Le Piper (q.v.) with whom Faithorne used to compete in a light-hearted way to demonstrate his powers. Buckeridge also states that he was 'a great Proficient . . . in Painting, especially in Miniature, of which there are many instances now in England', though the only works now ascribed to him to which the word 'miniature' is strictly applicable, are the portraits of Barbara, Countess of Castlemaine, after Lely (in the collection of the Duke of Buccleuch) and of an unknown lady (in that of the Hon. Donough O'Brien). The former clearly related to the drawing of Lady Castlemaine referred to by Pepys in his Diary under Nov. 7th, 1666, 'Called at Faythorns, to buy some prints for my wife to draw by this winter, and here did see my Lady Castlemaine's picture, done by him from Lilly's, in red chalke, and other colours, by which he hath cut it in copper to be printed. The picture in chalke is the finest thing I ever saw in my life I think.' Also in this connexion may be noted an illuminated pedigree of the Palmer family formerly (according to Neale) at Dorney Court, Bucks., which contained portraits by Faithorne of Lord and Lady Castlemaine. Also numbered among his acquaintances, John Smith (B. 1652 (?): D. 1742), the mezzotinter, and many of the writing-masters of the time, including John Seddon (B. 1644: D. 1700). Is said to have taught John Fillian (Fl. 1660–80) the engraver, and Thomas Hill (B. 1664: D. 1734) the portrait painter, and probably also William Faithorne II (B. 1656: D. 1701 (?)), the artist's son, known only as a mezzotinter. John Aubrey was another of the artist's friends to whom he presented his (Aubrey's) portrait, now in the Ashmolean. Married Mary, sister of 'the famous Captain Graund' (possibly the Captain Grant mentioned by Pepys). Died of a 'lingering consumption' in May, 1691, and was buried on the 13th of that month at St. Anne's, Blackfriars. According to Bagford, his death hastened by that of his son, William, in 1686, but this disproved by the bequest of two-thirds of his property to the younger Faithorne. Further evidence of his son's survival lies in the fact that his mezzotint plates were issued well into the reign of Queen Anne.

DRAWINGS IN OTHER COLLECTIONS: Ashmolean Museum (John Aubrey, 1666; An Unknown Man, 1679). Prof. J. Isaacs (A Divine). Mr. Edward Croft-Murray (A Young Man).

BIBL.: Bagford, Faithorne. Buckeridge, pp. 371–2. Neale, Ser. I, I, Dorney Court. Fagan, passim. D.N.B., XVIII, 1889, pp. 154–5 (with Bibl.). Bell & Poole, pp. 43–64. Hussey, Dorney Court, p. 176, figs. 7–9. Vertue, Index, p. 78. Woodward, passsim.

1. **JOHN RAY, F.R.S.** Bust turned half-l., with eyes looking to front, long grey hair, and grey moustache. Wearing broad white falling bands and a brown cloak draped over his shoulders. Dark grey background. In feigned oval. **Plate 124**

Crayons; 24·2 × 20 cm. (9½ × 7⅞ in.).

PROV.: Sir Hans Sloane, Bart., by whom it was bequeathed to the B.M., 1753.
Sloane, 407 (L.B.2).

ENGR.: By William Elder, in reverse, as the frontispiece to John Ray's *Stirpium Europearum . . . Sylloge*, 1694, his *Wisdom of God*, 1701, and his *Three Discourses*, 1732. (For later engravings and modifications of the portrait see *B.M. Engraved Portraits*, III, p. 548.)

BIBL.: *Sloane Antiquities, Pictures & Drawings*, No. 407 ('Mr. Ray in crayons by Faithorne'). Fagan, p. 91. Bell & Poole, p. 54.

[John Ray (B. 1627: D. 1705). One of the greatest of English naturalists. Was born at Black Norley, near Braintree, Essex, and educated at Catharine Hall and Trinity College, Cambridge. After a period as a lecturer in Greek and in mathematics, turned his attention to botany, making numerous tours in Great Britain, to collect material for his studies. In 1663–6 was on the Continent with three of his pupils, including Francis Willoughby, who was to collaborate in much of Ray's work. Was elected F.R.S. in 1667. Published, among other botanical works, his *Methodus Plantarum Nova* in 1682, and his *Historia Plantarum* in 1686–1704, which were important for their improvements in the classification of this science. In later life also studied entomology. Corresponded much with Sir Hans Sloane, many of his letters being amongst the Sloane MSS. The present drawing would show the sitter at about the age of 70.]

2. SIR EDMUND KING.

2. SIR EDMUND KING. Bust, perhaps imitating a coloured terracotta, on a pedestal. Head turned half-l., with eyes looking slightly to r. Wearing a heavy brown wig falling on his shoulders, broad white falling bands, and a rose-coloured cloak. Dark grey background. **Plate 125**

Water-colours and body-colours, over red and black chalk; 18·8 × 14·2 cm. (7⅞ × 5⅝ in.).

PROV.: As for No. 1. Kept in the Museum 'storeroom' till it passed into the keeping of the Dept. of P & D., 1857.
Sloane, 184 & 1847-3-26-5 (L.B.1).

BIBL.: *Sloane Antiquities, Pictures & Drawings*, No. 184 ('Sʳ Edmund Kings picture in crayons by Faithorn 1:1:6'). *Portraits transferred from Dept. of Antiquities* ('A Square Portrait of a Man in a flowing Wig & red drapery treated as a bust & placed on a pedestal. In body colours principally. This has suffered. In common black frame and glass'). Fagan, p. 91. Bell & Poole, p. 54.

[Sir Edmund King (B. 1629: D. 1709). Surgeon and physician. Was not only a successful practitioner, but also published the results of several important researches in medicine in the *Philosophical Transactions* of the Royal Society of which he became a Fellow in 1666. Kept a museum of medical specimens at his house in Little Britain which was always open to students. Appointed physician to Charles II and knighted in 1676. Attended that monarch during his last illness, and acted with great promptitude by bleeding him when he was struck by apoplexy on Feb. 2nd, 1684. Practised up to the age of 72, one of his last patients being the aged poet Sir Charles Sedley, the care of whom he handed on to Sir Hans Sloane.]

The present drawing should be compared with the two portraits of King, engraved respectively by R. Williams after Lely and by R. White after Kneller, which seemingly represent him as a much older man (*See B.M. Engraved Portraits*, II, p. 696). The authenticity of the drawing is, however, confirmed by its being listed in Sloane's own catalogue as a portrait of King.

3. SIR ORLANDO BRIDGEMAN, BART. H.L., with head turned half-l. and body half-r. Wearing a skull cap, broad lace-edged falling bands, and robes as Lord Keeper. Before him, the purse containing the Great Seal. **Plate 123**

Brush drawing in black wash, highly finished, over black lead, on vellum; 15·1 × 12 cm. (6 × 4¾ in.).

PROV.: Sir Hans Sloane, Bart., by whom it was bequeathed to the B.M., 1753. Formerly considered as having come from the Rev. C. M. Cracherode.

Sloane, 39. Formerly G.g.1–448

(L.B.3).

ENGR.: By William Faithorne for William Dugdale's *Origines Juridiciales, or Historical Memorials of the English Laws, Court of Justice, &c*; 2nd edn., 1671, following the *Chronica Series.* (For subsequent copies of the portrait see *B.M. Engraved Portraits*, I, p. 238.)

BIBL.: *Sloane Antiquities, Pictures & Drawings*, No. 39 ('Sᵣ Orlando Bridgman, a drawing'). *Fagan*, p. 90. *Bell & Poole*, p. 54.

[Sir Orlando Bridgeman (B. 1608/9: D. 1674). Lord Keeper of the Great Seal. Was the son of Dr. John Bridgeman, subsequently Bishop of Chester, and was educated at Queen's College, Cambridge. Was called to the Bar in 1632, acquiring a high legal reputation and becoming successively Chief Justice of Chester in 1638, and Attorney of the Court of Wards and Solicitor General to the Prince of Wales in 1640, in this latter year also was returned M.P. for Wigan and knighted. During the Civil War was a staunch Royalist, though at the Commonwealth he submitted to Cromwell and was permitted to practise privately, devoting himself to conveyancing. At the Restoration, his late attitude under the Commonwealth was forgotten, and he was made Sergeant-at-Law, Chief Baron of the Exchequer, and a Baronet. Presided at the trial of the Regicides which he conducted with characteristic moderation. Appointed Lord Keeper in 1667, and continued his policy of moderation and compromise, though he firmly opposed certain of Charles II's intentions with the result that he was deprived of his office in 1672. Died in retirement at Teddington.]

4. A YOUNG DIVINE(?). Bust turned half-l., with eyes looking to front, long dark hair falling in curls about the neck, and slight moustache and tuft under the lower lip. Wearing broad white collar and a black doublet buttoned to the neck.

Black, red and white chalks, on grey paper; 21 × 16·6 cm. (8¼ × 6½ in.).

PROV.: Rimell & Son, from whom it was purchased by the B.M., 1905.

1905–10–19–16.

The attribution of this drawing to Faithorne must be regarded as very tentative.

5. *Recto.* **JOHN STURT.** H.L., with body turned to r., head half-r., eyes looking to front, and long curling hair. Wearing a brown coat and lace cravat, and holding a sheet of paper. **Plate 123**

Crayons on copper; re-touched perhaps on the coat; in the original japanned and gilt (?) wood frame; 10·3 × 6·9 cm. (4 × 2⅝ in.). Frame: 18·9 × 15·4 cm. (7⅜ × 6 in.).

Verso. **PART OF A PEDIMENTAL DESIGN, PROBABLY FOR A TITLE-PAGE, AS YET UNIDENTIFIED, ENGRAVED ON THE COPPER.**

INSCR.: On a vellum label attached to the back board of the frame, by the sitter, John Sturt himself, in characteristically fine lettering: *John Sturt | Engraver | Born the 6, April | MDCL* [VIII] *| Drawn by the Celebrated | M.̣ Will :ᵐ Faithorne | . . . An du Noces, | MDCXCIII. | J. S. scripsit 1726. | Ætat 68.* Together with other and more recent labels, one with a transcript of Sturt's original, the other with an extract concerning Faithorne from Strutt's *Dictionary of Engravers*, and a printed label, *Collection of Dr. Williamson 280.*

PROV.: John Sturt. Edward Harley, 2nd Earl of Oxford (Sale, Cock, 12:iii:1741/2, Lot 2, purchased by 'West 10s 6d'). James West (Sale, Langford, 3:iv:1773, Lot 32, purchased by 'Thane 10 6'). John Thane (apparently not in any of his Sales or Catalogues). Read Adams (not apparently in his Sale, Sotheby, 27:v:1889). Dr. George C. Williamson (Sale, Sotheby, 31:i:1945, but not mentioned in the Catalogue). E. Wheeler, from whom it was purchased by the B.M., 1950.

1950–10–14–3.

ENGR.: By William Humphrey, in mezzotint, and published, 1774 (*From an original picture in the possession of Mr. Thane*), in reverse and with some modifications (*Chaloner Smith*, No. 16). In the mezzotint there appears on the paper held by the sitter a female nude figure.

BIBL.: *Walpole*, III, p. 911. *G. C. Williamson*, p. 39. *Vertue*, III, p. 62.

[John Sturt (B. 1658: D. 1730). Engraver and calligrapher. Was apprenticed to Robert White. Subsequently was associated with John Ayres, the writing-master, some of whose works on calligraphy he engraved. Published in 1717 his famous *Book of Common Prayer* engraved on 188 silver plates.]

According to his own inscription, Sturt is represented in this drawing at about the age of 35, in 1693. From the epithet 'celebrated' he suggests that it is the work of the elder Faithorne, and indeed in style the drawing has much in common with the latter's portraits of John Ray and Sir Edmund King listed above at Nos. 1 and 2. Vertue, moreover, definitely states (I, p. 43) that Faithorne 'did some few' drawings in this particular method of crayons on copper (following Edward Lutterell who was the first to practise it) in which the surface of the plate is roughened with a mezzotint rocker to hold the chalks. Faithorne died, however, in 1691, two years before the date given by Sturt for the execution of the drawing, and one can only conclude that Sturt, who wrote the inscription many years afterwards, must have been mistaken in the date, though this seems strange, seeing that this was such an important year in his life. Unfortunately no other record of his marriage has yet been found, which would help to solve this problem. An alternative explanation is that perhaps the portrait is by Faithorne's son, the younger William Faithorne (B. 1656: D. 1701); no drawings by him are known, but he was a respectable mezzotint engraver and, as this technique of working in crayons on copper is allied in a certain sense to mezzotint engraving, it is possible that he may have tried his hand at it.

Vertue, who saw the portrait about 1734, when in the possession of the 2nd Earl of Oxford, describes it thus: 'John Sturt Engraver born 6. April. MDCLVIII. his picture painted by Faithorne on Copper, dry colours. 1693. in poses̄ Earl of Oxford. little like him, when I knew him, from 1712. to his death'. A drawing by Vertue of Sturt at the age of 69, dated *Jan. 1727*, is in the Department.

(1852–2–11–381).

FORBES, ALEXANDER

Working in 1691
Topographical draughtsman

From his name and from the spelling of certain words in the inscriptions on his drawings was clearly of Scottish origin. Was probably an amateur. His plans of Chester, Coventry, Galloway, Nantwich, and Newcastle-under-Lyme (formerly in the Department of Prints and Drawings, L.B.1–4 & 6, but now in the Map Room) seem to be inspired by, but not copied from, the plans of towns which occur on John Speed's maps of the English Counties. His drawing of St. Michael's Church, Coventry, listed below, in its dry handling of pen and ink, is rather reminiscent of etchings after the topographical views of buildings by Daniel King.

1. ST. MICHAEL'S CHURCH, COVENTRY. Elevation of the N. side of the church with the tower and spire rising on the r. **Plate 128**

Pen and black ink; 43·2 × 42·1 cm. (17 × 16½ in.).

INSCR.: *Recto*, at the top, by the artist, on a pennant held by the figure of a man on a column, l., *A PROSPECT OF SAINT MICHAELS CHURCH IN COVENTRY. from yᵉ North*; on the plinth supporting the column, l., *THIS | Church is in lenth from— | the Northwest corner of the | Steeple, to the East end of yᵉ— | Chancell, 100 yards: But in | measuring, Remember, to allow— | 8, because yᵉ corner of yᵉ Church | covers so much of the Steeple.— | The Height of the Steeple to the | first Batlement is 50 yards. The | Height of yᵉ Octogon is 10 And | ane half in measuring of which | yow must allow 2 yards &* *ane | half because yᵉ lower Batlement— | hids so much of the foot of it. The | height of the Spyre is 42 yards | of the which yow must allow 2 | for the forgoing reason. On the foot of the plinth, A Scale of yards*, and *Done by Alexander Forbes anno Dom: 1691*. At the top, in the centre, on a separate slip of paper, *This Stately Church but view it well | Inside and out, ther's few excell, | Lofty, Spatious, Spyre so high, | It may be said to touch the Sky. | Built of good, firm, & lasting stone, | Carv'd curiously, and Lively done. |*

PROV.: Unknown. Formerly in an album labelled *British Topography*.
Old Crown (L.B.5).

FORSTER, THOMAS

B. *c.* 1677: Working till after 1712
Portrait draughtsman in black lead on vellum

Perhaps of Northumbrian origin. His date of birth fixed approximately by Vertue's mention of a self-portrait drawing inscribed *aeta. 31 1708*. One of the latest draughtsmen to work in the main XVII c. tradition of black lead on vellum, his style being characterized by great delicacy and decorative sense in rendering curls of the hair and wigs and the folds of the drapery worn by his sitters. Unlike his predecessors, Loggan (*q.v.*) and

Robert White (*q.v.*), rarely seems to have drawn persons of historical eminence and few of his portraits engraved. An important group of portraits, sold by Sotheby in 1954, included Francis, 2nd Baron Guilford, dated 1703, inscribed on the *verso*, *This for Ld. Kepr North*, and five others unidentified, dating from 1696 to 1699 (Sale, 17:xi:1954, Lots 45–8). A number of his sitters associated with James Butler, 2nd Duke of Ormonde, and with the Duke's life in Ireland. Perhaps identical with Thomas Forster, author of a drawing of the elevation of the Banqueting House, Whitehall, formerly in the collection of Mr. Randall Davies. Among his followers, working in the same medium and style of portrait drawing are Charles Forster (*Fl. c.*

1709–17) who was perhaps his son, and Mary Blencow or Blencowe, daughter of the judge, Sir John Blencowe (B. 1642: D. 1726), and later wife of Alexander Prescott of Thoby Priory, Essex. A portrait of a young gentleman by Mary Blencow is in the possession of Mrs. Hornby of 8 Old Palace Lane, Richmond, Surrey (1952).

BIBL.: *T.-B.*, XII, 1916, p. 224 (with *Bibl.*). *Foster, Cooper*, pp. 78–9. *Bell and Poole*, p. 73. *Old London Exhibition*, p. 43. *B.F.A.C., British born Artists*, pp. 40–3. *Vertue, Index*, p. 82.

DRAWINGS IN OTHER COLLECTIONS: *See* biography above and B.F.A.C., *British Born Artists*, pp. 32–4.

1. MARGARET or MARGERY HARCOURT. Bust, nearly H.L., turned half-r., with head turned half-l. and eyes looking to front. Wearing her hair in curls, and a low gown, above which her chemise shows.

Plate 127

Black lead on vellum; oval; 11·5 × 9·2 cm. (4$\frac{1}{2}$ × 3$\frac{5}{8}$ in.).

INSCR.: *Recto*, on the l., in black lead, by the artist, *Tho. fforster | delin. 1708*, and on the r., *MARG : HARCOVRT*.

PROV.: E. Daniell, from whom it was purchased by the B.M., 1861.
1861–8–10–91 (L.B.1).

BIBL.: *Bell & Poole*, p. 77. *Long*, p. 159.

[The sitter has not been identified with any certainty, but she may be identical with a certain Elizabeth Margaret Arabella Harcourt, daughter of Simon Harcourt of Pendley, Herts. (D. 1724), Clerk to the Crown. Or she may belong to the Harcourts of Burrough Hall, Staffs., in which family the first name of Margaret occurs. No Margery Harcourt has been traced (*See* William Harcourt-Bath, *A History of the Family of Harcourt*, 1930, p. 55 & 56).]

2. GEORGE ST. LO. Bust, with head to l., body to r. and eyes looking to front. Wearing a large curling wig falling on his shoulders, a fringed cravat and draped cloak. To the l. of his head, the sitter's arms with the motto, *PROTEO CONTRARIUS*.

Plate 126

Black lead on vellum; oval; 17·6 × 14·7 cm. (6$\frac{7}{8}$ × 5$\frac{3}{4}$ in.).

INSCR.: *Recto*, on the l., in black lead, by the artist, *Geo. St Lo Esq : | Commr. of | His (?) Majis : | Navy*, and on the r., *T. Forster. | delin— | 1704*.

PROV.: Joseph Mayor (Sale, Sotheby, 23:vii:1887, Lot 485). Purchased by Dr. John Percy through Messrs Hogarth (Sale, Christie, 17:iv:1890, Lot 454). Purchased by the B.M. at the Percy Sale, 1890.
1890–5–12–81 (L.B.2).

BIBL. & REPR.: *Percy Cat.*, pp. 40–3. *B.M. Reproductions*, III, 1893, p. 4 & Pl. XIII. *Foster*, pp. 78–9 & Pl. XC, No. 218 (incorrectly as by Robert White). *Bell & Poole*, p. 76. *Long*, p. 159.

[George St. Lo (B. 1658: D. 1718). Commissioner of the Navy. Fourth son of Edward St. Lo, of Knighton, Wilts. Served first as a lieutenant in the Navy from 1677/8 till 1682 when he was promoted captain of the 'Dartmouth'. Married Elizabeth Chiffinch in 1683. Wounded and captured by the French in 1689, but later repatriated. Made a Commissioner of Prizes in 1693, in which year he published his pamphlet, *England's Safety, or a Bridle to the French King*. Was Commissioner at Plymouth from 1695 to 1703. In 1697 was appointed to guard those at work on the construction of the Eddystone Lighthouse, who subsequently through his negligence were carried off by a French privateer. Became Resident Commissioner at Chatham in 1703, and Commander-in-Chief of ships in the Medway and at the Nore in 1712. Purchased the manor of East and West Yaldham, near Wrotham, Kent, in 1713. Was buried at Northfleet on Sept. 20th, 1718 (*See* R. D. Merriman in *The Mariner's Mirror*, 31, 1945, pp. 13–22).]

The present drawing would show St. Lo at the age of about 46. The engraved portrait of him by Joseph Nutter (*See B.M. Engraved Portraits*, IV, p. 13) has little in common with it, except the very large wig favoured by the sitter.

3. A MAN IN A NIGHT CAP. Bust turned half-r., with eyes looking to front. Wearing a night cap and a gown draped over his r. shoulder.

Black lead on vellum; oval; 9·1 × 6·8 cm. (3⅝ × 2⅝ in.).

INSCR.: *Recto*, on the r., in black lead, by the artist, *Thos. Forster | Delin 1705*.

PROV.: James Carter, from whom it was purchased by the B.M., 1906.

1906–7–23–2.

BIBL.: *Bell & Poole*, p. 77. *Long*, p. 159.

It is suggested in *Bell & Poole* (*See Bibl.* above) that this might be a self-portrait of the artist.

4. A MAN IN A LARGE WIG. Bust turned half-l., with eyes looking to front. Wearing a large curling wig, cravat and cloak draped over his l. shoulder.

Black lead on vellum; oval; 11·4 × 8·8 cm. (4⅜ × 3½ in.).

INSCR.: *Recto*, on the r., in black lead, by the artist, *T F* (monogram) | *1698*.

PROV.: E. Rawdon Smith, by whom it was presented to the B.M., 1954.

1954–11–3–428 (99).

FULLER, ISAAC

B. 1606 (?): D. 1672

History and decorative painter

Said by Redgrave to have been born in 1606, but the authority for this not given. Nothing known of his early training. Appears to have had Royalist sympathies, and was at Oxford during Charles I's stay in the city, as attested by the inscription on his portrait of the Cavalier poet John Cleveland (now in the collection of Lt.-Col. H. G. Sotheby) to the effect that this was painted at Oxford in 1644. Probably went abroad at the beginning of the Commonwealth. According to Buckeridge, studied many years in France under the history and decorative painter, François Perrier (B. 1590: D. 1650), thereby providing an early link in the association of French academism and English art which, later in the XVII c., was to play such an important part in the development of decorative painting in this country. May have worked with Perrier in Paris in 1645–50, at the time when he was engaged on his most important decoration, the Gallery of the Hôtel de la Vrillière, begun in 1645. Was certainly back in England by 1650 in which year was published his namesake Thomas Fuller's *A Pisgah-Sight of Palestine* for which Francis Cleyn designed and etched the frontispiece and Isaac Fuller a double-page plate (Bk. 5, p. 92) representing the costumes worn by Jewish men and women from the cradle to the grave. In 1654 published his drawing-book *Un Libro di Designare* of 15 etched plates, which is recorded by Vertue, though no copy is known today. On Sept. 18th, 1657, appears to have been commissioned by the Painter-Stainers' Company to paint a group of their 'Court of Assistants'. In 1658 was acclaimed by Sir William Sanderson as 'Fuller for story' among our 'Modern Masters comparable with any now beyond seas'. Soon after the Restoration painted a series of large pictures on wood, representing the adventures of Charles II after the Battle of Worcester, which Vertue saw in the Earl of Stafford's collection in 1743, and which are said to have found their way later to the Irish Parliament, subsequently being removed by Lord Clanbrassil to Tullamore Park. Was working again in Oxford before 1663 when Monconys noted on June 11th of that year his wall-paintings

of the *Resurrection* at the E. end and a *St. Francis* in a niche in All Souls Chapel. The *Resurrection* (in 'oil of turpentine' in imitation of 'fresco') also noted by Evelyn on Oct. 24th, 1664, as well as Fuller's other Oxford wall-painting of the *Last Judgment* at the E. end of Magdalen Chapel. Connected with the latter is the study of a floating figure in the N.G., Ireland, inscribed, *one of Fullers maid* (?) / *figures in Mag. Coll : Ox*. Painted for Wadham Chapel a *Last Supper* flanked on one side by Abraham and Melchisedek and on the other by the Israelites gathering manna, which is said to have been executed in brown crayon heightened with white on 'cloth of ash colour', the colours being fixed by some encaustic process. Also during his stay at Oxford made a copy of Dobson's *Decollation of St. John* (the original formerly at Wilton and, in 1951, at the Arcade Gallery) using his own models for the figures. By 1669 had returned to London, and was living in the parish of St. Giles-in-the-Fields, when he entered into a law-suit over payment for a scene of Elysium which he had executed for a production of Dryden's *Tyrannic Love* at Drury Lane. In 1670 painted his two full-blooded self-portraits (allegedly when drunk), now respectively in the Bodleian Library and the Queen's College, Oxford. The former painted for Daniel Rawlinson, owner of the Mitre Tavern in Fenchurch Street, for which hostelry Fuller also decorated a room with life-size mythological subjects described in detail by Vertue, who says in respect of a figure of Saturn that it showed the painter to have some knowledge of anatomy, though the 'fiery colours & distinct marking of the muscles make this appear like a body without a skin'. Also decorated rooms in two other taverns, the Crown in Smithfield and the Sun behind the Royal Exchange, besides painting a sign for the latter. His convivial habits referred to in John Elsum's epigram on the picture of '*A Drunken Sot, by an unknown Hand*'. According to Vertue painted a staircase ceiling in a house in Soho Square.

Vertue also notes a number of self-portraits by Fuller, including the two of him, with a beard, at Oxford, and one purchased by a Mr. Dorington in 1717 (a copy of which by Vertue is in the Dept., 1853–2–14–378), showing him beardless and, therefore, probably younger. The same authority mentions too Fuller's portraits of Cleveland (referred to above), and of Edward Pierce the sculptor (in the collection of Major J. H. Dent-Brocklehurst). Other portraits by, or attributed to, Fuller, listed by Mr. Collins Baker. 'History' pictures, outside his decorative work, included an allegory, *Fame and Honour treading down Envy*, in James II's collection, and a St. Mary Magdalen mentioned in Harleian MS. 2337. Etched two large plates of Tritons and seahorses and a small oval of profile heads. These show the same heavy cross-hatching as is visible in the two drawings described below, and in that at the V. & A. M., inscribed on the *verso*, *Fuller by himself*, which is connected with the Oxford portraits. This cross-hatching may be compared too with his old master Perrier's etchings of sculpture, *Icones et Segmenta Illustrium e Marmore Tabularum*, 1645. Died on July 17th, 1672, at Southampton Buildings, and was buried on July 18th, at St. Andrew's, Holborn. Does not appear to have left a Will. Was still of sufficient repute for his head to be included among those of distinguished artists which formed part of the temporary decorations at an entertainment given by John Talman at his lodgings in Rome in 1711.

Left two sons, Isaac and Nicholas, both of whom followed their father's profession. Nicholas said to have been an accomplished coach-painter, but to have died young. Isaac II's work often confused with that of his father. In 1678 painted the vestry ceiling of St. Lawrence Jewry and in 1679 was employed in the decoration of another City church, St. Stephen, Colman Street. May have painted the dome of St. Mary Abchurch (building completed in 1686), a work which Walpole attributes, but without giving his authority, to the elder Fuller. In 1681/2 was commissioned to paint a ceiling representing *Pallas triumphant with the Arts and Fame* for the hall of the Painter-Stainers' Company, a work which was probably not finished till 1683. The only known drawing by Isaac II is in the Witt Collection, a nude study in red chalk, dated *Feb 15th 1689*. Was probably still living in 1709 in which year was published the English edition of Cesare Ripa's *Iconologia* with an etched title and some plates by Isaac II, and other plates by Henry Cooke II.

BIBL.: *Sanderson*, p. 20. *Monconys*, II, p. 53. *Elsum*, p. 65. *Buckeridge*, pp. 313–4. *Walpole*, II, pp. 428–32. *Redgrave*, p. 162. *D.N.B.*, XX, 1889, p. 311. *Crace*, p. 12. *Evelyn, Diary*, III, p. 386. *Poole, Oxford Portraits*, I, p. 57, II, p. 119, & III, p. 26. *Baker, Lely*, I, pp. 124–9. *Wheatley & Cunningham*, III, p. 334. *Ward*, p. 89. *Hotson*, p. 250. *Wren Soc.*, X, p. 53, XVII, p. 4, & XIX, p. 25. *Vertue, Index*, p. 85. *Woodward, passim* & Pl. 21.

DRAWINGS IN OTHER COLLECTIONS: V. & A. M. N. G., Ireland.

1. HERCULES THE ARCHER. Hercules, in his lion skin, standing near a tree stump and drawing his bow towards the r.
Plate 130

Pen and dark brown ink; 10·9 × 8·6 cm. (4⅜ × 3⅜ in.).

INSCR.: Recto, at the foot, *x 15* (?).

PROV.: Hugh Howard. Dr. Robert Howard (Bishop of Elphin). The Earls of Wicklow. Charles Howard, 5th Earl, from whom it was purchased by the B.M., 1874. 1874–8–8–103 (L.B.2).

As stated in the biographical note above, the pen-work of this and the following drawing (No. 2), with its heavy cross-hatching, recalls the etchings of Fuller's master, François Perrier, and those of Fuller himself.

2. STUDY OF TWO FIGURES AMONG THE DAMNED IN MICHEL-ANGELO'S 'LAST JUDGMENT' IN THE SISTINE CHAPEL.

A woman about to strike a nude man, seen from behind, who drags her down towards him with one arm, while with the other he wards off her blow.

Plate 130

Pen and dark brown ink; $23 \cdot 4 \times 11 \cdot 5$ cm. ($9\frac{1}{4} \times 4\frac{1}{2}$ in.).

INSCR.: *Verso*, near the centre, *Fuller f* (?) (perhaps a signature).

PROV.: As for No. 1.
1874–8–8–104 (L.B.1).

The two figures appear on the r. of the third row in the *Last Judgment*. The present drawing is not, however, taken direct from the fresco, but from a study after this particular group by Vasari, which was etched by Jan de Bisschop in his *Paradigmata Graphices variorum Artificum*, 1671, Vol. II, Pl. 17. Fuller's drawing corresponds almost exactly in size with Bisschop's etching, so it seems likely that he copied this rather than Vasari's study.

GASCAR OR GASCARS, HENRI

B. 1634/5: D. 1701

Portrait painter

Born in Paris, perhaps the son of the sculptor Pierre Gasquart. As early as 1667 painted the striking portrait—very different from his later work—of the journalist Nicolas de Lafand ('le gazetier hollandais'), which was engraved by Pierre Lombart. *Agréé* of the *Académie* in 1671, and in the following year appointed *Peintre ordinaire du Roi*. Soon after, came to England with the engraver, Peter Vanderbank, at the invitation of Louise de Keroualle, Duchess of Portsmouth. Remained here perhaps till about 1680, during which time he represented the more decorative and pretty type of French Court portraiture (more generally associated with Pierre Mignard), his fellow-practioner in this manner being the Fleming Jacob Huysmans. A characteristic example of his work in England is his *James, Duke of York as Lord High Admiral*, in the National Maritime Museum, Greenwich. Traditionally said to have himself scraped a number of mezzotints published after his portraits (mainly of Court beauties). Outside portraiture, may have been the author of a curious representation, also engraved in mezzotint, of *Socrates & Xantippe*, lettered *H G delin . . . I Smith ex:*. Left England, probably about 1680, taking with him a fortune of more than £10,000. Was elected a Member of the *Académie* on Oct. 26th, 1680, on account of his portraits of the painters Louis (Ferdinand) Elle and Pierre de Sève, both now in the Louvre. In April 1681, took leave of the *Académie* 'pour un grand voyage' and probably went direct to Italy, where he imposed 'as much on the Italian noblesse, as he did on those of England'. Was in Venice in 1686 when he painted a portrait of 'Prince Maximilian Wilhelm', but lived mainly in Rome where he eventually died on Jan. 18th, 1701, being buried in the church of S. Lorenzo in Lucina.

BIBL.: *Buckeridge*, p. 375. *Walpole*, II, p.

464. *D.N.B.*, XXI, 1890, p. 34. *Chaloner Smith*, II, p. 523. *T.-B.*, XIII, 1920, p. 224. *Vertue, Index*, p. 86. *Waterhouse*, pp. 69, 70 & 85.

1. **CUPID HOLDING A DOVE.** H.L. figure of Cupid, partly draped in a striped cloth and with blue wings, leaning to r. on a bank and holding a dove which tries to escape. Beneath his r. arm, his quiver laced with a red ribbon. Dark wooded background with a late evening sky.   **Plate 145**

Oil-colours, highly finished; 11 × 8·8 cm. (4⅜ × 3½ in.).

INSCR.: *Verso*, in the centre, *par Gascar*.

PROV.: Richard Bull (Sale, Sotheby, 23:v:1881, Lot 51, 'One of Nell Gwynne's sons by Charles II, as Cupid playing with a dove'). Purchased by the B.M. at the Bull Sale, 1881.

1881–6–11–153 (L.B.1).

No other miniatures by Gascar are recorded, and the attribution of this rather insignificant little work to him rests solely on the old inscription on the *verso*. The identification of the subject with 'One of Nell Gwynne's sons' presumably derives from the fact that Gascar painted a portrait of Lord James Beauclerk, second son of Charles II by Nell Gwynne, represented as Cupid, of which there is a mezzotint attributed also to Gascar (*See Chaloner Smith*, II, p. 524, No. 2). This composition bears no relation to the present miniature.

GASPERS, JAN BAPTIST

[GASPARS, GASPAR, JASPER, JASPERS, JASPAR, CASPER]

B. 1620 (?): D. 1690 (?)

Portrait painter and draughtsman

Born in Antwerp where he was admitted as a member of St. Luke's Guild in 1641/2. Was a pupil of Thomas (Willeborts) Bosschaert (B. 1614: D. 1654), the imitator of Rubens and Van Dyck. According to Vertue, came to England during the Civil War, and is mentioned as purchaser in inventories of the sale of the King's collection, Vertue transcribing one entry under May 21st, 1650, 'Mr. Jan Baptist Jaspar, 44 pictures—[£]89'. Said to have worked for the Parliamentary leader, General Lambert. Was admitted as a member of the Painter-Stainers' Company on Sept. 6th, 1653, and on July 1st of the following year was chosen as 'Assistant of his Company'. After the Restoration entered Lely's studio and, according to Buckeridge, was employed 'to paint his postures which he performed very well' becoming known as 'Lely's Baptist'. After Lely's death (1680) was engaged with other assistants in finishing portraits which remained in the artist's studio. Subsequently worked for Sir Godfrey Kneller (*q.v.*) and John Riley (*q.v.*). Though known to his contemporaries principally as a painter of 'postures' and drapery (in which field Samuel Barker is named as a follower by Vertue), executed his own portraits, including those of Charles II (Painter-Stainers' Co.) and Thomas Hobbs (St. Bartholomew's Hospital), as well as history pieces. In this connexion Vertue mentions 'a large histori- call family peice & a curious picture of Cleopatra' at one time in the collection of the portrait painter, Thomas Murray (B. 1663: D. 1734). In the opinion of Buckeridge was 'a great judge of Painting and likewise emin- ent for his designs for tapestry having been an admirable draftsman in the academy'. Also executed working drawings after paintings for the mezzotinter J. Van Somer and the publisher Richard Tompson, at least one of which he appears to have engraved himself (*See* No. 1 below). Designed the emblematic frontispiece to the folio edition of the *Book of Common Prayer* engraved by David Loggan and

published in 1687. According to Vertue, died in 1692, and was buried at St. James's, Piccadilly, but no record of him appears in the Burial Register of the church for that year. An entry for Dec. 30th, 1690, of 'John Baptist' possibly refers to him. Vertue mentions Thomas Murray as the executor for Gasper's widow, stating that the latter owned a por- trait of the artist in addition to the pictures mentioned above.

BIBL.: *Painter-Stainers' Minutes*, II, p. 25 (Sept. 6th, 1653) and p. 171 (July 1st, 1674). *Buckeridge*, p. 356. *Walpole*, pp. 455 and 939. *D.N.B.*, XXI, 1890, pp. 55–6 (with *Bibl.*). *T.-B.*, XVIII, 1925, pp. 441–2 (with *Bibl.*). *Vertue, Index*, p. 86. *Waterhouse*, pp. 66 and 96.

1. THE LORDS GEORGE AND FRANCIS VILLIERS (?) AFTER VAN DYCK.
Both W.L. standing, Lord George to the front with head turned half-l., Lord Francis to the l., and looking over his l. shoulder. **Plate 129**

Red chalk; squared for transfer; 40 × 27·7 cm. (15¾ × 10⅞ in.).

INSCR.: *Recto*, at the foot, in a XVII c. hand, *J Baptist Jaspers*.

PROV.: Mrs. Campbell-Johnston, by whom it was presented to the B.M., 1888.
1888–12–21–5.

BIBL.: *Holmes, Villiers*.

[Lord George Villiers, 2nd Duke of Buckingham, whose father the 1st Duke was

murdered in 1628, was, together with his brother, brought up with the family of Charles I. He was to become the minister and notorious favourite of Charles II.]

Drawing for the mezzotint lettered *Lords John and Bernard Stuart* listed by Chaloner Smith (III, pp. 1379–80, No. 46) under the name of the publisher Richard Tompson. There seems to be little doubt that Gaspers was the actual engraver. The original oil-painting is in the N.G. (No. 3605). Sir Charles Holmes states the case for the re-identification of Van Dyck's subjects (*See* Bibl. above).

GASSELIN, FRANÇOIS (?)
Working c. 1683–1703
Topographical draughtsman

Of French origin. Christian name not known for certain. At Chatsworth (coll. Duke of Devonshire) is an album of drawings,

one of them being inscribed *par Gasselin*, which shows that their author was working in the environs of Paris between 1683 and

1692, and in London in 1693 (A view of *Ville Quinsington* (Kensington) dated *7 Oct 1693*). By the same hand is a view of the Old Manor House, Marylebone, in the Marylebone Public Library, inscribed *maribonne veut venant de Londre dè sinay a prest nature Je 1700—par Gasselin—*. Again by the same hand is a sheet of views of Windsor Castle, in the Royal Library, Windsor, which is dated *12–19 d'ous* (Août) *1703*. Nearly all the above are drawn in pen and brown ink with grey wash on narrow strips of paper and have inscriptions on them in this peculiarly spelt French. According to W. H. Manchée (*See* Bibl.) the Gasselin family were perhaps of Huguenot origin. *François Gasselin* appears in the Baptism Register of the French Church, Glasshouse St., as godfather to the son of Corneille François Gole on 16:vi:1701, and *François Gaslin* in that of St. Martin Orgars, as godfather to the son of Etienne Billon on 20:ix:1701. Sir Anthony Blunt suggests that the artist may be identical with a Noël Gasselin active in Paris in 1677.

BIBL.: *Manchée*, pp. 73 & 87. *Tabernacle, Glasshouse St. Registers*, p. 79. *St. Martin Orgars Register*, p. 3, No. 34. *Blunt, French Drawings*, p. 58, fig. 8, p. 59, No. 321.

DRAWINGS IN OTHER COLLECTIONS: *See* biography above. Also Mr. Iolo Williams and formerly Mr. J. E. Gardner, F.S.A.

1. PART OF ST. JAMES'S PALACE FROM THE S.E. View from the Great Yard leading from St. James's Park, looking towards the present Marlborough Chapel and the E. range of the Friary Court (not shown in correct perspective) on the l., with the turrets of St. James's Gate rising beyond it. On the extreme r., the wall of the garden of the former Friary which is seen in the background. **Plate 131**

Pen and brown ink with grey wash; 13.4×28.3 cm. ($5\frac{1}{4} \times 11\frac{1}{8}$ in.).

INSCR.: *Recto*, above various parts of the building, *St. jesme . . . la porte de St. jesme du Costé du pellemaille la Chapelle de St. jesme uéué du Costé du part* (parc), and below, on the l., *le Costé de St. jesme neue du Costé | du part*, and on the r., *. . . lantrée dan la Chapelle de St. | jesme du Costé dupart* (du parc).

PROV.: J. C. Crowle, by whom it was bequeathed to the B.M. in an extra-illustrated copy of the 1793 edn. of Pennant's *London*, 1811.

Crowle, Pennant, IV, No. 165.

BIBL. & REPR.: *Sheppard*, I, facing p. 6 and p. 9.

The above view is taken from a point inside what is now the garden of Marlborough House. The Chapel, designed by Inigo Jones, was built in 1623–27. Was stripped of its fittings during the Commonwealth and restored for Catherine of Braganza in 1662.

The apsidal end seen in the present drawing was removed probably about 1700, when Marlborough House was built. The Friary was established at the E. end of the Chapel, first with Capuchins in the time of Catherine of Braganza, and then with Benedictines who were expelled at the Revolution of 1688. Its site is occupied by part of Marlborough House. The E. range of the so-called Friary Court of the Palace, seen on the l. of the drawing, was destroyed by fire in 1809 and not rebuilt; the present Marlborough Rd. passes over the site (*See* Etched Plan of St. James's Palace in Crowle, *Pennant*, IV, No. 156; and *R.C.H.M., London, Monuments*, II, 1925, p. 118).

Another drawing by Gasselin, formerly in the collection of Mr. J. E. Gardner, showing the whole of the S. front of the Palace including that part seen in the present drawing, is reproduced by Canon Sheppard (*See* Bibl. & Repr.). It is characteristically inscribed, *le palast de St. jesme ueue du costé du jardin désinay a pres nature par Gasselin*.

2. MONTAGUE HOUSE FROM THE N.W. View from near the present Tottenham Court Road, looking over fields to Montague House in the distance, centre, with its tree-planted garden stretching out at the back. To the r., in mid-distance, the backs of the houses bordering on Great Russell Street.　　**Plate 132 (a)**

Pen and brown ink, touched with grey wash; 5·9 × 29·9 cm. (2⅜ × 11¾ in.); on an old mount bordered with brown wash; 10 × 33·6 cm. (4 × 13¼ in.).

INSCR.: *Recto*, at the top, *veuéé de montay gutant* (Montague House (?)) *du Costay qui re garde sur son jardin et sur la Coste ou est amesetet* (Hampstead) *et ayguet* (Highgate) *désynay a pres natures—*.

PROV.: Sir Henry Ellis, from whom it was purchased by the B.M., 1860.
1860–7–14–4.

The original Montague House was designed by Richard Hooke in 1678 for Ralph, 3rd Baron and subsequently 1st Duke of Montague. It was burnt in 1686, and was soon afterwards rebuilt by Pierre Puget. It is this second mansion which is seen in the above drawing. The British Museum was established in it in 1753, and it was eventually pulled down when the present building was erected in 1840–9. The fields at the back of Montague House were a favourite duelling-ground in the later XVII and earlier XVIII c.

3. LINCOLN'S INN GARDENS AND ST. PAUL'S FROM LINCOLN'S INN FIELDS. The gardens, consisting of closely planted trees, viewed from the other side of a low wall. In the distance, centre, the gable of the Hall (?) of Lincoln's Inn, and to the r., the dome of St. Paul's.　　**Plate 132 (b)**

Pen and brown ink, with grey wash; 9·3 × 37·5 cm. (3¾ × 14⅞ in.).

INSCR.: *Recto*, above the dome of St. Paul's, *ueue de St. paul*, and, at the foot, l., *le coin qui entre en oborne* [Holborn] *du jardin des a uoscat* [des avocats, *i.e.* the lawyers of Lincoln's Inn].

PROV.: Frederick Crace. John Gregory Crace, from whom it was purchased by the B.M., 1880.
1880–11–13–4376.

BIBL.: *Crace Cat.*, p. 534, Ptf. XXVIII, No. 41.

GERBIER, SIR BALTHAZAR

B. 1591/2: D. 1667 (possibly 1663)

Adventurer, diplomatist, architect and miniature painter

Born on Feb. 23rd, 1591/2, in Middelburg, the son of Anthony Gerbier, a Huguenot emigré. Claimed a certain 'Anthony Gerbier, Baron Douvilly' as his great-grandfather, and on occasion also styled himself 'Baron D'Ouvilly' or 'Doully'. Nothing known of upbringing but may have been a pupil of Hendrik Goltzius (B. 1558: D. 1617) of whom he wrote a eulogy *Eer ende Claght-Dicht: Ter Eeren . . . Henricus Goltius*, published in 1620. According to Sanderson 'had little of Art or merit; but was a common Pen-man'. Spent some time in Gascony with a brother. Knowledge of the 'framing of warlike machines' brought him to the notice of Prince Maurice of Orange who recommended him to Noel de Carron, Dutch Ambassador in London, with whom he came to England in 1616. Entered the service of the Duke of Buckingham who employed him in painting miniatures (for which he had a considerable reputation in his earlier years), 'contriving' houses and collecting works of art. In the Tanner Collection [Bodleian, MS. *Tanner*, 73, *ff.* 119–23] is in Gerbier's hand an undated list of selected pictures and statuary in a few private collections in Paris, some of which can be identified with some certainty with pictures known to be in Buckingham's collection in 1635. In the same collection is a letter written by Gerbier to the Duke in 1622 saying that he was awaiting a favourable ship for the despatch of his purchases and that 'they come both distended in their frames, for I durst not hazard them in rolls, the youngest being twenty-five years old, and therefore no longer supple and pliant'. In spite of this some of the pictures were sent in rolls wrapped in water-proofed cloth and packed in cases—notably the 'great peece of Titian' the *Ecce Homo*, now in Vienna, which was painted in 1543, and the Tintoretto of '*the woman in adulterie*' of about the same date. By 1648 most of the eleven pictures listed had been smuggled out of England and sold at Antwerp to support the second Duke in exile, and only the Titian and the Tintoretto can be identified with some certainty with existing pictures. Was given quarters in the Duke's residence, York House. In 1623 went with him and Prince Charles to Spain and painted a portrait of the Infanta which was sent to James I. In 1625 accompanied Buckingham to Paris where he met Rubens, with whom he afterwards became on intimate terms, corresponding with him on artistic and diplomatic matters and entertaining him on his visit to London in 1629. While on this visit Rubens painted a portrait group of the Gerbier family, now at Windsor. May have designed the York

Watergate, *c.* 1626 (also attributed to Inigo Jones and Webb, and claimed for Nicholas Stone by his great-nephew, Charles Stoakes), which was an adaptation of the *Fontaine de Medicis* in the Luxembourg gardens, completed shortly before his visit to Paris in 1625. Began his career as a secret agent when collecting pictures for Buckingham. After the Duke's murder in 1628, entered the service of the King. Planned a formal garden at Roehampton and saw to the casting of Le Sueur's equestrian statue of Charles I which was to stand in it. In 1631 appointed 'His Ma.ies Agent at Brussels', but in 1633 betrayed Charles's secret negotiations to the Infanta Isabella for 20,000 crowns. When Resident in Brussels corresponded with Weckerlin (Secretary to the Secretary of State) mainly about Gerbier's efforts to extract back pay from the Exchequer. Mention was, however, made of two portraits which he was sending for the King (Aug. 9th, 1636) —one of the Elector of Trèves by 'a good Master named Crayer' which Weckerlin noted in his Diary, 'his Majestie well liked' [*Turnbull Papers*, Reading. County Archives] and one of the Duke of Lorraine to which there is no further reference. In the same year (1636) Gerbier comments to Weckerlin that he had been offered '*le plus méchant libelle en peinture*' depicting Martin Luther dancing with a young nun accompanied by 'a gang of heresies'. Returned to England in Oct. 1638 to receive knighthood at Hampton Court. In 1639 negotiated with Jordaens for a series of canvases for the Queen's House at Greenwich. In 1641 was recalled from Brussels and appointed Master of the Ceremonies at the English Court. Took up the study of banking, and between 1641 and 1661 published a series of pamphlets on the theory of state-organized pawnbroking, but seems to have been unsuccessful in managing his own affairs, and, harassed by debts, left the country in 1643 to settle in Paris. Returned to England after the King's execution, and opened a short-lived academy at his house in

Bethnal Green, where such subjects were taught as philosophy, languages, mathematics, riding the 'great horse', dancing and fencing, some of the lectures being printed. At the sale of the Royal Collection bought a portrait of Charles I on horseback by Van Dyck and Titian's portrait of Charles V. In about 1651, with Lely and George Geldorp, put forward a proposal to decorate the palace of Whitehall with portraits and battlepieces illustrating the 'memorable achievements' of the Parliament, together with 'representations of the Council of State', destined for the Banqueting House. Went with his family to Holland in 1658, shortly afterwards sailing as commander of a Dutch colonial expedition to Guiana, but returning to Amsterdam in 1660. Returned to England at the Restoration and tried unsuccessfully to to regain royal favour, being suspended from his office of Master of Ceremonies at the end of 1660. Designed, however, the triumphal arches for Charles II's coronation in 1661, drawings for which are in the Burlington-Devonshire collection at the R.I.B.A. In 1662 began to rebuild the house at Hampstead Marshall for Lord Craven, in whose regiment his son, George, had served as a Captain; but died leaving Captain William Winde to finish the work. Published *A Brief Discourse Concerning the Three chief Principles of Magnificent Building* (1662) and *Counsel and Advise to All Builders* (1663). Usually said to have died in 1667 but in the *Calendar of State Papers* (Domestic) under the date, Aug. 24th, 1663, there is an appeal from his daughters *to the King for relief from the extremities of the starving condition in which they are left by their father's death, to whom £4,000 arrears were due from the late King*. The document itself is, however, undated and may have been misplaced, as a book by Gerbier appeared in 1665. Was buried in the church at Hampstead Marshall but no memorial was placed there for over 40 years. Edward Norgate in his treatise on miniature painting, *Miniatura* (1648–50) says: 'The best Crayons that ever I saw were those made by Sr Balthazer Gerbier after those soe celebrated Histories done by Raphaell of the banquets of the Gods, to be seene in the Pallazzo de Gigi in Longa Ara in Rome . . .' (Farnesina). As a miniaturist his style recalls that of Isaac Oliver; good examples of his work are in the Victoria and Albert Museum and the collection of the Queen of Holland. His portrait drawings, in fine pen and ink on vellum (*See* those described below), resemble the work of Hendrik Goltzius and Jan Wierix. Architectural and other drawings by him are in the Bodleian Library and the Pepys collection at Magdalene College.

BIBL.: *Sanderson*, p. 15. *Cheetham. Sainsbury, passim. B.N. Belgique*, VII, pp. 661–9. *D.N.B.*, XXI, 1890, p. 227. *De Boer*, pp. 129–60. *Baker, Lely*, II, p. 132. *Lugt, Le Portrait Miniature*, p. 15. *Norgate*, p. 74. *T.-B.*, XIII, 1920, p. 444. *Long*, pp. 168–9. *Croft-Murray, Rubens*, p. 90. *Vertue, Index*, p. 89. *Williamson, Stuart Portraits*, pp. 26–60. *Summerson*, pp. 85, 150, 337 (ch. 9, n. 6). *Philip. Inf.* from Prof. L. W. Forster.

1. FREDERICK V, ELECTOR PALATINE AND KING OF BOHEMIA, AFTER MIEREVELT. T.Q.L., standing, turned half-r., his l. hand resting on the pommel of his sword, his r. hand holding a baton. Wearing an embroidered doublet and trunk-hose, and, about his neck, a standing band and the medallion of the Lesser George suspended on a ribbon. On a table beside him, r., his helmet and gauntlet. Hanging drapery in the background. Within a feigned oval of scroll-work, hung with drapery and swags of fruit. **Plate 134**

Pen and brown ink, highly finished, on buff-toned vellum; $15 \times 12 \cdot 7$ cm. ($5\frac{7}{8} \times 5$ in.).

INSCR.: *Recto*, at the foot, r., by the artist, *Gerbier fc.*

Verso, in the lower l.-hand corner, *fr : v :-*, and *N1286.*

PROV.: Samuel Woodburn (Sale, Christie, 27:vi:1854, Lot 2383). Purchased by the B.M. at the Woodburn Sale, 1854.
1854–6–28–77 (L.B.1(b)).

BIBL.: *Long,* p. 169.

[Frederick V, Elector Palatine and King of Bohemia (B. 1596: D. 1632), son of the Elector Frederick IV whom he succeeded in 1610. Married Elizabeth, daughter of James I, in 1613 and was the father of Prince Rupert. Became head of the Protestant Evangelical Union, and in 1618, King of Bohemia, his action in accepting the crown marking the opening of the Thirty Years War. After losing both his kingdom and the Palatinate, died in comparative obscurity at Magdeburg.]

Gerbier's drawing is based on a portrait of Frederick by Mierevelt, of which two bust-length versions are known, one in the Mauritshuis at The Hague (No. 101), dated *Aetatis 16. / A⁰. 1613,* the other (in 1912) in the collection of Col. W. S. Noel of Stardens, Newent, Glos. There are two engravings connected with Mierevelt's portrait, one by Boëtius Bolswert dated *Aetat: 16 / 1613,* showing a three-quarter-length figure of Frederick, the other a bust-length, by L. Kilian. The present drawing comes nearest to Bolswert's engraving, though in the latter the r. hand is resting on a table (instead of holding a baton as in the drawing) and there is no helmet or gauntlet. The pattern of the embroidery on the costume in both the drawing and the two engravings is almost identical.

2. MAURICE, PRINCE OF ORANGE. The Prince in armour, with a pistol in his outstretched r. hand, mounted on his rearing charger, facing half-r. In the distance below, a battle, probably that of Nieuport, in progress. Within a small feigned oval medallion surrounded by scroll-work hung with swags of laurel and clusters of fruit. Below the medallion, a shield of arms surmounted by a crown and surrounded by the Order of the Garter. On a cartouche backed by a military trophy and surmounting another cartouche on which is the inscription beginning *Des plus preux . . . .* **Plate 133**

Pen and grey and brown ink, highly finished, on vellum; $16 \cdot 7 \times 10 \cdot 4$ cm. ($6\frac{5}{8} \times 4\frac{1}{8}$ in.).

INSCR.: *Recto,* on a ribbon at the top, *VIVE DE NASSOV / anno 1616;* round the medallion, *Maurice de Nasso*[u] *Princ*[e] *d'Orange etc:;* in a cartouche at the foot, *Des plus preux qui de Mars, on conduit les cohortes / Nassou, Nassou, Triomphe, invincible sans pair, / Il fait a son abort quitter Villes et portes / Et paroist en bataille, ainssi qu'un grand / esclair;* in the l.- and r.-hand lower corners, *B Ger*[b]*ier* (*B G* in monogram) *. . . fecit.*

PROV.: P. & D. Colnaghi, from whom it was purchased, 1862.
1862–2–8–3 (L.B.1(a)).

BIBL.: *Long,* p. 169.

[Maurice, Prince of Orange (B.1567: D. 1625), the second son of William the Silent, whose struggles against Spain he continued. Became Stadtholder in 1587 and was one of the foremost generals of his age. The arms beneath the drawing correspond with those he bore except in the third Grand-quarter, but the deviation may be attributed to inaccuracy. He was invested with the Order of the Garter on Feb. 4th, 1612/3.]

The date on the drawing, 1616, is that of the year in which Gerbier first came to England under the auspices of Prince Maurice who would have been 49 at the time. The drawing is closely connected with an equestrian portrait of Prince Maurice, engraved by E. de Paendre, which in its turn is based on another and younger portrait of him, engraved by Crispin van de Passe I, dated 1600, representing him at the Battle of Nieuport. The two engravings show the Prince holding a marshal's baton in his outstretched r. hand, instead of the less conventional pistol which appears in the drawing.

In the collection of the Queen of Holland is an oval miniature portrait of Prince Maurice, bust length in colours on vellum, by Gerbier (See G. C. Williamson, *History of Portrait Miniatures*, 1904, I, p. 36, Pl. XIX).

GIBBONS, GRINLING

B. 1648: D. 1721

Sculptor and wood-carver

Born on April 4th, 1648, in Rotterdam where his father, James Gibbons, was on business. Both his father and grandfather were Londoners, his great-grandfather having been a husbandman in the neighbourhood of Daventry. Nothing known of his upbringing, but may have spent his childhood in Holland, this perhaps justifying the belief that he was a Dutchman, as his father did not leave Rotterdam until after 1659. Having taken a small house in Deptford in which to work without interruption, was discovered there, while carving a copy of Tintoretto's *Crucifixion*, by John Evelyn, the diarist, on Jan. 18th, 1671, and by him was brought to the notice of the King and the nobility. Admitted freeman of the Drapers' Company by patrimony in 1672, subsequently taking up his livery in 1684 and holding several offices between 1704 and 1715. Married a certain Elizabeth (surname not known) and was the father of nine or ten children, five of whose births were registered at St. Paul's, Covent Garden, between 1678 and 1683. Appointed Master Carver to the Crown (1693) after Henry Phillips, the royal patronage being continued by James II, for whom Gibbons furnished the Catholic Chapel at Whitehall with a reredos and four figures of saints (or allegories) in white marble, which were praised by Evelyn. In addition to royal commissions for Windsor Castle, Kensington Palace, Hampton Court and St. James's Palace, worked for colleges in both universities, Christ's Hospital and many private houses. So great was the demand for his productions that he employed several assistants including John Seldon (D. 1715), Samuel Watson (D. 1715) and Arnold Quellin (B. 1653: D. 1686). A list of buildings containing woodwork executed by or under him includes Cassiobury, Petworth, Dalkeith Palace, Sudbury (Derbyshire), Trinity College (Oxford), Trinity College (Cambridge), St. Paul's Cathedral, Canterbury Cathedral and St. James's Church, Piccadilly. Among his sculptures in stone are the figures on the roof of Blenheim Palace, the Beaufoy and Churchill monuments in Westminster Abbey, the Chandos monument at St. Lawrence's, Whitechurch, the monument to G. Pole and his wife at Radbourne, Derbyshire, and the font at St. James's, Piccadilly. Died on August 3rd, 1721, and was buried a week later in St. Paul's, Covent Garden. Although best known today as a carver in wood, was also renowned in his own time as a sculptor in stone. Influenced by the Italian Baroque, elements in the Whitehall altarpiece having affinities with Bernini's Chapel of the Holy Sacrament in St. Peter's.

BIBL.: *D.N.B.*, XXI, 1890, pp. 259–61 (with *Bibl.*). Tipping. *T.-B.*, XIII, 1920, pp. 593–4 (with *Bibl.*). *Wren Soc., Index*, pp. 77–8. Osborne and Fisher. Vertue, *Index*, p. 90.

DRAWINGS IN OTHER COLLECTIONS: Westminster Public Library (design for the Churchill Monument). Society of Antiquaries (design for wall tablet, Clifton-on-Teme). Soane Museum (several drawings of chimney pieces reproduced in *Wren Soc.*, IV.

1. DESIGN FOR A MONUMENT FOR KING WILLIAM III AND QUEEN MARY II. A Baroque structure in the form of a triumphal arch under which the King and Queen stand on a pedestal behind a sarcophagus with two crowns, two sceptres and an orb on it. On either side and in front of the sarcophagus, female mourners, one of whom leans on a shield bearing the cross of St. George. The arch supported by four pairs of Corinthian columns in front of which stand figures symbolizing Hope, Justice, Truth and Charity. The entablature decorated on the front with stars of the Garter and relief panels of St. George and the dragon, and topped with trophies of arms, a lion and a unicorn. The centre of the arch covered by a canopy, the curtains of which are parted by angels blowing trumpets to disclose *putti* flying in clouds and carrying a celestial crown, a wreath, a palm and other symbols.

Plate 137

Pen and brown ink, with washes of grey, yellow and pink; 41·9 × 31·2 cm. (16½ × 12¼ in.).

PROV.: Richard Bull (Sale, Sotheby, 23:v:1881, Lot 72). Purchased by the B.M. at the Bull Sale.

1881–6–11–164 (L.B.2, as by William Kent).

BIBL.: *Wren Soc.*, V, p. 13.

This is clearly by the same hand as the design for a monument to Queen Mary II (All Souls, repr. *Wren Soc.*, V, frontispiece) and a number of chimney-pieces for Hampton Court (*Wren Soc.*, IV, Pls. XXVII–XLII) attributed to Grinling Gibbons. There is a small sketch of the drawing in an architect's notebook, in the Bodleian, which belonged to one of his assistants, possibly William Dickenson, who worked at Westminster Abbey under Wren's authority. A plan in the same note-book shows that the monument would have occupied the whole of the East end of the South aisle of Henry VII's Chapel.

2. STUDIES FOR A STATUE, PROBABLY FOR THAT OF EITHER CHARLES II, AT THE ROYAL HOSPITAL, CHELSEA, OR JAMES II NEAR THE NEW ADMIRALTY BUILDING. Two W.L. standing figures, crowned with laurel and wearing ancient Roman dress, a baton in the r. hand. That on the l., with r. hand extended holding the baton slightly downwards, l. hand resting on the hilt of a sword, and legs apart, the r. foot pointing outwards. That on the r., an alternative treatment, with r. hand holding the baton slightly to the rear, and l. hand extended, with fingers apart.

Plate 136

Pen and light brown wash; $11 \cdot 8 \times 15 \cdot 5$ cm. ($4\frac{5}{8} \times 6\frac{1}{8}$ in.).

INSCR.: *Recto*, in the lower r.-hand corner *GG* (probably not a signature).

PROV.: Robert Jackson, from whom it was purchased by the B.M., 1889.
1889-6-3-254 (1) (L.B.1).

BIBL.: *Peck*, II, p. 554. *Faulkner, Chelsea*, p. 58. *Bramston*, p. 253. *Walpole*, pp. 551–7. *D.N.B.*, XXI, 1890, p. 260. *Vertue*, I, 61, V, 58–9.

The attribution of this drawing to Grinling Gibbons does not seem unreasonable, in view of its apparent connexion with either the statue of Charles II in the main courtyard of the Royal Hospital, Chelsea, or with that of James II, formerly at Whitehall, and removed to its present site in 1948, outside the National Gallery fronting Trafalgar Square. Unfortunately the only other recorded drawing attributed to the sculptor (*See* above) has now disappeared, so it has been impossible to make any comparisons of style between it and the present one.

An attempt is here made to set forth the information about the two statues contained in the above bibliography. According to Peck, both were commissioned and set up at the expense of Tobias Rustat (B. 1606 (?): D. 1694), the Stuart supporter and benefactor of the universities of Oxford and Cambridge. Jointly they are said to have cost Rustat the sum of £1000.

There seems to be no doubt that the James II was designed by Grinling Gibbons. Bramston writes: 'On New Yeares Day [of 1686/7] a statue in brass was to be seen (placed the day before) [*i.e.* Dec. 31st, 1686] in the yard at Whitehall, made by Gibbons, at the charge of Toby Rustick, of the present King, James the 2d'. Vertue also notes having seen 'An Agreement made Signd & Seald—for a Statue. of King James

the Second to be made by M^r. Grinling Gibbons—for the sum of three hundred pounds. one half of the money to be paid down at the agreement, and 50 pounds more at the end of three months and the other hundred pounds to be paid when the Statue shall be compleatly finished—and set up— at bottom is the receit signed *Grinling Gibbons*. for the first payment 150 pounds and below. August 11. 1687. for the other fifty pounds paid to him by Tobias Rostat Esqr (Q^u the Statue in Chelsy Coll is said to be erected by Tob Rostat) . . . Q^u if this be for . . . . statue erected at his charge. because the top of this agreement where it was specified was torn off—.' Walpole, no doubt on the strength of this document, attributes, in his main text, the James II to Gibbons, though in a footnote he suggests that Vertue may have incorrectly read 'James II' for 'Charles II', probably in view of Vertue's confusing addition to his transcript, quoted above, which mentions the Charles II at Chelsea. Elsewhere Vertue records that 'The Statue of Brass, standing in Privy Garden against the banqueting house whitehall, of King James, the 2nd. was modelld & made by . . . Laurence (of Brussels) . . . & Devoot (of Mechlin) who was imployed by . . . Gibbons, carver to the King these men are still Living at Antwerp'. The names of Gibbons's assistants should properly be rendered as Dievoet and Laurens.

The Charles II at Chelsea seems to have been attributed in the past with less confidence to Gibbons. Vertue and Walpole, following him, both mention it in connexion with the James II, without, however, assigning it definitely to Gibbons, but Faulkner clearly does not consider it to be by him. More recent authorities, on the other hand, including Sir Lionel Cust, have accepted it as his work.

The dating of the two statues raises certain problems. Bramston states that the James II was erected on Dec. 31st, 1686. This, however, is contradicted by the agreement recorded by Vertue and quoted above, which refers to payments of £50 having been made on Aug. 11th, 1687, after the first three months of work on the statue. Thus there is a discrepancy of dates, and it seems likely that either Bramston's memory played him false, by recalling the erection of the statue as having been in 1686 rather than 1687, or that *Vertue* mis-transcribed the date 1687 for 1686 in the document.

According to Faulkner, the Charles II was erected at the same time as the James II. The earlier evidence of Peck, however, suggests rather that they were executed at different dates, as each statue appears to have been an individual present from Rustat to the monarch whom it commemorated.

The two statues are certainly near in style, and are to some extent complementary to one another. They are conveniently repro- duced side by side in the volume of the *Royal Commission on Historical Monuments* (II, 1925, Pl. 227). When compared with this repro- duction, it will be seen that the present drawing has something in common with both statues. The l.-hand figure of the drawing approximates to the Charles II, being girded with a sword on the l. side, standing with legs apart, the r. foot pointing outwards; the head looking over the r. shoulder and the outstretched r. hand holding the baton slightly downwards are, however, rather characteristic of the James II. The r.-hand figure somewhat resembles the James II in the position of the feet and in the absence of a sword, but its other features —the head looking to front, the r. hand holding the baton to the rear, and the l. hand extended—are common to neither statue.

3. STUDY FOR A STATUE, PROBABLY OF CHARLES II OR JAMES II.
W.L. standing figure, crowned with laurel and wearing ancient Roman dress, a baton in the r. hand, an orb supported by the r. elbow which is resting upon a plinth. The feet bare and slightly apart. **Plate 135**

Pen and light brown wash; cut off at the corners and torn across the middle; 11·3 × 5·8 cm. ($4\frac{3}{8} \times 2\frac{1}{4}$ in.).

PROV.: As for No. 2.
1889–6–3–254 (2).

See note to No. 2 with which it appears to be connected.

4. STUDY FOR A STATUE, PROBABLY OF CHARLES II OR JAMES II.
W.L. standing figure, crowned with laurel and wearing ancient Roman dress, a baton in the r. hand, an orb supported by the r. arm which is bent towards the chest. The feet slightly apart with the weight on the l. leg. **Plate 135**

Pen and light brown wash; cut off at the corners and torn across the middle; 11·2 × 5·7 cm. ($4\frac{3}{8} \times 2\frac{1}{4}$ in.).

PROV.: As for No. 2.
1889–6–3–254 (3).

See note to No. 2.

5. STUDY FOR A STATUE, PROBABLY OF CHARLES II OR JAMES II.
W.L. standing figure, crowned with laurel and wearing ancient Roman dress. The r. hand holding a baton pointed to the front, the r. arm supporting an orb and the l. hand on the hip. The feet slightly apart with the weight on the l. leg. **Plate 136**

Pen and light brown wash; cut off at the corners, and torn across the middle; $11 \times 5 \cdot 7$ cm. ($4\frac{1}{4} \times 2\frac{1}{4}$ in.).

PROV.: As for No. 2.
1889–6–3–254 (4).

See note to No. 2.

6. STUDY FOR A STATUE, PROBABLY OF CHARLES II OR JAMES II.

Fragment, upper part of W.L. standing figure, crowned with laurel and wearing ancient Roman dress, the r. hand holding a baton pointing outwards and downwards, the r. arm which supports an orb bent in to the middle.

Pen and light brown wash; the top corners cut off; $6 \cdot 2 \times 5 \cdot 7$ cm. ($2\frac{1}{2} \times 2\frac{1}{4}$ in.).

PROV.: As for No. 2.
1889–6–3–254 (5).

See note to No. 2.

GIBSON, RICHARD

B. 1615: D. 1690

Limner and portrait draughtsman in crayons

According to Long, was born perhaps in Cumberland. Grew only to 3 ft. 10 in. in height and was known as 'The Dwarf'. Became page to a lady living at Mortlake, who, noticing his talent for drawing, placed him with Francis Cleyn (q.v.) then designing for the tapestry works there. Vertue mentions having seen a small double portrait of Gibson and Cleyn 'both dresd in green habits, like Archers, with bowes & arrows', Gibson himself being 'a great Archer'. Later appointed a page at the court of Charles I, where he was a contemporary of another famous dwarf, Jeffrey Hudson, who was an inch shorter than Gibson. Achieved a considerable reputation as a limner, his most esteemed work being a copy of a head of Henrietta Maria after Van Dyck. The temporary disappearance of his limning of the parable of the Lost Sheep, a favourite piece in Charles I's collection, resulted in the suicide of the then keeper, Abraham van de Dort, in 1640. Shortly before the Civil War was married, in the presence of Charles and Henrietta Maria, to the Queen's dwarf,

Anne Shepherd, the nuptials being celebrated by Waller in his verses 'Design or chance makes others wive'. Was patronized also by Philip, 4th Earl of Pembroke, a double portrait of Gibson and his wife remaining in the Pembroke collection till about 1712, and Mrs. Gibson also appearing in Van Dyck's portrait of Mary Villiers, Lady Herbert (later Duchess of Richmond), in the Double Cube Room at Wilton. Must have been painted too about this time by Dobson. Remained in England during the Commonwealth, when (according to Buckeridge) he 'drew Oliver Cromwell several times', and when he himself was painted, leaning on a bust, by Lely in 1658 (perhaps the portrait mentioned by the Rev. Richard Warner as at Bowood in 1801). Probably took up drawing in crayons under Lely's influence, and like John Greenhill (q.v.), another member of the school, when working in that medium, imitated in his own signature the style of Lely's monogram and dating. His former patronage by the Protector did not apparently affect his position in Court circles after the

336

Restoration. Sir John Denham in his *Third Advice to a Painter*, published in 1667, p. 17, thus addresses him:

'Thow *Gibson*, that amongst the Navy small,
Of Marshal'd Shells, Commandst Admiral;
Thy self so slender, that thow shew'st no more
Than Barnicle new hatch't of them before:
Come mix thy water-Colours, and express,
Drawing in Little, how wee Do in less.'

Recorded by Charles Beale as having visited Mary Beale's studio on April 20th, 1672, in company with Lely. In the following year signed a miniature, *R Gibson fecit 1673*, now in the Palazzo Pitti, Florence. Taught Princess, later Queen, Anne. In his Will, drawn up as early as Nov. 11th, 1677, describes himself then as of the Parish of St. Martin-in-the-Fields, as owning two houses in Petty France, Westminster, and as still being in receipt of an annuity from the Earl of Pembroke. In 1677 was also invited to Holland to teach Princess Mary of Orange, later Queen Mary II. Lived at the Hague, and remained there perhaps till 1688. According to a memorandum appended by members of his family to his Will, died at about 10 o'clock on July 20th, 1690. Was buried on July 23rd at St. Paul's, Covent Garden, 'in yᵉ Church'. The following relatives mentioned in his Will: his wife Ann; his three daughters, Susan Penelope (Mrs. Rosse or Rose), Ann (later Mrs. Vrybergen), and Elisabeth; his brother and sister-in-law, Edward and Margaret Gibson; and his son-in-law, Michael Rosse or Rose (a jeweller). There is also a bequest to his 'worthy friend Mr. William Towers' (not identified) of his 'litle Birding Gun made by Harman Barne' (Prince Rupert's gunsmith). Owned a number of drawings by Polidoro da Caravaggio, formerly in the Arundel collection, which, though not mentioned in his Will, are known to have passed to his widow. One of these, touched up by Rubens, was acquired from her by the elder Richardson, and is now in the Ashmolean Museum. Mrs. Gibson is usually said to have died in 1709, but the record of the burial at St. Paul's, Covent Garden, of 'Ann Gibson Widʷ' on Dec. 21st, 1707, probably corrects this. All their children apparently of normal size. One daughter, Susan Penelope Rosse, known to have been a miniaturist. Other members of the family also followed artistic careers: Dirck Gibson, a sculptor at the Hague, and Edward Gibson, a portraitist in oil and crayons (both thought to have been the Dwarf's sons), and William Gibson, a miniaturist and collector of drawings (known to have been his nephew).

BIBL.: *Sanderson*, pp. 14 & 20. *Will, P.C.C. (Dyke), f. 22. Buckeridge*, p. 377. *D.N.B.*, XXI, 1890, p. 283 (with *Bibl.*). *St. Paul's, Covent Garden, Registers*, IV, pp. 130, 206. *T.-B.*, XIII, 1920, p. 602 (with *Bibl.*). *Long*, p. 171 (with *Bibl.*). *Vertue, Index*, p. 91. *Woodward*, pp. 36–7.

1. SELF-PORTRAIT. Head half-l. Wearing long curling hair and falling bands.

Plate 139

Red and black chalks, heightened with white, on buff paper; 22·5 × 17·8 cm. (8⅞ × 7 in.).

PROV.: Richard Bull (Sale, Sotheby, 23:v:1881, Lot 55). Purchased by the B.M. at the Bull Sale, through A.W. Thibaudeau, 1881.

1881–6–11–157 (L.B.1).

BIBL.: *Long*, p. 172.

2. A LITTLE GIRL. H.L., with body half-r. and eyes to front, standing or sitting at table covered with a brown cloth, on which she holds in her r. hand a doll, and in her l. a pack of playing-cards. Wearing a white coif over her fair hair, a red coral necklace, and a white collar and cuffs over a blue-green dress. Dark grey background.

Crayons; with stain marks at r., l. and lower border; $25 \times 19 \cdot 8$ cm. ($9\frac{7}{8} \times 7\frac{3}{4}$ in.).

Prov.: P. & D. Colnaghi, from whom it was purchased by the B.M., 1900.
1900–7–17–40.

BIBL. & REPR.: *Roberts*, pp. 316–17. *Foster, Cooper, Supplement*, p. 130. *Long*, p. 172.

3. A LITTLE GIRL. H.L., seated, with body half-l. and eyes to front. Holding in her lap a small basket of flowers. Wearing a white cap with rosettes at the ears, a pearl necklace, and a black dress with leading strings, a white stomacher, apron and sleeves. The background shaded in black round the lower part of the figure.

Plate 140

Black chalk and crayons on buff paper; with stain marks at r., l. and lower borders; $25 \cdot 1 \times 19 \cdot 8$ cm. ($9\frac{7}{8} \times 7\frac{3}{4}$ in.).

INSCR.: *Recto*, on the l., by the artist, *R G 1669.*

PROV.: As for No. 2.
1900–7–17–41.

BIBL. & REPR.: *Roberts*, pp. 316–17. *Foster, Cooper*, p. 54, Pl. LXIII. *Foster, Cooper, Supplement*, p. 120. *Long*, p. 172.

GREENHILL, JOHN

B. 1640–5: D. 1676

Portrait painter and draughtsman

Born at Salisbury, according to Sir Richard Colt Hoare, in 1645, but perhaps earlier than this date. Was the eldest son of John Greenhill, merchant and later registrar of the diocese of Salisbury, and of Penelope, daughter of Richard Champneys of Orchard Leigh, Somerset. The Greenhills were substantial yeomen from Steeple Ashton, Wilts., where their name first appears in the parish registers in 1561. Nothing known of his early training, but among his first essays in painting is the portrait of his great-uncle, James Abbott of Salisbury (B. 1584). By 1662 had moved to London and had presumably entered Lely's studio by Oct. 7th of that year, when he wrote to his family from an address in the Piazza, Covent Garden.

According to Vertue, lodged with Lely for a number of years and was no doubt employed as an assistant. His earliest known signed portrait, *Mother and Child*, dated 1665, probably of the same period as the *Mrs. Cartwright* (the actor's first wife) and other portraits at Dulwich. Made copies of Van Dyck's portraits, Vertue noting one in crayons at Wroxton. According to Buckeridge, obtained the jealously preserved secret of Lely's methods by observing him at work on Mrs. Greenhill's (the artist's wife's) portrait, for which he gave his master 'twelve broad pieces'. Seems to have set up on his own account as a portrait painter, probably about 1667, and to have achieved immediate recognition. Before his early death counted among his sitters: Charles II; James, Duke of York; John Locke; Anthony Ashley, 1st Earl of Shaftesbury as Lord Chancellor (1672); Sir William Davenant; Abraham Cowley; Simon, 5th Viscount Fanshawe; Seth Ward, Bishop of Salisbury (commissioned by the Corporation of Sarum on Oct. 30th, 1673), and Admiral Sir Edward Spragge. May also have painted landscapes, for according to Warner there was in 1801 at Hagley Hall, Worcs., a 'view on the River Charwell, by Greenhill', but the picture cannot now be identified. At one time lodged with Davenport, one of the followers of Lely (who made a copy of the latter's portrait of Mrs. Greenhill) and also with Parry Walton (D. c. 1700), painter and restorer of the King's pictures, in Lincoln's Inn Fields. Knew the Westphalian artist Gerard Soest (D. 1681) whose portraits Greenhill's early work somewhat resembles, and whom he is said to have introduced to a painter called 'Wildt', presumably a German. Associated with theatrical and literary circles and painted or drew crayon portraits of William Cartwright's two wives (Dulwich), Thomas Betterton as Bajazet (1663; Kingston Lacy), Joseph Harris as Cardinal Wolseley (1664; Magdalen College, Oxford). Mrs. Aphra Behn published a fulsome elegy on his death, and John Wilmot, Earl of Rochester, also commemorated him in a poem. According to Buckeridge was 'poetically inclined and very agreeable in conversation'. Fell into 'a debauched course of life', the result, it is said, of his association with stage players, and died at Parry Walton's house from a fall when drunk in Long Acre, after visiting the Vine Tavern. Charles Beale the elder noted that Greenhill died on May 19th, 1676. Apparently left no Will. Was buried at St. Giles-in-the-Fields, his wife, whose name has not been recorded, and several children, surviving him. She evi-

dently lived in poverty, as Lely allowed her a pension of £40 a year, but she 'grew crasy and died mad' not long afterwards. A John Greenhill, presumably a son, recorded as having been buried at St. Giles-in-the-Fields on Jan. 18th, 1697.

As a draughtsman Greenhill can be studied in his single etching, the portrait of his younger brother, Henry Greenhill, dated 1667, which owes much technically to Van Dyck's *Iconography*, and in the few crayon drawings known to be by him. The *Portrait of a Lady* at Oxford, is said, from a later inscription on the drawing, to be Catherine, Countess of Pembroke (which is unlikely). There is also a reference in a MS. catalogue of pictures at Hinton House, Somerset, to a portrait in crayons by Greenhill of Philip Herbert, 5th Earl of Pembroke, and his second wife, Catherine (probably after Van Dyck). Vertue quotes Thomas Gibson's opinion of Greenhill's crayon portraits as 'done . . . with great skill and perfection equal to any Master whatever'. They are very close in style to Lely as a comparison of the self-portrait (*See* No. 1 below) with his master's portrait of the artist (also in the B.M.) shows. His signed works either bear his name in full or the initials J.G., sometimes in monogram, in the manner of Lely. Many of his drawings passed into the possession of a relative, Mr. Blow. Unlikely that he worked in miniature though J. L. Propert claimed to have owned miniatures by Greenhill of Charles II and Catherine of Braganza.

BIBL.: *Hinton Portraits*, pp. 174 & 178. *Buckeridge* (1706), pp. 378–81. *Warner, N. England*, I, p. 86. *Hoare*, I, p. 247 and VI, p. 629. *T.-B.*, XIV, 1921, p. 571 (with *Bibl.*). *Waterhouse, Greenhill. B.F.A.C.*, 1938, p. 13, No. 12 and pp. 34–5, Nos. 72 & 73. *Vertue, Index*, p. 95. *Woodward, passim. Waterhouse*, pp. 74–5 and p. 243.

1. **SELF-PORTRAIT.** Bust turned half-l., with eyes looking to front. Wearing long curling hair and drapery over his shoulders. **Plate 141**

Black and red chalks, heightened with white, on buff paper; 23·9 × 19·4 cm. (9⅜ × 7⅝ in.).

INSCR.: *Recto*, on the l., in black chalk, by the artist, *JG* (monogram).

PROV.: W. B. Tiffin, from whom it was purchased by the B.M., 1886.

1886–11–23–1.

2. A LADY. Bust nearly H.L., lower portion lightly indicated. Head turned half-l., eyes lowered and facing front. Wearing pearl earrings, hair in ringlets and with a headdress lightly indicated.   **Plate 142**

Crayons on buff paper; 27·8 × 18·5 cm. (10⅞ × 7¼ in.).

PROV.: Campbell Dodgson, by whom it was bequeathed to the B.M., 1949.

1949–4–11–27.

GRIFFIER, JAN I

[OLD GRIFFIER]

B. *c.* 1646 or 1652: D. 1718

Topographical and history painter, draughtsman and etcher

Born at Amsterdam probably about 1646, this date being suggested by Walpole who states that he was 72 when he died in 1718. The *Album Studiosorum* of the Leyden Academy, dated July 14th, 1700, however, records a 'Joannes Griffier, Amstelo-Batavus, Picturam docens', aged 48, which, if it refers to the present artist, would make his date of birth 1652. Was apprenticed successively to a carpenter, a tile painter, a flower painter and to Roeland Roghman (B. *c.* 1620: D. 1686), the landscape painter and etcher. According to Deschamps and Walpole, also received tuition and advice from Roghman's circle of acquaintances including Adriaen van de Velde, Ruisdael and Rembrandt. After working in Rotterdam, came to England and settled in London soon after the Fire of which he painted a number of pictures. Was patronized by the 1st Duke of Beaufort. While in London, studied under his fellow-countryman, the landscapist, Jan Looten (B. 1618: D. *c.* 1681) and 'made great improvement became a more pleasant Painter then his Master'. Drew landscapes on the Thames from a yacht which he sailed between Wind-

sor and Gravesend. Was admitted a 'free-brother' of the Painter-Stainers' Company on Dec. 4th, 1677, and painted a landscape with ruins for their Hall. Married in England and, in 1695, returned to Holland with his family on his yacht which was wrecked off the Dutch coast. Spent the next ten or twelve years in Rotterdam, Enhuisen, Hoorn and Amsterdam. No doubt at the time learnt to imitate a number of older masters such as Elsheimer, Cornelius van Poelenburgh and Philips Wouwerman who contributed to form his later eclectic style. Returned to London and bought a house in Millbank where 'he liv'd somewhat retired towards his latter end'. Two of his sons, Jan II ('Young Griffier'; D. 1750) and Robert (B. 1688: D. *c.* 1760), were artists, the latter imitating his father's manner and according to Deschamps being the author of views on the Rhine usually attributed to Jan I.

As a draughtsman shows the influence of the Ruisdaels, and also has affinities with Andries Both (B. *c.* 1609: D. *c.* 1640) and Claes Pieter Berchem (B. 1620: D. 1683).

340

Was an accomplished etcher and executed five large etched plates of birds after Barlow (*q.v.*) published by E. Cooper as well as other unsigned smaller plates after the same artist. Also practised as a mezzotinter, engraving ten portraits after Lely, Kneller, Le Brun and others and another of a seated woman, published by Joseph Lloyd.

BIBL.: *Deschamps*, III, pp. 352–6. *Walpole* (1786), pp. 83–6. *D.N.B.*, XXIII, 1890, pp. 224–5. *T.-B.*, XV, 1922, pp. 26–7 (with *Bibl.*). *Vertue*, *Index*, p. 96.

DRAWINGS IN OTHER COLLECTIONS: Royal Library, Windsor. Viscount Radley.

1. STUDY OF WILLOWS ON THE BANKS OF A RIVER. View across a small river. In the foreground, at the water's edge, a fallen tree-trunk, centre, and r., the broken stump of a willow. On the far bank, two clumps of willows, between which a path winds upwards to a distant village with a church tower. **Plate 143**

Black chalk, heightened with white, on blue-grey paper; 39 × 57·5 cm. (15⅜ × 22⅝ in.).

PROV.: Messrs. Goupil, from whom it was purchased by the B.M., 1878. 1878–7–13–17 (L.B.1).

2. LANDSCAPE WITH TRAVELLERS. View from a stretch of undulating ground, through which, r., winds a road with travellers, some on foot, some on horseback, on it. To the l., wooded cliffs rising beyond a group of trees, and in the distance, r., low hills.

Black chalk, strengthened with brown wash, on blue-grey paper; 39·2 × 49·4 cm. (15⅜ × 19⅜ in.).

PROV.: John, Lord Northwick (Sale, Sotheby, 2:xi:1920, Lot 159). P. & D.

Colnaghi, from whom it was purchased by the B.M., 1920. 1920–11–16–35.

In style this drawing recalls some of the work of Herman Saftleven, who is said to have influenced both Jan and Robert Griffier.

3. STUDY OF A TURKEY-COCK. Standing in profile to r. **Plate 144**

Red and black chalks; 16·5 × 18·8 cm. (6½ × 7⅜ in.). Old mount; 20·5 × 22·5 cm. (8 × 8⅞ in.).

INSCR.: *Recto*, in the lower margin of the old mount, *griffr* (?).

PROV.: Freiherr Carl Rolas de Rosey (Lugt, No. 2237, Sale, Leipzig, Weigel, 5:ix:1864, Lot 4545). Miss Adeline Rowen, from whom it was purchased by the B.M., 1928. 1928–10–16–6.

GYLES, HENRY

B. 1645: D. 1709

Glass-painter

Born in Micklegate in the City of York, fifth child of Edmund (B. 1611: D. 1676) and grandson of Nicolas Gyles (B. 1551), bot glass-painters. Thus inherited an unbroke

341

tradition in his craft reaching back through his grandfather's contemporaries, the Thompson family, to late medieval times. In 1668, was working for his father (with whom he seems to have had serious differences) in York. Obtained only meagre patronage, chiefly for armorial work, since hostility to the pictorial representation of religious themes still persisted. Was fortunate in being able to observe outstanding examples of his craft left intact in the windows of York Minster and other churches of the city. Experimented in the manufacture of vitreous enamels which he used on the surface of his glass since supplies of coloured glass from Lorraine had ceased and Doctor Place, cousin of Francis Place (q.v.), had failed to discover satisfactory sources in Italy. Made sufficient coloured glass for use in the East window (now removed) of University College, Oxford (1682–92). Other important commissions were: an armorial window (1679) in the Merchant Taylors' Hall, York; the west window of the Guildhall, York (1682; destroyed 1942); a King David and St. Cecilia (1702) in the Fairfax Chapel at Denton-in-Wharfedale, Yorks; and an arms of Queen Anne (1704) for Trinity College Library, Cambridge. His work, found for the most part in the churches and houses of York and its vicinity, enjoyed a considerable reputation among his contemporaries (Thoresby considered the Denton window 'the noblest painted glass in the north of England') but compares unfavourably with that of his immediate predecessors, the Van Lings or of the next generation of glass-painters, William and Joshua Price. Gyles's importance rests rather in his preservation of a dying craft.

Belonged to the circle of York *virtuosi* which used to meet at his house in Micklegate, and was a close friend of the amateur artists, William Lodge (q.v.) and Francis Place (q.v.), the decorative painter Jacques Parmentier and the antiquary and historian Ralph Thoresby, advising the last on acquisitions for his collection in Leeds and presenting him with a piece of ancient stained glass from York Minster for his collection. Apparently also interested in the technique of miniature painting as he possessed a manuscript (B.M., Harl. MS. 6376), entitled the *Art of Limning*, a copy of Edward Norgate's *Miniatura*. A note on the fly-leaf reads *Henry Gyles Booke. Lent to S*^r *John Middleton. Jun. y*^e *7th 1702.* Gyles's interest in antiquarian subjects shown by a drawing of Stonehenge, once in Thoresby's collection and later in that of Mr. Paul Oppé. Was a collector of prints probably using them as models for his designs for glass-painting, *e.g.* the cherub on the sundial at Nun Appleton Hall (1670), after Titian. Complained in letters to Thoresby that he had received no payment up to that time for work done both at Oxford and Cambridge and seems after 1700 to have suffered extreme poverty. Died in 1709, leaving the residue of his estate to his wife Hannah Gyles and daughter, Rebecca. Was buried on Oct. 25th at the church of St. Martin-cum-Gregory, York. In his Will of July 3rd of that year, described himself as a glass-painter, this being the earliest recorded use of that term in connexion with the craft at York. Mr. Townley, a close friend of Gyles, wrote to Thoresby of his having died 'without leaving any behind him to transmit to posterity that art'.

The few surviving drawings attributed to Gyles are of unequal quality, the crayon portrait of himself (if actually by him, *see* No. 1 below) being much superior to the wash drawings for window designs now preserved at the City Art Gallery, York.

BIBL.: D.N.B., XXIII, 1890, p. 410 (with *Bibl.*). T.-B., XIV, 1921, p. 30 (with *Bibl.*). *Knowles, Gyles. Knowles, Sundials. Vertue, Index*, p. 91.

1. SELF-PORTRAIT. Bust, turned half-l., with eyes looking to front and long curling brown hair. The shoulders draped in a cloak, lightly indicated. Brown-grey background to the head. **Plate 138**

Red and black chalks strengthened with water-colours, on buff paper; 31·3 × 22·7 cm. (12¼ × 8⅞ in.).

INSCR.: *Recto*, by Ralph Thoresby, *yᵉ effigies of Mʳ Hen: Gyles the celebrated Glass-Painter at Yorke.*

PROV.: Thoresby. George Vertue (cannot be identified with any particular lot in his sales, Ford's, 16:iii & 17:v:1757). Horace Walpole (Sale, Robins, 28:vi:1842, Lot 270, p. 19). A. & E. Evans, from whom it was purchased by the B.M., 1852. 1852–2–14–372 (L.B.1).

BIBL. & REPR.: *Knowles, Gyles*, p. 53 & Pl. XXVII.

The attribution of this drawing to Gyles himself is suggested by Thomas Dodd who compiled the sale catalogue of Walpole's collection of engraved portraits, 1842. He describes it, p. 124, as 'Henry Giles . . . a beautiful crayon drawing, probably by himself'. The attribution may, of course, have already been attached to it when in Walpole's or even in Vertue's possession, but there is no evidence of this. It is undoubtedly the work of a skilled portrait draughtsman, but Gyles does not appear to have practised this branch of art. The inscription is clearly in Thoresby's hand (*See* B.M., Stowe MS. 746, *ff.* 23 & 140), and, as he was one of Gyles's intimate friends, it seems reasonable to suppose that the drawing might have been made by one of the artists who frequented the circle of *virtuosi* at the glass-painter's house. Of these the most likely would be John Lambert (D. 1701), son of the Parliamentarian general, who is known to have painted portraits and is described by Thoresby in his Diary as 'a most exact limner'. Another possible author would be Jacques Parmentier (B. 1658: D. 1730), who worked both as a history and a portrait painter in Yorkshire. A third would be Francis Place, who engraved a mezzotint portrait of Gyles, though apparently at a more advanced age than he is shown in the present drawing. Dodd's attribution has, however, been retained here, through lack of stronger evidence to contradict it. Thoresby mentions in his *Ducatus Leodiensis*, pp. 492 & 496, that he owned two portraits of Gyles, one being Place's mezzotint (which he acquired from Gyles's executors), the other apparently an oil-painting: there is no record of the present drawing in his *Catalogue*, but in view of the inscription, it is certain that the drawing at one time passed through his hands.

HAYLS, JOHN

D. 1679

Portrait painter and limner

Origin not known. Mentioned by Richard Symonds in his note-book of 1650–1 in connexion with a receipt for preparing vermilion which 'Mʳ Hales learnt from that of Mirauelt [*i.e.* Michiel Mierevelt] who lived in Holland in Prince Hen: time [Prince Henry of Orange] & should have come to England'. This rather ambiguous statement taken by some authorities to mean that Hayls actually studied under Mierevelt, either at the Hague or Amsterdam. The fact that the note-book was largely used in Rome has also suggested that Hayls may have been there with Symonds, but there is no other evidence to confirm this and the entries relating to him may equally well have been made after Symonds's return to London in 1652. Was of sufficiently high reputation in 1658 to be numbered by Sir William Sanderson among those 'rare Artizans' then practising portraiture in England: 'Walker, Zowst [Soest], Wright, Lillie [Lely], Hales, Shepheard, de Grange [Des Granges].' Is recorded by Pepys between 1666 and 1668, during which time Hayls painted the well-known portrait of the Diarist, in an 'Indian gowne', holding the music of his song *Beauty Retire* (now in the National Portrait Gallery, No. 211), Mrs. Pepys, Thomas Pepys (the Diarist's father) and Joseph Harris, the actor, as Henry V. Other authenticated portraits by him include Thomas Flatman the miniaturist and poet (engraved by Robert White), 'Mr. Morgan' (once at the Painter-Stainers' Hall), 'Mr. W. Finch' (noted by the elder Charles Beale), Colonel John Russell and the Ladies Anne and Diana Russell (at Woburn), and perhaps Richard Low the musician (engraved in mezzotint by Isaac Beckett as after 'Hays'). Further portraits attributed to him on stylistic grounds by Mr. Collins Baker. According to Buckeridge, was a 'competitor with Sir Peter Lely', and certainly his manner shows some affinity with that of Lely's earlier work. Is also said, by the same authority, to have been 'so excellent a copyist, that many of the portraits which he

did After Vandyck, pass at this day for originals of that ingenious man'. Painted at least one history-piece, *The Martyrdom of St. Sebastian*, at the Painter-Stainers' Hall. On hearing that Samuel Cooper had tried his hand at painting in oils, threatened to turn to limning, but, according to Vertue, does not seem to have been very successful in that branch of art. The drawing described below, if authentic, suggests that he may also have attempted book illustration, but nothing definite by him known in this field. In the collection of James Seamer (Seymour) were two miniatures of Hayls, one by himself, the other (dated 1656) by John Hoskins. A copy of the latter by Vertue is in the Department (1852-2-14-376). Vertue also mentions a portrait of Mrs. Hayls (the artist's wife) by William Claret. Is said to have lived in Southampton Street, Bloomsbury, later removing to a house in Long Acre, where in 1679, 'Comeing from the necessary house he dropt down dead in the Garden, being drest in a velvet suit ready to go to a Ld Mayor's feast.' Was buried at St. Martin-in-the-Fields on Dec. 27th of that year. Does not appear to have left a Will.

BIBL.: *Symonds, ff.* 15r. & 19r. *Sanderson*, p. 20. *St. Martin-in-the-Fields, Registers. Buckeridge*, p. 382. *Walpole*, II, p. 463. *D.N.B.*, XXV, 1891, p. 296 (with *Bibl.*). *Crace, Painter-Stainers' Pictures*, p. 11, No. 45. *Baker, Lely*, I, pp. 130-7. *T.-B.*, XVI, 1923, pp. 179-80 (with *Bibl.*). *Long*, p. 197. *Vertue, Index*, p. 104.

1. **A SHEPHERDESS.** T.Q.L. figure in a broad-brimmed hat and laced bodice over looped-up dress, holding in her r. hand a sheep-hook and pointing downwards with her l. A flock of sheep on the r., and on the l., a distaff and three bobbins.

Plate 145

Pen and ink, with light brown wash; indented (?); 10·1 × 7·9 cm. (4 × 3⅛ in.).

PROV.: W. Rickard, by whom it was presented to the B.M., 1893.
1893-2-21-1 (L.B.1).

This appears to be a design for a book illustration, so far not identified, perhaps emblematic of the production of wool. The reason for attributing it to Hayls is obscure, and there are certainly no other book illustrations by this artist recorded with which it might be compared.

HOLLAR, WENCESLAUS

B. 1607: D. 1677
Topographical etcher and draughtsman

Born in Prague, July 13th, 1607, eldest son of Jan Hollar, a Bohemian official in the service of Rudolf II, and Margaret, daughter of David Löw von Löwengrün und Bareyt. Little known of his early career, but the brief account of his life inscribed on his engraved self-portrait (1647) after Jan Meyssens states that he was naturally inclined to miniature painting and illumination (one signed miniature landscape, dated 1637, belongs to Mr. E. Schilling) but was obstructed by his father ('beaucoup retardé par son père') who is said to have intended him for a legal career. Aubrey, his earliest biographer and a close acquaintance, states that Hollar as a boy 'tooke a delight in draweing of Mapps' and claims to have seen some of these early works. According to a modern biographer, became the pupil of Egidius Sadeler (B. 1570: D. 1629), engraver to the Imperial Court, who persuaded him to take up etching. The earliest date found in his work, 1623, on the *View near Gravesend* (See No. 1 below, and note) cannot be taken as authentic and there is no supporting evidence of such an early visit to England. A few etched plates can be assigned to the years 1625 and 1626, at least two of which are after Dürer. Left Prague in 1627, probably either for religious or professional reasons, and settled for a short period in Frankfurt, where he was apprenticed to Matthäus Merian (B. 1593: D. 1650), the topographical etcher and publisher, assisting with the production of topographical landscapes, city plans and architectural designs. In 1628 moved to Strasburg by way of Stuttgart and began to work independently apart from commissions for Jacob van der Heyden, among others. The following year undertook a journey along the Rhine and settled in Cologne where in 1630 he was working for the publishers Abraham Hogenberg and Gerhardt Altzenbach. Visited Holland in 1634 and in 1635 published in Cologne his *Amoenissimae aliquot locorum Effigies . . .*, a set of views of Rhenish and Dutch cities. In April 1636 joined the suite of Thomas Howard, First Earl of Arundel, then on his way to the Imperial Court, who employed him to make a graphic record of the embassy's travels, but William Crowne's *True Relation of all the Remarkable Places . . . in the Travels of the Earle of Arundel . . .*, 1637, makes no mention of him although he is reputed to have illustrated the original MS. of this work, once in the possession of the Duchess of Portland, but now lost. In addition to those described below, a group of 20 drawings illustrating the journey along the Rhine and Danube are preserved at Chatsworth and similar large groups at Berlin and Prague, besides etchings, one of which is inscribed *Hollar delineavit . . . in Legatione Arundeliana ad Imperatorem* (Parthey, No. 735). Arundel mentions the artist in a letter to the Rev. W. Petty, dated May 1636: 'I have one Hollarse wth me who drawes and eches Printes in stronge water quickely, and wth a pretty spiritt,' and secured for him from the Emperor Ferdinand II the right to use his mother's title and coat of arms. In 1636 returned with his patron to England and resided in Arundel House, of which he etched several views. Also began the task of reproducing many of the most notable works in his patron's collection. One of his earliest English etchings, the large *View of Greenwich* (1637), dedicated to Queen Henrietta Maria, probably used to effect his introduction at Court, though Vertue notes that he was never able to win the full approval of Van Dyck 'because he could not so well enter that master's true manner of drawing'. Nevertheless executed some of his finest plates after Van Dyck, among them portraits of Charles I and his Queen (1640). Was also appointed drawing-master to Charles, Prince of Wales, probably also to Prince James, and was commissioned to execute portrait and allegorical plates for Puget de la Serre's *Histoire de l'Entrée de la Reyne Mère du Roy très Chrestien . . . dans les Pays Bas* and *L'Entrée de la Reyne Mère du Roy très Chrestien dans la Grande Bretaigne*, both published in 1639, the latter in commemoration of a visit of Maria de Medici to her daughter Queen Henrietta Maria. In 1640 appeared the first of Hollar's important costume works, the *Ornatus Muliebris Anglicanus*. About the same time was attached to the Duke of York as 'serviteur domestique' but the duties involved in this office not known. Married on July 4th, 1641, at Arundel House, Mrs. Tracy, 'my ladie's [Countess of Arundel's] wayting woman' who, according to Nagler, assisted him in his work and who bore him a son John, and a daughter, the former 'an ingeniose youth' who 'drew delicately' and who died of the plague at the age of seventeen. After the outbreak of the Civil War when the royal patronage ceased and Arundel went into exile at Antwerp, undertook plates of notable events such as Strafford's trial and execution, the trial of Laud, the destruction of Cheapside Cross, and illustrations to John Vicars' *A Sight of yᵉ Transactions of these latter Years emblemized with*

engraven plats which men may read without spectacles, 1646. Also produced the extensive costume series, *Theatrum Mulierum*, 1643, and portraits of Milton and Pym.

Vertue records Hollar's capture at the Siege of Basing House (surrendered Oct. 14th, 1645), but, if true, must have been made prisoner the year before the garrison's surrender, escaping the same year to Antwerp, where he executed plates dated 1644. No doubt intended to seek there the assistance of Arundel who left for Italy soon after. Was forced to work for engraver-publishers, among whom were: Jan Meyssens (B. 1612: D. 1670), Hendrik van der Borcht (B. c. 1620; joined the Legation of Arundel in 1636), Cornelis Galle (B. 1576: D. 1650) and F. van den Wyngaerde (B. 1614: D. 1679). Became a member of St. Luke's Guild in 1645. His output of etched and engraved plates enormous, and included portraits after Van Dyck and many of the Italian masters and other plates after Elsheimer, Dürer and Holbein. Is also thought to have executed at Antwerp the series of seashells (*Parthey*, Nos. 2187–2224) which may have influenced Rembrandt to etch a similar plate. Returned to England in 1652, possibly at the invitation of Elias Ashmole, Sir William Dugdale or John Aubrey. Was arrested on his arrival and only released on the intercession of Dugdale. May have been proscribed for his services to the Royalists, since a letter now in the British Museum from the artist to Dugdale asks him to arrange for the removal of his name 'from the book in which it is inscribed'. Lived and worked for a time with William Faithorne (q.v.) near Temple Bar. Forced by lack of patronage to work by the hour at a low rate for publishers such as Peter Stent and John Ogilby, engraving book illustrations which included plates for Ogilby's *Vergil*, 1654, Dugdale's *Warwickshire*, 1656, and Sir Robert Stapleton's *Juvenal*, 1660. According to Francis Place (q.v.), Stent paid Hollar only 30/– for the *View of Greenwich* mentioned above, which Vertue considered 'very well deserved ten or £15'. After leaving Faithorne, lodged with Stent and John Overton, another print-seller. His fortunes not improved materially by the Restoration, which supplied the subject for one of his finest etched plates, the *Coronation of Charles in Westminster Abbey* for Ogilby's *Entertainment of his Most Excellent Majestie Charles II*, 1662. About the same time, executed inset views of London, Greenwich, Woolwich, Erith and Gravesend for Sir Jonas Moore's *Map of London and the Thames*, dated 1662 (London Museum). Petitioned the king for assistance, who recommended his unfinished map of London to the Lord Mayor, and requested him to enable Hollar to complete it. Obtained, possibly in Nov., 1666, the appointment of 'King's scenographer or designer of Prospects' and in 1667 received a grant of £50. Two year's later, 1669, was sent with Lord Henry Howard's expedition to Tangier to make drawings of the town and fortifications (*See* Nos. 28–41 below), for which he received only £100. Married a second time in 1665 Honora . . . (the date of his first wife's death unknown) and had several children by her. At this period, according to Vertue, lived in Bloomsbury. The catastrophes of the Plague and the Fire adversely affected his ability to obtain patronage. Apart from the Tangier commission, seems to have depended entirely on book illustration for a meagre living, executing plates for: *Multae et Diversae Avium Species*, 1671 (?), after Francis Barlow (*q.v.*); Ashmole's *Institution of the laws and ceremonies of the most noble Order of the Garter*, 1672; Vol. III of Dugdale's *Monasticon*, 1673; Thoroton's *The Antiquities of Nottinghamshire*, 1677, and Sandford's *Genealogical History*, 1677. Fell into increas-

ing poverty and debt and died at his house in Gardiner's Lane, Westminster, according to Place, so poor that 'before his departure. the bayliffs came and siez'd all he had, which gave him a great disturbance & he was heard to say they might have stayd till he was dead. he left a widow & two daughters . . . .' Was buried at St. Margaret's, Westminster, on March 28th, 1677, the addition of crosses against the entry in the register apparently indicating that a bishop performed the service. Below his name have been added the words 'the famous'.

Had few known pupils, but Richard Gaywood (B. *c.* 1630: D. *c.* 1711), the engraver, describes himself as Hollar's 'quondam discipulus', and Thomas Neale, the etcher (*Fl.* mid-XVII c.), is said to have been a pupil. Peregrine Lovell (*Fl.* mid-XVII c.) was another follower and imitated Hollar's manner in his portrait and figure etchings. Hollar was the primary influence in English topographical art during the later XVII and early XVIII c., particularly in the work of Francis Place (*q.v.*), his friend but never his pupil, Daniel King (*q.v.*), John Dunstall (*q.v.*), David Loggan (*q.v.*), Robert White (*q.v.*), Sir Martin Beckman (*q.v.*) and Thomas Phillips (*q.v.*).

Vertue states that Hollar's widow some years after his death sold a large volume of his works to Sir Hans Sloane which no doubt formed the basis of the Museum collection.

BIBL.: *D.N.B.*, XXVII, 1891, pp. 160–2 (with *Bibl.*). Hind, *Hollar. T.-B.*, XVII, 1924, pp. 376–9 (with *Bibl.*). Dostal. Hind, *Studies*, V. Urzidil. Sprinzels. Vertue, *Index*, pp. 116–17. Woodward, pp. 23–5, 34 & 49.
DRAWINGS IN OTHER COLLECTIONS. See *Sprinzels*.

[1-11]. VIEWS IN ENGLAND.

1. VIEW NEAR GRAVESEND. View from a high bank on the Kentish side, looking W. over the Thames Estuary. On the crest of the bank, l., two men, one standing, the other seated, regarding the prospect. On the shore below, r., a horse and cart coming into the foreground. In mid-distance, a group of buildings with a cloud of smoke hanging over them, and away to the r., shipping in mid-stream.

Plate 152

Pen and ink with grey wash; 6·2 × 18 cm. (2½ × 7⅛ in.).

INSCR.: *Recto*, at the top, in the centre, by the artist, *bey Gravesend in England*, and in the lower l.-hand corner, *WH:* (monogram) *1623*.

PROV.: W. & G. Smith, from whom it was purchased by the B.M., 1850.
1850–2–23–193 (L.B.13).

BIBL.: *Hind*, p. 21. *Sprinzels*, p. 113, No. 368.

The inscription at the top of the drawing is clearly in Hollar's hand; but the 'signature' and date, 1623, in the lower l.-hand corner are almost certainly later additions. Mr. Hind does, however, very tentatively suggest that it might indicate an earlier visit to England, and states that the drawing itself appears to be an early work. Dr. Sprinzels dates it about '1643–77' (by which presumably he means after Hollar's return to England in 1652), and regards the 'signature' and date as a later addition.

cf. Cornelis Bol, No. 1, for another view of Gravesend of this period.

2. HAMPTON COURT AND A SUNDIAL. Distant view of the Palace, looking N.W. along the Thames. To the l., three of the tower-like gazebos which dotted the gardens. Below, a separate study of a sundial composed of a pile of books surmounted by a figure of Time.

Plate 166

Metalpoint; 10·6 × 11·4 cm. (4⅛ × 4⅜ in.).

INSCR.: *Recto*, at the top, in the centre, by the artist, *Hampton Court*.

PROV.: Sir Thomas Lawrence (*Lugt*, No. 2445). W. & G. Smith, from whom it was purchased by the B.M., 1850.
1850–2–23–190 (L.B.8a).

BIBL. & REPR.: *Popham, Hollar*, p. 29, Pl. 33.

A leaf from a sketchbook, of which another leaf is described at No. 50.

3. LONDON AND OLD ST. PAUL'S FROM THE THAMES. View looking N.E. down the river, from a point above the Savoy (?), Old St. Paul's dominating the prospect. The landmarks to the l. of the Cathedral difficult to identify, as the drawing is unfinished, but may perhaps be recognized as follows, from l. to r.: the Savoy, a square church tower surmounted by four pinnacles (St. Sepulchre's (?)), the garden of Somerset House (?), the hall and garden of the Temple, the tower of St. Bride's but without its four pinnacles (?), the tower of St. Anne's, Blackfriars (?), Old St. Paul's. To the r. of the Cathedral, from l. to r.: the tower of St. Mary-le-Bow, the tower of St. Martin's in Thames Street (?), the spire of St. Lawrence Poulteney, the spire of St. Dunstan-in-the-East, and the Tower of London. **Plate 149**

Pen and brown ink; 8·8 × 29·4 cm. (3½ × 11⅝ in.).

INSCR.: *Recto*, on the mount, in the r.-hand corner, *Hollar*, and in the centre, *923*.

PROV.: Sir J. C. Robinson (*Lugt*, No. 1433). A. W. Thibaudeau, from whom it was purchased by the B.M., 1882.
　1882–8–12–489.

Dating from before 1666, the year of the Great Fire. The old attribution to Hollar appears to be correct. The rather free handling of the drawing is comparable with that used by the artist in portraying distant buildings in other London views, *e.g. Westminster and the Thames* (No. 5 in this Catalogue), *London from Milford Stairs* in the Pepysian Library, Magdalene, Cambridge (*Sprinzels*, p. 107, No. 331 & Pl. 49, No. 248), etc. There is no etching by Hollar which corresponds exactly with the present drawing, but it may be compared with the r.-hand half of *The Prospect of London and Westminster* (Parthey, No. 1013; Hind, No. 18) in its first (or 'pre-Fire') state. A rather similar view is represented in a drawing by M. van Overbeck, inscribed *Pauls Churche*, in the Louvre, placed with anonymous German drawings.

4. LONDON: THE TOWER. View looking N.E. across the Thames towards the fortress on the far bank, with the Traitors' Gate in the centre and the White Tower rising beyond it. On the extreme l., the Byward and Bell Towers, and to the r., the Lantern, Cradle and Salt Towers. Anchored in the foreground, r., a three-masted ship flying the St. George's flag (customary for merchant ships at the time), in mid-stream, two barges, and by Tower Wharf other vessels.　　　　**Plate 146**

Pen and ink over black lead, lightly tinted in water-colours; 11·1 × 28·3 cm. (4⅜ × 11⅛ in.).

INSCR.: *Recto*, at the top, in the centre, by the artist, *Den Tower van London*, and on the river, *Thamesis fluvius*.

PROV.: P. & D. Colnaghi, from whom it was purchased by the B.M., 1859.
　1859–8–6–389 (L.B.9).

ETCH.: Connected with the etching by Hollar, *Castrum Royale Londinense vulgo the Tower* (Parthey, No. 908; Hind, No. 22).

BIBL. & REPR.: Hind, pp. 20 & 51, No. 22, & Pl. IX. *Sprinzels*, p. 109, No. 340.

Dated by Dr. Sprinzels about 1637–43.

5. LONDON: WESTMINSTER AND THE THAMES FROM LAMBETH HOUSE. View looking N. down the river from near Lambeth Stairs, with Lambeth House (or Palace) on the bank, r., flanked by trees. On the far bank, from l. to r., Westminster Abbey, Westminster Hall and Clock House, Whitehall, Scotland Yard, Suffolk (or Northumberland) House, and the other palaces formerly bordering the river at this point, York House, Durham House, Salisbury House, the Savoy, and Somerset House. In the foreground, at the end of Lambeth Stairs, a number of wherries, one of which is putting off with a load of passengers. In mid-stream, l., a loaded barge.　　　　**Plate 148**

Pen and brown ink over black lead; 15·1 × 40·1 cm. (6 × 15¾ in.).

INSCR.: *Recto*, in the lower r.-hand corner, by the artist, *W: Hollar. Dᵉ . . .* , and above

HOLLAR

the appropriate buildings, also by the artist, *Wesminster Abby*, *Parlament house* (St. Stephen's Chapel), *Suffolke house*, *Lambeth house*.

> *Verso*, at the top, *Sketches of Hollar* —·15—.

PROV.: Messrs. Hogarth, from whom it was purchased, 1882.

> **1882–8–12–224** (L.B.11).

BIBL. & REPR.: *Hind*, p. 21 & Pl. IX. *Vasari Soc.*, Pt. XV, 1934, No. 4. *Sprinzels*, p. 107, No. 328, & Pl. 59, No. 298.

Dated by Dr. Sprinzels about 1637–43. The view should be compared with that in the l.-hand half of *The Prospect of London and Westminster* (*Parthey*, No. 1013; *Hind*, No. 18).

6. LONDON: WESTMINSTER ABBEY.

View from the S. bank of the Thames, just above Lambeth Palace, looking N. over the river. On the opposite bank, the Abbey, with Henry VII's Chapel and the Chapter House, dominating the centre of a cluster of rose-tinted buildings, which include the low battlemented tower, perhaps Edward III's Jewel House. In the distance, l., the country to the W. of Hampstead, and on the extreme l., in the foreground, the corner of a building, apparently an addition to the original design and drawn on the old mount.

Pen and light brown ink over black lead, tinted in water-colours; $7 \cdot 1 \times 13 \cdot 2$ cm. ($2\frac{7}{8} \times 5\frac{1}{4}$ in.). The old mount, $11 \cdot 5 \times 17 \cdot 9$ cm. ($4\frac{1}{2} \times 7$ in.).

INSCR.: *Recto*, at the top, by the artist, *Westminster bey . . . London*; in the upper r.-hand corner, *55*; on the old mount, in the lower r.-hand corner, *hollar*.

PROV.: J. P. Heseltine (Sale, Sotheby, 29:v:1935, Lot 317). P. & D. Colnaghi, from whom it was purchased by the B.M. through the Malcolm Exchange Fund, 1935.

> **1935–6–8–3** (Malcolm Add. 109).

ETCH.: Study for the view of Westminster Abbey in Hollar's panorama, *The Prospect of London and Westminster Taken from Lambeth* (*Parthey*, No. 1013; *Hind*, No. 18).

BIBL. & REPR.: *J. P. Heseltine*, No. 24. *Vasari Soc.*, Series 2, Pt. V, 1924, No. 15. *Hind, Miscellaneous*, p. 23, Pl. XA. *Sprinzels*, p. 325, No. 325, & Pl. 20, No. 137.

EXH.: B.F.A.C., *Early Drawings and Pictures of London*, No. 9.

Dated by Dr. Sprinzels about 1637–43. The drawing corresponds almost exactly with the view in the etched *Prospect of London and Westminster*, with two small differences: a group of buildings, which, in the drawing, appear in the distance, l., between the Abbey and a clump of trees, are omitted in the etching; and the tower of St. Margaret's, which, in the etching, appears on the r. of the Abbey, is not shown in the drawing. It would seem that the drawing once formed part of a much longer view, extending on either side of the present sheet of paper, from which it was cut at some early date and laid down on a mount. It was at this time, too, that the curious addition to the design on the l. was probably made, in a darker ink and by a less accomplished hand than the main part of the drawing. Perhaps this addition was intended to represent part of Lambeth Palace; if so, it is incorrectly placed in relation to the rest of the view. More likely it was merely intended to give scale to the foreground of the composition after the drawing had been mounted. The l. half of the *W* of *Westminster* in the inscription was cut off and has been re-written on the old mount immediately above the addition.

350

7. LONDON: WHITEHALL PALACE. View looking W. from an inlet of the Thames in the Surrey shore, with part of Lambeth Marsh, planted with trees, appearing in the l. foreground. On the opposite bank, Whitehall Palace with the Banqueting House rising in the centre and Whitehall Stairs below it. On the r., Scotland Yard, and on the extreme r., the tower of old St. Martin-in-the-Fields and the S.W. turret of Suffolk (or Northumberland) House. On the river, numerous wherries, two of which are seen in the foreground, the one leaving, the other approaching the shore. **Plate 147**

Pen and ink, lightly tinted in water-colours; 9·8 × 29·3 cm. (3⅞ × 11⅝ in.).

INSCR.: *Recto*, at the top, in the centre, by the artist, *White Hall. Palatium Regis*, and on the river, *Thamesis fluvius*.

PROV.: As for No. 4.
1859–8–6–390 (L.B.10).

ETCH.: Perhaps connected with the etching by Hollar, *Palatium Regis prope Londinum vulgo Whitehall* (Parthey, No. 1039; Hind, No. 85).

BIBL.: *Hind*, p. 74, No. 85; *Sprinzels*, p. 104, No. 312.

Dated by Dr. Sprinzels about 1637–43.

8. QUEENBOROUGH CASTLE, SHEPPEY, KENT. View looking N.E. across a stretch of open flat ground known as Queenborough Marsh toward the Castle, a circular building girt with round towers and enclosed within a circular curtain wall, in which is the gatehouse flanked also by round towers. In the distance, high ground at the l. extremity of which is a tower, perhaps indicating the village of Minster. Further to the l., the Thames Estuary with ships on it. In the foreground, groups of figures approaching the Castle. **Plate 150**

Pen and ink over black lead, tinted in water-colours; 10·2 × 27 cm. (4 × 10⅝ in.).

INSCR.: *Recto*, at the top, by the artist, *Qvinborow Castle in Engelland*.

PROV.: As for No. 4.
1859–8–6–387 (L.B.14).

ETCH.: Study for the etching, on a greatly reduced scale and with modifications, by Hollar, *Quinboro Castle, in the Ile of Shepy* (Parthey, No. 948).

BIBL. & REPR.: *Sprinzels*, p. 113, No. 369, & Pl. 56, No. 284.

As Queenborough was demolished pro-

bably soon after 1650 (*See* below) and is here shown intact, it seems likely that this drawing was executed during Hollar's first stay in England in 1637–43.

Queenborough Castle was built by Edward III about 1361–7, from designs by William of Wyckham, to defend the Isle of Sheppey and the strip of water between it and the Kentish mainland. It was repaired by Henry VIII in 1536 probably as part of his coastal defences. After the death of Charles I it was annexed by the Parliament, surveyed in 1650, and eventually demolished. Hollar's view corresponds closely with the description of the Castle in the Parliamentary survey quoted in E. Hasted's *History . . . of Kent*, II, 1782, p. 656.

9. RICHMOND PALACE, SURREY. View looking N. from the Twickenham bank of the Thames across the river to the opposite bank, on which stands that part of the Palace known as the Privy Lodgings. To the l., the Great Orchard dominated by the 'spire' of the Livery Kitchen. To the r., part of the gallery surrounding the Privy Garden. In the foreground, two ladies preceded by a gentleman walking along the bank to the r. In mid-stream, l., a wherry, and moored against the far bank, r., a pleasure-barge. **Plate 152**

Pen and ink over black lead, with brown-grey wash; $8 \cdot 1 \times 12 \cdot 4$ cm. ($3\frac{1}{8} \times 4\frac{7}{8}$ in.).

INSCR.: *Recto*, at the top, in the centre, by the artist, *Richmond*; on the river to the r., *Thamesis fluvius*; and at the foot, in the centre, also by the artist, *W: Hollar fecit*.

   Verso, in the lower l.-hand corner, *1526* and *No. 20*:–.

PROV.: Uvedale Price (Sale, Sotheby, 3:v:1854, Lot 102). Purchased by the B.M. at the Uvedale Price Sale, 1854.

   1854–5–13–7 (L.B.12).

ETCH.: Study for the central portion of the etching by Hollar, *RICHMOND*, dated *1638* (*Parthey*, No. 1058; *Hind*, No. 109).

BIBL. & REPR.: *Hind*, pp. 21 & 82. *Cundall*, p. xiii & Pl. 8. *Sprinzels*, p. 113, No. 365.

The date, *1638*, on the related etching proves that the date suggested by Dr. Sprinzels for this drawing, *1643–77*, is incorrect. The view in the etching is considerably more extended, and shows several modifications, including a deeper foreground in which a group of figures are coming ashore from a pleasure barge, and a three-masted ship moored against the far bank to the r. of the Palace.

Richmond Palace, one of the favourite residences of the Tudor sovereigns, was founded in 1499 by Henry VII on the site of the Palace of Sheen. In 1501 he rechristened it Richmond in honour of his own former title of Earl of Richmond (in Yorkshire). Queen Elizabeth died in the Palace in 1603. It later, for James I's sons, Prince Henry and Prince Charles, became one of the principal repositories of their art collections. Sequestrated under the Commonwealth it gradually fell into decay, the greater part being eventually pulled down in Queen Anne's reign, leaving only the gateway and the range of buildings at r. angles to it known as the Wardrobe (*See Cundall*, pp. 1–7, and Estella Cave, *Memories of Old Richmond*, 1923, pp. 299–313).

The present drawing should be compared with Anthonis van den Wyngaerde's drawing of the S. front of the Palace in the Bodleian Library, Oxford (*Sutherland-Clarendon*, Vol. 171, pp. 11 & 12). For other early views *see Cundall*, Pls. 2, 5, 6, 7 & 8.

10. STERBOROUGH CASTLE, LINGFIELD, SURREY. View looking probably N.W., from a stretch of open ground, to the Castle, a moated quadrilateral building, with round angle towers capped by pointed roofs, and a gatehouse, approached by a trestle bridge on which two men are walking. Clumps of bushes at the water's edge, r. and l., and in the distance, trees and a line of low hills. **Plate 151**

Pen and ink over black lead, lightly tinted in water-colours; $10 \cdot 7 \times 25 \cdot 9$ cm. ($4\frac{1}{4} \times 10\frac{1}{4}$ in.).

INSCR.: *Recto*, at the top, by the artist, *Starburow in England*.

PROV.: As for No. 4.
   1859–8–6–388 (L.B.15).

BIBL. & REPR.: *Sprinzels*, p. 114, No. 371, & Pl. 55, No. 279.

As Sterborough Castle is said to have been demolished under the Commonwealth (*See* below) and is here shown in a fairly good state of repair, it seems likely that this drawing was executed during Hollar's first stay in England in 1637–43, or soon after his return here in 1652.

Sterborough Castle, originally known as Prinkham, was fortified by Reginald de Cobham, later Lord Cobham, in 1342. During the Civil War it was garrisoned for the Parliament, but never attacked. It appears to have been demolished under the Commonwealth. During the XVIII c. a new house was erected near the site by Sir James Burrow, who, according to Manning and Bray (*History and Antiquities . . . of Surrey*, II, 1809, pp. 340–7), owned 'a rude drawing of the ichnography of this castle, and of the moat which surrounded it, and a very rude ancient map . . . in a corner of which is a small sketch of the upright of the castle. It appears to have had a round tower at each corner, with domes thereon, shews the drawbridge, and that there was a court in the middle'. The castle emplacement still exists today surrounded by its moat.

11. WINDSOR CASTLE, THE QUADRANGLE. View looking W. along the grass-grown Quadrangle towards the Keep or Round Tower which rises on its mound in the centre, approached, r., by a covered ascent. On the l., the S. range of buildings including, from l. to r., the Augusta Tower, the Black or York Tower, the King's or 'Rubbish' Gate, the Earl Marshal's or Maid of Honour's Tower, and the Lieutenant's Tower. On the r., the N. range, including, from l. to r., King John's Tower, the Gate to the King's Lodgings or Spicery Gatehouse, the Private Chapel, and St. George's Hall. In the centre, two women crossing the Quadrangle, and to the r., three musketeers marching into the foreground. In the background, r., other soldiers with a cannon.

Pen and brown ink, partly ruled, tinted with water-colours and body-colours and strengthened with gum, on vellum; 17·8 × 57·2 cm. (7 × 22½ in.).

INSCR.: *Recto*, towards the lower r.-hand corner, by the artist, *Wenceslaus Hollar delineavit*.

PROV.: The Rev. C. M. Cracherode, by whom it was bequeathed to the B.M., 1799. **G.g.3–359** (L.B.30).

BIBL.: *Cracherode Cat.*, p. 84, No. 359. *Hind*, p. 21. *Sprinzels*, p. 112, No. 362.

A finished drawing no doubt based on sketches made in company with Elias Ashmole at Windsor in 1659, as recorded by Ashmole in his diary (Bodleian Library) under May 25th of that year: 'I went to Windsor, and took Mr. Hollar with me to take views of the Castle'. A smaller and less elaborate version of approximately the same subject is in the Bodleian Library (*See Sprinzels*, p. 112, No. 363 (b), & Pl. 51, No. 259).

The Quadrangle is here shown in its medieval state before the extensive rebuilding of the N. range in 1674–82.

[12–27]. VIEWS ON THE CONTINENT.

12. AMSTERDAM FROM THE 'LEEUWEN OR BLAUWE BOLWERCK'.
View looking S.W. from the northernmost bastion of the city with a windmill in the open foreground, r. On the l., part of the stockade of the 'Nieuwe Waell' and the estuary of the river Y with several vessels on it. In the centre, mid-distance, the

masts of shipping, and beyond, to the r., the city with the Nieuwe Kerk (?) and the towers of the Jan Roopoort and the Westerkerk.

Pen and ink, with washes of light brown and blue; 15·1 × 28 cm. (6 × 11⅜ in.).

INSCR.: *Recto*, above the city, in black lead, probably by the artist, *Amsterdam* (very faint); in the lower margin, in ink, *Hollar* (?) *fect* (probably not a signature).

PROV.: R. P. Roupell (Sale, Christie, 12:vii:1887, Lot 919). George Salting, by whom it was bequeathed to the B.M., 1910. **1910–2–12–106.**

BIBL. & REPR.: *Sprinzels*, p. 79, No. 155, & Pl. 22, No. 151.

About 1634.

The topography of the drawing has been identified through C. J. Visscher's plan, *Amstelodamum, Celebre Emporium Formâ Planâ* (c. 1630).

13. *Recto*. **THE HARBOUR AT AMSTERDAM.** View looking N. from a reedy bank at the entrance to the S. moat defending the city, just opposite the 'Rijsen Hooft' with the Zuyder Kerk beyond it on the extreme l. In the l. foreground, a ship laid up within the stockade of the 'Oude Waell', and near her, guns lying on a low wharf. In the distance, a fleet in the river Y. **Plate 153**

Pen and ink with grey wash, tinted in water-colours; 14·6 × 37·3 cm. (5¾ × 14⅝ in.).

INSCR.: At the top, in the centre, by the artist, *Zu Amsterdam . . . W H.* (monogram) *1634*; and on the extreme l., *Zuyder Kerck.*

Verso. **TWO STUDIES OF A DUTCH EAST INDIAMAN.**

Pen and ink.

INSCR.: At the foot, in the centre, *Of Mr: Hllrs Drawing*; in a different hand, *Hollar*; and in the lower l.-hand corner, by William Esdaile, *1834 W E 10x.*

PROV.: Sir Thomas Lawrence (*Lugt*, No, 2445). William Esdaile ((?) Sale, Christie, 20:vi:1840, but not identifiable). P. & D.

Colnaghi, from whom it was purchased by the B.M., 1862. **1862–7–12–193** (L.B.17).

BIBL. & REPR.: *Sprinzels*, p. 80, No. 157, & Pl. 18, No. 121 (*recto*).

The topography of the drawing on the *recto* has been identified through C. J. Visscher's plan, *Amstelodamum, Celebre Emporium Formâ Planâ* (c. 1630).

14. AUGSBURG FROM THE S.E. ((?) AFTER MERIAN). View over low-lying meadows through which winds the river Lech. In the background, the walled city with its many churches and other public buildings, prominent among which is St. Ulric on the l. **Plate 155**

Pen and ink, tinted in water-colours; 11·6 × 29·5 cm. (4⅝ × 11⅝ in.).

INSCR.: *Recto*, at the top, in the centre, by the artist, *Augspurg.*

Verso, by the Rev. C. M. Cracherode, *CMC.* (monogram) *1786*.

PROV.: As for No. 11.
G.g. 2–244 (L.B.25).

ETCH.: By Hollar, the l. half only, with
modifications to the foreground and on a
slightly reduced scale, and with the lettering,
M. Merian delin. W Hollar fecit. 1665 (Parthey,
No. 758).

BIBL. & REPR.: *Cracherode Cat.*, p. 59, No.
244. *Sprinzels*, p. 99, No. 283, & Pl. 27,
No. 168.

The lettering on Hollar's etching noted
above would suggest the present drawing is
based on an original by the elder Merian.
The view is indeed taken from approximately
the same angle as Merian's large engraved
prospect of Augsburg, *Avgvsta Vindelicorvm*,
but from a point considerably further away
from the city. No other engraved view of
Augsburg by Merian taken from this angle is
known to exist. The date on Hollar's etching
indicates that it was made during the artist's
second stay in England.

15. BONN ON THE RHINE FROM THE N.E. View across the river to the walled city which stands on the far bank. On the l., the Zoll and the spire of the Münster. In the foreground, men standing and sitting, and a boat moored against the shore. **Plate 154**

Pen and ink, with washes of blue, brown and
grey; the lower r.-hand corner repaired;
10·4 × 26·6 cm. (4 × 10½ in.).

INSCR.: *Recto*, above the city, by the artist,
Bonn, on the river, *Rhenus fluvius*, and in the
lower r.-hand corner, *W. Hollar* (partly
damaged).
    Verso, by the Rev. C. M. Crache-
rode, *CMC.* (monogram) *1786*.

PROV.: As for No. 11.
G.g. 2–245 (L.B.23).

BIBL. & REPR.: *Cracherode Cat.*, p. 59, No.
245. *Sprinzels*, p. 77, No. 134, & Pl. 27,
No. 166.

This drawing should be compared with
the engraving (dated 1575) in Braun and
Hogenberg's *Civitates Orbis Terrarum*, II,
No. 33, which is taken from approximately
the same view-point.

16. DELFHAVEN FROM THE E. View from the entrance to one of the two canals which intersect the town. In the foreground, a tongue of land, protected by an embankment, with boats moored by it and houses on the extreme r. Beyond, the entrance to the other canal approached from the river Maas on the l. by a small Dutch vessel. On the far side of the second canal, a corresponding tongue of land with two ships anchored at the end of it, a clump of trees in the centre, and a line of houses on the r. Other shipping in the river, l., and in the centre distance, the town of Schiedam.

Pen and ink, tinted in water-colours;
9·8 × 27 cm. (3⅞ × 10⅝ in.).

INSCR.: *Recto*, above the respective towns,
by the artist, *Delfshaven* and *Shiedam*.

PROV.: Jonathan Richardson I (*Lugt*, No. 2184, (?) Sale, Cock, 23:i:1746/7, Lot 45). (?) William Esdaile (Sale, Christie, 20:vi:1840, Lot 555). P. & D. Colnaghi, from whom it was purchased by the B.M., 1862.

1862-7-12-194 (L.B.18).

ETCH.: By Hollar, the central portion only, with modifications and with the lettering, *Zu Delfshauen*, in the series *Amoenissimae aliquot Locorum . . . Effigies*, 1635, No. 21 (*Parthey*, No. 715).

BIBL. & REPR.: *Sprinzels*, p. 79, No. 154, & Pl. 53, No. 274.

17. DÜREN, THE 'WEILER PFORT'. View looking S.E. from the outer bank of the moat which surrounds the town, opposite to the fortified gate known as the 'Weiler Pfort' which stands on the far bank, r. In the foreground, l., a man with a dog, and a clump of trees at the water's edge.

Pen and brown ink, with washes of grey and brown; 12·8 × 25·6 cm. (5 × 10 in.).

INSCR.: *Recto*, at the top, in the centre, by the artist, *By duren*.

PROV.: As for No. 1.
1850-2-23-194 (L.B.20).

BIBL. & REPR.: *Sprinzels*, p. 82, No. 171, & Pl. 13, No. 84.

The 'Weiler Pfort' appears as No. 29 in Hollar's own bird's-eye view of Düren, dated 1634 (*Parthey*, No. 841).

18. LIPPSTADT FROM THE E. View from the river Lippe, which winds through low-lying meadows in the foreground, towards the town.

Pen and brown ink with grey wash; 8·9 × 25·3 cm. (3½ × 10 in.).

INSCR.: *Recto*, at the top, towards the r., by the artist, *Lippe*, and on the river, *Lippe fl.*

PROV.: Sir Hans Sloane, Bart., by whom it was bequeathed to the B.M., 1753.
5214-10 (L.B.19(b)).

BIBL. & REPR.: *Sloane Cat.*, p. 128, No. 10. *Sprinzels*, p. 81, No. 162, & Pl. 10, No. 60.

19. MELATEN. A group of cottages and a building with a bell-turret (perhaps a chapel), surrounded by trees. A stream in the foreground, l.

Pen and brown ink; 5·2 × 10·9 cm. (2 × 4¼ in.).

INSCR.: *Recto*, at the top, in the centre, by the artist, *Melaten, bey Cölln*; in the lower r.-hand corner, also by the artist, *1633*; and in the upper l.-hand corner, 2 6 $\overset{s\ d}{}$ (?).

PROV.: As for No. 18.
5214-9 (L.B.21(a)).

BIBL.: *Sloane Cat.*, p. 128, No. 9. *Sprinzels*, p. 79, No. 151.

Melaten lies due W. of Cologne. Most of it is now occupied by a large graveyard, originally a burial ground, dating from the XVII c., for victims of the plague. The only old building which has survived is a XIV–XV c. chapel, now in the graveyard, perhaps the building seen in the present drawing.

20. MILTENBERG FROM THE N.E. View from the S. bank of the Main, looking downstream round a bend in the river, on which stands the town dominated by its castle and backed by wooded hills.

Pen and ink with washes of brown and grey, tinted with blue; 9·6 × 24·5 cm. (3¾ × 9⅝ in.).

PROV.: As for No. 11.

G.g. 2–243 (L.B.26).

INSCR.: *Recto*, at the top, in the centre, by the artist, *Miltenburg*, and on the river, *Moenus fluvius*.

BIBL. & REPR.: *Cracherode Cat.*, p. 59 No. 243. *Sprinzels*, p. 89, No. 218, & Pl. 25, No. 161.

Verso, by the Rev. C. M. Cracherode, *CMC.* (monogram) *1786*.

21. CASTLE OF PFALZ. View across the Rhine, with a barge in the foreground, to the castle with the steep bank of the river beyond. Within an oval.

Pen and ink with brown wash; 5·8 × 8·2 cm. (2¼ × 3¼ in.).

BIBL. & REPR.: *Sloane Cat.*, p. 137, No. 73. *Sprinzels*, p. 86, No. 200, & Pl. 8, No. 52.

PROV.: As for No. 18.

5214–73 (L.B.29(a)).

22. RANNARIEDL ('RANDERIGL') FROM THE S.W. View looking down the Danube in mid-stream, presumably from one of Lord Arundel's house-barges, two others of which are seen at some distance away. On the high wooded l. bank, the castle of Rannariedl, and on the r., clumps of trees. Hills in the distance.

Pen and ink, with washes of brown, grey and blue; 10·5 × 23·6 cm. (4⅛ × 9¼ in.).

PROV.: As for No. 11.

G.g. 2–246 (L.B.24).

INSCR.: *Recto*, at the top, towards the l., by the artist, *Randerigl*, and on the river, *Danubius fluvius*.

ETCH.: By Hollar, with slight modifications and on a much reduced scale (*Parthey*, No. 777).

Verso, by the Rev. C. M. Cracherode, *CMC.* (monogram) *1786*.

BIBL. & REPR.: *Cracherode Cat.*, p. 59, No. 246. *Sprinzels*, p. 94, No. 252, & Pl. 32, No. 182.

23. RHEINECK FROM THE N.W. View looking up the Rhine in mid-stream, with Lord Arundel's barge flying a flag with the cross of St. George in the foreground. On the r., at the summit of a wooded hill, the castle of Rheineck, and further off, l., also crowning a hill, the ruins of Hammerstein. In the distance, Andernach.

Plate 157

Pen and ink, with blue-grey wash, touched with red on the flag of the barge; a section in the sky on the l. of the Castle, repaired; 10·6 × 27·6 cm. (4⅛ × 10⅞ in.).

INSCR.: *Recto*, above the three landmarks, by the artist, *Reineck, Hammerstein,* and *Andernach*; on the river, *Rhenus fluvius*; and at the foot, towards the l., *9 :Maij* [1636].

Verso, by the Rev. C. M. Crache-rode, *CMC.* (monogram) *1786.*

PROV.: As for No. 11.

G.g. 2–247 (L.B.22).

BIBL. & REPR.: *Cracherode Cat.*, p. 59, No.

247. *Sprinzels*, p. 84, No. 187, & Pl. 27, No. 167.

Dating from 1636. *Cf.* the etched view of the Rhine near Rheineck in the same direction but from a point further downstream (Parthey, No. 743).

24. NEAR STRASBURG.

24. NEAR STRASBURG. View along the bank of the river Ill, outside the main city, looking S.E. towards the E. suburb which appears in the distance, l., with the Gronenburger Thor (?) and the churches of St. Aurelian and St. Margaretha. In the foreground a figure swimming in the river and another at the water's edge, and on the r., the angle of a house from which extends a wall along the river bank with trees behind it.

Pen and brown ink, with washes of brown and grey, over black lead; 13·2 × 26·6 cm. (5¼ × 10½ in.).

INSCR.: *Recto*, at the top, in the centre, by the artist, *Beij Strassburg*, and towards the lower r.-hand corner, *1.6.30.*

PROV.: As for No. 1.

1850–2–23–195 (L.B.27).

BIBL. & REPR.: *Sprinzels*, p. 74, No. 116, & Pl. 10, No. 62.

Cf. No. 25 which is very similar in handling; also the etchings (Parthey, Nos. 723, 751–6, & 764), the original drawings of which appear to have been made in 1629–30, though the etchings were not carried out till 1643 and 1665 when Hollar was in England.

25. DISTANT VIEW OF STRASBURG FROM THE S.W.

25. DISTANT VIEW OF STRASBURG FROM THE S.W. View, from near an inlet of the river Ill, looking over a stretch of open ground. In the distance, l., clumps of trees, and r., the city, above which rise the tower of St. Peter's Church and the W. front of the Cathedral.

Pen and brown ink, with washes of grey and brown; 9·5 × 18·9 cm. (3¾ × 7½ in.). Old mount; 17·5 × 25·7 cm. (6⅞ × 10⅛ in.).

INSCR.: *Recto*, in the lower r.-hand corner, *W. Hollar Fecit* (probably not a signature), and at the top, *Straasburgh.* On the old mount, in the lower margin, *W: Holaar fe:* (not a signature).

PROV.: J. C. Spengler (*Lugt*, No. 1434). Sir Henry Williams-Wynn. Henry Bertie Williams-Wynn. Mrs. Stanley Leighton. Miss Rachel Leighton, by whom it was presented to the B.M., 1940.

1940–4–13–78.

See note to No. 24.

26. WAGENINGEN FROM THE S.W.

26. WAGENINGEN FROM THE S.W. View from the grassy l. bank of the Lower Rhine, looking upstream, with a barge and other small vessels on it. On the far bank, l., the town with churches (unidentified) prominent among its buildings. A line of trees and hills in the distance, r. **Plate 156**

Pen and ink, tinted in water-colours; 11 × 27·6 cm. (4¼ × 10⅞ in.).

INSCR.: *Recto*, at the top, in the centre, by the artist, *Wageningen*, and on the river, *Rhenus fluvius.*

PROV.: Thomas Dimsdale (*Lugt*, No. 2426). W. & G. Smith, from whom it was purchased by the B.M., 1850.
1850–2–23–192 (L.B.28).

BIBL. & REPR.: *Sprinzels*, p. 80, No. 156, & Pl. 18, No. 122.

27. WESEL FROM THE S.

View from the Rhine looking towards the r. bank where are moored barges beside a crane. In the background, the town with the churches of St. Wilbort, l., and St. Anton, r., and a windmill in the centre between them.

Pen and brown ink over black lead; (7·5 × 25·5 cm. (3 × 10 in.).

BIBL. & REPR.: *Sloane Cat.*, p. 128, No. 11. *Sprinzels*, p. 80, No. 159, & Pl. 57, No. 286.

INSCR.: *Recto*, in the upper r.-hand corner, by the artist, with the point of a brush, *wesel*, and on the river, in the lower r.-hand corner, in pen and ink, *Rhenûs fl.*
Verso, in ink, not by the artist, *Wesel.*

PROV.: As for No. 18.
5214–11 (L.B.19).

ETCH.: Study for the etching by Hollar, *Vesalia . . . Wesel* (Parthey, No. 900).

Another version by Hollar of the same subject, in pen and ink tinted in water-colours, is in the Kupferstichkabinett, Berlin (See E. Bock, *Die Deutschen Meister*, I, p. 191, No. 3301, and *Sprinzels*, p. 80, No. 160, & Pl. 13, No. 83). In the same collection is a view of St. Wilbort and the windmill, taken from a different angle also by Hollar, in pen and ink, tinted in water-colours (See Bock, I, p. 191, No. 3324, & II, Pl. 161, No. 3324, and *Sprinzels*, p. 80, No. 161). This latter corresponds with the etching *Zu Wesel* (Parthey, No. 714).

[28–41]. DRAWINGS OF TANGIER

and surroundings by Hollar during, or soon after, his official visit there in 1669. These fall into two groups: finished and mainly highly-coloured drawings from the Sloane and Esdaile collections (Nos. 29, 32, 33, 35, 36, 40–2), and less finished, perhaps preliminary, studies from the Skinner collection (Nos. 30, 31, 34, 37–9).

Eight other drawings from the Tangier series are in the collection of Sir Bruce Ingram. Another, a large finished drawing (similar to those in the Sloane Collection), representing the *Prospect of the Bay of Tangier from the South East* and connected with the etching, *Parthey*, No. 1188, is in the Ashmolean Museum (formerly in the Bodleian Library), Oxford (*Sutherland-Clarendon*, Vol. 171, p. 104). All the known drawings of the series, with the exception of the Ashmolean example, have been listed by Dr. Sprinzels.

After his return to England Hollar published a series of twelve etchings, *Divers Prospects in and about Tangier . . . London 1673* (Parthey, Nos. 1187–98), together with three long *Prospects of Tangier* (Parthey, Nos. 1199–1201) and a *Mapp of the Citty . . .* (Parthey, No. 1202). Some of these can be connected with the drawings.

[Tangier became a British possession, as part of Catherine of Braganza's dowry, in 1662. It was abandoned by Charles II in 1683 and the fortifications were blown up.]

HOLLAR

Views of the place before and after destruction were made by Thomas Phillips, the military engineer (*q.v.*). Oil paintings, traditionally ascribed to Dirck Stoop, of Tangier at the time of the evacuation, are in the collection of the Earl of Dartmouth and in 1948 were lent to the National Maritime Museum, Greenwich. For a full account of the British occupation of Tangier see E. M. G. Routh's *Tangier, England's Lost Atlantic Outpost*, 1912.

The following drawings are listed according to the order in which they are arranged in the solander containing them.

28. TANGIER FROM THE S.W. View from a grassy slope, below Catherine Fort, traversed by roads leading to the town with its fortifications, prominent among which is Peterborough Tower flying a flag bearing a red saltire edged with white on a blue ground. Beyond the town, r., the bay curving round by Old Tangier to Cape Malabata, and in the distance, the Spanish coast and Gibraltar. In the foreground, l., a group of four officers in conference, approached by another, and below them, Whitehall Fort. On the r., a party of red-coated musketeers marching up the road to Tetouan.   **Plate 158 (b)**

Pen and brown ink, with grey wash and water-colours; on three conjoined sheets; 32·3 × 88·9 cm. (12¾ × 35⅛ in.).

INSCR.: *Recto*, at the top, by the artist, *Prospect of TANGIER from the Land | it beeing the South-West Side*; the landmarks identified with their names; at the foot, towards the r., by the artist, *W. Hollar delineavit | 1669*.

PROV.: As for No. 18.
5214–19 (L.B.33(b)).

ETCH.: By Hollar, with modifications in

the foreground, and with the title, *Prospect of TANGIER from the S. West* (Parthey, No. 1199).

BIBL. & REPR.: *Sloane Cat.*, p. 129, No. 19. Routh (*See* prefatory note to this series of drawings), p. 156. *Sprinzels*, p. 114, No. 374. *Vertue*, IV, p. 197.

No such flag as that shown on Peterborough Tower is known to have existed, and it seems likely that this is a misrepresentation of the Union Flag, which indeed is correctly shown in the related etching (*Parthey*, No. 1199).

29. TANGIER FROM THE S.W. Study for No. 28 and taken from the same viewpoint, but without figures. On the l., a separate slip of paper (5 × 13·9 cm.), hinged to the drawing, showing an alteration in the lie of the land on which stands Whitehall Fort.   **Plate 158 (a)**

Pen and brown ink, with washes of brown and grey and water-colours; on five conjoined pieces of paper; 31 × 79·8 cm. (12¼ × 31⅜ in.).

INSCR.: *Recto*, at the top, by the artist, *Tangier from S.W.*; the landmarks identified with their names; in the upper r.-hand

corner, in a later hand, *Handed over to Lieut. Skinner Royal Eng^rs | by his Father— in 1872—*.

PROV.: Lt.-General William Skinner, R.E. J. Skinner. Lieut. Monier Skinner, R.E. War Office, whence it was transferred to B.M., Dept. of MSS., 1887. Transferred to Dept. of Prints & Drawings, Nov. 1932.

1932–11–3–3.

BIBL.: *B.M., Cat. Add. MSS.,* 1889, p. 278, No. 33,233 (9). *Sprinzels,* p. 114, No. 375.

30. TANGIER FROM THE S. View from a grassy slope taken from a point rather more to the E. than in Nos. 28 and 29, showing the outlying forts which encircle the town, from l. to r.: Charles Fort, Catherine Fort, Whitehall, Fount Fort, Bridges Fort, and Cambridge Fort. In the centre, Peterborough Tower (flying the same flag as in No. 28) from which the town with its fortifications descends to the Bay. In the distance, the coast of Spain and Gibraltar.   Plate 159 (a)

Pen and ink, with grey wash and water-colours; on six conjoined pieces of paper; 19·3 × 109·2 cm. (7⅝ × 43⅛ in.).

INSCR.: *Recto,* at the top, by the artist, *Tangier from the Land, it beeing the South Side;* the landmarks identified with their names; in the upper r.-hand corner, in a later hand,

Handed over to Lieut!. Monier Skinner Royal Eng.ʳˢ | by his Father in 1872—.

PROV.: As for No. 29.

1932–11–3–5.

BIBL.: *B.M., Cat. Add. MSS.,* 1889, p. 278, No. 33,233 (9). *Sprinzels,* p. 114, No. 373.

31. VIEW FROM PETERBOROUGH TOWER, TANGIER CASTLE. View from the summit of the Tower, which commands an extensive prospect to the S.W. over grassy and undulating country, dotted in mid-distance with outlying forts. Immediately below, in the centre, a bastion on which are groups of red-coated soldiers conversing. To the l., part of the town and its fortifications, including Catherine Fort, and on the extreme l., the bay. To the r., a party of musketeers on the path leading to Henrietta Fort, and below, on the extreme r., Whitby Mole and the Atlantic Ocean.   Plate 160 (b)

Pen and brown ink, with water-colours; on nine conjoined pieces of paper; 28·1 × 102·2 cm. (11⅛ × 40⅛ in.).

INSCR.: *Recto,* at the top, by the artist, *A Prospect of the Lands and Forts, within yᵉ Line of Communication | before Tangier, now in the Possession of the English, drawne from Peter-borow | Tower, by Wenceslaus Hollar, his Majᵗⁱᵉˢ designer, in September A.º 1669;* the landmarks identified with their names.

PROV.: As for No. 18.

5214–20 (L.B.34(b)).

BIBL. & REPR.: *Sloane Cat.,* p. 129, No. 20. *Routh* (See prefatory note to this series of drawings), p. 296. *Sprinzels,* p. 116, No. 387, & Pl. 60/61, No. 301. *Vertue,* IV, p. 197.

32. THE SETTLEMENT AT WHITBY, W. OF TANGIER. View looking N.W. from the road to Tangier which leads down a slope from the l. to the settlement, r. A group of buildings round a courtyard overlooking the shore from which a curved mole runs out into the sea. Below, in the centre, a large number of men quarrying the cliff beyond which the ground rises steeply in a line of grassy hills ending in Cape

Spartel. In mid-distance, Henrietta Fort, and below it, near the water, another fort, The Drop (or Devil's Drop). In the foreground, a man and woman followed by another man driving a pack-ass descending the road towards Whitby, while four musketeers ascend it on the l. in the direction of Tangier.　　　**Plate 160 (a)**

Pen and brown ink, with grey wash and water-colours; on seven conjoined pieces of paper; 28 × 97·9 cm. (11 × 38½ in.).

INSCR.: *Recto*, at the top, by the artist, *Prospect of Whitby by Tangier, where the | Stone for the Mould is fetsh'd, and the Workmen | doe quarter, drawne from the S.E. by W.H.*, and in

the lower r.-hand corner, by the artist, *W. Hollar fecit 1669.*

PROV.: As for No. 18.
5214–21 (L.B.34(a)).

BIBL.: *Sloane Cat.*, p. 129, No. 21. *Sprinzels*, p. 116, No. 386. *Vertue*, IV, p. 197.

33. *Recto.* **OUTLYING FORTS IN THE VICINITY OF TANGIER.** An extensive prospect, from near the E. end of the town looking S.W. over undulating and grassy country. In the foreground, Bridges Fort and beyond it, Fount Fort. Further off, l., on an eminence, Monmouth Fort, from which a palisade runs down the slope to the l. From near Bridges Fort, a road disappearing over the brow of a hill. In the distance, r., Charles Fort.

Black lead, strengthened in part with pen and ink and tinted in water-colours; on eight conjoined pieces of paper; 10·6 × 124·6 cm. (4¼ × 49⅛ in.).

INSCR.: The landmarks identified with their names, together with other notes by the artist.

Verso. **FOUR SEPARATE VIEWS OF OUTLYING FORTS.** (1) Catherine Fort and Norwood Fort from the N.E. (2) Distant view of Charles Fort from the E. (3) The path leading down to Whitehall Fort, looking E., with part of the city on the l. (4) James Fort and Ann's Fort from the N.

Black lead, with slight grey wash; damaged and partly obliterated.

INSCR.: The various landmarks identified by their names.

PROV.: As for No. 29.
1932–11–3–6.

BIBL.: *B.M., Cat. Add. MSS.,* 1889, p. 278, No. 33,233 (9). *Sprinzels*, p. 116, No. 388.

34. TANGIER FROM THE W. View from a grassy slope looking towards the town, with Peterborough Tower on the l. and the bay in mid-distance, centre. On the r., undulating country dotted with outlying forts. On the extreme l., the distant coast of Spain. In the foreground, two red-coated musketeers marching towards the l., and below, three horsemen riding away towards the r. up the opposite bank.
　　　Plate 159 (b)

Pen and brown ink, with grey wash and water-colours; on four conjoined pieces of paper; 22·8 × 84·9 cm. (9 × 33⅝ in.).

INSCR.: *Recto*, at the top, by the artist, *Prospect of TANGIER from the West*; the landmarks identified with their names; in the lower r.-hand corner, by the artist, *W. Hollar fecit. 1669.*

PROV.: As for No. 18.
5214–17 (L.B.32).

ETCH.: The central portion etched, with modifications to the foreground, by Hollar,

with the lettering, *Prospect of yᵉ lower part of Tangier, from the hill West of White-hall* (Parthey, No. 1190).

BIBL. & REPR.: *Sloane Cat.*, p. 129, No. 17. *Sprinzels*, p. 115, No. 376, & Pl. 60/61, No. 300. *Vertue*, IV, p. 197.

35. TANGIER FROM THE SEA. View looking S. over the water towards the city and fortifications, prominent among which are York Castle, the Upper Castle and Governor's House, and Peterborough Tower. On the l., the mole jutting out into the sea, and on the extreme r., the settlement of Whitby with Charles Fort on the hill above it. In the immediate foreground, two naval vessels, an English two-decker l. and a ketch r., under way, flying the red ensign. **Plate 161 (b)**

Pen and brown ink, with grey wash and water-colours; on five conjoined slips of paper; 21·3 × 90·7 cm. (8⅜ × 35⅝ in.).

INSCR.: *Recto*, at the top, by the artist, *Prospect of TANGIER from the Sea | it being the North side, opposite to Spaine. | 1669. by W. Hollar*; the landmarks identified by their

names; in the lower r.-hand corner, *W. Hollar fecit.*

PROV.: As for No. 18.
5214–18 (L.B.33(a)).

BIBL. & REPR.: *Sloane Cat.*, p. 129, No. 18. *Sprinzels*, p. 115, No. 380, & Pl. 60/61, No. 199. *Vertue*, IV, p. 197.

36. TANGIER FROM THE SEA. Study for No. 35 and taken from the same viewpoint, but without the ships. **Plate 161 (a)**

Pen and brown ink, with grey wash and water-colours; on three conjoined sheets of paper; 16·4 × 86·2 cm. (6½ × 34 in.).

INSCR.: *Recto*, at the top, by the artist, *Tangier from the Maÿne Sea and Opposite to Spaÿne | it beeing ye (?) North Side*; the landmarks identified with their names; at the top, in a later hand, (*By Sir Martin Beckman*) and *Handed over to Lieutᵗ. Monier Skinner Rˡ Engʳˢ | by his father in 1872. J.S.*

PROV.: As for No. 29.
1932–11–3–4.

BIBL. & REPR.: *B.M., Cat. Add. MSS.*, 1889, p. 278, No. 33,233 (9). *Sprinzels*, p. 115, No. 379, & Pl. 59, No. 296.

The attribution is no doubt due to the fact that Beckman (*q.v.*) was at Tangier, seven years before Hollar's visit, and during his stay there made plans of the town and its surroundings for which he drew up a scheme of fortification. Two of these plans, drawn on vellum, are in the Dept. of Printed Books (K. 117.77 & 78).

37. TANGIER FROM THE BAY. View looking W. over the water, with the town and Irish Battery on the l., and the main fortifications, York Castle, the Upper Castle, and Peterborough Tower, on rising ground in the centre. On the r., the mole juttin out diagonally into the foreground, and beyond it, three ships standing out to sea.

Pen and brown ink, with grey wash, tinted in water-colours; on two conjoined sheets of paper; 15·2 × 81·4 cm. (6 × 32⅛ in.).

INSCR.: *Recto*, at the top, by the artist, *Tangier from the Bay it being the East Side*; the landmarks identified with their names; at the top, in a later hand, *By Sir Martin Beckman.* and *Handed over to Lieut!. Monier Skinner R! Eng.ʳˢ | by his father in 1872. J S.*

PROV.: As for No. 29.
1932–11–3–2.

ETCH.: By Hollar, with ships added on the l. and other modifications, and with the title, *Prospect of TANGIER from the East* (Parthey, No. 1200).

BIBL. & REPR.: *B.M., Cat. Add. MSS.*, 1889, p. 278, No. 33,233 (9). *Sprinzels*, p. 116, No. 382, Pl. 62, No. 308.

38. TANGIER FROM THE STRAITS OF GIBRALTAR. Prospect of the Barbary Coast, extending from Apes Hill (Abyla) and Cape Malabata, l., to Cape Spartel, r., looking S. over the water towards the Bay of Tangier with Tangier to the r.

Pen and brown ink, with grey wash, tinted in water-colours; on six conjoined pieces of paper; 10·9 × 112·5 cm. (4⅜ × 44 in.).

INSCR.: *Recto*, at the top, by the artist, *Coast of Barbary within the Streigts opposite to Spaine | at a Leagues distance*; the landmarks identified with their names; at the foot, in a later hand, *Handed over to Lieut! Monier Skinner R! Engrs | by his Father in 1872.*

PROV.: As for No. 29.
1932–11–3–1.

BIBL. & REPR.: *B.M., Cat. Add. MSS.*, 1889, p. 278, No. 33,233 (9). *Sprinzels*, p. 116, No. 385, & Pl. 63, No. 309.

39. THE STRAITS OF GIBRALTAR FROM TANGIER. Prospect of the Spanish coast seen from across the Straits, looking N. from Tangier opposite which is Tarifa (Teriffa). On the extreme r., Gibraltar and the coast of Malaga. Three ships, at various distances away, in the Straits.

Pen and brown ink, with grey wash, tinted in water-colours; on two conjoined sheets of paper; 9·8 × 62·9 cm. (3⅞ × 24¾ in.).

INSCR.: *Recto*, at the top, by the artist, *Prospect of the Straights of Gibraltar from Tangier*, and below, *Coast of Spain*; the landmarks identified with their names.

PROV.: William Esdaile (*Lugt*, No. 2617. Sale, Christie, 20:vi:1840, Lot 556). W.B. Tiffin, from whom it was purchased by the B.M., 1854.
1854–8–13–23 (L.B.31(a)).

BIBL. & REPR.: *Sprinzels*, p. 116, No. 384(a), & Pl. 63, No. 313.

40. THE STRAITS OF GIBRALTAR FROM THE W. APPROACH. Prospect of the Barbary Coast, seen from across the Straits, looking S.E., extending from Ceuta and Apes Hill (Abyla), l., to Cape Spartel, r., with the Bay of Tangier in the centre.

On the extreme l., the Mediterranean Sea, and on the r., the Atlantic Ocean. In the foreground, r., an English ship and a felucca.

Pen and brown ink, with grey wash, tinted in water-colours; on two conjoined sheets of paper; 10·4 × 63·1 cm. (4⅛ × 24⅞ in.).

INSCR.: *Recto*, at the top, by the artist, *Prospect of the Straights of Gibraltar as you come | from Cadiz from about the middle yᵉ Chanell*; below, *Coast of Barbary*, and the landmarks identified with their names.

PROV. As for No. 39.
1854-8-12-24 (L.B.31(b)).

BIBL. & REPR.: Sprinzels, p. 116, No. 384(b), & Pl. 63, No. 312.

41. PLAN OF THE SETTLEMENT OF WHITBY NEAR TANGIER.

Pen and brown ink, partly ruled, with washes of brown and blue; 29·7 × 35·3 cm. (11⅝ × 13⅞ in.).

INSCR.: *Recto*, at the top, by the artist, *Groundplott of Whitby by Tangier 1669*; some of the features identified with their names, others with letters referring to a key in the upper l.-hand corner; in the lower l.-hand corner, by the artist, *W. Hollar fecit*.

PROV.: As for No. 18.
5214-15 (L.B.36).

BIBL.: *Sloane Cat.*, p. 128, No. 15. Sprinzels, p. 116, No. 389. *Vertue*, IV, p. 197.

[42-46]. PORTRAIT AND FIGURE STUDIES.

42. STUDY OF A WOMAN IN BLACK. W.L. figure, in profile, walking on a pavement towards the r. Wearing a wide-brimmed black hat with high crown, a white collar, and a black tunic over a long black gown. Her hands tucked into a muff or her sleeves. Her figure sharply silhouetted against a yellow lighted background.

Plate 163

Oil-colours on paper; 19 × 11 cm. (7½ × 4⅜ in.).

INSCR.: *Verso*, at the top, *W C. Nᵒ 5*.

PROV.: As for No. 18.
5214-3 (L.B.4).

BIBL.: *Sloane Cat.*, p. 127, No. 3. Sprinzels, p. 61, No. 20.

See note to No. 43.

43. STUDY OF A WOMAN IN BLACK, WEARING A HOOD. W.L. figure, in profile, walking towards the r. Wearing a black hood concealing her face, a cape over her shoulders, and a long black gown, a fold of which she holds before her while the skirt trails out behind. The upper part of her figure sharply silhouetted against a yellow lighted background, the lower part in shadow.

Plate 164

Oil-colours on paper; 18·7 × 10·4 cm. (7⅜ × 4⅛ in.).

INSCR.: *Verso*, at the top, *W.C N4*.

PROV.: As for No. 18.
5214-4 (L.B.5).

BIBL.: *Sloane Cat.*, p. 127, No. 4. *Sprinzels*, p. 61, No. 19.

The attribution to Hollar of this interesting oil-sketch and of its companion (No. 42) must date from at least the time of Sir Hans Sloane. In technique they are unlike any known work by Hollar, though in subject they may be compared with his etchings of female costume, *Theatrvm Mvliervm* (Parthey, Nos. 1804–1907) and *Ornatvs Mvliebris Anglicanus, 1640* (Parthey, Nos. 1778–1803). In particular the present sketch is not unlike the figure of the woman in hood and mask in the latter series (*Parthey*, No. 1789). The two subjects are each called in the *Sloane Catalogue* 'costume of a German Lady in Black with hood on'.

44. PHILIP, 4th EARL OF PEMBROKE, AFTER VAN DYCK. Bust, turned half-r., with eyes looking to front. Wearing long curling hair, moustache and pointed beard, broad lace-edged collar, and the Lesser George hanging from his neck by a ribbon.

Pen and ink, with grey wash, touched with pen and light brown ink in the hair; oval; $7 \cdot 6 \times 5 \cdot 7$ cm. ($3 \times 2\frac{1}{4}$ in.).

INSCR.: *Recto*, on either side of the bust, by the artist, l., *A. Van Dyck | Pinx.*, and r., *W. Hollar | delin.*

PROV.: The Rev. C. M. Cracherode, by whom it was bequeathed to the B.M., 1799.
G.g. 1–446 (L.B.1(a)).

ENGR.: By William Faithorne (*Fagan*, p. 53) or by George Glover (*Colvin & Hind*, p. 150, and *B.M. Engraved Portraits*, III, p. 440, No. 8).

BIBL.: *Cracherode Cat.*, p. 99, No. 446. *Sprinzels*, p. 60, No. 6.

[Philip Herbert, 4th Earl of Pembroke and 1st Earl of Montgomery (B. 1584: D. 1650). After enjoying royal favour under James I and Charles I, sided with the Parliament during the Civil War. Was a great patron of the arts and especially of Van Dyck, and rebuilt parts of his seat, Wilton House, on a magnificent scale to the designs of Salomon de Caus and John Webb.]

The present drawing does not correspond exactly with any of the known portraits of Lord Pembroke by Van Dyck.

45. WILLIAM OUGHTRED. Bust, turned three-quarter l. Wearing moustache and beard, skull-cap and broad white collar.   Plate 166

Black lead; $7 \cdot 2 \times 7 \cdot 1$ cm. ($2\frac{7}{8} \times 2\frac{3}{4}$ in.).

INSCR.: *Recto*, in the upper r.-hand corner, by the artist, *M.ͬ Oughtred | Hollar deli . . . .*

PROV.: As for No. 44.
G.g. 1–449 (L.B.1(b)).

BIBL.: *Cracherode Cat.*, p. 99, No. 449. *Sprinzels*, p. 60, No. 7, & Pl. 2, No. 17.

[William Oughtred (B. 1575: D. 1660). Mathematician and divine. Was rector of Albury in Surrey from 1610 to the time of his death. Published his well-known textbook on algebra and arithmetic, *Clavis Mathematicae*, in 1648, for which Hollar etched, as a frontispiece, a portrait of the author.]

The portrait differs from the present drawing in that it shows the sitter H.L. turned slightly to r. (*Parthey*, No. 1477). Both John Evelyn (*Numismata*, 1697, p. 341) and John Aubrey (*Natural History and Antiquities of . . . Surrey*, 1718, IV, pp. 70–1) mention the etched portrait with high approbation.

46. PORTRAIT OF A LADY. H.L., turned half-l., with eyes looking to front. Wearing a small coif on the back of her head, a broad collar over the shoulders of her dark gown, and earrings. In an oval. **Plate 166**

Pen and ink on vellum; 7·2 × 6·5 cm. (2⅞ × 2⅝ in.).

INSCR.: *Verso*, in the upper r.-hand corner, *Tr* (?) *2.*

PROV.: P. & D. Colnaghi, from whom it was purchased by the B.M., 1863. **1863–11–14–745** (L.B.2).

BIBL. & REPR.: *Sprinzels*, p. 60, No. 11, & Pl. 11, No. 65.

[47–51]. MISCELLANEOUS.

47. *Recto.* **STUDY OF A MUFF.** A fur muff with a brocade or embroidered band round the centre. **Plate 165**

Brush drawing in black wash, heightened with white, on a grey prepared ground; 6·9 × 9·6 cm. (2¾ × 3¾ in.).

Verso. **PART OF A STUDY OF NIOBE.** Niobe looking up at, and fleeing from, Apollo's bow and arrow, part of which appear in the upper l.-hand corner.

Red chalk, strengthened with pen and ink.

PROV.: As for No. 18. **5214–7** (L.B.6).

ETCH.: The muff only, by Hollar, in

reverse, with the date *1647 (Parthey*, No. 1946).

BIBL. & REPR.: *Sloane Cat.*, p. 127, No. 7. *Parker. Sprinzels*, p. 61, No. 21, & Pl. 2, No. 12 (the muff only).

48. DESIGN FOR THE TITLE-PAGE TO 'CLIDAMAS OR THE SICILIAN TALE', 1639. A double scrolled cartouche adorned with festoons of fruit and inscribed *CLIDAMAS | or | The Sicilian Tale | by I. S. | LONDON | Printed by Th: Paine. | 1639.* At the top, kneeling on the cartouche, a *putto*, supporting on either side of him a wreathed medallion, containing scenes from the novel, *viz.*: l., a fight between galleys, probably those of the Duke of Medina Sidonia and of the pirate Martoll (pp. 45–57) or of the King of Tunis (pp. 105–7); and r., a man greeting a woman, perhaps intended for Hormisda presenting the enchanted gloves to Callanthia or Florella (p. 118). The whole composition on a brown ground. **Plate 165**

Pen and brown wash over black lead; 12·3 × 7·4 cm. (4⅞ × 2⅞ in.).

INSCR.: *Recto*, in the lower l.-hand corner, *B.*

PROV.: John Bagford. Robert Harley, 1st Earl, and Edward Harley, 2nd Earl of

Oxford. Purchased by the B.M., 1753. Transferred to Dept. of Prints & Drawings, 1814. **E.e. 2–35** (L.B.7).

ETCH.: By Hollar, with modifications of the scrollwork of the cartouche (*Parthey*, No. 2655; *Johnson*, p. 27, No. 1).

BIBL. & REPR.: *Drawings Presented and Purchased*, p. 50. *Sprinzels*, p. 68, No. 78, & Pl. 4, No. 25.

The identity of 'I.S.', the author of this little romantic novel, has not been established.

49. *Recto.* **A SEA FIGHT.** An English two-decker, with a St. George's flag at the main, seen starboard bow view, engaged with a smaller ship to the r. of uncertain nationality.

Pen and ink, with grey wash, tinted in watercolours; 8·4 × 8·9 cm. (3¼ × 3½ in.).

Verso. **A SMALL DUTCH VESSEL.**

Pen and ink.

INSCR.: In the upper l.-hand corner, 6.

PROV.: W. & G. Smith, from whom it was purchased by the B.M., 1850.
1850–2–23–189 (L.B.29(b)).

BIBL. & REPR.: *Sprinzels*, p. 69, No. 87, & Pl. 8, No. 54.

50. A PAIR OF STOCKS, AND TWO MEN READING A PAPER (AFTER JACOB DE GHEYN). At the top, a pair of stocks with six leg holes. Below, two men, the elder, l., wearing glasses, looking over the shoulder of the younger, r., who holds a sheet of paper.

Metalpoint; 10·5 × 11·1 cm. (4⅛ × 4⅜ in.).

PROV.: Sir Thomas Lawrence (*Lugt*, No. 2445). W. & G. Smith, from whom it was purchased by the B.M., 1850.
1850–2–23–191 (L.B. 8(b)).

BIBL. & REPR.: *Popham, Hollar*, p. 29. *Altena*, p. 27, Pl. 4.
A leaf from a sketchbook of which another is described at No. 2.

The two men are copied from figures in the centre of the picture by Jacob de Gheyn II of *Julius Caesar dictating his despatches on horseback* at Ham House. De Gheyn seems to have been in London in 1618 and again in 1622 (*See Altena*, p. 15) and may have painted this picture either for Sir Thomas Vavasour, first owner of Ham, or his successor, John Ramsay, Earl of Holderness.

51. THE HEAD AND HIND LEGS OF A HORSE'S CARCASS.

Metalpoint; 16·3 × 15·4 cm. (6⅜ × 6 in.).

INSCR.: *Recto*, in the upper r.-hand corner, 45 or 48.

PROV.: Vivant-Denon (*Lugt*, No. 779). Sir Thomas Lawrence (*Lugt*, No. 2445). J. P. Heseltine, from whom it was purchased by the B.M., 1886.
1886–5–13–3.

BIBL.: *Popham, Hollar*, p. 30.

A leaf from a sketchbook. Three other studies of dead horses from the same book, numbered 46, 47 and 49, are in the Louvre (Vallardi Coll., Nos. 02401, 02402 & 02404), and a fourth is in the collection of the late Mr. Paul Oppé.

HONDIUS, ABRAHAM

B. between 1625 and 30: D. 1691

Animal, genre and history painter

Born at Rotterdam, the son of the city stone-mason, Daniel Abramsz Hondius. Buckeridge gives the following account of his work: 'He was a Painter whose manner was universal. He drew history, landskip [including, according to Auction sale catalogues, "Several Ruined Pieces"], cielings, and small figures; but above all the rest, beasts and hunting pieces were his principal study. In all these kinds his colouring was often extravagant, and his draft as commonly uncorrect. He delighted much in a fiery tint, and a harsh way of pencilling, so that few of his pictures being without this distinguishing mark, his Paintings are easy to be known.' His earliest recorded picture, a *Wild Boar Hunt* (coll. A. Friedman, Stockholm) dated *1651*. Other early pictures include a *Hunting Party outside an Inn*, 1653 (Lady Chesham Sale, Christie's, 13:vii:1951, Lot 12) and a *Bear Hunt* (Sale, Hotel Drouot, Paris, 22:v:1925). Married Gertruyd Willems van der Eyck in 1653. Most of his works signed with the Latin form of his name *Hondius*, but one, a *Return from the Hunt* (Hallwyl Museum, Stockholm) is signed and dated *A D Hondt 1657*. Was still living in Rotterdam in 1659, but is said to have removed to Amsterdam by the following year. May perhaps have gone almost immediately to Italy, and have spent some considerable time there as suggested by his *Roman Carnival at Night* (Gemälde-Gallerie, Schwerin) dated *1660* and his *Battle of the Nicolotti and Castellani on the Ponte dei Pugni at S. Barnabà, Venice* (Hauser Sale, Sotheby, 23:vi:1937, Lot 52) dated *1666*. Also at this period painted religious subjects, including a *Nativity* (Barbier Sale, Brussels, 12–13:vi:1912), dated *1669*, which shows strongly the influence of Jan Lys. Other pictures, mainly animal and sporting subjects, recorded with the dates between 1662 and 1670. In England by 1674 and painted a view of the frozen Thames (London Museum) dated *1677*. Also in 1677 painted his celebrated *Dog Markett*, noted by Vertue as in a Mr. Halstead's Sale in 1726, and now, or lately in the collection of Mr. G. Massey, London. Vertue also noted 'a large picture bear bating by Hondius—much like Snyders' in Thomas Rawlinson's Sale, 1734. Other pictures of a similar nature, presumably painted in England, include a *Bull baiting* signed *Abraham Hondivs 1678*, and four hunting scenes panelled into the walls of the Dining Room at Easton Neston. His activities as a ceiling-painter not recorded, at least as far as this country is concerned, though a curious allegorical composition of the *Elements* (?), once in the possession of Mr. F. Drey, may indicate what he was prepared to do in this vein. Etched a number of animal and sporting subjects, including a large plate of a *Wild Sow and her Litter attacked by Hounds*, a *Man with a Hare and Hounds* (published by John Smith) and a set of six animal subjects with a title-page of *Two Hunters and Hounds* (published by R. Thompson). His self-portrait, holding a board with a drawing of Minerva on it, engraved in mezzotint by John Smith. Lived first on Ludgate Hill, and later in the parish of St. Dunstan's in the West. His first wife probably dead before he came to England, as Walpole (apparently quoting Vertue, though the reference has not so far been found) says that he was a man of humour, and that one of his maxims was that 'the goods of other men might be used as our own; and that finding another man's wife of the same mind, he took and kept her till she died, after which he married'. According to Buckeridge was 'for many years, afflicted with the gout so severely, that he had prodigious swellings, and chalk-stones in most of his joints, the effects of a sedentery and irregular life.' Eventually died from the effects of this 'distemper in September, 1691, at the Blackmores hd against Water Lane [now Whitefriars St.] Fleetstreet', and was buried on the 17th of that month 'in a woollen shroud' in the 'U. G.' [Upper Ground] of St. Bride's, his name being recorded as 'Abraham Hondiens, painter'. In his Will, made on Sept. 10th, 1691, bequeathed to his wife Sarah 'two peeces of Landskipp half Lengths, And eight of [his] best small peeces, with [his] owne picture', the rest of his pictures to be sold to defray the funeral expenses. To his son Abraham (also a painter) he bequeathed for 'his owne proper use' his 'prints, books and drawings'.

BIBL.: *St. Bride's Register*, 17:ix:1691. *C.C.L.* 43, *f.* 296. *Buckeridge*, p. 389. *Walpole*, II, p. 440. *D.N.B.*, XXVII, 1891, pp. 241–2 (with *Bibl.*). *T.-B.*, XVII, 1924, pp. 434–5 (with *Bibl.*). *Vertue, Index*, p. 117. *Vertue*, VI, p. 234. *Ogden*, p. 221 (*Index*). *Witt, Repr.*

1. A GREYHOUND BITCH. Standing in profile to l., her tail between her legs. **Plate 167**

Black chalk; 20·7 × 32 cm. (8⅛ × 12⅝ in.).

INSCR.: *Recto*, in the lower l.-hand corner, by the artist, *Abraham Hondiūs / 1682.*

PROV.: Edward Verrall Lucas, by whom it was presented to the B.M., 1910.
1910–12–2–48.

BIBL.: *Delbanco*, p. 41.

According to the date, this and the following three studies (Nos. 2–4) would have been made in England.

2. TWO STUDIES OF A SPANIEL. Both showing him lying on the ground towards the l., one with his head up and tongue lolling, the other asleep. **Plate 168**

Black chalk; 19·6 × 33·5 cm. (7¾ × 13¼ in.).

PROV.: As for No. 1.
1910–12–2–49.

BIBL. & REPR. *Delbanco*, p. 41, Pl. 19.

3. FOUR STUDIES OF A DOG ASLEEP, LYING TOWARDS THE R.

Pen and brown ink over black chalk; 8 × 15·7 cm. (3⅛ × 6⅛ in.).

PROV.: As for No. 1.
1910–12–2–50.

4. A MASTIFF. Half-crouching towards the r., growling, with his l. paw outstretched.

Black chalk; 19·4 × 30·1 cm. (7⅝ × 11⅞ in.).

PROV.: As for No. 1.
1910–12–2–51.

BIBL. & REPR.: *Delbanco*, p. 40, Pl. 20.

JOHNSON OR JONSON, CORNELIUS

B. 1593: D. 1661/2
Portrait painter

Born in London, and baptized at the Dutch Church in Austin Friars on Oct. 14th, 1593. Son of Cornelius Johnson (or Jansz), and Jane le Grand, mentioned in the *Return of Aliens* for 1588 as then living in Duke's Place, Aldgate. The family, first of Cologne and then of Antwerp, probably settled in London at the time of the Duke of Alba's persecution in 1568. Nothing definite known of the artist's training, but Mr. Collins Baker thinks that he may have studied under the younger Marcus Gheeraerts, while his early pictures show the influence of Mytens and of Mierevelt. His earliest portrait dated 1617. Became one of the leading English artists of his day, being patronized by James I and Charles I, and was made by the latter 'His Majesty's servant in ye quality of picture maker'. Charged 'five broad pieces' (about £5) for a head, the bust size being a favourite with him. On July 16th, 1622, married Elizabeth Beke of Colchester. Up to 1636 lived in Blackfriars, and, for a time after that date with Sir Arnold Braems, a Netherlandish merchant, at Bridge near Canterbury, painting many portraits in that locality. Supplied Sir Theodore Mayerne with a note on the preparation of *Orpiment* (yellow arsenic or King's yellow), this being written in English, presumably by the artist himself. His later portraits show the influence of Van Dyck. Mr. Long and Mr. Edwards note a number of miniatures in oil on copper by him, and Mr. Long also refers to Johnson's acquaintance with John Hoskins, the well-known limner. The few drawings attributed to him, all in chalks, include, besides the one listed below, a near life-size and highly finished study of a widowed lady, in 1878 in the collection of the Queen of Saxony (Repr. in Dept.), another study of a widowed lady in the collection of Mr. C. R. Rudolf and a copy (formerly in the collection of Mr. Henry Oppenheimer) of a portrait group in oil in the collection of Sir George Leon, Bart. Retired to Holland in 1643, probably on account of the outbreak of the Civil War, his pass being dated Oct. 10th. Resided successively at Middleburg (where he joined the Guild of St. Luke), Amsterdam (1646), and The Hague (1647). Died, probably at Utrecht or Amsterdam, in the winter of 1661/2. Had a son, Cornelius III, who was practising as a limner in Utrecht as late as 1698. Another member of the family, his nephew, Theodore Roussel (Russel) was well-known for his small copies of portraits by Van Dyck and Lely. Various aliens called Cornelius Janssen or Johnson (which must have been a common name in the Netherlands) are mentioned in the Huguenot Soc. Publications, but none appears to be connected with the artist or his family.

BIBL.: *Mayerne, f.* 152. *Buckeridge,* p. 391. *Walpole,* I, p. 211. *D.N.B.,* XXIX, 1892, pp. 248–9. *Cust, Johnson. Baker, Johnson. Schneider. Edwards. Maison. Miller. Baker, Lely,* I, pp. 74–86. *Huguenot Society Publications,* X, Pt. II, p. 413. *Finberg. Long,* pp. 245–6. *Vertue, Index,* pp. 129–30. *Waterhouse,* pp. 38–9.

1. PORTRAIT OF A MAN, SAID TO BE THE ARTIST. Bust to r., with head turned half-r. and eyes to front. Wearing light-coloured or white hair falling in curls, slight moustache and tufted beard, and a cloak draped over his r. shoulder. In a feigned oval of scrollwork. **Plate 169**

Black chalk, heightened with white, on blue-grey paper; 27·1 × 22·1 cm. (10⅝ × 8¾ in.).

INSCR.: *Recto*, at the foot, to the r., *Se ipse Corn Iohnson delin.*

PROV.: W. H. Carpenter, by whom it was presented to the B.M., 1856.
    1856–1–12–379.

BIBL.: *Baker, Johnson. B.F.A.C.*, 1938, pp. 35–6 (No. 75).

In style this drawing is closely related to one in the collection of Mr. C. R. Rudolf, a portrait of a widowed lady, inscribed *C. Jons. van Keulen*, which in its turn appears to be connected in pose and costume with an oil-painting by Johnson, dated *1655*, formerly in the collection of Mrs. Joseph (*See Finberg*, p. 36, & Pl. LXXIX). Mr. Collins Baker

considers the present drawing to be an engraver's copy from an oil-painting, and its appearance certainly suggests this; it has in fact affinities with the later drawings kept as studio records by Edward Byng and others of the Kneller period. With regard to the inscription stating that it represents the artist, the drawing may be compared with the self-portrait engraved by Conrad Waumans during Johnson's lifetime in 1649, and with the portrait in a family group by Adriaen Hanneman (*See Schneider*, Pls. A–C). In both of these paintings, the sitter has light-coloured curling hair and a tufted beard and moustache, but the face in each case is rounder than in the drawing. As far as the picture in the N.P.G. is concerned (No. 1887), this has now been discredited as a self-portrait of Johnson, and certainly the present drawing has no connexion with it.

JOHNSON, THOMAS

Fl. c. 1634–76

Topographical and history painter, draughtsman and etcher

His earlier biography mainly derived from the Minutes of the Painter-Stainers' Company. First mentioned there on Jan. 24th, 1634, when he attended the company's court with the younger Robert Peake, Robert Greenbury and others. On Oct. 5th, 1640, was 'chosen into the Lyvery' and appointed to act as Steward on Lord Mayor's Day. On Dec. 4th of that year referred to as a 'picture-maker' when he complained of being insulted by one Powell, and on Dec. 16th appeared, in company with Marcus Garret (Gheeraerts), Gilbert Jackson, Thomas Brooker, Greenberry (Greenbury) and Thomas Eykes, to ask for freedom of the company as a measure of protection against 'the number of strangers & others who daily increase in & about this City'. His name further recorded in 1640/1 when he again

attended the court of the company. Is last mentioned in the Minutes of Oct. 8th, 1652, when he was appointed Renter Warden. During the mid-Commonwealth period worked at Canterbury where he made two drawings, a view of the Cathedral (noticed by Vertue in the Chapter Library, where it still hangs), signed and dated *F* (*sic* for *T*) *Johnson 1651*, and a distant prospect of the city from the North (Mr. Iolo Williams), signed *Tho. Johnson delin.*, which was etched by Hollar (*Parthey*, No. 961). Also painted a view of the inside of the Cathedral (in the collection of the late Mr. W. D. Caroë) dated *1657*, showing the Parliamentarian iconoclasts breaking the glass. Other views of Canterbury by him published as etchings by Hollar and Daniel King in Dugdale's *Monasticon*, 1655, and King's *Cathedrall and Convent-*

uall Churches, 1656. In 1657 and 1658 respectively painted two religious subjects, one of *Christ in the house of Mary and Martha* (coll. Mr. W. H. Woodward, 1926) the other of *St. Jerome in a church* (coll. the Earl of Berkeley). Later worked in Bath, where he executed the drawing described below, which is dated 1675, and where he etched a view of the Queen's Bath. Also drew a plan of the 'Hott and Cross Baths', etched by John Oliver in 1676. By 1685 appears to have returned to Canterbury, when as 'Mr. Johnson of Canterbury' he showed at a meeting of the Royal Society on May 13th of that year 'a curious prospect of the Cathedral of that city drawn by himself in oil-colours'. A garden prospect with an unidentified mansion and a distant view of the sea, lettered *T. Johnson Invent* and no doubt by the present artist, was engraved by William Sherwin (impression at the Society of Antiquaries, *Album, Westminster, Whitehall, St. James's etc.*, VI, p. 68). May be counted, with John Dunstall (*q.v.*), Daniel King (*q.v.*) and (later) Francis Place (*q.v.*), as one of the group of native topographical draughtsmen round Hollar, whose style Johnson certainly imitated in his distant view of Canterbury, though not in his later drawing of Bath. Has sometimes been wrongly identified with the portrait-engraver in line and mezzotint of the same name.

BIBL.: *Painter-Stainers' Minutes*, I, pp. 146, 149, 152, 153, 155, 160, 186, II, p. 20. *Bird*, IV, p. 399. *Walpole*, II, p. 370. *T.-B.*, XIX, 1926, p. 91 (with *Bibl.*). *B.F.A.C.*, p. 36, No. 76. *Vertue, Index*, p. 127.

1. THE KING'S BATH AND THE QUEEN'S BATH AT BATH, LOOKING

W. On the r., the King's Bath, and on the l., the Queen's Bath, both full of bathers of both sexes, watched by spectators from the surrounding balcony and houses. One house on the W. side with its parapet inscribed *ANNÆ REGINÆ* [*Anne of Denmark*] *SACRVM 1618*.   **Plate 171**

Pen and ink, with grey wash; indented for transfer; 33·5 × 47 cm. (13⅛ × 18½ in.).

INSCR.: *Recto*, at the top, in the centre, referring to various features of the baths, *A. Kings | B Queens bath | C the Kitchen under the Cros | D this table on the wall | in this Charakter—BLADVD, SON TO LVDHVDEB-RAS, | THE EIGHT KING OF THE BRITAINS | FROM BRUTE, A GREAT PHILOSOPHER | AND MATHEMATITIAN: BRED AT ATHENS, | AND RECORDED THE FIRST DISCOVERER, | AND FOVNDER OF THESE BATHES, EIGHT | HUNDRED SIXTY AND THREE YEARES | BEFORE CHRIST, THAT IS TWO THOWSAND | FIVE HVNDRED THIRTY FIVE YEARS | SINCE | ANNO DOMINI 1672 | E the dry Pump | F Bladuds picture | G the Parlor | H Francis Stoner of | Stoner Knight 1624*. [With an oval shield of arms], and in the lower l.-hand corner, *T. Johnson Delineāt 1675*.

PROV.: Messrs. Ellis and White, from whom it was purchased by the B.M., 1881. **1881–6–11–85** (L.B.1).

The King's Bath, the oldest of the baths, was so called since at least the XIII c. The wooden pavilion in the centre, known as the Cross, erected over the hot spring in 1663/4, replaced an earlier pavilion, and the recesses below it on the E. and W. sides were called the Kitchen from the high temperature of the water at this point. In the niche on the S. side was a statue, erected in in 1624 with the balustrade round the Bath, of Bladud, the mythical ancient British king and traditional founder of the bath. The adjoining New Bath was re-named the Queen's Bath in honour of Anne of Denmark's first visit in 1613 which the artist mistakenly gives as 1618.

JONES, INIGO

B. 1573 : D. 1652

Architect, painter and designer of stage scenery

Born in the parish of St. Bartholomew-the-Less, Smithfield, July 15th, 1573, the son of Inigo Jones, a cloth worker (D. 1573). Nothing known of his upbringing but he probably began his artistic career as a painter, the earliest reference to him, as 'Henygo Jones, a picture maker' occurring in a list of rewards, gifts, etc., in the household accounts of the Earl of Rutland. Said to have begun by painting landscapes, and one traditionally attributed to him is at Chatsworth. Was possibly in Italy in 1601 and is also said to have visited Denmark. Designed scenery for *The Masque of Blackness*, produced Jan. 6th, 1605, the first of a long line of court entertainments presented in conjunction with Ben Jonson (with whom he later quarrelled) as well as Samuel Daniel, Thomas Campion, George Chapman (to whom he erected a monument in 1634), Sir William Davenant and others. In his designs was influenced by the scene painters of the Tuscan court, Alfonso and Giulio Parigi, and probably also by Jacques Callot. In 1609 visited Paris 'carrying letters for His Majesty's service'. In 1611 was appointed surveyor to Prince Henry who died next year. Left for Italy with Lord Arundel in 1613, visiting Vicenza, Venice (where he met Scamozzi), Bologna (where he met Guercino aged 23 and drew his portrait), Rome, Naples, Genoa and Turin, returning in 1614. Used a copy of Palladio's *I Quattro Libri Dell' Architettura* (now at Worcester College, Oxford) as a commonplace book, keeping notes and measurements of antique buildings in it. Also kept a sketch book (now at Chatsworth) for copying paintings and drawings, showing him to have studied the work of Parmigianino, Polidoro, Fra Barto-lommeo, Andrea Schiavone, Raphael and Michelangelo. In 1615 made Surveyor of the King's Works. Appears as Member of Parliament in 1621. In 1628 took as pupil John Webb (B. 1611 : D. 1672) who married Jones's kinswoman, Anne. In 1634 made surveyor for the renovation of St. Paul's, taking no payment for his work there. Remained loyal to the King throughout the Rebellion, lending him £500 in 1642. On Oct. 14th, 1645, taken prisoner at Basing House and fined, but next year was pardoned, his estate being restored. On July 29th, 1650, made his Will, and two years later on June 21st, 1652, died at Somerset House and was buried beside his parents in St. Benet's Church on June 26th. Was reputed to have died a Catholic but Gregorio Panzani, Papal agent to this country from 1634, writing in 1636 called him 'puritanissimo fiero', probably indicating that he was a free thinker rather than a Puritan. Was largely responsible for the introduction into England of a true taste for Italian achievements in art through his splendid settings for the masques and through his foundation of the English Palladian school, which became a ruling influence in the architecture of this country. Also had a wide knowledge of Italian painting and advised collectors, notably Charles I, Lord Arundel and Lord Pembroke. Does not appear to have practised as an architect before his appointment as Surveyor in 1615, and the ascription to him of several 'Jacobean' houses, said to have been designed before his visit to Italy in 1614, cannot be maintained; nor did he design, as is often stated, the Gothic chapel of Lincoln's Inn. Authentic works by him include: The Queen's House, Greenwich (1616–35), Gateway at Oatlands

(1617), Banqueting House, Whitehall (1619–22), Gateway at Beaufort House, Chelsea (1621), Queen's Chapel at St. James's (1623–7), Queen's Chapel at Somerset House (1629–35), St. Paul's Covent Garden (1638: burnt and rebuilt 1795), Winchester Cathedral screen (finished 1638), Wilton House (1649). His style in domestic architecture and stage scenery continued into the Commonwealth period by his relative and assistant John Webb. His influence also to be seen in the work of Sir Roger Pratt at Coleshill. As a draughtsman shows the influence of the Italian Mannerists, especially Parmigianino and Andrea Schiavone. His scenic designs are naturally allied to those of the Parigi, the landscapes in them having affinities with the early drawings by Guercino. The purely architectural drawings rather naturally seem to have been influenced by those of Palladio, many examples of which he had collected.

BIBL.: *Simpson & Bell. Gotch. Wittkower. Gordon. Vertue, Index, p. 127. Wittkower, Inigo Jones. Keith. Gotch, Itinerary.*

1. THE DEATH OF LUCRETIA. Lucretia leaning back in a chair, supported by her father, l., while her husband pulls the dagger from her breast, and a maid bends over her from behind.

Pen and brown ink; outline indented: 25·3 × 18·6 cm. (10 × 7¼ in.).

PROV.: Sir Hans Sloane, Bart., by whom it was bequeathed to the B.M., 1753.
5224–3 (L.B.1).

BIBL.: *Sloane Cat.*, p. 179.

The head of Lucretia appears to have been taken from an etching of the Entombment by Parmigianino (*Bartsch*, XVI, 8, 5).

2. ELEVEN STUDIES OF HEADS ARRANGED IN THREE ROWS. Six of elderly bearded men, three of whom wear Phrygian caps, and five of young women.

Plate 170

Pen and brown ink; 25·1 × 19·5 cm. (9⅞ × 7⅝ in.).

PROV.: As for No. 1.

BIBL.: *Sloane Cat.*, p. 181.
5224–23 (L.B.2).

According to the catalogue of the Sloane Collection the above heads are said to be copied from Parmigianino; the head in the r.-hand top corner seems to derive from that of the Virgin in an etching of the Circumcision (*Bartsch*, XVI, 44, 10) while the old man, lower l., seems to be enlarged from a head in an etching of the Nativity (*Bartsch*, XVI, 7, 3). The others have not been identified with any known compositions.

3. STUDY OF TWO HEADS, PERHAPS AFTER POLIDORO. One of a woman looking down, the other of an elderly bearded man.

Pen and brown ink; 7·9 × 9·9 cm. (3¼ × 3⅞ in.).

PROV.: Hugh Howard. Dr. Robert Howard (Bishop of Elphin), and the Earls of Wicklow. Charles Howard, 5th Earl, from whom it was purchased by the B.M., 1874.
1874–8–8–127 (L.B.3a).

The head of the woman is not unlike two

studies in the Duke of Devonshire's Sketch-book, *f.* 10 *recto*, beside which is inscribed *dell polidor | a dissegnio*, thus indicating that they are probably copies from that master.

4. *Recto.* BUST OF A MAN WITH A POINTED BEARD. In profile to l.

Plate 172

Pen and brown ink; 9·5 × 7·8 cm. (3¾ × 3⅛ in.).

Verso. **PART OF A DECORATIVE COMPOSITION.** A scroll terminating in a *putto* and an eagle.

PROV.: As for No. 3.
1874–8–8–128 (L.B.3c).

The profile head on the *recto* appears, from the fashion of the pointed beard, to be a study of one of Inigo Jones's contemporaries, and, from its form, to have been copied perhaps from a medallion or some other relief.

5. HEAD OF A CHILD, PERHAPS AFTER RUBENS. In profile to l., looking down.

Pen and brown ink; 6·2 × 5·8 cm. (3⅜ × 2¼ in.).

PROV.: As for No. 3.
1874–8–8–129 (L.B.4c).

6. THREE STUDIES OF FEMALE HEADS. The first looking to r. and upwards, the second to l. and slightly upwards, the third to l., seen from beneath, fore-shortened.

Pen and brown ink; 10·4 × 16·2 cm. (4⅛ × 6⅜ in.).

PROV.: As for No. 3.
1874–8–8–130 (L.B.4d).

7. HEAD OF AN OLD MAN. In profile to r., bearded and bald.

Pen and brown ink; 7·9 × 7 cm. (3⅛ × 2¾ in.).

PROV.: As for No. 3.
1874–8–8–131 (L.B.3b).

8. THREE STUDIES OF HEADS AND SHOULDERS. An old man in the act of prayer and two youths, all looking to l.

Pen and brown ink; 7·8 × 11·4 cm. (3⅛ × 4½ in.).

PROV.: As for No. 3.
1874–8–8–132 (L.B.4a).

9. *Recto.* HEAD OF A MAN IN SOFT CAP, PROBABLY AFTER A GERMAN ORIGINAL. In profile to l.

Plate 172

Pen and brown ink; 8·7 × 5·5 cm. (3⅜ × 2⅛ in.).

Verso. **STUDY OF A PAIR OF LEGS.**

Plate 172

Pen and brown ink.

INSCR.: *Verso*, on the r., by the artist, *Inigo Jon*[es] and *J Inig*.

PROV.: As for No. 3.
1874–8–8–133 (L.B.4b).

10. SHEET OF STUDIES. In two rows. In the upper, from l. to r., a nude man carrying a dish, the head of a youth in profile to the l., and probably the same youth, full face. In the lower, from l. to r., a l. hand, a small nude figure partly draped, the head of a woman looking back over her l. shoulder, and a mouth, l. eye, l. ear and nose, probably of the youth noticed above. **Plate 173**

Pen and brown ink; 14·7 × 19·8 cm. (5¾ × 7⅞ in.).

Prov.: As for No. 1.
1874–8–8–134 (L.B.3d).

INSCR.: Verso, with part of a letter: *Mr. Damport* [Davenport (?)] *I desire that you would bee pleased | to lett Mr. : Surveyoᵣ : under-stand that yesterdaie here | was Mr. Dethicke gent to usher* [sic for 'usher to' (?)] *the Kinge and the Princes | gent usher; and they have given order to have | all the house and Princes lodgs made ready against | thursdaie; the yeomen hangers are at worke; and | they saie the Kinge and Prince intend to tarrey | here wᵗʰ: the Prince (and Prince* [struck out]*) Electoᵣ : and | Prince Robert* [sic for 'Prince Rupert' (?)]*; the glazeinge willbee the greates[t] matter that now I have to d . . . [do (?)] wch will be abound | in Tiltya:* [sic for 'Tiltyard'] *lodgs by reason the staire-cases | upp the Towers and other places must bee glassed | that did not use[d] [d struck out] to bee glased in Sumer; I shall | allsoe want the materialls in this warrant | extreamely by reason I have not anie at all in | stoare; and all the Princes lodgs must be used | and there is neither tables Cubbards; nor fformes | as yett: the matts in the Kings; Queenes; and | P[rinces] [cut away] lodges (?) as [t]hey will verey well [s]erve.*

The woman's head in the centre of the lower row, looking back over her left shoulder, should be compared with a rather similar study in the Duke of Devonshire's Sketch-book, *f.* 12 *recto*, at the foot of the page.

The letter which appears on the *verso* is addressed to a certain 'Mr. Damport' who is to notify 'Mr. Surveyor' that the King and the Prince intend to stay in company with the 'Prince Elector' and 'Prince Robert' at one of the royal residences. The writer of the letter has not as yet been identified. One 'John Damporte' a Carpenter appears in the Audit Office's declared accounts; in 1636 a payment of £75 was made to 'Humfrey Dethick' who may be identical with a man of that name who seems to have been a proctor in the Court of High Commission. Mr. Surveyor is presumably Inigo Jones. Prince Rupert and Prince Charles Lewis, the Prince Elector, accompanied Charles I and the Prince of Wales on a royal progress from July 18th to Sept. 21st, 1636. It has not yet been possible to identify the palace which may well be Theobalds.

[11–15.]. ELEVATIONS AND PLAN FOR WHITEHALL PALACE. Colen Campbell recorded that 'after much Labour and Expence I have at last procured these excellent Designs of *Inigo Jones* for *White-hall* from that ingenious Gentleman *William Emmet* of *Bromley* in the County of *Kent*, Esq; from whose Original Drawings the following 5 Plates are publish'd, whereby he has made a most valuable Present to the Sons of Art.' Miss Whinney has suggested that they were by some draughtsman in Jones's office other than John Webb. When he had them engraved Colen Campbell made a number of alterations, forcing elevations and plan to correspond and chastening the design. Notes in black-lead seem to be late 18th or early 19th century hand.

11. PLAN OF THE PRINCIPAL STORY. Plan of a palace with five courtyards, arranged symmetrically, with square towers at the four corners.

Pen and brown ink; damaged along the lower edge and in the upper r.-hand corner; 34·5 × 44·5 cm. (13½ × 17½ in.).

INSCR.: *Recto*, at the top, in black lead, *East* and *Plan of the First and Principal floor of the Palace at Whitehall*. At the l. side, in brown ink, *600 ft. Depth*.

PROV.: William Emmett. G. W. de Norman by whom it was presented to the B.M. 1848.
1848–8–5–22 (L.B.15).

ENGR.: *Vitruvius Britannicus*, II, Pls. 2–3.

REPR.: *Walpole Soc.*, XXXI, Pl. XVIa. *Architectural Review*, 1912, p. 346, Fig. 14.

BIBL.: *Campbell*, II, Fig. 14. *Gotch, Whitehall*, pp. 333–64. *Whinney*, p. 72.

This plan would have entailed the removal of the Banqueting House; as it stands the Palace would project into the river.

12. THE WEST WING FROM THE EAST. Drawn geometrically as to the centre and in perspective as to the wings. The interior of a large courtyard, with an elaborate entrance gateway, centre, which is joined by a two storied range to twin buildings one of which appears to be the Banqueting House. At either end a return wing joins the main building beneath a tower crowned by a cupola.

Pen and brown ink; in two sections; 30·4 × 123·8 cm. (12 × 48¾ in.).

INSCR.: *Recto*, in blacklead, over r.-hand building, *This part is executed and is | now the Chapel at Whitehall—having been | designed for a Banquetting Room*. Of an inscription in the same hand, in the centre, only the words *Palace, West* and *original* remain legible.

PROV.: As for No. 11.
1848–8–5–14 & 1848–8–5–15 (L.B.5 & 6).

ENGR.: H. Hulsbergh in *Vitruvius Britannicus*, II, Pls. 4–7.

REPR.: *Gotch*, Fig. 15. *Whinney*, Pl. XVIc.

BIBL.: See No. 11.

The return wings do not seem to have been included in the plan though the obliterations make this an uncertain point; they are not, however, shown on North or South elevations. The pediments on the Banqueting House windows are incorrectly arranged.

13. THE EAST FRONT. A long building of two stories with five pediments, two of which are broken. At either end is a square pavilion of three stories from the roof of which rises a drum supporting a cupola crowned by a lantern.

Pen and brown ink; in two sections, each of two conjoined sheets; 28·4 × 118·8 cm. (11⅛ × 46¾ in.).

INSCR.: *Recto*, in blacklead, *Whitehall*

Palace | Elevation toward the East | this is Jones's original.

PROV.: As for No. 11.
1848–8–5–12 & 1848–8–5–13 (L.B. 1 & 2).

ENGR.: H. Hulsbergh in *Vitruvius Britan-nicus*, II, Pls. 8–11.

BIBL.: As for No. 11.

In *Vitruvius Britannicus* Campbell reduced the number of windows on this elevation and replaced the broken pediments with un-broken ones.

14. THE SOUTH FRONT. A two story building, the lower floor of which forms an open arcade, the skyline being broken by two pediments and a number of statues. At either end is a three storied pavilion as in No. 13.

Pen and brown ink; in two sections, the r.-hand section damaged; $31 \cdot 3 \times 101 \cdot 5$ cm. ($12\frac{1}{4} \times 40\frac{1}{8}$ in.).

INSCR.: *Recto*, in black lead, *Whitehall Palace | [ele]vation towards the South | . B. this is Jones's original*.

PROV.: As for No. 11.

1848–8–5–10 & 1848–8–5–11 (L.B. 7 & 8).

ENGR.: H. Hulsbergh in *Vitruvius Britan-nicus*, II, Pls. 12–15.

REPR.: *Whinney*, Pl. XVIB.

BIBL.: As for No. 11.

15. SECTION FROM NORTH TO SOUTH FROM THE WEST. A three story building divided by four two story cross ranges into three courts. The middle court has in the centre an ornamented pavilion of four stories.

Pen and brown ink; r.-hand part damaged and repaired, $26 \cdot 2 \times 120$ cm. ($10\frac{3}{8} \times 47\frac{1}{4}$ in.).

INSCR.: *Recto*, in black lead, *White Hall Palace looking East | Jones's original*.

PROV.: As for No. 11.

1848–8–5–16 . . 17 (L.B. 3 & 4).

ENGR.: H. Hulsbergh in *Vitruvius Britan-nicus*, II, Pls. 16–19.

BIBL.: As for No. 11.

[16–18]. PLANS FOR A LARGE PALACE. These formed, with the designs for Whitehall and Colen Campbell's adaptations of them, part of the collection of William Emmett (*q.v.*) of Bromley, who described them in a letter preserved in a MS. volume of notes on architecture now among the Norman papers in the County Record Office at Maidstone:—

A True Copy of Letter I sent to Coll. Richard King concerning a very grand Designe of a Building, in order to show it to my Lord Bolingbrooke. Mr. Benson ye Chancelor of ye Excheqr. and ye Honble George Clarke Esqr.
Sr

Understanding by my Brother Emmett yt Mr. Clarke had lately seen a very great Plan or Designe for the Rebuilding White Hall, which he believes to be of Inigo Jone's own Drawing & Designing, I set myself immediately to ye perusing of a very large & noble Designe yt I have by me, ye account of which I here send you. The Hand yt drew it I am not able to determine, but submitt my self to better Judges—neither is it so neatly drawn as I have seen some Designes—handled, but this I may venture to say, that as it is ye largest, so I take it to be ye most Masterly & regular Design for the Beauty and symmetry of Architecturekeeping closely to the Best manner of ye Ancients yt yet I ever saw. There is some Writeing upon it with black lead either in Spanish or Italian, but ye few words that are laegible I take to be Italian, indeed ye whole is so Obliterated yt no sence can be made of it so as to know what ye Designe is, though I have tryed it with the best Glasses I could get.

There being no Scale to this Designe I have with great care Calculated one to it. And find ye front of this Designe to be 4304 feet, and in Depth 1920 Feet, which being Multiplied together Contains 8,263,680 Superficial Feet, and reducing them to Acres find yt this vast Designe Stands upon 189 Acres and a half of Ground, and 9060 Superficial Feet. whole Designe is Divided into Nine parts or Sections, and is again subdivided into three Equal Parts.

That which I take to be the Principal Front of this Designe consists of 13 Faces and Frontispieces, three of which are very large and uncommon, but very Grand, and of equal Dimentions, the other Frontispieces do not exceed a bow a 4th. part of one of ye great ones, the rest of ye Breaks and Faces to ye number of Seven make up ye Entire Front.

The Opposite Front Consists of ye same Sections, and is made up of 25 Breakes Faces & Frontispieces, Three of which are large and of equal Dimentions, with 5 Breakes & Faces to each Frontispieces, ye rest of ye Breakes and Faces to ye Number of 22 make up the Entire Front.

These Nine Parts or Sections which Constitute this great Designe, contain 57 Principal Courts & Quadrangles, of Square & oblong Figures, of great Dimentions, besides abundance of smaller Courts in each Section.

The first Section begining from ye laft hand contains 8 Principal Quadrangles. The Second, 3 very large ones. The Third answers to ye First. The Fourth hath also Eight Quadrangles, but differs from ye /d and first. The Fifth w.ch is ye center of ye Building contain 3 Quadrangles equal in Dimentions to ye Second Section.

So yt these four Sections to ye left hand contain 27 Principal Courts & Quad-rangles, ye other four Sections to ye right hand are ye same in Number & Dimen-tions, and exactly answer to ye four Sections on ye left hand, And ye Section in ye Middle haveing 3 Quadrangles which answer to ye Second and seventh, makes this great Designe to Consist of 57 Principal Courts & Quadrangles. Indeed ye whole Designe is Wonderfull & Surprising.

Sr if a Sight of this Designe would in ye least be Acceptable to my Lord Bolingbrooke, the Chancelor of the Excheqr. Mr. Clarke, or your Self, be pleased to Command it

I am Sr with all Respect your Obedient humble Servant to Command.

Bromley.   Willm Emmett.

May 1713.

From this it is clear that Emmett supposed all the sheets to join forming one plan for a ground floor; it is more probable that the 'three equal parts' were intended to be three stories. Even so the palace would have had some 18 courtyards, most of which were long and narrow, and it seems that a street was intended to run through it, crossed by 5 bridges. In the centre of the main front there appear to have been twin towers. The whole design is so obviously unpractical that it may well be an amateur's fantasy.

16. THE GROUND FLOOR. A lower floor plan with colonnades, and, in one courtyard, a faintly indicated garden.

Pen and brown ink and black lead; indented; (i) (upper l.) & (ii) (lower l.) damaged, particularly on lower and upper edges respectively; (i) 23·8 × 35 cm. (9¼ × 13¾ in.); (ii) 27 × 36 cm. (10⅝ × 14¼ in.); (iii) 43·2 × 33·8 cm. (17 × 13⅜ in.).

INSCR.: *Recto*, in black lead, in colonnade, upper l., *Strada*.

PROV.: As for No. 11.

1848–8–5–10, 19 & 23.

17. THE MAIN FLOOR. Incomplete plan of the *piano nobile*.

Pen and brown ink; indented; in two separate sections; (i) 43·5 × 32·5 cm. (17 × 12⅞ in.), (ii) 51·7 × 33·2 cm. (20⅜ × 13⅛ in.).

PROV.: As for No. 11.

1848–8–5–20 & 23 (included in L.B. 16–20).

18. AN UPPER FLOOR. Incomplete plan for an upper floor.

Pen and brown ink, black lead, indented; in two separate sections; (i) 50·3 × 32·5 cm. (19¾ × 12⅞ in.), (ii) 50·4 × 34·2 cm. (19¾ × 13½ in.).

INSCR.: *Recto*, in black lead, on l. sheet, *Il piano d . . .* [the rest illegible].

PROV.: As for No. 11.

1848–9–5–18 & 21 (included in L.B. 16–20).

DE JONGH, CLAUDE

B. *c.* 1600: D. 1663

Topographical painter and draughtsman

Born about 1600, or rather earlier (to judge from his first dated drawing of 1615). Though supposed by Weale and later writers to have been born in Utrecht, no documentary evidence of this. Does not appear to be connected with any of the other Dutch artists of this name. The first mention of him occurs in 1627 when he is recorded as a master in the painters' gild at Utrecht. Later documents concerning him also relate to Utrecht, and he presented a mountain landscape to the Hospital of St. Job of that city in 1638.

Other records, one of a court case of 1630/1, another of a lottery of 1633/4, in which a landscape of the artist was disposed of, connect him also with Haarlem. Married first Adriana Carpenter, an Englishwoman (?), secondly Juliana van Pisa of Nijmegen on July 18th, 1643. On July 29th, 1645, a son, Herman, was baptized at the Geertekerk, Utrecht. No documentary evidence known to exist of de Jongh's residence in England. The dates inscribed on his English drawings, 1615, 1625, 1627 and 1628 suggest short visits to this country, mainly to Kent and London, for the purpose of collecting material for paintings which he completed in Holland and of which the finest and best known is the view of Old London Bridge (Iveagh Bequest, Ken Wood) dated 1630. About twenty years later, executed three other paintings of the subject based on a variant of this picture. These cannot have have been done direct from nature and there is no suggestion that de Jongh returned to England at this period. Died at Utrecht in 1663 and was buried on March 16th in the Buurkerk.

His style reflects the current continental taste for the picturesque and in general connects him with Van Goyen and the Haarlem school. In particular his use as a draughtsman of the broken line and the convention of tightly-looped foliage has close affinities with the work of Esaias van de Velde.

DRAWINGS IN OTHER COLLECTIONS: Royal Library, Windsor (*Puyvelde, Flemish Drawings*, Nos. 249 & 250, as Keirincx). Guildhall. Witt Coll. (Courtauld Institute). Boymans Museum, Rotterdam (*Cf.* No. 2 below).

BIBL.: *Weale, Kunstbode*, p. 268. *Wurzbach*, p. 761. *T.-B.*, XIX, 1926, p. 131 (with *Bibl.*). *Hayes* (with *Bibl.*).

1. A RUINED CASTLE, PERHAPS INTENDED FOR ROCHESTER FROM THE N.W. A mound topped by a Norman keep with corner turrets. In the foreground, a broken wall. Trees on the hillside a little to r. In the upper r.-hand corner, a slight sketch of part of the keep.   Plate 174

Pen and brown ink, with washes of brown and grey; 18 × 31·8 cm. (7⅛ × 12½ in.).

PROV.: Sir Hans Sloane, Bart., by whom it was bequeathed to the B.M., 1753.
5214–103 (L.B., IV, p. 379).

BIBL.: *Sloane Cat.*, p. 141, No. 103. *Hayes*, p. 6.

Wrongly described in the *Sloane Catalogue* as 'a portion of the Ruins of Kenilworth Castle'. The ruins correspond, however, fairly closely with those seen in Samuel and Nathaniel Buck's *The North West View of Rochester Castle*, 1735.

2. *Recto.* A VILLAGE STREET, WITH A RUINED WALL. View along a rough road, with a ruined wall pierced by an Elizabethan doorway on the r. In mid-distance, a line of cottages.   Plate 179

Pen and brown ink, with brown wash; 20·3 × 29 cm. (8 × 11⅜ in.).

Verso. DETAIL OF TWO COTTAGES.

Pen and brown ink, with brown wash.

INSCR.: In the lower r.-hand corner, by the artist, *in Aprill* [1]628.

PROV.: As for No. 1.
5214–104 (L.B., IV, p. 379).

BIBL. & REPR.: *Sloane Cat.*, p. 141, No. 104. *Hayes*, p. 7, fig. 10.

Probably wrongly described in the *Sloane Catalogue* as 'View in the Village of Kenilworth'. In the Boymans Museum, Rotterdam, is another view of the same street looking in the opposite direction. It is in the same manner and is inscribed on the *recto*, *C. D. IONGH*, and on the *verso*, *.D.J.1628* (?), and in a later hand, *Claude de Jongh 1660*.

It is on this basis that Prof. J. S. van Gelder has suggested the attribution to De Jongh of the present group of drawings.

3. COLLEGIATE OR MONASTIC BUILDINGS. View towards a group of partly ruined medieval buildings, approached, r., by a road passing through two arches. In the background, r., a long range pierced by Gothic windows and topped by a high-pitched roof. **Plate 177**

Pen and brown ink, with brown wash; 20·4 × 29·9 cm. (8 × 11¾ in.).

INSCR.: *Verso*, in the lower l.-hand corner, in black lead, by the artist, *the 6 (?) off May* / [16] *2*[7(?)].

PROV.: Baron J. G. Verstolk van Soelen (Sale, Amsterdam, de Vries, Brondgeest & Roos, 22:iii:1847, Lot 303, 'Wenceslaus Hollar—deux dessins a la plume et au bistre, representant chacun une ancienne abbaye en ruine'). Purchased, with No. 4, by the B.M. at the Verstolk Sale, 1847.
1847–3–26–11 (L.B., IV, p. 379).

BIBL.: *B.M., Drawings Presented & Purchased*, p. 50. *Hayes*, p. 4. *Inf.* from Mrs. James Tudor-Craig.

Wrongly identified, on its acquisition by the B.M., as 'Winchester House, Southwark'. The buildings have certain affinities with those of St. Augustine's Monastery, Canterbury, as shown in Daniel King's etching after Thomas Johnson, in Sir William Dugdale's *Monasticon*, 2nd edn., 1718, I, p. 9, but the resemblance is not strong enough to warrant a definite identification with that building.

4. THE SAME BUILDINGS AS IN NO. 3. View within the courtyard, with the second of the two archways mentioned in No. 3 on the l. On the r., a similar long range pierced by a Gothic window and entered by two square-topped Tudor doors. **Plate 176**

Pen and brown ink, with brown wash; 20·4 × 30·9 cm. (7¾ × 12⅜ in.).

INSCR.: *Verso*, in the lower l.-hand corner, in black lead, *hoogh 7½* / *briet 12 dm.*, and in the lower r.-hand corner, in ink, by the artist, *The 8 off M* [ay] / . *Anº 1627* (?).

PROV.: As for No. 3.
1847–3–26–12 (L.B., IV, p. 379).

BIBL.: *B.M., Drawings Presented & Purchased*, p. 51. *Hayes*, p. 4. *Inf.* from Mrs. James Tudor-Craig.

See Note to No. 3.

5. RUINS OF A MONASTIC BUILDING, PERHAPS AT CANTERBURY. View looking towards a late Gothic arched gateway, with Norman remains on the r. On the l., a high-pitched roof rising beyond the wall. **Plate 178**

Pen and brown ink, with brown wash; 20·2 × 31·9 cm. (8 × 12⅝ in.).

INSCR.: *Recto*, in the lower l.-hand corner, in ink, by the artist, *the 26 off Aprill* / *1627*.

PROV.: E. Daniell, from whom it was purchased by the B.M., 1861.
1861–11–9–509 (L.B., IV, p. 379).

BIBL.: *Hayes*, p. 4.

6. THE BLOCKHOUSE AT GRAVESEND. View looking S. down the Thames from the Kentish shore, with the Blockhouse in the foreground, r. In the distance, l., the Essex shore.   **Plate 175**

Pen and brown ink, with brown-grey wash; 17·6 × 36·4 cm. (7 × 14⅜ in.). Old mount; 18·7 × 37·4 cm. (7⅜ × 14¾ in.).

PROV.: P. & D. Colnaghi, from whom it was purchased by the B.M., 1949. 1949–2–12–5.

BIBL.: *Hayes*, p. 4.

For another view of the same building and a historical note on it, *see* Cornelis Bol, No. 1.

KING, DANIEL

Fl. from 1630: D. *c.* 1661

Topographical and antiquarian draughtsman and etcher

Son of William King, a baker of Chester, where he was apprenticed to a local (perhaps heraldic) painter, Randle Holme the elder, from 1630 to 1640. Appears in the *Memorandum* presented on St. Luke's Day (Oct. 18th), 1639, by the Painters' Co. of Chester. In 1640 recorded as a journeyman along with a 'Mr. Blackburne' (Richard Blackborne (?), *See Walpole*, III, p. 835) and John Dixon, a glass-painter, and again, in 1641, with a certain Mr. Poyntz. After carrying on business on his own account for some years in his native city, removed to London where he studied etching under Hollar (*q.v.*), whose style he followed, though with a certain dryness and lack of technical skill. A similar comment may be made on his surviving drawings listed below. Drew and etched, sometimes in collaboration with his master, the plates for several topographical and antiquarian works, including Dugdale's *Monasticon*, 1655, *The Vale Royall of England*, 1656 (with text by William Smith and others), *The Cathedrall and Conventuall Churches*, 1656, and *An Orthographical Designe of severall Viewes upon Ye Road in England and Wales*, 1660 (?). Outside the field of topography, published a translation of Gerard Desargues'

Universal Way of Dyaling, 1659. Also executed a drawing of the Great Auk (B.M. Add. MS. 27362). His literary powers not considered as very high by his contemporaries, at least by Sir William Dugdale, who told Anthony Wood that King was 'a most ignorant, silly fellow', and, moreover, 'an errant knave'. Though he does not appear to have practised miniature, wrote a treatise, *Miniatura or the Art of Limming*, which is pirated from various sources (original MS. in B.M., Add. MS. 12,461). Dedicated this to Mary Fairfax, daughter of the Parliamentarian general and subsequently Duchess of Buckingham, and, as the artist is known to have resided near York House in the Strand, home of the Duke of Buckingham, may have lived latterly under her protection. Despite his living in London kept up his connexion with the Chester Painters' Company and is recorded in their St. Luke's Day *Memorandum* up to 1661 when the word *mort* is written against his name. According to Anthony Wood, married a woman who afterwards robbed and left him, and is said to have died of a broken heart at his lodging near York House.

BIBL.: *Chester Painters, Apprentices. Chester*

384

Painters, Expense Bk. (kindly communicated by Mr. S. M. Gold). *Walpole*, III, pp. 891 & 970. *D.N.B.*, XXXI, 1892, p. 126 (with *Bibl.*). Wood, *Athenae Oxon*, III, p. 503. *Long*, p. 252.

DRAWINGS IN OTHER COLLECTIONS: City Art Gallery, York.

1. YORK MINSTER, ELEVATION OF THE E. END.   Plate 180

Pen and ink, with grey wash, and additions in red chalk; indented for transfer; 26·4 × 18·1 cm. (10⅜ × 7⅛ in.).

INSCR.: *Recto*, in the lower margin, Sr *Thomas Tucker of S*. . . . (?).

PROV.: P. & D. Colnaghi, from whom it was purchased by the B.M., 1932.

1932–11–15–10.

ETCH.: By the artist in reverse, in *Dugdale, Monasticon*, (1718 edn.) p. 276, III, with the lettering, *Ecclesiae S^{ti} Petri Eborac: | facies orientalis* and *The East Prospect of the Church of St. Peter of yorke*.

The inscription on the drawing is perhaps intended as the name of the prospective donor of the plate. *Sir Thomas Tucker*—if that is the correct interpretation—has now, however, been identified; and the actual name of the donor as given on the plate itself is, *JOHANNES ESTOFTE | ar.* [miger], 'Estofte' standing perhaps for 'Estouteville' which was indeed a Yorkshire family.

KNELLER, SIR GODFREY, BART.

B. 1646 (or 1649): D. 1723

Portrait painter

Born in 1646 or 1649, at Lübeck (the earlier date derived from the inscription on his monument in Westminster Abbey, the later date given by Vertue). His father, Zacharias Kniller (this being the original form of the surname) worked as a portrait and history painter, and held the post of architect and chief surveyor to the city. Intended for a military career, and to that end entered Leyden University 'where he applied himself to the mathematics, particulary to fortification'. Subsequently turned his attention to painting which he studied at Amsterdam under Ferdinand Bol, also taking an occasional lesson from Rembrandt. An early painting by him, dated *1668*, in the Museum at Lübeck, representing an aged philosopher, reflects this training in the Rembrandt school.

Walpole says, but without giving his authority, that he had also heard that one of Kneller's masters was 'Francis Hals'. If the elder, and famous Hals (B. 1580: D. 1666) is meant, this unlikely statement would refer to an earlier stage in Kneller's artistic career. Went to Italy in 1672 where he 'studied at Rome under the favourable influence of Carlo Marat and the Chevalier Bernini'. Later removed to Venice where he was patronized by the Donati, 'Gartoni' (Garzoni (?)), and other noble families. Came to London, in 1675, and lodged with a Hamburg merchant, Jonathan Banks, whose portrait he painted. The Banks portrait seen by the then secretary to the Duke of Monmouth, John Vernon, who sat to Kneller (portrait now in N.P.G., No. 2963), this leading to a commission to paint the Duke himself (portrait now at Goodwood (?)), and finally Charles II, thus ensuring the artist's reputation. May have travelled on the Continent a second time between 1678 and 1682, revisiting Italy, but was certainly in England in 1681 when he painted the 3rd Earl of Salisbury. According to Buckeridge, was later sent by Charles II to Paris to paint the portrait of Louis XIV, returning thence in 1685. Succeeded Lely as the main fashionable portraitist, and built up a huge practice, counting among his sitters most of the persons of rank, wealth and eminence of his day. Seems, according to Pope, to have seen little even of important sitters, working from a single sketch of the head. Also delegated much of his accessory work, such as the painting of draperies and architectural ornament, to assistants, who included John James Backer (q.v.), Edward and Robert (?) Byng (q.v.), J. Baptist Gaspars. (q.v.), Marcellus Laroon I, Jan Pieters III, 'John Reiters', 'Weedman' (Wiedmann (?)), and 'Swartz' (Schwartz). His portraits in consequence of very uneven quality, though in those where he was obviously interested personally in the sitters— such as the 'Chinese Convert' (Kensington Palace), Matthew Prior (Trinity College, Cambridge), and the Members of the Kitcat Club (National Portrait Gallery)—he shows considerable brilliance of handling and insight into their characters. His style probably at first influenced by Maratta, and latterly by the school of French Baroque portraiture headed by Rigaud and Largillière. Much of his work engraved by the accomplished mezzotinter, John Smith. Among the most interesting of the drawings by, or attributed to him below, are his life-size studies of faces, representing a preliminary stage in portrait making which he may have originally learnt from Maratta (See 1952–10–11–11), and which was adopted by subsequent painters such as Jonathan Richardson. Occasionally attempted history and decorative painting, and by

tradition is said to have executed a ceiling at Hanworth House, Middlesex, and to have helped Laguerre on his own staircase at Whitton. Also offered, a few months before his death, to decorate the staircase at Canons for the Duke of Chandos. His only surviving essays in this field are the three feigned statues, of the Farnese Hercules, the Medici Venus, and the Belvedere Apollo, painted for Pope's Villa at Twickenham, and now at Cirencester House. In 1688 appointed Principal Painter to William III. Was knighted in 1691/2, and created a baronet in 1715. Also made a Knight of the Holy Roman Empire in 1700. Lived successively in York Buildings (c. 1676), Durham Yard (c. 1676–8) and, with increasing business, in the Piazza, Covent Garden (c. 1681–1702). Finally settled in Great Queen St., Lincolns Inn Fields, and also purchased an estate at Whitton near Twickenham, where he built a magnificent house with a staircase painted by Louis Laguerre (q.v.). In 1711, founded (with other artists), and became Governor of, the first organized academy of painting in England, which had its seat at his house in Great Queen St. A number of studies, listed for convenience here under Edward Byng (See pp. 207–58), but obviously by different members of the academy, testify to its activities. Married Mrs. Susannah Grave (née Cawley; See pp. 230–1, f. 55r.), but had no children by her, his eventual heir being Godfrey Huckle Kneller, son of Agnes Huckle, Kneller's illegitimate daughter by Mrs. Voss (See p. 247, f. 38v.). Died, according to his monument in Westminster Abbey, on Oct.. 26th, 1723, at his house in Great Queen St., and was buried in his garden at Whitton. The monument was executed by Rysbrack, based probably on Kneller's own design (See No. 27 below). In his Will left instructions for his pictures to be finished by Edward Byng (See pp. 204–5). Refers to his house in Great Queen St., then (1723) 'in possession of the Portugal Envoy', where there were 'six pictures of mine and my Wife's Relations painted by myself and now in my Great Dining Room . . . and also three pictures [unspecified] put up for Ornament over the doors of the said Room'. Mentions too his house in Wild St. (also in the neighbourhood of Lincolns Inn Fields) 'now or late in the possession of Mrs. Carpenter'. Made bequests to his brother Andrew Kniller (of Hamburg, B. 1649), Capt. William Cawley (no doubt a relative of his wife's), Elizabeth Springall (wife of Thomas Springall of Henley), and Ann Wickham (wife of White Wickham of Windsor). Among his trustees were Bayn-brigg Buckeridge (of New Windsor, B. 1668: D. 1733), author of the greater part of *An Essay towards an English School*, including Kneller's *Life* in the 3rd edition).

BIBL.: *Will (P.C.C., Richmond, f. 261)*. *Buckeridge*, pp. 393–8. *Walpole*, II, pp. 586–98. *Baker, Lely*, II, pp. 75–94. *T.-B.*, XX, 1927, p. 596 (with *Bibl.*). *Whitley*, I, passim. *Killanin*, passim. *Vertue, Index*, pp. 134–6. *Vertue*, VI, 12, 70, 72, 162, 163, 168–9, 178. *Woodward*, passim. *Waterhouse*, passim. *Hatfield MS.*, No. 9, p. 323.

[1–11]. LARGE STUDIES OF HEADS. These may probably be considered as preliminary stages in portrait-making.

1. JOHN CHURCHILL, 1st DUKE OF MARLBOROUGH. Head alone, turned half-l. Wearing light-coloured and curling wig. **Plate 183**

Black, red and white chalks, and stump, on green-grey paper; 36·8 × 23·8 cm. (14⅜ × 9¼ in.).

PROV.: P. & D. Colnaghi, from whom it was purchased by the B.M., 1860.
1860–7–14–35 (L.B.1).

[John Churchill, 1st Duke of Marlborough (B. 1650: D. 1722), the famous military commander.]
Study for the portrait of the Duke in early middle age at Blenheim (*See Scharf*, p. 26).

2. *Recto.* **A LADY.** Head turned slightly to l., with curling hair falling on her shoulder.

Black chalk and stump, touched with white, on brown-grey paper; 39·2 × 28·4 cm. (15⅜ × 11⅛ in.).

Verso. **A LADY.** H.L., seated nearly to front, resting on her l. arm. Wearing a cap loosely tied below her chin and a low-necked dress. A slight sketch of her head on the r.

Black chalk, touched with white.

PROV.: As for No. 1.
1860–7–14–36 (L.B.2).

The suggestion that this drawing represents Sarah, Duchess of Marlborough, is most improbable.

3. ADMIRAL GEORGE CHURCHILL. Head turned slightly to r., with eyes looking to front. Wearing curling wig. **Plate 182**

Black chalk and stump, touched with red and white, on blue-grey paper; 38 × 27·2 cm. (15 × 10¾ in.).

PROV.: As for No. 1.
1860–7–14–37 (L.B.3).

[George Churchill (B. 1654: D. 1710). Younger brother of the Duke of Marlborough. Commissioner of the Admiralty in 1699–1702, Rear Admiral in 1701, and Admiral of the Blue in 1702. Was notorious for his rapacity and incompetence.]

The present drawing does not appear to correspond with the portrait by Kneller of Churchill in the National Maritime Museum, Greenwich, and the old identification with the Admiral must, therefore, be considered as doubtful.

4. A LADY. Head turned slightly to l., with curling hair.

Black chalk, touched with red and white, on buff paper; 38·1 × 23·5 cm. (15 × 9¼ in.).

PROV.: As for No. 1.
1860–7–14–38 (L.B.4).

Inf. from Miss Patricia Wilkinson.

Related to a portrait by Kneller, now known only through a copy in the Museum of Fine Arts, Boston (George Nixon Black Bequest, 1929). The suggested identification with Anne Sutherland, Countess of Sunderland, is most improbable.

5. A YOUNG MAN. Head turned slightly to r., with eyes looking to front. Wearing curling wig lightly indicated.

Black chalk, touched with red and white, on blue-grey paper; 32 × 25·4 cm. (12⅝ × 10 in.).

PROV.: As for No. 1.
1860–7–14–39 (L.B.5).

The suggestion that this drawing may represent William, Duke of Gloucester, Queen Anne's only son, is doubtful.

6. *Recto.* A LADY. Head nearly full face, with eyes looking to front.

Black chalk, touched with red and slightly with white, on buff paper; 37·8 × 23·3 cm. (14¾ × 9⅛ in.).

Verso. A LADY AS DIANA. Head in profile to r., with long pointed nose and hair dressed in curls, a crescent above.

Red chalk, shaded with black chalk and stump.

PROV.: P. & D. Colnaghi, from whom it was purchased by the B.M., 1870.
1870–10–8–2376 (L.B.7).

7. *Recto.* A LADY. Head turned half-l., with eyes looking to front. Wearing long curling hair, a circlet of pearls over it, and pearl earrings.

Black chalk and stump, touched with red and white, on brown-grey paper; 39·2 × 25·8 cm. (15¼ × 10⅛ in.).

Verso. **HEAD OF A WOMAN, PROBABLY AFTER THE ANTIQUE.**

Black chalk, touched with white.

PROV.: As for No. 6.
1870–10–8–2377 (L.B. 6).

8. *Recto.* **A YOUNG MAN.** Head turned half-l., with long curling hair, a lock of which falls on his l. shoulder.

Black chalk, strengthened with oiled chalk and heightened with white, on light brown-grey paper; 27·7 × 22·7 cm. (10⅞ × 9 in.).

Verso. **STUDY OF A NUDE MAN SEEN FROM BEHIND.**

Black chalk.

PROV.: As for No. 6.
1870–10–2378 (L.B., as by Sir John Baptist Medina, 3).

When acquired by the B.M. this drawing was attributed to Kneller, but was later placed with drawings by Sir John Baptist Medina, under whose name it was catalogued by Mr. Binyon. In handling, however, it has far more in common with Kneller's work, and the old attribution, therefore, has been reverted to.

9. *Recto.* **A CHILD.** Bust, nearly full-face, with head slightly inclined towards the r.

Black chalk, touched with white and red, on grey paper; 30·6 × 28 cm. (12 × 11 in.).

Verso. **A LADY.** Head and neck turned slightly to r., with eyes looking to front.

Black chalk, touched with white.

PROV.: As for No. 6.
1870–10–8–2380 (L.B. 11, as by Lely).

10. HENRY PURCELL. Head turned half-l., and slightly thrust forward. Wearing long curling hair or wig, only partly indicated.   **Plate 184**

Black chalk, retouched on the jaw, on lilac paper; 40·1 × 27·2 cm. (15¾ × 10¾ in.).

PROV.: Dr. Charles Burney, in 1793 (Sale, White, 8:viii:1814, Lot 1031, 'An undoubted original drawing, *Head of Purcell* by Sir G. Kneller', purchased by 'Bartleman £1 1s'). 'Bartleman', probably James Bartleman ((?) Sale, White, 20:ii:1822, Lot 1426, 'Small Head of Purcell, after Kneller . . .'). Edward Cheney (Sale, Sotheby, 4:v:1885, Lot 955, not mentioned, but with drawings attributed to Jonathan Richardson). Purchased at the Cheney Sale by the B.M., 1885.

1885–5–9–1897 (L.B., as attributed to Jonathan Richardson the Elder, Vol. III, p. 228).

ENGR.: By T. Holloway, 1798 (*from a Drawing by Sʳ Godfrey Kneller in the possession of Dr. Burney*).

BIBL. & REPR.: *Callcott, f.* 22. *Cumming, Purcell. Holmes. Grove,* VI, p. 1002. *Schotes,* II, p. 121. *Zimmerman,* pp. 139 (No. 19) & 144, Pl. I.

[Henry Purcell (B. 1658 or 9: D. 1695). The most celebrated English native-born musician. Composer of *The Fairy Queen*, *King Arthur*, *Dido* and other dramatic music, and of numerous vocal and instrumental works.]

The present drawing is closely connected with the oval portrait of Purcell, attributed to Kneller, now in the National Portrait Gallery (No. 2150) and formerly in the collections of Joah Bates, Mr. Henry Littleton, and Mr. Barclay Squire. A rectangular version of this picture, also attributed to Kneller, formerly in the collection of Mr. G. W. Hastings of Barnard's Green House, Great Malvern, was sold at Sotheby's on 18:vi:1947, Lot 25(e), and in 1948 was in the possession of Mr. H. M. Calmann. A third portrait, apparently connected with this type, was formerly at Dulwich College, and, according to *B.M. Engraved Portraits*, III, p. 524, No. 12, was engraved by W. N. Gardiner in Harding's *Biographical Mirrour*. This reference cannot be traced.

The old attribution of the present drawing also to Kneller dates back at least to Dr. Burney, and has been retained here for convenience. The handling, however, bears little resemblance to that of the authenticated portrait-studies by that master (e.g. Nos. 1, 3, 11 in this Catalogue). The later alternative attributions are equally unsatisfactory.

With regard to its history when in Dr. Burney's collection, Dr. Callcott, writing of the 'Graduates' Meeting' (*See Bibl.*), states that in 1793 'Dr. Burney having in his possession an original drawing of Purcell of which the merit appeared considerably great it was proposed in honour of our Countryman and the Society to publish an engraving of it at the joint expence. The delay of the artist, together with the resignations & death of several members who had pledged themselves to support the undertaking render the future publication extremely hypothetical, as the concern is now entirely limited to the risque of a few'. It seems unlikely that the proposed engraving mentioned by Dr. Callcott is identical with the one by Holloway published in 1798. The latter is an octavo-size plate and looks as if it had been intended for the illustration to some book which so far, however, has not been identified.

---

11. ALEXANDER POPE. Bust, in profile to l., looking slightly upwards. Wearing a wreath of ivy in his curling hair, and drapery about his shoulders. **Plate 185**

Black chalk, heightened with white and touched with red, on yellowish-brown oiled paper; made up in the lower l.-hand corner; $46 \cdot 5 \times 37 \cdot 5$ cm. ($18\frac{1}{4} \times 14\frac{3}{4}$ in.).

PROV.: Edward Byng (q.v.). Mrs. E. A. Roberts, from whom it was purchased by the B.M., 1888.

1888–7–19–65 (L.B.14).

[Alexander Pope (B. 1688: D. 1744). The most renowned English poet of the early XVIII c.]

The present drawing is connected with the portrait by Kneller, dating from 1721, in the collection of the Earl of Sefton at Croxteth Hall, Liverpool. Another version of this, from the collection of H. M. Pym, was sold at Christie's, 22:xi:1912, Lot 68. It was engraved in mezzotint by John Faber II in 1738 (*See B.M. Engraved Portraits*, III, p. 489, No. 23). A rather similar portrait, attributed to Jonathan Richardson I, is in the N.P.G. (No. 1179).

[12–14]. SMALL STUDIES, PROBABLY FROM THE LIFE.

12. LEBECK. H.L., turned half-r., eyes looking to front. Wearing a kerchief over his head and coat unbuttoned at the top.   **Plate 188**

Black chalk, touched with white, on blue-grey paper; 28 × 21·3 cm. (11 × 8⅜ in.).

PROV.: As for No. 11.
1888–7–19–68 (L.B.11).

[Lebeck (*Fl.* 1710). Proprietor of a tavern in Half Moon St. or Chandos St.]

The study is connected with the portrait (present whereabouts unknown), subsequently engraved in mezzotint by Andrew Miller, 1739. A copy after the oil painting appears in one of the Byng sketch-books (*See* p. 249, *f.* 46*r*.).

13. A YOUNG LADY. Bust, with head turned half-l., the shoulders lightly indicated.

Black chalk, on blue-grey paper; irregularly cut; 27·2 × 21·7 cm. (10¾ × 8½ in.).

PROV.: As for No. 11.
1888–7–19–70 (L.B.12).

INSCR.: *Recto*, in the lower r.-hand corner, by the artist, *G K*, and above, *Polde--* (?), the remainder of the word illegible.

14. A NEGRO PAGE. Two studies in the same pose, one slighter than the other. T.Q.L., standing, turned half-l., looking back over the l. shoulder, and pointing upwards with the l. hand.

Black chalk, touched with white, on blue-grey paper; 28·1 × 22·5 cm. (11 × 8¾ in.).

PROV.: As for No. 11.
1888–7–19–77 (L.B.15).

INSCR.: *Recto*, in the lower r.-hand corner, by the artist, *G K*, and at the foot, in the centre, in white chalk, *72* (?)/*1642*.

Perhaps a study for the page in Kneller's *Mary Davies* at Audley End. The prototype for this is possibly the negro in Van Dyck's *Henrietta of Lorraine* at Ken Wood.

[15–20]. COPIES FROM PORTRAITS. Three of these, Nos. 16, 17 and 18, certainly belong to the type of studio copy from a finished picture kept for record purposes, and it is significant that these were acquired from a collateral descendant of one of Kneller's assistants, Edward Byng (*See* p. 207). No. 15, though less certainly connected with Kneller, may also belong to this class of drawing. No. 19, a juvenile performance, is taken from a print.

15. A MILITARY COMMANDER. W.L., standing, his r. arm outstretched, his l. hand holding a baton. Wearing a long curling wig and armour, his helmet on a bank beside him, l. In the distance, l., a landscape, and on the r., a curtain.

Black chalk, touched with red and heightened with white, on brown-grey paper; 28 × 19·1 cm. (11 × 7½ in.).

PROV.: John Deffett Francis, by whom it was presented to the B.M., 1875.
1875–4–10–2 (L.B., as by Sir Peter Lely, 8).

This drawing was listed by Mr. Binyon as by Lely. It clearly belongs, however, to a rather later period, the figure suggesting the type of portrait generally associated in this country with Kneller.

16. CHARLES FITZROY, 2nd DUKE OF GRAFTON. H.L., with body turned slightly to r., head slightly to l. and eyes looking to front, his r. hand held to his breast. Wearing a night cap, and an open shirt and coat.

Black and white chalks, with grey wash, on blue-grey paper; $26 \cdot 8 \times 19 \cdot 4$ cm. ($10\frac{1}{2} \times 7\frac{5}{8}$ in.).

PROV.: As for No. 11.
1888–7–19–66 (L.B.10).

[Charles Fitzroy, 2nd Duke of Grafton (B. 1683: D. 1757). Son of Henry, 1st Duke, whom he succeeded in 1690. Held a number of appointments under the Crown, and was Viceroy of Ireland in 1720–4.]

The original picture, one of the Kit-Cat portraits, is in the N.P.G. (No. 3210). Another drawing after this portrait appears in one of the Byng sketchbooks (See p. 245, f. 22v.).

17. A YOUNG MAN. T.Q.L., standing, turned half-l. and looking to front. Wearing a long curling wig falling on his shoulders, coat, and drapery round his waist.

Black chalk, touched with white, on blue-grey paper; $37 \cdot 7 \times 27 \cdot 5$ cm. ($14\frac{3}{4} \times 10\frac{3}{4}$ in.).

PROV.: As for No. 11.
1888–7–19–67 (L.B.13).

18. THREE CHILDREN. Heads: on the l., a girl turned slightly to r.; in the centre, a second girl turned slightly to l., and in the lower r.-hand corner, a third, also a girl (?), turned slightly to l.

Black and red chalks, heightened with white, on oiled brown paper; irregularly cut; $17 \times 24 \cdot 9$ cm. ($6\frac{5}{8} \times 9\frac{3}{4}$ in.).

PROV.: As for No. 11.
1888–7–19–78 (L.B.16).

REPR.: Killanin, Pl. 40.

19. Recto. **HENRY THE PIOUS, DUKE OF SAXONY.** H.L., turned half-r. Wearing mail and holding a sword on his r. shoulder.

Pen and brown ink; $20 \cdot 5 \times 15 \cdot 4$ cm. (8×6 in.).

INSCR.: In the lower l.-hand corner, Gottfride Kniller / Anno. 16.n.g. (i.e. 'nach geburt').

Verso. **A HEAD LOOKING DOWNWARDS.**

Pen and brown ink.

PROV.: As for No. 11.
1888–7–19–80 (L.B.24(a)).

REPR.: Recto, Killanin, Pl. 37.

The drawing on the recto is copied from a woodcut in Nicolaus Reusner's Icones sive Imagines Impp. Regvm, Principvm, Electorvm, et et Dvcvm Saxoniae . . . , 1597, No. 33.

20. QUEEN ANNE. W.L., seated, with head turned slightly to l. and body slightly to r., holding on her l. knee the orb. On a throne supported at the top by cherubs. Wearing a royal mantle over her dress.

Pen and brown ink with grey wash; 32·2 × 20·2 cm. (12¾ × 8 in.).

PROV.: As for No. 11.
1888–7–19–69 (L.B.9).

Probably a studio record after the portrait, painted in 1702 at the Queen's accession, of which several versions exist, among them one at Drumlanrig, another at Cirencester House, and a third at Deane Park, Northants.

[21–22]. **STUDIES OF ANIMALS.** Both identified as having been used as accessories in portraits.

21. *Recto.* **A GREYHOUND.** Seen from behind, and looking upwards to the r.

Plate 186

Black chalk, on blue paper; 28·4 × 22·5 cm. (11⅛ × 8⅞ in.).

REPR.: *Killanin*, Pl. 41.

Verso. **A FAMILY GROUP.** A Lady seated to r., her arm round a little girl standing beside her, r., while further to the r. is a boy.

Black chalk, lightly sketched.

PROV.: As for No. 11.
1888–7–19–73 (L.B.21).

The study of the greyhound on the *recto* was used in the portrait-group of Richard

Boyle, Lord Clifford (later 3rd Earl of Burlington), and his sister Lady Jane Boyle, now at Chatsworth, but cut down and with two figures added to the composition. This picture, in its original state, was engraved in mezzotint in reverse by John Smith, *c.* 1701 (*C.S.*, No. 53).

22. A DOE. Standing in profile to l., looking upwards, the legs studied in alternative positions.

Plate 187

Black, yellow and white chalks, on buff paper; 31·4 × 25·5 cm. (12⅜ × 10 in.).

BIBL. & REPR.: *Killanin*, p. 54, & Pls. 42 & 46.

INSCR.: *Recto*, in the upper r.-hand corner, *G K* (signature).

PROV.: As for No. 11.
1888–7–19–75 (L.B.20).

Study used in the portrait-group of Lionel Sackville, Lord Buckhurst, and his sister Lady Mary Sackville, now at Knole, engraved in mezzotint by John Smith, *c.* 1695 (*C.S.*, No. 27).

[23–25.] **ACADEMIC STUDIES** belonging to the same class of material, emanating from Kneller's workshop and academy, as that described on pp. 264–7.

23. A NUDE MAN. W.L., half kneeling to l., with eyes looking upwards and his r. knee raised.

Black chalk, on blue-grey paper; 28·7 × 28·1 cm. (11¼ × 11 in.).

INSCR.: *Recto*, in the lower r.-hand corner, by the artist, *G K*.

PROV.: As for No. 11.
1888–7–19–71 (L.B.18).

24. HANDS AND FOREARMS. On the r., two female forearms, one with the l. hand pointing downwards, the other with the r. hand outstretched holding some object. On the l., offsets from three sketches of hands.

The studies on the r. in black, red and white chalks, the offsets on the l. from black chalk only; on blue-grey paper; folded in the centre; 26·6 × 39 cm. (10½ × 15¼ in.).

INSCR.: *Verso*, in the upper l.-hand corner, by the artist, *G K*.

PROV.: As for No. 11.
1888–7–19–72 (L.B.19).

25. *Recto.* THREE STUDIES OF A NUDE MAN. W.L., seen from behind(?), standing in different positions, and holding a staff in his l. hand.

Pen and brown ink; 13·6 × 19 cm. (5⅝ × 7½ in.).

INSCR.: In the lower r.-hand corner, by the artist, *G K*.

REPR.: *Killanin*, Pl. 38.

Verso. A NUDE MALE TORSO AND LEGS.

Pen and brown ink.

PROV.: As for No. 11.
1888–7–19–79 (L.B.24(b)).

[26–27]. STUDIES FOR, AND AFTER, SCULPTURE.

26. STUDY OF THE 'DIANE DE VERSAILLES'. W.L. figure of the goddess, seen as if walking towards the front, her head in profile to l., plucking with her r. hand an arrow from her quiver, and holding with her l. a deer which leaps beside her.

Black and red chalks; 30·6 × 20 cm. (12 × 7⅞ in.).

INSCR.: *Recto*, in the lower r.-hand corner, by the artist, *G Kneller. desinyé a Verlalie [i.e.* Versailles] / *apree La Statue don La / Gallerie d' Roy.*

PROV.: Hugh Howard. Dr. Robert Howard (Bishop of Elphin) and the Earls of Wicklow. Charles Howard, 5th Earl, from whom it was purchased by the B.M., 1874.
1874–8–8–2261 (L.B.25).

Study of the statue, known as the 'Diane de Versailles' or 'Diane à la Biche', now considered to be a Roman replica of a Greek type of the IV c. B.C. It was brought to France from Rome in the reign of François I, and was successively in the châteaux of Mendon and Fontainebleau, the old 'Salle des Antiques' at the Louvre, and the Grande Gallerie at Versailles, where it remained till the Revolution, when it was returned to the Louvre (*See* W. Fröhner, *Notice de la Sculpture Antique du Musée Impérial du Louvre*, 1869, I, pp. 122–5, No. 98). Kneller probably made the present drawing when he was sent to France to paint the portrait of Louis XIV.

27. DESIGN FOR THE ARTIST'S OWN MONUMENT. A bust of the artist, with head turned half-r., flanked by two cherubs, that on the l. seated on the ledge of the curved-sided inscription tablet below, that on the r. supporting a medallion portrait-relief of Lady Kneller in profile to r. The composition surmounted by a canopy with looped-up drapery and a central cartouche for a coat of arms. Below the inscription tablet, a cherub's head flanked by palm branches.　　　**Plate 181**

Black chalk; 46·5 × 33·3 cm. (18⅛ × 13⅛ in.).

INSCR.: *Verso*, at the foot, *Sr Godfy Knellers monum^t Westm^r Abby*.

PROV.: As for No. 11.
1888–7–19–81 (L.B.17).

BIBL.: *Vertue*, III, p. 43. *Killanin*, Pl. 84.

Study for the monument executed by John Michael Rysbrack and placed on the N. wall of the choir in Westminster Abbey. Vertue notes in 1730: 'Lately sett up in Westminster Abbey the Monument of Sr Godfrey Kneller K^t & Baronet. the Moddel was made by M. Rysbrack. before the death of Sr Godfrey. & by his direction. the Monument by him was intended to be erected in Whitton Church (near Twittenham) where he was buried.— but in the place most conspicuous or pleasing to him, for the placing it was already a small Monument for Mr Pope's father. which he could not prevail to get remov'd therefore it was erected at Westminster. there being left by his will 300^{ll} or thereabouts to pay for it. [Kneller was actually buried in his own garden at Whitton, and the monument was to have been set up in Twickenham Church] Mr. Bird Statuary also made a model & designs. for it. the bas-relieve of his Ladys head was so directed by him [Kneller]. (tho not so properly). rather it shoud have been some alusion to the Art of Painting— another omission happend. of his great gold chain & medal. about his neck the bust being done from a sketch of his [Kneller's] unfinisht. & therein omitted. & wanting proper directions. the statuary is to be excus'd—.'

The present drawing is clearly connected in design with Rysbrack's finished monument, but there are certain notable differences in the latter: the bust of Kneller looks to the r. and wears a cap, and there is no canopy. The drawing itself, however, is not like Rysbrack's usual studies for monumental sculpture, examples of which are in the Department. Indeed, it is nearer in handling to Kneller's own manner, and this combined with Vertue's evidence (quoted above) that Kneller made at least one sketch for his monument, would justify maintaining the old attribution to him.

KNELLER, JOHN ZACHARY

B. 1644: D. 1702

Limner, decorative and still-life painter

Born at Lübeck on Oct. 16th, 1644. Son of Zacharias Kniller and elder brother of Sir Godfrey Kneller (*q.v.*), in whose company he probably studied under Ferdinand Bol. Painted, in the Rembrandt manner, a *Young Scholar*, now in the Museum at Lübeck, which forms a pendant to his brother's *Aged Philosopher*, dated *1668*, in the same collection. Accompanied Godfrey on his travels in Italy, and subsequently in 1677 painted, jointly with him, 'a piece of the Roman ampitheatre'—presumably the Colosseum. Came to London (possibly with his brother), where he painted oil portraits 'in small, very neat', later extending this particular branch of art to include miniatures in water-colour, in which medium he copied several of Godfrey's portraits. Three miniatures, all signed *I Z K*, are known: two, in oil on copper, of William III and the Duchess of Manchester in the Victoria and Albert Museum; and one of James II in the collection of Earl Beauchamp. Also achieved some success as a painter of still-life, and (according to Walpole, who however does not quote his authority) 'in

fresco [and] architecture', which suggests that he may have acted as assistant to one of the several decorative history painters of the Verrio-Laguerre school. A portrait of him by Godfrey engraved by Richard Collin for Sandrart's *Academia*. Another portrait of him, by Jan Wyck, recorded by Vertue as in the possession of Dr. William Barnard, Bishop of Derry. Died in Covent Garden in 1702, and was buried in the Church of St. Paul there on Aug. 31st.

BIBL.: *Buckeridge*, p. 392. *Walpole*, II, p. 598. *D.N.B.*, XXXI, 1892, p. 243. *St. Paul's, Covent Garden, Registers*, p. 184. *T.-B.*, XX, 1927, p. 600. *Long*, p. 254. *Vertue, Index*, p. 137. *Killanin, passim*.

1. A HOG. Standing in profile to l., the forelegs studied in alternative positions.

Plate 189

Black chalk on blue-grey paper; 20·5 × 26·7 cm. (8 × 10½ in.).

INSCR.: *Recto*, in the lower l.-hand corner, *J Kf*.

PROV.: Mrs. Roberts, from whom it was purchased by the B.M., 1888.

1888–7–19–76 (L.B. 23, as by Sir Godfrey Kneller).

KNYFF, LEONARD

B. 1650: D. 1722

Landscape, still-life and animal painter and draughtsman

Born on Aug. 10th, 1650, in Haarlem, the third son of Wouter Knyff (B. c. 1607: D. c. 1693), a landscape painter, from whom he probably received his artistic training. By 1681 was living in the parish of St. Martin-in-the-Fields (presumably in the house in which he later held auctions in Westminster adjoining the stairs 'going up to the House of Lords', with 'one door in the Old Palace yard the other over against the Painted-Chamber'), but known to have returned to Holland on two occasions, once in 1693, and again in 1695 when a pass was issued for 'Mr.

Leonard Knife, a protestant, to go to Harwich or Gravesend for Holland'. Was among those aliens on behalf of whom a warrant was sent to the Attorney General on June 8th, 1694, to prepare a bill for the great seal to make them 'free denizens of England'. In Holland had specialized in still-life, but in England turned his attention mainly to topography, painting bird's-eye views of country seats, including old Chatsworth and old Clandon. Began holding picture auctions at least as early as 1695 and quite probably earlier. Apparently one of the most prolific of the landscape painters whose works are listed in the auction catalogues. Most of his pictures sold at auctions or through dealers. Employed in 1699–1702 by Arthur Ingram, 3rd Viscount Irwin, for whom he painted a portrait of his lordship with a gun and dog in a landscape (Temple Newsam), two pictures of hounds and hares (Earl of Halifax), and a prospect of Temple Newsam (now lost). Drew many of the buildings of which views appear in the first volume of Kip's *Britannia Illustrata* (1707). His portrait was painted by Simon Du Bois. Died in 1722, not in 1721 as is generally stated, between April 16th, when he made his Will ('very weak in body and in hourly expectation of death') and Sept. 2nd, when it was proved. Directed that he should be buried in the 'New Chapple, Westminster',

and bequeathed £1,700 in South Sea Co. stock to his wife, son and daughter. His executors, John Boulter and John Coushmaker, each received £20 and 'two pictures a peice such as they shall choose out of those of mine own painting'. Of the four drawings listed below, No. 1 is in the style of his work for *Britannia Illustrata* while Nos. 3 and 4 recall the studies of buildings in black chalk and grey wash of Thomas Wyck (B. 1616: D. 1677).

BIBL.: *Will*, P.C.C., *Marlboro*, f. 240. *C.S.P. Dom.*, 1694/5, p. 172; 1695, p. 35. *D.N.B.*, XXXI, 1892, p. 338. *Grant*, p. 21. *T.-B.*, XXI, 1927, pp. 44–5 (with *Bibl.*). *Vertue, Index*, p. 137. *Honour, Knyff, passim. Ogden, Index*, p. 221.

1. BIRD'S-EYE VIEW OF WHITEHALL, ST. JAMES'S PARK, ARLINGTON HOUSE, AND ST. JAMES'S PALACE.

View taken from above the river, in midstream, opposite Whitehall, looking N.W. In the foreground centre, at the water's edge, the landing-stairs and Queen Mary's Garden, backed by the Queen's Apartments built from Wren's design in 1687–8. Behind this building, slightly to the r., the Great Hall and Chapel, and slightly to the l., the Pebble Court with Grinling Gibbons's statue of James II, beyond which rises the Banqueting House, with the Great Court Gate beside it, r. Further to the r., Scotland Yard, and the main thoroughfare of Whitehall, bordered on the far side by the Horse Guards and the Admiralty Building (which occupied the site of Wallingford House from 1694 till the erection of the present Admiralty in 1722–6). To the l. of the prospect, the Privy Garden surrounded by a group of buildings, including the Cock Pit, the Great Covered Tennis Court, James II's Roman Catholic Chapel and the turrets of the Holbein Gate, and the Privy Gallery. In the background, St. James's Park with the Canal and Rosamond's Pond, l., Arlington House at its far extremity, and St. James's Palace lying away to the r. **Plate 190**

Pen and brown ink over black lead; unfinished; 33·6 × 48·8 cm. (13¼ × 19¼ in.).

PROV.: J. C. Crowle, by whom it was bequeathed, in an extra-illustrated copy of Pennant's *London*, to the British Museum, 1811.

Crowle-Pennant, Pt. IV, No. 8 (now mounted separately).

ENGR.: By R. Sawyer in *Smith, Westminster Suppl.* (Pl. 24).

BIBL.: *B.M., MS. Maps . . . and Topographical Drawings*, II, p. 44. L.C.C., *Survey of London*, XIII, 1930, pp. 111–12 & Pl. 5. *Wroth*, pp. 258–60.

The date of the drawing must be between 1694, when the predecessor of the present

Admiralty building was erected, and 1698 when the Palace was destroyed by fire. Another more finished version in pen, ink and wash is in the Westminster Public Library. In the foreground is shown a floating 'musical summer house', known as the Royal Diversion or the Folly', also seen in Knyff's view of Somerset House, engraved by Jan Kip (*Britannia Illustrata* (1724 edn., I, Pl. 6).

2. WESTMINSTER, OLD PALACE YARD, LOOKING N., PROBABLY FROM THE GARDEN OF LINDSAY HOUSE.

On the extreme l., the Jewel Tower with Hawksmoor's coping and classical windows (which replaced the medieval battlements and fenestration in 1718–19), and Westminster School; in mid-distance, the Abbey with the apse of Henry VII's Chapel and the entrance to St. Margaret's Lane beyond it; and on the extreme r., the S. gable of Westminster Hall (?).   **Plate 192**

Pen and brown ink with grey wash; 22·2 × 41·7 cm. (8¾ × 16⅜ in.).

PROV.: Thomas Allen (Sale, King & Lochee, 14:v:1807, Lot 223 (?)). Richard Grenville, 1st Duke, and Richard Grenville, 2nd Duke of Buckingham (Sale, Sotheby 8:viii:1849, Lot 225, as by 'Canaletti'). Frederick Crace. John Gregory Crace, from whom it was purchased by the B.M., 1880.

1880–11–13–2589.

AQT.: By F. C. Lewis in *Smith, Westminster*, p. 34.

BIBL.: *Crace Cat.*, p. 330, Ptf. XV, No. 1 (as 'supposed by *Canaletti*', *c.* 1740).

Obviously drawn in the same manner as No. 1, but with the addition of grey wash.

3. BERKELEY CASTLE FROM THE E.

View looking towards the Castle which stands on rising ground with a line of trees below it. On the r., the parish church with its detached tower.

Brush drawing in grey wash over black lead; 27·8 × 67·7 cm. (11 × 26¾ in.).

INSCR.: *Verso*, in the upper r.-hand corner, *prospects by Mr. Knife / 1676* (referring also to No. 4).

PROV.: Lt.-General William Skinner, R.E. J. Skinner. Lieut. Monier Skinner, R.E. War Office, whence it was transferred to the B.M. Dept of MSS., 1887. Transferred to Dept. of Prints & Drawings, 1948.

1948–11–26–9.

BIBL.: *B.M., Catalogue Add. MSS.*, 1882–7, 1889, p. 278, No. 33, 233 (3).

This view corresponds in part with the r.-hand portion of the Castle as seen in S. & N. Buck, *Antiquities*, 1774, I, Pl. 97. A later view, corresponding more closely with the present drawing but without the church, is seen in the engraving by A. Birrell after F. Gresse, 1790.

Berkeley Castle is said to have been founded soon after the Conquest, but was considerably added to at subsequent dates. It was the scene of Edward II's murder in Sept., 1327.

4. BERKELEY CASTLE FROM THE S.

Near view of the Castle which stands on rising ground with a line of trees below it.   **Plate 191**

Brush drawing in grey wash over black lead; $25 \cdot 9 \times 45 \cdot 3$ cm. ($10\frac{1}{4} \times 17\frac{7}{8}$ in.).

PROV.: As for No. 3.
1948–11–26–10.

BIBL.: *B.M., Add. MSS.*, 1882–7, 1889, p. 278, No. 33, 233 (3).

This view corresponds with the central portion of the building seen in Kip's bird's-eye prospect in *Nouveau Theatre de la Grande Bretagne*, II, 1724, Pl. 7, and in S. & N. Buck, *Antiquities*, 1774, I, Pl. 97.

LAGUERRE, LOUIS

B. 1663: D. 1721

History and decorative painter

Born at Versailles, where his father, a Catalan, was keeper of the royal menagerie to Louis XIV, who became the boy's godfather. Entered a Jesuit college, where the education he received was to be of considerable use to him in his career as a history painter. Was prevented by an impediment of speech from becoming a priest, and, having a talent for drawing was enrolled as a student at the Académie Royale. In 1682 won 3rd prize for painting in the *Prix de Rome*, the subject being *Cain bâtit la ville d'Hérioch*, and in 1683 took the same place for sculpture with his *Invention des forges . . . par Tubal-Cain*. According to Vertue also studied under Le Brun whose influence is indeed very marked in much of Laguerre's work. Came to England with an architectural painter, Ricard, about 1684, and became an assistant to Verrio (*q.v.*) with whom Laguerre's name is inseparably linked in the history of decorative painting in England through the well-known couplet in Pope's *Epistle to the Earl of Burlington*, 1731. Probably worked with Verrio on his last commissions at Windsor, and certainly helped him to complete the large painting of *James II giving Audience* for the hall of Christ's Hospital, *c.* 1686–7. First recorded as working on his own in 1687–8, for William, 4th Earl of Kingston, at Thoresby near Nottingham. Employed as a master-painter by William Cavendish, 1st Duke of Devonshire, between 1689 and 1697, at Chatsworth, where some of his best work is to be found, on the scheme of decoration for the Hall, State Rooms and Chapel. The architectural and other subsidiary work there carried out by Ricard, but the names of the other assistants not recorded. Between 1691 and 1701 worked for William III at Hampton Court, his commissions including the roundels of the *Labours of Hercules* and the *Four Seasons* in the Fountain Court, and the restoration (with disastrous results) of Mantegna's *Triumph of Julius Caesar*. Other houses where his work at this period can be seen are Sudbury Hall (1691), Burghley and Wollaton Hall (both *c.* 1698), Castle Bromwich (1698–1700; an interesting series of letters from the architect Captain William Winde (*q.v.*), relating to this is in the archives of the Earl of Bradford). Succeeded Verrio, on the latter's retirement about 1705, as the leading history and decorative painter in this country. In 1711 became one of the Directors of the newly-founded academy in Kneller's house in Great Queen Street. Worked much for the Duke of Marlborough, first at Marlborough House, St. James's (*c.* 1713), and then at Blenheim (*c.* 1720). Borrowed from French models for his decorative schemes in both of these houses. The wall-paintings of the Duke's campaigns at Marlborough House are inspired by Louis XIV's victories as painted by A. F. van der Meulen and others at Marly, and the layout and subject-matter of the Saloon at Blenheim, showing the nations of the world appearing behind the parapet of a colonnade, are based on Le Brun's *Escalier des Ambassadeurs* at Versailles. Among other important commissions were the staircase of Sir Godfrey Kneller's country seat at Whitton (*c.* 1710), several ceilings at Canons (after 1713), the staircase at Petworth (after 1714), and the staircase at Buckingham House. In lighter vein than his usual mythological decorations was a 'Revel of Punch painted gratis, in Chiaroscuro [*i.e.* monochrome] a Bacchanalian Procession round a Room, the Revel of Punch carried in Triumph for a famous Club of Vertuosi held in Drury Lane'. Brought to the school of Baroque painting, founded in England by Verrio, the more sober characteristics of his native French classicism and a more harmonious sense of colour. From Laguerre's paintings, according to Vertue, 'most of the Present History painters learnt the Manner of such works. Sir James Thornhill first'. Certainly Thornhill's style has much affinity with that of certain of Laguerre's later works especially the staircase at Petworth. Found in Thornhill a serious rival to whom, in 1715, he lost the coveted commission of painting the dome of St. Paul's Cathedral. Clearly in emulation of the panels in the dome of St. Paul's, painted scenes from the life of Christ and single figures of the Evangelists and the Christian Virtues, all in monochrome, in the church of St. Lawrence, Whitchurch, Edgware (after 1714) at the expense of the Duke of Chandos. Supplanted Thornhill in the decoration of Blenheim. Designed a panel of tapestry, intended for the House of Lords, representing the Commissioners for England and Scotland presenting the Act of Union to Queen Anne, 1706. This was not woven, but

the oil sketch eventually passed to Vertue who mentions another sketch by Laguerre 'in two Colours' or 'in Chiar Obscure' for tapestry into which were introduced figures of Queen Anne and the Duke of Marlborough. A third painting by Laguerre of a similar type, but in the full colours, showing 'the Duke of Malbro. introduc'd by Victory to the Queen & Prince Eugene with him, france & bavaria overturn'd on the ground, with Cullours Armes & Standard & Trophies, Ec' was intended as a design for a huge enamel on copper to be executed by Charles Boit. [Perhaps related to these is a drawing in crayons (now in the collection of Mr. Iolo Williams) which when at Strawberry Hill was attributed to Laguerre by Walpole, who wrote on the old mount, *a Design for a Set of Tapestry of Queen Anne's Victories, by Laguerre, in which were to have been represented the Queen, Prince Eugene, the Duke of Marlborough and her principal Generals & Ministers . . . .* But it also bears the name *La fosse*, i.e. Le Brun's pupil, Charles de la Fosse (B. 1636: D. 1716), and of the two attributions this may be the correct one.] Laguerre occasionally painted easel pictures, including one of *Andromeda* which he presented to the Painter-Stainers' Company, and another of *Christ and the woman of Samaria* engraved in mezzotint by Jean Simon. Besides his early work with Verrio at Christ's Hospital and the occasional introduction of the figure of a contemporary person into his wall-paintings, also painted easel portraits, including one of Jan van Son, the flower painter. Designed two title-pages, one for Jean Tijou's *A new Booke of Drawings . . . containing several[l] sortes of Iron worke,* 1693, engraved by Paul van Somer, the other for Caius Velleius Paterculus's *Historia Romana,* London, 1718, engraved by Louis du Guernier.

In 1709 was living between Shepherd's Market and Brick Street, Piccadilly, but subsequently moved into the parish of St. Martin-in-the-Fields. Married Jean Tijou's daughter Eleanor, and by her had a son, John

(D. 1748), who achieved some success as an actor and singer. Died suddenly of apoplexy on April 20th, 1721, at Lincoln's Inn Theatre where he had gone to see his son act. Was buried in the churchyard of St. Martin-in-the-Fields. According to Vertue, John Laguerre also inherited some of his father's talent and combined this with his life on the stage by executing 'paintings & drawings for the playhouses [scene paintings (?)]' besides publishing his drawings of scenes from Dogget and Hippisley's ballad-opera *Flora; or Hob in the Well*, precursors with Hogarth's prison scene in the *Beggar's Opera* of the theatrical pictures made so popular by Zoffany and others in the later XVIII c.

BIBL.: *Kingston Accts. Bridgeman-Winde, Letters*, 1698–1700. *Walpole*, II, pp. 645–8. *Guiffrey & Barthelmy*, pp. 14–15. *Vertue, Index*, p. 138. *Baker, Chandos, passim. Thompson, Chatsworth, passim.*

DRAWINGS IN OTHER COLLECTIONS: Mr. Brinsley Ford and Prof. J. Isaacs (unused studies for ceilings at Chatsworth). Mr. Iolo Williams (design for tapestry, *see* above).

1. **THE JUDGMENT OF PARIS.** Scene in front of a wooded bank. On the l., Paris seated, with Mercury behind him, offering the golden apple to Venus who stands in the centre, attended by Cupid. Behind her to the r., Minerva and Juno, the latter with her head shielded by a mantle held over her by an *amorino*. Further to the r., nymphs and a river god.   **Plate 194**

Pen and brown ink, with grey wash, over black lead; 15·3 × 24 cm. (6 × 9½ in.). Old mount; 25·2 × 34·1 cm. (9⅞ × 13⅜ in.).

INSCR.: *Recto*, on the old mount, at the foot, by Jonathan Richardson II, *Laguerre*, and at the top, by Horace Walpole, *Judgment of Paris*.

PROV.: Jonathan Richardson II (?) (Sale, Langford, 6:ii:1772, Lot 72, or 7:ii:1772, Lot 39, or 11:ii:1772, Lot 40). Horace Walpole (Sale, Robins, 23:vi:1842, Lot 1266, No. 31, purchased by Graves). E. Parsons, from whom it was purchased by the B.M., 1929.

1929–3–11–2.

2. **MOSES RETURNING FROM MOUNT SINAI WITH THE TABLES OF THE LAW** (*Exodus*, XXXIV, 29). Moses standing, l., at the foot of the path leading up the mountain, holding the Tables of the Law. Further to the l., two men looking at him, and on the r., the Israelites, some of whom kneel in adoration.   **Plate 193**

Pen and brown ink, with light washes of grey and brown; partly stained with oil; 11·2 × 22·4 cm. (4⅜ × 8¾ in.). Old mount; 20·9 × 31·7 cm. (8¼ × 12½ in.).

INSCR.: *Recto*, on the old mount, at the foot, by Jonathan Richardson II, *Laguerre*, and at the top, by Horace Walpole, *Moses giving the Law*.

PROV.: Jonathan Richardson II (*Lugt*, No. 2170. Sale, Langford, 6:ii:1772, Lot 72, or 7:ii:1772, Lot 39, or 11:ii:1772, Lot 40). Horace Walpole (Sale, Robins, 23:vi:1842, Lot 1266, No. 30, purchased by Graves). E. Parsons, from whom it was purchased by the B.M., 1929.

1929–3–11–3.

LAROON, MARCELLUS II

[LAURON]

B. 1648/9 or 53: D. 1701/2

Genre and drapery painter, and mezzotint engraver

Born at The Hague, according to his son, Marcellus III, in 1648 or 9, but according to Buckeridge in 1653. Younger son of an indifferent portrait and landscape painter, also named Marcellus. A drawing in pen and ink on vellum, in the collection of Lord Methuen (copied from an etching by Place after Barlow), representing a hawk attacking poultry, and signed and dated *M Laurens* (*M L* in monogram) *fec Æt* $75\frac{1}{2}$ *1696*, is presumably by this first Laroon and supplies the date of his birth as *c.* 1620. Marcellus I also executed a commemorative design representing an interior scene in the Bank of England, where it still is. Studied in his native city with his father, and, for a short time, with an unknown history painter. According to Vertue, was 'of loose conversation and *morals* suteable to his birth and education, being *low* and *spurious*', and (it may be added) suitable also to the branch of art which he was generally to practise. Came to England with his father when young and studied, presumably portraiture, under 'one La Zoon' (perhaps Lely's assistant Sonnius, or 'Zonius' as Vertue calls him), but left him for B. Flessiers with whom he finished his apprenticeship. Lived some time in Yorkshire, and (according to Vertue) during that period (*c.* 1661/2) knew Rembrandt at York, the only literary evidence for that master's visit to England. Also knew Henry Gyles the glass painter (*q.v.*), and as 'Mr. Lorowne' is mentioned in no very flattering terms in letters dating from *c.* 1682 to Gyles from his nephew James Smith. By 1674 had removed to London, when on July 15th of that year he appears in the Minutes of the Painter-Stainers' Company as having 'ap-

peared and paid his Quarteridge and promised to bring his proofe peece'. Married, before 1679, Elizabeth, daughter of Jeremiah Keene, a builder of Little Sutton, near Chiswick. From June 1680, lived at Bow St., Covent Garden. According to Buckeridge, 'made it his endeavour to follow nature very close, so that his manner was wholly his own. He was a general painter [apparently attempting most branches] and imitated other masters hands exactly well. He painted well, both in great and little, and was an exact draughtsman; but he was chiefly famous for drapery [in portraits] wherein he exceeded most of his contemporaries', and in this last capacity assisted Sir Godfrey Kneller (*q.v.*). Tendered (Oct. 13th, 1684) the 'draught' for a portrait of the King (James II) which the Court of Governors of Christ's Hospital on the recommendation of the 'Schooles Committee' had agreed (June 24th, 1684) should be 'sett up at the upper end of the New Mathematicall Schoole'. The draught was 'very well liked and approved off' by the Court which, however, demurred at the fee asked by 'Mr Morsellis Lorone Limner', namely 'first for £50 and afterwards for £40, the house to find the frame'. He was told that if he did well 'upon Ticking, not Canvas according to the figures they would give him £30, the which he said was but little'. Subsequently, however, (Feb. 24th, 1684/5), Sir John Moore, the President of the Court, reported from the chair that 'at a Comm. in Christ's Hospital 24 Jany 1684/5. The said persons having received and considered off the picture drawn by Mr Lauron . . . agreed to allow him twenty four pounds and one Guinney to

402

buy him a paire of Globes in full payment for the said picture which the said Mr Lauron accepted of . . .' (*Christ's Hospital Committee Book Minutes MS.*). On his own account, painted a portrait of Caius Gabriel Cibber the sculptor, one of Egbert van Heemskerck the drollery painter (formerly in the collection of Dr. Coxe Macro), and, in the grand manner, of John, 3rd Lord Lovelace, signed and dated *Mar. Lauron fecit 1689* (at Wadham College, Oxford). According to the example described by Chaloner Smith (IV, p. 1605, No. 36) would have drawn the original of R. Williams's mezzotint of Queen Mary II. A miniature, with Messrs. H. Blairman in 1951, of the Duke of Monmouth (after an original by Laurence Cross in the collection of the Duke of Portland) also probably by him. Was more at home, however, in portraying the well-known characters in the London streets of his day, his drawings of them being published by Pierce Tempest as the well-known series of engravings, *The Cryes of the City of London* (1st edn., with 40 Pls., 1687/8, 4th edn., with 74 Pls., 1689), which have much in common with their Parisian counterparts of the same period by J. B. Bonnart (*See* **1938–3–11–5** (114–41)). Rather in the same vein are his *genre* scenes, including Dutch drolleries and monks listening to confession, in the manner of Heemskerck, some of these being engraved in mezzotint by himself, others by John Smith, and one by Francis Place (*q.v.*), a fellow member of the York *virtuosi*. Etched a series of drolleries, again in the

manner of Heemskerck, and a small camp scene in that of Thomas Wyck. Painted a 'history piece', the *Deliverance of Andromeda*, engraved in mezzotint by Smith and, in a completely different field, fine studies of a sparrow-hawk and a spaniel, about 1670 (Sale, Sotheby, 31:i:1951, Lot 121). Other works include the originals of a series of plates on fencing, engraved by William Elder, with the title, *The Art of Defence*, 1699 (two issues, one published by Philip Lea, the other by G. Beckett. Is said by Vertue to have drawn a representation of the coronation procession of William and Mary, 1689, presumably the one engraved by Samuel Moore (**1934–2–17–76**). Among his pupils were his three sons, the eldest of whom, Marcellus III, at one time a captain in the army and an actor, became well known as a painter and draughtsman of conversation pieces and fashionable gatherings. Another pupil, Thomas Pembroke (*See Buckeridge*, p. 408), is said to have painted history and portraits. Died of consumption at Richmond on March 11th, and was buried there on March 15th, 1701/2, his name being entered in the register as 'Marcelius Laroon of par. St. Pauls, [Covent] Gardeing, paintr.'.

BIBL.: *Buckeridge*, p. 401. *Bodleian MS., Eng. misc. C 346*, p. 259. *Smith, Nollekens*, II, p. 257. *C.S.*, IV, p. 1605, No. 36. *Richmond Registers*, I, p. 264. *Poole, Oxford Portraits*, III, p. 219, No. 32. *Knowles, Gyles*, pp. 65–6. *Vertue, Index*, p. 140. *Inf.* from Dr. Robert Raines.

[1–2]. DRAWINGS CONNECTED WITH *THE ART OF DEFENCE*

1. THE SWORD AND DAGGER GUARD. Two men fencing, shown with their swords in their l. and their daggers in their r. hands, he on the l. parrying with his dagger his opponent's sword in tierce. On the ground, the wig belonging to the man on the r.   **Plate 195**

Brush drawing in brown wash, over black lead, indented for transfer; 17·9 × 29·6 cm. (7 × 11⅝ in.).

INSCR.: *Recto* bears traces of lettering cut away at the foot.

PROV.: Hugh Howard. Dr. Robert Howard (Bishop of Elphin), and the Earls of Wicklow. Charles Howard, 5th Earl, from whom it was purchased by the B.M., 1874.

1874–8–8–2262 (L.B.9).

ENGR.: By W. Elder, correctly in reverse, with the lettering, *The Sword and Dagger Guard: The Sword that offers first is Defended by ye Dagger*, in THE ART OF DEFENCE, Pl. 8.

2. *Recto*. **A FENCING SCENE.** The man on the r. transfixing his opponent, l., who has attempted unsuccessfully to parry the former's lunge in cart. **Plate 197**

Black chalk on blue-grey paper; 27·6 × 45·1 cm. (10⅞ × 17¾ in.).

Verso. **A FENCING SCENE.** The man on the r. on guard, the man on the l. drawing his sword. On the ground, a wig lying between them, and a hat on the r.

Plate 198

Black chalk on blue-grey paper.

PROV.: Edward and Robert Byng. C. W. B. W. Roberts, their great-great nephew. G. R. Harding, from whom it was purchased by the B.M., 1897.

1897–8–13–9 (113).

The present drawing formed part of a large collection of sketchbooks and studies mainly by Edward and Robert Byng (*q.v.*),

who worked, like Laroon, as drapery painters in Kneller's studio. Included in this series was also a drawing by John James Baker or Backer, another of Kneller's assistants (*q.v.*).

Neither *recto* nor *verso* of the present sheet corresponds with any of the plates in *The Art of Defence*, but their subjects are sufficiently related in style to the engravings of that work to suggest that they were probably intended as studies for it.

3. *Recto*. **HORSES.** Three main studies: a horse's head turned half-l.; another turned slightly to r.; and a foreleg. Also slight studies of another foreleg, and horses galloping. **Plate 196**

Black and white chalks, on blue-grey paper; 30·1 × 22·3 cm. (11¾ × 8¾ in.).

REPR.: *Killanin*, Pl. 8, as by Kneller.

Verso. **PULCINELLA DANCING IN PROFILE TO L.**

White chalk, on blue-grey paper.

PROV.: Mrs. Roberts, from whom it was purchased by the B.M., 1888.

1888–7–19–74 (L.B., as by Sir Godfrey Kneller, 22).

This sheet was acquired with a group of drawings, all from the same source, most of which are by Sir Godfrey Kneller (*See* under his name, Nos. 11–14, 16—25, 27). The present studies, however, do not appear to

be by his hand, though they probably originated in his studio. In style they come near to that of Laroon and should be compared with No. 2 above. The Pulcinella on the *verso* in particular seems to have points in common with the fencers, notably in the drawing of the hands and of the costume. This figure should also be compared, from the point of view of subject, with the *Commedia dele' Arte* personages described below (Nos. 4–11), though there is some doubt that these are correctly attributed to Laroon.

[4–11]. DRAWINGS CONNECTED WITH THE COMMEDIA DELL' ARTE.

Some of these correspond with well-known types described in P. L. Duchartre's *The Italian Comedy*, 1929; others, however, have not been identified, and may be of local French or Netherlandish origin. They should be compared with the twelve engravings of *Commedia dell' Arte* figures published by Nicolas Bonnart, impressions of which are in the Department (1938–3–11–204 . . . 215). Some of the present drawings have been indented in preparation for engraving, but no prints directly connected with them have so far been found.

Purchased in 1852 from A.E. Evans as by 'Laroon', these drawings were catalogued by Mr. Binyon under 'Marcellus Laroon I' (*i.e.* II). The attribution is not an unlikely one, as they are not far removed in style from *The Cryes of the City of London*. It is possible, however, that they may have belonged to a series of twenty-four, formerly in the collection of Horace Walpole, which were described in the Strawberry Hill Sale of 23:vi:1842, Lot 1251, as 'Pantomimical Characters, dancing, singing, etc., very spirited by an anonymous artist', and which are known to have been purchased there by Evans. The following Lot, No. 1252, certainly contained drawings by Marcellus Laroon, and this may have resulted in his name also becoming attached subsequently to the 'Pantomimical Characters'.

4. A PUPPET SHOWMAN.

Standing on a platform and holding a short wand or flute to which he points. Wearing a round white hat, a doublet, petticoat breeches and a pink cloak, with a collar of teeth about his neck and a large wallet in front of him. In the background, his show-box with two puppets representing Punch and Judy at the top.   **Plate 199**

Pen and ink, with grey wash and water-colour, over black lead; indented for transfer; 26·4 × 18·5 cm. (10⅜ × 7¼ in.).

PROV.: Horace Walpole (?) (*See* introductory note to this series of drawings). A. E. Evans & Sons, from whom it was purchsaed by the B.M., 1852.

1852–2–14–412 (L.B.8).

The collar of teeth round the neck of the showman in the present drawing suggests that he also practises tooth extraction. In this connexion it is interesting to note that the Frenchman, Jean Brioché, one of the most celebrated puppet-masters of the XVII c. and the first to produce Polichinelle (Punch) on the puppet stage, achieved a considerable reputation as a dentist (*See* Philippe Le Bas, *Dictionnaire Encyclopedique de la France*, III, 1841, pp. 390–1). Tooth extraction indeed seems to have been not infrequently accompanied by some form or other of theatrical entertainment at fairs in the XVII and XVIII c. There are numerous pictures of the period depicting this.

5. AN UNIDENTIFIED CHARACTER.

Laughing and dancing, with hands outstretched and r. leg raised. Wearing a pink cap, light blue doublet with pink and blue slashed sleeves, breeches and green stockings. In the background, a landscape with a river and trees and a group of buildings on its bank.

Pen and ink, with grey wash and water-colours, over black lead; indented for transfer; 26·4 × 18 cm. (10⅜ × 7⅛ in.).

6. A FOOL. Standing on a terrace, laughing, with his hands clasped before him and his legs apart. Wearing a feathered cap with long ears, ruff, pink doublet with bells and green ribbons, petticoat breeches and green stockings. In the background, the head of a flight of steps and a distant landscape. **Plate 200**

Pen and ink, with grey wash and water-colours, over black lead; indented for transfer; 27·6 × 18·7 cm. (10¾ × 7⅜ in.).

PROV.: As for No. 4.
1852–2–14–414 (L.B.4).

7. MEZZETINO. Standing, with head turned to r. as if speaking, his l. arm outstretched. Wearing a pink and light blue bonnet and a pink and light blue striped doublet and breeches, with green stockings. Trees in the background, lightly indicated.

Pen and ink, with grey wash and water-colours, over black lead; indented for transfer; 26·9 × 18·8 cm. (10⅝ × 7⅜ in.).

PROV.: As for No. 4.
1852–2–14–415 (L.B.2).

Mezzetino was one of the best-known of the valets in the *Commedia dell' Arte*. Towards the end of the XVII c. the Franco-Italian actor Angelo Constantini is said to have introduced the red and white striped costume, seen here, when interpreting the character (*See Duchartre*, p. 171).

8. AN UNIDENTIFIED CHARACTER. Dancing, with one hand holding the brim of his hat and the other resting on his hip, his l. leg raised. Wearing a striped pink and blue conical hat, a mask with black curving moustache and tufted beard, a pink and yellow doublet with striped green and white apron, pink breeches, and a light blue and yellow cloak. In the background, which suggests a stage back-cloth, a wooded knoll and a long, low building. **Plate 201**

Pen and ink, with grey wash and water-colours, over black lead; 26·2 × 18·8 cm. (10¼ × 7⅜ in.).

The mask of this character suggests that of Scaramuccia, but the costume is entirely different (*See* No. 10).

PROV.: As for No. 4.
1852–2–14–416 (L.B.6).

9. AN UNIDENTIFIED CHARACTER. Dancing, with his hat in his l. hand, and looking towards the r. Wearing a mask, a doublet and breeches ornamented with a flame pattern of pink and light green, and pink stockings blue-gartered. In the background, farm-buildings and trees.

Pen and ink, with grey wash and water-colours, over black lead; indented for transfer; 26·7 × 18·5 cm. (10½ × 7¼ in.).

PROV.: As for No. 4.
1852–2–14–417 (L.B.7).

10. SCARAMUCCIA. Walking towards the l. with a guitar in his r. hand, and looking over his l. shoulder. Wearing a black bonnet, a mask with black moustache and tufted beard, falling ruff, black doublet, breeches, stockings, and cloak over his l. arm. In the background, trees and buildings, lightly indicated.

Pen and ink, with grey wash and water-colours, over black lead; $27 \cdot 5 \times 18 \cdot 7$ cm. ($10\frac{7}{8} \times 7\frac{3}{8}$ in.).

PROV.: As for No. 4.
1852–2–14–418 (L.B.1).

Scaramuccia was one of the several varieties of the swaggering captain in the *Commedia dell' Arte*, and later took on some of the attributes of the valet. He was always dressed in black (*See Duchartre*, pp. 236–47).

11. PULCINELLA. Dancing, in profile to l., on a terrace. Wearing a feathered hat, mask with hooked nose and glasses, ruff, doublet with large buttons and protuberant stomach, breeches with long cannons and a short cloak. In the background, a garden with trees and a clipped hedge, and a group of figures.   **Plate 202**

Pen and brown ink, with grey wash, over black lead; indented for transfer; $27 \cdot 5 \times 18 \cdot 6$ cm. ($10\frac{3}{4} \times 7\frac{3}{8}$ in.).

PROV.: As for No. 4.
1852–2–14–419 (L.B.3).

Pulcinella, later Polichinelle in France and Punch in England, was one of the most ancient characters in the *Commedia dell' Arte*. Witty and impertinent on the one hand, and fawning and cowardly on the other, he played many different roles.

LELY, SIR PETER

B. 1618: D. 1680
Portrait painter and draughtsman

Born at Soest in Westphalia, according to Houbraken on Sept. 14th, 1618. Son of Johan van der Faes, a well-to-do Dutch infantry captain (known as Lely from the name 'In de Lely' of his house at The Hague) and Abigail van Vliet. Studied at Haarlem under Frans Pietersz de Grebber (B. *c.* 1573: D. 1649), where his name appears in the register of St. Luke's guild for 1637. Two drawings from this period survive, a signed chalk and wash landscape of Haarlem (?), now in the Birmingham City Art Gallery, and an interior scene with figures, in pen and wash, signed and dated 1639 (Colnaghi, 1956). The date of his arrival in England probably 1641, on the occasion of William of

Orange's marriage to Princess Mary, as stated by Houbraken and Graham, but Houbraken mistakenly gives the date of that event as 1643. Vertue states that the artist first worked with Isaac Sailmaker (B. 1633: D. 1721), the marine painter, and for George Geldorp (D. *c.* 1658) the portraitist, at his house in Drury Lane. In his early period, according to Graham, 'Pursu'd the natural bent of his *Genius* in *Landtschapes* with *small Figures*, and *Historical Compositions*'. Graham and Richard Lovelace (*Peinture, a Panegyrick to the best Picture of Friendship, Mr. Pet. Lilly*) indicate that his work in this field met with small success. His earliest known signed painting, a *Diana and her Nymphs* (Nantes

Museum), dated either 1640 or 1646. By 1647 had secured the patronage of Algernon, 10th Earl of Northumberland, Van Dyck's principal patron, whose portrait by Van Dyck Lely may have copied and who, as guardian of the royal princes, may have commissioned him to paint the *Children of Charles I* (Petworth) and the *Charles I and the Duke of York* (1647, Syon House). Also found employment with Northumberland's relations, William, 2nd Earl of Salisbury, and Robert, 2nd Earl of Leicester, and during the Civil War and Protectorate continued to paint portraits and a few subject pictures. Was made free of the Painter-Stainers' Company on October 26th, 1647, together with George Wild, Thomas Rawlins, and Richard Lovelace for whose volume of poems (1649) he designed frontispieces. Even by 1650 considered by some to be England's leading painter, and was then already living in the house in the Piazza, Covent Garden, where he eventually died. With Geldorp and Balthazar Gerbier (*q.v.*) submitted to the Commonwealth government at some period before April 1653 an abortive proposal to decorate the 'Great Room [Banqueting Hall] and galleries' at Whitehall with paintings of events during the life of the Long Parliament. In 1656 visited Holland with Hugh May, later Clerk of Works under Wren at Windsor. Was appointed in 1661 Principal Painter to the King, being granted in October of that year a pension of £200 'as formerly to Van Dyck' and became naturalized the following year. Maintained an elaborate studio organization (Pepys mentions a strict time-table of sitters kept by Lely) which necessitated the employment of assistants who included Joseph Buckshorn (Bokshorn; B. *c.* 1670: D. 1755) and Prosper Henricus Lankrink (B. 1628: D. 1692), the artist-collector who painted backgrounds and draperies; Jan Baptist Gaspars (*q.v.*) who painted 'postures'; and Thomas Hawker and Sonnius who were later engaged in finishing Lely's pictures. Apart from these numbered among his

pupils and followers Mary Beale (*q.v.*), John Greenhill (*q.v.*), the French artist Nicolas Largillière, who worked in Lely's studio from 1674–8, and William Wissing (*q.v.*). Vertue also mentions other minor followers: William Bonett, Davenport, Jeremiah Davison, John Dixon, the amateur Sir John Gawdie, Bart., and Henry Tilson (*q.v.*). Was accepted as an arbiter of taste and his authority at Court, according to the same source, helped Grinling Gibbons to secure the royal patronage. Had no serious rivals as a portrait painter after the Restoration, although Gerard Soest (B. 1637: D. 1681) and Michael Wright (B. 1617 (?): D. 1700 (?)) had respectable practices and Jacob Huysmans (B. 1656: D. 1696) found support in the Catholic section of the Court. There was a tradition that Lely retired to Richmond or Kew after Simon Verelst became fashionable, and his practice may have been jeopardized by the success of the foreign painters who won popularity in certain circles at Court. Was secretive about his technique as a portrait painter, to judge from references in Charles Beale's diaries and Buckeridge's account of Greenhill. Was knighted at Whitehall on Jan. 11th, 1679, receiving a grant of arms. Died suddenly on Nov. 30th, 1680, while still engaged on a full programme of portraits, and was buried in St. Paul's, Covent Garden. Left a son John (*See* No. 26 below) and a daughter Anne (*See* No. 27 below) (B. 1662) by Ursula, 'his reputed wife', whose name appears in the register of that church as the mother of 'Peter [baptized and buried in January 1673] son of Peter Lelly'. She herself was buried there on Jan. 11th, 1673.

Lely's great collection which Buckeridge described as 'the best chosen . . . of any of his time' consisted of about 160 paintings and 10,000 drawings and prints (mainly of the Italian School, Dutch Italianists and Caravaggisti) primarily acquired from the collections of Charles I, Arundel, Buckingham and Geldorp. It was sold by auction in 1682,

1688 and 1693. Roger North, Lely's executor, put the collection in order and stamped each of the drawings and prints with Lely's mark.

Lely as a draughtsman is well represented in the Department and the examples of his work listed below are arranged according to their various categories, each with an introductory note.

BIBL.: Sanderson, pp. 20, 36 & 46. B.M., Additional MS., 16174. Graham, pp. 343–5. Buckeridge, pp. 402–4. Nichols & Bruce, Wills, pp. 133–7. North, Lives, III, pp. 190–209. Baker, Lely, pp. 138–77 and passim. Osborne, Letters, pp. 50, 59, 106, 109, 114, 192, 234 & 261. T.-B., XXIII, 1929, pp. 13–15 (with Bibl.). Lee. Glück, Reflections. Toynbee, Early Portraits. Borenius, Lely's Coll. Puyvelde. Ogden, Lely's Coll. Waterhouse, Van Dyck. Toynbee, Lely's Early Work. Ilchester. Vertue, Index, pp. 143–5. Woodward, pp. 27–54. Beckett, Lely. Waterhouse, pp. 57, 62–7, 72, 84–5, 88 and 150. Van Luttervelt. Vertue, VI, pp. 161–3. Inf. from Mr. Oliver Millar.

[1–16]. STUDIES OF FIGURES TAKING PART IN THE CEREMONIES OF THE ORDER OF THE GARTER ON ST. GEORGE'S DAY, APRIL 23rd.

The following belong to a large group of studies connected with the ceremonies of the Order of the Garter on St. George's Day, April 23rd. There are no contemporary records of these drawings—they do not appear, for instance, in Lely's sale catalogue—and the first notice of them found so far is in the catalogue of an anonymous sale by De Leth at Amsterdam on March 23rd, 1763, in which is described an album containing sixteen of them, all being attributed to Lely. This by no means represents the complete group, however, for at least thirty drawings are now known. Besides the sixteen in the British Museum, examples have been identified in the following collections: Amsterdam, Chr. P. van Eeghen (1. A Poursuivant). Amsterdam, Mensing (1. A Knight bowing). Amsterdam, Rijksmuseum (1. A Poursuivant. 2. A Knight, wrongly said to be the Chancellor). Berlin, Print Room (1. Two Heralds). Cambridge, Mass. Fogg Art Museum (1. Two Poor Knights of Windsor). Chatsworth Estates Co. (1. A Knight bowing). Paris, Institut néerlandais, Frits Lugt (1. A Knight, perhaps the King). The Hague, Baron Victor de Stuers (1. A Knight, barehead, perhaps William Cavendish, 1st Duke of Newcastle). Leningrad, Hermitage Museum (1. A Knight. 2. Two Canons of Windsor). London, Courtauld Institute, Witt Coll. (1. Two Heralds). London, Victoria & Albert Museum (1. A Poursuivant). Oxford, Ashmolean Museum (1. The Chancellor, Sir Henry de Vic. 2. A Knight). Sacramento, Calif., E. B. Crocker Art Gallery (1. Two Canons of Windsor). Vienna, Albertina (1. Two Heralds).

The technique of these drawings appears to be the same in every case: black chalk, much re-drawn with oil-charcoal and heightened with white, on blue-grey paper; some are, or appear to be, offsets and even double-offsets (Nos. 13–15), the probable use of which will be referred to below. As a whole, though more detailed in handling, they have affinities, both in size and appearance, with Van Dyck's studies for portraits made in England (See Hind, Dutch & Flemish Drawings, II, pp. 65–72), which would explain the former long-standing, but incorrect, ascription of the Vienna example to that master.

One, at least, of the present series (No. 3) is recognizable as a portrait of the Prelate of the Order, Bishop Morley, and it can be assumed that most of the remaining studies are also from the life, as, for instance, the Usher of the Black Rod, Sir Edward Carteret, and the Register of the Order, Bruno Ryves (No. 2), the blind poor Knight (No. 12) who is probably Captain Richard Vaughan, and—outside the British Museum series—the bareheaded Knight in the Stuers collection, who may be William Cavendish, 1st Duke of Newcastle. Captain Vaughan was admitted a Poor Knight in 1663, and this date may be taken as the earliest at which the drawings could have been made. The other limiting date would be 1671, the year in which the Chancellor of the Order, Sir Henry de Vic (No. 15), died.

These studies are nearly always spoken of as representing figures in a Garter Procession, but reference to Elias Ashmole's *Institution . . . of the Most Noble Order of the Garter*, 1672, certainly suggests that three of those not included in the British Museum series from their poses are taking part in other ceremonies of the Order on St. George's Day: the two Knights bowing, respectively at Chatsworth and in the Mensing collection at Amsterdam, might be making their 'reverences' either to the Sovereign before setting out for the Chapel (*Ashmole*, p. 548), or before taking up their places in the Choir for the start of the Grand Procession (*Ashmole*, p. 566), or when making their offerings (*Ashmole*, p. 583), or to the Sovereign, in the Presence Chamber, before passing into St. George's Hall for the dinner (*Ashmole*, p. 589); and the bareheaded Knight in the Stuers collection would probably be standing uncovered at the moment during the dinner when the Garter King of Arms proclaims the Stiles of the Sovereign (*Ashmole*, p. 592). Most of the drawings, however, do seem to be concerned with the Procession, which was—and still is—the most picturesque feature of the Garter ceremonies.

The actual purpose for which the drawings were made remains obscure. It is possible that they are connected with some project for wall decoration, perhaps a revival of that originally planned by Van Dyck, about 1641, for the Banqueting House at Whitehall, to be carried out in tapestry; and it may be significant that Lely owned Van Dyck's original oil-sketch of a Garter Procession (now in the collection of the Duke of Rutland) which appears to have been one of the subjects included in the scheme. Oddly enough, Ashmole, who devotes a substantial section of his chapter XXI to an account of pictorial representations of processions in the past, makes no mention of Van Dyck or Lely as having contemplated a work of this kind. But it seems just worth while referring to an account of Burford House (the Duke of St. Albans) at Windsor in Mrs. J. H. Pye's *A Short View of the Principal Seats . . . in and about Twickenham*, 1767, p. 19, where there was a 'gallery of the Knights of the Garter, all whole lengths, done by Van Dyke and Sir Peter Lely'. An account of the same house in an anonymous guide, *Windsor, and Its Environs*, 1768, pp. 76–7, refers to this gallery as the 'Billiard-room'. The names of the alleged painters are not given, but those of the Knights represented are; and, with the exception of Prince Rupert, all were created by Charles II, so Van Dyck's supposed authorship can probably be ruled out altogether. Lely, on the other hand could well have executed these portraits, but whether they can have had anything to do with the present drawings it is impossible to say, as the house has been modified and the pictures have disappeared.

There is too, in *Ashmole*, pp. 576–7, an etching by Hollar representing the Garter Procession of 1671, and Mr. Binyon thought that Lely's drawings might have been made on this same occasion. But Hollar made no real attempt, as Lely did, to depict recognizable individuals such as Bishop Morley and Captain Vaughan, though perhaps his Chancellor (Sir Henry de Vic) has something in common with Lely's. There may, however, be some more definite point of contact between the drawings and the etching in the fact that Lely probably intended to portray, according to a well-established convention (*Cf.* Denis van Asloot's *Ommeganck* in the Victoria & Albert Museum) a long cortège winding into the distance such as Hollar shows: and for this purpose he drew his figures moving both to left and right, besides taking offsets from them as a further aid in working out how they were to be placed in such a composition. (A parallel use of offsets is to be found among the drawings of the Van de Veldes, *Cf.* p. 521.) The diminutive Poor Knight walking beside his seemingly gigantic companion in No. 11, may also be a device to facilitate composition, the figure in this case being scaled down, so that it should be seen in correct proportion when occupying a place near the head of the Procession in the background, as indeed the Poor Knights do in Hollar's etching.

BIBL.: *Schwabe. Bell, Letter. Kleinmann*, Ser. II, Pl. 5. Lugt, *Dutch Catalogue, Berlin. Van Eeghen*, p. 22, No. 61, Pl. 7. *Fellowes*, p. 36. *Benisovich. Woodward*, pp. 34, 50. *Millar, Charles I. Inf.* from Sir Owen Morshead, Mr. Frits Lugt, Mr. J. L. Nevinson and Mr. John Woodward.

1. ONE OF THE SOVEREIGN'S CANOPY-BEARERS. Walking towards the l. and looking up at the canopy (not seen) which he supports by a pole held before him. Wearing a dark doublet over petticoat breeches, and large cannons over his stockings. **Plate 203**

Black oiled chalk, heightened with white, on blue-grey paper; the upper corners cut off and made up; 50 × 23·4 cm. (19⅝ × 9¼ in.).

PROV.: Anon. Sale, Amsterdam, De Leth, 23:iii:1703, Lot 24, 'een Standaert-dragger, hoog 20 duim, breed 10½ duim,' purchased by Johan van der Marck, or Lot 28, 'een standaart-draeger hoog 19 duim, breed 19 duim,' purchased by Fouquet (?). Johan van der Marck (Sale, Amsterdam, Hendrick de Winter & Jan Yver, 29:xi:1773, Lot 1439, 'Een Ridder een Standaart houdende . . . h. 18½ b. 16 duim' (?)). Dirk Versteegh (Sale, Amsterdam, de Vries & Roos, 2nd Partie,

3:xi:1823, Lot 9 (?), described, however, as 'Une feuille avec trois nobles seigneurs'). Baron J. G. Verstolk de Soelen (Sale, Amsterdam, de Vries, Brondgeest, & Roos-22:iii:1847, Lot 332, 'Trois chevaliers de l'ordre de la Jarretiere, en costume, avec tous les attributs'). Purchased at the Verstolk Sale by the B.M., 1847.

1847–3–26–15 (L.B.16(1)).

BIBL.: *Benisovich*, p. 80.

The drawing traditionally is said to represent a standard-bearer. The subject is, however, clearly one of the bearers of the canopy over the Sovereign as seen in Hollar's etching of *The Grand Procession* mentioned above. According to *The Order of the Ceremonies Used at the Celebration of St. Georges Feast at Wind-* sor . . . , 1671, p. 11, these canopy bearers were 'certain Gentlemen of the *Privy-Chamber* appointed by the *Lord Chamberlain*'.

2. SIR EDWARD CARTERET, USHER OF THE BLACK ROD, AND BRUNO RYVES, DEAN OF WINDSOR AND REGISTER OF THE ORDER. On the l., Sir Edward Carteret in his mantle, holding in his r. hand the Rod, tipped with a lion rampant, to which he points with his l. hand, while he looks round at Bruno Ryves, who walks beside him, r., wearing a skull-cap and mantle and holding the Red Book of the Order before him. Plate 205

Black oiled chalk, heightened with white, on blue-grey paper; on two conjoined sheets; 45·5 × 39 cm. (18 × 15⅝ in.).

INSCR.: *Recto*, in the lower l.-hand corner, *King of Armes met een / satijne mantel*, and in the r.-hand corner, *root / Deeken van Windsor Registermeest* [er].

PROV.: Dirk Versteegh (Sale, Amsterdam, de Vries & Roos, 2nd Partie, 3 :xi:1823, Lot 9 (?), described, however, as 'Une feuille avec trois nobles seigneurs'). Baron J. G. Verstolk de Soelen (Sale, Amsterdam, de Vries, Brondgeest, & Roos, 22 :iii:1847, Lot 332, 'Trois chevaliers de l'ordre de la Jarretiere, en costume, avec tous les attributs'). Purchased at the Verstolk Sale by the B.M., 1847.

1847–3–26–16 (L.B.16(2)).

[Sir Edward Carteret (D. 1683), 5th son of Sir Philip de Carteret, Deputy Governor of Jersey in Charles I's reign (*See* Arthur Collins, *A History of the Noble Family of Carteret*, 1756, p. 34). Was knighted by Charles II, and became Usher of the Black Rod and a member of the household of James, Duke of York (later James II). His sister Margaret married Sir Henry de Vic, Bart., Chancellor of the Order (*See* No. 15).

Bruno Ryves (B. 1596: D. 1677). Educated at Oxford. Vicar of Stanwell and chaplain to Charles I. During the Civil War published his Royalist newspaper *Mercurius Rusticus* from 1642 onwards. In 1646 appointed Dean of Chichester, but not installed till 1660. Carried money to Charles II during his exile. Appointed Dean of Windsor, 1660, and Register of the Order of the Garter, 1660/1.]

3. GEORGE MORLEY, BISHOP OF WINCHESTER AND PRELATE OF THE ORDER. Walking towards the l. and looking over his l. shoulder. Wearing a skull-cap, moustache and pointed beard, and a mantle over a rochet and cassock. Holding in his outstretched r. hand an academic cap. Plate 204

Black oiled chalk, heightened with white, on blue-grey paper; 50·3 × 35 cm. (19⅞ × 13⅞ in.).

INSCR.: *Recto*, at the foot, *The Prelate of the Order* (partly obliterated).

PROV.: John Thane (*Lugt*, No. 1545. Apparently not in any of his catalogues or

sales). Henry Graves, from whom it was purchased by the B.M., 1862.

1862–7–12–647 (L.B.16(3)).

BIBL. & REPR.: *Woodward*, p. 50, and Pl. 36.

[George Morley (B. 1597: D. 1684). Had a distinguished ecclesiastical career in which he showed himself to be a staunch church-man and Royalist, though with leanings to-wards Calvinism. Virtually acted as chaplain to the Royalists in exile at St. Germain, and latterly at The Hague and Antwerp. After the Restoration became successively Dean of Christ church, Oxford, and Bishop of Wor-cester, and finally, in 1662, Bishop of Win-chester and Prelate of the Order of the Garter. Was noted for his wit and hospitality, and enjoyed the friendship of many well-known figures of the day, including Edmund Waller and Lord Clarendon.]

The present drawing shows his characteris-tically short hair and closely cut beard which are also such features of the later por-traits of him by Lely, though these show him with his face much fallen in through the loss of his teeth (*See B.M. Engraved Portraits*, III, p. 281).

4. TWO CANONS OF WINDSOR. Walking together towards the l. and convers-ing, he on the l. with his hands outspread. Both wearing skull-caps and mantles over their surplices and cassocks, he on the r. holding an academic cap in his l. hand.

Black oiled chalk, heightened with white, on blue-grey paper; 52·2 × 37·7 cm. (20½ × 14⅞ in.).

INSCR.: *Recto*, in the lower r.-hand corner, *Cannons of the Order*.

PROV.: As for No. 3.
1862–7–12–645 (L.B.16(14)).

5. TWO CANONS OF WINDSOR. Walking together towards the l., he on the l. in profile, bearded, his r. hand held to his breast, he on the r. looking back over his l. shoulder. Both wearing skull-caps and mantles.

Black oiled chalk, heightened with white, on blue-grey paper; 52·4 × 38·3 cm. (20¾ × 15⅛ in.).

INSCR.: *Recto*, at the foot, towards the r., *Cannons of the Order*.

PROV.: As for No. 3.
1862–7–12–648 (L.B.16(5)).

6. TWO CANONS OF WINDSOR. Walking together towards the l., he on the l. turning to look back, he on the r. with his l. hand outstretched. Both wearing skull-caps and mantles, and holding academic caps in their r. hands.

Black oiled chalk, heightened with white, on blue-grey paper; 51·5 × 38 cm. (20¼ × 15 in.).

INSCR.: *Recto*, at the foot, in the centre, *Cannons* (very faint).

PROV.: As for No. 3.
1862–7–12–651 (L.B.16(6)).

7. TWO CANONS OF WINDSOR. Walking together towards the l., he on the l. turning to speak to his companion. Both wearing skull-caps and mantles over surplices and cassocks, he on the l. holding a book, he on the r. an academic cap.

Plate 207

Black oiled chalk, heightened with white, on blue-grey paper; 53·2 × 37·8 cm. (21 × 14⅞ in.).

INSCR.: *Recto*, at the foot, *The Prebends of Windsor in blacke . . . an* (partly obliterated).

PROV.: As for No. 3.

1862–7–12–652 (L.B.16(7)).

8. TWO POOR KNIGHTS OF WINDSOR. Walking together towards the l. Both wearing mantles, he on the l. bare-headed and holding a round hat before him, he on the r. wearing a skull-cap and holding a stick.

Black oiled chalk, heightened with white, on blue-grey paper; 53·9 × 39·5 cm. (21¼ × 15⅝ in.).

INSCR.: *Recto*, at the foot, towards the l., *Poor Knights*.

PROV.: As for No. 3.

1862–7–12–644 (L.B.16(8)).

9. TWO POOR KNIGHTS OF WINDSOR. Walking together towards the l. and conversing. Both bare-headed and wearing mantles, he on the l. with a stick.

Black oiled chalk, heightened with white, on blue-grey paper; 51·2 × 37·6 cm. (20¼ × 14⅞ in.).

INSCR.: *Recto*, at the foot, in the centre, *Poor Knights*.

PROV.: As for No. 3.

1862–7–12–646 (L.B.16(9)).

10. TWO POOR KNIGHTS OF WINDSOR. Walking together towards the l. and conversing. Both wearing mantles over their cassocks, he on the l. with a skull-cap on his head and holding a stick, he on the r. bare-headed and holding a broad-brimmed hat in his l. hand. **Plate 208**

Black oiled chalk, heightened with white, on blue-grey paper; 53 × 38·1 cm. (20⅞ × 15 in.).

PROV.: As for No. 3.

1862–7–12–649 (L.B.16(10)).

11. TWO POOR KNIGHTS OF WINDSOR. Walking together towards the l. and conversing. Both wearing skull-caps and mantles over their cassocks, he on the r. holding a broad-brimmed hat in his r. hand. The figure on the l. of the same size as the others in the series, that on the r. drawn on a reduced scale. **Plate 206**

Black oiled chalk, heightened with white, on blue-grey paper; 49·6 × 37·5 cm. (19½ × 14¾ in.).

INSCR.: *Recto*, at the foot, in the centre, *Poor Knights*.

PROV.: As for No. 3.

1862–7–12–650 (L.B.16(11)).

12. CAPT. RICHARD VAUGHAN, A POOR KNIGHT OF WINDSOR. A blind man with eyes closed, leaning on a stick as he feels his way towards the l. Wearing a skull-cap, and mantle over his cassock. **Plate 212**

Black oiled chalk, heightened with white, on blue-grey paper; 45·1 × 33·6 cm. (17¾ × 13¼ in.).

PROV.: Anon. (Sale, Amsterdam, De Leth, 23:iii:1763, Lot 17, 'een blinde Ridder . . . hoog 17½ duim, breed 13 duim', purchased by Yver (?)). Dirk Versteegh (Sale, Amsterdam, de Vries & Roos, 2nd Partie, 3:xi:1823, Lot 9 (?), described, however, as 'Une feuille avec trois nobles seigneurs'). Baron J. G. Verstolk de Soelen (Sale, Amsterdam, de Vries, Brondgeest, & Roos, 22:iii:1847, Lot 332, 'Trois chevaliers de l'ordre de la Jarretiere, en costume, avec tous les attri-

buts'). Purchased at the Verstolk Sale by the B.M., 1847.

    1847–3–26–17 (L.B.16(12)).

BIBL.: *Benisovich*, p. 80.

[Capt. Richard Vaughan (B. 1620: D. 1700). Of the family of Vaughan of Pantelas, Carnarvon. Fought with much courage in the Royalist army during the Civil War, sustaining 'great sufferings in his means and hurts in his body', and losing his sight. Was admitted a Poor Knight on July 15th, 1663, died June 5th, 1700, and was buried in St. George's Chapel, Windsor.]

13. A KNIGHT OF THE ORDER OF THE GARTER. Standing, his head in profile to r., his body turned half-r., his r. hand outstretched and pointing. Wearing the robes and collar of the Order, with a plumed cap on his head.   **Plate 210**

Black oiled chalk, heightened with white, on blue-grey paper; 50·4 × 26·7 cm. (19⅞ × 10½ in.).

PROV.: George Morant (Sale, Christie, 21:iv:1847, Lot 990, 'Van Dyck—two studies of Knights in their robes'). Purchased at the Morant Sale by the B.M., 1847.

    1847–5–29–12 (L.B.16(13)).

14. A KNIGHT OF THE ORDER OF THE GARTER. Walking to r. and looking slightly upwards. Wearing the robes and collar of the Order, with a plumed cap on his head.   **Plate 209**

Black oiled chalk, heightened with white, on blue-grey paper; 49·6 × 32·3 cm. (19⅝ × 12¾ in.).

INSCR.: *Recto*, in the lower r.-hand corner, 17.

PROV.: As for No. 13.

    1847–5–29–11 (L.B.16(14)).

15. SIR HENRY DE VIC, CHANCELLOR OF THE ORDER. Walking in profile towards the l. Wearing a long curling wig and a mantle, and holding before him the Purse of the Order.

Double offset (?) from black chalk, heightened with white, on blue-grey paper; 46·8 × 28·2 cm. (18⅜ × 11⅛ in.).

PROV.: Purchased in Florence, 1944. E. Croft-Murray, by whom it was presented to the B.M., 1946.

    1946–7–13–1267a.

[Sir Henry de Vic (B. c. 1599: D. 1671). Probably a native of Guernsey. For nearly twenty years was English Resident in Brussels under Charles I, and was created a Baronet during the Royal exile at St. Germain, 1649. Appointed Chancellor of the Order of the Garter in 1660, which office he held till the end of his life.]

This drawing is probably an offset from an offset from the original drawing in the Ashmolean Museum (formerly in the Bodleian Library), Oxford (*Sutherland-Burnet*, II, p. 722). This would explain why it is so faint and why it is in the same sense as the original which also shows the figure walking towards the l.

16. TWO POOR KNIGHTS OF WINDSOR. Walking together towards the l., he on the l. turning back to speak to his companion. Both bare-headed, bearded and wearing mantles.

Plate 211

Black oiled chalk, heightened with white, on blue-grey paper; $53 \cdot 8 \times 35$ cm. ($21\frac{1}{4} \times 13\frac{7}{8}$ in.).

INSCR.: *Recto*, in the lower l.-hand corner, on a separate slip, *arme | Ridders Almes Knights | de mantel violet den rock* [rok=coat] . . . .

Verso, in the lower l.-hand corner, *Sophia Sir P Lilly*.

PROV.: Anon. Sale, Amsterdam, de Leth, 23:iii:1763, Lot 25 (?) 'twee arme Ridders, hoog 21 duim, breed 14 duim'. Purchased by Abr. Falc. Dr. Johannes Jantzen, from whom it was purchased by the B.M., 1955.

1955-4-16-1.

BIBL.: *Benisovich*, p. 80.

[17–29]. PORTRAIT STUDIES AND RELATED DRAWINGS. The following section mainly consists of portraits from the life. Among them are some of the bust-length studies in crayons on buff or grey paper, which are so characteristic of Lely as a draughtsman (*See* Nos. 20, 22, 24, 28). His works in this medium are lighter and freer in handling than the crayons in full colour executed, at a slightly later period, by Edmund Ashfield (*q.v.*) and Edward Lutterell (*q.v.*); yet they seem to have been regarded by Lely as finished enough works in themselves, for most of them are boldly signed by him, and examples which appeared in his sale are described in the catalogue (*Burl. Mag.*, LXXXIII, p. 188) as having been '*in Ebony frames*', implying that they were intended to be hung on the wall. In one instance alone can one of them perhaps be related to a known oil-painting, though it cannot be regarded as a direct study for it: this is the drawing of a *Young Girl* belonging to Lady Islington (*Woodward*, Pl. 39), which certainly has affinities with Lely's portrait of Elizabeth Seymour (B. *c.* 1654: D. 1695), 1st wife of Thomas Bruce, 2nd Earl of Aylesbury (*Cf.* the Earl of Cardigan, *The Life and Loyalties of Thomas Bruce*, 1951, p. 30; kindly communicated by Mr. C. F. Bell). In his particular use of crayons Lely was followed by his pupil John Greenhill (*q.v.*), the dwarf Richard Gibson (*q.v.*), T. Thrumton (*q.v.*), and, at a later date, by Mary Beale and Michael Dahl (*q.v.*). Of the remaining drawings, No. 29 is related to the above-mentioned crayons in style, but not in technique; Nos. 26 and 27 are slight and intimate sketches of the artist's children; No. 17 is also probably an intimate study; Nos. 18, 19, 21, 23 and 25 may or may not be studies for use in the process of portrait manufacture.

17. HEAD OF A WOMAN SEEN FROM BEHIND. Turned l., the hair partly coiled on top, partly falling in ringlets at the side.

Black chalk, heightened with white, on brown-grey paper; 16·9 × 15 cm. (6⅝ × 5⅞ in.).

PROV.: Lely (Lugt, No. 2092). Sir Joshua Reynolds (Lugt, No. 2364. Cannot be identified in any of his sales). Richard Payne Knight, by whom it was bequeathed to the B.M., 1824.

O.o.9–52 (L.B., as by Van Dyck, 59).

BIBL.: Payne Knight Cat., p. 127, No. 52. Binyon, Drawings of English Women, p. 79.

Like No. 18 this drawing was formerly attributed to Van Dyck, though Mr. Binyon points out that it is 'very near to Lely'. The coiffure suggests a period about 1645, when Lely would still have been working, early in his career, under Van Dyck's influence.

18. STUDY OF A WOMAN'S R. FOREARM AND HAND HOLDING UP DRAPERY.

Black chalk, the hand touched with red and white chalks, on brown-grey paper; 33 × 21·1 cm. (13 × 8¼ in.).

PROV.: Lely (Lugt, No. 2092). Sir Joshua Reynolds (Lugt, No. 2364. Cannot be identified in any of his sales). Mr. Farrer, from whom it was purchased by the B.M., 1845.

1845–12–8–8 (L.B., as by Van Dyck, 58).

BIBL.: Binyon, Drawings of English Women, p. 79.

Following the traditional attribution Mr. Binyon lists this drawing with those by Van Dyck, though he notes that it is 'very close in manner to Lely's style'. It is indeed very reminiscent of the handling of the latter's crayon drawings (See Nos. 20, 22, 24 & 28).

19. AN ELDERLY MAN IN ACADEMIC DRESS. T.Q.L., seated, turned half-r., and looking to front, his l. hand on the arm of his chair, his r. to his breast. Wearing a skull-cap, long white hair, bands, and apparently a Doctor's gown.

Black chalk, touched with white, on brown-grey paper; 27·7 × 27·3 cm. (10⅞ × 10¾ in.).

PROV.: Jonathan Richardson II (Lugt, No. 2170, but not identifiable in his sale, Langford, 5–13:ii:1772). Thomas Thane (Sale, Sotheby, 16:vi:1846, Lot 150 or 152 (?)). Purchased at the Thane Sale by the B.M., 1846.

1846–7–9–19 (L.B., IV, p. 284, as 'School of Van Dyck').

BIBL. & REPR.: Hind, Dutch & Flemish Drawings, II, p. 79, Pl. XL.

This drawing is obviously by a follower of Van Dyck's, but not by the master himself. Mr. Binyon has suggested an attribution to William Dobson, and Mr. C. F. Bell to Lely. Stylistically it bears some relationship to the drawings of the Garter Procession listed above at Nos. 1–16.

20. Recto. JOHN GREENHILL. Bust in profile to r., with eyes looking slightly downwards, and long straight hair falling on his shoulders which are lightly indicated.

Plate 213

Black, red and white crayons on grey paper; 27·3 × 20 cm. (10¾ × 7⅞ in.).

Verso. SLIGHT SKETCH OF A MALE FIGURE IN PROFILE TO L.

Black chalk.

INSCR.: In the lower r.-hand corner, in ink, *J Greenh . . . l* (partly obliterated).

PROV.: Jonathan Richardson II (*Lugt*, No. 2170. Sale, Langford, 7:ii:1772, Lot 24 or 68). Sir J. C. Robinson, by whom it was presented to the B.M., 1857.
1857–11–14–213 (L.B.2).

BIBL. & REPR.: *Waterhouse, John Greenhill.*

[John Greenhill (B. 1640–5 (?): D. 1676). Portrait-painter and pupil of Lely].

In Mr. Waterhouse's opinion the drawing on the *recto* was made about 1662 when Greenhill entered Lely's studio. Mr. Waterhouse also suggests that Greenhill's self-portrait in oils in the Dulwich Gallery (No. 418) belongs to the same period. The self-portrait drawing in the B.M. (*See* p. 339) he dates about 1664. The features in all three portraits agree fairly well.

21. A GENTLEMAN. Bust, turned half-r. Wearing a wig falling in long curls on the shoulders and a cravat.

Plate 215

Red chalk, heightened with white, on buff paper; 21·5 × 14·2 cm. (8½ × 5⅝ in.).

INSCR.: *Recto*, at the foot, *P Lely* (not a signature).

PROV.: P. & D. Colnaghi, from whom it was purchased by the B.M., 1865.
1865–7–8–129 (L.B.1).

22. A LADY. Bust turned three-quarter l. Wearing her hair in ringlets, and a veil as a hood over her head, tied loosely under her chin. Her dress lightly indicated.

Plate 218

Black, red and white crayons on grey-brown paper; 23·4 × 17·9 cm. (9¼ × 7 in.).

INSCR.: *Recto*, on the l., by the artist, *P Lely* (P.L. in monogram).

PROV.: Dr. H. Wellesley (Sale, Sotheby, 30:vi:1866, Lot 851). Purchased at the Wellesley Sale by the B.M., 1866.
1866–7–14–34 (L.B.5).

BIBL. & REPR.: *Binyon, Drawings of Englishwomen*, p. 78, Pl. IIa. Baker, *Lely Drawings*, p. 340. Baker, *Lely and Kneller*, p. 40. *Connoisseur*, May, 1930, LXXXV, p. 302. *Woodward*, p. 50, Pl. 40.

The old identification of the sitter as Barbara, Duchess of Cleveland, seems to be untenable.

23. A LADY, PERHAPS ELIZABETH, COUNTESS OF NORTHUMBERLAND. T.Q.L., moving towards the l., her eyes looking to front, her r. arm extended, and her l. hand holding before her a fold of her dress.

Black chalk, heightened with white body-colour and touched with red in the features, on oiled paper; 15·3 × 12·9 cm. (6 × 5⅛ in.).

PROV.: Dr. H. Wellesley (Sale, Sotheby, 30:vi:1866, Lot 857). Purchased at the Wellesley Sale by the B.M., 1866.
1866–7–14–35 (L.B.7).

In its curious handling of the medium, this drawing may be compared with No. 29. The pose of the figure suggests a connexion with the painting, now at Hampton Court, of Elizabeth, daughter of Thomas Wriothesley, 4th Earl of Southampton, who married firstly Jocelyn Percy, 11th Earl of Northumberland, and secondly Ralph Montague, 1st Duke of Montague (*See* Baker, *Hampton Court*, p. 90,

No. 202). This portrait was engraved in mezzotint by Thomas Watson in 1779 (C. S., IV, p. 1551, No. 5). The figure also somewhat resembles, but in reverse, that of the Hon. Mrs. Katherine Neville, engraved in mezzotint by Alexander Browne after Van Dyck (C. S., I, p. 116, No. 25).

24. A LADY. Bust with head in profile to l., her hair, which falls in ringlets about her neck, partly covered by a small kerchief. Wearing low-necked dress.　　**Plate 214**

Black, red and white crayons, on grey-brown paper; 24·4 × 18·4 cm. ($9\frac{5}{8}$ × $7\frac{1}{4}$ in.).

INSCR.: *Recto*, on the l., by the artist, *P Lely* (*P L* in monogram).

PROV.: Spencer (*Lugt*, No. 1530. Probably in the Sale, Philipe, 10–17:vi:1811, but no copy of the catalogue available for consultation). Esdaile (*Lugt*, No. 2617; Sale,

Christie, 25:vi:1840, Lot 1264, 'Portrait of a lady in crayons', purchased by Colnaghi). Wellesley (Sale, Sotheby, 30:vi:1866, Lot 863). Purchased at the Wellesley Sale by the B.M., 1866.
　　　1866-7-14-36 (L.B.6).

BIBL. & REPR.: *Binyon, Drawings of Englishwomen*, p. 78, Pl. IIa. *Baker, Lely Drawings*, p. 338. *Baker, Lely and Kneller*, p. 40.

25. JOHN MAITLAND, 1st DUKE OF LAUDERDALE. Bust turned half-l., with eyes looking to front. Wearing a long curling wig, moustache, and cravat.
Plate 216

Black chalk and stump, heightened with white on buff paper; 18·2 × 16·8 cm. ($7\frac{1}{8}$ × $6\frac{5}{8}$ in.).

INSCR.: *Recto*, in the lower r.-hand corner: *D. Lauderdale*.

PROV.: Hugh Howard. Dr. Robert Howard (Bishop of Elphin). The Earls of Wicklow. Charles, 5th Earl, from whom it was purchased by the B.M., 1874.
　　　1874-8-8-2263 (L.B.4).

BIBL. & REPR.: *Airy*, facing p. 200. *Binyon, Vasari Soc.*, Pt. II, 1906/7, No. 31. *Baker, Lely Drawings*, p. 337. *Baker, Lely and Kneller*, p. 40.

[John Maitland, 1st Duke of Lauderdale (B. 1616: D. 1687). Rose to prominence as a partisan of the Covenant. Later gained an extraordinary influence over Charles II, and exercised practically supreme control over Scotland throughout his reign, being the 'L' of the Cabal. Was noted for his immense ability, his brutal force and debauched character.]

The present drawing bears some similarity to the Duke in Lely's double portrait of him and his Duchess, now at Ham House, which was engraved in mezzotint by I. (R. (?)) Williams (C. S., IV, p. 1604, No. 32). Lauderdale married Elizabeth Murray, widow of Sir Lionel Talmash, in 1671/2 and was created Duke in 1673, so probably this portrait and the present drawing date from that time when Lauderdale would have been about 57.

26. JOHN LELY. As a child. Head turned three-quarter l. and looking upwards.
Plate 222

Black chalk; 13·1 × 12·4 cm. ($5\frac{1}{8}$ × $4\frac{7}{8}$ in.).

INSCR.: *Recto*, on the l., by the artist, *P. Lely* (*P L* in monogram) *fecit*, and on the r.. also by the artist, *Mr John Lely*.

PROV.: As for No. 25.
1874–8–8–2264 (L.B.9).

[John Lely, Lely's son, by an unknown Englishwoman (*See* biography above) who was first the artist's mistress and subsequently his wife. Nothing known of him except that he married Elizabeth, daughter of Sir John Knatchbull, 2nd Bart.]

27. ANNE LELY. As a young girl. Bust, with head in profile to l., and hair dressed in curls. The body, lightly indicated, turned half-l.   **Plate 222**

Black chalk; 12·9 × 12·2 cm. (5 × 4¾ in.).

INSCR.: *Recto*, in the lower l.-hand corner, by the artist, *P Lely* (*P L* in monogram) *fecit*, and in the lower r.-hand corner, also by the artist, *Mis Lely*.

PROV.: As for No. 25.
1874–8–8–2265 (L.B.10).

[Anne Lely. Sister of John Lely (No. 26). Subsequently married a Mr. Froud, and died in childbirth.]

28. SIR CHARLES COTTERELL. Bust turned half-l., with long hair falling on the shoulders. Wearing a broad white collar and dark-coloured doublet, with his personal badge as Master of Ceremonies (*See* No. 31) suspended on his breast.
Plate 220

Black, red and white crayons on brown-grey paper; 27·7 × 19·4 cm. (10⅞ × 7⅝ in.).

INSCR.: *Recto*, on the l., by the artist, *P. L.* (in monogram) *fe*.

PROV.: Sir Andrew Fountaine (Sale, Christie, 10:vii:1884, Lot 832). Purchased by the B.M. at the Fountaine Sale, 1884.
1884–7–26–25 (L.B.3, as a portrait of Edmund Waller).

BIBL. & REPR.: *D.N.B.*, LIX, 1899, p. 126. Baker, *Lely Drawings*, p. 339. Baker, *Lely*, pp. 39–40.

This drawing was said, in the Fountaine Sale Catalogue, to be a portrait of Edmund Waller, the poet and politician, and this identification was accepted with reservations by Mr. Collins Baker, who suggested that the drawing might be related to the youthful portrait of Waller at Holkham. The correct identification as Sir Charles Cotterell, at the age of about 45 in 1660, has been confirmed by Mr. T. Cotterell-Dormer. For another portrait of Cotterell and a biographical note on him *See* No. 31.

29. A LADY. Nearly H.L., turned half-l. Wearing her hair in ringlets, and a low-necked dress with bare shoulders.   **Plate 217**

Black chalk and white oil-paint, on brown-toned paper; 24·6 × 18·2 cm. (9¾ × 7⅛ in.).

PROV.: Nathaniel Hone (*Lugt*, No. 2793, but not identifiable in any of his sales). H. S. Reitlinger (Sale, Sotheby, 27:i:1954,

Lot 171). Purchased at the Reitlinger Sale by the B.M., 1954.
1954–2–13–6.

The scale of the drawing and the pose of the figure are similar to those of Lely's well-known portrait-studies in crayons (*Cf.* Nos. 22 & 24). The technique, on the other hand, is most unusual, though it seems to bear some relationship to that of No. 23. Another drawing of a lady, in precisely the same manner and also formerly in the Hone collection, is in the Museum at Truro, where it has been attributed to Mary Beale (*See Penrose*, p. 26, No. 231).

[30–33]. COPIES AFTER PORTRAITS IN OILS.

30. A LADY. Head turned half-r., with eyes looking to front and hair dressed in ringlets. Wearing pearls in her hair, and pearl earrings and necklace.

Black chalk, heightened with white, on dark greenish-grey paper; 29·6 × 22·8 cm. (11⅝ × 9 in.).

In manner this drawing much resembles the head of Sir Edward Littleton (No. 32) and would appear to be by the same hand.

PROV.: P. & D. Colnaghi, from whom it was purchased by the B.M., 1870.
1870–10–8–2379 (L.B.14).

31. SIR CHARLES COTTERELL. Bust turned to l., with head turned half-l., and eyes looking to front. Wearing a light-brown wig falling in curls on his shoulders, lace cravat, and dark brown drapery. Suspended on his breast, his personal badge, given him by Charles II, bearing the device of 'a hand coming out of a white cloud, holding a palm branch for peace', and surmounted by a crown set with brilliants. In a feigned oval. **Plate 219**

Oil-colours on paper; 20·3 × 16·8 cm. (8 × 6⅝ in.).

PROV.: Richard Bull (Sale, Sotheby, 23:v:1881, Lot 81). Purchased by the B.M. at the Bull Sale, through A. W. Thibaudeau, 1881.
1881–6–11–167 (L.B., p. 55, as 'after Lely').

[Sir Charles Cotterell (B. 1615: D. 1701). Son of Sir Clement Cotterell, Groom Porter to James I and Charles I. Was educated at Queens' College, Cambridge, until he was 17, and then travelled on the Continent, with the sons of the 4th Earl of Pembroke. On his return in 1636 took service in the Pembroke family, and later with the King, being appointed in 1641 assistant to Sir Balthazar Gerbier, then Master of Ceremonies. Followed the King during the Civil War, and, being made Master of Ceremonies in place of Gerbier (who had deserted the Royal service), was knighted in 1644. In 1649, went into exile at Antwerp, and subsequently became steward of the household or 'Hofmaster' to Elizabeth, Queen of Bohemia. At the Restoration, was reinstated as Master of Ceremonies, which post he held with great distinction till 1686, being succeeded in the office, which was made an hereditary one, by his son Sir Charles Lodowick Cotterell. On April 22nd, 1661, the day before that of Charles II's coronation, was invested by that monarch with a gold chain and medal enamelled on the obverse with the device of 'a hand coming out of a white cloud, holding a palm branch for peace, with the motto *Beati Pacifici*', and on the reverse with that of 'a hand gauntletted coming out of a black cloud with lightning and the motto *Dieu et mon droit*'.

This badge to be personal to himself and to his successors in office, each having the right to claim from the Jewel Office so many ounces of gold at every coronation to make a new one.]

The present little painting was described in the Bull Sale as a 'Portrait of a Nobleman' and by Mr. Binyon as a self-portrait by Lely. In view of the badge depicted in it, however, there seems to be no doubt that it represents Sir Charles Cotterell, and it should be compared with two portraits of him at Rousham, Oxon., respectively ascribed to Sir Godfrey Kneller (1683) and John Riley (1687). Both of these show the sitter in the same attitude as in the present painting, and wearing a large curling periwig, a lace cravat, and his badge. From the point of view of facial characteris-

tics the present painting comes nearest to the Kneller portrait, in which Sir Charles has a thin moustache. In the Riley portrait he is clean shaven.

From its small size and finish the present painting has the appearance of being a reduced replica of a life-size portrait (somewhat in the manner of Edmund Ashfield's and Theodore Russell's copies from Van Dyck and Lely) rather than a preliminary sketch for such. Its quality is high enough, however, to suggest that it may well be by Lely himself.

Another version of the same size, in pen and ink with brown wash heightened with white, is in the Pierpont Morgan Library (*See Morgan*, III, No. 202).

32. EDWARD, 1st LORD LITTLETON OF MOUNSLOW, AFTER VAN DYCK (?). Head turned half-r., with eyes looking to front, curling hair, moustache and tufted beard. Wearing a skull-cap and ruff.

Black chalk, heightened with white, on blue-grey paper; damaged and made up at the corners; $28 \cdot 4 \times 21 \cdot 2$ ($11\frac{1}{8} \times 8\frac{3}{8}$ in.).

PROV.: Edward Cheney (Sale, Sotheby, 4:v:1885, Lot 955 (?), but not mentioned). Purchased at the Cheney Sale by the B.M., 1885.

1885-5-9-1671 (L.B.12).

[Edward, 1st Lord Littleton (or Lyttleton) of Mounslow (B. 1589: D. 1645). Succeeded his father Sir Edward Littleton as Chief Justice of North Wales in 1621, and thenceforth had a fairly distinguished legal and parliamentary career, as Solicitor General, 1634, Chief Justice of the Common Pleas, 1640, and finally Lord Keeper, 1641, in which year he was also created Lord Littleton. Steered a middle course between the King and Parliament, finally siding with

the former, for whom he raised a regiment of foot consisting of members of the legal profession, of which he became colonel in 1644. Died at Oxford.]

This drawing is connected with the T.Q.L. portrait of Littleton in Lord Chief Justice's robes, of which a number of versions exist, including one in the National Portrait Gallery (No. 473). The original, of which the whereabouts is unknown, has been given to Van Dyck (*See* Cust, *Anthony Van Dyck*, p. 278, No. 133), and an early mezzotint after it by R. Williams (*C. S.*, p. 1605, No. 33) bears his name. The drawing itself cannot be by Van Dyck; and, rather than being an original study, looks more like an early life-size copy of the head in the oil-painting, perhaps used in the process of manufacturing replicas of this. In handling it has some affinity with that of the head of a lady, No. 30.

33. A LADY. T.Q.L., seated, turned half-l., her eyes looking to front, her hair falling in ringlets about her neck. Wearing a low-necked dress and holding on her r. knee a scallop shell.

Grey wash on grey paper; 36·7 × 27·6 cm. (14½ × 10⅞ in.).

PROV.: Mr. Fawcett, from whom it was purchased, 1888.

1888–1–16–16 (L.B.13).

No doubt a copy from an oil-painting, and probably belonging to the type of drawing made in the studio for record purposes (*Cf.* introductory note to Byng, Nos. 2–8, pp. 206–7). The original has not yet been identified, but, from the pose and style of coiffure of the sitter, it would probably have dated from *c.* 1660.

[34–5]. MISCELLANEOUS SUBJECTS.

34. A NYMPH CARRIED OFF BY A SATYR. A nymph, seen from behind, caught up by a satyr, who clasps her round the waist and holds her against his breast. Blue drapery falling at her side and between her legs. In the background, a rock.

Plate 221

Crayons, partly strengthened with body-colours; apparently partly indented; 38·9 × 28·5 cm. (15¼ × 11¼ in.).

PROV.: Richard Payne Knight, by whom it was bequeathed to the B.M., 1824.

O.o.10–177 (L.B.15).

BIBL.: *Payne Knight Cat.*, p. 146, No. 177.

The influence of Rubens and Jordaens is apparent in this study which is unlike any other type of drawing attributed to Lely, though he is known to have painted a number of mythological subjects. In the working up of the crayons and use of body-colours it recalls the methods employed by the later XVII c. pastellists, in particular Edward Lutterell (*q.v.*). It may be noted, as a coincidence, that in the catalogue of Richard Cosway's Sale of 478 pictures, p. 25, Lot 53, appeared, as by Lely, a 'Pan and Syrinx . . . one of those high-finished little pictures which Sir Peter used to paint when he first came to England'. (The name of the auctioneer and the date of this sale are unknown, as the catalogue is apparently not recorded in *Lugt*, and the Print Room copy lacks the title-page, which would have supplied the necessary information.) In Lely's own collection, also, was 'Of *Jacomo Palma*, A Satyr, with a Naked Nymph big as the Life' (*See Burl. Mag.*, LXXXIII, 1943, p. 186).

35. STUDIES OF A HALF NUDE WOMAN AND A MAN. Left: the woman, probably a mythological or allegorical figure, seated to r., looking down, her l. arm across her breast, the lower part of her body draped. Right: the man, T.Q.L., also seated to r., his head turned half-r., his r. hand resting on a lyre (?) which he holds on his knee; wearing a periwig and drapery.

Pen and brown ink over black and red chalks; 17·6 × 17·4 cm. (7 × 6⅞ in.)

INSCR.: *Recto*, in the lower l.-hand corner, 49.A.

PROV.: The Rev. C. M. Cracherode, by whom it was bequeathed to the B.M., 1799.

F.f.4–49.

BIBL.: *Cracherode Cat.*, p. 119, No. 49. Described in the *Cracherode Cat.* as 'English'. Clearly by a follower of Van Dyck, and dating, according to the man's coiffure, from about 1680, which facts have suggested the present attribution to Lely.

LE PIPER, FRANCIS

D. 1695

Amateur draughtsman

The son of Noel Le Piper, or Lepipre, who came from a prosperous Walloon family which had settled in England, presumably to escape religious persecution, at the end of the XVI c., and owned property in Canterbury. Nothing known of the date or place of his birth. Buckeridge, from whom all our knowledge of him derives, says that he received a 'liberal education . . . but his Genius leading him wholly to *designing*, he cou'd not fix to any particular science, or business, besides the art to which he naturally inclined. Drawing took up all his time and all his thoughts; and being of a gay facetious humour, his manner was humorous or comical'. Travelled widely in Europe and even visited Cairo. Is said to have etched on silver plates which his friends used as lids for tobacco boxes. Spent much of his life in taverns where many of his drawings were made but were not preserved. On one occasion he competed with William Faithorne (*q.v.*) in drawing portraits in charcoal on trenchers. Particularly frequented the Mitre Tavern in Stocks Market where, according to Buckeridge, 'there is a room called the *Amsterdam*, which is adorned with his pictures in black and white. The room takes its name from his pieces, which representing a Jesuit, a Quaker preaching, some other preachers of most religions, that were liable to be expos'd contained as many sectaries as were to be found in Amsterdam.' The painting of the Quaker probably resembled a mezzotint engraving by Isaac Beckett after Egbert van Heemskerk of the same subject. Was a 'great admirer and imitator of Augustine Caracci, Rembrant, Van Rhine's and Hemskirk's manner of Design', and is said to have been 'always in raptures when he spoke of Titian's colouring' though he appears never to have worked in colour himself. Is said to have produced 'designs' which Isaac Beckett engraved in mezzotint but none of these has been identified. Nor are any examples of his landscapes known, which were said to be skilful. Drew several of the heads for Sir Paul Rycaut's *History of the Turks* (1687) which were engraved by William Elder (*Fl.* 1680–1700). Late in life took to modelling bas-reliefs in wax. Dissipated his father's fortune, then with his inheritance from his mother, again lived so freely that he fell into a fever 'and making use of an ignorant surgeon to Let him blood, the fellow prick'd an artery, which accident proved mortal'. Died, unmarried, in Aldermanbury and was buried in the church of St. Mary Magdalene, Bermondsey, on July 23rd, 1695. His portrait engraved in mezzotint by Edward Lutterell (*q.v.*), referred to by Walpole as Lutterell's best work. All his known drawings are in the B.M. and show a talent for caricature which looks forward to Hogarth whose master Nichols said he was, but as Hogarth was not born until 1697 this can only be possible in a spiritual sense. In 1816 Mr. Davies, a bookseller in the Strand, had twelve small pictures by Le Piper of scenes from *Hudibras* on which it was thought probable that Hogarth had based his series. The first illustrated edition of *Hudis bras* was published 1709/10 with engravings which have many affinities with both of Hogarth's series, and may also derive from Le Piper. The drawings numbered 2–4 below show the influence of Dutch 'drollery', which was also felt by Hogarth, whose style is more closely anticipated in No. 1.

BIBL.: St. Mary Magdalene, *Bermondsey Register. Buckeridge*, pp. 409–13. *Walpole*, III, p. 960. *Nichols*, pp. 349–50. *D.N.B.*, XXXIII, 1893, p. 66. B.M., *Engraved Portraits*, III, p. 51, No. 1. *Vertue, Index*, p. 147.

1. READING THE NEWS.

1. READING THE NEWS. Caricature study of a man, H.L., with a broad-brimmed hat on his head and spectacles on his nose, reading by the light of a candle, which he holds, a news-sheet, the *LONDON* . . . . **Plate 224**

Pen and ink, with grey wash; 16·6 × 16·7 cm. (6⅕ × 6⅝ in.).

INSCR.: *Verso*, at the top, *N? 119*.

PROV.: Sir Hans Sloane, Bart., by whom it was bequeathed to the B.M., 1753.
5224–80 (L.B.1).

BIBL.: *Sloane Cat.*, p. 189, No. 80.

2. TWO OLD MEN CONVERSING.

2. TWO OLD MEN CONVERSING. Caricature study of two H.L. figures, one on the l., with a hooked nose and broad-brimmed hat, turning round to speak to his companion in a skull-cap and cassock buttoned to the throat. **Plate 223**

Brush drawing in grey wash, strengthened with pen and brown ink; 10·6 × 13·7 cm. (4¼ × 5⅜ in.).

PROV.: As for No. 1.
5237–40 (L.B.2(c)).

BIBL.: *Sloane Cat.*, p. 274, No. 40.

Adapted from two of the heads in No. 3.

3. SIX GROTESQUE HEADS OF OLD MEN.

3. SIX GROTESQUE HEADS OF OLD MEN. In two rows of three each, including a Jew in a fur cap, a man grinning, a man in a broad-brimmed hat, and a friar. **Plate 223**

Pen and brown ink; 10·2 × 12·9 cm. (4 × 5 in.).

PROV.: As for No. 1.
5237–41 (L.B.2(a)).

BIBL.: *Sloane Cat.*, p. 274, No. 41.

4. FIVE GROTESQUE HEADS OF OLD MEN.

4. FIVE GROTESQUE HEADS OF OLD MEN. In a single row. Three wearing conical caps.

Pen and light brown ink, the background washed with brown; 6·8 × 16·8 cm. (2⅝ × 6⅝ in.).

PROV.: As for No. 1.
5237–42 (L.B.2(b)).

BIBL.: *Sloane Cat.*, p. 274, No. 42.

LODGE, WILLIAM

B. 1649: D. 1689

Amateur draughtsman and etcher

Born July 4th, 1649, son of William Lodge, a Leeds merchant, and Elizabeth, whose grandfather Richard Sykes was a prosperous cloth trader and one of the first aldermen of the newly incorporated Borough of Leeds (1629). Educated at a school in Leeds, and Jesus College, Cambridge, and afterwards studied law at Lincoln's Inn, but inheriting an income of £300 a year, did not find it necessary to practise. At Cambridge spent some of his leisure time painting and drawing: he wrote to his mother 'I make painting only a recreation an hour after dinner or so, no hindrance in it but rather a furtherance to things of greater concernment'; and received some instruction from the amateur artist, John Lambert, son of the Parliamentary general. In 1669, accompanied Thomas, 2nd Viscount Fauconberg, on his mission as English ambassador to Venice. Travelled extensively in Italy and the south of France and drew, mainly for the purpose of etching, views and monuments particularly in the neighbourhood of Rome, and in Provence. After his return to England in 1671 (according to the Latin inscription of a certain Captain Fisher on a portrait of the artist) became one of the group of York *virtuosi* and a close friend of Henry Gyles the glass-painter (*q.v.*), and of Francis Place the amateur artist (*q.v.*) who executed a portrait of Lodge in mezzotint. Made long excursions on foot with Place in England and Wales, sharing his interests as draughtsman, anti-quary and angler. According to the Leeds historian, Ralph Thoresby (to whose wife Lodge was related), both artists were arrested in Wales as Jesuit spies at the time of the Popish Plot (1678). On these journeys drew numerous views, many of which he afterwards etched, such as those of the Monument and Lambeth House, of York, Leeds, Durham, Newcastle, Berwick, Car-lisle, Edinburgh and Glasgow. Some of his English and Italian drawings were later presented to Thoresby by Lodge's cousin, Henry Watkinson, Chancellor of the diocese of York, and are now preserved in Leeds Public Library. Published in 1679 a transla-tion of Giacomo Barri's *Viaggio Pittoresco d'Italia* (1671) under the title of *The Painter's Voyage of Italy in which all the famous Paintings of the most eminent Masters are particularized* . . . , the first foreign guide book of its kind to appear in English. In his translation Lodge makes some additions, notably a list of the pictures in the Septale collection in Milan. He added five etched portraits of artists, a frontispiece and map of Italy. Etched for Dr. Martin Lister plates of shells and fossils as illustrations to papers in *The Philosophical Transactions of the Royal Society*, and a plate representing 34 types of spiders.

Is said by Vertue to have engraved por-traits including one of Oliver Cromwell and his page, but none is now traceable, and to have 'painted some few pictures from the life in Oil, but was no mighty labourer in Art, having enough to live on without it. being all his life single'. Perhaps painted the large view of York from the south (York Art Gallery) which is closely connected with his etching, *The Ancient and Loyall Citty of York*. As a draughtsman is inferior to Place and worked mainly with a fine pen, his drawings being considered rather as studies for etch-ings than as finished works in themselves.

Died at Leeds on Aug. 27th, 1689, having in his Will directed that he should be buried with his mother at Gisburn in Craven,

Yorks, but because of an accident to the hearse, was buried in the choir of Harewood Church. Thoresby notes in his diary that Lodge presented two bells to St. Peter's Church, Leeds.

BIBL.: *Thoresby, Ducatus*, pp. 77, 497 and 541. *Thoresby, Diary*, I, pp. 132, 250 and 421.

Redgrave, p. 274. *D.N.B.*, XXXIV, 1893, pp. 66–7 (with *Bibl.*). *T.-B.*, XXXIII, 1929, pp. 311–12 (with *Bibl.*). *Vertue, Index*, pp. 149–50. *B.F.A.C., British Born Artists*, 1938, p. 40, No. 88. *Ogden, Index*, p. 222.

DRAWINGS IN OTHER COLLECTIONS: City of York Art Gallery.

1. OLD SOMERSET HOUSE, FROM THE S. BANK OF THE THAMES. View looking across the Thames from below Cupid's (or Cuper's) Stairs, with a watergate in the foreground, r. On the opposite bank, Old Somerset House, with the Great Gallery in the centre, and the clock-turret rising beyond it. To the l., Somerset Yard and Stairs, and on the extreme l., part of the Savoy. On the extreme r., the Strand Bridge. In the upper r.-hand corner, part of the Great Gallery redrawn on a larger scale. **Plate 225**

Pen and brown ink; 13·8 × 29·6 cm. (5½ × 11⅝ in.).

INSCR.: *Recto*, by the artist, towards the top, with corrections.

PROV.: Ralph Thoresby (from the same source as Nos. 2 & 3. Sale, Whiston Bristow, 7:iii:1764, Lot 66 (?)). E. Daniell, from whom it was purchased by the B.M., 1866, with a drawing of Tynemouth by Francis Place, also from Thoresby's coll. (*See* p. 446, No. 26).
1866–11–14–676 (L.B.1).

Somerset House was built by Edward Seymour, Duke of Somerset and Protector, between about 1547 and the time of his execution in 1552. Subsequently it passed to the Crown, when it was used as a minor royal residence and as lodgings for the nobility and court officials. In the XVII c. additions were made to it from the designs of Inigo Jones, including the Great Gallery, which according to Colen Campbell (*Vitruvius Britannicus*, I, p. 4) was erected in 1662. In 1776 it gave place to the present building designed by Sir William Chambers.

2. THE MONUMENT, FROM THE W. View looking towards Monument Yard from Fish St., which crosses the foreground. In the centre, the pedestal alone of the Monument, the details of sculpture being omitted. To the r., at the corner of the Yard and Fish St., a shop with the sign of the Sun, the corresponding houses to the l. not fully drawn in. A few figures in the street indicated. **Plate 226**

Pen and brown ink, partly over pencil; 30·3 × 41 cm. (11⅞ × 16⅛ in.).

INSCR.: *Recto*, at the top, in ink, by Ralph Thoresby, *The Monument at London / by M.* Lodge.

PROV.: As for No. 1.
1866–11–14–677 (L.B.3).

ETCH.: Preliminary study for the etching by Lodge, published by Faithorne, in which the entire column is shown, the surrounding houses seen in detail, and the street peopled with figures.

BIBL.: *Thoresby, Ducatus*, p. 497. *Vertue, Index*, p. 150.

The Monument to commemorate the Fire of London was erected, 1671–7, from the designs of Sir Christopher Wren, the sculpture being executed by Caius Gabriel Cibber and Edward Pierce (*See Wheatley and Cunningham*, II, pp. 557–8, for a full account). Thoresby considered Lodge's etching to be the best representation of the Monument.

3. LINCOLN'S INN FIELDS. View looking E. from the centre of the square, where the two paths crossing it intersect, the foreground peopled with groups of figures. To l. and r., rows of houses known respectively as Newman's Row and Portugal Row, and in the distance, l., Old Southampton Buildings and Lincoln's Inn Garden, and r., Lincoln's Inn itself with the tower of St. Sepulchre's rising beyond.

Plate 227

Pen and brown ink; 20·9 × 48·7 cm. (8¼ × 19⅛ in.).

INSCR.: *Recto*, in the upper l.-hand corner, in ink, by the artist, with corrections and other notes; and, at the foot, by Ralph Thoresby, *Lincolns Inn London by M.ʳ Lodge*.

PROV.: As for No. 1.
1866–11–14–678 (L.B.2).

Lincoln's Inn Fields, one of London's earliest squares, was up to 1618 a piece of waste ground frequented by beggars and idlers. It was subsequently laid out in walks by order of a Commission under Francis Bacon, with the assistance of Inigo Jones, and bordered with houses on three sides, the fourth towards Lincoln's Inn being left open (*See Wheatley and Cunningham*, II, pp. 392–4, for a full account).

LOGGAN, DAVID
B. 1635: D. 1692
Portrait and topographical engraver and draughtsman

The earliest (and possibly first-hand) account of the artist is given by his contemporary, Joachim von Sandrart. Born in Danzig in 1635 (if the inscription *aet.20.1655* on the self-portrait noted by Vertue is correct), son of John Loggan, merchant or consul, resident there. Was of Scottish descent and probably belonged to that branch of the family mentioned by Anthony Wood, the Oxford historian, as living near Idbury, Oxfordshire. First studied under Willem Hondius (B. *c.* 1597: D. *c.* 1658), in Danzig and then worked for seven years with Crispin de Passe, the younger (B. *c.* 1589: D. *c.* 1667) in Amsterdam. Came to London between 1656, when certain of his engravings were published in Holland, and 1658 when he drew his earliest English portraits in black lead on vellum (Sandrart mentions a portrait of Oliver Cromwell (D. Sept. 3rd, 1658). In his topographical work was influenced by Hollar (*q.v.*) with whom he collaborated, engraving some of his drawings and contributing with him some of the portrait illustrations to Dugdale's *Origines Juridiciales*, 1666. Was commissioned in 1662 to design the title-page of a folio edition of the *Book of Common Prayer* and executed plates for John Ogilby's *Homer his Odysses*, 1665, including the portrait of James, 1st Duke of Ormonde after the artist's own drawing (*c.* 1652; V. & A. Mus.). On June 15th, 1663, married at St. Sepulchre's, London, Anna Jordan, of an Oxfordshire family, by whom he had at least two sons, the younger, John (B. 1672: D. 1722) becoming a fellow of Magdalen College, Oxford. Wood first refers to the artist as living at Nuffield, near Nettlebed, Oxon., in 1665 (Sandrart says that he left London to escape the Plague), thereafter noting in his diary frequent meetings with him in Oxford taverns. Mentions lending him 'the old map of Oxon.', no doubt encouraging him to undertake the famous series of engraved plates, *Oxonia Illustrata* which was finally published in 1675 as a companion-piece to Wood's *History and Antiquities of the University of Oxford*, 1674. Was granted, by royal warrant, 4,000 reams of paper, customs free, 'he having undertaken a great and expensive work to draw and impress all the Colleges of Oxford'. Probably through Wood became intimately associated with the circle of scientists and antiquaries which included Ashmole, Thomas Hobbes, Robert Hooke, Seth Ward, Bishop of Salisbury and John Aubrey. Aubrey noted in the manuscript copy of his *Naturall Historie of Wiltshire*, 'Mr. David Loggan drew my picture anno 1686, which is in his hands to be engraven for this book.' On March 30th, 1669, secured the office of 'public sculptor' to the University at a stipend of 20/- per annum. Was then living in Holywell (Oxford) where he had set up a press. Had already made progress with the Oxford plates when Cosimo III, Grand Duke of Tuscany, visited the University in May of that year, Loggan 'showing him the draught of the colledges and presenting him the picture of the king in sarsenet [the Duke] rewarded him with 5 ginnyes' (Wood). Also in 1669, undertook his first known commission for the University, i.e. two engraved views of the Sheldonian Theatre, for which he was paid £15. Matriculated in 1672, no doubt in order to gain additional privileges at Oxford, and in 1675 became a naturalized subject. Must have relied on considerable assistance in undertaking the Oxford plates. The Dutch engraver, Michael Burghers, is known to have come from Amsterdam to Oxford in 1672 to work for Loggan. Vertue mentions as apprentices Robert White (*q.v.*) who 'assisted him in the drawing of many buildings' and Edward le Davis (B. 1640 (?): D. 1684 (?)), and speaks of 'one Kickers', perhaps another Dutchman, who 'drew the views & draughts of the Colleges of Oxford (for D. Loggan) & those of Cambridge in partnership with him: & they both went to Scotland & there he drew the views in Theatrum Scotiae'. Also according to Vertue, brought into England the Dutchman Abraham Blooteling (B. 1632: D. 1698), the mezzotinter, and the engravers Gerard Valck (B. 1626 (?): D. 1720) and Abraham de Blois (*Fl.* 1690–1720). His work at Cambridge followed a similar course. Was engaged on the *Cantabrigia Illustrata* from 1676 until 1690, when he was made engraver to the University, but continued to hold his office at Oxford until his death, when Burghers was appointed to succeed him. His other commissions at Cambridge included an engraving of Wren's design for Trinity College Library, published in 1676. Was provided with a workshop and press in Trinity College, but was not in permanent residence there, visiting Cambridge only as necessary to supervise his work. Continued to live in London 'next door to the Golden Head in Leicester Fields' where most of his portraits were executed and where he died. Was buried on Aug. 1st, 1692, at St. Martin-in-the-Fields.

Was with the elder William Faithorne and Robert White (*q.v.*) among the foremost miniature draughtsmen of his time. Using the same black lead and Indian ink medium, his drawings are often not easily distinguishable from White's. Must have learnt to work in this manner in Holland and thus constitutes a link between the Dutch and English schools of portrait miniature. Besides portrait drawings, executed a large number of engravings *ad vivum*, usually for frontispieces. Vertue states that both Robert

White and Michael van der Gucht (B. 1660: D. 1725) helped him in his portrait engraving. For a full list of Loggan's portrait drawings and engravings *ad vivum*, *see Bell and Poole*.

BIBL.: *D.N.B.*, XXXIV, 1893, p. 87–9 (with *Bibl.*). *Loggan, Cantabrigia* (ed. *Clark*), Introduction. *Mills. Bell and Poole. Long*, p. 277. *T.-B.*, XXIII, 1929, p. 330 (with *Bibl.*). *Hooke, Diary, passim. Vertue, Index*, p. 150. *Woodward*, pp. 28, 38 and 53. *Vertue*, VI, pp. 182 and 184.

1. GEORGE MONK, 1st DUKE OF ALBEMARLE. Bust turned half-r., with eyes looking to front, long curling hair, moustache, and slight tuft under the lower lip. Wearing lace falling bands over his doublet. **Plate 228**

Black lead on vellum; oval; 9·4 × 7·5 cm. (3¾ × 3 in.).

PROV.: Sir Hans Sloane, Bart., by whom it was bequeathed to the B.M., 1753.

Sloane, 13.

BIBL.: *Sloane Antiquities*, No. 13 ('A man's head in black lead by Faithorn'). *Portraits transferred from Dept. of Antiquities*, No. 19 ('Gen: Monk, by Faithorne in B. lead. 13. Eaten by worm in one spot').

[George Monk, 1st Duke of Albemarle (B. 1608: D. 1670). The celebrated general and statesman, who was mainly responsible for the Restoration of the monarchy in 1660.]

This drawing is ascribed to Faithorne in Sir Hans Sloane's catalogue (*See Bibl.* above), but the sitter's name is not given, and the identification with General Monk, which is not an improbable one, can only date from after the time the drawing was acquired by the Museum. It should be compared with the engraved portrait of Monk by Loggan (*See B.M. Engraved Portraits*, I, p. 21, No. 10), and this has suggested the present attribution to Loggan rather than the traditional one to Faithorne. This attribution is further strengthened by the fact that its handling is so near to known examples of Loggan's work, especially No. 4 listed here.

2. RICHARD ALLESTREE, D.D. Bust turned half-r., with eyes looking to front. Wearing a black skull-cap, long curling hair or wig, slight moustache, broad white bands, and academic gown.

Black lead, the face slightly touched with light brown wash (?), on vellum; oval; 12·3 × 9·6 cm. (4⅞ × 3¾ in.).

INSCR.: *Recto*, on the r., *DL/167–*(?) (partly obliterated and covered by the subsequent monogram), and below it *DL* (monogram).

PROV.: The Rev. C. M. Cracherode, by whom it was bequeathed to the B.M., 1799.

G.g.1–474 (L.B.3).

ENG.: By the artist, in the same sense and on the same scale (*ad Vivum delin.*), as the frontispiece to Allestree's *Forty Sermons*, 1684.

[Richard Allestree (B. 1619: D. 1681). Born at Uppington, Shropshire. Was educated at Christ Church, Oxford, where he became Moderator in Philosophy and varied his academic career with military service in the Royalist cause of which he was a staunch supporter. Subsequently acted as a secret messenger between Charles II and his supporters in England during the Commonwealth. At the Restoration became a Canon of Christ Church, in 1663 Chaplain to Charles II and Regius Professor of Divinity at

Oxford, and in 1665 Provost of Eton. Was noted for his wide learning and his ability as a preacher and a tutor. Died in London.]

If the date on the drawing has been read correctly, this would show the sitter between the ages of 51 and 60.

3. THOMAS BARLOW, BISHOP OF LINCOLN. Bust turned half-r., with eyes looking to front. Wearing a skull-cap, long hair, moustache and small tufted beard, and broad white falling bands over an academic gown.

Black lead on vellum; the body only lightly indicated; 9·1 × 7·8 cm. (3⅝ × 3⅛ in.).

INSCR.: *Recto*, in the upper r.-hand corner, *Bp Barlow*.
Verso, at the foot, *Loggan. | Dr Barlow Bishop Lincoln*.

PROV.: W. Young Ottley. The Rev. C. M. Cracherode, by whom it was bequeathed to the B.M., 1799.
G.g.1–477 (L.B.2).

ENGR.: Study probably for the portrait engraved by the artist in the same sense but on a slightly larger scale (*ad Vivum Sculp*), 1672 (*See B.M. Engraved British Portraits*, I, p. 121, No. 1).

BIBL. & REPR.: *Cracherode Cat.*, p. 103, No. 477. *Foster, Cooper*, Pl. LXXXVII, No. 211. *Bell & Poole*, p. 62. *Long*, p. 277.

[Thomas Barlow (B. 1607: D. 1691). Born at Long-gill, Orton, Westmorland. Educated at the Queen's College, Oxford. Renowned for his learning and as the author of *Cases of Conscience*, 1692, and other works, in some of which his strong anti-Papist leanings are apparent. Was a 'trimmer' in politics, maintaining his position both under the Commonwealth and at the Restoration. Became Bodley's Librarian in 1642, Provost of Queen's in 1657, and Bishop of Lincoln in 1675. Died at his Palace of Buckden.]

The present drawing no doubt dates from about 1672, the date of the engraving with which it is connected and which shows the sitter as Provost of Queen's and Lady Margaret Professor of Divinity, at about the age of 65.

4. CHARLES II. Bust turned half-r., with eyes looking to front. Wearing a long curling wig, thin moustache, and broad lace falling bands over a patterned doublet. In front of him, part of a stone parapet.   **Plate 229**

Black lead on vellum; oval; 9·5 × 7·4 cm. (3¾ × 2⅞ in.).

PROV.: As for No. 2.
G.g.1–495 (L.B.1).

BIBL. & REPR.: *Cracherode Cat.*, p. 105, No. 495. *Foster, Cooper*, Pl. LXXXV, No. 207. *Bell & Poole*, p. 63. *Long*, p. 277.

The present drawing may be compared with the portrait of Charles II, drawn, engraved and published by Loggan (*See B.M. Engraved Portraits*, I, p. 402, No. 125). They both show the King in the same pose, but differ in the treatment of the eyes, the wig, and in details of the costume.

5. PETER MEWS, BISHOP OF WINCHESTER. Bust turned slightly to r., with eyes looking to front. Wearing a black skull-cap on his white curling hair, thin white moustache, a black patch covering a wound received at Sedgemoor, falling bands and chimere.   **Plate 228**

Black lead on vellum; oval; 12 × 9·3 cm. (4¾ × 3¾ in.).

PROV.: William Esdaile (?) (Sale, Christie, 25:vi:1840, Lot 1274). W. B. Tiffin, from whom it was purchased by the B.M., 1854.
1854-8-12-34 (L.B.4).

ENGR.: Study for the portrait engraved by the artist in the same sense but on a larger scale (*ad vivum sculpsit*), which is lettered below, *Reverendus admodum in Christo Pater, D^{nus} PETRUS MEWS Wintoniensis | Episcopus, Nobilissimi Ordinis a Pericelide dicti Praesul . . .* (*See B.M. Engraved Portraits*, III, p. 230). In the second state the badge of Prelate of the Order has been added.

BIBL.: *Bell & Poole*, p. 63. *Long*, p. 277.

[Peter Mews (B. 1619: D. 1706). Born at Purce Candle near Sherborne, Dorset. Educated at St. John's College, Oxford. Served in the Royalist army and later as a secret agent. After the Restoration had a distinguished ecclesiastical and academic career in which he became President of his College in 1667, Vice-Chancellor of the University in 1669, Bishop of Bath and Wells in 1672, and Bishop of Winchester and Prelate of the Order of the Garter in 1684. Though loyal to the King (to the extent of being present at the battle of Sedgemoor when he directed the fire of the royal cannon), supported the Fellows of Magdalen College and the Seven Bishops in their opposition to James II.]

The present drawing probably dates from soon after 1685, the year of Sedgemoor, when the sitter was aged about 66, as it shows the patch he wore over the wound which he received in the battle. Another drawing of him, in black lead on vellum, very near to the present example, is in the National Portrait Gallery (No. 637).

6. A GENTLEMAN. Bust turned half-r., with eyes looking to front. Wearing a long curling wig, lace cravat, with drapery over his r. shoulder, and ribbons on his sleeves. **Plate 230**

Black lead, the face slightly touched with light brown wash (?), on vellum; oval; 12·6 × 10·4 cm. (5 × 4 in.).

INSCR.: *Recto*, at the foot, on the r., *D.L. fecit | 1674.*

PROV.: W. B. Tiffin, from whom it was purchased by the B.M., 1854.
1854-8-12-35 (L.B.5).

BIBL.: *Bell & Poole*, p. 62. *Long*, p. 277.

There is perhaps some resemblance between the sitter in this drawing and that in another portrait by Loggan, dated 1673, of the Pierpont Morgan Library, said to be of 'Sir — Blount (?)' (*See* C. Fairfax Murray, *J. Pierpont Morgan Collection of Drawings*, 1912, III, No. 5). It has nothing to do with Loggan's engraved Sir Henry Blount (B. 1602: D. 1682), the traveller, dated 1679 (*See B.M. Engraved Portraits*, I, p. 205).

7. A DIVINE, SAID TO BE RALPH CUDWORTH. Bust turned slightly to r., with eyes looking to front. Wearing long hair, slight moustache and tufted beard, broad white bands, and academic gown.

Black lead, the face slightly touched with light brown wash; oval; 14·2 × 11·9 cm. (5⅝ × 4¾ in.).

INSCR.: *Recto*, on the r., *D: Loggan | delin; | 1666.*

PROV.: W. B. Tiffin, from whom it was purchased by the B.M., 1857.
1857–5–9–31 (L.B.6).

BIBL. & REPR.: Foster, Cooper. Pl. LXXXVIII, No. 212. Bell & Poole, p. 61. Long, p. 377.

This drawing was acquired as a portrait of Ralph Cudworth (B. 1617: D. 1688), leader of the Cambridge Platonists and author of *The true Intellectual System of the Universe*, 1678, but it in no wise corresponds with the portrait of him by Loggan, said to have been drawn in 1684, which was engraved by George Vertue as the frontispiece to Cudworth's *A Treatise concerning Eternal and Immutable Morality*, 1731.

8. A YOUNG DIVINE.
Bust turned slightly to r., with eyes looking to front. Wearing long curling hair or wig, broad white bands, and academic gown. In the background, l., a vase of flowers with the *Holy Bible* and another book in front of it, and r., a female bust in a niche.

Black lead, the face slightly touched with light brown wash; on vellum; 13·1 × 11·0 cm. (5⅛ × 4¾ in.).

INSCR.: *Recto*, on the r., *D.L. fecit / 1677.*

PROV.: Messrs. P. & D. Colnaghi, from whom it was purchased by the B.M., 1870.
1870–10–8–2381 (L.B.7).

BIBL.: *Bell & Poole*, p. 62, under 1677. *Long*, p. 277.

The objects in the background of this drawing appear to have been added by another and less skilled hand.

9. MRS. BAILY.
Nearly H.L., turned half-l., with eyes looking to front. Wearing widow's weeds with a black hood over a peak, and a gown with full sleeves.

Plate 229

Black lead on vellum; oval; 14·2 × 11·3 cm. (5⅝ × 4½ in.).

INSCR.: *Verso*, on the l., *Drawn by D Loggan 1668.*

PROV.: The Rev. F. O. White, from whom it was purchased by the B.M., 1881.
1881–11–12–154 (L.B.8).

BIBL. & REPR.: Foster, Cooper, Pl. LXXXVIII, No. 214. Bell & Poole, p. 63. Long, p. 277.

[This drawing was acquired with the title 'Mrs. Baily', but there is no further clue as to the identity of the sitter. She may, however, have some connexion with Thomas Bayly, D.D. (D. 1657 (?)) Royalist and (later) Catholic divine, Sub-Dean of Wells, and author of *Herba Parietis . . . ,* 1650.] A portrait of Dr. Bayly, said to be by Loggan, was engraved in mezzotint by Richard Earlom in Samuel Woodburn's *100 Portraits of Illustrious Characters,* 1810–15, No. 4 (See Chaloner Smith, I, p. 261).

10. JOHN WILMOT, 2nd EARL OF ROCHESTER.
H.L., turned half-r., with eyes looking to front. Wearing a long curling wig, lace cravat, and a richly patterned doublet with a shoulder-knot of ribbons.

Plate 231

Black lead, the face tinted in light brown wash; on vellum; 13·6 × 11·6 cm. (5¾ × 4⅝ in.).

INSCR.: *Recto*, at the foot, on the r., *D.L. delin / 1671.*

C.E.D.

PROV.: Miss Warre (Sale, 1874. Purchased by Miss Adair). Miss Adair, by whom it was presented to the B.M., 1903.

1903–3–9–1.

BIBL. & REPR.: *D.N.B.*, LXII, 1900, p. 66. *Vasari Soc.*, Ser. I, Pt. IV, 1908–9, No. 35. *Bell & Poole*, p. 62.

[John Wilmot, 2nd Earl of Rochester (B. 1647: D. 1680). Celebrated for his wit, his lyric and satiric verse, and his profligacy.]

The identification of the sitter in the present drawing is a traditional one. The contours of the face and the set of the eyes correspond fairly closely with those in the two engraved portraits of Rochester by Robert White (one after Lely) and the portrait of him crowning his monkey at Warwick Castle (*See B.M. Engraved Portraits*, III, p. 596). From the date on it, the drawing would show him at about the age of 24.

The brown wash on the face is of a stronger tint than is usually the case with these black lead portrait drawings by Loggan and his contemporaries.

11. A GENTLEMAN. Nearly H.L., turned half-r., with eyes looking to front. Wearing long curling hair or wig, upturned moustache, and broad white falling bands over a doublet with slit sleeves. **Plate 230**

Black lead on vellum; 9·4 × 7·7 cm. (3¾ × 3 in.).

PROV.: James Carter, from whom it was purchased by the B.M., 1906.

1906–7–23–1.

This drawing was traditionally ascribed to Loggan when acquired by the B.M. The costume of the sitter suggests that it was executed about 1660.

12. A DIVINE. Nearly H.L., turned half-r., with eyes looking to front. Wearing a black skull-cap, long curling hair, moustache and pointed beard, broad white falling bands and academic gown. **Plate 231**

Black lead, the face slightly touched with brown wash; on vellum; oval; 14·8 × 12·6 cm. (5⅞ × 5 in.).

INSCR.: *Recto*, on the r., in brown ink, by the artist, *R.G. | Æt: Suæ 77 | An° D: 1667*, and in black lead, *D: Loggan— | delin: |1667*.

PROV.: John Grimston. Lady Waechter de Grimston, by whom it was presented to the B.M., 1937.

1937–2–15–4.

LUTTERELL, EDWARD

[LUTTRELL, LUTTREL]

Working from about 1673: D. after 1723

Portrait draughtsman in crayons and mezzotint engraver

Accounts of the artist's origin and early life are confusing and to some extent contradictory as Mr. Bell states (*See Bibl.*). By some authorities, notably Strickland, said to have been born in Dublin about 1650 for which date there appears to be no authority. Possibly connected with the family of Luttrell of Luttrelstown near Dublin. Early in his career seems to have settled in London, becoming a law student in New Inn. Vertue states that he had no regular teaching but drew for pleasure, the practice leading him eventually altogether from his legal studies. Buckeridge, however, states that he learnt from Edmund Ashfield and so improved on his instruction that he 'multiplied the variety of colours to effect any thing; as also found out a method, unknown before, to draw with those chalks or *crayons*, on copper-plates, either by the life or historically'. The earliest known date connected with his work, 1673, appears on his mezzotint plate of Anthony, 1st Earl of Shaftesbury, as Lord Chancellor, after Greenhill. Mr. Bell, however, points out that the 'date' is no doubt that of the painting executed when Shaftesbury was in office, and that the print is almost certainly later. His crayon drawings date from 1684 and are characterized by hot reddish flesh tones and signed *E. Lutterell* (the spelling favoured by the artist) or *E. L.*, sometimes in monogram. They were executed in dry pastel, sometimes strengthened with washes of body-colour. It is likely that in order to avoid the unsightly stains made by using fixative on paper, Lutterell turned from that medium to copper-plate (as indicated above) which he roughened with a rocker to hold the chalks. According to Vertue, Lutterell claimed that 'he was the first that lay'd grounds on copper for to draw in Crayons. after him Mr. Faithorne the Graver did some few' (*See* above, p. 315). Evelyn notes in his *Diary* for Aug. 14th, 1694, that he saw in the house of his cousin, George Evelyn of Nutfield, a group of the latter's ten children 'all painted in one piece, *very well*, by Mr. Luttrell, in crayons on copper, and seeming to be as finely painted as the best miniature'. This special technique relates Lutterell's

crayons to his experiments in mezzotint, in which he may be counted a pioneer. Vertue relates an involved story of the artist's efforts to obtain the secret of the process from Blois, the assistant of Abraham Blooteling through the printseller and publisher, Floyd. Is said to have learnt the art from Paul van Somer (not John, as Vertue states). Vertue also associates the artist with Isaac Beckett, another pioneer of mezzotint, with whom he entered into a business relationship doing 'many heads for him being very quick and drew better so that Beckett us'd after to finish and ploish [polish] them up'. At one period Lutterell was working at Westminster, as at the back of an unsigned crayon drawing by him belonging to Mr. Alfred Kohnstamm, is a printed label, *Drawn by Edward Luttrell in Peter's Street, near Masham Street in Westminster*, and the first state of his mezzotint of Francis Higgins (*Chaloner Smith*, No. 10), is lettered *sold by M. Luttrell in Westminster Hall*. Vertue relates that he was instrumental in recommending a painted ceiling in Soho Square done by the decorative painter Henry Cooke to Sir Godfrey Copley, thus securing patronage for that artist and promoting his reputation. An entry in the Marriage Register of St. James's, Clerkenwell (*Harl. Soc., Registers*, XIII, 1887), '1675/6, Feb. 1. Edward Lutterell & Jane Smith' possibly refers to the artist. Drew some of the royal portraits for Kennet's *History of England*, 1706. Although 1710 sometimes given as the year of his death, is mentioned by Vertue in 1711 among the twelve directors of Kneller's Queen Street academy, and in 1723 is included in a list of 'Living painters of Note in London & their pictures by whom painted. . . . Mr. Lutterel (painter in Crayons) by himself several.—one head as big as life'.

BIBL.: *Buckeridge*, p. 355. Bell, *Portrait Drawings*, pp. 9–17. *T.-B.*, XXIII, 1929, p. 482 (with *Bibl.*). Vertue, *Index*, p. 167.

1. BEN JONSON, AFTER ABRAHAM BLYENBERCH (?). H.L., turned slightly to l., with eyes looking to front. Wearing short dark hair, close-cropped light-coloured beard, white collar, black doublet and cloak over his r. shoulder. Light brown background. In a feigned oval.

Crayons; $34 \cdot 6 \times 25 \cdot 5$ cm. ($13\frac{5}{8} \times 10$ in.).

PROV.: William Frederick, 2nd Duke of Gloucester, by whom it was bequeathed to the B.M., 1853.
Gloucester-Clarendon, VII, 12 (1853–1–12–332).

[Ben Jonson (B. 1572: D. 1637). The famous poet and dramatist.]
Though the drawing is unsigned, the rather coarse handling of the crayons and the hot flesh tint have suggested the attribution to Lutterell. A number of versions of the original oil-painting exist: two in the N.P.G. (Nos. 363 & 2752), at Knole, and in the collections of the Duke of Portland (Welbeck Abbey) and Mr. T. Cotterell-Dormer (Rousham). Vertue in 1730 engraved one version, then belonging to Lord Somers, as by Gerard Honthorst, which is obviously a wrong attribution. Mr. David Piper of the N.P.G. suggests as the possible author, the Antwerp painter, Abraham Blyenberch (*Fl.* 1621–2), who is recorded, under the name of 'Blyemberch', as having painted a portrait of James I (*See T.-B.*, IV, 1910, p. 145).

2. JAN DE WAEL, AFTER VAN DYCK. Bust, turned half-l., eyes looking to front. Ruddy complexion, brown-grey moustache and pointed beard. Wearing black skull-cap and doublet, and greyish-white ruff.

Crayons and body-colours; stained along the l., r. and lower edges; $22 \cdot 4 \times 18 \cdot 4$ cm. ($8\frac{3}{4} \times 7\frac{1}{8}$ in.).

INSCR.: *Recto*, very faintly in the upper l.-hand corner, by the artist, *E Luttrell*.

PROV.: Richard Bull (Sale, Sotheby, 23:V:1881, Lot 89). Purchased by the B.M. at the Bull Sale, through A.W. Thibaudeau, 1881.
1881–6–11–172 (L.B.1).

BIBL.: *Bell, Portrait Drawings*, p. 16.

Adapted from Van Dyck's etched portrait of Jan de Wael in the *Iconographie* (*Wibiral*, No. 17) which, however, is a H.L. figure with the l. hand showing. No oil painting of this portrait is known to have existed, so the colouring of the present pastel may be assumed to be Lutterell's own.

3. A GENTLEMAN. Bust, turned to r., and head half-r. Wearing dark brown wig, white cravat and brown-black drapery.

Crayons and water-colours; $31 \cdot 9 \times 25 \cdot 7$ cm. ($12\frac{1}{2} \times 10\frac{1}{8}$ in.).

INSCR.: *Recto*, on the r., by the artist, *E Lf*[ec] *1684*.

PROV.: Not known. Presented anonymously to the B.M., 1926.
1926–3–10–2.

Very badly rubbed and much of the original work lost, especially on the face. Has been roughly retouched.

4. AN EARLY SEVENTEENTH-CENTURY DIVINE(?). Bust, turned half-r., with eyes looking to front. Brown hair and large forked beard. Wearing white collar and black gown over red doublet.

Crayons and body-colours; 25·3 × 19·9 cm. (9⅞ × 7¾ in.).

INSCR.: *Recto*, on the r., by the artist, *Lutterell fecit 1694.*

PROV.: Samuel Woodburn (Sale, Christie, 12:vi:1860, in Lot 1081). Sir Thomas

Phillipps. T. Fitzroy Phillipps Fenwick. Presented anonymously to the B.M., 1946. **1946–7–13–1169.**

BIBL.: *Popham, Fenwick*, p. 241, No. 1.

Copy of an early XVII c. portrait. The sitter has not as yet been identified.

5. REMBRANDT'S MOTHER, AFTER REMBRANDT. H.L. figure of an old woman with a ruddy complexion, turned slightly to r. and looking down, her l. hand on her breast, holding a pair of spectacles. Wearing a kerchief and gown, and an olive-green scarf striped with white round her neck.   **Plate 232**

Crayons and body-colours over black lead; 32·2 × 24·6 cm. (12¾ × 9¾ in.).

INSCR.: *Recto*, on the r., by the artist, *E L* (monogram).
> *Verso*, in red chalk,
> *4 Clowns at Cards upon a Barrell*
> *Heated wth Ale began to Quarrell*
> *They Roard & Raved Curst & Swore*
> *Their best* [crossed out] *In the midst of*
>   *this uproar*
> *From Words to Blows* [crossed out]
> *Offensive Weapons up they took*
> *One a Flail tother a ffork*
> *One (?) Wife came in wth too* [th] *& nail to*
>   *opposse the Fork & help the Fl* [ail]
> *Tother to assist her Forked Spouse*
> *Valued neither Cutts nor Blows*

PROV.: Purchased at a sale at Messrs. Foster and Foster, 1938. E. Croft-Murray, by whom it was presented to the B.M., 1946. **1946–8–13–1.**

Adapted from Rembrandt's etching of his Mother, 1631 (Hind, *Rembrandt's Etchings*, No. 50), with considerable modifications, including the contour of her face which has here been lengthened, the scarf which has been added round her neck, and the spectacles placed in her hand. No original oil-painting of this particular portrait of Rembrandt's Mother appears to exist from which this crayon drawing might have been copied, so it must be assumed that the colouring is Lutterell's own. It is interesting to note that in the Landesmuseum, Kassel, are two crayon drawings by Lutterell, of Rembrandt's Father and Mother, signed *E L* and dated *1706.*

The lines inscribed on the *verso* of the present drawing have not as yet been identified. In form, however, they are not unlike certain of John Elsum's *Epigrams upon the Paintings of the most eminent masters . . . ,* London, 1700, especially those on subjects by Adriaen Brouwer.

6. JAN LUTMA, AFTER REMBRANDT. Bust of an old man with white hair and beard, turned half-l. and looking down. Wearing black skull-cap and black coat. Greyish-green and brown background.   **Plate 233**

Crayons and body-colours; 31·7 × 24 cm. (12½ × 9½ in.).

PROV.: As for No. 5. **1946–10–24–1.**

A pendant to No. 4. Adapted from Rembrandt's etching of Jan Lutma, 1656 (Hind, *Rembrandt's Etchings*, No. 290), only the bust being shown, the remainder of the body, the chair and other accessories, and the background, all being omitted. As in Nos. 2, 5 and 7, the colouring may be assumed to be Lutterell's own.

7. REMBRANDT. Bust, with head turned to front and body in profile to l. Wearing a grey bonnet, yellow hair, moustache and beard, and a plum-coloured cloak. Dark grey background.

Crayons and body-colours; 32·8 × 25 cm. (12⅞ × 9⅞ in.).

INSCR.: *Recto*, on the l., by the artist, *Luttrell fe*.

PROV.: M. Cooper and W. Lilly, from whom it was purchased by the B.M., 1957.

1957–2–14–1.

Adapted from Rembrandt's etched self-portrait, 1639 (Hind, *Rembrandt's Etchings*, No. 168). As in Nos. 2, 5 and 6, the colouring may be assumed to be Lutterell's own.

8. A WOMAN WITH BARED BREASTS. Bust, with head nearly in profile to r., and body to front. Wearing grey-green drapery on her head and shoulders and a red dress. Brown-grey background.

Crayons and body-colours; 32·5 × 24·8 cm. (12¾ × 9¾ in.).

INSCR.: *Recto*, on the r., by the artist, E L (monogram).

PROV.: As for No. 7.
1957–2–14–2.

MANBY, THOMAS

B. 1633 (?): D. 1695

Landscape painter and draughtsman

Possibly the Thomas Manby who was baptized at St. Martin-in-the-Fields on May 30th, 1633, son of William and Barbara Manby. Nothing known of his early life. The only contemporary references to him found in Mary Beale's diary (*q.v.*). An entry in 1672 records Manby as the source of her information for the painter Isaac Fuller's death in July of that year. Another entry for Feb. 16th, 1676, shows him collaborating with Mary Beale in a portrait of the Countess of Clare, wife of the 3rd Earl (Welbeck Abbey), for which Manby painted the landscape background. For this he was recompensed by Mrs. Beale with ' 2 ounces of very good Lake. of my makeing—& 1 oz ½ pink'. In Sept., 1676, she sent to him 'a little Italian book *il partito di Donni*. about painting' [Antonio Francesco Doni, *Disegno . . . partito in piu ragionamenti, ne quali si tratta dell Scoltura et Pittura*, 1549] and in April, 1681, lent him 'my Leonardo da Vinci trattato della Pittura which I had from Mrs. Flatman'. Buckeridge, ten years after Manby's death, writes of him as 'a good *English* Landskip-Painter, who had been several times in Italy, and consequently painted much after the *Italian* manner'. The group of drawings attributed to him all in fact of Italian scenes, mainly ruins. Executed in grey wash, sometimes with pen outline, they are reminiscent of the manner of Jan Asselyn, Bartholomeus Breenbergh and Manby's fellow-countryman, Francis Place (*q.v.*). The dates of his visits to Italy not known but probably finally returned to this country before 1685, as Buckeridge says that 'he was famous for bringing over [from Italy] a good Collection of pictures, which were sold at the *banqueting*-house about the latter end of king Charles IId's Reign'. Subsequently entered into partnership, as a picture dealer, with Edward Pierce, a sculptor (*q.v.*). Died in Nov., 1695, and was buried at St. Martin-in-the-Fields on the 24th of that month. St. Martin's Burial Register also includes an entry for Nov. 18th of the same year of Esther Manby, perhaps a relative though not the artist's wife since letters of administration were granted to his widow and heirs. Manby and Pierce's 'curious Collection of Books, Drawings, Prints, Models & Plaster Figures' was offered for auction on Tuesday, Feb. 4th, 1695/6 'at Mr. John Cocks, the Golden Triangle in Long Acre, to be continued daily till sold'.

BIBL.: *Buckeridge*, p. 406. *Poole, Pierce. St. Martin-in-the-Fields Registers (Harleian Soc.,* LXVI, 1936, p. 94). *Williams, Manby. Vertue, Index*, p. 169. *Williams*, p. 6.

DRAWINGS IN OTHER COLLECTIONS: V. & A. M. Mr. Iolo Williams. Mr. Leonard Duke.

1. ROMAN RUINS, PROBABLY IN THE BATHS OF CARACALLA. View of a two-storied arched and vaulted building. Plate 234

Brush drawing in grey wash; 33·6 × 38·3 cm. (13⅛ × 15⅛ in.).

INSCR.: *Recto*, in the upper l.-hand corner, *Manby 1⁸*.

PROV.: Patrick Allan-Fraser (Sale, Sotheby, 10:vi:1931, Lot 149). Iolo Williams, by whom it was presented to the B.M., 1956. 1956-4-14-1.

2. ROMAN RUINS, PROBABLY IN THE BATHS OF CARACALLA. View of a two-storied arched and vaulted building Plate 235

Brush drawing in grey wash; 22·9 × 25·5 cm. (9 × 10 in.).

INSCR.: *Recto*, in the upper l.-hand corner, *Manby 3⁸*.

PROV.: As for No. 1. 1956-4-14-2.

3. A STONE BRIDGE OVER A WATERFALL.

Brush drawing in grey wash; 12 × 18·5 cm. (4¾ × 7¼ in.).

PROV.: As for No. 1. 1956-4-14-3.

4. RUINS OF HADRIAN'S VILLA. View towards a wooded and rocky bank, beyond which rises a tall mass of ruined masonry. Plate 236

Pen and ink, with grey wash; 28·7 × 21·3 cm. (11⅜ × 8⅜ in.).

INSCR.: *Verso*, in the centre, probably by the artist, *The Ruens of Adrians/Villa.*

PROV.: As for No. 1.
1956-4-14-4.

MARSHALL, ALEXANDER

[MARSHAL]

B. 1639 (?): D. 1682

Amateur limner and flower painter

Described on his gravestone, formerly in Fulham Church, as 'descended from an honourable family' and in the *Freind Catalogue (See Bibl.)* as 'a Gentleman' who 'had an independent fortune and painted merely for his Amusement'. May conceivably be identified with Alexander Marshall, born at Loxbeare, Devon, in 1639, the son of the Rector of that parish who was also called Alexander. Nothing known about his upbringing, but perhaps an early work by him is in oil-painting on panel (in the collection of Prof. Thomas Bodkin) representing the siege of Magdeburg in 1631, signed *ALEX. MARSHAL. F.* but not dated, which is probably based on an engraving of the same subject in Matthaüs Merian's *Teatrum Europaeum* (Abelinus), II, 1637, p. 356. Another early work would have been a limning representing *A Philosopher of the second century.* / *Meditating on Death & Immortality.* . . . Signed and dated *A. MARSHAL.* / *1650,* the original of which is now lost, though it is known through a copy (dated *1785*), belonging to the late Mr. A. P. Oppé. In the *Musaeum Tradescantianum,* 1656, is listed 'A Booke of Mr. TRADESCANT'S choicest Flowers and Plants, exquisitely limned on vellum, by Mr. *Alex: Marshall'.* This volume not apparently in either the Bodleian Library or the Ashmolean Museum. Marshall is also mentioned by Sir William Sanderson, 1658, among 'Our Modern Masters comparable with any now beyond Seas . . . *Marshall* for *Flowers* and *Fruits'.* According to the *Freind Catalogue* is 'said to have had a particular art of extracting Colors out of the Natural Flowers' which 'Secret though left behind him, died with those to whom he intrusted it'. Refers himself to this technique in a letter written from Castle Ashby to Thomas Povey, F.R.S., on Nov. 30th, 1667, and states that, though he is 'giving over water-colours, finding it tedious and forcible to the eyes', he intends to practise in oil as he hopes that his 'colours will shew themselves as beautiful in oil as water; though many will say that it is needless for oil-colours to be so orient or beautiful in painting'. Is also said to have used the technique in executing some of the drawings in the *Florilegium Alexandri Marshall,* his most important extant work, now bound in two volumes, in the Royal Library at Windsor (*Cupboard Y*). These drawings consist mainly of flowers but some are of animals, birds, insects and shells, and one (the only figure-subject) of two men, partly copied from Rubens's *Christ bearing the Cross,* engraved by Paulus Pontius in 1632 (*Rooses,* No. 274). The greater number executed in opaque water-colours, and the figure-subject (*f. 155*) in blue wash, heightened with white on blue-grey paper. The signatures *A. Marshall (A.M* in monogram) and *A M* (in monogram) occur in Vol. II, *ff.* 155 & 157–9. The flower-studies inscribed on the *verso*, r., presumably by the artist himself with their Latin and English names, the Guernsey Lily (Vol. II, *f.* 151) inscribed: *this flower was sent me by Generall Lambert august 29 1659 fro / Wimbleton.* The Parliamentary general is credited with having introduced that flower into England, and with being himself a flower painter (*See D.N.B.*, xxxii, 1892, p. 17), so he may have practised this art under Marshall's guidance. Again according to the *Freind Catalogue*, 'lived many years in great friendship with Dr Compton Bishop of London (Henry Compton, B. 1632: D. 1713) and died in his Palace at Fulham; where he planted several Cedars of Libanus (still growing there) and raised many Other Exotics from America & Other Countries, the first that are known to have been raised in this Island.' On Aug. 1st, 1682, Evelyn went to 'the Bishop of London at Fulham, to review the additions which Mr. Marshall had made to his curious book of flowers in miniature, and collection of insects'. Died on Dec 7th, 1682, and was buried in Fulham Church, his gravestone mentioning his marriage to 'Dorothea [Dorothy] daughter of Francis Smith of noble birth'. Apparently made no Will, but administration of his goods granted to his widow on Jan. 3rd, 1683. She is said to have been offered £500 by the French Ambassador for the *Florilegium*, but refused, and subsequently bequeathed it with other of Marshall's works 'and valuable Curiosities' to her nephew, Dr. Robert Freind (B. 1667: D. 1751), Headmaster of Westminster. In 1724 Vertue saw 'at Dr. Friends [*sic*] Westminster several limnings pretty large done by Alex Marshal some copied after Vandyke pretty justly, but his flesh colours painted very carefully, no invention of his own, some small heads by the life not ill done, about 40 or 50 years ago'. The *Florilegium* descended to Robert Freind's son, Dr. William Freind (B. 1715: D. 1766),

Dean of Canterbury, and its contents were listed in detail in his catalogue (the *Freind Catalogue*) under the heading *Volume H.1. Florilegium Alexandri Marshall.* Also recorded there, under the heading *Volume H.2.*, are a copy of Thomas Moffet's *Theatre of Insects*, 1658, with MS annotations and drawings by Marshall, and another volume entitled '*Mr Marshall^s Insects*' in which was inserted 'a Head drawn upon blue Paper by Mr Marshall; supposed to be the Portrait of Himself done by his own hand'. These are evidently the 'curious book of flowers' and the 'collection of insects' mentioned by Evelyn. The volumes probably sold in Dr. Freind's sale (Langford, 14:xii:1768; *See Lugt, Ventes*, No. 1650). Subsequently the *Florilegium* found its way to Brussels where it was purchased in 1818 for John Mangles of Hurley, Bucks., who rebound the contents in two volumes and inserted a highly misleading note as to the origin of the drawings and their author. Mangles later presented the volumes to George IV, through whom they passed into the Royal Library at Windsor. Other recorded works by Marshall include: (1) A picture or drawing, once in the Sloane Collection but now disappeared, of 'Strange Birds &c. of Mareschall'; (2) 'A curious drawing in water colours, of a droll subject, very finely executed by Marshal' listed in John Thane's Catalogue for 1773, p. 99, No. 3763; (3) a miniature of the Countess of Dysart, signed *Alex* (?) *Marshal*, seen by Mr. Long; and (4) a small painting on panel of Christ at the Column, perhaps after Van Dyck, signed in gold *Alex Marshal*, also mentioned by Mr. Long.

BIBL.: Marshall's gravestone, formerly in Fulham Church (communicated by Canon A. J. G. Hawes). *Musaeum Tradescantianum*, p. 41. *Sanderson*, p. 20. *Mrs. Marshall's Will* (P.C.C., *Young*, 215). *Freind Catalogue*, *ff.* 129–36. *Birch*, II, pp. 230–1. *Evelyn, Diary*, Aug. 1st, 1682. *Sloane, Antiquities, Pictures and Drawings*, No. 78. *Walpole*, II, p. 536.

Marshall, I, p. 110 & *App.*, pp. 29–30. *T.-B.*, XXIV, 1930, p. 141. *Long*, p. 289. *Vertue, Index*, p. 171. *Blunt, Tulipomania*, p. 31. *Oppé, English Drawings*, pp. 74–5.

[1–33]. The following drawings, when first acquired by the B.M., were mounted in an album, which was probably lettered with Marshall's name, or may have contained some other indication of his authorship. Unfortunately this album, and any documentary information it may have contained, disappeared when the drawings were re-arranged on separate mounts. The attribution to Marshall may probably be accepted, as the drawings are not far removed in style from those in the Windsor albums described in the biographical note above, though the latter are more naturally composed. In view of their technique of water-colours on vellum, it would be tempting to connect the present series of drawings with the missing 'Booke of Mr. TRADESCANT'S choicest Flowers', but the types here represented do not correspond with the rarities in Tradescant's garden which one imagines would have been depicted.

1. LARGE CRIMSON AND WHITE AND SMALL PURPLE ANEMONES, TIED WITH BLUE RIBBON.

Water-colours over metal-point, shaded with grey and heightened with white; 18 × 11·3 cm. (7⅛ × 4½ in.).

PROV. Miss Cecilia Ashe, from whom it was purchased by the B.M., 1878.

1878–12–14–59 (L.B. 6a).

2. YELLOW AND CRIMSON TULIP, PURPLE MALLOW AND CRIMSON ANEMONE, TIED WITH BLUE RIBBON.

Water-colours over metal-point, strengthened with body-colour, on vellum; 18 × 11·4 cm. (7⅛ × 4½ in.).

PROV.: As for No. 1.

1878–12–14–60 (L.B.6b).

3. CRIMSON AND WHITE TULIP, WHITE CHERRY BLOSSOM AND BLUE HYACINTH, TIED WITH YELLOW RIBBON.

Water-colours over metal-point, shaded with grey wash, on vellum; 18 × 11·3 cm. (7⅛ × 4½ in.).

PROV.: As for No. 1.

1878–12–14–61 (L.B.6c).

4. BLUE CLEMATIS, PINK COLUMBINE AND PURPLE FRITILLARY, TIED WITH CRIMSON RIBBON.

Water-colours over metal-point, heightened with white, on vellum; 18 × 11·2 cm. (7⅛ × 4⅜ in.).

PROV.: As for No. 1.

1878–12–14–62 (L.B.9a).

5. YELLOW AND CRIMSON TULIP, BLUE CONVOLVULUS AND CRIMSON GLADIOLUS, TIED WITH ORANGE RIBBON.

Water-colours over metal-point, on vellum; 17·8 × 11·3 cm. (7 × 4½ in.).

PROV.: As for No. 1.

1878–12–14–63 (L.B.9b).

6. WHITE AND CRIMSON TULIP, PURPLE LARKSPUR AND YELLOW NARCISSUS, TIED WITH BLUE RIBBON.

Water-colours over metal-point, shaded with grey wash, on vellum; 18 × 11·4 cm. (7⅛ × 4½ in.).

PROV.: As for No. 1.
1878–12–14–64 (L.B.9c).

7. CRIMSON ANEMONES AND PURPLE AMARANTHUS (?), TIED WITH BLUE RIBBON.

Water-colours over metal-point on vellum; 18 × 11·3 cm. (7⅛ × 4½ in.).

PROV.: As for No. 1
1878–12–14–65 (L.B.7a).

8. WHITE NARCISSI AND PINK ROSE, TIED WITH BLUE RIBBON.

Water-colours over metal-point, shaded with grey wash, on vellum; 17·9 × 11·3 cm. (7 × 4½ in.).

PROV.: As for No. 1.
1878–12–14–66 (L.B.7b).

9. PINK ROSE, ORANGE TAGETES AND BLUE HYACINTH, TIED WITH PINK RIBBON.

Water-colours over metal-point, heightened with white, on vellum; 18 × 11·3 cm. (7⅛ × 4½ in.).

PROV.: As for No. 1.
1878–12–14–67 (L.B.7c).

10. PURPLE IRIS, PINK ANEMONE AND YELLOW COMPOSITE, TIED WITH CRIMSON RIBBON.

Water-colours over metal-point on vellum; 17·9 × 11·2 cm. (7 × 4½ in.).

PROV.: As for No. 1.
1878–12–14–68 (L.B.10a).

11. YELLOW TAGETES, BLUE LOVE-IN-A-MIST AND PINK, TIED WITH CRIMSON RIBBON.

Water-colours over metal-point on vellum; 18 × 11·3 cm. (7⅛ × 4⅜ in.).

PROV.: As for No. 1.
1878–12–14–69 (L.B.10b).

12. WHITE AND CRIMSON TULIP, PINK, AND YELLOW AND RED RANUNCULUS, TIED WITH BLUE RIBBON.

Water-colours over metal-point, shaded with grey wash, on vellum; 18 × 11·2 cm. (7⅛ × 4⅜ in.).

PROV.: As for No. 1.
1878–12–14–70 (L.B.10c).

13. PURPLE AND BLUE IRISES, AND VIOLETS, TIED WITH PINK RIBBON.

Water-colours over metal-point on vellum; 18·1 × 11·5 cm. (7⅛ × 4½ in.).

PROV.: As for No. 1.
1878–12–14–71 (L.B.11a).

14. PINK ROSES TIED WITH BLUE RIBBON.

Water-colours over metal-point on vellum; 18·1 × 11·3 cm. (7⅛ × 4½ in.).

Prov.: As for No. 1.
1878–12–14–72 (L.B.11b).

15. CRIMSON AND YELLOW TULIP AND BLUE CONVOLVULUS, TIED WITH PURPLE RIBBON.

Water-colours over metal-point, heightened with white, on vellum; 17·9 × 11·4 cm. (7 × 4½ in.).

Prov.: As for No. 1.
1878–12–14–73 (L.B.11c).

16. PURPLE COLUMBINE AND PURPLE AND CRIMSON ANEMONES, TIED WITH CRIMSON RIBBON.

Water-colours over metal-point on vellum; 17·9 × 11·4 cm. (7 × 4½ in.).

Prov.: As for No. 1.
1878–12–14–74 (L.B.8a).

17. ORANGE TURK'S CAP, CRIMSON AND WHITE ANEMONE AND PURPLE HEARTS–EASE, TIED WITH BLUE RIBBON.

Water-colours over metal-point, shaded with grey wash and heightened with white, on vellum; 18 × 11·4 cm. (7⅛ × 4½ in.).

Prov.: As for No. 1.
1878–12–14–75 (L.B.8b).

18. CRIMSON ANEMONE, YELLOW TAGETES AND YELLOW HOOP PETTICOAT, TIED WITH PURPLE RIBBON.

Water-colours over pencil, shaded with grey wash, on vellum; 17·9 × 11·3 cm. (7 × 4¼ in.).

Prov.: As for No. 1.
1878–12–14–76 (L.B.8c).

19. YELLOW AND RED, AND WHITE AND RED TULIPS, TIED WITH ORANGE RIBBON.

Water-colours over metal-point, shaded with grey wash, on vellum; 18 × 11·4 cm. (7⅛ × 4½ in.).

Prov.: As for No. 1.
1878–12–14–77 (L.B.1a).

20. RED AND WHITE, AND PURPLE ANEMONES, TIED WITH BLUE RIBBON.

Water-colours over metal-point, shaded with grey wash, on vellum; 18 × 11·4 cm. (7⅛ × 4½ in.).

Prov.: As for No. 1.
1878–12–14–78 (L.B.1b).

21. RED AND WHITE, AND PURPLE ANEMONES, TIED WITH YELLOW RIBBON.

Water-colours over metal-point, shaded with grey wash, on vellum; 17·8 × 11·4 cm. (7 × 4½ in.).

Prov.: As for No. 1.
1878–12–14–79 (LB.1c).

22. RED AND WHITE TULIP, AND WHITE AND RED, AND PURPLE AND RED ANEMONES, TIED WITH BLUE RIBBON.

Water-colours over metal-point, shaded with grey wash, on vellum; 18·1 × 11·4 cm. (7⅛ × 4½ in.).

PROV.: As for No. 1.

1878–12–14–80 (L.B.2a).

23. WHITE AND YELLOW, PURPLE, AND RED ANEMONES, TIED WITH YELLOW RIBBON.

Water-colours over metal-point, shaded with grey wash, on vellum; 18 × 11·4 cm. (7⅛ × 4½ in.).

PROV.: As for No. 1.

1878–12–14–81 (L.B.2b).

24. CRIMSON AND WHITE ANEMONES, TIED WITH CRIMSON RIBBON.

Water-colours over metal-point, shaded with grey wash, on vellum; 18 × 11·3 cm. (7⅛ × 4½ in.).

PROV.: As for No. 1.

1878–12–14–82 (L.B.2c).

25. CRIMSON AND WHITE, PURPLE AND WHITE, AND CRIMSON AND YELLOW TULIPS, TIED WITH ORANGE RIBBON.

Water-colours over metal-point, shaded with grey wash and heightened with white, on vellum; 18·1 × 11·6 cm. (7⅛ × 4⅝ in.).

PROV.: As for No. 1.

1878–12–14–83 (L.B.3a).

26. WHITE AND CRIMSON, WHITE AND PURPLE, AND WHITE AND ORANGE TULIPS, TIED WITH YELLOW RIBBON.

Water-colours over metal-point, shaded with grey wash, on vellum; 18 × 11·3 cm. (7⅛ × 4½ in.).

PROV.: As for No. 1.

1878–12–14–84 (L.B.3b).

27. WHITE AND CRIMSON, AND ORANGE ANEMONES, TIED WITH BLUE RIBBON.

Water-colours over metal-point, shaded with grey wash, on vellum; 17·5 × 11·3 cm. (6⅞ × 4½ in.).

PROV.: As for No. 1.

1878–12–14–85 (L.B.3c).

28. WHITE AND CRIMSON, WHITE AND PURPLE ANEMONES AND A DOG'S TOOTH VIOLET (SHOWN PINK), TIED WITH BLUE RIBBON.

Water-colours over metal-point on vellum; 17·9 × 11·2 cm. (7 × 4⅜ in.).

PROV.: As for No. 1.

1878–12–14–86 (L.B.4a).

29. WHITE AND PINK, AND VIOLET ANEMONES AND YELLOW TULIP, TIED WITH BLUE RIBBON.

Water-colours over metal-point on vellum; 17·9 × 11·2 cm. (7 × 4⅜ in.).

PROV.: As for No. 1.

1878–12–14–87 (L.B.4b).

30. WHITE AND CRIMSON, AND PURPLE ANEMONES, TIED WITH DULL RED RIBBON. Plate 237

Water-colours over metal-point, heightened with white, on vellum; 18·1 × 11·3 cm. (7⅛ × 4½ in.).

PROV.: As for No. 1.
1878–12–14–88 (L.B.4c).

31. YELLOW AND CRIMSON, BLUE AND CRIMSON AND WHITE AND CRIMSON TULIPS, TIED WITH MAUVE RIBBON. Plate 237

Water-colours over metal-point, shaded with grey wash, on vellum; 18 × 11·3 cm. (7⅛ × 4½ in.).

PROV.: As for No. 1.
1878–12–14–89 (L.B.5a).

32. YELLOW AND CRIMSON, WHITE AND CRIMSON AND WHITE AND PURPLE TULIPS, TIED WITH BLUE RIBBON.

Water-colours over metal-point, shaded with grey wash, on vellum; 17·8 × 11·2 cm. (7 × 4⅜ in.).

PROV.: As for No. 1.
1878–12–14–90 (L.B.5b).

33. PURPLE, WHITE AND CRIMSON TULIP, WHITE AND CRIMSON ANEMONE, AND YELLOW VIOLET, TIED WITH CRIMSON RIBBON.

Water-colours over metal-point, shaded with grey wash, on vellum; 18 × 11·3 cm. (7⅛ × 4½ in.).

PROV.: As for No. 1.
1878–12–14–91 (L.B.5c).

MEDINA, SIR JOHN BAPTIST

B. 1659: D. 1710

Portrait painter and book illustrator

Born at Brussels, where his father, Medina de Caustanais, a Spanish officer, had settled. Studied painting there under the portrait and genre painter François du Chatel. Married Joanna Maria van Dael, by whom he is said to have had 21 or 22 children. Came to England in 1686 and practised first in London as a portrait painter, later obtaining commissions to the value of £500 in Scotland, through the good offices of his patron, the 5th Earl of Leven. Went there in 1688, bringing with him a large number of 'postures and half-lengths' to which he attached heads thereby completing the work in one year. Paid another short visit to England, during which time he designed twelve plates for the fine but inaccurate edition of Milton's *Paradise Lost*, published by Tonson in folio in 1705, and later in 12mo in 1711. Also designed illustrations to Ovid's *Metamorphoses*, which, however, were not engraved. Returned with his family to Scotland, where he continued his practice as a portraitist, and where he attained the same kind of position as did his contemporary Kneller in England. Painted most of the Scottish nobility, and the series of 'professors' in the Surgeons' Hall, Edinburgh. Self-portraits of him are in the Surgeons' Hall, Edinburgh (painted in 1708) in the Uffizi (presented to the Grand Duke of Tuscany by the Duke of Gordon). Was also the author of a remarkable 'conversation picture', apparently signed *Medina/C.H.* now at Nostell Priory, of five musicians said (probably incorrectly) to represent the members of the Cabal. A number of his portraits were engraved during, or soon after his life-time. Vertue's comment on him points to his having tried his hand at other branches of painting besides portraiture: 'He painted with great freedom, a clever pencil and good colouring. He drew and painted historical subjects very well and had a fine taste in landscape and would have made a good history painter had he lived where suitable encouragement were to be met with'. Among his pupils in Scotland were William Aikman (B. 1682: D. 1731) the portraitist, and Andrew Hay the picture dealer. Was knighted in 1707, the last to receive this dignity in Scotland before the Union in May of that year. Died in Edinburgh on Oct. 5th, 1710, and was buried in the churchyard of the Greyfriars at Edinburgh. His Will in the Library of the Writers to the Signet at Edinburgh. His son, John Medina II (D. 1764), and his grandson, John Medina III (B. 1721: D. 1796), also followed the same profession.

BIBL.: *Walpole*, II, pp. 610–11. *D.N.B.*, XXXVII, 1894, pp. 203–4. Baker, *Lely*, II, pp. 211–12. *B.M. Engraved Portraits*, VI, p. 519. *T.-B.*, XXIV, 1930, p. 328 (with *Bibl.*). *Vertue, Index*, p. 176.

1. *Recto*. **GRINLING GIBBONS.** Bust, turned half-r., with head nearly to front and eyes looking to l., wearing long curling hair or wig, cravat, and a cloak draped over his shoulder. **Plate 238**

Red and black chalk, heightened with white, on buff paper; 22·7 × 17·2 cm. (9 × 6¾ in.). Old mount; 25 × 18·3 cm. (9⅞ × 7⅛ in.).

INSCR.: In the upper r.-hand corner, by the artist, *J. Medina / D.º*; and on the old mount, at the foot, by George Vertue, *J Medina Eques ad vivum delin.* and *G Gibbons Sculptor* & (not completed).

Verso. **STUDY OF A PAIR OF LEGS.**

Red chalk.

PROV.: George Vertue (cannot be identified with any particular lot in his sales, Ford, 16:iii: & 17:v:1757). Horace Walpole (Probably in Sale, Robins, 28:vi:1842, Lot 1270, but not specified. Purchased by A. E. Evans). A.E. Evans, from whom it was purchased by the B.M., 1852.

1852-2-14-375 (L.B. 1).

BIBL. & REPR.: *Connoisseur*, LXXXVI, 1930, pp. 285 & 332. For the biography of Grinling Gibbons, *see* pp. 332–3.

This drawing shows Gibbons perhaps as a rather younger man than he appears in the portraits of him by Closterman and Kneller (*See B.M. Engraved Portraits*, II, p. 325).

2. **ROBERT DALZELL, 5th EARL OF CARNWATH.** Bust, turned to r., head half-r. and eyes looking to front. Wearing a large curling wig and armour. Against a shaded background within a feigned oval.

Brush drawing in grey wash, touched with pen and ink and heightened with white, on blue-grey paper; 28·4 × 20·2 cm. (11⅛ × 7⅞ in.).

INSCR.: *Recto*, at the foot, in the l.-hand corner, *De Medina fect*, and in the r.-hand corner, *Rob : Dalziel Earl of Canwarth*.

PROV.: Richard Bull (Sale, Sotheby, 23:v:1882, Lot 93). Purchased by the B.M. at the Bull Sale, 1881.

1881–6–11–173 (L.B.1).

BIBL. & REPR.: *Connoisseur*, LXXXV, 1930, pp. 324-5.

[Robert Dalzell, 5th Earl of Carnwath (B. *c.* 1687: D. 1737). Son of Sir John Dalzell, Bart. of Glencoe, whom he suc-ceeded in 1689. Succeeded to the Earldom of Carnwath on the death of his kinsman, John, 4th Earl, in 1702. Took part in the Rising of 1715, and was captured at Preston. Was attainted and sentenced to death. Escaped execution, but forfeited his peerage honours. Married four times. Died at Kirkmichael.]

In handling, this drawing clearly belongs to the large group of portrait-drawings in pen and grey wash on blue-grey or drab paper belonging to the Lely-Kneller schools, of which the largest number in the collection are those by, or attributed to, the brothers Edward and Robert Byng. The present example is not comparable in quality with the authentic portrait-drawing by Medina of Grinling Gibbons (No. 1 above), and is most likely a copy of an oil painting.

3. SAMSON SLAYING A PHILISTINE, AFTER GIAMBOLOGNA. Samson, seen in profile to l., with upraised jaw-bone in his r. hand, about to strike the Philis-tine whom he holds down with his l. hand. **Plate 239**

Black chalk on light buff paper; 53 × 32·3 cm. (20¾ × 12¾ in.). Old mount; 56·1 × 36 cm. (22⅛ × 14¼ in.).

INSCR.: *Recto*, in the lower r.-hand corner, S*r* *John Medina 1690*.

PROV.: Dr. E. Peart (*Lugt*, No. 891). Sale, Christie, 29:iv:1822, Lots 11 or 134).

Capt. John Elliott, from whom it was pur-chased by the B.M., 1933.

1933–11–28–1.

Presumably after the sculpture now in the V. & A. Museum. If drawn directly from this, must have been executed at York House, where the group was preserved, between 1624 and the early XVIII c.

OLIVER, PETER

[OLIVIER]

B. 1594: D. 1648

Limner

Eldest son of Isaac Oliver, the miniaturist (*q.v.*) by his first wife. Was no doubt in-structed by his father, whose style he fol-lowed closely and whose reputation he seems to have equalled or even surpassed in the opinion of contemporaries like Norgate. Inherited his father's 'drawings and lim-nings', and completed the 'large fine limning', the *Burial of Christ* (*See* p. 23, No. 11), intended for the King's collection, and left unfinished by the elder Oliver at his death (1617). Executed in addition to portrait miniatures, history pieces in miniature, copies of paintings by Titian, Correggio, Van Dyck and Raphael, of which a number were in the Royal Collection. Walpole notes that history pieces comprised most of the thirteen works by the younger Oliver listed as being in the collections of Charles I and James II. Norgate writes, 'Histories in Lymning are strangers in England till of late Yeares it pleased a most excellent King to comand the Copieing of some of his owne peeces, of Titian, to be translated into English Lymning, which indeed were admirably performed by his Servant, Mr. Peter Olivier'. Additional evidence of royal patronage found in the exchequer accounts for 1635 when £100 paid to him for work ordered, or completed, for the King. Among his more influential patrons was Sir Kenelm Digby of whose family he, as well as his father, made a number of portraits. Norgate also refers to landscapes drawn by Oliver with the point of the brush and to his work in crayons, and eulogizes the artist, claiming him to be the superior of Giulio Clovio. Vertue suggests that in addition to histories and portraits, Oliver was occupied at Court in assisting Inigo Jones with designs for costumes for the masque. The same writer says that Oliver also collaborated with Francis Barlow by drawing the figures in designs for etchings and that he etched a few small history pieces, but only one etched plate by Peter Oliver known, a half-length figure of a woman after Parmigianino, signed *P.O.* Among his self-portraits was one (formerly at Strawberry Hill, now belonging to the Earl of Derby) in black lead on vellum, signed *P.O./se ipse fecit*, with a head of Mrs. Oliver on the *verso*.

The records of marriages for 1626 and 1638 which concern Pierre Olivier and Pierre Ollivier, given in *Cust*, probably do not relate in either instance to the artist. His wife known to have been called Anne and named in his Will, dated Dec. 12th, 1647, as his sole heir and executrix. There seem to have been no children. Resided at Isleworth where he died. Was buried on Dec. 22nd, 1647, at St. Anne's, Blackfriars, next to his father, to whose memory Peter erected a monument.

The King's interest in the artist's work continued after the Restoration. Anthony Russell provided Vertue with the account, inherently probable, of Charles II's acquisition from Oliver's widow of the best of the collection of his duplicate portraits. In return she received a pension of £300. The story goes on to tell how the King squandered this collection on his mistresses, the news of which provoked the widow to an abusive outburst, as a result of which the King stopped her pension.

BIBL.: *Walpole*, I, pp. 221–6. *D.N.B.*, XLII, 1895, p. 149. *Cust, Foreign Artists*, p. 30. *Norgate*, pp. 47, 54–5, 72–3. *Long*, pp. 320–3 (with *Bibl.*). *T.-B.*, XXV, 1931, p. 599. *Vertue, Index*, p. 194. *Woodward*, pp. 20 and 46. *Derby Miniatures*, pp. 43 & 44, No. 10. *Vertue*, VI, pp. 5, 8, 55 and 161.

DRAWINGS IN OTHER COLLECTIONS: Ashmolean.

1. **STUDIES OF FIVE HEADS.** Three in profile to l., including one of a woman and of a man caricatured in the manner of Leonardo, and two, in profile to r., of an old bearded man and a youth. **Plate 240**

Pen and light brown ink, with light brown wash; 7·8 × 7·1 cm. (3 × 2¾ in.).

INSCR.: *Recto*, in the lower r.-hand corner, by the artist, *PO*.

2 F

C.E.D.

PROV.: Jonathan Richardson, I (*Lugt*, No. 2184. Sale, Cock, 23:i:1746/7, Lot 48). Nathaniel Hone (not identifiable in his Sale, Hutchins, 7–15:ii:1785). Richard Payne Knight, by whom it was bequeathed to the B.M., 1824.

O.o.5–1 (L.B.1).

BIBL.: *Payne Knight Cat.*, p. 176, No. 1.

2. THE PENITENT MAGDALEN. H.L., looking upwards to l., her hands clasped together. Before her a crucifix, an open book, a skull and a jar. In the background, a rock and foliage.   **Plate 240**

Brush drawing in black, touched with pen and ink (?); the corners cut off; 8·7 × 6·2 cm. (3⅜ × 2⅜ in.).

PROV.: A. G. Grant, from whom it was purchased by the B.M., 1956.

1956–8–2–1.

INSCR.: *Recto*, in the upper l.-hand corner, by the artist, *P Oliver/fecit*.

PHILLIPS, THOMAS

B. 1635(?): D. 1693

Military engineer and draughtsman

First mentioned in a letter from James, Duke of York, who appointed him master-gunner of the *Portsmouth* in 1661. Held that rank at the Tower in 1672 and later that year at Sheerness. His career as a military engineer included periods in the Channel Islands (1679–80), the Isle of Wight (1683), Tangier (1683–4), where he served as third engineer under Major—later Sir Martin—Beckman, in the Earl of Dartmouth's expedition to demolish the defences, and Ireland (1684). Numerous maps, charts and views by him connected with the defences of several of these areas are preserved. In December, 1685, was appointed second engineer, remaining in London at the Board of Ordnance as adviser on problems of defence until the Revolution. Continued in the same rank under William and Mary, except for a brief interlude when he was dismissed from his post for refusing to serve under the Duke of Schomberg. Took part in the expedition against the French coast in 1692 and in the latter part of the following year sailed with Captain Benbow as chief engineer in the operations against St. Malo when he directed the bombardment. Died on Nov. 22, 1693, at sea as a result of firing the powder-ship, *Infernal*, off the sea-wall of that town.

His work included not only the painstaking plans and prospects of fortifications required by his office, executed in the tradition of Hollar, but also drawings of sea battles, apparently commissioned by Charles II, since the artist is recorded as petitioning unsuccessfully for a pension, quoting as a precedent the grants to the two Van de Veldes (*q.v.*) for the same type of work. A number of drawings of the Battles of Solebay (1672) and Texel (1673), as well as designs for mortars, in the collection of the Earl of Dartmouth (now on loan to the National Maritime Museum) can be attributed to Phillips.

BIBL.: *D.N.B.*, XLV, 1896, pp. 214–215

(with *Bibl.*). *Routh. Navy Records*, Pls. for XXXIV, and LVII (1923), pp. 470–1. *Eagleston*, Pls. V–VIII. *B.M., Eng. Topographical & Landscape Drawings*, p. 13.

DRAWINGS IN OTHER COLLECTIONS: B.M., Dept. of MSS. and Map Room (*King's Topography*, LI, 49). National Maritime Museum.

1. TANGIER FROM THE SEA. Unfinished view of the fortifications, looking S.E., with the mole and harbour in the distance, l. On the l. of the defences, York Castle with its prominent square tower. In the foreground, on the shore, figures outlined in brown ink but uncoloured: on the r., a team of three horses drawing a cart loaded with stones, and men standing by; on the l., two men on horseback.   Plate 162 (b)

Pen and brown ink over black lead, with water-colours; on two conjoined sheets; 20·7 × 59·7 cm. (8⅛ × 23½ in.)

PROV.: Sir Hans Sloane, Bart., by whom it was bequeathed to the B.M., 1753.
5214–16 (L.B. 37, as by Hollar).

In connexion with the above drawing may be noted an advertisement in the *London Gazette*, No. 1997, Jan. 5th–8th, 1684/5: 'There are Four Large Prospects of Tangier, curiously engraven on copper-plates, Two of Towns, and Two of the Ruins after it was Demolished, taken by Mr. Tho. Phillips one of his Majesties Principal Engineers . . . Sold at Mr. John Berries Mapmaker at the Sign of the Globe at Charing-Cross, at Mr. Lords, a Picture-shop in Westminster-Hall, and at his Shop in Chancery-Lane, at Mr. Holfords, a Book-seller at the Sign of the Crown in Pall-mall, at Mr. John Sellers, on the Royal Exchange, and at his House in Wapping.'
Cf. also Hollar's etching, *York Castle from the North West* (*Parthey*, No. 1191).

PIERCE, EDWARD II

[PEARCE]

B. *c.* 1635: D. 1695

Sculptor and 'mason-contractor'

Son of Edward Pierce I (B. 1598: D. 1658), well-known in his day as a decorative painter who is also known to have painted scenery for Inigo Jones. Date of birth unknown but probably about 1635 as he was made a freeman, by patrimony, of the Painter-Stainers' Company in 1656. Nothing known of his upbringing but probably lived at his father's house in Aldersgate. Married Anne Smith on Oct. 22nd, 1661, in the church of St. Michael Bassishaw. Before 1660 modelled terra-cotta busts of Milton and Cromwell and carved the latter in marble. From 1663–5 worked under Sir Roger Pratt at Horseheath, Cambridgeshire. At some time between 1667 and 1688 worked under Capt. William Winde (*q.v.*) at Hampstead Marshall. Worked from 1671 with Sir Christopher Wren under whom in that year he began the rebuilding and furnishing of St. Lawrence Jewry. Cast a bronze bust, and carved a marble one, of Cromwell (1672) and next year carved the marble bust of Wren now in the Ashmolean. The doorway carved by Pierce for the Painter-Stainers' Hall in 1675 has been attributed to Grinling Gibbons, as has much of his work. Worked in 1676 at Sudbury Hall, Derbyshire. In 1678 was

451

appointed one of the carvers at St. Paul's. Made the dragon weathervane for St. Mary-le-bow in 1650 and in the same year was made mason-contractor for St. Clement Danes in partnership with John Shorthose. Took as apprentice Richard Crutcher who was later to carve the Clayton monument in Bletchingley church, Surrey. Carved the wooden statue of Sir William Walworth for the Fishmongers' Hall and in the same year (1682) began work at St. Matthew, Friday Street, where he carved the pulpit, font-cover and reredos. In partnership with William Stanton was appointed mason-contractor for St. Andrew's Holborn (1684); their work took seven years to complete. Carved a statue of Queen Elizabeth for the Fishmongers' and one of Edward III for the Skinners' Company, neither surviving though the Skinners possess a model for theirs. In 1688 carved a bust of Thomas Evans, Master of the Painter-Stainers' Company. When working with C. G. Cibber on garden urns at Hampton Court (1690), was involved in a dispute over the piers which were alleged to be unsound. His last work apparently the design and erection of the Seven Dials column (1694). Died in 1695 and was buried in St. Clement Danes; his Will proved on April 20th. Enjoyed considerable reputation as a sculptor on his own and also worked as a 'shop keeper' employing five men and a mason-contractor.

BIBL.: *D.N.B.*, XLV, 1896, pp. 257–8. *Seymour. T.-B.*, XXVI, 1932, p. 599. *Wren Soc., Index*, p. 160. *Vertue, Index*, p. 208.

DRAWINGS IN OTHER COLLECTIONS: Soane Museum (designs for monuments from Talman coll.). V. & A. M. (design for reredos from Talman coll.). Ashmolean M. (design for a bust, probably a preliminary design for Sir William Walworth).

1. DESIGN FOR A MONUMENT TO GEORGE VILLIERS, 2nd DUKE OF BUCKINGHAM.

An elaborate Baroque structure in the form of a pavilion, the central feature of which is a cupola, rising above a canopy hung with drapery and decorated with a shield (blank) surmounted by the ducal coronet and encircled by the Garter. Beneath this canopy, the Duke and Duchess recumbent on a sarcophagus, supported by nude slaves, behind which rises an obelisk surrounded by military emblems. Below the sarcophagus, an infant with a coronet beside it, lying on drapery supported by two weeping cherubs. To r. and l. of the canopy, in niches flanked by Corinthian columns, standing figures of the Duke and Duchess as in life, pointing towards the sarcophagus. At the top, on the cupola, Fame blowing a trumpet, and on the attic, two genii holding wreaths, a lion, a dragon, and two trophies of arms. On either side of the pavilion, an obelisk topped by a coronet, and seated along the step below, figures symbolizing Faith, Hope, Wisdom and Fortitude.   **Plate 242**

Pen and brown ink over black lead, with washes of grey and brown, perhaps indicating the parts to be carried out respectively in marble and gilded bronze; 50·5 × 49·5 cm. (19$\frac{7}{8}$ × 19$\frac{1}{2}$ in.).

INSCR.: *Recto*, by John Talman, at the foot, to the r., *Designed by Edwd. Pierce for y^e Duke of Buckingham to be Set up in Westminster Abby.*

PROV.: John Talman (*Lugt*, No. 2462. Sale, 4–10:iv:1728, Lot 23 or 132 (?)). Richard Bull (Sale, Sotheby, 23:v:1881, Lot 106). Purchased at the Bull Sale, through A. W. Thibaudeau, by the B.M., 1881.

1881-6-11-176 (L.B.2).

BIBL.: *Poole, Pierce*, pp. 38 & 44.

[George Villiers, 2nd Duke of Buckingham (B. 1627/8: D. 1687). 2nd son of the 1st and great Duke. Celebrated as a wit of his age, and notorious for his profligacy and unscrupulous politics. Was the original of Zimri in Dryden's *Absolom and Achitophel*. Married Mary, daughter and heiress of Lord Fairfax, the Parliamentarian General. Buried in the family vault in Henry VII's Chapel, Westminster Abbey, where later his Duchess (D. 1704) was also laid. No monument was set up to their memory.]

There is apparently no contemporary or early mention of Pierce's having designed such a monument, but there seems no reason to doubt the attribution in Talman's inscription. One cannot date the drawing with any certainty. The representation of the Duchess beside her husband on the sarcophagus would suggest, at first sight, that the design was made after her death in 1704, but this is impossible as Pierce himself died in 1695. The monument may therefore have been commissioned by the Duchess after the Duke's death in 1687; or, following the custom of the time, it might even have been commissioned by the Duke himself during his life-time, with the idea of commemorating both himself and the Duchess. Mrs.

Poole (*op. cit.*, p. 38), gives the date of the drawing as 1687-8. The introduction of the dead infant into the design also presents a problem. The coronet beside it would indicate that it was the Duke's heir who had predeceased him, but, so far, this child has not been identified. Brian Fairfax (*Life of George Villiers, Duke of Buckingham, in A Catalogue of the . . . Pictures of George Villiers, Duke of Buckingham*, 1758, p. 37) states rather ambiguously that the Duke 'had no children by his dutchess, nor heirs capable of inheriting his estate or title'; and no more precise information has been provided on this point by the other authorities consulted.

Vertue mentions (*Walpole Soc.*, Vol. XVIII, 1930, p. 69), on the authority of John Talman, 'several drawings of Edw. Pierce. a curious Architect & Carver. a great assistant of Sr Christo. Wren.' Mrs. Poole (*op. cit.*, p. 43), quoting this note, suggests that these drawings belonged to Dr. George Clarke; but, from Vertue's original wording, this would not necessarily appear to be so, and it seems possible that the drawings in question actually belonged to Talman himself, in which case the present design for the Duke of Buckingham's monument would have been one of them.

2. THE PILLAR AT SEVEN DIALS, LONDON. Elevation of a Doric pillar on a pedestal, with a pinnacle at the top surrounded by sundials (left blank in the drawing), three of which are shown.
Plate 241

Pen and brown ink, with grey wash; 50·8 × 31·3 cm. (20 × 12⅜ in.).

INSCR.: *Recto*, at the foot, *A Stone Pillar with Sun-Dyals, to which are directed 7 Streets in St Giles's Parish, commonly | called the Seven Dyals, formerly a Lay stall. designed & drawn by Edwd: Pierce sculpto* [r]; also the scale to which the drawing is made and measurements in feet and inches on various ledges of the pedestal.

PROV.: Richard Bull (Sale, Sotheby, 23:v:1881, Lot 107). Purchased at the Bull

Sale, through A. W. Thibaudeau, by the B.M., 1881.

1881-6-11-177 (L.B.1).

BIBL.: *Poole, Pierce*, pp. 38 & 43.

This is presumably Pierce's original drawing of the pillar (perhaps made for an engraving, not carried out), which formerly stood in the parish of St. Giles-in-the-Fields at the meeting-place of what formerly were seven separate streets; now known as Mercer St., Earlham St., Monmouth St., and

Short's Gardens. According to the inscription on the drawing this point was originally a lay-stall, or refuse pit. Evelyn, under the date Oct. 5th, 1694, mentions having seen the pillar, which is said to have been erected by Thomas Neale (D. 1699 (?)), Master of the Mint and promoter of several lotteries, who also is known to have initiated the building of the surrounding streets. Though the name of the locality derives from the dials on the pillar, there were actually only six of these. In 1773, the pillar was removed, and eventually was re-erected at Weybridge (*See Wheatley and Cunningham*, III, p. 234, for a full account). As far as can be ascertained, there is no contemporary or early reference to Pierce as its designer.

[3–6]. The following four drawings were attributed to William Talman in the Bull Sale, and as such were acquired by the B.M. and catalogued by Mr. Binyon. There seems to be no doubt, however, that they are by the same hand as No. 1 (which, incidentally, also came from the Bull collection), and have now, therefore, been placed with drawings by Edward Pierce. All of them have the gold stencilled border characteristic of drawings from John Talman's collection, and like No. 1 they may originally have formed part of the series of Pierce's drawings which, according to Vertue, probably belonged to John Talman (*See* note to No. 1).

3. DESIGN FOR A MONUMENT TO A DIVINE, TO BE CARRIED OUT IN BLACK AND WHITE MARBLE.

A niche-like structure, flanked by Corinthian columns and topped by a scroll-cartouche, left blank for a coat of arms. Within, an urn hung with leafy swags and supported on a tall plinth at the foot of which is the figure of the divine in a gown and bands, a book in his hand, reclining on a sarcophagus. The sides of the monument showing alternative treatments : that on the l. with a flaming urn at the top, and a weeping cherub, holding a palm-branch, seated on a volute; that on the r. with a burning lamp at the top, and a panel-trophy of books, scrolls, pens and an ink-well, on the pilaster.

Pen and brown ink with grey wash; with gold stencilled border; 36·5 × 29·5 cm. (14⅜ × 11⅝ in.).

INSCR.: *Recto*, in the upper r.-hand corner, probably by John Talman, *109*.

PROV.: John Talman (*Lugt*, No. 2462. Sale, 4–10:iv:1728, Lot 23 or 132 (?)). Richard Bull (Sale, Sotheby, 23:vi:1881, Lot 133). Purchased at the Bull Sale, through A. W. Thibaudeau, by the B.M., 1881.

1881–6–11–189 (L.B., as by William Talman, 2).

4. DESIGN FOR A MONUMENT TO A VISCOUNT, HIS WIFE AND CHILD, TO BE CARRIED OUT IN BLACK AND WHITE MARBLE.

A sarcophagus with two ledges, the upper one supporting the reclining effigy of the Viscount, the lower one that of his wife whose l. hand rests on the shoulder of her infant son, seated beside her. Behind the Viscount, a plinth supporting an urn, about which is looped a curtain falling from a canopy, topped by a Viscount's coronet and branches of palm and oak. On the front of the sarcophagus a scrolled cartouche, left blank, also surmounted by a coronet. The whole composition against a dark ground, no doubt intended for black marble, following the contours of the monument.

Plate 243

Pen and brown ink, with washes of grey and brown; with gold line border; 42 × 29·4 cm. (16½ × 11½ in.).

INSCR.: *Recto*, at the foot, the scale to which the drawing is made; and in the upper r.-hand corner, probably by John Talman, 99.

PROV.: As for No. 3.

1881–6–11–190 (L.B., as by William Talman, 3).

5. DESIGN FOR A MONUMENT TO A BISHOP, TO BE CARRIED OUT IN BLACK AND WHITE MARBLE.

An altar-like structure, backed by a reredos which is surmounted by a mitre above a shield left blank for a coat of arms. Upon the altar, a group of appropriate objects resting on a cushion, including a mitre, a skull, books, and branches of palm and laurel; and on the front, a piece of drapery intended for an inscription, backed by crossed pastoral staffs. The sides of the monument showing alternative treatments; that on the l. with a flaming urn, that on the r. with a lighted candle.

Plate 244

Pen and brown ink, with washes of brown and grey; with gold stencilled border; 37 × 28·5 cm. (14½ × 11¼ in.).

INSCR.: *Recto*, in the upper r.-hand corner, probably by John Talman, *103*.

PROV.: John Talman (*Lugt*, No. 2462. Sale, 4–10:iv:1728, Lot 23 or 132 (?)). Richard Bull (Sale, Sotheby, 23:v:1881, Lot 135). Purchased at the Bull Sale, through A. W. Thibaudeau, by the B.M., 1881.

1881–6–11–191 (L.B., as by William Talman, 4).

6. DESIGN FOR A MONUMENT TO A BISHOP, TO BE CARRIED OUT IN BLACK AND WHITE MARBLE.

A shallow urn with gadrooned sides, supported on a plinth with a stepped foot. Upon the urn, a group of appropriate objects, including a mitre, a skull, books, and branches of palm and laurel.

Plate 245

Pen and brown ink, with washes of brown and grey; with gold stencilled border; 25·1 × 22·9 cm. (9⅞ × 9 in.).

INSCR.: *Recto*, at the foot, the scale to which the drawing is made, and in the upper r.-hand corner, probably by John Talman, 7.

PROV.: As for No. 5.

1881–6–11–192 (L.B., as by William Talman, 5).

Clearly an alternative design for No. 5.

PLACE, FRANCIS

B. 1647: D. 1728

Topographical draughtsman, etcher and antiquary

Born at Dinsdale, Co. Durham, the fifth son of Rowland Place and Catherine, daughter and heiress of Charles Wise of Copgrove, Yorks. Articled in 1665 to an attorney at Gray's Inn, where his father had been admitted in 1633. Shortly afterwards the Plague offered him the excuse for leaving a profession he disliked. Subsequently settled at York, where he lived at the Manor House within the precincts of the ruins of St. Mary's Abbey. Became a member of the group of *virtuosi* of that city which included Ralph Thoresby the antiquary, William Lodge the engraver (*q.v.*), Martin Lister the physician and zoologist, Henry Gyles the glass-painter (*q.v.*), Jacques Parmentier the decorative painter, and John Lambert, amateur artist and eldest son of the Parliamentary general. Place's own antiquarian interests are evident from his work and Francis Drake, in his *Eboracum*, says that the artist supplied him with the dimensions of St. Mary's Abbey. While in London made the acquaintance of Hollar, by whose work he was greatly influenced throughout his life, though to his regret, was never actually his pupil. Is primarily regarded as an amateur, but evidently from an early date undertook professional commissions as an etcher which sometimes necessitated his presence in London. His first recorded work dates from about 1666 and, executed in collaboration with Hollar (*q.v.*), illustrates John Ogilby's English edition of Nieuhoff's *An Embassy from the East India Company to the . . . Emperour of China*, published in 1669. Also published a series of views of Greenwich Observatory and other topographical plates, together with two series of imaginary Italianate coast-scenes. Etched the plates for

his friend Martin Lister's *Godartius of Insects*, published at York in 1682, and a series of animals and birds after Barlow in collaboration with Jan Griffier (*q.v.*). A reference to his etched works occurs in a letter of 1686 to Place from Pierce Tempest, the London printseller. Considered also as one of the pioneers of mezzotint, his best plate being the portrait of Richard Tompson. Another rare plate is the mezzotint, the *Three Boers*, after Brouwer (York Art Gallery). Executed other portraits in this medium of his friends, Lodge, Lambert and Gyles. As a draughtsman worked in pen and ink occasionally washed with grey or brown and tinted in watercolour. In his more detailed topographical drawings strongly influenced by Hollar, but his freer landscape drawings show strong affinities with contemporary Netherlandish work. His treatment of light on broken masonry recalls the Roman views of Bartholomeus Breenbergh (B. 1599: D. 1659) and Thomas Wyck (B. *c.* 1616: D. 1677), and his rendering of trees and rocks is similar to that of Jan Wyck (B. *c.* 1645: D. 1702) and Anthonie Waterloo (B. 1609 or 1610: D. 1690). Many of his drawings made during long tours on foot, sometimes in company with William Lodge who like Place was a keen fisherman. Travelled in South Wales, largely Pembrokeshire, in 1678, parts of North Wales in 1699–1700, the eastern coastal areas of Ireland in 1698–9, and Scotland in 1701. Must also have visited the Low Countries, as in Sir Bruce Ingram's collection there are five drawings of the coastal areas of Antwerp and The Hague, and a number of his etched plates bear the name of Dutch publishers like Hugo Allardt, and Frederick de Witt. Later, to judge from his dated drawings, seems to have confined his travels to Yorkshire, one of his finest works being a large panoramic view of Scarborough Castle and harbour. Both Francis Drake and Ralph Thoresby in their histories of York and Leeds (*See Bibl.* below) incorporate as illustrations plates by or after Place, and Thoresby in his Diary mentions drawings executed by the artist, who accompanied him on his travels in the neighbourhood of Leeds. Place's last known drawing, of Hull, is dated 1722. Also worked in crayons, Surtees alluding in 1823 to several 'admirable' drawings in this medium then in the collection of the antiquary, George Allan of Grange. Executed crayon portraits, said to be of William Penn and his second wife Hannah, formerly in the possession of Sir Henry Havelock-Allan, Bart., and sold at Sotheby's on June 18th, 1957, Lot 434. Essentially a *virtuoso* and universally described as 'ingenious', his other activities including the manufacture of stoneware which he undertook as a paying proposition from 1683 to about 1693. Thoresby possessed one of his cups in his museum at Leeds among numerous other objects presented by Place, and another, formerly in the collection of Horace Walpole, is in the Victoria and Albert Museum. A small self-portrait in oils at Hospitalfield, Arbroath, shows the artist holding one of his cups and doubtless expresses the importance he attached to this craft.

Communicated in 1716 an invaluable account of the life of Hollar to Vertue who subsequently visited him in 1727 at York, in company with Lord Oxford. Died the following year and was buried at St. Olave's, York.

Details of the family history contained in a recently discovered notebook written by Place Parrott and Richard Parrott, grandsons of the artist. Francis Place there recorded as having been married twice, first to Mrs. Ann Wilkinson in 1693, later to Mrs. Ann Wintringham, and having had one daughter, Elizabeth, by the first, and two daughters, Ann and Frances, by the second marriage. A number of his drawings came into the possession of Wadham Wyndham who married his youngest daughter, Frances. Others passed through his second daughter, Ann, to a descendant by marriage, Patrick Allan-Fraser of Hospitalfield, Arbroath, whose collection came on to the market in 1931.

BIBL.: *Thoresby, Ducatus, passim.* Drake, pp. 331-2 & 577. *Strutt, II, pp. 232–3. Thoresby, Diary, II, pp. 170 & 174. Thoresby, Correspondence, II, p. 92. Surtees, Durham, III, p. 238. D.N.B., XLV, 1896, p. 390 (with Bibl.). Thoresby Soc., XXI, 1912, pp. 180, 215 & 221. Hake. Maher. Maher, Drogheda. T.-B., XXVII, 1933, p. 128 (with Bibl.). Vertue, Index, p. 209. Toppin. Woodward, pp. 24, 25, 26 & 53. Moorman. Williams, pp. 8–11. Lemaitre, pp. 19–21. Inf.* from Mr. P. Tomory and Mr. J. Jacob.

DRAWINGS in OTHER COLLECTIONS: Sir Bruce Ingram. Patrick Allan-Fraser, Art College, Hospitalfield, Arbroath. V. & A. M. N. M. Wales. York City Art Gallery. Mr. Leonard Duke. Mr. Iolo Williams.

[1–4]. DRAWINGS PROBABLY FROM THE SAME SKETCHBOOK. This sketchbook, with leaves measuring approximately 10 × 22.5 cm. (4 × 8¾ in.), was at some remote date dismembered, perhaps by the artist himself. The views include York, Sheriff Hutton Castle, Scarborough, Bridlington, Hull, Boston Stump, and Ely, a number of them being in circular compartments, which recall Place's etched roundels of Italian coast scenes (*Hake*, 31–55). The present circular views may also have been intended as studies for etchings, but do not appear to have been carried out as such. None of the drawings is dated so it is not possible to say when the sketchbook was in use. The fragment should, however, be compared with the complete book, recording a tour of Wales in 1678, which is in the V. & A. Museum, E 1506–1931.

1. These leaves are inlaid together, with the following drawings: (*a*) *Recto* of leaf 1, (*b*) *Verso* of leaf 1 and *Recto* of leaf 2, (*c*) *Verso* of leaf 2 and *Recto* of leaf 3, (*d*) *Verso* of leaf 3.

(*a*) A SLIGHT LANDSCAPE SKETCH.

Brush drawing in grey wash; 10·1 × 22·7 cm. (4 × 8⅞ in.).

(*b*) BARNARD CASTLE. View from the W. of the ruined Castle on its hill, l., above the Tees, which is crossed in mid-distance by a bridge with groups of houses beyond it. On the r., in a circular compartment, another and slighter view of the Castle.

Pen and brown inks, with grey wash; the slighter view in black lead; 10·1 × 22·7 cm. (4 × 8⅞ in.), and 9·5 × 21·6 cm. (3¾ × 8½ in.).

INSCR.: At the top, incorrectly, by the artist, *Baynards Castle*; beside the large square tower, *make this lower than | the round tower*, and on the Tees, *river*.

It is rather strange that Place, a north countryman, should have given this incorrect version of the place-name, *Baynards Castle*, which is actually that of the famous London river-side fortress destroyed in the Great Fire.

(*c*) THE SOUTH BLOCKHOUSE AT HULL, WITH A DISTANT PROSPECT OF THE LINCOLNSHIRE COAST. View, from the N.E. shore of the Humber, looking over the water towards the Lincolnshire coast, with vessels anchored in the estuary. In the foreground, r., the Blockhouse, on the bastion of which flies a standard.

Pen and brown ink, with washes of grey and (on the water) blue; 9·5 × 21·6 cm. (3¾ × 8½ in.), and 10·3 × 22·4 cm. (4 × 8¾ in.).

INSCR.: At the foot, *one of the Block Houses att Hull*, and above the distant coast, *Lincoln Shire*.

REPR.: *Hake*, Pl. LXXXVII (*a*) & (*b*).

(*d*) A GROUP OF SADDLED HORSES, WITHIN A CIRCULAR COMPARTMENT; AND A MAN SKETCHING.

Pen and ink, and black lead; 10·3 × 22·4 cm. (4 × 8¾ in.).

PROV.: Frances (Place) Wyndham. Wadham Wyndham (*See* No. 10). Parrott (Perrott) Family (?). W. & G. Smith, from whom it was purchased by the B.M., 1850.

1850–2–23–816*, 824, & 816 (L.B. 18, 30, 28).

2. Two leaves, inlaid together, with the following drawings: (*a*) *Verso* of leaf 1 and *Recto* of leaf 2, (*b*) *Verso* of leaf 2, (*c*) *Recto* of leaf 1. **Plate 246**

(*a*) BRIDLINGTON QUAY. View looking along the beach from the S., with the jetty running out into the sea, r. Beyond, l., on a high bank, a row of houses.

Pen and brown ink, with grey wash; 10·1 × 45 cm. (4 × 17¾ in.).

INSCR.: At the top, *Bridlington Key*.

REPR.: *Hake*, Pl. LXXXIII (*a*).

(*b*) TWO VIEWS AT YORK, IN CIR-
CULAR COMPARTMENTS. That on the l.
with the round tower of the North St.
Postern, looking N.W. across the Ouse
towards St. Mary's Tower. That on the r.,
looking N.W. towards the city, with the
Minster rising in its midst and Clifford's
Tower on the r.

Pen and ink, with slight grey wash;
$10 \times 22 \cdot 5$ cm. ($4 \times 8\frac{7}{8}$ in.).

INSCR.: Below the l.-hand compartment,
The Tower where y^e: . . . The (?) *Bote Gate at
Yorke*; below the r.-hand compartment, *Yorke
from the River ouse . . . w^{th}out Skeldergate
Posterne.*

(*c*) A GROUP OF ROCKS, WITH TWO
FIGURES SEATED AMONGST THEM.

Pen and brown ink; $10 \cdot 1 \times 22 \cdot 4$ cm.
($4 \times 8\frac{7}{8}$ in.).

PROV.: As for No. 1.
1850–2–23–808 (L.B.24).

3. Two leaves, inlaid together, with the following drawings: (*a*) *Verso* of leaf 1 and
Recto of leaf 2, (*b*) *Verso* of leaf 2, (*c*) *Recto* of leaf 1.

(*a*) DISTANT VIEW OF SCARBOROUGH.
An extensive view taken from the cliffs
S.W. of the town, which is seen in mid-
distance at the foot of the headland surmounted by the Castle. To the r., the sea,
and in the foreground, l., a man on horseback passing through a gap in a hedge.

Pen and brown ink tinted in water-
colours; $10 \times 43 \cdot 5$ cm. ($4 \times 17\frac{1}{8}$ in.).

INSCR.: At the top, by the artist, *Scarborough from . . . Burlington Rode distanc about
2 m ha* (?) (the last word illegible), with
other slight notes.

REPR.: *Rowntree*, p. 231, Fig. 68.

(*b*) DURHAM CATHEDRAL, THE S. SIDE.

Pen and ink; unfinished; $10 \times 20 \cdot 9$ cm.
($4 \times 8\frac{1}{4}$ in.).

(*c*) SHERIFF HUTTON CASTLE, AND
CLIFFORD'S TOWER, YORK. Two separate views in circular compartments. The
former, on the l., a view from the S.E.
angle of Sheriff Hutton Castle, looking S.
towards the distant city of York. The latter,
on the r., a view looking N.W. from the
bank of the Ouse, a barge in the foreground and Clifford's Tower on a mound
beyond.

Pen and black and brown inks, with grey
wash; $10 \cdot 2 \times 22 \cdot 5$ cm. ($4 \times 8\frac{7}{8}$ in.).

INSCR.: Below the l.-hand compartment,
by the artist, *Part of Sheriff . . . Hutton Castle.*

PROV.: As for No. 1.
1850–2–23–829 (L.B.25).

4. Three leaves, inlaid together, with the following drawings: (*a*) *Verso* of leaf 1 and
Recto of leaf 2, (*b*) *Verso* of leaf 2 and *Recto* of leaf 3, (*c*) *Verso* of leaf 3, (*d*) *Recto* of
leaf 1. **Plate 247 (a)**

(*a*) YORK FROM THE S.E. Views from an
open piece of ground, looking towards the
city, with the tower of Fishergate Postern
on the l., and the ruins of St. George's
Church on the r. Beyond, the following
buildings from l. to r.: Bishop Hill (St.

Mary) the Elder, Bishop Hill (St. Mary) the
Younger, York Castle, Clifford's Tower, St.
Mary's Castlegate, All Hallows, St. Samp-
son's, York Minster, and, behind St.
George's, the spire of St. Dennis's.

Pen and ink, with grey wash; $10 \cdot 1 \times 44 \cdot 5$ cm. ($4 \times 17\frac{1}{2}$ in.).

INSCR.: At the top, by the artist, *Yorke from Fisher gate Barr* (the last word substituted for *Posterne*); the principal features marked with letters referring to a key in the upper r.-hand corner, *A The castle | b bishop hill ye Lower | c bishop y.e Higher | d Clifords Tower | E S.t Maryes Castle gate | F All Hallowe, in the pauement | g S.t Samsoons | H. the Minster | I St Denis Walmgate | K christchurch | L the Ruines of S.t George | M Edwards Tower* (Fishergate Postern).

1850–2–23–834.

(*b*) ELY. Distant view of the Cathedral and city from the N., looking over fields which slope gently into the foreground.

Pen and ink with brown wash; $10 \cdot 3 \times 43 \cdot 9$ cm. ($4\frac{1}{8} \times 17\frac{1}{4}$ in.).

INSCR.: At the top, by the artist, *Elly*.

The W. tower of the Cathedral is here shown with the spire which was removed shortly before 1802.

(*c*) BOSTON STUMP, LINCOLNSHIRE. View from the W. towards Boston Church, with its lofty tower rising in the centre.

Pen and brown ink; $10 \cdot 5 \times 21 \cdot 5$ cm. ($4\frac{1}{8} \times 8\frac{5}{8}$ in.).

INSCR.: Near the tower, by the artist, *boston church*, and above the tower, *Hier* [Higher].

(*d*) VIEW OVER OPEN COUNTRY.

Pen and ink; $10 \cdot 3 \times 22 \cdot 3$ cm. ($4\frac{1}{8} \times 8\frac{7}{8}$ in.).

PROV.: As for No. 1.

1850–2–23–835 (L.B.5).

5. BERWICK CASTLE. View looking S.E. from the high ground overlooking the Tweed, which appears below in the centre, with undulating country beyond. On the l., the walls of the Castle with a square tower rising beyond them. On the r., a group of figures ascending a slope.

Pen and ink, with washes of grey and brown slightly tinted in blue; $12 \cdot 6 \times 41 \cdot 3$ cm. ($5 \times 16\frac{1}{4}$ in.).

INSCR.: *Recto*, at the foot, by the artist, *Part of Barwick castle*, and on the river, *twede*.

Verso, at the foot, in a later hand, *Part of Barwick Castle.*

PROV.: As for No. 1.

1850–2–23–807 (L.B.31).

6. BRIDLINGTON BAY. View looking N. along the curving shore, backed by cliffs on the l. On the r., a choppy sea, with various craft on it.　　**Plate 246**

Pen and brown ink, with brown wash; $15 \cdot 7 \times 40 \cdot 8$ cm. ($6\frac{1}{4} \times 16$ in.).

INSCR.: *Recto*, in the lower l.-hand corner, *By Bridlington.*

Verso, at the foot, *Bridlington Bay F Place Delin.*

PROV.: As for No. 1.

1850–2–23–809 (L.B.26).

7. *Recto*. BYLAND ABBEY. Near view from the S. of the ruins of the Dormitory, looking towards a wall pierced by windows and arches, beyond which, l., is one of the pinnacles of the W. front. In the foreground, a man seated on a bank.

Pen and ink, with grey wash; 31·3 × 19·7 cm. (12¼ × 7¾ in.).

INSCR.: At the foot, by the artist, *Part of the Ruines of Byland Abbie.*

Verso. **BYLAND ABBEY.** Near view of part of the ruins.

Washes of grey and brown, partly outlined with pen and ink.

PROV.: As for No. 1.

1850–2–23–810 (L.B.19).

INSCR.: At the foot, by the artist, *Part of the Ruines of Byland Abbie,* and in the lower l. hand corner *F P.*

8. BYLAND ABBEY. View from the interior of the Church, with part of the vaulted N. aisle on the r., and the W. front on the l.

Pen and ink over black lead, with light brown wash; 17·9 × 18 cm. (7⅛ × 7⅛ in.).

PROV.: As for No. 1.

1850–2–23–811 (L.B.20).

INSCR.: *Recto,* at the foot, by the artist, *a peece of byland Abbie 1713.*

9. CLEVELAND PORT (CARGO FLEET), YORKSHIRE. View looking over an open piece of ground, crossed by a stone wall, towards a group of buildings, with a round tower, centre, an old lighthouse (?), l., and a cottage, r. Beyond, a boat on the stocks, and in the distance, the towers of a castle. In the lower l.-hand corner, a separate sketch of a woman.

Pen and brown ink, with washes of grey and green; 22 × 33·5 cm. (8⅝ × 13⅛ in.).

INSCR.: *Recto,* by the artist, at the foot upside-down, *Cleevland*; repeated, in a later hand, at the top, *Cleeveland.*
   Verso, in the lower l.-hand corner, *F. Place delin* (probably not a signature).

PROV.: As for No. 1.
1850–2–23–812 (L.B.22).

The title of this drawing is so given on the strength of the inscription, but, as far as can be judged from the topographical details, it may well not be the correct one. There are, or were, for instance, in the neighbourhood of Cleveland Port, no important castle ruins such as appear in the distance of this view. It is also curious that the artist's original inscription, *Cleevland,* should appear upside down; this is quite out of keeping with his normal practice, and might suggest that the inscription does not refer at all to the view represented in the drawing, but to some other which may perhaps have been drawn on a conjoined sheet of paper since detached.

10. DUNSTANBURGH CASTLE. View looking E. towards the Castle, which stands on a hill, r. Below, l., cornfields, and beyond, the sea with various craft upon it.

Pen and grey and brown inks, with grey wash; 12·5 × 42·8 cm. (5 × 16⅞ in.).

INSCR.: *Recto,* at the foot, by the artist, *The Ruines of Dunstenbrough Castle in Northum-*

berland in A? *1678*, and in the lower r.-hand corner, also by the artist, *F.P.*

      Verso, in ink, in a later hand, *Bath. Jan: 11, 1762. Given me that Ev. by Wadham*

Wyndham, Esq at his own House; his Lady was Daughter to M.? Place, who made this Drawing.

PROV.: As for No. 1.

1850–2–23–813 (L.B.32).

11. EASBY ABBEY. View looking N. across the Swale towards the Abbey ruins which stand above the wooded far bank, with the Refectory prominent in the centre. Subsidiary farm buildings on the r.

Brush drawing in brown wash over black lead; on two conjoined sheets; 14·5 × 43·4 cm. (5¾ × 17⅛ in.).

INSCR.: *Recto*, at the top, by the artist, *Easby Abby . . . by Richmond*, and in the lower l.-hand corner, *Easby Abie by Richmond*.

PROV.: As for No. 1.

1850–2–23–814 (L.B.21).

12. HULL, FROM THE N.E. General prospect of the town from a stretch of open ground, crossed by a fence. On the r., the N. Blockhouse, and in the distance, the tower of Holy Trinity Church.

Pen and brown ink, with washes of brown and grey; 12·3 × 40·7 cm. (4⅞ × 16⅛ in.).

Verso, the same in a later hand, and, probably not by the artist, *F. Place delin.*

INSCR.: *Recto*, at the foot, by the artist, *Hull from Holderness side.*

PROV.: As for No. 1.

1850–2–23–815 (L.B.27).

13. *Recto*. KINGSTON BASIN, HULL. View looking N.E. across the Basin, with the town of Hull on the opposite shore, the tower of Holy Trinity Church rising in the centre, and the S. Blockhouse on the extreme r.

Pen and brown ink, with washes of grey and blue; 18·2 × 44·6 cm. (7⅛ × 17½ in.).

INSCR.: At the top, by the artist, *The South Side of Kingstone upon | Hull*; the principal

features marked with letters referring to a key, *a the Towne house | b the Light house | c the block house | D Miton Port | E Beverley Port | F the Church |.*

Verso. **SLIGHT SKETCHES OF MEN SEATED**

Pen and brown ink.

REPR.: *Hake*, Pl. LXXXIII (*b*).

PROV.: As for No. 1.

1850–2–23–817 (L.B.29).

14. KNARESBOROUGH CASTLE FROM THE S.W. View of part of the Castle ruins from below the cliff on which they stand, a pathway crossing the foreground.

Pen and brown ink, with brown wash; 17·7 × 35·6 cm. (7 × 14 in.).

PROV.: As for No. 1. 1850–2–23–818 (L.B.13).

INSCR.: *Recto*, in the lower r.-hand corner, *Part of the Ruines of Knaisborough Castle.*

15. KNARESBOROUGH CASTLE. View looking from the W. across the Nidd towards the Castle ruins which stand at the top of a high bank, the Keep prominent in the centre. Below, to the l., a water-mill, and a dam across the river. In the foreground, r., two men, one standing, the other sitting on the shore.

Pen and brown ink, with washes of brown, grey and light blue; 20·8 × 53·9 cm. (8¼ × 21⅛ in.).

PROV.: As for No. 1. 1850–2–23–819 (L.B.40).

REPR.: *Hake*, Pl. LXXXII (*b*).

INSCR.: *Recto*, at the foot, by the artist, *Part of Knaisborough Castle wth the Mills 1711,* together with other notes.

Verso, in another hand, *F Place delin.*

16. *Recto.* **KNARESBOROUGH CASTLE FROM THE S.** View from below the cliff on which stands the Castle, looking up to part of the ruins. The undulating foreground crossed by a path leading from the r.

Washes of brown and grey over black lead, partly strengthened with pen and brown ink; 19·6 × 30·7 cm. (7¾ × 12⅛ in.).

INSCR.: At the foot, by the artist, *Part of the ruines of Knaisborough Castle: 1711.*

Verso. **MILLS BELOW KNARESBOROUGH CASTLE.** View looking from the W. across the Nidd towards a water-mill and cottages on the far bank grouped at the foot of the cliff below the Castle.

Grey wash over pencil.

INSCR.: In the upper r.-hand corner, *F. Place del.* (upside down).

PROV.: As for No. 1. 1850–2–23–820 (L.B.14).

The group of buildings on the *verso* is also seen in No. 15.

17. KNARESBOROUGH CASTLE, THE KEEP. Near view of the ruins of the Keep from the S., with the foreground sloping away to the r. **Plate 250**

Pen and brown ink, with brown wash; 32·1 × 41·3 cm. (12⅝ × 16¼ in.).

INSCR.: *Recto*, in the lower l.-hand corner, by the artist, *Part of the ruines of | Knaisborough Castle |1703 | F :P :.*

Verso, in the lower l.-hand corner, by another hand, *F. Place deli.* and in the upper l.-hand corner, *92 Perrott.*

PROV.: As for No. 1. 1850–2–23–821 (L.B.15).

18. THE DROPPING WELL, KNARESBOROUGH. The steep and cavernous rock, l., in wooded surroundings, with the water dropping from it into a pool below.

Plate 251

Grey wash partly outlined with pen and brown ink; 32·4 × 40·8 cm. (12¾ × 16 in.).

INSCR.: *Recto*, at the foot, by the artist, *The Droping well Knaisborough F :P.*

Verso, in the lower l.-hand corner, by another hand, *F. Place delin* and in the upper l.-hand corner, *92 Perrott* (partly covered).

PROV.: As for No. 1.
1850–2–23–822 (L.B.16).

19. THE DROPPING WELL, KNARESEBOROUGH. View of the rock from the side opposite to that shown in No. 18, with a flight of steps on the l.

Grey wash, partly outlined with pen and brown ink; 32·1 × 40·6 cm. (12⅝ × 16 in.).

INSCR.: *Recto*, in the lower r.-hand corner, by the artist, *The Droping well Knaisborough F P.*

Verso, in the upper l.-hand corner, by another hand, *92. Perrott*, and in the lower l.-hand corner, *F Place delin.*

PROV.: As for No. 1.
1850–2–23–823 (L.B.17).

REPR.: *Hake*, Pl. LXXXI (*a*).

20. *Recto*. **MIDDLEHAM CASTLE.** View of part of the ruins, the principal feature of which is a square tower rising in the centre above a wall pierced by embrasures.

Pen and brown ink, with washes of brown and grey; 31 × 36·1 cm. (12¼ × 14⅛ in.).

INSCR.: At the foot, to the r., by the artist, *Part of the Ruines of Midlam Castle 1711*, and in the l.-hand corner, *F.P.* (probably not a signature).

Verso. **MIDDLEHAM CASTLE, A BREACH IN THE WALL.**

Pen and brown ink, with brown wash, over black lead; the drawing confined to the upper l.-hand quarter of the sheet; 18 × 15·2 cm. (7 × 6 in.).

INSCR.: At the foot, by another hand, *pt. of Midlham Castle 1711*, and in the upper r.-hand corner, *92 Perrott*, and in the lower l.-hand corner, *29/6*.

PROV.: As for No. 1.
1850–2–23–825 (L.B.39).

The drawing on the *recto* should be compared with the similar (but of course later) view engraved in Edward Dayes's *Works*, 1805, p. 104.

21. *Recto*. **PICKERING CASTLE FROM THE N.W.** View from the side of a hill looking over a small valley towards the Castle on its mound, with a road curving up to it on the r. In the foreground, on the extreme r., two men beside a tree.

Pen and brown ink, with grey wash; 20·3 × 41·1 cm. (8 × 16¼ in.).

Verso. **PART OF THE NAVE OF A CHURCH WITH A PORCHWAY.**

INSCR.: At the foot, by the artist, *Pickering Castle from Catt-gate hill 1715;* transcribed, in a later hand, at the top, *Pickering Castle from Cattgates Mill 1715;* and

in the lower l.-hand corner, in another hand, *F Place delin.* Top l. corner *Perrott.*

PROV.: As for No. 1.
1850–2–23–826 (L.B.12).

22. PART OF RICHMOND CASTLE. View, perhaps within the cockpit, looking towards a wall, pierced by a round-headed gateway and ending, l., in a quadrangular tower, perhaps that at the S.E. angle of the Castle.

Pen and brown ink, with washes of brown and grey; 14·4 × 22·4 cm. ($5\frac{5}{8}$ × $8\frac{3}{4}$ in.).

Verso, by another hand, *F. Place delin.*

INSCR.: *Recto,* by the artist, *p.t of Richmond Castle 1689* and *part of Richmond Castle.*

PROV.: As for No. 1.
1850–2–23–827 (L.B.11).

23. RICHMOND CASTLE FROM THE S.E. View from the Swale valley, with the town of Richmond set in a hollow in mid-distance, centre, and the Castle with its tall Keep crowning the hill on the r. In the foreground, l., a man standing beside his horse.

Pen and ink, with grey wash, the foliage tinted in green; 17·7 × 29·3 cm. (7 × $11\frac{1}{2}$ in.).

Verso, in a later hand, *An elegant View of Richmond Castle and | Part of the Town.*

PROV.: As for No. 1.
1850–2–23–828 (L.B.9).

INSCR.: *Recto,* at the foot, by the artist, *The South east side of Richmond Castle w.th part of the Toune in 1674.*

[24–25]. The following drawings, with views of Scarborough and Richmond Castles, are apparently from the same sketchbook, with leaves measuring approximately 11.5 × 22 cm. ($4\frac{1}{2}$ × $8\frac{3}{4}$ in.), which at some remote date was dismembered, perhaps by the artist himself.

24. SCARBOROUGH CASTLE, FROM THE N.W. General prospect of the Castle on its rocky headland, with the Keep rising in the centre. On the l., a glimpse of the sea.

Pen and light brown ink, with washes of light brown and grey, over black lead; on two conjoined leaves; 11 × 42·1 cm. ($4\frac{3}{8}$ × $16\frac{5}{8}$ in.).

PROV.: As for No. 1.
1850–2–23–830 (L.B.23).

REPR.: *Hake,* Pl. LXXXII (*a*).

INSCR.: *Recto,* at the foot on the r., by the artist, *Scarborough Castle from the Nor West.*

25. Three leaves, inlaid together, with the following drawings: (*a*) *Recto* of leaf 1, (*b*) *Verso* of leaf 1 and *Recto* of leaf 2, (*c*) *Verso* of leaf 2 and *Recto* of leaf 3, (*d*) *Verso* of leaf 3.

(*a*) VIEW OF A SEAPORT. Slight sketch.

Black lead; 11·5 × 22 cm. (4½ × 8¾ in.).

(*b*) SCARBOROUGH CASTLE, FROM THE S.W. General prospect of the Castle on its rocky headland, with the sea to the r.

Pen and light brown ink, with light brown wash; 11·5 × 44·8 cm. (4½ × 17⅝ in.).

INSCR.: At the foot, by the artist, *Scarborough Castle West Side*.

(*c*) RICHMOND CASTLE, FROM THE S.W. General prospect of the Castle from nearby, with the Keep rising on the l., and the ground sloping away to the r.

Pen and light brown ink, with light brown wash, over black lead; 11·3 × 44·1 cm. (4⅜ × 17⅜ in.).

INSCR.: At the foot, by the artist, *Richmond Castle* [repeated at the top in black lead].

A more finished version by Place of this view is in Sir William Worsley's collection.

(*d*) VIEW OVERLOOKING A BAY. Slight sketch, with indications of figures.

Black lead, touched with pen and brown ink; 11·3 × 21·5 cm. (4½ × 8½ in.).

PROV.: As for No. 1.

1850–2–23–831 (L.B.10, only the view of Richmond Castle being described).

26. TYNEMOUTH LIGHTHOUSE, PRIORY, AND CASTLE FROM THE N. View from the shore looking towards a line of cliffs, at the top of which are, from l. to r., the Lighthouse, the ruins of the Priory, and the Castle. To the l., the sea.

Pen and ink, with grey wash, the grass at the top of the cliffs tinted in greenish yellow; 16·7 × 47·5 cm. (6⅝ × 18¾ in.).

INSCR.: *Recto*, the top, by the artist, *Tinmouth Castle & Lighthouse*, continued by Ralph Thoresby, *by the Ingenious M.* *Francis Place*; and at the foot, by the artist, *Fra Place Fecit*.

PROV.: Thoresby (Sale, Whiston Bristow, 77:iii:1764, Lot 66 (?)). Purchased by the B.M. from E. Daniell, 1866, with three drawings by William Lodge (*q.v.*) also from Thoresby's coll., 1866.

1866–11–14–679 (L.B.33).

BIBL.: *Thoresby, Ducatus*, p. 497.

27. YORK FROM ST. GEORGE'S CLOSE. General prospect of the city, looking N.W. from without the walls. From l. to r. can be seen the following buildings: the spire of St. Martin's Micklegate, the spire of All Saints', the Council Chamber, St. Olave's, St. Martin's Coney St., St. Michael's, Clifford's Tower with the Castle Mills below it, York Castle with the spire of St. Mary's and York Minister beyond and the Sessions House to the r., St. Saviour's, Fishergate Postern, the spire of St. Dennis's, Fishergate Bar, and St. Margaret's. The undulating fields of St. George's Close in the foreground, with a clump of willows on the l., and a man and woman standing on the r. **Plate 247**

Pen and grey and brown inks, the foreground being tinted in pale green; on two conjoined sheets; 17·4 × 75 cm. (6⅞ × 29½ in.).

INSCR.: *Recto*, at the top, *York S.E. by S.*

PROV.: As for No. 1.

1850–2–23–837 (L.B.2).

28. *Recto.* YORK, FROM WITHOUT CASTLEGATE POSTERN.

View on the Ouse, looking N.W. At some distance away on the r., York Minster, Clifford's Tower, York Castle and the Prison. In the centre, the tower of St. Michael's. To the l., the spire of All Saints', the Ouse Bridge with the Council Chamber, and the tower of St. Martin's Coney St. In the foreground, men fishing from the river bank, and further off, other figures drying linen.

Pen and light brown ink, with light brown wash over black lead; 16·1 × 30·7 cm. (6⅜ × 12⅛ in.).

Verso. SLIGHT SKETCH OF TWO ANGLERS.

Pen and brown ink.

INSCR.: In the lower l.-hand corner, not by the artist, *Place delin*; at the foot, in the centre, by the artist, *York from without Castle Gate postern*; in the upper r.-hand corner, in a later hand, *4 Yo* (partly cut away).

PROV.: As for No. 1.

1850–2–23–833 (L.B.1).

29. YORK, FROM OPPOSITE ST. MARY'S TOWER.

View looking N.E. across the Ouse. On the opposite bunk, from l. to r., St. Olave's, St. Mary's tower, St. Mary's Abbey, the Manor Yard, and in the centre, York Minster.

Pen and ink over black lead, the r.-hand half unfinished; 12·9 × 40·6 cm. (5 × 16 in.).

INSCR.: *Verso*, in the upper r.-hand corner, *N⁰ 1 York.*

PROV.: As for No. 1.

1850–2–23–832 (L.B.4).

30. YORK FROM ST. MARY'S TOWER.

View looking S.E. along the Ouse, with St. Mary's tower in the foreground, l. In the centre, a barge on the river being towed towards the city, where the following buildings are seen from l. to r.: the Water Tower, the Guildhall, St. Martin's Coney St., All Hallows, North St. Postern, the spire of St. Mary's, St. Michael's, All Saints', spire of St. Martin's Micklegate.

Pen and ink, with grey wash, the roofs of the houses and some other features tinted in reddish-brown wash; on two conjoined leaves; 10 × 44·9 cm. (3⅞ × 17¾ in.).

INSCR.: *Recto*, at the top, by the artist, *York from beyond the water Tower at Sᵗ Maryes*; the church spires and towers and other buildings marked with letters referring to a key in the upper r.-hand corner, *A Sᵗ Martins coney Streete | b All hallowes pavement | c the water Tower | d Sᵗ Maryes castle gate | E Sᵗ*

Michaels | F All S^{ts}_. :Streete | g S^t_. Mar : Mic : gate | H the common Hall. | ; and, below, stone wall.

PROV.: As for No. 1.
1850–2–23–834 (L.B.3).

ETCH.: The l.-hand half of this drawing probably used as a study for the view of York etched by the artist (*Hake,* 17), which later appeared as an illustration to *Drake,* p. 33.

Cf. No 29 which is a view taken from the opposite bank of the river, looking E. towards St. Mary's tower.

31. YORK, ST. MARY'S ABBEY. View looking N.E. across the Ouse, with various craft on it, towards the opposite bank where stand the Abbey ruins and St. Olave's Church at the top of rising ground, and the Manor Yard and St. Mary's tower on the l.

Pen and brown ink, with grey wash; 18·9 × 31·3 cm. (7½ × 12⅜ in.).

INSCR.: *Recto,* at the top, *Prospect of S^t_. Mary's Abby near York.*
Verso, in the upper r.-hand corner,

eight lines erased and now almost illegible and in the lower r.-hand corner, by the artist, *No. 6 Sep 4* [16] *98.*

PROV.: As for No. 1.
1850–2–23–841 (L.B.8).

32. YORK FROM THE S.W.; VIEW FROM SKELDERGATE POSTERN. View from the r. bank of the Ouse, looking across the river, with an extensive prospect of the city on the far side. From l. to r., the following landmarks: the Ouse Bridge with the Council House, St. Martin's Coney St., St. Michael's, York Minster, All Hallows, St. Mary's Castlegate, Clifford's Tower, the Castle Mills, York Castle, St. Dennis's, and Fishergate Postern. In the foreground, r., the prow of a boat.

Plate 248

Pen and ink, with washes of grey and brown; 22 × 56·9 cm. (8¾ × 22⅜ in.).

INSCR.: *Recto,* at the foot, by the artist, *A View of York from without Skeldergate postern,* and the principal features marked with letters referring to a key in the upper r.-hand corner, *A The Minster | b all Hallowes | c St Maryes Castle gate | d S^t_. Michael's | S^t_. Martin's | F S^t_. LLoyd | & the Common hall | G Clifords tower | H y^e_. Castle | J S^t_. Denis | K*

ows Bridge | 1 Edwards tower | m. Skeldergate Posterne | n Castlegate Posterne | P part of y^e_. Mannor.
Verso, in the lower l.-hand corner, *F. Place delin.* (not a signature), and in the upper l.-hand corner, *92 Perrott,* and in the upper r.-hand corner, *No. 7 York.*

PROV.: As for No. 1.
1850–2–23–836 (L.B.37).

33. YORK, THE OUSE BRIDGE. Near view of the Bridge from mid-stream, looking S., showing the houses, l., and the Council Chamber, r., built over the side arches.

Pen and brown ink, with washes of brown and grey; on two conjoined sheets; 11·7 × 29·6 cm. (4⅝ × 11¾ in.).

INSCR.: *Recto,* at the top, by the artist, *Ous Bridg York 1703. Between the Butments or first Spring of the Arch 83½ Feet or 27⅔ yards.*

PROV.: As for No. 1.   REPR.: *Hake*, Pl. LXXXI (*b*).
1850–2–23–839 (L.B.6).

34. YORK, THE OUSE BRIDGE. Near view of the Bridge, looking S., with the
main arch, l., and the Council Chamber built over the side arches, r.   **Plate 252**

Pen and ink, with grey wash; 21·8 × 27·9   *Verso*, in a later hand, *York N° 6*
cm. (8⅜ × 11 in.).   *Ousebridge* and *R. Perrott*.

INSCR.: *Recto*, below the main arch, by the   PROV.: As for No. 1.
artist, *bring the Arch Lower*.   1850–2–23–840 (L.B.7).

35. YORK, VIEW FROM CLIFFORD'S TOWER. View looking S.E. over York
Castle towards a wide expanse of country through which winds the Ouse from
the r., with Fulford Chapel on its bank in mid-distance, and further off, the village
of Fulford itself.   In the foreground, the Castle Yard enclosing, from l. to r., the
Sessions House, the Prison, and the Jury House. Below, to the r., the Castle Mills.
                                                                        Plate 249

Pen and brown ink, with brown wash, tinted   *Dutch super (?) Royall and french are 26 In^{ches}*
in water-colour; on three conjoined sheets;   *and a ½ and 18 : High* (probably a reference to
27·1 × 61·2 cm. (10⅝ × 24¼ in.).   sizes of paper); in a later hand, not by the
                                                  artist, *F Place delin*, and in yet another hand,
INSCR.: *Recto*, by the artist, with place   *N° 8 York Castle*.
names and other notes.
        Verso, by the artist, *York Castle as* PROV.: As for No. 1.
It appears from Cliffords Tower An^o/1710, and 1850–2–23–838 (L.B.38).

36. A ROCKY ISLAND. View across a stretch of water, with ships lying at anchor,
towards the island formed of two precipitous rocks, one seen beyond the other to
the l. On the island, a few buildings including a bastion at the water's edge, r. In the
foreground, l., a small cliff with a boat moored by it.

Pen and brown ink, with grey wash, on buff-   etched 'Series of Italian Views' (*Hake* 24–9).
toned paper; 12·7 × 22·7 cm. (5 × 8⅞ in.).   One of these (*Hake* 27) shows a rocky island,
                                                  the outline of which is not unlike that of the
PROV.: As for No. 1.   one seen in the present drawing. Place is not
1850–2–23–843 (L.B.34).   known to have visited the Mediterranean,
                                                  and it is probable that he was inspired in
This is almost certainly an imaginary sub-   these particular subjects by contemporary
ject, and in style is connected with Place's   Continental masters.

37. *Recto.* **STUDIES OF THE FEMALE COMMON MALLARD** (*Anas
platyrhyncha*). Seven studies of heads in various positions.

Pen and brown ink, with brown wash;   INSCR.: In the lower r.-hand corner, not
20 × 31·7 cm. (7⅞ × 12½ in.).   by the artist, *F. Place*.

Verso. **TWO STUDIES OF THE COMMON MALLARD.** One of the head in profile to l., the other a slight sketch of the bird floating on water.

Pen and brown ink, with brown wash.

INSCR.: In the lower l.-hand corner, not by the artist, *F. P. delin.*

PROV.: William Wells (Christie, 22:i:1857, Lot 361). Purchased at the Wells Sale by the B.M., 1857.

1857–1–10–26 (L.B.35).

38. STUDIES OF WATERFOWL. The heads of the following, from l. to r.: the Common Mallard (*Anas platyrhyncha*), the Red-breasted Merganser (*Mergus serrator*), and above, the Common Scoter (*Melanitta nigra*). **Plate 253**

Pen and brown ink, with grey wash, tinted in water-colours; 20·2 × 31·9 cm. (8 × 12½ in.).

INSCR.: *Recto*, by the artist, above the mallard, *The head of a Mallard*, beside the Merganser, *The head of a | fishing fowle*, below the Scoter, *The black diver or Scoter w^{ce} is discrib'd | in M^r. Willoghbys booke this was | Kild upon Ous 170⅞ the whole | body is black feete and all*; in the lower r.-hand corner, not by the artist, *F. Place.*

PROV.: As for No. 37.

1857–1–10–27 (L.B.36).

The inscription below the Scoter refers to Francis Willughby's *Ornithologiae Libri Tres*, 1676 (English edn. 1678), where the bird is described on pp. 280–1 and illustrated in Pl. LXXIV.

RILEY, JOHN

[RYLEY, ROILY, ROYLE]

B. 1646: D. 1691

Portrait painter

Born, according to Vertue, in the parish of St. Botolph's, Bishopsgate, though the registers of that church do not record this. Son of John Riley (not Thomas Riley, as Walpole supposed). The elder Jonathan Richardson, whom Vertue quotes, says that the artist first took lessons from the Westphalian portraitist, Gerard Soest (D. 1681) and from Isaac Fuller (*q.v.*), but left them while still young and 'began to practisse after the Life'. His reputation not fully established until after Lely's death in 1680 when he was introduced to Charles II by William Chiffinch (Closet Keeper to Charles II) whose portrait he had painted. On Sept. 15th, 1682, was given the freedom of the Painter-Stainers' Company 'by redemption', which suggests that by then he had arrived at some standing in his craft. Made no concessions to fashionable taste, 'studying Life rather than following any particular Manner,' a judgment in keeping with Charles II's famous remark on seeing Riley's portrait of him, 'Is this like me? Then oddsfish, I am an ugly fellow.' His best portraits were in fact of humble subjects like the *The Scullion* (Christ Church, Oxford), James II's housemaid, *Bridget Holmes* (1686; Windsor Castle) and *Mrs. Elliot*, a nurse of the royal household (c. 1690; Kensington Palace). Was a member of St. Luke's Club, one of the earliest and best-known of artists' societies. In Dec. 1688, was appointed jointly with Kneller (q.v.) Principal Painter to William and Mary. Though he enjoyed some aristocratic patronage, never achieved the popularity of his German colleague, perhaps because of his unfashionable preference for 'realistic' portraiture. Worked with John Baptist Closterman (q.v.), normally painting the heads while his partner undertook the draperies and 'postures'. His pupils included Anthony Russell (B. 1663 (?): D.1742), another of Vertue's informants, Edward Gouge (fl. 1715) and of greater importance, Thomas Murray (B. 1663: D. 1734) and the elder Jonathan Richardson (B. 1665: D. 1745) who formed a link between Riley and Hudson, the first master of Reynolds. Bequeathed to Richardson (who married his niece and managed the family affairs after his death) paintings and drawings to the value of '7 or 800 [pounds]'. Richardson also drew Riley's portrait (B.M.) in black lead on vellum and that of Jochebed Riley

(B.M.), probably the artist's stepmother, since she was only eleven years old at the time of his birth. Died on March 27th, 1691, at his house in the parish of St. Giles, and was buried on March 30th, at St. Botolph's, Bishopsgate. His brother Thomas Riley (See note to No. 1 below) whom Vertue also mentions as an artist, died the same year.

Only one drawing (No. 1 below) can with any certainty be attributed to the artist, although the Nude Man (Oppé collection) is by tradition given to Riley. Chalk drawings of female heads (V. & A. and Sir Bruce Ingram) which have been attributed to Riley are more probably by Michael Dahl (q.v.).

BIBL.: Will, P.C.C., 71 (Vere), P.S. Min., Sept. 15th, 1682. St. Botolph's, Bishopsgate, Register, II, 1893. Baker, Lely, II, pp. 20–33. T.-B., XXVIII, 1934, with Bibl. to that date. Vertue, Index, p. 222. Woodward, pp. 35 & 40. Waterhouse, pp. 88, 96–7, 100, 105 and 128.

1. PORTRAIT OF A MAN, PERHAPS THOMAS RILEY. Head alone, turned half-r., bearded, and wearing a broad-brimmed hat turned up on one side. Plate 260

Black chalk, heightened with white chalk, on light buff paper; 24·5 × 17·6 cm. (9⅝ × 6⅞ in.).

INSCR.: Verso, in the lower r.-hand corner, Mr Tho. Riley, and at the top, C.11. On one side of a slip cut from the old mount, in the handwriting of Horace Walpole, by J. Riley; on the other, in a later hand, John Riley B. 1646 D. 1691 / Purchased at Strawberry Hill Sale 1842 / The words 'by J Riley' are in the hand-writing of Horace Walpole / B.D. [Dr. Barry Delany], and again B.D.

PROV.: Horace Walpole (Sale, Robins, 23:vi:1842, Lot 1266, No. 60). Purchased by Henry Graves & Co. at the Walpole Sale. Dr. B. Delany (Sale, Sotheby, 5:vi:1872,

Lot 105). E. Daniell, from whom it was purchased by the B.M., 1872.
1872–10–12–3383 (L.B.1).

The inscription on the verso of the drawing suggests that this may be a portrait of Thomas Riley, mentioned in the artist's will as being his brother, and also described as such by Cust (D.N.B., XLVIII, 1896, p. 307). He may be identified with the Thomas Riley who was buried, 12:x:1691, aged 43, at St. Botolph's, Bishopsgate, where (as mentioned above) John Riley himself was interred. The drawing, however, may perhaps represent an older man than Thomas Riley could have been at the time of its making. Cust also states that Thomas Riley was an actor, and presumably was prompted in this by Walpole's footnote (*Anecdotes*, ed. Wornum, 1862, Vol. II, p. 606): 'One Thomas Riley was an actor, and has a copy of verses addressed to him in Randolph's poems. This might be the painter's father. In the same place are some Latin verses by Riley, whom I take to be the painter himself.' These two sets of verses are actually prefixed to Thomas Randolph's comedy, *The Jealous Lovers*, 1632, pp. vii & xii (reprinted at the end of the 3rd edn. of his *Poems*, 1640–3, pp. vii & xii); the first (p. vii) is addressed by Randolph '*To his deare Friend*, Thomas Riley'; the second (p. xii), a Latin poem of ten hendeca-syllabic lines, is addressed to 'Randolpho suo' by 'Thom. Riley'. The writer of the article on Randolph in the *D.N.B.* (XLVII, 1896, p. 282) refers to this Thomas Riley as a member of Trinity College, and a friend of the poet's. He would appear to have been an amateur rather than a professional actor, and probably took part in the original production of *The Jealous Lovers*, which, according to the title-page of the play, was 'presented to their gracious Majesties at CAMBRIDGE by the Students of Trinity-Colledge'. Walpole's suppositions, therefore, are completely groundless: the painter's father was not named Thomas, so he cannot be identified with Randolph's friend; the set of Latin verses is signed by Thomas not John Riley; and in any case neither the painter nor his brother Thomas could have been concerned with these verses, published as they were some 14–16 years before either was born.

ROUSSEAU, JACQUES

B. 1630: D. 1693

Landscape painter

Born in Paris of a Protestant family. Not known where he received his earliest training. Went to Rome and there met the Dutch landscapist Herman van Swanevelt whose sister he married. Perfected himself in landscape under Swanevelt's guidance and became an accomplished painter of ruin-pieces and perspectives. After his return to France was admitted to the Académie on Sept. 2nd, 1662, with the special permission of the King, which was necessary on account of his religion. Was employed at the Hotel Lambert in Paris, where he decorated the walls of the gallery with a series of upright landscapes (still extant), at Versailles, where he painted two perspectives in the Salle de Venus (still extant), and at Marly, where he painted a perspective on a wall joining the outlying pavilions and an order of corinthian pilasters, trophies and devises on the exterior of the main building (all destroyed). Through the revocation of the Edict of Nantes 1685 was compelled to abandon this last mentioned work, which was completed by his pupil, Philippe Meusnier. On leaving France, first went to Switzerland, then to Holland and finally to England, where he entered the service of the Duke of Montague who employed him at Montague House and settled on him a pension of £200 a year. Was responsible for the landscape and architecture in the wall painting on the staircase and in the saloon there, the figures being by Charles Delafesse and Jacques Parmentier. During his stay in England 'further improved himself in the study of landskip, and added beautiful groups of trees to the many drafts he made after nature, in several parts of this kingdom' (*Buckeridge*). Three pictures, probably all landscapes, bought from him by William III in 1693 for £100. Other pictures of ruin-pieces, also no doubt painted for

William III, still appearing as over-doors in the King's First and Second Presence Chambers at Hampton Court. Etched a number of landscapes from designs by Annibale Carracci and by himself. Lived till the year of his death in Soho Sq., and was buried in the neighbouring church of St. Anne, Dec. 22nd, 1693. Was described by Parmentier to Vertue as 'a tall lusty Man, of stately carriage, regular, very honest, but a little reserv'd'. Was also of a most charitable disposition and bequeathed almost all his fortune to the poor of the French Protestant church in England.

BIBL.: *St. Anne's Burial Register* (*inf.* from Mr. G. F. Osborn). *Versailles & Marly*, pp. 36 & 364–5. Buckeridge, pp. 416–17. Bickham, *Deliciae*, pp. 75–6 (as by Rosso Fiorentino!). Dezallier, *Environs*, pp. 64–149. Martyn, I, p. 45. *Beauties of England*, I, p. 102. Scharf, *Watercolours*. T.-B., XXIX, 1935, pp. 113–14. Wren Soc., VI, p. 778. Vertue, II, pp. 21, 85; III, 23–4; IV, pp. 43, 74–5. *Vertue, Index*, p. 226.

1. LANDSCAPE WITH A DISTANT LAKE. View from a wooded dell looking out through a gap in the trees towards a stretch of water. In mid-distance, a tower on a spit of land, and beyond, a range of hills. **Plate 254**

Pen and ink with grey wash; 18·3 × 29·2 cm. (7$\frac{1}{8}$ × 11$\frac{1}{2}$ in.). Old mount, 30·7 × 41·4 cm. (12$\frac{1}{8}$ × 16$\frac{1}{4}$ in.).

PROV.: Jonathan Richardson II (*Lugt*, No. 2170. Sale, Langford, 5–13:ii:1772 (?)).

Maj. Gen. Sir Willoughby Rooke. The Rev. Willoughby Rooke. J. E. Rooke. Miss Muriel H. Williams, from whom it was purchased by the B.M., 1927.

1927–4–11–8.

RUPERT, PRINCE PALATINE OF THE RHINE
B. 1619: D. 1682
Amateur draughtsman, etcher and engraver in mezzotint

Born at Prague, 3rd son of Frederick V, King of Bohemia and Elector Palatine, and Elizabeth, daughter of James I of England. After Frederick's overthrow by the imperial forces in 1620, went into exile with the rest of the family at the Hague. On March 16th, 1628, matriculated at the University of Leyden, and may have attended there the lectures of Franciscus van Schooten, professor of mathematics and military architecture, and an amateur draughtsman. Is recorded by his sister Sophie in her memoirs as developing a talent for drawing by this time, and may have been taught by Gerard van Honthorst, who according to Buckeridge, gave lessons to the ex-Queen Elizabeth and her children, besides painting their portraits. Another member of the family, Rupert's sister Louise, also showed some skill as a painter. Came to England with his elder brother, Prince Charles Louis in 1636, and on that occasion Van Dyck painted his portrait. At Archbishop Laud's suggestion made, with his brother, M.A. of Oxford, and entered in the books of St. John's College. During the next two years, campaigned with the Elector Palatine's army in Westphalia, being accompanied, probably as military draughtsman, at the siege of Breda in 1637, by the Sienese Giuliano Periccioli, who had previously in

England acted as drawing master to Prince Charles (later Charles II) and had designed scenery for the court masques. In 1638 was taken prisoner at the Battle of Vlotho, and during a three years' captivity at Linz is supposed to have spent much of his time in practising drawing. By this time was also executing etchings in the manner of Callot, one of them being dated 1636, and another (described by Andresen) bearing the inscription, *Daz hat Pfalzgraf Rub. in seinem Arrest zu Linz gradirt*. Returned to England at the outbreak of the Civil War (1642) to take up his commission as General of the King's Horse and after the defeat of the royal cause followed the Court into exile at St. Germain. The theory that he learnt the secret of mezzotint from Ludwig von Siegen (B. 1609: D. 1680) in 1654 when resident in Brussels is derived from Leon Laborde's *Histoire de la gravure en manière noire*, 1839 (pp. 85–6). But no evidence that Rupert was in Brussels in that year. References in letters to William VI of Hesse-Cassel and in particular passages in a MS. (Christ Church, Oxford) of John Evelyn (*q.v.*) provide evidence that Rupert at least invented the rocker. His claim to be the inventor of mezzotint, put forward by Evelyn, is, to judge from his extant plates, probably stronger than that of von Siegen. Among the 17 plates recorded as by or attributed to Rupert are the self-portrait after Titian (inscribed *ANNO 1657 Wien*), the *Great Executioner* after Ribera (1658; Altere Pinakothek, Munich), probably executed at Frankfurt, and *The Standard Bearer* after Pietro della Vecchia (previously at the Schönborn Gallery, Vienna). Met in 1658 the Dutch artist Wallerant Vaillant (B. 1623: D. 1677) to whom he revealed the new process and whom he probably brought to England after the Restoration. Was the pioneer of mezzotint in this country, and became the master of William Sherwin who in 1669 dedicated a portrait of Charles II to Rupert in this medium. In 1663 showed his process (together with a contrivance for drawing buildings in perspective) to the French traveller Balthasar de Monconys then on a visit to London. In addition to his naval and political duties played a prominent part in the intellectual and artistic life of his time, and became a founder member of the Royal Society in 1660. Another artist under his patronage was the Frenchman Lefèvre (whether Rolland [B. 1608: D. 1677] or Valentine [B. 1642: D. 1682] is not clear), who, according to Vertue, 'had a Particular Excellence in staining Marble'. Vertue also records 'a piece of Marble in a frame' of the *Woman taken in Adultery*, mentioned by same authority as 'curiously painted and stained by Pr. Rupert' and doubtless executed under Lefèvre's influence. Sat to the leading portraitists of the time: Dobson, Walker, Lely (*q.v.*), Michael Wright, and Kneller (*q.v.*). His portrait by the first mentioned was engraved by William Faithorne (*q.v.*) who styled himself 'painter to Prince Rupert'. In 1668 became Constable of Windsor Castle (an office held until his death), establishing there a laboratory where he engaged in scientific experiments largely concerned with the improvement of guns, firearms and ammunition. Few of his drawings now known. In the sales (1739–41) of the collection of the painter Charles Jervas were 'some small figures drawn loosely with the pen', inscribed *dessinati per il principe Ruberto a Londra, 23 Septembro*.

Bequeathed part of his collection of pictures, including paintings by Van Dyck, Honthorst, and Lely, to his natural daughter Ruperta, later the wife of General Howe, Envoy Extraordinary to the Court of Hanover. Vertue notes that these were sold by public auction after her death in 1740, but no catalogue recorded.

BIBL.: Evelyn MS., No. 52, *ff*. 307–8. *Azzolini*, Pt. II, pp. 388–90. *Monconys*, Pt. II, pp. 79–80. *Strutt*, II, pp. 283–4. *Walpole*, III, pp. 922–6. *Chaloner Smith*, I, pp. xxvi–xxx, & IV, pp. 1772–5. D.N.B., XLIX,

1897, pp. 405–17 (with *Bibl.*). *Hauck, passim. Evelyn, Sculptura,* pp. 130–1. *Russell,* pp. 20, 130, 323. *Hind, Studies,* VI. *T.-B.,* XXIX, 1935, pp. 214–15 (with *Bibl.*). *Inf.* from Miss Orovida Pissarro.

DRAWINGS IN OTHER COLLECTIONS: Mr. John Evelyn.

1. A MORTAR MOUNTED ON A BOAT. A small vessel with beak-shaped prow to r. on which is mounted a mortar with a man attending it. On the l., three other men, two of whom are rowing, and on the prow to the r. of the mortar, a fifth standing with a staff in his hand. At the top, a cross-section of the mortar loaded with grape-shot and powder. **Plate 256**

Pen and brown wash over black lead; 17·1 × 18·6 cm. (6¾ × 7⅜ in.).

INSCR.: *Verso,* in the lower r.-hand corner, *P. Rupert.*

PROV.: Hugh Howard. Dr. Robert Howard (Bishop of Elphin). The Earls of

Wicklow. Charles Howard, 5th Earl, from whom it was purchased by the B.M., 1874.
1874–8–8–2273 (L.B.1).

The vessel represented is of the Mediterranean galley type. The mortar is the common chambered type in use since Elizabethan times.

2. STUDIES OF HEADS. Thirteen studies of male and female heads, the bust of a young man with flowing hair, and a small sketch of a pikeman marching towards the l. **Plate 256**

Pen and brown ink; 15 × 19 cm. (5⅞ × 7½ in.).

INSCR.: *Recto,* with the address, *ffor his Highness Prince Rupert* (being part of a letter or a packet addressed to the Prince).

PROV.: As for No. 1.
1874–8–8–2274 (L.B.2).

3. LANDSCAPE. On the l., a road between two trees, with a woman and a boy on it. In the background r., a building with a square tower. **Plate 257**

Black lead, the l.-hand section tinted with brown; 7 × 13·9 cm. (2¾ × 5½ in.); old mount; 14·5 × 21·2 cm. (5¾ × 8⅜ in.).

INSCR.: *Recto,* in the l.-hand tree, by the artist, *Rp.* below a coronet; on the old mount at the foot, by Jonathan Richardson I, *Prince Rupert.*
Verso, on the old mount, probably by Richardson, with inventory marks (?).

PROV.: Jonathan Richardson I (*Lugt.,* No. 2184. Sale, Cock, 10:ii:1746/7, Lot 44). Sir Edward Marsh, by whom it was bequeathed to the B.M., through the N.A.C.F., 1953.
1953–5–9–1.

Probably a sketch for an etching.

SIBERECHTS, JAN

[SYBRECHTS]

B. 1627: D. c. 1700

Landscape painter and draughtsman

Born in Antwerp and baptized on Jan. 29th, 1627, the son of Jan Siberechts, sculptor, and Susanna Mennens. Nothing definite known of his early training as a painter. By some authorities thought to have visited Italy between 1645 and 1648, though no documentary evidence of this. Became a member of the Antwerp Guild of St. Luke between Sept. 18th, 1648, and Sept. 17th, 1649. Married Maria Anna Croes on Aug. 2nd, 1652, their two daughters, Susanna Maria and Catherine Françoise, being baptized in 1653 and 1655. Is said to have been brought to England by George Villiers, 2nd Duke of Buckingham, who had been impressed by Siberecht's landscapes which he saw in Antwerp on his way home from an embassy to France in 1670. Was still living with his wife and family in Antwerp in 1672, but was probably in England by 1674 when he painted the *Coach and Six Horses* (considered to be an English type of vehicle) now at Squerryes Court. In 1677 painted the view from Richmond Hill, the first of many representations of this classic scene, now at Easton Neston. Of all the XVII c. Netherlandish landscapists to come here, perhaps the one who most appreciated the English countryside, this being especially noticeable in his water-colours of views near Chatsworth in the B.M. (*See* No. 2), the Whitworth Gallery at Manchester and in the Rijksmuseum at Amsterdam. The drawing at Manchester, signed *Wooten & Sybrecht*, and the fact that the figures in this drawing are by the same hand as those in No. 2 appears to establish a link between Siberechts and John Wootton (B. 1682 (?): D. 1765), the sporting artist. By May 14th, 1687, was definitely established in London when he signed a procuration for some inheritance which fell due in Antwerp. Buckeridge states that he stayed with the Duke of Buckingham 'and he did a great Number of those Pictures for him at *Cliveden* House. However, after three or four years stay with him, he left him and perform'd several Pieces for the nobility and gentry of *England*, among whom he was for some time in vogue'. In Holland had specialized in the painting of pastoral and *genre* scenes in the manner of Berchem and Waterloo. Subsequently in England would have used this style when executing quasi-decorative paintings which he was occasionally called upon to do. Captain William Winde (*q.v.*) writing to Lady Bridgeman about the decorations at Castle Bromwich remarked: 'If instead of ye Historiacal picture of M^r La Gerre (for an overdoor) y^r Ladp should be pleased to have a Landscap of Mr Syberechts but I prefer M^r La Gerres desine [as] moore proper for ye place'. Vertue, who had no high opinion of Siberechts's ability said that the landscapes done by him for the Duke of Portland were 'not much esteemed —or valued I suppose done for furniture' and recorded 'at Cheveley a Seat of the late Ld Dovers built about 1680. many picturesque landskips, Views, over doores chimneys in the house painted by Sebright. Wyke.' In a more individual style also painted prospects of English country houses and widely viewed landscapes; in this manner are the bird's-eye views of Longleat, Wollaton, Bayhall, Nannau Hall (1696) and Clevely. In 1698 painted a view of Henley and in 1699 of the Peak in Derbyshire, the latter being his last recorded picture, and the date, that of a drawing also of the Peak (Rijksmuseum, Amsterdam). In the 'Schedule of the receipts and payments by Henry Guy Esq., for the secret services of his late Majesty Charles II and the late King James II successively between Lady Day 1679 and Christmas day 1688' is a payment of £28 4s. od. 'To *John Sibrechte* in full of two bills (as is supposed) for the linnens sold by his [younger] daughter Francis [*sic* for Françoise] Quellin, Viz. £12 11s. 6d. for the Children of the Chappell delivered to Mrs. Bradcourt and £15 12s. 6d. for the use of the Chappell.' From this it seems probable that Frances married firstly the sculptor Artus Quellin III

(B. 1653: D. 1686) and secondly Quellin's foreman Jan Van Ost (or Nost). Buckeridge writing in 1706 states that Siberechts died 'about three Years ago in *London*, and lies Bury'd in St. James's Church [Piccadilly], being 73 Years old'. This statement not confirmed, however, by the registers of that church, and Siberecht's name not yet traced in any other London burial registers consulted.

BIBL.: *Buckeridge*, p. 421. *Grant*, I, p. 16, & III, Pl. 1. *Fokker. T.-B.*, XXX, 1936, p. 579. *Wren Soc.*, VII, p. 131. *Vertue, Index*, p. 239.

1. A FELLED TREE.

A leafless tree on the bank of a lake in which stand two cows and a sheep. Beyond the lake, undulating parkland. **Plate 258**

Black lead, water-colours and body-colours; 16·6 × 40·1 cm. (6½ × 15¾ in.).

PROV.: J. C. Blofeld, from whom it was purchased by the B.M. 1909.
1909–4–6–8.

BIBL. & REPR.: *Blofeld Cat.* ('A very curious drawing by Sybrecht of a cut down tree and castle'). *Hind, Dutch & Flemish Drawings*, II, p. 131, Pl. LXVII. *Fokker*, p. 112.

2. VIEW OF BEELEY, NEAR CHATSWORTH.

A river bordered by trees running through undulating fields and wooded hills into the distance. In the middle distance, l., the village of Beeley and in the foreground, r., a man and a woman on horseback and two men on foot, one with two dogs. **Plate 259**

Water-colours and body-colours touched with white; 28·5 × 45·5 cm. (11¼ × 17¾ in.).

INSCR.: *Recto*, along the top '*Bely in darbyshair 22 Augusti 1694 J. Sybrecht. f.*'

PROV.: William Harris, 6th Earl of Malmesbury (Sale, Christie, 21:iv:1950, Lot 102). H. M. Calmann from whom it was purchased by the B.M., 1952.
1952–4–5–10.

The figures in the above drawing may be by the young John Wootton (*See* biography above). A similar drawing at the Rijksmuseum, Amsterdam, inscribed *By Chatworth/in Derbyshire* is also dated 1694.

TALMAN, JOHN

B. 1677: D. 1726

Architect, collector and antiquarian draughtsman

Born in London in 1677, the eldest son of the architect William Talman (B. 1650: D. 1719). Nothing known of upbringing or education. Was in Holland and Germany sketching landscapes in 1698 and probably made his first visit to Italy at about this time. Between 1705 and 1708 was in London and Norfolk (where his father leased the manor of Ranworth) drawing medieval and Jacobean monuments. In 1707 made proposals in a letter to Thomas Madox for a society of *virtuosi* realised ten years later in the Society of Antiquaries of which he was the first president. In 1708 made alternative designs for rebuilding All Souls College in Italian Gothic or Classical style, and presented a design for paving the dome area of St. Paul's in coloured marbles. Left for Italy with William Kent in July 1709. After a perilous voyage they reached Gibraltar in September and Leghorn in October. After a few weeks in Pisa, went to Florence and thence to Rome in April 1710. In Pisa and Florence commissioned artists including Agostino Cornacchini (B. 1685: D. 1740), Giovanni Casini (B. 1689: D. 1748) Santi Santucci (*Fl.* 1713), Francesco Bartoli (B. 1675: D. *c.* 1730) and Giuseppe Grisoni (B. 1699: D. 1769) with whom he returned to England, to make drawings for him of architecture, church ornaments and regalia. Negotiated the sale of the drawings collected by Padre Resta, from the Cav. Marchetti to Lord Somers, and acted as an amateur dealer in prints and drawings. De La Mottraye, in his *Travels,* gives an account of Talman in Rome. In 1713 his father petitioned for the restitution of the Comptrollership of the Works, stating that 'Yr. petr. has made, and is still Collecting by his son abroad, the most valuable Collection of Books, Prints, Drawings &c, as is in any one person's hands in Europe, as all the artists in Towne well know, and your petr. has kept his son abroad these seven years [*sic*] to view the most famous buildings in Italy . . . .' Returned home in 1715. Married Frances Cockayn of Hinxworth, Herts. in 1718 and the next year made his Will providing for his burial in Hinxworth church. Presumably returned to Italy and made drawings in Venice in 1719. On Jan. 7th, 1724/5 a description of the Talman collection was given to the Spalding Gentlemen's Society. Began the sale of his collection in 1725. Died on Nov. 3rd, 1726, and was buried as he had directed. The remainder of his collection, containing over 1600 architectural drawings alone, was dispersed at a sale in April, 1727 (*Daily Journal,* 25:iv:1727). Two volumes are in B.M. In his early landscapes (at the R.I.B.A.) showed great delicacy of feeling under the influence of Hollar. For the antiquarian drawings used a strong, sketchy technique. His fondness for coloured drawings is illustrated in the interior of Norwich Cathedral (Society of Antiquaries) and a church in Gibraltar (Witt Library) as in his designs incorporating coloured marble. Showed remarkable interest in Byzantine art. Designed fantastic buildings, the most interesting being the West front of a Cathedral in Italian Baroque.

BIBL.: *Talman-Aldrich, passim. D.N.B.,* LV, 1898, p. 351. *T.-B.,* XXXII, 1938, p. 418. *Wren Soc., Index,* p. 222. *Vertue, Index,* p. 256.

DRAWINGS IN OTHER COLLECTIONS: The Society of Antiquaries. R.I.B.A. Library. V. & A. M. Witt Library. Worcester Coll., Oxford. Mr. Iolo Williams.

1. DUCAL CROWN OF VENICE. A red *cornu* of the traditional form worn by the Doge, with gold embroidered border.

Water-colours heightened with gold; $31 \cdot 9 \times 23 \cdot 5$ cm. ($12\frac{1}{2} \times 9\frac{1}{4}$ in.).

INSCR.: *Recto*, at the foot, by the artist, *The Horn or Crown w:^{ch} y^e Doge of Venice weareth on less Solemn occasions, | as in Time of Lent, . . . and in a later hand, J. Talman, del: 1719.*

PROV.: John Talman. F. Harvey, from whom it was purchased by the B.M., 1893. 1893–4–11–10–12 (L.B.1).

It would appear that this drawing was made on Talman's last visit to Italy. It, and No. 2, are mounted in a volume which contains coloured drawings of regalia and ecclesiastical vestments by Francesco Bartoli (Bertoli) and Giuseppe Grisoni.

2. COIF WORN BY THE DOGE OF VENICE. The simple cambric cap worn underneath the *cornu*.

Pen and brown ink, with blue wash; $33 \cdot 3 \times 29 \cdot 5$ cm. ($13\frac{1}{8} \times 11\frac{3}{4}$ in.).

INSCR.: *Recto*, at the foot, by the artist, *A Coif of very fine Cambrick which ye Doge of Venice | weareth under his Crown, and I. Talman delin. 1719.*

PROV.: A for No. 1. 1893–4–11–10–14.

3. THE SANDAL OF ST. BERNARD. A cloth sandal with a thick sole, decorated with palmette ornament.

Pen and brown ink, with washes of brown, red and blue; $21 \cdot 7 \times 34 \cdot 8$ cm. ($8\frac{1}{2} \times 13\frac{3}{4}$ in.).

INSCR.: *Recto*, at the toe of the shoe, by the artist, *J: Talman delin. 1719.*, and at the bottom, also by the artist, *The Sandal which S$^{t.}$ Bernard, Abbot of Valombrosa in Tuscany, used when he celebrated | Mass; it is kept in ye Treasury of y^e said Abby; it is adorned with gilt leather layd on Silk of divers | colours, y^e Sole is very thick of cork & covered with flowered Silk; y^e upper part is tyed with latchets of red ruban.*

PROV.: Sir Hans Sloane, Bart., by whom it was bequeathed to the B.M., 1753. Transferred from the Dept. of MSS., 1928. 5239–45. 1928–3–10–91–45.

In the V. & A. M. (E.79–185–1940) there is a small sketch in pen and ink of this shoe, also by John Talman, inscribed, *Sandalo pontificale di St Bernardo Abbato di Vallambrosa.*

THRUMTON OR THRUMPTON, T.

Working 1667–73

Portrait draughtsman in crayons

No biographical details known, except through the three recorded drawings signed by him, from which it may be seen that he worked in London between 1667 and 1673. The sheet of accomplished studies in the Ashmolean Museum, Oxford, with the heads of a young man and Mary Carleton, dated *1667*, has certain affinities with Lely's portrait-drawings in crayons. Thrumton's other recorded drawings are less sensitive in handling; and apparently characteristic of them is the use of black wash to strengthen the shadows. A mezzotint portrait of *Georg, Lord Palmer*, lettered *T. Th. . . . ton Pinx* and *W. Sherwin fec*, is described by Russell (*See Bibl.*) as perhaps after Thrumton.

BIBL.: Bell, *Portrait Drawings*, pp. 6–8. Russell, II, p. 252, No. 1059. *Baker and Constable*, p. 54, Pl. 68. *B.F.A.C.*, p. 52.

DRAWINGS IN OTHER COLLECTIONS: List in *B.F.A.C.*

1. PORTRAIT OF A LADY. Bust, turned half-l., with eyes looking to front. Brown hair with corkscrew curl falling on either shoulder. Wearing a pearl necklace and earring, and a brown low-necked dress with blue-green drapery. Dark grey background. **Plate 261**

Crayons, strengthened, with black wash, over pencil; 27·7 × 22·7 cm. (10⅞ × 8⅞ in.).

PROV.: E. Denney, from whom it was purchased by the B.M., 1936. **1936–7–2–1.**

INSCR.: *Recto*, on the l., by the artist, *Trumpton* (or *Frumpton*) *Fe | Londini 1672 | Thrumpton;* the beginning of each line damaged and retouched.

TILSON, HENRY

B. 1659: D. 1695

Portrait painter and draughtsman in crayons

Born, according to Buckeridge, in London but this contradicted by Vertue's account (compiled from information given to him by the artist Thomas Hill (B. 1661: D. 1734)), which states that he was born in Yorkshire. Son of Nathaniel Tilson of Rochdale, Yorks., and grandson of Henry Tilson, Bishop of Elphin (B. 1576: D. 1655). Studied under Lely (*q.v.*) and was considered one of his most promising pupils, lodging with him until his death in 1680. Appears also to have worked with Kneller, in whose studio he met the Swedish portraitist, Michael Dahl (*q.v.*), a joint production of these three painters being a portrait of Margaret Brownlow at Belton. Went with Dahl to Italy via Paris, in 1685, and visited Venice, Florence and finally Rome where during the year 1686/7 painted a small portrait in oils of the Hon. Thomas Arundel and drew in crayons the head of the scientist and heretic, Giuseppe Francesco Borri (Hansteen coll., Oslo), besides making crayon copies of works by Correggio, Titian and the Carracci. Vertue mentions a self-portrait 'with a pencil in his hand leaning on a bust' dated 1687. Also noted by Vertue is the artist's portrait by Dahl, dated 1686, and another of him in the possession of 'Mr. Armstrong Painter' (Vertue). Returned to England by way of Germany about 1678/9. At first found difficulty in renewing his connexions. Was paid £12 for a drawing (now lost) of Dr. Richard Busby, the famous headmaster of Westminster, from which it seems probable that Robert White executed his engraving. His *Sir William Dolben* (Guildhall) close in style to Dahl. A whole group of posthumous portraits (at Westminster School, Christ Church, Oxford, and the N.P.G.), at least one of which is attributed to Dahl, may also have been based on Tilson's drawing. Eventually found a patron in a certain Mrs. Green, 'a woman of great wealth & Interest [who] . . . recommended Mr. Tilson every where and procurd him a deal of Business'. Tilson conceived a passion for her which induced in him a state of melancholy. In return for the gift of his self-portrait, she gave him some embroidered caps and 'some curious Indian hankerchiefs', which in his madness he interpreted as meaning that the caps were 'to put over his eyes' while he hanged himself with the handkerchiefs. Despite all efforts 'to get him in company to move this Frenzy', one day 'retird into his Closett & with a pistol shot [himself] thro' the heart . . . to the great regret of his Friends & the surprise of his Patroness who suspected nothing of his concerns'. At the time of his suicide lived in Portugal Row in Lincoln's Inn Fields. Appears in the Burial Register of St. Giles-in-the-Fields for Nov. 25th, 1695, as 'Mr. Henry Tilson carried away' (i.e. his body was transferred for burial elsewhere). Was, as Vertue states, buried at St. Dunstans-in-the-West, on Nov. 25th (the name spelt in the register, ffilson), not at St. Clement Danes as Buckeridge supposed. Vertue writes that 'he had particular genius for Crayons, in which he perform'd admirably well'. His few surviving works in this medium show a use of colour nearer to the later manner of crayon drawing developed by Edmund Ashfield (q.v.) than to that of his master, Lely. Dr. Barry Delany owned a portrait by Tilson of 'Thomas Turner Esq. in crayons, fine' (Sotheby, 5:vii:1872, Lot 134). The Armstrong mentioned above, perhaps Tilson's pupil, may be identified with Nicholas Armstrong, apprenticed in 1671 to one William Mills, and with a draughtsman of that name, author of a group of crayon portraits at Narford Hall.

BIBL.: St. Giles-in-the-Fields, Burial Register. St. Dunstans-in-the-West, Burial Register. B.M. Lansdowne MS., No. 655, f. 29. Buckeridge, p. 426. D.N.B., LVI, 1898, pp. 400–401. Poole, Oxford Portraits, III, 1898, pp. 35–7. T.-B., XXXIII, 1939, p. 173 (with Bibl.). Nisser, passim. Vertue, Index, p. 260. Woodward, p. 35. Waterhouse, pp. 73, 101, 102, 103. Inf. (concerning portraits at Westminster School) from Mr. John Carleton.

1. A LADY. Bust, turned half-l., with eyes to front, her right hand to her breast. Wearing her hair loose on her shoulders, and a low-necked dress with drapery shaded in red. Light green background.   **Plate 262**

Black chalk and crayons, rather rubbed; on buff paper; made up at the four corners; 26·8 × 20 cm. (10⅝ × 8 in.).

INSCR.: Recto, in the lower l.-hand corner, by the artist, *H T* (monogram) *ilson* (almost obliterated) / *1683*.
Verso, in another hand, presumably transcribing the other, *H. Tilson* / *1683*.

PROV.: C. H. Collins Baker, from whom it was purchased by the B.M., through the H. L. Florence Fund, 1934.

1934–7–10–3.

BIBL. & REPR.: Baker, Tilson, passim. Woodward, p. 35.

2. A LADY. Bust, turned half l., with eyes looking to front and dark brown hair falling in a long curl on her l. shoulder. Wearing a blue scarf over a purple low-necked dress with scalloped sleeves. Brown background within a feigned oval.   **Plate 263**

Crayons; $25 \cdot 6 \times 19 \cdot 9$ cm. ($10\frac{1}{8} \times 7\frac{3}{4}$ in.).

PROV.: Mrs. C. Stuart Bunning, from whom it was purchased by the B.M., 1955. 1955-3-15-3.

3. *Recto.* A NUDE WOMAN SEATED, AND ANOTHER FIGURE.

Red chalk on blue-grey paper; $24 \cdot 8 \times 19 \cdot 5$ cm. ($9\frac{3}{4} \times 7\frac{5}{8}$ in.).

Verso. A PAINTER'S PALETTE AND BRUSHES, AND A KNIFE.

Red Chalk.

PROV.: As for No. 2.
1955-3-15-4.

Both very roughly sketched, and used as backing to No. 2.

4. A DEMON OR SATYR.

Red chalk on blue-grey paper; $23 \cdot 4 \times 18$ cm. ($9\frac{1}{4} \times 7\frac{1}{8}$ in.).

PROV.: As for No. 2.
1955-3-15-5.

INSCR.: *Verso*, in red chalk, by the artist, *May Y^e 3^d 1679 | H T | 1679 | 2001 | London H.*

Very roughly sketched, like No. 3, and used as backing to No. 2. The above inscription has suggested the attribution to Tilson of these drawings.

TOUROUDE, MICHEL

[TOURARDE]

Fl. 1678

History and decorative painter

Of French or Flemish origin. Recorded as one of the assistant-painters working under Antonio Verrio (*q.v.*) at Windsor Castle, 1678.

BIBL.: *C.S.P. Dom., Addenda, 1678,* p. 525.

1. DESIGN FOR THE FRONTISPIECE TO SOME HISTORICAL WORK.

History seated at a table writing, and Time standing on her l., pointing to a globe. Above, Fame blowing her trumpet.

Plate 255

Red chalk with grey wash; $15 \times 9 \cdot 3$ cm. ($5\frac{7}{8} \times 3\frac{5}{8}$ in.).

ENGR.: By Pierre Vandrebanc (Pieter van der Banck), with the lettering *Touroude de . . . Vandrebanc fe.*

PROV.: Iolo Williams, by whom it was presented to the B.M., 1954.
1954-4-27-5.

The book has not so far been identified. It is interesting to note that Van der Banck also engraved three of Verrio's Windsor ceilings.

VAN DER MEULEN, PIETER

[Vandemeulen, Mulen]

B. 1638: D. after 1685 (?)

Battle and landscape painter

Born in Brussels in 1638, and baptized on April 28th at the church of St. Nicholas. Younger son of Pieter van der Meulen and Marie Stocmans, and brother of Louis XIV's battle painter Adam François van der Meulen. Settled in Paris where he lived in the rue de la Reale. Aug. 15th, 1653, became apprenticed to his brother, in whose steps he followed as a painter of battle and hunting subjects. Married firstly (in Flanders (?)) Marie van Snelleghem, by whom he had a daughter Madeleine (later the wife of the Flemish landscape and battle painter Frans Dominic Nollet). Married secondly, in Paris, Marie Bachelier, by whom he had a son François (B. 1664) and a daughter Catharine (B. 1665). Is said by his earliest English biographer, 'J.B.', to have 'applied himself to sculpture, in which he distinguished himself', and to have brought 'his wife with him to England in 1670, where he continued several years with Peter van Bloemen [battle and animal painter] and Largilière [Nicolas de Largillière, the portraitist]'. This mention of him as a sculptor perhaps indicates a confusion (also made by other authorities) with Laurens van der Meulen of Malines (B. 1645: D. 1719), a carver who is known to have been an assistant to Grinling Gibbons in 1678. The alleged date of his arrival here, 1670, also doubtful, as he is known to have been present in Paris in 1671 at the burial of one of the children of his brother Adam François, while Largillière was not in England till 1674–8. His portrait painted by Largillière and engraved in mezzotint by Isaac Beckett, on which he is definitely described as *Pictor*. Is recorded in the Minutes of the Painter-Stainers' Company, under Sept. 13th, 1682, when as 'Mr. Peter Vandemeulen' he was 'admitted as a fforeigne Brother . . . and promised a proofe peice'. According to Walpole (who does not quote his authority) was employed by William III in painting battle subjects, and would therefore have practised in his brother's manner here, along with other battle painters such as Dirk Maas, Jan Wyck (q.v.), Johan Vanderhagen (tapestries in the Bank of Ireland, Dublin), Louis Laguerre (q.v.; Marlborough's victories at Marlborough House), and the anonymous masters of the painted staircase at Charlcote Park, the Siege of Namur at Hawkstone Park, and the series of Marlborough's victories formerly at Tewin Water. According to 'J.B.' probably died in England.

BIBL.: *Painter-Stainers' Minutes*, II, p. 272. *J.B.*, p. 108. *Walpole*, II, p. 608. *Immerzeel*, p. 222. *C. S.*, I, p. 52, No. 95. *B.N.*, *Belgique*, XIV, pp. 692–3. *T.-B.*, XXIV, 1930, p. 452. *Vertue, Index*, p. 266.

1. **A GENERAL RIDING OVER A BATTLEFIELD.** In the foreground men and horses lying dead or dying. Beyond them mounted men, in armour, among them the general and his standard bearer. On a hill, l., a castle. On a plain below, r., the remains of a body of men and transport moving away towards a distant town. **Plate 268**

Pen and brown ink over black chalk outlines, with grey wash; 25·5 × 42·2 cm. (10 × 16⅝ in.).

PROV.: E. Daniell, from whom it was purchased by the B.M., 1876.
1876–7–8–2382.

VAN DER VAART, JAN

B. 1647: D. 1727

Landscape, portrait and still-life painter, mezzotint engraver

Born in Haarlem in 1647. Said by Vertue to have studied under Thomas Wyck in England but as Wyck's only recorded visit was in 1666/7 it is more probable that he received his artistic education in Holland. Came to England in 1674 and settled in London. Painted drapery for William Wissing (*q.v.*) some of whose portraits he engraved in mezzotint. After Wissing's death worked as a portrait-painter on his own. Painted imaginary Italianate landscapes (at least one of which was engraved in mezzotint). Also enjoyed a reputation as a painter of still-life, Vertue recording that he had done 'very surprizing pictures of dead pa[r]tridges that have deceiv'd the sight being so naturally painted that the picture has not been known from ye bird itself. & fiddles he has painted so deceivingly to ye eye, that all who have seen them were surprizd. The Duke of Devonshire has one done by him in his collection that is finely done.' Subsequently, owing to failing eyesight, gave up portraiture. In 1713 sold off his pictures and bought a house in Covent Garden where he lived until his death, still painting a little, but working mainly as a picture restorer, which, according to Vertue, proved a lucrative occupation. He was 'imployed by most of the great people that collect paintings, haveing great prices & thereby profitted more at the latter end of his time than any other wayes'. Is traditionally said to have instructed John Smith in the art of mezzotint engraving. Died in 1727 (not 1721 as stated by most authorities) and was buried on March 30th of that year at St.

Paul's, Covent Garden, 'in ye South isle in ye Church under the Pews no. 17 & 18'. Vertue's obituary of him says: 'he was of an affable good temper, quiet an easy, very regular & sober a Man inoffensive generally vallu'd and esteemd by all his profession no wayes ostentatious a constant labourouror to his last & tho a man of an abstemious constitution was now and then afflicted with the gout but of a Gentle feavour after two or three weeks illness he dyd a batchelor of a good age'. In his Will, made on Feb. 18th, 1727, and proved on March 29th, bequeathed some £1200 to various relatives, friends and servants, and the residue of his property to his nephew and executor, 'John Arnold alias Spornevelt' who is described by Vertue as a 'painter who had livd with him between thirty & forty years'. Other legatees included Sarah Arnold and Sebastian Spornevelt, respectively sister and half-brother to John Arnold, and 'Sybil Kerseboom, spinster', presumably a relative of one of the painters of that name. Portraits by Van der Vaart are in the Guildhall Library (William III and Mary), at Burghley House (Lady Williams represented as the Magdalene), Wilton House (Margaret Sawyer, Countess of Pembroke) and Squerryes Court, Kent (Mr. and Mrs. Warde, 1715) where there are also two landscapes by him. Painted the drapery for Wissing's portrait of Princess, later Queen, Anne (N.P.G., Edinburgh) and Frances Teresa Stuart, Duchess of Lennox. With J. Kerseboom, painted a full length portrait of the Duke of Leeds in 1704 (property of H.M. Ministry of Works). Also executed the *trompe l'œil* of a fiddle hanging on a door of the State Music Room at Chatsworth.

BIBL.: *D.N.B.*, LVIII, 1899, p. 103. *St. Paul's, Covent Garden, Register*, 1908, p. 300. *T.-B.*, XXXIV, 1940, p. 20. *Vertue, Index*, p. 267. *Thompson, Chatsworth*, p. 156.

1. LANDSCAPE WITH A QUARRY. View from near a path leading down into a quarry on the far side of which, at the top, stands a small house. In the foreground, r., a mass of rock, and in the distance, l., a mountain. **Plate 265**

Brush drawing in grey and light brown over black lead; on two conjoined sheets, perhaps from a sketch book; 30·8 × 41·2 cm. (12⅛ × 16⅛ in.).

PROV.: Hugh Howard. Dr. Robert Howard (Bishop of Elphin). The Earls of Wicklow. Charles Howard, 5th Earl, from whom it was purchased by the B.M., 1874. 1874–8–8–90 (L.B.1).

2. FRAGMENT OF A SKETCHBOOK. Now containing 11 leaves, filled with landscape studies, which in handling resemble very closely No. 1 above.

20·5 × 14 cm. (8 × 5½ in.).

f. 1r.

INSCR.: In the upper r.-hand corner, *Min. 37* (the number struck out); further down, in another hand, *Bibliothecae Sloanianae Min: 259.* and *114* (struck out); and still further down, on a separate slip of paper, in yet another hand, *Min. 259 | Several views done | with Indian Ink.*

ff. 1v. & 2r. VIEW AT THE FOOT OF A ROCKY HILL WHICH DESCENDS FROM R. TO L.
  Brush drawing in washes of grey and light brown.

  INSCR.: Paginated in the upper r.-hand corner of *f.* 2r., *8.*

ff. 2v. & 3r. VIEW FROM THE SIDE OF A HILL LOOKING OVER UNDULATING AND WOODED COUNTRY.
  Brush drawing in grey wash.

  INSCR.: Paginated in the upper r.-hand corner of *f.* 3r., *9.*

ff. 3v. & 4r. VIEW FROM THE FOOT OF A ROCKY HILL. A rocky hill descending from the l., overlooking a river which curves away to the r., passing a castle with boats moored beside it.
  Brush drawing in grey wash, touched with light brown.

  INSCR.: Paginated in the upper r.-hand corner of *f.* 4r., *10.*

ff. 4v. & 5r. ROCKY CLIFFS WITH AN INLET OF THE SEA ON THE R.
  Brush drawing in washes of light brown and grey.

  INSCR.: Paginated in the upper r.-hand corner of *f.* 5r., *11.*

ff. 5v. & 6r. A RIVER SCENE. View from midstream, looking towards a wooded bank, against which boats are moored. On the r., a fortified wall.
  Brush drawing in grey wash.

  INSCR.: Paginated in the upper r.-hand corner of *f.* 6r., *12.*

f. 6v. BLANK.

f. 7r. A PONTOON BRIDGE SPANNING A RIVER, WITH A PARTLY WOODED BANK IN THE BACKGROUND.
Brush drawing in grey wash.

INSCR.: Paginated in the upper r.-hand corner, *13.*

ff. 7v. & 8r. PARTLY RUINED FORTIFICATIONS ON A RIVER BANK, WITH A GATE IN THE DISTANCE, R., APPROACHED BY A BRIDGE.
Brush drawing in grey wash.

INSCR.: Paginated in the upper r.-hand corner of 8r., *14.*

f. 8v. BLANK.

f. 9r. A RUINED BASTION RISING FROM A DITCH, WITH A DRAWBRIDGE ON THE R., AND A TOWER IN THE DISTANCE.
Brush drawing in grey wash.

INSCR.: Paginated in the upper r.-hand corner, *15.*

ff. 9v. & 10r. SPUR OF A ROCKY HILL DESCENDING FROM THE R., WITH A VIEW OVER HILLY AND WOODED COUNTRY TO THE L.
Brush drawing in washes of grey and brown.

INSCR.: Paginated in the upper r.-hand corner of *f. 10r.*, *16.*

f. 10v. BLANK.

f. 11r. A STEEP AND ROCKY HILLSIDE.
Brush drawing in washes of grey and brown.

INSCR.: Paginated in the upper r.-hand corner, *17.*

f. 11v. VIEW LOOKING ACROSS A VALLEY TOWARDS A STEEP AND ROCKY HILLSIDE, PARTLY COVERED WITH TREES.
Brush drawing in washes of grey and brown.

PROV.: Sir Hans Sloane, Bart., by whom it was bequeathed to the B.M., Dept. of MSS., 1753. Formerly bound with a sketch-book with drawings in red chalk by William Courten or Charleton (Sloane MS. 5251) from which it was separated when transferred to the Dept. of Prints and Drawings, 1928.
1928–3–10–93

VAN DE VELDE, WILLEM I

B. 1611: D. 1693

Marine painter and draughtsman

Born at Leiden, the son of a sea-captain of Flemish origin. Vertue says that he was the brother of Cornelis van de Velde, also a maritime painter, but the relationship of the latter to him uncertain. Probably accompanied his father to sea on the expedition to Grave in 1622. Married in 1631, in Leiden, Judith van Leeurven, who became the mother of William the younger (*See* p. 488). Moved to Amsterdam some time before the birth of his second son Adriaen in 1635, his career as a maritime painter probably beginning about this time. Not known whether he studied under any master. By 1639 was of sufficient eminence for one of his compositions of a sea battle to appear under a portrait of Admiral

Marten Tromp, engraved by C. van Dalen, together with one by his close friend, Simon de Vlieger (B. *c.* 1600: D. 1653). No evidence, however, that the latter influenced his work. After 1634 carried out fairly regular commissions for the Dutch navy, and was recognized as the foremost marine draughtsman of his day. In 1653 officially described as 'Draughtsman of the fleet', being given the use of a galliot by the Dutch Admiralties, and from this time began to make his characteristic sequences of panoramic drawings of actions and other events 'by way of a journal'. Was present at many of the important naval battles of the Anglo-Dutch Wars, including Scheveningen (1653), the Sound (1658), Lowestoft (1665), The Four Days (1666), and Solebay (1672). Spent the periods between these expeditions in his studio, chiefly on paintings in monochrome (*grisailles*). His patrons included not only the Dutch Admiralties and private individuals in Holland, but also such distinguished foreigners as Ferdinand II, Grand Duke of Tuscany. In 1660 accompanied the Restoration squadron to England, where he received gifts from Charles II. Thirteen years later, during the French invasion of Holland, was forced to leave his country for England, where he arrived, probably in the winter of 1672/3, and found immediate favour at Court. Was granted £100 from the King in 1674 for 'taking and making drafts of sea-fights' and was given the use of a ketch by the English Admiralty. Together with Willem the younger, made his studio in the Queen's House, Greenwich, which may subsequently have become his residence. Carried out in England the same kind of commissions as in Holland, including 'journal' drawings of such events as Mary of Modena's progress from Calais to London (1673), the voyage to Holland of Princess Mary and William of Orange after their marriage (1677), and,

outside his normal subject matter, the military reviews on Hounslow Heath (1687–8, Boymans Museum). Continued to receive a royal pension up to the Revolution. In 1691 moved to Sackville Street, where he died two years later. Was buried in St. James's, Piccadilly, on Dec. 16th, 1693.

Was an accomplished and painstaking draughtsman and, Vertue says, always used, when working in his studio, the replica of a ship as a model. His earliest known drawings, dating from about 1638, are executed in pen and ink, frequently on vellum, and anticipate in technique his *grisailles* or monochrome drawings in pen or brush on white prepared grounds of canvas or panel, a medium first used by Hendrik Goltzius. Later developed a characteristic style, suited to his need for taking rapid notes of naval engagements while at sea, with outlines of black chalk or black lead, afterwards strengthened with broad grey washes. Still occasionally used detailed pen-work in his more finished drawings, such as the designs for the Texel and Solebay tapestries, and the series connected with the journey of William of Orange and Princess Mary to Holland. Made frequent use of offsets from his own drawings, probably as a means of correcting details, and taking copies in reverse of compositions.

BIBL.: *Buckeridge*, pp. 431–2. *T.-B.*, XXXIV, 1940, p. 203 (with *Bibl.*). *Vertue*, *Index*, p. 265. *Williams*, pp. 11, 167 and 197–200. *Robinson*, pp. 3–15. *Inf.* from Mr. M. S. Robinson.

DRAWINGS IN OTHER COLLECTIONS: Sir Bruce Ingram, whose collection with a few exceptions has been added to that of the National Maritime Museum. V. & A. M. Rijksmuseum, Amsterdam. Boymans Museum, Rotterdam.

VAN DE VELDE, WILLEM II

B. 1633: D. 1707
Marine painter and draughtsman

Born in Amsterdam, the eldest son of Willem van de Velde, the elder (*q.v.*), and brother of Adriaen van de Velde (B. before 1635: D. 1672). For a brief period was perhaps a pupil of his father's friend, Simon de Vlieger (B. *c.* 1600: D. 1653). Married on March 23rd, 1652, in Amsterdam, Petronella la Maire, from whom, however, he separated in the following year. Married his second wife, Magdalena Walraven four years later. From the beginning of his career worked closely with his father, though it is unlikely that he accompanied him to sea on the earlier expeditions with the Dutch fleet in the 1660's, and must thus have relied entirely on his father's material for his own versions of naval exploits at this time. Probably came to England with the elder Willem late in 1672, and in 1674 received from the King, together with his father, a warrant for £100 for putting 'the said drafts [of his father's sea-fights] into colours'. Was also associated with his father in the production of tapestry designs and portraits of individual ships. As a painter in oils was certainly the more accomplished artist of the two, Vertue rating him as the best painter of sea pieces in England and probably in Europe. As a draughtsman is difficult to distinguish from his father at this period, especially as there is evidence that he frequently worked on the latter's drawings and offsets. Subsequently, from about 1685, developed a use of pen and brown ink outline peculiarly his own. Visited Holland in 1686 when he executed the picture of the shipping in the Y (Rijksmuseum) for the harbour-master's room at Amsterdam. An order of 1694 refers to him for the first time officially as 'Draughtsman to the British fleet' but few drawings survive from his two expeditions to Spain in that and the following year. His last drawing is dated 1707, the year of his death at Millbank (?) where he had owned a house since the previous year which passed to his son-in-law, John Burgess. Was buried on April 11th at the same church as his father, St. James's, Piccadilly. Had two sons, Willem—also a marine painter who copied his father's work and died after 1708 in Holland—and Cornelis or Cornelius who married at Knightsbridge Chapel on August 8th, 1699, Bernarda van der Hagen, the daughter of an artist. A third child, Sarah, married as her second husband Simon Du Bois, the artist (*q.v.*) and later the John Burgess mentioned above. Vertue records her as owning several portraits of the Van de Velde family.

The Van de Veldes, more especially the younger, much influenced the later XVIII c. school of English marine draughtsmen, in particular Dominic Serres and his son, John Thomas Serres.

BIBL.: *T.-B.*, XXXIV, 1940, pp. 203–4 (with *Bibl.*). *Vertue, Index*, p. 265. *Williams*, pp. 11, 167 & 197–200 *Robinson*, pp. 3–17. *Inf.* from Mr. M. S. Robinson.

DRAWINGS IN OTHER COLLECTIONS: *See* Van de Velde, I, p. 487.

[1–57]. HISTORICAL EVENTS AND DATED DRAWINGS. The following are listed in the order of events and are mounted in three albums. Drawings made up to the year 1672, while the Van de Veldes were still in Dutch service, are dated in the catalogue entries according to the New Style Calendar (where the New Year begins on January 1st), which had already come into force in Holland. After 1672, when the artists had come to England, they are dated according to the Old Style (where the New Year began on March 25th), which was still used in England at that time, there being ten days difference between the two calendars.

1. DUTCH SHIPS IN THE CHANNEL BETWEEN THE HELDER AND TEXEL, 1643.

Black chalk and black lead, with grey wash; 23·7 × 79 cm. (9½ × 31¼ in.).

INSCR.: *Recto*, in the upper l.-hand corner, *ind't Helder en Tessel 1643* [within the Helder and Texel 1643]; and in the lower l.-hand corner, in black lead, *28*.

PROV.: William Courten (?). Sir Hans Sloane, Bart., by whom it was bequeathed to the B.M., 1753.

5214–53 (L.B., Van de Velde I, 1).

BIBL.: *Sloane Cat.*, p. 134, No. 53.

By W. Van de Velde I.

2. THE DUTCH FLEET LYING AT ANCHOR BEFORE TERSCHELLING, OCT. 1658.

Offset from black chalk (?), with grey wash, strengthened with black lead; on three conjoined sheets; 23 × 107·3 cm. (9⅛ × 42¾ in.).

INSCR.: *Recto*, in the upper l.-hand corner, by W. Van de Velde II, *1658 d state floot, die naer denmerka gingh uit assistensie van d coningh van denmerke,* [1658 the States fleet which went to Denmark to the assistance of the King of Denmark]; and in the upper r.-hand corner, in black lead, *t Leggen voor der schellng* [lying before Terschelling].

PROV.: E. Daniell, from whom it was purchased by the B.M., 1877.

1877–10–13–976* (L.B., Van de Velde I, 25 (2)).

BIBL.: *Van Rijsewijk*, I, p. 24.

By W. Van de Velde I.

See note to No. 3.

3. THE DUTCH FLEET ROUNDING THE POINT OF SKAGEN IN JUTLAND, OCT. 22 (N.S.), 1658, ON THE EXPEDITION AGAINST THE SWEDES.

Black chalk, with grey wash, strengthened with black lead; on three conjoined sheets; 31·5 × 100 cm. (12⅜ × 39¼ in.).

INSCR.: *Recto*, at the top in the centre, in black lead, gone over in ink by another hand, *No 8 T soorby by Juidtlant eersth to* (in black lead, *ij . . . mende*) *den 22 octob 1658 | & voor by na de houck van schagen seijllende | de sommige schepen haer soldaten onstenende* [Saeby near Jutland arriving there first 22nd October 1658 and sailing past the point of Skagen some of the ships disembarking their sol-

diers]; and in the lower r.-hand corner, in black lead, *2*.

PROV.: As for No. 1.

5214–27 (L.B., Van de Velde I, 3).

BIBL.: *Sloane Cat.*, p. 130, No. 27. *Van Rijsewijk*, I, p. 24.

By W. Van de Velde I.

On Oct. 17th, 1658, the Dutch fleet set out on an expedition to assist the Danes against the Swedes. The fleet was not heard of till Oct. 29th, when it was near Skagen, the northernmost point of Jutland. *Soorby*, referred to in the inscription on the present drawing, is probably identical with Saeby which is beyond Skagen on the E. coast of Jutland and which the fleet is known to have reached on Oct. 30th.

William Courten's former ownership of this and other Van de Velde drawings in the Sloane collection has been suggested by the hand which has gone over, and, in some cases, transcribed the original inscriptions (*See* also note to No. 44).

4. THE DUTCH FLEET AT ANCHOR NEAR LESSÖ IN THE SOUND, OCT. 31 (N.S.), 1658. ON THE EXPEDITION AGAINST THE SWEDES. Among the ships can be identified, from l. to r., the 'Halve Maan', the 'Eendracht' (flagship of Admiral van Wassenaar Obdam, commander-in-chief of the expedition), and the 'Kleine Eendracht'.

Black chalk, with grey wash, strengthened with black lead; on four conjoined sheets; $41 \cdot 2 \times 112$ cm. ($16\frac{1}{4} \times 43\frac{1}{2}$ in.).

INSCR.: *Recto*, in the upper r.-hand corner, in black lead, *nota V int.* | *winter praetie* [winter expedition]; *No 17* | *no 17*; and *geteickent* (?) *op donderdach . . . ij . . . den 31 Oct* (?) | *daer den adml voor ofte onder lesouten* | *ancker leijt & de cappiteijn v-maent haer* | *heerlick te comporteeren* [drawn on Thursday . . . the 31 Oct . . . when the admiral lay at anchor before and under lessö & the captains were exhorted to acquit themselves honourably], *alwaer wij van daer* | *inde nanacht ofte tegens den dach tsijl gingen soo det mij niet mogelick was daer een teickening van*

te maecken & te becomen [as we set sail from there after midnight or towards morning, it was not possible to make & obtain a drawing of it]. To l. and r. of the ships, in black lead, *20*.

PROV.: As for No. 1.
5214–46 (L.B., Van de Velde I, 2).

BIBL.: *Sloane Cat.*, p. 133, No. 46.

By W. Van de Velde I.

Though there is no indication of Courten's possible ownership of this drawing, as in the case of No. 3, one may assume that it reached Sir Hans Sloane from the same source, in view of its belonging to the same series.

5. THE DUTCH FLEET AT ANCHOR NEAR ZEALAND, DENMARK, NOV. 4–7 (N.S.), 1658, ON THE EVE OF THE BATTLE OF THE SOUND. On the l. is the 'Halve Maan' (*Cf.* No. 4).

Black chalk, with grey wash, strengthened with black lead; on three conjoined slips; $17 \cdot 3 \times 37 \cdot 3$ cm. ($6\frac{3}{4} \times 14\frac{5}{8}$ in.).

INSCR.: *Recto*, in black lead, partly gone over in ink by another hand, *gesicht van zelant vande Baye* (in black lead, *uijt te sien na de* | *uijterste houck*) [view of Zealand from the Bay looking out to the outermost point]; in

the lower l. and r. hand corners, in black lead, *10*.

PROV.: As for No. 1.
5214–36, 37 (L.B., Van de Velde I, 4).

BIBL.: *Sloane Cat.*, p. 131, Nos. 36 & 37.

By W. Van de Velde I.

On Nov. 8th, 1658, was fought the Battle of the Sound between the Dutch and the Swedes.

See notes to Nos. 3 & 4.

6. VISIT OF THE STATES GENERAL TO THE DUTCH FLEET, NOV. 1664.

On the extreme l., apparently from its flag, an English yacht, and further off to the r. of her, the yacht of the States General. In the centre, r., beyond the end of the jetty, the flagship of Admiral van Wassenaar Obdam.

Black chalk, with grey wash; on three conjoined sheets; 36·7 × 96·5 cm. (14⅜ × 38 in.).

INSCR.: *Recto*, in the upper l.-hand corner, in black lead, *1664*; and in the lower l.-hand corner, in black lead, *25 / t' Jacht van staten generael / ((?) in de) vloot* [the yacht of the States General (in the) fleet].

PROV.: As for No. 1.

5214–51 (L. B., Van de Velde I, 5).

BIBL.: *Sloane Cat.*, p. 134, No. 51. *Van Rijsewijk*, I, p. 28.

By W. Van de Velde I.

The presence here of an English yacht is curious, seeing that England was on the point of war with Holland, and the inscription, which clearly refers to the yacht of the States General in the background, most confusingly appears below this English vessel.

See note to No. 4.

7. THE DUTCH FLEET TEN DAYS BEFORE THE BATTLE OF LOWESTOFT, JUNE 2 (N.S.), 1665.

Black chalk, with grey wash; 16·3 × 42 cm. (6⅜ × 16½ in.).

INSCR.: *Recto*, in the lower l.- and r.-hand corners, in black lead, *12*; and in the l.-hand lower corner, in ink, *W.V.V.J.*

    Verso, in the upper l.-hand corner, in black lead, gone over incorrectly in ink, *dunslach* (sic for *dingsdach*) *den 2 Junij 1665 dit aen malkar pil* (sic for *zeil(en)*) */ for de vloet met de praste natelangt pil* (sic for *natelang &*

zil) / gaet [The assembling of the fleet on Tuesday, June 2nd, 1665 and how it afterwards set sail with the prizes].

PROV.: As for No. 1.

5214–39 (L.B., Van de Velde II, 2).

BIBL.: *Sloane Cat.*, p. 132, No. 39.

By W. Van de Velde II.

See note to No. 3.

8. THE DUTCH FLEET BEFORE THE BATTLE OF LOWESTOFT, JUNE 11 (N.S.), 1665.

In the centre the flagship of the commander, Admiral van Wassenaar Obdam.

Black chalk, with grey wash, strengthened with black lead; on four conjoined sheets; 19·8 × 128·2 cm. (7¾ × 50½ in.).

INSCR.: *Recto*, at the top, on the l., in black lead, *No 2*; at the top, in the centre, in

black lead, *woensdach* (altered to *donderdach*) *d 11 Juij 1665 daer eenich goet ujt den ad¹ gegeven / wert inde gallijods on ruijmte te geven donderdach nademiddach / ontrent 6 a 7 uuren* [Wednesday (altered to Thursday) the 11 June 1665 as some goods from the admiral's ship are being put in galliots to have more room, Thursday afternoon about 6 to 7 o'clock]; at the foot, under the respective ships, the names of the commanders and ships, in black lead, *ad^l jan everts* [Lieut.-Admiral Jan Evertsen], *schram* [Vice-Admiral V. Schram,] *7 wolde* [the 'Zevenwolden'], *stellingwerff* [Lieut.-Admiral A. Stellingwerf], *graef tijt verdrijff* [Capt. A. de Graef in the 'Tijdverdrijf'], *heer obdam* [Admiral van Wassenaar Obdam], *amsterdam* [the 'Amsterdam'], *verhulst* [Capt. A. Van der Hulst], *tromp* [Vice-Admiral Cornelis Tromp].

PROV.: John Thane (*Lugt*, No. 1544. Sale, George Jones, 26:ii:1819, Lot 244 or 245). Samuel Woodburn (Sale, Christie, 27:vi:1854, Lot 2477 (?)). W. B. Tiffin, from whom it was purchased by the B.M., 1854.

1854-8-12-18 (L.B., Van de Velde I, 6).

BIBL.: *Van Rijsewijk*, I, p. 31.

By W. Van de Velde I.

On June 11th, (N.S.), 1665, the Dutch fleet came in sight of the English, and Admiral van Wassenaar Obdam, the Dutch commander-in-chief, prepared his ship for battle.

9. THE DUTCH FLEET ON THE EVE OF THE BATTLE OF LOWESTOFT, JUNE 12 (N.S.), 1665.

Black chalk, with grey wash, strengthened with black lead; on two conjoined sheets; 27·5 × 46·1 cm. (10$\frac{3}{4}$ × 18$\frac{1}{8}$ in.).

INSCR.: *Recto*, at the top, in the centre, in black lead, *N° 4*; in the upper l.-hand corner, in black lead, *geteickent op vrijdach de 12 Junij 1665 op de namiddach ontrent 4 a 5 uuren, | boven de wint vande engelse armade Leggende & drijven heel moij & stil weder de wint z. oost | soo dat de schepen uijt den anderen moete blijven door behulp van met de sloupen te boucsiaerden* [drawn on Friday the 12 June 1665 in the afternoon about 4 to 5 o'clock being to windward of the English fleet drifting in very fine and still weather, the wind S. East, so that the ships had to be kept apart by taking them in tow of the boats]; and under three ships to the l., respectively, in black lead, *terlon* [Capt. Treslong (?)], *cor everts*

[Vice-Admiral Cornelis Evertsen I], *tromp* [Vice-Admiral Cornelis Tromp].

PROV.: Rev. W. D. Conybeare, (Sale, Sothebys, 22:xii:1857, Lot 22). Purchased at the Conybeare Sale, through A. E. Evans & Sons, by the B.M., 1857.

1857-12-22-15 (L.B., Van de Velde I, 7).

BIBL.: *Van Rijsewijk*, I, p. 32.

By Van de Velde I.

June 12th (2nd O.S.) was spent by the two fleets in manoeuvring for the windward position, ultimately obtained by the English commanded by the Duke of York (later James II). The actual battle began at sunrise on Saturday, June 13th (3rd O.S.), and resulted in the defeat of the Dutch.

10. THE BATTLE OF LOWESTOFT, JUNE 13 (N.S.), 1665. The English fleet passing to windward of the Dutch. Van de Velde's galliot on the r.

Black chalk, with grey wash; on five conjoined sheets; 30·9 × 198·8 cm. (12$\frac{1}{8}$ × 78$\frac{1}{8}$ in.).

INSCR.: *Recto*, in the upper l.-hand corner,

in black lead *het 3^d teickende 2 (3)^d actije & geschiedenis ontrent na 8 uuren & 9 uuren | W.V.V.* [the 3rd drawing (of the) 2nd action & event from about 8 o'clock to 9 o'clock | W.V.V.]; towards the centre, in black lead, verkeerde dach / engelse vloot (struck out) [wrong day / English fleet]; l. to r., in black lead, *prins robbert* [Prince Rupert], *de graeff van zandtwits montagu* [the Earl of Sandwich & Montagu], *vis ad lauson* [Vice-Admiral Sir John Lawson], / *L ad¹ Kortenaer* [Lieut.-Admiral Kortenaer], *blau* (blue), *de heer askue* [Vice-Admiral Sir George Ayscue], *de heer tromp / de heer vis ad¹ tromp* [Vice-Admiral Cornelis Tromp], *duck de Jorck* [Duke of York], *de heer van obdam* [Admiral van Wassenaar Obdam], *engels brander* (?) *kidts* [English fireship (?) ketch], *L ad¹ jan*

everts [Lieut.-Admiral Jan Evertsen], *banckert* [Vice-Admiral Adriaen Banckert], *stellingwerff* [Lieut.-Admiral A. Stellingwerf].

PROV.: As for No. 2.

1877–10–13–9790* (L.B., Van de Velde I, 25 (5)).

BIBL.: *Van Rijsewijk*, I, p. 32.

By W. Van de Velde I.

A 'galliot' was a small two-masted vessel used for carrying dispatches.

11. ADMIRAL DE RUYTER TAKING OVER THE COMMAND OF THE DUTCH FLEET FROM ADMIRAL TROMP, AUG. 18 (N.S.), 1665.

Black chalk, with grey wash; 19·3 × 51·4 cm. (7⅝ × 20¼ in.).

INSCR.: *Recto*, in the upper l.-hand corner, in black lead, *dijto dijnxdach nade middach de heeren staten general* (?) / *varen van tromp na delfslant om daerop over to gaen* / *den 18 Augustij 1665* [ditto on Tuesday afternoon the gentlemen of the States General departed from Tromp to (the) 'Delfland' to embark in that ship 18 August 1665]; and at the foot, to the r., in black lead, *de ruijter met de heer van borel* [De Ruyter with Heer van Borel].

PROV.: As for No. 9.
1857–12–22–13 (L.B., Van de Velde I, 8).

BIBL.: *Van Rijsewijk*, I, p. 34.

By W. Van de Velde I.

Admiral Cornelis Tromp, in the absence of De Ruyter, was given the command of the fleet which was to fetch home the Dutch Indiamen which had sailed for Bergen in Norway, after the defeat at Lowestoft. De Ruyter, however, returned some days before the fleet set out; and was appointed to the supreme command, whereupon Tromp asked for his discharge, but was persuaded to remain. The present drawing shows the moment when the three Deputies of the States General, who were to accompany the expedition, left Tromp's ship, the 'Liefde' for De Ruyter's, the 'Delfland'. Van Borel, mentioned in the above inscription, was one of the three Commissioners who accompanied De Ruyter on this expedition.

12. A COUNCIL OF WAR IN THE DUTCH FLEET ON THE WAY TO BERGEN, AUG. 25 (N.S.), 1665. On the l., boats approaching De Ruyter's flagship, the 'Delfland', which is flying a pendant at the mizzen peak as a signal for a council of war.

Black lead; 19 × 51·1 cm. (7½ × 20⅜ in.).

INSCR.: *Recto*, in the upper l.-hand corner, in black lead, *dit geteickent op dijnxdach den 25*

augustij 1665 / *nademiddach pesiaering* [this drawn on Tuesday the 25 August afternoon holding a council of war].

PROV.: As for No. 9.

1857–12–22–16 (L.B., Van de Velde I, 9).

BIBL.: *Van Rijsewijk*, I, p. 34.

By W. Van de Velde I.

See note to No. 11.

13. THE DUTCH INDIAMEN FROM BERGEN, JOINING THE FLEET OFF THE COAST OF NORWAY, SEPT. 6 (N.S.), 1665.

Black chalk, with grey wash; on four conjoined sheets; $22 \cdot 7 \times 162 \cdot 5$ cm. ($8\frac{7}{8} \times 64\frac{1}{2}$ in.).

INSCR.: *Recto*, on a separate slip of paper, in the upper l.-hand corner, in black lead, *geteickent op sonnendach smorgens vanden 6 september 1665 soo de generaele | vloot haer onder noorwegen boven ons verthoont de wint meest n. oost doch | stille & labber koelte* [drawn on Sunday morning 6 September 1665 as the main fleet shows itself near Norway to windward of us the wind mostly n. east yet still and soft breeze]; under one of the ships to the r., in black lead, *t raethuis* (?) *van haerlem*; and under four others, further to the r., *oostijndije* [East Indiamen].

PROV.: Paul Sandby (*Lugt*, No. 2112, probably Sale, Christie, 16:iv:1817, Lots 65–75). Rev. W. D. Conybeare, (Sale, Sotheby, 22:xii:1857, Lot 22). Purchased at the Conybeare Sale, through A.E. Evans & Sons, by the B.M., 1857.

1857–12–22–17 (L.B., Van de Velde I, 10).

BIBL.: *Van Rijsewijk*, I, p. 35.

By W. Van de Velde I.

Though De Ruyter's fleet arrived off the Norwegian coast about Sept. 6th (N.S.), it was compelled by the wind to leave again on the next day, and did not return till Sept. 14th. The elder Van de Velde accompanied De Ruyter and landed at Bergen on Sept. 6th. He made many drawings of this expedition now in the Boymans Museum, Rotterdam. In the National Maritime Museum, Greenwich, is another drawing belonging to the series, showing the Indiamen coming out of Bergen, which would be the incident immediately preceding that shown in the present drawing.

14. DUTCH FISHING VESSELS IN THE NIEUWE DIEP, 1666.

Black lead, with grey wash; $22 \cdot 3 \times 57$ cm. ($8\frac{3}{4} \times 22\frac{1}{2}$ in.).

INSCR.: *Recto*, in the lower r.-hand corner, in ink, *W.V.V J.*

Verso, in the upper l.-hand corner, in black lead, *niewe diep wijt tesien 1666* [looking out from the Nieuwe Diep 1666]; in another hand, in ink, *niew diep*; and in the centre, in black lead, *152*.

PROV.: As for No. 9.

1857–12–22–7 (L.B., Van de Velde II, 5).

Perhaps by W. Van de Velde II.

15. VIEW OVER AN ESTUARY, WITH A 'WEYSCHUIT' MOORED IN THE FOREGROUND, L., AND SHIPS LYING OFF IN THE DISTANCE, R., MAY 31st (N.S.), 1666.

Black chalk, with grey wash; $15 \cdot 2 \times 41$ cm. ($6 \times 16\frac{1}{8}$ in.).

INSCR.: *Recto*, in the upper l.-hand corner, *den 31 meij 1666 getekent H—u.* [the 31 May

1666 drawn H—u]; and in the upper r.-hand corner, *W.V.V.J.*

PROV.: Samuel Woodburn (Sale, Christie, 27:vi:1854, Lot 2463). Purchased at the Woodburn Sale, through W. B. Tiffin, by the B.M., 1854.

1854–6–28–78 (L.B., Van de Velde II, 20).

By W. Van de Velde II.

A 'weyschuit'—'meadow boat'—was a small Dutch open boat with a straight raking stem usually rigged with a sprit. It was originally used on farm waterways, and later on estuaries, for agricultural purposes.

16. THE DUTCH FLEET AT ANCHOR BEFORE THE BATTLE OF THE FOUR DAYS, OFF THE NORTH FORELAND, JUNE, 1666. Van de Velde's galliot on the l.

Black lead, with grey wash; on four conjoined sheets; 20·4 × 164 cm. (8 × 64⅝ in.).

INSCR.: *Recto*, in the upper l.-hand corner, in black lead, *Woensdag de 9 Junij 1666 no 1* (?) [Wednesday the 9th June 1666 no 1]; at the top, towards the centre, in black lead, *op woensdach de 9 Junij 1666 tegen de avont soo de wint | . . . den donder bùije oost & ono liep no 2*, [on Wednesday 9 June 1666 about night-fall as the wind / after the thunder went round to the East & ENE no 2]; to the r., *de vlagge begint* (?) *oost te waeijen . . . | . . . de vlage z west geweijt . . . | . . . no 3* [The flag begins to blow to the East . . . | . . . the flag blows S. West . . . | . . . no 3].

PROV.: As for No. 2.

1877–10–13–981* (L.B., Van de Velde I, 25 (7)).

BIBL.: *Van Rijsewijk*, I, pp. 38–40.

By W. Van de Velde I.

[Albemarle and Prince Rupert were put in joint command of the English fleet which set sail on May 3rd (N.S.), 1666. Rupert was detached with twenty ships to prevent a junction between the French and Dutch, but during his absence, the Dutch appeared off the North Foreland. On June 11th Albemarle attacked and was worsted, and Rupert returning on June 13th, the day indicated by the date of the present drawing, could do no more than save Albemarle from destruction.]

Other drawings representing the Battle of the Four Days are in the Rijksmuseum, Amsterdam, and the Boymans Museum, Rotterdam.

17. THE DUTCH FLEET BECALMED THE DAY BEFORE THE BATTLE OF THE FOUR DAYS, JUNE 10 (N.S.), 1666.

Black lead, with grey wash; on three conjoined sheets; 22·2 × 174·7 cm. (8¾ × 68⅞ in.).

INSCR.: *Recto*, in the upper l.-hand corner, in black lead, *No 1 tleggen vande vloot te weten de 2 esquadrens vande | adl de ruijter met van nes | & tromp & van meppelen geteickent op donderdach | ontrent 5 a 6 uren soo de fictalij*

schepen na dunckerken | gesonden werden [No 1 The lying of the fleet namely the two squadrons of / Admiral de Ruyter with Van Nes / & Tromp & Van Meppelen drawn on Thursday about 5 to 6 o'clock when the victualling ships were sent to Dunkirk]; towards the centre, on a separate slip of paper, in black lead, *dit zijn de 2 dagen voor tgevecht 1666 | met de ruijter* [these are the 2 days before the battle 1666 / with De Ruyter], and at the foot, below Van de Velde's galliot, in black lead, *mijn gallijodt den ouden W van de velde* [my galliot the elder W Van de Velde].

PROV.: As for No. 2.

1877–10–13–983* (L.B., Van de Velde I, 25 (9)).

BIBL.: *Van Rijsewijk*, II, p. 174.

By W. Van de Velde I.

See note to No. 16.

18. A COUNCIL OF WAR IN THE DUTCH FLEET, ON THE DAY BEFORE THE BATTLE OF THE FOUR DAYS, JUNE 10 (N.S.), 1666. On the r., De Ruyter's flagship with boats bringing officers to the council.

Black lead, with grey wash; on three conjoined sheets; 22·2 × 173 cm. (8¾ × 68⅜ in.).

INSCR.: *Recto*, in the upper l.-hand corner, in black lead, *3*; towards the centre, *2*; at the top, towards the r., in black lead, *No I. pesiaring int cleijn op donderdach voormiddach den 10 Jnij 1666 / de wint noch hebbende meest n. oost* [small council of war on Thursday before noon 10 June 1666 the wind being mostly n. east]; and at the foot, below the ships, in black lead, *Hiddes* [Lieut.-Admiral Tjerk Hiddes (of the Friesland squadron)], *fries,*

fries, fries [ships of the Friesland Squadron], *meppelen* [Lieut.-Admiral Meppel], *tromp* [Lieut.-Admiral Cornelis Tromp].

PROV.: As for No. 2.

1877–10–13–982* (L.B., Van de Velde I, 25 (8)).

BIBL.: *Van Rijsewijk*, I, p. 38.

By W. Van de Velde I.

See note to No. 16.

19. THE BATTLE OF THE FOUR DAYS, JUNE 11–14 (N.S.), 1666. A council of war in the Dutch fleet early on the second day of the battle.

Black chalk, with grey wash, strengthened with black lead; on four conjoined sheets; 20·7 × 153·2 cm. (8⅛ × 60⅜ in.).

INSCR.: *Recto*, in the upper l.-hand corner, on a separate slip, in black lead, . . . (the first line illegible) / *saterdach smorgens vroúg soo onse vloot / leijt en wacht om te verwachten de afgedwaelde schepen / & de heer tromp die op een ander schip was overgegaen / de engelse vloot hier boven ons verthoont die geen wint / noch water over en* . . . [. . . / Saturday early in the morning as our fleet lies waiting for the scattered ships and Tromp who had gone on board another ship / the English fleet here above us (i.e. to windward of us) which (having) no wind / nor water besides . . .]; towards the centre, on a separate slip, in black lead, *Saterdach den*

12 Junij 1666, (in a later hand) *No 3* [Saturday the 12 June 1666 No 3]; in the upper r.-hand corner, on a separate slip, in black lead, *conte Gúisse & de prins van Monaco comen hier aen boort / vande ruijter alsoo tschip daer die heeren op geweest waeren verbrant / was te weten duijvenvoorden otto van treslon No 22*. [Conte de Guise & the prince of Monaco come here on board / (the ship of) De Ruyter, the ship in which these gentlemen had been burnt namely the 'Duijvenvoorde' (Capt.) Otto van Treslon No 2] 2; below the ships, from l. to r., *van nes* [Lieut.-Admiral van Nes (in the 'Eendracht')], *Koenders* [Vice-Admiral Coenders (in the 'Groningen')], . . . *everts* [Rear-Admiral Cornelis Evertsen (in the 'Zierikzee')], on the extreme r., *hiddes* [Lieut.-Admiral Tjerk Hiddes (in the 'Groot

Frisia')]; at the foot, centre, on a separate slip, in black lead, *de engelse vloot soo zij leijt en drijft passende op ons voornemen*, (in a later hand) *No 7* [the English fleet as it lies waiting for our decision No 7]; to the r., on a separate slip, in black lead, *ad de ruijter pesiaert*, (in a later hand) *No 6* [Ad^l De Ruyter holds a council of war No 6]; and beside it, on another slip, in black lead, *vis adl de liefde*, (in a later hand) *No 5*. [Vice-Admiral De Liefde No 5].

PROV.: As for No. 2.
1877–10–13–978* (L.B., Van de Velde I, 25 (4)).

BIBL.: *Van Rijsewijk*, I, p. 41.

By W. Van de Velde I.

See note to No. 16.

20. THE BATTLE OF THE FOUR DAYS, JUNE 11–14 (N.S.), 1666. The Dutch fleet bearing down to attack on the second day of the battle. Van de Velde's galliot in the centre, l.

Black lead, with grey wash; on five conjoined sheets; 24·4 × 190·8 cm. (9½ × 75¼ in.).

INSCR.: *Recto*, in the upper l.-hand corner, on a separate slip, in black lead, *no 2 saterdach smorgens de 12 Junij 1666 soo de staten vloot | op den vijant avanceert hebbende wint rúijmer alsoo veranderden & waren . . .* [no 2 Saturday morning the 12 June 1666 the States (Dutch) fleet advancing on the enemy having a fair wind so changing & were . . .]; in the centre, below a ship to the l., in black lead, *van nes* [Lieut.-Admiral Van Nes (in the 'Eendracht')]; and at the foot, on a separate

slip, in black lead, *utrecht goskens . . . evers* [the 'Utrecht' Capt. Goskens . . . Evertsen], transcribed below in ink *Utrech Goskens, Capt Evers*.

PROV.: As for No. 2.
1877–10–13–977* (L.B., Van de Velde I, 25 (3)).

BIBL.: *Van Rijsewijk*, I, p. 41.

By W. Van de Velde I.

See note to No. 16.

21. THE BATTLE OF THE FOUR DAYS, JUNE 11–14 (N.S.), 1666. The second day of the battle, when De Ruyter, having lost his top-mast, transferred his pennant to Lieut.-Admiral Van Nes in the 'Eendracht'. Van de Velde's galliot shown twice, in the centre and on the extreme r.

Black lead, with grey wash, on eight conjoined sheets; 32·5 × 242·7 cm. (12⅞ × 95⅝ in.).

INSCR.: *Recto*, at the top, from l. to r., in black lead, *van nes de daer wen . . . | actije soo den ad^l de . . . de engelse vloot . . .* [Van Nes there . . . | action as the admiral the . . . English fleet . . .], *actije soo den h . . .* [action as the . . .], *den vijant seijlt soo hoog als . . . | so dat onse schepen de wenden &*

dwars strooms . . . | als vervolgens no 8 kan bemerkt werden [the enemy sailing as close to the wind ((?) as possible) / so that our ships tacking across the tide . . . | as can be seen in the following no 8]; at the foot, in black lead, *lad^l meppelen* [Lieut.-Admiral J. Meppel], *van nes soo de vloot passeert | de wempel op de groote steng* [Van Nes as the fleet was passing / the pennant at the masthead], *loopt uijt de vloot* [sailing out of the fleet] *blau* [blue], *askue prins roijael* [Admiral Sir George

Ayscue in the 'Royal Prince'], *de zon van amsterdam* / . . . *Bloem* [the 'Zon' of Amsterdam / (commanded by) Van Bloem], *slepen vande visad schram* [towing of Vice-Admiral Schram], *blau* [blue (Vice-Admiral Sir Thomas Teddeman)], *root* [red (Vice-Admiral Sir Joseph Jordan in the 'Royal Oak')], *Mijn gallijodt* [my galliot]; transcribed in English in ink, *Rear adm. Mettelin, Run out of the ffleet, Askue Prince Royall, the sun*

of amsterdam / *comand by van bloom, The Towing away of vice-Admirall Scram, Van de Velde—Galliot.*

Prov.: As for No. 2.

1877–10–13–980* (L.B., Van de Velde I, 25 (6)).

By W. Van de Velde I.

See note to No. 16.

22. THE BATTLE OF THE FOUR DAYS, JUNE 11–14 (N.S.), 1666. The Dutch fleet pursuing the English on the third day of the battle. Van de Velde's galliot in the centre.

Black chalk, with grey wash; 22·2 × 57·1 cm. (8¾ × 22⅜ in.).

Inscr.: *Recto*, in the upper l.-hand corner, in black chalk, *dese actije geschiede op pijnxterdach int vervolgen ontrent na middagge so* . . . (partly cut away) *van de voorste schepen* / *vier uuren de 13 Junij 1666 nu jagen wij haer & Ao 1665 op denselven 13 Junij jougen zijons* / *1* [this action took place on Whitsunday as we were pursuing about afternoon when . . . of the foremost ships at four o'clock of 13 June 1666 now we chase them & A⁰ 1665 on the same 13 June they chased us, 1]; at the foot, in black lead, under the respective ships, from l. to r., the names of the commanders, etc., *L adr van nes* [Lieut-Admiral Van Nes], *utrecht goskens* [the 'Utrecht' Capt. Goskens],

gouda [the 'Gouda'] *t vertuin, brander* [the 'Fortuin' ('Fortune') fireship], *hielst* [Vice-Admiral Van der Hulst in the 'Spiegel'], *hollander*; and in the lower r.-hand corner, in ink, *W.V.V.J.* (probably a copy of W. Van de Velde's signature).

Prov.: As for No. 9.

1857–12–22–14 (L.B., Van de Velde I, 11).

Bibl.: *Van Rijsewijk*, I, p. 43.

By W. Van de Velde I.

The reference in the inscription to June 13th, 1665 (the previous year) recalls the Dutch defeat at the Battle of Lowestoft.

23. DURING THE BURNING OF THE DUTCH MERCHANTMEN OFF THE ISLANDS OF VLIELAND AND TERSCHELLING, AUG. 18–20 (N.S.), 1666.

Black lead, with grey wash, strengthened with pen and brown ink; 21·3 × 106·5 cm. (8⅜ × 41⅞ in.).

Inscr.: *Recto*, at the top, in the centre, l., in black lead, *stille weder bij na kalm* [still weather nearly calm]; at the top, in the centre, r., in black lead, *in dese tropp ontrent de 40 schepen westers vaerders*, reworded above in ink, *dese troppe schepen zijn westers vaerders tussen*

de 40 ende 50 sterck [in this group of ships are westbound merchantmen between 40 and 50 strong]; at the top, on the r., in ink over black lead, *tussen de 80 ende 90 noortsvaerders ende oosters waerders al meest verbrant* [from 80 to 90 northbound merchantmen and eastbound merchantmen nearly all burnt]; above the ships from l. to r., in black lead, *de engelse schep leggende* / *ter ancher onde derscheling schout bij nacht van roo vlagge* [the

English ships lying at anchor near Ter-schelling the rear admiral with the red flag] *vaertuig voor derschelling, engels vergadt met 4 a 5 branders* [vessels off Terschelling. English frigate with 4 or 5 fireships], *3 genees vaerders die niet verbrant zijn & waren (?) | naet verbranden vande schep op gedreven—met de | avont vloet* (above the ships in the centre, l.) [3 Genoese merchantmen which were not burnt & after the burning of the ships drifted with the evening tide], *beg* (above a ship in the centre, r.), *dese 3 genues vaerders* [these 3 Genoese merchantmen] | *10 a 12 schepen legende* (?) (above and below the ships on the extreme r.) [10 to 12 ships lying]; at the foot, below the ships, from l. to r., in black lead, *het leste deseijn | 24* [the last drawing | 24] *buijsen* [herring boats], *Hamburger boeijer* [Hamburg hoy] | *frans spiegel* [French stern] *leger* [soldiers], *capt toll* [Capt. Toll (Commander of the 2nd convoy)] | *tol | adelaer inde brant* [on fire], *capt adelaer | capt Adelaer in brant* [Capt. Adelaer (commander of the 1st convoy) on fire], *verbrunt wiuck* [burnt wreck], *de grlnt* [the shingle], | *oostindienschip* [East Indiaman], *Wracken in de brant* [wrecks on fire], *onse sloepe loopt* [our boats rowing away], *engels sloup schietend* [English boat firing], *engels kidts* [English ketch], *dese ontrent 80 a 90 schepen dat bij terschelling hals . . .* [these ships about 80 to 90 which near to Terschelling . . .).

Verso, in a later hand in ink, *The burning of the Dutch Fleet in the Vlie by Sir Robert Holmes, Anno 1665* (incorrectly for 1666).

PROV.: As for No. 1.

5214–50 (L.B., Van de Velde I, 12).

BIBL.: *Sloane Cat.*, p. 134, No. 50. *Van Rijsewijk*, II, p. 173.

By W. Van de Velde I.

Following up the victory of St. James's day, July 25th (O.S.), 1666, the English commanders detached Sir Robert Holmes, Rear-Admiral of the Red, with a small squadron to destroy the Dutch shipping at Vlieland and Terschelling. Piloted by the traitor Laurens Heemskerk, he arrived on August 18th, and destroyed about 150 merchantmen with fire ships.

According to Buckeridge (p. 431) the elder Van de Velde 'is said to have conducted the English fleet to the burning of Schelling', but there is no evidence that he left the Dutch service before 1672. He might have been present at the Terschelling action, but on the Dutch side, as witnessed by this and the following drawing (No. 24). An oil-painting of the subject, with some features in common with the present drawing, is in the Royal Collection at Buckingham Palace.

24. THE BURNING OF THE DUTCH MERCHANTMEN OFF THE ISLANDS OF VLIELAND AND TERSCHELLING, AUG. 18–20 (N.S.), 1666.

Black chalk, with grey wash, strengthened with black lead and pen and brown ink; on four conjoined sheets; 58·3 × 87 cm. (22⅞ × 34¼ in.).

INSCR.: *Recto*, in the upper l.-hand corner, *hier het dorp van der schelling in de | brant beneffens eenig cleijn vaertuigen* [here the village of Terschelling in flames together with some small ships]; at the top, to the r., in ink, *hier zijn verbrant indese twee tropp(en)*

soo wester | & ooster als noorts vaerders over 16 schepen [here were burnt in these two groups west and east as well as northbound merchant-men more than 16 ships]; in the r.-hand margin, centre, in ink, *hier boven schel- | ling hal(s) . . . | 10 a 12 sche(pen) | behouwen & | gesalvaert de | 3 genees vaerde . . .* [here above Terschelling 10 to 12 ships remained and were saved 3 Genoese merchantmen], and below, *hier verscheijd . . . | vaertuij ind. | brant inde sloot* [here various vessels on fire in the creek]; at the foot in the centre, in ink, partly illegible, ... *waijt ... eloot ... alwaer de Legger beie* [... blowing ... when the Army ...].

PROV.: Hugh Howard. Dr. Robert Howard (Bishop of Elphin), and the Earls of Wicklow. Charles Howard, 5th Earl from whom it was purchased by the B.M., 1874.

1874–8–8–98 (L.B., as by Van de Velde II, 66).

BIBL.: *Van Rijsewijk*, II, p. 173.

Perhaps by W. Van de Velde I, retouched by W. Van de Velde II.

See No. 23.

25. THE BURNING OF THE DUTCH MERCHANTMEN OFF THE ISLANDS OF VLIELAND AND TERSCHELLING, AUG. 18–20 (N.S.), 1666.

Pen and ink, with washes of grey and brown; 28·8 × 45·4 cm. (11$\frac{3}{8}$ × 17$\frac{3}{4}$ in.). Old mount: 40·1 × 56·5 cm. (15$\frac{3}{4}$ × 22$\frac{1}{4}$ in.).

INSCR.: *Recto*, in the upper l.-hand corner, *... van ter schellingh en Vlie den 19 en 20 Augusti Ao 1666*—[... of Terschelling and Vlie the 19 and 20 August Ao 1666]; and in the lower l.-hand corner, in ink, *W.V.V J.*

Verso, on the old mount, in ink, *N: 78 / Vandervelde . . . A: D: 1779—*

PROV.: Henry John Peachey, 3rd Lord Selsey (Sale, Sotheby, 29:vi:1872, Lot 2631).

Purchased at the Selsey Sale by the B.M., 1872.

1872–7–13–444 (L.B., Van de Velde II, 1).

BIBL.: *Van Rijsewijk*, II, p. 173.

By W. Van de Velde II.

See Nos. 23 & 24. The drawing is not contemporary with the event, however, as it belongs to the artist's latest manner (*Cf.* Nos. 48, 50, 51, 55, 56, 57, & 105, etc.).

26. THE DUTCH FLEET AT SEA, THREE DAYS (?) BEFORE THE BATTLE OF SOLEBAY, JUNE 3 (N.S.), 1672. On the l., the 'Gouda' with the Rear-Admiral's flag, and on the r., the flagship of Lieut.-Admiral van Ghent.

Black chalk, with grey wash, partly strengthened with pen and brown ink; 24·7 × 44 cm. (9$\frac{3}{4}$ × 17$\frac{1}{4}$ in.).

INSCR.: *Recto*, in the upper l.-hand corner, in black chalk, *den 3 Junij 1672 (?) / 2 / 1* (partly illegible and cut away); and above the ships, *gouda* and *gent*.

PROV.: John Henderson, by whom it was presented to the B.M., 1863.

1863–1–10–224 (L.B., as by Van de Velde II, 7).

Probably by W. Van de Velde I.

27. THE DUTCH FLEET BEFORE THE WIND ON THE EVE OF THE BATTLE OF SOLEBAY, JUNE 6 (N.S.), 1672. The Dutch fleet sailing from r. to l. In the l. foreground Van de Velde's galliot.

Black chalk, with grey wash, strengthened with black lead; on two conjoined sheets; 25·6 × 159 cm. (10$\frac{1}{8}$ × 62$\frac{1}{2}$ in.).

INSCR.: *Recto*, at the top, in the centre, in black lead, *hier* ... (remainder of line illegible) / *voor de wint naet voorlant te seyllen* ...

(three words illegible) / . . . *moet aen te grijpen godt geve zijn de segen & heijl . . . / bewaer ons lieve vaderlant—zijnde . . . en de . . . ent ontrent.* / *6 uuren de 6 Junij 1672 pijnxter maenendag.* [here . . . sailing before the wind to the Foreland . . . must engage, God give victory and salvation . . . save our dear fatherland—being . . . about 6 o'clock the 6 June 1672 Whitsun Monday]; below the ships, from l. to r., in black lead, *van de velde* (below his galliot), *de visad sweers*, [the Vice-Admiral Sweers], *de heer de ruijter* [De Ruyter]; and above the ships on the r., in black lead, *v liefde*, [Vice-Admiral de Liefde], *esquadre van zeeuwen* [the squadron of Zeeland]. On a separate sheet, in ink, *A View of the Dutch Fleet on the 6th of June 1672, being the Day before the Fight at Solbay.*

PROV.: As for No. 1.
5214–49 (L.B., Van de Velde I, 13).

BIBL.: *Sloane Cat.*, p. 134, No. 49. *Van Rijsewijk*, II, p. 178.

By W. Van de Velde I.

The Battle of Solebay (Southwold Bay) was fought on June 7th, (N.S.), 1672, between the English fleet, under James, Duke of York, and the Dutch, under De Ruyter. The action ultimately went in favour of the English, but fog enabled De Ruyter to withdraw.

See note to No. 4.

28. THE BATTLE OF SOLEBAY, JUNE 6 (N.S.), 1672, FROM 7 TO 9.30 A.M. To the l., De Ruyter in the 'Zeven Provincien' and the Duke of York in the 'Royal Prince'. In the centre, the burning of Lord Sandwich's flagship, the 'Royal James'.

Black chalk, with grey wash, strengthened with black lead; on six conjoined sheets; 35·4 × 230·7 cm. (13⅞ × 90¾ in.).

INSCR.: *Recto*, in the upper l.-hand corner, in black lead, *dynsdag van smorgens ten 7* (altered from 6) *uuren / 9 u* (?) *half 10 uuren toe* [Tuesday from 7 o'clock of the morning to half past 9]; at the top, to the l., in black lead, . . . (the first line illegible and partly crossed out) / *dit is al wederom op zijn rechte plaets geleijt neen naer het / boven uijt gehaelt is gaet & moet hier geleijt werden daer den 10 de opstaet* / (in ink) *dit schrift is niet te seggen* [this is again put in its right place not raised up to the top and must be put here where the 10th stands / this writing is not correct]; above the ships, from l. to r., in black lead, *franse met de zeeuwen* [French with the Zeeland squadron], *ladl van nes / de eendracht* [Lieut.-Admiral van Nes / in the 'Eendracht'], *vis ad Spraag / root londen* [Vice-Admiral Spragg / of the Red in the 'London'], *heer de ruijter* [de Ruyter], *ducke de Jorck / de prins* [Duke of York / in the 'Prince'], *d sweers* [Admiral Sweers], *root / de siarles* [red / the 'Charles'], *blau ad = zantwits / de roijael James* [blue Ad. Sandwich / in the 'Royal James'], *b, een inde / brant* [one on fire], *blau* [blue], *gent met de roo vlag / laet waeijen* [Lieut.-Admiral van Ghent with the red flag flying], *blau visad / . . . . sovvereijn.* [blue Vice-Admiral / . . . 'Royal Sovereign' (?)]; below the ships, from l. to r., in black lead, *zeelant van rotterdam* ['Zeeland' of Rotterdam], *schip schielandt* [ship 'Schieland'], *de maecht van dordrecht* [the 'Maid of Dordrecht'], *schip delft* [ship 'Delft'], *vergadt agata* [frigate 'Agatha'], *brakel soo vande blu ad¹ seer schadeloos / off raeckt na dat hij lang aen zijn boort / vast gelegen had* [Brakel as he gets loose from the Admiral of the Blue very much damaged after having been a long time fast alongside his ship]; *hessen* [the 'Essen'], *gedion / gijdijon* [Gideon / Gideon], *de schout bij nacht haen seer / reddeloos* [the Rear-Admiral de Haen much / damaged]; *dolf . . . ijn* [the 'Dolphin' (Admiral van Ghent)]; and in the lower l.-corner, *21*.

PROV.: As for No. 1.

5214–47 (L.B., Van de Velde, I, 14).

BIBL.: *Sloane Cat.*, p. 133, No. 47. *Van Rijsewijk*, II, p. 178.

By W. Van de Velde I.

Van Brakel in the 'Groot Hollandia', of 60 guns and 300 men, lay alongside the 'Royal James', of 100 guns and 800 men, for an hour and a half.

See note to No. 4.

29. THE BATTLE OF SOLEBAY, JUNE 7 (N.S.), 1672, FROM 10 A.M. TILL NOON. In the centre, foreground, the artist's own galliot, and to the l., the burning of the 'Royal James'. On the extreme l., in the distance, the French squadron.

Black chalk, with grey wash, strengthened with black lead; on five conjoined sheets; 35·5 × 218·3 cm. (14 × 86⅛ in.).

INSCR.: *Recto*, in the upper l.-hand corner, in black lead; . . . *vervolgens van 10 uuren tot smiddags toe* / (in another hand) & . . . *s dit gesicht ontrent middach* [the following from 10 o'clock till noon / & . . . this view about noon]; above the ships in black lead, *de fransen hier int verschiet bij na ofte wel grote-mijlen / van ons met de zeeuwen doende zijnde* [the French here hardly in sight or a good many miles / away from us fighting with the Zee-landers], *heeft 4 branders in brant geschoten dat / wij gesien hebben als ick tegens de heer de ruijter oock geseijt hebbe* [has set four fireships on fire which we have seen and which I have told de Ruyter about], *van nes* [Lieut.-Admiral van Nes], *schiet los* [guns firing], *schiet gaet los door brander* [guns firing because of a fireship], *adl van bloeu vla soo / int brant sonder hulp bij hem / dat ick geloof veel volck gebleven is* [the Admiral of the Blue (Sandwich) lay on fire without help near him and as I believe many died there], *schiet los* [guns firing], (at the top of the mainmast) *sweers* [Vice-Admiral Sweers], *en ander ad*^{l} *blau . . . plats van verbrant* [(ship of) another Admiral of the Blue in place of (the one which was) burnt], *de duck op de michiel / blau* [the Duke in the 'Michael' / blue], *root v.d. duck Jorck / groot steng wech prins* [red flag of the Duke of York / the 'Prince's' main topmast down],

root schout bij nacht / de siarles, [Rear-Admiral of the Red (Sir John Harman) / in the 'Charles'], *W. blau* (blue), *visd liefde* [Vice-Admiral de Liefde], *gent*, [Lieut.-Admiral van Ghent], *blu visd / hebbende / de louf* [Vice-Admiral of the Blue (Sir Joseph Jordan) / to windward]; below the ships, from l. to r., in black lead, *teickenaer vande veldens gallijodt* [the draughtsman Van de Velde's galliot], *hier blijft de Jouswa* [here founders the 'Joshua'], *van onse schepen branders* [our fireships], *d sweers* [Vice-Admiral Sweers], *visd Schram / Schram / schram* [Vice-Admiral Schram]; and in the lower l.-hand corner, in black lead, *22*; other inscriptions illegible.

Verso, in the r.-hand margin in ink, *Int kleijn vant t Jaer 72 — ackoerderende met de / hooge orrisont* [small version of the Year 72 — agreeing with the / (drawings) with the high horizon].

PROV.: As for No. 1.

5214–48 (L.B., Van de Velde I, 15).

BIBL.: *Sloane Cat.*, p. 133, No. 48. *Van Rijsewijk*, II, p. 179.

By W. Van de Velde I.

At noon the Duke of York had to leave his ship, the 'Royal Prince', and went on board the 'St. Michael'. The inscriptions were corrected after the artist came to England in the Autumn of 1672. That on the *verso* may refer to drawings prepared by him for the well-known series of tapestries, presenting various stages of the battle, woven at the Great Wardrobe in Hatton Garden by Francis and Thomas Poyntz in 1674–6 (*See* Margaret Jourdain in *Country Life*, March 16th, 1929, pp. 351–3).

See note to No. 4.

30. THE BATTLE OF SOLEBAY, JUNE 7 (N.S.), 1672, NOON. The English fleet sailing from r. to l., with the Dutch before them on the l. On the extreme r., the 'Royal Sovereign' (Sir Joseph Jordan, Vice-Admiral of the Blue), whose three-turreted quarter-gallery is identifiable from the drawing. **Plate 275 (a)**

Black chalk, with grey wash, strengthened with black lead; on five conjoined sheets; 34·5 × 235·5 cm. (13½ × 92¾ in.).

INSCR.: *Recto*, in the upper l.-hand corner, in black lead, partly gone over by another hand in ink, . . . (two lines illegible) *middag tot 3 uuren . . . passeert is op dynsdag de 6* (altered from 7) *Junij 1672* [mid-day to 3 o'clock . . . has happened on Tuesday the 6 (7) June 1672]; *No 4* (gone over in ink); in the upper r.-hand corner, in black lead, *No 3*; above the ships, in black lead, partly gone over by another hand in ink, *t verschiet gevecht tussen zeeuwen | & het franse esquadre* [the distant encounter with firing between the Zeelanders & the French squadron], *Londen spragg* (in ink) [the 'London' Vice-Admiral Spragg], *duch de Jorck | op de ander schip | de michiel* [Duke of York | in the other ship | the 'Michael'], *ruijter* [de Ruyter (in the 'Zeven Provincien')], *root* [red (flag)], *gent* [Lieut.-Admiral van Ghent), *root* [red (flag)], *kenthorn* (gone over in ink) [Rear-Admiral Kempthorne], *haen* [Rear-Admiral de Haen], *root* (gone over in ink) [red (flag)], *bl* [blue (flag)], referring to the 'Royal Sovereign', *bl visad heeft de louft* (gone over in ink) [Blue Vice-Admiral to windward]; below the ships, in black lead, *veldens gallyodt* (in ink) | *veldens gallijodt* [Van de Velde's galliot], *vande veldes gallijodt ick was door de | blauw esquadre afgesneden soo dat de ruijter & | tgeene ontrent hem was int verschiet gesicht most | teickenen* (gone over in ink) [Van de Velde's galliot. I was cut off by the blue squadron so that I had to draw de Ruyter & what was around him from a distance], *stavoren raeckt hier verre | inde partije* (gone over in ink) [the 'Staveren' gets here far | into battle], and (referring to the 'Royal Sovereign') *bla* [blue].

PROV.: As for No. 1.
5214–26 (L.B., Van de Velde I, 16).

BIBL.: *Sloane Cat.*, p. 130, No. 26. *Van Rijsewijk*, II, p. 179.

By W. Van de Velde I.

See notes to Nos. 3 & 44.

31. THE BATTLE OF SOLEBAY, JUNE 7 (N.S.), 1672, FROM 2 TO 5 P.M. View from ahead of the Dutch and English fleets standing to the S. Eastward. In the foreground, l., the artist's galliot.

Black chalk, with grey wash, strengthened with black lead; on five conjoined sheets; 35·3 × 177·8 cm. (13⅝ × 70 in.).

INSCR.: *Recto*, at the top, in the centre, in black lead, gone over by another hand in ink, *geteickent van 2 uurren tot 5 urren duerende | van tgeen in die tijt gepasseert is* [drawn from 2 o'clock to 5 o'clock of what happened at that time]; *No 5* (altered from 4); above the ships, from l. to r., in black lead, partly gone over by a later hand in ink, *Root vlag blijft vor | op de prins | op de voorsteng* [Red flag remains at the 'Prince's' fore topmasthead], *gent* [Lieut.-Admiral van Ghent], *desswerius* [Capt. David Swerrius (in the 'Beschermer'),] *vis adr liefde* [Vice-Admiral de Liefde), *her Ruijter* [Lieut.-Admiral de Ruyter], *Jan nes* [Rear-Admiral Jan van Nes], *Schram* [Vice-Admiral Schram], *vlug* [Rear-Admiral David Vlugh], *van nes* [Admiral Aert van Nes] *root* (twice) [red (flags)], *op S Machiel* (crossed out) [(the Duke of York) on board the 'St. Michael'], *hier Londen naer onderrechtig | vande duck de Jorck selfs aen mij gedaen* [here the 'London' as the Duke of York has himself instructed me], *de Siarles root* [the 'Charles' red (flag)], *Londen* (crossed out) *alwaer de ducke | op overgaet | Machiel* [the 'London' (crossed out) where the Duke of York went on board | the 'St Michael']. Below the ships, from l. to r., in black lead, partly gone over by another hand in ink, *13 Josuwa* (twice) *afgebleven* [remains of the 'Joshua], *Veldes gallijoot* [Van de Velde's galliot], *Veldens Gallyot, vergadt hessen* [the frigate 'Essen'], *tschip oosterwijck* [the ship 'Oosterwijk'], *schout bij nacht den haen* [Rear-Admiral de Haen], *13, 14, d sweers* [Vice-Admiral Sweers], *comedtstar* [the 'Komeetster'], *14*.

PROV.: As for No. 1.

5214–41 (L.B., Van de Velde I, 17).

BIBL.: *Sloane Cat.*, p. 132, No. 41. *Van Rijsewijk*, II, p. 179.

By W. Van de Velde I.

The incident represented occurred about 5 o'clock, when the Duke of York transferred his flag from the 'St. Michael' (*See* No. 29) to his third ship, the 'London'. As it was blowing 'a fine gale' the Duke's boat took three-quarters of an hour to reach the latter ship, and during that time Sir Robert Holmes kept the Standard flying in the 'St. Michael' until he saw it put up in the 'London', indicating that the Duke had gone on board (*See Navy Records Society*, Vol. LXXXVI, 1946, pp. 164–86). This may account for the artist's having thought that the Duke was still in the 'St. Michael' at the time; he has indeed pasted a slip of paper subsequently over the place where the 'St. Michael's' Standard would have been, and added a Standard to the main topmasthead of the 'London'. As in the case of No. 29, these corrections would have been made after Van de Velde came to London in 1672.

See notes to Nos. 3 & 44.

32. CHARLES II'S VISIT TO THE FLEET AFTER THE BATTLE OF SOLEBAY, 1672. In the centre, the 'Royal Prince'.

Brush drawing in grey wash, over black lead; 16·2 × 32·7 cm. (6⅜ × 12¾ in.).

PROV.: John Sheepshanks (*Lugt*, No. 2333). Purchased by W. & G. Smith 1836, from whom it was bought by the B.M. in the same year.

1836–8–11–537 (L.B., as by Van de Velde II, 13).

BIBL.: *Sheepshanks Cat.*, p. 98, No. 537.

The present drawing is probably by an imitator of the Van de Veldes' style. It is clearly connected with the two authentic representations of the subject by W. Van de Velde II, which exist as a drawing and an oil painting in the National Maritime Museum. There is also a mezzotint, printed in green, by Elisha Kirkall, apparently after the latter.

33. DEFENCE OF THE 'ROYAL PRINCE' AT THE BATTLE OF TEXEL, AUG. 11th (O.S.), 1673. On the l., the flagship of the Dutch Lieut.-Admiral, Cornelis Tromp, and in the distance, r., the 'Royal Prince'.

Pen and brown ink, with grey wash; 6·9 × 14·7 cm. (2⅝ × 5¾ in.).

INSCR.: *Recto*, in the upper l.-hand corner, in black lead, *37*.

PROV.: As for No. 1.
5214–62 (L.B., Van de Velde II, 41a).

BIBL.: *Sloane Cat.*, p. 136, No. 62.

By W. Van de Velde II.

The Battle of Texel was the last of three actions fought in the summer of 1673 during an attempted Anglo-French invasion of Hol-land by sea. Admiral Sir Edward Spragge was in command of the rear division of the fleet and found himself opposed to Tromp, with whom he became fiercely engaged. Spragge's flagship, the 'Royal Prince', was so badly damaged in the fight that the admiral had to shift his flag successively to two other ships, during which operation he was drowned. Despite her condition, however, Capt. John Cox continued to defend the 'Royal Prince' throughout the remainder of the action, and thus managed to save her.

Related pictures are in the National Maritime Museum and the Rijksmuseum, Amsterdam.

34. AN INCIDENT CONNECTED WITH THE EMBARKATION OF MARY OF MODENA, NOV., 1673, AT SOME POINT W. OF CALAIS WHICH APPEARS IN THE DISTANCE, L.

Black chalk; on three sheets; 34·4 × 96·7 cm. (13½ × 38 in.).

INSCR.: *Recto*, at the top, in black lead, *no 1*, and to the l., *hier* (?) *sijn de trompeters* . . . (?) *met* . . . / *troop van den duck de York* [here are the trumpeters . . . with . . . / troop of the duke of York]; in the centre, from l. to r., in black lead, *Kalis in vrangrijck* [Calais in France], *pier hoeft* [pier head], *pier hooft* / *de W zijde* [pier head / the W. side]; below, from l. to r., in black lead, *gras* [grass], *al sinchel* [all shingle], *vis afslaan* (?) [fishing boats pushing off (?)], *al schinchel, al Sinchel* [all shingle], *modder gront* [muddy ground].

PROV.: As for No. 2.
1877–10–13–975* (L.B., Van de Velde I, 25 (1)).

By W. Van de Velde I.

Princess Mary of Modena was married by proxy to James, Duke of York, on Sept. 30th (O.S.), 1673. She travelled overland through France and embarked for England at Calais, arrived at Dover where she was met on Nov. 21st by the Duke. Together they came by road from Dover to Gravesend, where they were received on Nov. 26th by Charles II, and so proceeded with him by barge up the Thames to Whitehall.

Other drawings connected with this event are in the National Maritime Museum and in the collection of Sir Bruce Ingram.

35. THE ARRIVAL OF CHARLES II AT GRAVESEND TO RECEIVE MARY OF MODENA, NOV. 26 (O.S.), 1673. View looking down the Thames, with the forts of Tilbury, l., and Gravesend, r. Plate 275 (b)

Black chalk, with grey wash, strengthened with pen and ink; on four conjoined sheets and one slip; made up at the top; 32·7 × 110·3 cm. (12⅞ × 43⅜ in.).

INSCR.: *Recto*, at the top, in the centre, in black lead, *No 2*.

PROV.: Samuel Woodburn (Sale, Christie, 27:vi:1854, Lot 2459 (?)). Purchased at the Woodburn Sale, through W. B. Tiffin, by the B.M., 1854.

1854–6–28–80 (L.B., as by Van de Velde II, 70).

By W. Van de Velde I.

See note to No. 34.

36. THE ARRIVAL OF MARY OF MODENA OFF GRAVESEND, NOV. 26 (O.S.), 1673.
In the centre, two separate incidents shown; on the l., Charles II, accompanied by the Duke of Monmouth, handed into the Duke of York's barge; on the r., the Duke of York and Mary of Modena handed into the King's barge.

Black chalk, with grey wash, strengthened with pen and ink; on four conjoined sheets; $29 \cdot 5 \times 112 \cdot 2$ cm. ($11\frac{5}{8} \times 44\frac{1}{4}$ in.).

INSCR.: *Recto*, at the top, on the l., three lines in black chalk, illegible; in, the centre, in black chalk, *no 5 segge 6* [no. 5 should be 6]; to the r., *dit W*; in the centre, l., above the royal barge, in black chalk, *ducke . . . de prins*; and at the foot, below the two incidents, in black chalk, gone over in ink by W. Van de Velde II, *duck de monmout* [Duke of Monmouth], *de koning komt bij de Jonge dúcsesse van Jorck úijt zijn baersie / inde dúck baersie over* [the King comes to the young Duchess of York from his barge into the Duke's barge], *dúcke de Jorck met de dúcsesse gaen hier over met de koning inde / Roijael baersie & paseren alsoo de revier tot wietehal toe* [the Duke of York with the Duchess go over with the King into the / royal barge & so pass on the river to Whitehall]. In the lower r.-hand corner, in black lead, *de m. c. ens ver* [bij] *wolets* [. . . passing Woolwich].

PROV.: Mr. Keogh, from whom it was purchased by the B.M., 1879.

1879–8–9–599 (L.B., as by Van de Velde II, 67).

BIBL.: *Van Rijsewijk*, II, p. 228.

By W. Van de Velde I.

See note to No. 34.

37. MARY OF MODENA'S PROGRESS UP THE THAMES, SALUTED BY THE SHIPS OFF DEPTFORD, NOV. 26 (O.S.), 1673.

Black chalk, with grey wash; on three conjoined sheets; $19 \cdot 5 \times 72 \cdot 7$ cm. ($7\frac{5}{8} \times 28\frac{3}{4}$ in.).

INSCR.: *Recto*, at the top, in the centre, in black chalk, almost illegible, *passeren van det.oo.t no 9* [passage of Deptford no 9]; to the r., in black chalk, *v-gadt* [frigate]; in the upper r.-hand corner, in ink, probably by W. Van de Velde II, *een vergadt* [a frigate], *het paseren & actije voor dettvort* [the passage and action before Deptford].

PROV.: Samuel Woodburn (Sale, Christie, 27: vi:1854, Lot 2459 (?)). Purchased at the Woodburn Sale, through W.B. Tiffin, by the B.M., 1854.

1854–6–28–79 (L.B., Van de Velde I, 24).

By W. Van de Velde I.

See note to No. 34.

38. THE ENGLISH FLEET AT ANCHOR, c. 1673. In the foreground, l., the artist's ketch.

Black lead, with grey wash, partly strengthened with pen and brown ink; 28 × 44·2 cm. (11 × 17⅜ in.).

INSCR.: *Recto*, at the foot, below the ketch, in black lead, *velde*, and in the upper l.-hand corner, *4434* (?).

PROV.: As for No. 26.

1863–1–10–225 (L.B., as by Van de Velde II, 8).

By W. Van de Velde I.

This drawing was probably made soon after the artist and his son arrived in England in 1672. It shows the ketch which in this country replaced the galliot used by him when in Dutch service.

39. AN ENGLISH FRIGATE SALUTING, AS A BARGE PULLS AWAY FROM HER, 1674.

Brush drawing in grey wash, touched with pen and black ink, over black lead; 15·6 × 20·7 cm. (6⅛ × 8⅛ in.).

INSCR.: *Recto*, in the lower l.-hand corner, in ink, *w.v.velde 1674*

PROV.: Richard Payne Knight, by whom it was bequeathed to the B.M., 1824.

O.o.11–246 (L.B., Van de Velde II, 12).

BIBL.: *Payne Knight Cat.*, p. 155, No. 246. By Van de Velde II.

40. THE BURNING OF FOUR CORSAIR SHIPS AT TRIPOLI BY SIR JOHN NARBROUGH, JAN. 14 (O.S.), 1675/6.

Black chalk, with grey wash, slightly touched with pen and ink on a ship in the foreground; 29·4 × 45·3 cm. (11⅛ × 17¾ in.).

INSCR.: *Recto*, in the upper l.-hand corner, in ink, by W. Van de Velde II, *Tripoli S Jan alborgh* [for 'Narbrough']; in the upper r.-hand corner, in black chalk, *Tripoli | S Jan alborgh*, and over it, in ink, also by Van de Velde II, *Tripoli, komander S Jan alborgh. vier Tursee schepen | verbrandt. een smer-nes, varder bleef legge was. | bij naght, met elf sloepen d selfe verbrant*, [Tripoli, Sir John Alborgh (Narbrough) commanding. Four Turkish ships / burnt. A Smyrna trader which remained lying there was likewise burnt in the night by eleven boats], *2 vand salopen quamen in acsi tegen een smal Tursee | barckentijn noch een schip van Tunnis | massant man* [2 of

the boats were in action with a small Turkish barquentine and also a merchantman from Tunis]. On a separate slip of paper, in black chalk, *tripoli | 4 turcsische | verbrant | een smerens | voorder blef | lege bij nach | met elf slope | d komander S Jan alborgh* (similar to the inscription on the drawing itself); on another slip, in black chalk, *11 bots ofte slope in al waer | van 2 in acsi ware vegtende tege | een turckse smal barckentijn | noch een schip van tunijs masant | man Tripoli* (similar to the inscription on the drawing itself).

PROV.: As for No. 24.

1874–8–8–96 (L.B., as by Van de Velde I, 21).

Probably by W. Van de Velde II. The artist, however, was not present at the action.

A more finished drawing of the subject, from the same viewpoint, is in the National Maritime Museum (No. 530), and the painting connected with both this and the present drawing is in the Royal Collection, formerly at Hampton Court and now at Buckingham Palace.

41. WILLIAM, PRINCE OF ORANGE, AND PRINCESS MARY AT ERITH ON THEIR WAY TO HOLLAND, NOV. 19 (O.S.), 1677. Towards the centre, the yacht 'Mary', with the Prince and Princess on board, hoisting sail. Other yachts and ships to l. and r. Erith in the background.

Black chalk, with grey wash, strengthened with black lead; on four conjoined sheets; $32 \cdot 2 \times 100 \cdot 8$ cm. ($12\frac{5}{8} \times 40\frac{1}{8}$ in.). Old mount; $40 \cdot 3 \times 55 \cdot 7$ cm. ($15\frac{3}{4} \times 21\frac{7}{8}$ in.).

INSCR.: *Recto*, at the top, to the l., in black chalk, *geteickent op maenendach soo wij een weijnig tijt bij | herift ten ancker gelegen had door stilte & en wenig | wint krijgende onder seil gaen no 4(3) seg no 10* [drawn on Monday when we had ridden at anchor a little time near Erith owing to the calm & getting some wind we set sail]; at the foot, below the vessels, in black chalk, repeated in ink, in the margin, *de grahont* [the 'Greyhound'], *de porsmout* [the 'Portsmouth'], *de Marije alwaer de roijael princes in was* [the 'Mary' in which the Princess Royal was], *de navij* [the 'Navy'], *de Anne, de Katerijne, de siarlet* [the 'Charlotte'], *de soldaete* [the 'Saudadoes'].

PROV:. Marseille Holloway, from whom it was purchased by the B.M., 1872.

1872–1–13–373 (L.B., Van de Velde I, 22).

BIBL. & REPR.: *Van Rijsewijk*, II, p. 230. C. M. Gavin, *Royal Yachts*, 1932, pp. 267–8.

By W. Van de Velde I.

William of Orange married Princess Mary on Nov. 4th (O.S.), 1677, and on Nov. 19th set out for Holland. They were accompanied by the King and other members of the Royal Family as far as Erith, where they embarked in the yacht 'Mary'.

The elder Van de Velde went as official artist and recorded the incidents of the journey, the greater part of the 56 drawings which he made being in the Boymans Museum, Rotterdam. They were among his most elaborate works, and were shown by him to Sir Joseph Williamson, Secretary of State, with a letter of recommendation from Capt. Gunman, commander of the 'Mary' yacht (*See* P.R.O., State Papers, 29, 400, *f.* 107).

See No. 77 for a portrait of the 'Mary'.

42. WILLIAM, PRINCE OF ORANGE, AND PRINCESS MARY SALUTED AT SHEERNESS ON THEIR WAY TO HOLLAND, NOV. 20 (O.S.), 1677. The 'Mary', wearing her special standard, in the foreground, l., followed on the r. by the other yachts, 'Katherine', 'Charlotte', 'Portsmouth', 'Navy', 'Greyhound', and 'Anne'. In the distance, the fort at Sheerness firing a salute, to which the 'Mary' replies.

Black chalk, with grey wash, strengthened with black lead; on two conjoined sheets; $32 \cdot 3 \times 82 \cdot 5$ cm. ($12\frac{5}{8} \times 32\frac{3}{8}$ in.). Old mount; $40 \cdot 3 \times 55 \cdot 7$ cm. ($15\frac{3}{4} \times 22$ in.).

INSCR.: *Recto*, in the upper l.-hand corner, in black chalk, gone over in ink, *soo wij dijnxdag smorgens sernesse passeeren & den | prins van orangie met eerschooten begroet wert no*

14 [as we pass Sheerness on Tuesday in the morning and the Prince of Orange is welcomed with salutes, no 14]; in the lower margin, in ink, from l. to r., *de marije alwaer den prins van orangie met | de roijaell princes doen mael in waren* [the 'Mary' with the Prince of Orange and the Princess Royal on board], *het kosteel siarnesse* [the castle of Sheerness], *de katarijn* [the 'Katherine'], *de siarlet Jacht* [the 'Charlotte' Yacht], *de portsmout Jacht* [the 'Portsmouth' Yacht], *de navij Jacht* [the 'Navy' Yacht], *de grahont* [the 'Greyhound'], *de Anne*

Verso, in the upper l.-hand corner, in black lead, *van mijn Journal | . . . an zij dooluchtig hoogh | van orangie* [from my Journal / for his serene highness / of Orange]; and at the foot, in black lead, in a later hand, *The fleet in attendance | on the Prince of Orange.*

PROV.: As for No. 41.
1872–1–13–373 (1) (L.B., Van de Velde I, 23).

BIBL. & REPR.: *Van Rijsewijk*, II, p. 231. C. M. Gavin, *Royal Yachts*, 1932, pp. 267–8.

By W. Van de Velde I.

The Royal party was becalmed at Sheerness, and had to go overland by Canterbury to Margate where it was picked up again by the yachts on Nov. 28th. The standard worn by the 'Mary' during the voyage was designed specially for the occasion; it combined the Stuart and Orange arms on a red ground.

43. THE VISIT OF CHARLES II WITH LORD BERKELEY TO THE 'TIGER' AT SHEERNESS, 1681 (?). Ships, with ketches in the foreground, l., and the fort at Sheerness to the r.

Black chalk, with grey wash, strengthened with black lead; on three conjoined sheets; 18·6 × 87 cm. (7¾ × 34⅜ in.).

INSCR.: *Recto*, in the upper l.-hand corner, in black lead, by the artist, *no 5*; in another and later hand, *Portsmouth*, and in yet another hand, *Sheerness*.

PROV.: As for No. 9.
1857–12–22–8 (L.B., as by Van de Velde II, 3).

By W. Van de Velde I.

44. THE LAUNCH OF THE 'ROYAL SOVEREIGN' AT CHATHAM, SEPT. 30 (O.S.), 1684. A long line of ships lying in ordinary. Figures on the shore in the foreground.

Black chalk, with grey wash, strengthened with black lead; on three conjoined sheets; 28·8 × 110 cm. (11¼ × 43¼ in.).

INSCR.: *Recto*, in the upper l.-hand corner, in black lead, *4* (?); below the ships, from l. to r., in black lead, some being transcribed above in ink by another hand, *de Londen, de Londen, de dúc-es* [the 'Duchess'], *winsor kastell* [the 'Windsor Castle'], *de siarles* [the 'Charles'], *de opdreijvende* (?) *breta . . .* [the drifting 'Britannia'], *de nepthuin* [the 'Neptune'], *de breda*, [two three-deckers, possibly the 'Royal Prince' and the 'Royal Sovereign' (inscriptions illegible)], *de roijall oock* [the 'Royal Oak'], *de sudtfolck* [the 'Suffolk']. *de heinerijte* [the 'Henrietta'], *de fictorij* [the 'Victory']; and in the lower l. and r.-hand corners, *4*.

PROV.: As for No. 1.
5214–28 (L.B., Van de Velde I, 19).

BIBL.: *Sloane Cat.*, p. 130, No. 28. *Van Rijsewijk*, II, p. 228.

By W. Van de Velde I.

Other drawings representing this event are in the National Maritime Museum, Greenwich, and the Boymans Museum, Rotterdam.

The hand, which has attempted to transcribe in ink the original inscriptions on this and Nos. 45 and 46, is very similar to an informal one used by William Courten (*See* Sloane MSS., 3962, *ff.* 227–30). This has suggested that Courten originally owned these and other Van de Velde drawings in the Sloane Collection (*See* No. 3).

45. THE LAUNCH OF THE 'ROYAL SOVEREIGN' AT CHATHAM, SEPT. 30 (O.S.), 1684. A long line of ships lying in ordinary. Figures on the shore in the foreground, l.
Plate 290 (a)

Black chalk, with grey wash, strengthened with black lead; on three conjoined sheets; 29·4 × 108·5 cm. ($11\frac{1}{2}$ × $42\frac{3}{4}$ in.).

INSCR.: *Recto*, in the upper l.-hand corner, in black lead, [n]*o 6*; at the foot, below some of the ships, from l. to r., in black lead, *s Joris* [the 'St. George'], *Londen | de Londen* [the 'London'], *de siarles* [the 'Charles'], *de ducses* [the 'Duchess'], *de Winsor kastel* [the 'Windsor Castle'], *de bretadie* [the 'Britannia'], *de albemaele* [the 'Albemarle'], *nepthunije* [the 'Neptune'], *de prins* [the 'Prince']; transcribed above, sometimes incorrectly, in ink, *de Doris, de Londen, de Charles, de Duches, de Winsor Castle, de Breda,*

de Albemarle, de Royal Prins; and in the lower l. and r. hand corners, *3*.

PROV.: As for No. 1.

5214–29 (L.B., Van de Velde I, 18).

BIBL.: *Sloane Cat.*, p. 130, No. 29. *Van Rijsewijk*, II, p. 228.

By W. Van de Velde I.

Described in the *Sloane Cat.* as 'The English Fleet in Ordinary in the Medway', and by Mr. Binyon as the visit of Charles II to Tilbury.

See notes to Nos. 3 & 44.

46. THE LAUNCH OF THE 'ROYAL SOVEREIGN' AT CHATHAM, SEPT. 30 (O.S.), 1684. In mid-distance, centre, a yacht, with a flag at the masthead.

Black chalk, with grey wash, strengthened with black lead, on two conjoined sheets; 29·7 × 68 cm. ($11\frac{5}{8}$ × $26\frac{3}{4}$ in.).

INSCR.: *Recto*, in the upper l.-hand corner, in black lead, *2*; in the lower l. and r.-hand corners, in black lead, *15*; below the ships, from l. to r., in black lead, and transcribed above in ink, in another hand, *de breda* ['Breda'], *roijael ooke* [the 'Royal Oak'], *sudtfolck* [the 'Suffolk'], *fictorij* [the 'Vic-

tory'], *de heinerijte* [the 'Henrietta'] incorrectly transcribed as *de Windrijffe*.

PROV.: As for No. 1.

5214–42 (L.B., Van de Velde I, 20).

BIBL.: *Sloane Cat.*, p. 132, No. 42. *Van Rijsewijk*, II, p. 228.

By W. Van de Velde I.

See notes to Nos. 3 & 44.

47. THE LAUNCH OF A THREE-DECKER, PROBABLY THE 'ROYAL SOVEREIGN', AT CHATHAM, SEPT. 30 (O.S.), 1684. The three-decker on

the l., with other ships at anchor between her and the shore, r. On the extreme r., buildings on a quay with a crane.

Black chalk, and grey wash, strengthened with black lead; on two conjoined sheets; 20·5 × 95·9 cm. (8 × 37⅜ in.).

INSCR.: *Verso*, in the upper r.-hand corner, *H*; in the lower r.-hand corner, in ink, by a former collector, *no 14 Mar 26 84*; and in the upper l.-hand corner, *12447*.

PROV.: 'H' (unidentified mark (?)). Rev. W. D. Conybeare, (Sale, Sotheby, 22:xii:1857, Lot 22). Purchased at the Conybeare Sale, through A. E. Evans & Sons by the B.M., 1857.

1857–12–22–18 (L.B., as by Van de Velde II, 4).

Probably by W. Van de Velde I.

A drawing of the same incident, inscribed *de nieu opgemaeckte souvereijn* is in the Boymans Museum, Rotterdam (No. 202a. b). This has enabled the subject of the present drawing and Nos. 44—46 to be identified.

48. SHIPPING IN THE Y AT AMSTERDAM, 1686. On the l., Lieut.-Admiral Cornelis Tromp's flagship, the 'Gouden Leeuw', seen from the stern.

Pen and brown ink, with grey wash, over preliminary black chalk; 21 9 × 45 cm. (8⅝ × 17⅞ in.).

INSCR.: *Recto*, in the lower l.-hand corner, *W. V. V.*, and on a separate slip of paper below, *het Originale Schilderij van Willem Van de Velde geschildert in 1686. is met eenige Verandering | hoewel ten principaalsten Gevolgt nadere Teekening van hem, het Stuk is te vinden, | en te zien in de Schreijershoeksthoorn te Amsterdam, en is een onbetaalbaar Stuk | the original painting by William Van de Velde painted in 1686 is (with some alterations | though imitated in the essentials) after this drawing by him. The painting may be | seen at the Schreyershoeks. tower at Amsterdam and it is of inestimable value.*

PROV.: Benjamin West (*Lugt*, No. 419, Sale, Christie, 10.vi.1820, Lot 69, purchased by Hume). William Beckford (not identified in any of his sales). W. B. Tiffin, from whom it was purchased by the B.M., 1849.

1849–10–3–167 (L.B., Van de Velde II, 6).

By W. Van de Velde II, in his latest manner (*Cf.* Nos, 25, 50, 51, 55, 56, 57, & 105, etc.).

Study for the picture, dated *1686*, formerly in the Harbour Master's room in the Schreierstoren, at Amsterdam, and transferred to the Rijksmuseum in 1808 (See *Catalogue of the Pictures . . . in the Rijksmuseum*, 1927, p. 197, No. 2469).

49. THE DESTRUCTION OF THE FRENCH SHIPS IN THE BAY OF LA HOGUE BY SIR GEORGE ROOKE, MAY 23–24 (O.S.), 1692.

Pen and brown ink with grey wash; 12·5 × 27·4 cm. (4⅞ × 10¾ in.).

INSCR.: *Recto*, in the lower l.-hand corner, *W.V.V.*

PROV.: A. C. Poggi (*Lugt*, No. 617. Sale, T. Philipe, 25:iv:1801, Lot 37). Sir J. C. Robinson. John Malcolm. J. W. Malcolm, from whom it was purchased by the B.M., 1895.

1895–9–15–1333.

BIBL.: *Malcolm Cat.*, p. 260, No. 858.

By W. Van de Velde II.

On May 19th (O.S.), 1692, Admiral Edward Russell with a combined English and Dutch fleet defeated the French, under the Comte de Tourville, off Cap Barfleur. The subsequent action (May 23rd—24th) of Sir George Rooke's burning the French ships in the Bay of La Hogue is also shown in Nos. 50 & 51.]

50. THE DESTRUCTION OF THE FRENCH SHIPS IN THE BAY OF LA HOGUE BY SIR GEORGE ROOKE, MAY 23–24 (O.S.), 1692.   Plate 270

Pen and brown and black inks, with washes of grey and brown, over black chalk; 29·9 × 46·7 cm. (11¾ × 18⅜ in.). Old mount: 35·3 × 52·2 cm. (13⅞ × 20½ in.).

INSCR.: *Recto*, at the top to the l., *het branden der franse schepen te La Hogue no 5: 1692 1.2.3.junij* [here burn the French ships at La Hogue *no 5: 1.2.3. Junij* (according to the New Style)], and in the lower l.-hand corner *W.V.V J 1692*.
　　　　Verso, in the centre, *N76 Vandervelde. A;D; 1779–*

PROV.: As for No. 41.

1872–7–13–443 (L.B., Van de Velde II, 68).

By W. Van de Velde II, in his latest manner (*Cf.* Nos. 25, 48, 51, 55, 56, 57 & 105, etc.). Though dated against the signature, *1692*, this drawing corresponds exactly with its pendant, No. 51, and was probably made at the same time, *i.e.* 1701.

51. THE DESTRUCTION OF THE FRENCH SHIPS IN THE BAY OF LA HOGUE BY SIR GEORGE ROOKE, MAY 23–24 (O.S.), 1692

Pen and brown and black inks, with washes of grey and brown, over black chalk; on two conjoined sheets, 24·9 × 43·4 cm. (9¾ × 17 in.). Old mount; 36 × 54·2 cm. (14⅛ × 21⅜ in.).

INSCR.: *Recto*, at the top to the l., *La Hogue 1692 1.2.3. Junij*, (according to the New Style); and in the lower l.-hand corner, *W V Velde J. Ao 1701*.
　　　　Verso, in the centre, in ink, *N:77 / Vander Velde . . . A:D: 1779*.

PROV.: As for No. 41.

1872–7–13–445 (L.B., Van de Velde II, 69).

By W. Van de Velde II, in his latest manner (*Cf.* Nos. 25, 48, 50, 55, 56, 57 & 105, etc.).

After the battle off Cap Barfleur, three French ships ran ashore near Cherbourg, and twelve took refuge in the Bay of La Hogue where they were burnt by Sir George Rooke. This incident is represented in the present drawing and No. 50, which, however, from the date against the signature would appear to have been made nine years after the event.

52. LAUNCH OF THE 'RUSSELL' AT PORTSMOUTH, 1692.

Black lead, with pen and brown ink and brown-grey wash; 20·7 × 27·1 cm. (8⅛ × 10⅝ in.).

INSCR.: *Verso*, in the upper l.-hand corner, *Reesijille* [the 'Russell'].

PROV.: As for No. 26.

1863–1–10–220 (L.B., Van de Velde, II, 10(a)).

By W. Van de Velde II.

The 'Russell' was built at Portsmouth in 1692, and carried 80 guns. She was rebuilt in 1709 (*See* Anderson, *English Ships, 1649–1702*, pub. by Society for Nautical Research (*Occasional Publication*, No. 5), p. 43, No. 736).

53. SKETCHES, IN SIX COMPARTMENTS, OF SHIPS, PRESUMABLY INTENDED TO SHOW HOW THESE SHOULD BE PLACED IN A COMPOSITION, 1693.

Pen and brown ink; made up in the lower l.-hand corner; 36·9 × 23·8 cm. (14½ × 9⅜ in.).

INSCR.: *Recto*, below the sketches, in ink, by W. Van de Velde II, *daer sijn veel groette opseervasie, in het begenne vanden | schilderij, ofte men het mest bruijn. ofte meest light | wil maecke; moet men op het voor stel merkere | als de Loght ende d selfs natuer van koluer | de Linijes van son, en wint, als oock de selfe | hoegh ofte middelmaectigh, naer het schonst ver | kies vant het goet, d schessen dan, van ordenansie | ofte schepen onderseijl, hier naer, ofte het doen | van voele ich hebbe daer toe te verkiese in den | beginne. | W.V.V.J. | 1693.* [there is much to be observed in beginning a picture, whether it should be mostly dark or mostly light. One must take into consideration such things as the atmosphere and the exact colouring, the directions of the sun and of the wind and also its precise strength or moderation for the most pleasing choice, the sketches of guns or of ships under sail here shown and many others I have to make a choice of before beginning. W.V.V.J. 1693.]

PROV.: As for No. 24.

1874–8–9–94 (L.B., Van de Velde II, 29).

By W. Van de Velde II. In the same style as No. 76.

54. AN ENGLISH FLAGSHIP DRIVEN ON TO THE ROCKS, 1701.

Black chalk, strengthened with black lead; 23·8 × 38·8 cm. (9⅜ × 15⅜ in.).

INSCR.: *Recto*, in the lower r.-hand corner, in black lead, by the artist, *W.V.V J. 1701.*

Verso, on the l., in ink, *Mʳ Lordt allefaes schesse* [Mr Lordt all these sketches (?)].

PROV.: Sir Hans Sloane, Bart., by whom it was bequeathed to the B.M., 1753.

5214–43 (L.B., Van de Velde II, 32).

BIBL.: *Sloane Cat.*, p. 132, No. 43.

By W. Van de Velde II.

'Mr Lordt' (Lord or Lort (?)) has not been identified.

55. A FLAGSHIP BECALMED, WITH YACHTS SALUTING IN THE DISTANCE, R., 1704.

Pen and brown ink, with grey wash; 13·7 × 20·2 cm. (5⅜ × 8 in.).

INSCR.: *Recto*, in the lower l.-hand corner, in black chalk, *35*; and towards the r., in ink, *W.V.Velde J 1704.*

PROV.: As for No. 54.
5214–60 (L.B., Van de Velde II, 40b).

BIBL.: *Sloane Cat.*, p. 135, No. 60.

By W. Van de Velde II, in his latest manner (*Cf.* Nos. 25, 48, 50, 51, 56, 57 & 105, etc.).

56. ENGLISH SHIPS BECALMED, 1704.

Pen and brown ink over black chalk, 15·1 × 18 cm. (5⅞ × 7⅛ in.).

INSCR.: *Recto*, in the lower l.-hand corner, in black chalk 36 (?); and below it, in ink, *W V V J 1704.*

PROV.: As for No. 54.
5214–61 (L.B., Van de Velde II, 41b).

BIBL.: *Sloane Cat.*, p. 136, No. 61.

By W. Van de Velde II, in his latest manner (*Cf.* Nos. 25, 48, 50 ,51, 55, 57 & 105, etc.).

57. TWO SHIPS SCUDDING IN A HEAVY SEA, 1706.

Pen and brown ink on blue-grey paper; 15·2 × 22·3 cm. (6 × 8¾ in.).

INSCR.: *Recto*, at the foot, *W. V. Velde J 1706.*

PROV.: As for No. 32.
1836–8–11–534 (L.B., Van de Velde II, 42).

BIBL.: *Sheepshanks Cat.*, p. 97, No. 534.

By W. Van de Velde II, in his latest manner (*Cf.* Nos. 25, 48, 50, 51, 55, 56 & 105, etc.).

[58–97]. PORTRAITS AND NEAR VIEWS OF SHIPS. The following are listed in chronological order of acquisition and registration, and are mounted on separate mounts.

58. THE 'WOOLWICH' FROM THE PORT QUARTER.

Grey wash over an offset (?) from black chalk; 21·9 × 28·8 cm. (8⅝ × 11¼ in.).

INSCR.: *Recto*, at the foot, *The whoole withs 1676 : maert 22.*

PROV.: P. H. Lankrink (*Lugt*, No. 2090. Apparently not in his first sale, Smith-Basset, 23:i:692; but perhaps in the second one, Cocks, 22:ii:1694, of which no catalogue, however, is known to exist). Sir Hans Sloane, Bart., by whom it was bequeathed to the B.M., 1753.
5214–24 (L.B., as by Van de Velde II, 59).

BIBL.: *Sloane Cat.*, p. 130, No. 24.

The first 'Woolwich' was a sloop built at Woolwich in 1673 and wrecked in 1675. The second ship of that name, the one represented in the present drawing, was built in 1675, also at Woolwich, and rebuilt in 1702. She carried 54 guns (See Anderson, *English Ships, 1649–1702*, pp. 32, No. 557, & 33, No. 571.

It has not been possible to establish where this portrait was made, as the extant log-book of the second 'Woolwich', in the P.R.O. (Adm. 51/4398), only begins in the year 1679. The quality of the drawing suggests that it is the work of a follower rather than of either of the Van de Veldes themselves. A drawing, by apparently the same hand and inscribed in the same writing, of the 'Royal Charles' (formerly the 'Naseby'), dated *1672*, is in the Rijksmuseum (*See The Mariner's Mirror*, Vol. II, 1912, p. 238 & Pl. facing).

59. STERN OF A DUTCH SHIP. Painted with a bird's-eye view of a country house, and elaborately carved with figures of warriors and lions. Plate 285

Grey wash over black chalk; 36·7 × 30 cm. (14$\frac{1}{2}$ × 11$\frac{3}{4}$ in.).

INSCR.: *Recto*, in the lower l.-hand corner, *8*.

PROV.: As for No. 1.
5214–25 (L.B., Van de Velde II, 62).

BIBL.: *Sloane Cat.*, p. 130, No. 25.

This is no doubt one of the several Dutch ships named after country houses, *e.g.*: *Huis Abcoude, Huis te Elswoud*, etc. (*See Vreugdenhil*, p. 42, No. 815, & p. 43, No. 840). So far the present example has not been identified.

By W. Van de Velde II.

60. THREE DUTCH FISHING BOATS 'PINKS' ON THE SHORE.

Black lead, with grey wash, 24·5 × 40 cm. (9$\frac{5}{8}$ × 15$\frac{5}{8}$ in.).

INSCR.: *Recto*, in the lower r.-hand corner, *5*.

Verso, in the lower r.-hand corner, *5 Shillings*.

PROV.: As for No. 1.
5214–31 (L.B., as by Van de Velde II, 23).

BIBL.: *Sloane Cat.*, p. 131, No. 31.

A 'Pink' was a small fishing boat about 20 ft. long.

61. THE 'ZEVENWOLDEN' FROM THE PORT QUARTER. Plate 271

Grey wash over an offset (?) from black chalk redrawn in black lead; 32·7 × 41 cm. (12$\frac{7}{8}$ × 16$\frac{1}{8}$ in.).

INSCR.: *Recto*, in the upper l.-hand corner, in black lead, *7wolde adm van vrieslant 1665*; in the lower l.-hand corner, in ink, *W.V.Velde J*; and in both lower corners, *7*.

Verso, in the lower l.-hand corner, in ink, *genamt d seeven Wolde, is gevoort / bij den ad miral van Vrislant, stelinghwerf 1665* [called the 'Zevenwolden', is commanded / by the Admiral of Friesland Stellingwerf *1665*], and in the upper l.-hand corner, *stellingwerf*.

PROV.: As for No. 1.
5214–33 (L.B., Van de Velde II, 61).

BIBL.: *Sloane Cat.*, p. 131, No. 33.

By W. Van de Velde II.

The 'Zevenwolden', the second ship of that name, was bought in 1664 by the Friesland Admiralty, and carried 54–58 guns. She was the flagship of Admiral Stellingwerf at the Battle of Lowestoft in 1665, when he was killed in her and she was captured by the English. She was re-captured by the Dutch in 1666 (*See Vreugdenhil*, p. 25, No. 447). She also appears in the drawing of the Dutch fleet at the Battle of Lowestoft (No. 10).

62. THE 'ZON', FROM THE STARBOARD QUARTER.   Plate 272

Grey wash over an offset (?) from black chalk, re-drawn with black lead and touched with pen and ink; the paper extended by two slips to the r.; 23·3 × 39·3 cm. (9⅛ × 15½ in.).

INSCR.: *Recto*, across the stern of the ship, *DE SON IS MYN NAEM*; in the lower l.-hand corner, in ink by W. Van de Velde II, *W.V.V.J*; on either side, in black lead, *18*; and in the lower r.-hand corner, in black lead, *K*(= *Keer* [turn]).

PROV.: As for No. 1.
5214–44 (L.B., Van de Velde II, 60).

BIBL.: *Sloane Cat.*, p. 133, No. 44.

By W. Van de Velde II.

Three Dutch ships of this name are recorded, all belonging to the Amsterdam Admiralty; the first built in 1640, carrying 44–48 guns, and last mentioned in 1666; the second hired in 1688, and carrying 52 guns; and the third built in 1694, carrying 50–52 guns, and last mentioned in 1712 (*See Vreugdenhil*, p. 6, No. 69, p. 45, No. 885, & p. 50, No. 991).

Another drawing of this ship is in the National Maritime Museum (No. 22), and an offset is in the V. & A. M. (No. 4700).

63. THE ROYAL YACHT 'CLEVELAND', CLOSE-HAULED IN A STRONG BREEZE, SEEN, AT SOME DISTANCE AWAY, FROM THE PORT QUARTER.
Plate 269

Pen and brown ink, with grey wash; 15·3 × 19·5 cm. (6 × 7⅝ in.).

INSCR.: *Recto*, in the upper r.-hand corner, *40*.

PROV.: As for No. 1.
5214–64 (L.B., Van de Velde II, 39).

BIBL.: *Sloane Cat.*, p. 136, No. 64.

By W. Van de Velde II.

The Royal Yacht 'Cleveland' was built at Portsmouth in 1671, and sold in 1716. She carried 8 guns (*Anderson*, p. 28, No. 460).

The present drawing is a study for an oil painting in the collection of Sir Bruce Ingram (*See* C. M. Gavin, *Royal Yachts*, 1932, Pl. III). Other drawings of the 'Cleveland' are in the National Maritime Museum (No. 438) and in the collection of Sir Bruce Ingram. *See also* No. 123.

64. A DUTCH TWO-DECKER FROM THE STARBOARD QUARTER. With an elaborately decorated stern incorporating the arms of the City and Admiralty of Amsterdam, and a female figure with a book on the tafferel.

Offset from black chalk, partly re-drawn in black lead; 32·4 × 50·2 cm. (12¾ × 19¾ in.).

PROV.: Richard Payne Knight, by whom it was bequeathed to the B.M., 1824.
O.o.10–234 (L.B., as by Van de Velde II, 63).

BIBL.: *Payne Knight Cat.*, p. 153, No. 234.

65. QUEEN CATHERINE OF BRAGANZA'S YACHT, THE 'SAUDADOES', FROM THE STARBOARD BOW.   Plate 277

Offset from black chalk, re-drawn in black lead; 31·3 × 39·7 cm. (12¼ × 15⅝ in.).

INSCR.: *Recto*, in the lower l.-hand corner, in black lead, *de soldate* (a misinterpretation of the yacht's name).

Prov.: As for No. 64.

O.o.10–235 (L.B., as by Van de Velde II, 64).

Bibl.: *Payne Knight Cat.*, p. 153, No. 235.

The Yacht 'Saudadoes' (Saudados', 'Soda-lis') was built at Portsmouth in 1670. She was rebuilt in 1673 as a sixth-rate with 8–10 guns, and as such appears in Samuel Pepys's *Register of Ships* in 1686. She was captured by the French in 1696 (*See Anderson*, p. 27, No. 451, & p. 31, No. 531).

66. THE STERNS OF THREE ENGLISH SHIPS, c. 1685, FROM THE STARBOARD QUARTERS. Plate 273

Black lead; 36·1 × 49·8 cm. (14¼ × 19½ in.).

Prov.: As for No. 13.

1857–12–22–1 (L.B., as by Van de Velde II, 55).

This drawing was perhaps made when James, Duke of York, visited Chatham on the occasion of the launch of the 'Royal Sovereign' on Sept. 30th, 1684 (*See* Nos. 44–47).

67. AN ENGLISH TWO-DECKER, c. 1680, FROM THE STARBOARD BOW.

Black chalk; 31·4 × 41·2 cm. (12⅜ × 16¼ in.).

Inscr.: *Recto*, in the lower l.-hand corner, in brown ink, by the artist, *W. V. V. J.*

Prov.: Rev. W. D. Conybeare, (Sale, Sotheby, 22:xii:1857, Lot 22). Purchased by the B.M., at the Conybeare Sale, through A. E. Evans & Sons, 1857.

1857–12–22–2 (L.B., Van de Velde II, 56).

By W. Van de Velde II.

68. THE 'HAPPY RETURN', FROM THE PORT QUARTER. Plate 276

Black lead, with grey wash; extended by an additional slip at the top; 36·3 × 43·5 cm. (14¼ × 17⅛ in.).

Inscr.: *Recto*, in the lower l.-hand corner, in black lead, by the artist, *happie retorn, rebijlt ' black wal.*

Prov.: As for No. 13.

1857–12–22–3 (L.B., Van de Velde II, 54).

Probably by W. Van de Velde II.

Built originally at Yarmouth in 1654, when she was called the 'Winsby', this ship carried 44–54 guns. She was re-named the 'Happy Return' at the Restoration in 1660, and was captured by the French in 1691, entering their service as the 'Heureux-Retour'. She was condemned in 1709 (*See Anderson*, p. 14, No. 214, and *Le Conte*, p. 15, No. 261). There is no record of her having been rebuilt at Blackwall, as suggested in the inscription on the present drawing.

Two finished portrait-drawings of this ship, both dated 1678, are in the collection of Sir Bruce Ingram; one is inscribed, *d'hapritorn vertimert 1678*, the other *d'haperitorn neu vertumbert 1678*.

69. THE 'OLIFANT', FROM THE PORT QUARTER, WITH ANOTHER SHIP IN MID-DISTANCE, R. Plate 283

Black chalk; 31·5 × 42·3 cm. (12⅜ × 16⅝ in.).

Inscr.: *Recto*, at the foot, in the centre, *35.*

PROV.: As for No. 13.
1857–12–22–4 (L.B., as by Van de Velde II, 27).

The 'Olifant' was built for the Amsterdam Admiralty in 1666, and carried 82 guns. She was declared obsolete in 1686 (*See Vreugdenhil*, p. 30, No. 565).

70. AN ENGLISH TWO-DECKER, c. 1675, FROM THE STARBOARD BROADSIDE, WITH TOPSAILS LOOSED ON THE CAP. Plate 278

Black lead; $37 \cdot 3 \times 44 \cdot 5$ cm. ($14\frac{3}{4} \times 17\frac{1}{2}$ in.).

PROV.: As for No. 13.
1857–12–22–6 (L.B., as by Van de Velde II, 53).

71. ENGLISH FISHING VESSELS NEAR THE SHORE.

Black lead, with grey wash, $36 \cdot 2 \times 48 \cdot 8$ cm. ($14\frac{1}{8} \times 19\frac{1}{4}$ in.).

PROV.: As for No. 13.
1857–12–22–9 (L.B., as by Van de Velde II, 28).

72. TWO ENGLISH TWO-DECKERS, c. 1675, FROM THE PORT BROADSIDE, WITH THEIR SAILS LOOSED.

Black lead, with grey wash; $29 \cdot 1 \times 39 \cdot 7$ cm. ($11\frac{3}{8} \times 15\frac{5}{8}$ in.).

PROV.: As for No. 13.
1857–12–22–11 (L.B., as by Van de Velde II, 52).

73. A DUTCH FRIGATE, c. 1665, FROM THE STARBOARD BOW.

Offset from black lead; $24 \times 35 \cdot 8$ cm. ($9\frac{1}{2} \times 14\frac{1}{8}$ in.).

INSCR.: *Recto*, in the lower l.-hand corner, by the artist, *W.V.V.J*; and in the lower r.-hand corner, *N. 1*.

PROV.: As for No. 26.
1863–1–10–221 (L.B., Van de Velde II, 57).

By W. Van de Velde II.

Another offset of this subject is in the National Maritime Museum (No. 257).

74. A DUTCH 'FLUTE', FROM THE STARBOARD BOW.

Black lead, with grey wash; $23 \cdot 2 \times 29 \cdot 4$ cm. ($9\frac{1}{8} \times 11\frac{1}{2}$ in.).

PROV.: As for No. 26.
1863–1–10–222 (L.B., as by Van de Velde II, 58).

A 'flute' was a Dutch ship with a bulbous hull and upward tapering stern, specially designed for trading in the Mediterranean.

75. TWO ENGLISH TWO-DECKERS, c. 1675, PASSING EACH OTHER.

Black lead, with grey wash; $29 \cdot 3 \times 40$ cm. ($11\frac{1}{2} \times 15\frac{3}{4}$ in.).

PROV.: As for No. 26.
1863–1–10–223 (L.B., as by Van de Velde, II, 51).

76. STUDIES OF A BARGE, THE HULL OF A HAMBURG SHIP, A FIGUREHEAD, AND THE STERNS OF THREE GENOESE SHIPS.

Pen and brown ink; 29 × 23·6 cm. (11⅜ × 9¼ in.).

INSCR.: *Recto*, by the artist, above the barge, *roodt, dit boijsel blau, root van binne* [red, this top-strake blue, red withinboard], and below it, *geel d regeling, 5 reme, de kolúer vand roeijers / oranje, en haer kappe* [the rail yellow, 5 oars, the colour of the rowers / orange, and their caps]; against the Hamburg ships, *met een finke net* [with a grating (over the waist)] *root d flagh / hamborgh tornsens wit* (against a sketch of the arms of Hamburg) [the flag red, Hamburg towers white], *de steng doorgeschoten* (referring to the lower study) [the topmast struck]; above and against the figurehead, twice, *sinnewesse* [emblem]; against the Genoese ship on the l., *wit/root* (on the flag) [white/red], *orke nohach* (referring to the emblem on the stern) [Noah's ark], *dubbelle lagh* [double deck]; against that in the centre, *romijnne* (referring to the quarter figures) [Roman], *3 figuere int hack / ,,brot''* [3 figures on the tafferel], *10 stucke* [10 guns], *dubbelle langh* [double deck]; against that on the r., *d vlagh wit / root kruijs* [the flag white / red cross], *beelt werck / al groen / selfs d / grondt* [carved work / all green even the / background], *balkoni* [balcony]; and at the foot, *Te vrage ofte het al was ijser schut ofte eenigh mataei* [To ask whether it is all iron ordnance or some other metal].

PROV.: As for No. 24.
1874–8–8–95 (L.B., Van de Velde II, 30).

By W. Van de Velde II, in his latest manner, and in the same style as No. 53.

77. THE ROYAL YACHT 'MARY', FROM THE PORT QUARTER.

Offset from black chalk, with grey washes, touched with pen and ink, on two conjoined sheets of paper; 48 × 86·5 cm. (19 × 34 in.).

INSCR.: *Recto*, in the upper l.-hand corner, by the artist, *het Jaght dat aen de Konningh van / engelant wieert veereert vandesen staet* [the Yacht which was offered to the King of England by this state]; and in the lower l.-hand corner, *W.V.V J.*

PROV.: As for No. 24.
1874–8–8–97 (L.B., Van de Velde II, 65).

REPR.: C. M. Gavin, *Royal Yachts*, 1932, p. 270.

By W. Van de Velde II.

The 'Mary', a yacht carrying 8 guns, was presented to Charles II by the City of Amsterdam in 1660. She was wrecked in 1675 (*See Anderson*, p. 20, No. 292).

78. AN ENGLISH TWO-DECKER FROM THE STARBOARD QUARTER, AND ANOTHER IN MID-DISTANCE.   Plate 281

Black lead, with grey wash; 44 × 27·6 cm. (17¼ × 10⅞ in.).

INSCR.: *Recto*, in the lower r.-hand corner, in black lead, by the artist, *W V V*, gone over by a later hand, *W. V. Velde*.

Prov.: George Salting, by whom it was bequeathed to the B.M., 1910.

1910–2–12–220.

Perhaps by W. Van de Velde II.

79. AN ENGLISH TWO-DECKER, c. 1680, FROM THE PORT BOW, WITH TOPSAILS LOOSED.

Offset from black chalk, re-touched in black lead, with grey wash; 42·2 × 30 cm. (16⅝ × 11⅞ in.). Old mount; 49·3 × 37·2 cm. (19⅜ × 14⅝ in.).

Prov.: Paul Sandby (*Lugt*, No. 2112. Probably sale, Christie, 17:iv:1817, Lots 65–75). Capt. Walter Dasent, R.N., by whom it was bequeathed to the B.M., 1940.

1940–12–14–1.

A Rear-Admiral's flagship, with his flag at the mizzen.

80. AN ENGLISH TWO-DECKER, c. 1680, FROM THE STARBOARD BOW, BEFORE THE WIND.   Plate 280

Offset (?) from black chalk, re-touched in black lead, with grey wash; 41·5 × 31·5 cm. (16⅜ × 12⅜ in.). Old mount; 51·4 × 37·5 cm. (20¼ × 14¾ in.).

Prov.: As for No. 79.

1940–12–14–2.

81. A SHIP CLOSE-HAULED, FROM THE PORT BOW, WITH ANOTHER SHIP BEYOND, BEFORE THE WIND.

Black chalk, with grey wash, re-touched in part with pen and brown ink; with an additional slip on the r.; 30·5 × 27 cm. (12 × 10¾ in.). Old mount; 44·1 × 38·8 cm. (17⅜ × 15¼ in.).

Inscr.: *Recto*, on the r., referring to the further vessel, in ink, *L* (twice) and *light*.

Prov.: As for No. 79.

1940–12–14–3.

By W. Van de Velde II.

82. A LARGE DUTCH GALLIOT, FROM THE PORT BOW.

Offset (?) from black chalk, with grey wash, re-touched with black lead; 41·8 × 31·7 cm. (16⅜ × 12½ in.). Old mount; 51·2 × 37·3 cm. (20⅛ × 14¾ in.).

Prov.: As for No. 79.

1940–12–14–4.

A galliot was a small two-masted vessel used for carrying dispatches.

83. AN ENGLISH THREE-DECKER, c. 1670, WITH A RICHLY DECORATED STERN INCORPORATING THE ROYAL ARMS AND A FIGURE OF JUSTICE, FROM THE PORT QUARTER.   Plate 274

Offset (?) from black chalk, with grey wash, re-touched in black lead; with an additional slip on the l.; 37·3 × 52·9 cm. (14⅝ × 20⅞ in.). Old Mount; 48·5 × 64 cm. (19⅛ × 25⅛ in.).

INSCR.: *Recto*, in the lower r.-hand corner, in black lead, by the artist, *ick heb om de wille van Monsr Scrudt mijn dess . . . | de afdruckxsels hier van gekomen na dat ick noch b . . . | wassen in . . . . engels & andere . . . schepen bouck le . . .* [I have at the request of Monsr Scrudt my . . . / the offsets taken from these after that I still . . . / washes in English & other . . . ships . . . .]

PROV.: As for No. 79.
1940–12–14–5.

Probably by W. Van de Velde II.

The inscription confirms the use made by the Van de Veldes of offsets (apparent in the weak outlines of many of their drawings), when a study of a single ship or of some more elaborate composition was required in reverse. A similar method was employed by Lely in the case of his drawings of the procession of the Knights of the Garter (*Cf.* p. 411).

84. A DUTCH TWO-DECKER, c. 1665, FROM THE PORT BOW, BECALMED.

Offset from black chalk, re-touched in black lead, with grey wash; on two conjoined sheets; 58·9 × 40·5 cm. (23⅛ × 15⅞ in.). Old mount; 63 × 46 cm. (24¾ × 18⅛ in.).

PROV.: As for No. 79.
1940–12–14–6.

A Vice-Admiral's flagship, with his flag at the fore.

85. PROBABLY THE 'MIDDELBURG', FROM THE STARBOARD BOW, WITH SAILS SHAKING.

Offset (?) from black chalk, re-touched in black lead, with grey wash; 35·4 × 47·3 cm. (14 × 18⅝ in.). Old mount; 49 × 61 cm. (19⅛ × 24 in.).

INSCR.: *Recto*, in the lower l.-hand corner, by the artist, *t v-gadt | [m]iddelbuch | . . . leijst 1659* [the frigate / 'Middelburg' / . . . 1659].

PROV.: As for No. 79.
1940–12–14–7

A number of ships named the 'Middelburg' are recorded, but the one with which the present drawing may be identified was a frigate built for the Zeeland Admiralty in 1653, which carried 40 guns. She is last heard of in 1693 (*See Vreugdenhil*, p. 16, No. 274).

86. TWO DUTCH TRANSPORT VESSELS, A 'KAAG' (L) AND A 'TJALK' (R), RESPECTIVELY FROM THE PORT AND THE STARBOARD BOW.

Offset (?) from black chalk, re-touched in pen and black ink, with grey washes, on blue-grey paper; 43 × 53·9 cm. (16⅞ × 21⅝ in.). Old mount; 43·9 × 54·7 cm. (17¼ × 21½ in.).

PROV.: As for No. 79.

1940–12–14–8.

A 'Kaag' was a small Dutch boat with a raking stem. A 'tjalk' was used mainly on inland waterways.

87. A DUTCH YACHT, c. 1660, WITH A FEMALE FIGURE ON HER STERN, FROM THE PORT QUARTER. At the top a small offset of part of another ship.

Plate 279

Black chalk and black lead; $42 \cdot 1 \times 31 \cdot 3$ cm. ($16\frac{1}{2} \times 12\frac{1}{4}$ in.). Old mount; $44 \cdot 7 \times 34 \cdot 2$ cm. ($17\frac{1}{2} \times 13\frac{1}{2}$ in.).

PROV.: As for No. 79.

1940–12–14–9.

88. A DUTCH TWO-DECKER, c. 1675, FROM THE PORT QUARTER, FIRING A SALUTE, A BARGE APPROACHING HER STARBOARD SIDE.

Black lead; $37 \times 29 \cdot 5$ cm. ($14\frac{5}{8} \times 11\frac{5}{8}$ in.). Old mount; $45 \cdot 9 \times 38 \cdot 8$ cm. ($18\frac{1}{8} \times 15$ in.).

INSCR.: *Recto*, in the lower l.-hand corner, by the artist, *W.V.V.J.*

PROV.: As for No. 79.

1940–12–14–10.

By W. Van de Velde II.

89. A DUTCH FLAGSHIP, c. 1675, FROM THE STARBOARD BOW, CLOSE-HAULED IN A BREEZE.

Black lead; $38 \cdot 8 \times 30 \cdot 2$ cm. ($15\frac{1}{4} \times 11\frac{7}{8}$ in.). Old mount; $50 \cdot 5 \times 37 \cdot 7$ cm. ($19\frac{7}{8} \times 14\frac{7}{8}$ in.).

INSCR.: *Recto*, in the lower l.-hand corner, by the artist, *W.V.V.J.*

PROV.: As for No. 79.

1940–12–14–11.

By W. Van de Velde II.

90. AN ENGLISH TWO-DECKER, c. 1675, FROM THE STARBOARD BOW.

Black chalk and black lead; $38 \cdot 1 \times 29$ cm. ($15 \times 11\frac{1}{2}$ in.). Old mount; $49 \cdot 7 \times 36 \cdot 9$ cm. ($19\frac{1}{2} \times 14\frac{1}{2}$ in.).

INSCR.: *Recto*, in the lower l.-hand corner, by the artist, *W.V.V J.*

PROV.: As for No. 79.

1940–12–14–12.

By W. Van de Velde II.

91. A DUTCH 'ADVICE VESSEL' OF THE ZEELAND ADMIRALTY, FROM THE PORT BOW, A BARGE TOWING AHEAD.

Black chalk; $38 \cdot 6 \times 29 \cdot 8$ cm. ($15\frac{1}{8} \times 11\frac{3}{4}$ in.). Old mount; $48 \cdot 6 \times 37 \cdot 5$ cm. ($19\frac{1}{8} \times 14\frac{3}{4}$ in.).

INSCR.: *Recto*, at the foot, *zeeus advijs vaertuijgh* [Zeeland advice boat].

PROV.: As for No. 79.

1940–12–14–13.

Probably by W. Van de Velde II.

92. THE 'ROYAL ESCAPE', FROM NEARLY THE STARBOARD BROADSIDE.

Plate 282

Black chalk and black lead; $29 \cdot 5 \times 45$ cm. ($11\frac{5}{8} \times 17\frac{3}{4}$ in.). Old mount; $36 \cdot 8 \times 52$ cm. ($14\frac{1}{2} \times 20\frac{1}{2}$ in.).

INSCR.: *Recto*, in the upper r.-hand corner, by the artist, *dit is het vartúijgh waer | d koningh Karel sigh mede | salferde flugtende úijt engelen*

/ ick hebbehet noch perfetter [this is the vessel in which / King Charles saved himself / fleeing out of England / I have (another) more perfect]; and in the lower l.-hand corner, *W V V J*.

PROV.: As for No. 79.
1940–12–14–14.

By W. Van de Velde II.

The smack in which Capt. Nicholas Tattersal took Charles II on his memorable flight to France in 1651. She was subsequently purchased by the King in 1660, and named the 'Royal Escape'. She was rebuilt in 1714 (*See Anderson*, p. 20, No. 291).

This drawing probably served as a study for the oil-painting of the 'Royal Escape' by W. Van de Velde II, signed *W. V. Velde*, in the collection of Sir Bruce Ingram. Another portrait of the 'Royal Escape', differing considerably from Sir Bruce Ingram's picture is in the Royal Collection at Buckingham Palace; it is identical with that mentioned by *Vertue* (IV, p. 92) as being in the catalogue of James II's pictures (1687): '(Van de Velde) a little seapeice with the bark that carried the King to France.' In the National Maritime Museum there is also a drawing by W. Van de Velde II of a vessel very similar to that in the present study, and this, too, may therefore be a portrait of the 'Royal Escape'.

93. AN ENGLISH SLOOP OF WAR, FROM NEARLY THE PORT BROADSIDE.

Black lead; 36 × 47 cm. (14$\frac{1}{8}$ × 18$\frac{1}{2}$ in.). Old mount; 43·1 × 54·2 cm. (17 × 21$\frac{1}{4}$ in.).

PROV.: As for No. 79.
1940–12–14–15.

94. A DUTCH FLAGSHIP WITH SAILS SHAKING, FROM THE STARBOARD BOW.

Pen and black and brown ink; 16·6 × 18·8 cm. (6$\frac{1}{2}$ × 7$\frac{3}{8}$ in.). Old mount; 22·5 × 24·8 cm. (8$\frac{7}{8}$ × 9$\frac{3}{4}$ in.).

PROV.: Miss Julia Sharpe, by whose Executors it was presented to the B.M., 1946.
1946–4–13–186.

95. AN ENGLISH FISHING VESSEL, FROM THE STARBOARD BROADSIDE; IN THE FOREGROUND, A WHERRY.

Black lead, with grey wash; 22·7 × 19·8 cm. (8$\frac{7}{8}$ × 7$\frac{3}{4}$ in.). Old mount; 25·1 × 22 cm. (9$\frac{7}{8}$ × 8$\frac{5}{8}$ in.).

PROV.: As for No. 94.
1946–4–13–187.

96. AN ENGLISH SHIP BECALMED, FROM THE STARBOARD BOW.

Grey washes, over black lead; on two conjoined strips; 22·8 × 12 cm. (9 × 4$\frac{3}{4}$ in.). Old mount; 24·8 × 14 cm. (9$\frac{3}{4}$ × 5$\frac{1}{2}$ in.).

PROV.: As for No. 94.
1946–4–13–188.

97. STERN OF A DUTCH SHIP, PERHAPS THE 'PRINS WILLEM'. Richly carved on the tafferel with allegorical figures, one seated in the centre with a tilting lance, a second on the r. with the arrows of the Seven Provinces, and a third on the l. with a palm branch representing Victory. Above, the arms of Orange, and

below, figures with the shields of the Seven Provinces, and the arms of the Admiralty of the Maas.

Plate 284

Grey wash over an offset from black chalk; a narrow strip added on the r.; 38·3 × 27·1 cm. ($15 × 10\frac{5}{8}$ in.). Old mount; 39·8 × 28·7 cm. ($15\frac{5}{8} × 11\frac{1}{4}$ in.).

PROV.: As for No. 94.
1946-4-13-189.

A number of ships named the 'Prins Willem' are recorded, but the one with which the drawing may be connected was built for the Maas Admiralty in 1653 and carried 42-44 guns. She was lost at sea in 1656 (*See Vreugdenhil*, p. 17, No. 290).

[98–147]. MISCELLANEOUS SHIPPING. The following are listed in chronological order of acquisition and registration, and are mounted in two albums.

98. FOUR STATES YACHTS AT ANCHOR, L., AND SMALL CRAFT BEACHED IN THE FOREGROUND.

Black lead, with grey wash; 24·4 × 39·9 cm. ($9\frac{5}{8} × 15\frac{3}{4}$ in.).

INSCR.: *Recto*, in the lower l. & r.-hand corners, 6.

PROV.: As for No. 54.
5214-32 (L.B., as by Van de Velde II, 25).

BIBL.: *Sloane Cat.*, p. 131, No. 32.

99. FISHERMEN IN A 'WEYSCHUIT' HAULING A NET IN THE FORE-GROUND, L., A 'FLUTE' SEEN FROM THE STERN ON THE R.

Black chalk, with grey wash; 19·4 × 31·2 cm. ($7\frac{5}{8} × 12\frac{1}{4}$ in.).

INSCR.: *Recto*, in the upper l.-hand corner, in black lead, *28*, and in the lower r.-hand corner, *8*.

PROV.: As for No. 54.
5214-34 (L.B., as by Van de Velde II, 22).

BIBL.: *Sloane Cat.*, p. 131, No. 34.

For the 'weyschuit' and the 'flute', *See* respectively Nos. 15 & 74.

100. AN ENGLISH 'HOOKER' BEFORE THE WIND.

Black chalk touched with white, on light buff paper; 17·7 × 28·5 cm. ($7 × 11\frac{1}{4}$ in.).

INSCR.: *Recto*, at the foot on both sides, in black lead, *9*, and in the lower l.-hand corner, in black lead, by the artist, *W. V. V J*.

PROV.: As for No. 54.
5214-35 (L.B., Van de Velde II, 36).

BIBL.: *Sloane Cat.*, p. 131, No. 35.

By W. Van de Velde II.

A 'hooker' was a two-masted square-rigged merchant vessel, either English or Dutch.

101. A SHIP IN A GALE, DRIVING ON TO THE ROCKS.

Black chalk, strengthened with black lead, the sea touched with white; 28·2 × 35·5 cm. (11 × 14 in.).

INSCR.: *Recto*, towards the foot, on either side, in black lead, *11*; and in the lower r.-hand corner, in ink, by the artist, *W. V. V J*.

PROV.: As for No. 54.
5214–38 (L.B., Van de Velde II, 33).

BIBL.: *Sloane Cat.*, p. 132, No. 38.

By W. Van de Velde II.

102. A 'WATERSCHIP', WITH A DUTCH SHIP AT ANCHOR BEYOND, c. 1665.

Black lead, with grey wash; 21 × 32·4 cm. (8¼ × 12¾ in.).

INSCR.: *Recto*, in the lower l. and r.-hand corners, in black lead, *19*.

PROV.: As for No. 54.
5214–45 (L.B., as by W. Van de Velde II, 24).

BIBL.: *Sloane Cat.*, p. 133, No. 45.

The 'waterschip' was used in Holland for towing ships over the shallows.

103. A 'FLUTE', L., AND ANOTHER DUTCH MERCHANT SHIP TOWED BY 'WATERSCHIPS'.

Brush drawing in grey wash, over black lead; 19·1 × 31·2 cm. (7½ × 12¼ in.).

INSCR.: *Recto*, in the lower l.-hand corner, in black lead, *27*.

PROV.: As for No. 54.
5214–52 (L.B., as by W. Van de Velde II, 21).

BIBL.: *Sloane Cat.*, p. 134, No. 52.

For the 'flute' and the 'waterschip', *See* respectively Nos. 74 & 102.

104. A DUTCH SHIP, BROAD ON THE PORT TACK, AND TWO OTHERS IN THE OFFING.

Black chalk and black lead; 16·2 × 21 cm. (6⅜ × 8¼ in.).

INSCR.: *Recto*, in the lower l.-hand corner, in black lead, *30*; and in the lower r.-hand corner, in black lead, by the artist, *W* (*V. V J* cut away).

PROV.: As for No. 54.
5214–54 (L.B., Van de Velde II 35b).,

BIBL.: *Sloane Cat.*, p. 134, No. 54.

By W. Van de Velde II.

105. TWO STUDIES, ONE ABOVE THE OTHER, OF AN ENGLISH SHIP CLOSE-HAULED.

Pen and brown ink, with grey wash, over black lead; 29·1 × 17·8 cm. (11½ × 7 in.).

INSCR.: *Recto*, in the upper r.-hand corner, in black lead, *29*.

PROV.: As for No. 54.
5214–55 (L.B., Van de Velde II, 38).

BIBL.: *Sloane Cat.*, p. 135, No. 55.

By W. Van de Velde II, in his latest manner (*Cf.* Nos. 25, etc., & 108, 109, 132).

106. A DUTCH 'FLUTE' BEFORE A STRONG BREEZE.

Black lead; the horizon line ruled; 16·4 × 20·5 cm. (6½ × 8⅛ in.).

INSCR.: *Recto*, in the lower l.-hand corner, in black lead, *31*; and below it, in black lead, by the artist, *W V V J*.

PROV.: As for No. 54.
5214–56 (L.B., Van de Velde II, 34a).

BIBL.: *Sloane Cat.*, p. 135, No. 57.

By W. Van de Velde II.

For the 'flute', *See* No. 74.

107. DUTCH SMALL CRAFT IN A STRONG BREEZE.

Black lead, 16·3 × 20·7 cm. (6⅜ × 8⅛ in.).

INSCR.: *Recto*, in the lower l.-hand corner, in black lead, *32.*; and below, in black lead, by the artist, *W.V.V J* (partly cut away).

PROV.: As for No. 54.
5214–57 (L.B., Van de Velde II, 34b).

BIBL.: *Sloane Cat.*, p. 135, No. 56.

By W. Van de Velde II.

108. TWO YACHTS AT THE ENTRANCE TO A CREEK WITH OTHER SMALL CRAFT.

Pen and brown ink, with grey wash; the corners made up; 12·4 × 18·8 cm. (4⅞ × 7½ in.).

INSCR.: *Recto*, in the lower r.-hand corner, in black lead, *33*.

PROV.: As for No. 54.
5214–58 (L.B., Van de Velde II, 40a).

BIBL.: *Sloane Cat.*, p. 135, No. 58.

By W. Van de Velde II, in his latest manner (*Cf* Nos. 25, etc., & 105, 109, 132).

109. AN ENGLISH FLAGSHIP BECALMED, SALUTING.

Pen and brown ink, with grey wash, the sky touched with white; the corners made up; 14·8 × 18·9 cm. (5⅞ × 7½ in.).

INSCR.: *Recto*, in the lower l. & r.-hand corners, in black lead, *34*.

PROV.: As for No. 54.
5214–59 (L.B., Van de Velde II, 37b).

BIBL.: *Sloane Cat.*, p. 135, No. 59.

By W. Van de Velde II, in his latest manner (*Cf.* Nos. 25, etc., & 105, 108, 132).

110. A DUTCH 'FLUTE' BEFORE THE WIND.

Black lead, with grey wash, partly gone over in pen and brown ink; 16·5 × 18·8 cm. (6½ × 7⅜ in.).

INSCR.: *Recto*, in the upper r.-hand corner, in black lead, *38*.

PROV.: As for No. 54.
5214–63 (L.B., as by W. Van de Velde II, 37a).

BIBL.: *Sloane Cat.*, p. 136, No. 63.

III. A KETCH BEFORE THE WIND.

Black lead; 14·6 × 19·3 cm. (5¾ × 7⅝ in.).

INSCR.: *Recto*, in the upper r.-hand corner, in black lead, *39*.

Probably by W. Van de Velde II.

For the 'flute', *See* No. 74.

PROV.: As for No. 54.
5214–65 (L.B., as by W. Van de Velde II, 35a).

BIBL.: *Sloane Cat.*, p. 136, No. 65.

112. A DUTCH SHIP, L., A GALLIOT, R., AND OTHER SHIPPING WITH A QUARTERING BREEZE.

Grey washes, strengthened with pen and black ink, over black lead; 26 × 43 cm. (10¼ × 16⅞ in.).

PROV.: The Rev. C. M. Cracherode, by whom it was bequeathed to the B.M., 1799.
F.f.4–140 (L.B., as after W. Van de Velde II, p. 270).

BIBL.: *Cracherode Cat.*, p. 133, No. 140.

An XVIII c. copy, perhaps by Charles Gore, after W. Van de Velde II.

113. A MEDITERRANEAN SEAPORT, WITH A GENOESE SHIP ON THE R.

Pen and brown ink, with grey wash; on two conjoined sheets; 21·5 × 20·3 cm. (8½ × 8 in.). Old mount; 27·2 × 25·8 cm. (10¾ × 10⅛ in.).

INSCR.: *Recto*, in the lower l.-hand corner, *W.V.V J*

PROV.: As for No. 112.
G.g.2–297 (L.B., Van de Velde II, 15).

BIBL.: *Cracherode Cat.*, p. 70, No. 297.

By W. Van de Velde II. An imaginary composition in the style of Abraham Storck.

114. DUTCH FISHING BOATS NEAR A SHORE.

Pen and brown ink, with grey wash, over black lead (?); 15·5 × 21·1 cm. (6⅛ × 8¼ in.). Old mount; 25 × 30·5 cm. (9¾ × 12 in.).

PROV.: As for No. 112.
G.g.2–298 (L.B., Van de Velde II, 16).

BIBL.: *Cracherode Cat.*, p. 70, No. 298.

By W. Van de Velde II.

115. DUTCH SMALL CRAFT NEAR THE SHORE.

Pen and brown ink, with grey wash; 9 × 16·2 cm. (3½ × 6⅜ in.).

PROV.: P. H. Lankrink (*Lugt*, No. 2090, Sale, Smith-Basset, 23:i:1693, Lot 9, 150 or 173 (?), though these may have been oil paintings). The Rev. C. M. Cracherode (*Lugt*, No. 606), by whom it was bequeathed to the B.M., 1799.

G.g.2–299 (L.B., as by Van de Velde II, 48b).

BIBL.: *Cracherode Cat.*, p. 70, No. 299.

Given in the *General Inventory* of 1837 to Ludolf Bakhuysen, but in the *Cracherode Catalogue* to W. Van de Velde II, which latter seems to be the more likely attribution.

116. DUTCH SMALL CRAFT GOING TO WINDWARD.

Pen and brown ink, with grey wash; 10·2 × 15·6 cm. (4 × 6⅛ in.).

PROV.: As for No. 115.
G.g.2–300 (L.B., as by Van de Velde II, 48a).

BIBL.: *Cracherode Cat.*, p. 70, No. 300.

Given in the *General Inventory* of 1837 to Ludolf Bakhuysen, but in the *Cracherode Catalogue* to W. Van de Velde II, which later seems to be the more likely attribution.

117. DUTCH SMALL CRAFT BEATING TO WINDWARD IN A BREEZE.

Pen and brown ink, with grey wash; 12·8 × 20 cm. (5 × 7⅞ in.).

PROV.: As for No. 64.

O.o.10–137 (L.B., as by Van de Velde II, 44).

BIBL.: *Payne Knight Cat.*, p. 139, No. 137.

118. SHIPS WRECKED ON A ROCKY COAST.

Brush drawing in grey wash, over black lead; 15·2 × 20 cm. (6 × 7⅞ in.).

INSCR.: *Recto*, at the foot, in the centre, by the artist, *W.V.V J*

PROV.: As for No. 64.
O.o.10–232 (L.B., Van de Velde II, 45).

BIBL.: *Payne Knight Cat.*, p. 153, No. 232.

Presumably by W. Van de Velde II. The signature is apparently in his hand.

119. STATES YACHTS AND OTHER VESSELS BECALMED.

Brush drawing in grey wash, over black lead, strengthened with pen and black ink; 17·2 × 32·2 cm. (6¾ × 12⅝ in.).

INSCR.: *Recto*, in the lower r.-hand corner, by the artist, *w.v.velde F.*

PROV.: As for No. 64.
O.o.10–233 (L.B., Van de Velde II, 19).

BIBL.: *Payne Knight Cat.*, p. 153, No. 233.

Presumably by W. Van de Velde II.

120. AN ENGLISH SHIP AT ANCHOR IN A BAY, DRYING SAILS.

Pen and black ink, with grey wash; 14·8 × 26·1 cm. (5⅝ × 10¼ in.).

INSCR.: *Recto*, in the lower l.-hand corner, by the artist, *w.v.velde Junʳ*

PROV.: As for No. 64.

O.O.10–244 (L.B., Van de Velde II, 17).

BIBL.: *Payne Knight Cat.*, p. 155, No. 244.

Presumably by W. Van de Velde II.

121. DUTCH VESSELS BECALMED NEAR THE SHORE.

Pen and black ink, with grey wash; 21·9 × 30·8 cm. (8⅝ × 12⅛ in.).

PROV.: As for No. 64.

O.O.11–245 (L.B., as by W. Van de Velde II, 18).

BIBL.: *Payne Knight Cat.*, p. 155, No. 245.

Perhaps an XVIIIc. imitation of the style of the Van de Veldes.

122. ENGLISH SHIPS AT ANCHOR, c. 1700.

Pen and brown ink, with washes of grey and brown; 13·5 × 19·5 cm. (5¼ × 7⅝ in.).

INSCR.: *Recto*, in the lower r.-hand corner, *W vd Velde*.

    Verso, at the top, in black lead *getekent als ick was te gaen naer . . .* [drawn as I was to go to . . .].

PROV.: As for No. 32.

1836–8–11–538 (L.B., Van de Velde II, 11a).

BIBL.: *Sheepshanks Cat.*, p. 98, No. 538.

By W. Van de Velde II (?).

The signature on the *recto* is not the normal one used by Willem Van de Velde II to whom the drawing would naturally be attributed.

123. ENGLISH SHIPS AT ANCHOR, c. 1700. In the distance, r., the Royal Yacht 'Cleveland'.

Pen and brown ink, with washes of grey and brown over black lead; 13·3 × 19·1 cm. (5¼ × 7½ in.).

INSCR.: *Recto*, in the lower r.-hand corner, *W vd Velde*.

    Verso, at the top in black lead, *Jaght d kleeflant om* (?) *dit geteke . . .* [Yacht Cleveland to this drawn . . .].

PROV.: As for No. 32.

1836–8–11–539 (L.B., as by Van de Velde II, 11b.

BIBL.: *Sheepshanks Cat.*, p. 98, No. 539.

By W. Van de Velde II (?). *See* note to No. 122. For a near view of the 'Cleveland', *see* No. 63.

124. A STATES YACHT AND OTHER DUTCH CRAFT BECALMED.

Pen and brown ink, with water-colour, heightened with white; 16·1 × 13·2 cm. (6⅜ × 5¼ in.).

PROV.: As for No. 32.

1836–8–11–804 (L.B., Van de Velde II, 49).

BIBL.: *Sheepshanks Cat.*, p. 115, No. 19 (?).

The penwork suggests the latest manner of W. Van de Velde II. The tinting in water-colour, which seems to be contemporary, is the only recorded instance of this medium among his drawings.

125. A SMALL SHIP BEING TOWED PAST A LARGER SHIP AT ANCHOR.

Black chalk; $26 \cdot 6 \times 44 \cdot 7$ cm. ($10\frac{1}{2} \times 17\frac{5}{8}$ in.).

PROV.: As for No. 13.

1857–12–22–5 (L.B., as by Van de Velde II, 26).

126. A DUTCH SHIP, BROADSIDE VIEW, WITH FORE TOPSAIL AND MIZZEN LOOSED.

Black chalk, with grey wash; the upper corners cut off; $8 \cdot 7 \times 9 \cdot 1$ cm. ($3\frac{3}{8} \times 3\frac{5}{8}$ in.).

INSCR.: *Recto*, in the lower l.-hand corner, in black lead, by the artist, *W*

PROV.: As for No. 67.

1857–12–22–10 (L.B., Van de Velde II, 43a).

By W. Van de Velde II.

127. A MEDITERRANEAN SEAPORT WITH ENGLISH SMALL CRAFT.

Black chalk, with grey wash, strengthened with black lead; $9 \cdot 1 \times 18 \cdot 5$ cm. ($3\frac{5}{8} \times 7\frac{3}{8}$ in.).

PROV.: As for No. 67.

1857–12–22–12 (L.B., Van de Velde II, 43b).

Probably by W. Van de Velde II.

128. DUTCH SHIPS AT ANCHOR, AND A STATES YACHT UNDER SAIL, R.

Black lead, with grey wash, touched with pen and brown ink on the yacht; $15 \cdot 4 \times 29$ cm. ($6\frac{1}{4} \times 11\frac{3}{8}$ in.).

PROV.: As for No. 26.

1863–1–10–226 (L.B., Van de Velde II, 46b).

By W. Van de Velde II.

129. A 'KAAG' PASSING THE END OF A PIER.

Black chalk strengthened with black lead; $19 \cdot 2 \times 26 \cdot 8$ cm. ($7\frac{1}{2} \times 10\frac{1}{2}$ in.).

INSCR.: *Recto*, in the lower l.-hand corner, in black lead, by the artist, (W)*V. V. J* (partly cut away); and, in the lower r.-hand corner, in black lead, *K* (for '*keer*' = 'turn over').

PROV.: As for No. 26.

1863–1–10–227 (L.B., Van de Velde II, 47).

By W. Van de Velde II.

For the 'kaag', See No. 86.

130. VIEW FROM THE DUTCH COAST WITH SHIPPING, A FORT ON THE L.

Black chalk, with grey wash, strengthened with black lead; $20 \cdot 1 \times 32$ cm. ($7\frac{7}{8} \times 12\frac{5}{8}$ in.).

INSCR.: *Recto*, in the lower r.-hand corner, in black lead, *N.5.*

PROV.: As for No. 26.

1863–1–10–228 (L.B., Van de Velde II, 10b).

Probably by W. Van de Velde II.

131. AN ENGLISH FLAGSHIP AT ANCHOR, WITH A YACHT UNDER HER STERN.

Black lead, with grey wash, touched with pen and brown ink; $27\cdot7 \times 45\cdot9$ cm. ($10\frac{7}{8} \times 17\frac{3}{4}$ in.).

PROV.: As for No. 26.

1863–1–10–229 (L.B., Van de Velde II, 9).

By W. Van de Velde II.

INSCR.: *Recto*, in the lower l.-hand corner, in black lead, *N.2.*

132. AN ENGLISH YACHT AT THE ENTRANCE TO A CREEK.

Pen and brown ink, with grey wash; the horizon line ruled; $15\cdot6 \times 18\cdot3$ cm. ($6\frac{1}{8} \times 7\frac{1}{4}$ in.).

PROV.: As for No. 26.

1863–1–10–230 (L.B., Van de Velde II, 46a).

By W. Van de Velde II, in his latest manner (*Cf.* Nos. 25, etc., & 105, 108, 109).

INSCR.: *Recto*, in the lower l.-hand corner, in grey wash, by the artist, *W.V.V J*

133. A DUTCH SHIP BECALMED, WITH A BOAT PULLING TOWARDS HER.

Black lead, with grey wash, touched with pen and ink; $21\cdot7 \times 28\cdot4$ cm. ($8\frac{1}{2} \times 11\frac{1}{4}$ in.).

PROV.: Marseille Holloway, from whom it was purchased by the B.M., 1872.

1872–10–12–3323 (L.B., Van de Velde II, 14).

By W. Van de Velde II, but perhaps redrawn in part by a later hand.

INSCR.: *Recto*, above the ship, in black lead, *blaū*; to the l., in black lead, *L.*; and, in the lower l.-hand corner, in pen and ink, by the artist, *W.V V J* (mostly cut away).

134. SHIPS CLOSE-HAULED IN A FRESH BREEZE.

Pen and dark grey ink; the horizon line and other planes ruled; $19\cdot4 \times 30\cdot6$ cm. ($7\frac{5}{8} \times 11\frac{7}{8}$ in.).

PROV.: As for No. 24.

1874–8–8–93 (L.B., Van de Velde II, 31).

By W. Van de Velde II.

No doubt intended to illustrate some point in perspective.

INSCR.: *Recto*, in the upper l.-hand corner, in black lead, by the artist, *W.V.V J*

135. ATTACK ON A BARBARY STRONGHOLD, WITH A GALLEY IN THE FOREGROUND, R., AND OTHER SHIPS TO THE L.

Pen and brown ink, with grey wash, over black lead; $5\cdot9 \times 7\cdot2$ cm. ($2\frac{1}{4} \times 2\frac{7}{8}$ in.).

PROV.: G. Leembruggen (Sale, Amsterdam, Brakke Grond, 5: iii: 1866, Lot 673).

John Malcolm. J. W. Malcolm, from whom it was purchased by the B. M., 1895.

1895–9–15–1332.

BIBL.: *Malcolm Cat.*, p. 259, No. 857.

By W. Van de Velde II.

136. SHIPPING BECALMED NEAR THE SHORE, WITH AN ENGLISH YACHT SALUTING IN THE FOREGROUND, L.

Black chalk, touched with pen and brown ink; 13·5 × 32·5 cm. (5¼ × 12¾ in.).

INSCR.: *Recto*, over the boats on the l., in black lead, *rora* [sunlight]; and in the lower r.-hand corner, in black chalk, by the artist, *W.V.V I*

PROV.: Sir Thomas Lawrence (*Lugt*, No. 2445). John Malcolm. J. W. Malcolm, from whom it was purchased by the B.M., 1895.

1895–9–15–1334.

BIBL.: *Malcolm Cat.*, p. 260, No. 859.

By W. Van de Velde II.

137. A 'KAAG' BEFORE A FRESH BREEZE.

Pen and brown ink, with grey wash, over black lead; 15·4 × 23·8 cm. (6⅛ × 9⅜ in.).

INSCR.: *Recto*, in the lower r.-hand corner, on a spar, in brown ink, *W V Velde*

PROV.: G. Leembruggen (Sale, Amsterdam, Brakke Grond, 5:iii:1866). Baron J. G. Verstolk van Soelen (Sale, Amsterdam,

4-7:xi:1867). John Malcolm. J. W. Malcolm, from whom it was purchased by the B.M., 1895.

1895–9–15–1335.

BIBL.: *Malcolm Cat.*, p. 260, No. 860.

For the 'kaag', *See* No. 86.

138. A DUTCH FLAGSHIP, L., WITH A 'KAAG', R., BECALMED.

Brush drawing in grey wash, strengthened with black lead; 15·5 × 20 cm. (6⅛ × 7⅞ in.).

INSCR.: *Recto*, in the lower l.-hand corner, on a spar, in ink, by the artist, *W V V*

PROV.: Muller. G. Leembruggen (*Lugt*, No. 2988; Sale, Amsterdam, Brakke Grond,

5:iii:1866, Lot 663). John Malcolm. J. W. Malcolm, from whom it was purchased by the B.M., 1895.

1895–9–15–1336.

BIBL.: *Malcolm Cat.*, p. 260, No. 861.

Presumably by W. Van de Velde II. The signature, however, is not his usual one.

139. A STATES YACHT AND DUTCH SHIPS BECALMED.

Brush drawing in grey wash over black lead; 15·6 × 24·9 cm. (6⅛ × 9¾ in.).

PROV.: Sir J. C. Robinson. John Malcolm. J. W. Malcolm, from whom it was purchased by the B.M., 1895.

1895–9–15–1337.

BIBL.: *Malcolm Cat.*, p. 260, No. 862.

140. AN ENGLISH FLAGSHIP BECALMED.

Pen and brown ink; 8·9 × 10·6 cm. (3½ × 4¼ in.).

1900–8–24–149 (L.B., Van de Velde II, 50a).

PROV.: Henry Vaughan, by whom it was bequeathed to the B.M., 1900.

By W. Van de Velde II.

141. A DUTCH SHIP, WITH A GALLIOT UNDER HER STERN, R. OTHER SHIPS IN THE OFFING, L.

Brush drawing in grey wash over black lead; 20·6 × 15·3 cm. (8⅛ × 6 in.).

INSCR.: *Recto*, in the lower l.-hand corner, in brown ink, *W. V. V.*

PROV.: As for No. 140.

1900–8–24–150 (L.B., as by W. Van de Velde II, 50b).

Probably by W. Van de Velde, I.

For the 'galliot', *See* No. 82.

142. A DUTCH YACHT WITH A 'WATERSCHIP' AT ANCHOR IN THE FOREGROUND. OTHER SHIPS TO L. AND R.

Brush drawing in grey wash over black chalk, touched with pen and grey ink; 16·7 × 30·2 cm. (6⅝ × 11⅞ in.).

INSCR.: *Recto*, in the lower r.-hand corner, in grey wash, by the artist, *W. V. V J*

PROV.: George Salting, by whom it was bequeathed to the B.M., 1910.

1910–2–12–215.

By W. Van de Velde II.

For the 'waterschip', *See* No. 102.

143. A 'BOEIER' UNDER SAIL, AND A DUTCH SHIP AT ANCHOR IN THE BACKGROUND, R.

Black lead, with grey wash; 14·3 × 22·8 cm. (5⅝ × 9 in.).

PROV.: R. P. Roupell (Sale, Christie, 14:vii:1887, Lot 1232). George Salting,

by whom it was bequeathed to the B.M., 1910.

1910–2–12–216.

A 'boeier' was a small 'round' Dutch vessel used for fishing and transport.

144. TWO DUTCH SHIPS BECALMED AND DRYING SAILS.

Brush drawing in grey wash over black lead; 17 × 28·4 cm. (6¾ × 11⅛ in.).

PROV.: R. P. Roupell (Sale, Christie, 14:vii:1887, Lot 1220 (?)). George Salting,

by whom it was bequeathed to the B.M., 1910.

1910–2–12–217.

145. DUTCH SHIPS BECALMED, WITH BOATS IN THE FOREGROUND.

Brush drawing in grey wash over black lead; $15 \times 41 \cdot 2$ cm. ($5\frac{7}{8} \times 16\frac{1}{4}$ in.).

PROV.: R. P. Roupell (Sale, Christie, 14:vii:1887, Lot 1224 (?)). George Salting, by whom it was bequeathed to the B.M., 1910.

1910–2–12–218.

By W. Van de Velde II.

146. DUTCH FISHING 'PINKS' NEAR THE SHORE, WITH OTHER SHIPS BECALMED IN THE BACKGROUND.

Brush drawing in grey wash, over black lead; $14 \cdot 7 \times 40 \cdot 6$ cm. ($5\frac{3}{4} \times 16$ in.).

PROV.: As for No. 142.
1910–2–12–219.

By W. Van de Velde II.

For the 'pink', *See* No. 60.

147. THE DUTCH FLEET AT ANCHOR.

Black lead, with grey wash; $15 \cdot 4 \times 41 \cdot 4$ cm. ($6 \times 16\frac{1}{4}$ in.).

INSCR.: *Recto*, in the lower l.-hand corner, *W. V. V. J* (very faint).

PROV.: As for No. 142.
1910–2–12–221.

By W. Van de Velde II.

VAN DIEST, ADRIAEN

B. 1655/6: D. 1705

Landscape painter and etcher

Born at The Hague, the son and pupil of a marine painter, probably Jeronymus van Diest (B. 1631: D. 1673) who was the son of Willem van Diest (*fl.* 1610–63). Said to have come to England with his father in 1673. Came under the patronage of the Earl of Bath, patron of Jan Siberechts, who encouraged him to draw the ruined castles of Devonshire and Cornwall. An entry in the Painter-Stainers' order book, March 6th, 1676/7, records that 'Mr. Adrian Van Diest appeared and promised to give his proofe piece he lives with Vaubert in Durham Yard'. Married Huberta, daughter of Adam Colonia (*q.v.*); four of their children were baptised at the Dutch Church of Austin Friars between 1686 and 1691. Vertue states that his portrait was painted in Rome by an English artist, but there is no other evidence of travel in Italy. Painted many Italianate landscapes most frequently as decorative panels. At the Countess of Dover's house in Albemarle Street, Vertue noted 'in the Roomes & over the doors & chimneys adornd with the works of Vandiest, in Landskapes, many of his best manner'. His view of Sprotborough near Doncaster engraved in mezzotint by Bernard Lens. Etched a number of landscapes from his own works but before completing the series died of gout, and was buried in St. Martin-in-the-Fields on Feb. 9th, 1704/5. According to Vertue, his 'reputation & workes will be ever valuable as long as these endure' and Buckeridge considered his 'distances have a peculiar tenderness and his clouds a freedom that few have arrived at'. His style in painting and etching strongly imitative of Salvator Rosa.

BIBL.: *Buckeridge*, p. 428. *Moens*, p. 19. *D.N.B.*, LVIII, 1899, p. 104. *T.-B.*, IX, 1913, p. 250. *Grant*, p. 20. *Vertue, Index*, p. 63.

1. TREES ON THE BANK OF A RIVER OR POND. An inlet of water with trees on the far bank, centre, and bushes on a slope to the r. On the l., a fisherman wading in the water with a net, and in the distance, another figure seated beneath the trees.   **Plate 264**

Black chalk, heightened with white, on blue-grey paper; 22 × 26·9 cm. (8⅝ × 10½ in.).

PROV.: Richard Payne Knight, by whom it was bequeathed to the B.M., 1824. **O.o.11–269** (L.B.1).

BIBL.: *Payne-Knight Cat.*, p. 158, No. 269.

VERELST, SIMON

[VARELST, VER ELST]

B. 1644: D. after 1710 (?)

Flower and portrait painter

Born at The Hague on Aug. 21st, 1644. Younger son of Pieter Verelst, portrait, *genre*, and still-life painter of Antwerp, and later of Dordrecht and The Hague, and brother of Harman Verelst (B. 1641/2: D. 1699), flower and portrait painter. In early life lived and worked with Harman, and became a member of the Guild of St. Luke at The Hague in 1666. Came to London in 1669, and lodged near his compatriot, Jan Looten the landscape painter, in St. James's Market, where Pepys (who calls him Evereest) visited him on April 11th of that year, and was shown 'a little flower pot of his drawing'. Quickly made a reputation with his flower-pieces, many of which would no doubt have been used as decorative over-doors and over-mantels. Acclaimed in this field by Prior in his lines on *A Flower painted by Simon Varelst*, which were to inspire the subject of a picture by Angelica Kauffman, 'Flora finishing a Flower for Varelst' (1826; in the collection of the Hon. Anne Rushout at Wanstead Grove). Was 'piqued' by the 2nd Duke of Buckingham into attempting portraiture, and launched a new fashion in this art by introducing floral decoration. His portrait of Buckingham in this manner was 'so crouded . . . with fruits and sun-flowers' that Charles II, when he saw it, thought that it actually was a flower-piece. Another example, still extant, is his *Louise de Keroualle, Duchess of Portsmouth, as Flora*, now at Hampton Court. Though Vertue was informed on one occasion that Verelst was 'stiff & laborious [and] therefore succeeded not', yet generally his work as a portraitist seems to have been admired for its high finish and to have obtained good prices. Was joined in England by his brother Harman, with whom he went (in company with the landscape painter Adriaen de Hennin and the history painter Jacques

Parmentier) on a short visit to France in 1680. In 1685, when painting Mary, wife of the seventh Duke of Norfolk, was offered a bribe by her lover, Sir John Germaine, to admit the ownership of a shirt and waistcoat of Sir John's which had been discovered by the Duke's agent. Verelst refused, and, when divorce proceedings were instituted by the Duke in 1691, was called as a witness. Was inordinately vain, a fault which lost him at least one important sitter, the 1st Earl of Shaftesbury. Eventually became mad, and on his recovery, found that he was out of vogue. Besides still-life and portraits, is said to have painted two history-pieces, one a 'Venus naked under a tree' in James II's collection, the other of an unknown subject, in which he attempted to unite the drawing of Raphael with the colouring of Titian, Rubens or Van Dyck. Perhaps identical with the 'S.

Verelst who wrongly informed Vertue that Harman Verelst came to England in Charles II's reign and Simon in William III's. Is said to have died at an advanced age at his house in Suffolk Street, Haymarket, but the date not known, though Walpole states that he was still alive in 1710, and there is no record of him in the Registers of either St. Martin-in-the-Fields or St. James's, Piccadilly, where he might have been buried. Buckeridge notes that Harman had several sons and a daughter, all trained in their father's profession, and among these must be the Willem, Maria and J. Verelst noted by Mr. Collins Baker.

BIBL.: *Neale*, Ser. II, iii (*Wanstead Grove, Essex*). *Walpole*, *II*, pp. 464–6. *D.N.B.*, LVIII, 1899, p. 249. *Baker*, *Lely*, II, pp. 65–6. *Vertue*, *Index*, p. 273.

1. A WOMAN, PERHAPS REPRESENTING FLORA OR SPRING. Draped figure of a woman seated at the foot of a column, l., against which she leans her r. elbow. Holding up with her r. hand part of her veil, and looking down at a bunch of flowers in her lap. On the r., a vase with a flowering tree in it. **Plate 266**

Red chalk, strengthened with light brown-grey wash; $16 \cdot 1 \times 13 \cdot 4$ cm. ($6\frac{3}{8} \times 5\frac{1}{4}$ in.).

PROV.: William Fawkener, by whom it was bequeathed to the B.M., 1769. 5213–34.

BIBL.: *Fawkener Cat.*, p. 58, No. 34.

The old attribution in the *Fawkener Catalogue* is to 'Verelst'. This seems to be not inconsistent with the figure subjects of Simon Verelst, with their floral accessories, for example the portrait of Louise de Keroualle, Duchess of Portsmouth, at Hampton Court (*See Baker, Hampton Court*, p. 155, No. 194).

VERRIO, ANTONIO
B. 1639 (?): D. 1707
History and decorative painter

Said by Domenici to have been born in Lecce about 1639 (*See* below). His father, Giovanni Verrio, who is described in the Cathedral Registers there as *Lycensis*, was certainly of that city. Two other members of the family recorded, both named Giuseppe, the elder

being the painter of a picture of St. Irene, 1639, for the church of the Teatini in Lecce, the other, Antonio's brother, shown as having had four children between 1653 and 1661 by his wife Lucrezia (Bibba). Antonio may have received his first lessons from the older Giuseppe, but is also said by Domenici to have studied in Venice. Was certainly living in Lecce in 1655, already a married man at the early age of 16 (?). By his wife Massenzia (Tornese) had a son Cristofero Gaetano, born Jan. 15th, 1656. Worked much for the Jesuits, for whom he decorated a 'macchina di Quarant' Ore' with scenes from the *Story of Joseph* (two of which are still in the church of the Buon Consiglio at Lecce) and a signed picture of *St. Francis Xavier appearing to the dying Padre Mastrilli* (now in the Convitto Palmieri). Was still in Lecce in 1659 when his second son, Oronzo Cristofero, was born on March 5th. Moved to Naples where in 1661 painted the ceiling of the Farmacopea of the Jesuit College with a representation of *Christ healing the sick*, which he signed with his name, his place of birth, the date and his age at the time— twenty-two. (It was from this description that Domenici obtained the date of Verrio's birth.) Travelled widely, no doubt becoming familiar with the main schools of Baroque painting in Rome, Bologna and Genoa. Arrived in France in 1666, near Toulouse, and was employed by Pierre Paul de Riquet, constructor of the Canal du Midi, in painting two rooms of his château of Bon Repos with the story of Psyche and a representation (no longer extant) of the Virtues. According to another authority, the French dramatist Jean Palaprat, was summoned by Riquet from Florence to execute these decorations. Afterwards settled in Toulouse itself where he painted two altarpieces (both now in the Musée des Augustins), one for the *Carmes Déchaussées*, the other for the *Capucins*. Other paintings by him at Toulouse were formerly in the collection of the Marquis de Pins and the Baron de Puymauris. Married as his second (?) wife Françoise Dangely (De Angeli) by whom he had two sons, Jean Baptiste and François ('Francisco'), the former having been born in Toulouse on July 3rd, 1668. By 1671 was in Paris, where, according to Palaprat, he associated with

theatrical circles and knew Molière. On May 2nd, 1671, petitioned the Académie for reception, submitting a painting of the *Baptism of Christ*. The subject chosen for his reception-piece was *Les Divertissements du Roi a la plasse Dunquerchx alegoriquement*. Is said to have come to England at the invitation of Ralph Montague, later 1st Duke of Montague, when, as Ambassador Extraordinary to the French Court, Montague was recalled in 1672. First worked here for Henry Bennet, 1st Lord Arlington, at his country seat of Euston (destroyed by fire in 1902), and his town house (predecessor of Buckingham Palace in St. James's Park). Quickly established a reputation, and in 1674 was appointed by Charles II designer to the tapestry works at Mortlake, and perhaps to show off his powers in this field painted the easel picture of the *King's Sea Triumph* now at Hampton Court. Was naturalized on May 5th, 1675, and in the same year embarked on his most important commission, the decoration of the newly constructed North range at Windsor Castle, where he fixed for him and the succeeding generation, the patterns for Baroque wall and ceiling painting in England. The work, which was much admired by John Evelyn (*q.v.*), including twelve ceilings, the King's Chapel and St. George's Hall, and was completed by 1678. Only three ceilings survived George IV's reconstruction of the castle. Also at this time (1681–after 1687), executed a large painting for the hall of Christ's Hospital representing the King (first Charles II, subsequently altered to James II) giving audience to the governors, masters and children of the foundation. In this shows considerable talent as a portraitist, as demonstrated too by the single portrait of Charles II (also at Christ's Hospital) and that of Sir Christopher Wren in the Sheldonian Theatre, Oxford, afterwards completed by Sir Godfrey Kneller (*q.v.*) and Thornhill (*q.v.*). After the death of Charles II, continued in high favour with the Court and decorated for James II, in preparation for the Catholic rite, Henry VIII's

Chapel in St. George's, Windsor, and a chapel at Whitehall, the consecration of the latter being recorded by Evelyn. Was also made principal 'Gardener and Surveyor' to the King and in this capacity laid out the garden at St. James's which, according to Evelyn, he 'made a delicious paradise', and where he had a house and lived in great state. Was a member of two of the earliest recorded artists' clubs in England, the Society of Virtuosi of St. Luke, and the Society of Painters. Designed for the latter the invitation card to their St. Luke's Feast, on Nov. 24th, 1687, at the Painter-Stainers' Hall. At the Revolution, 1688, retired from Court patronage to execute a number of private commissions, among them the decoration for John, 5th Earl of Exeter, of six rooms and a staircase at Burghley, Northants., completed in 1697/8 and now Verrio's most important extant work. Was also employed extensively at Chatsworth and Lowther Hall. Is said to have been persuaded by Lord Exeter to return to royal service under William III. Worked intermittently at Windsor between 1694 and 1702, perhaps refurbishing his earlier paintings there, and at Hampton Court, c. 1700-4, where he painted the Banqueting House, the King's Staircase, three ceilings and the Queen's Drawing Room, his most familiar but hardly his most successful productions. Probably retired soon after because of failing eyesight, and is said to have receive an annual pension of £200. The self-portrait (?) inscribed *Cieco Antonio | O il povero Verrio* (N.P.G. No. 2890) no doubt dates from this time. Died on June 15th, 1707, at his residence in Hampton Court, having made bequests to his two sons, Jean-Baptiste and Francisco, and to his grandchildren Jean-Baptiste and Mary, who were to receive all his 'household goods, plate and pictures and other ffurniture'. His burial place not known. Among his numerous assistants and followers were Louis Chéron (*q.v.*), Henry Cooke (*q.v.*), Louis Laguerre (*q.v.*) and Michel Touroude (*q.v.*).

BIBL.: Lecce, Registers, 3:i:1650, 8:viii:1651, 14:v:1653, 17:i:1656, 6:iii:1659, 13:viii:1661. De Domenici, III, p. 173 (2nd edn. III, p. 378). Panettera, p. 53. Artisti Salentini, pp. 11 & 31. De Simone, I, pp. 62-3. Malliot, passim. Biographie Toulousaine, II, pp. 480-1. Palaprat, I, Préface, e–eij. Toulouse, Registers, f. 60. Arch. Art. Français, pp. 119-20. Montaiglon, I, p. 361. Thomson, p. 299. Evelyn, passim. Vertue, Index, pp. 273, 274. Walpole, II, pp. 467-71. Verrio, Windsor, passim. Hope, Windsor, passim. Pote, pp. 62 & 415-26. Pyne, I, between pp. 87 and 179, & II, between pp. 32 & 66. Verrio, Burghley, passim. Thompson, Chatsworth, passim. Wren Soc., XX, p. 234. Fiennes, passim. Baker, Verrio, passim.

1. **DESIGN FOR AN ALLEGORICAL COMPOSITION.** A prince in antique Roman dress, holding an olive branch, and surrounded by three female figures symbolising Royal Power, Justice and Humility, all borne forward from the r. on clouds. In the centre, three other female figures welcoming the prince's arrival on earth, one of them kneeling and offering him a crown. Behind them, l., a throne, sheltered by a canopy held up by *putti*, beside which crouches a woman with a lap-dog (?). In the background, a military commander pointing to the halberds of a group of soldiers.

Plate 267

Pen and brown ink, with brown wash over red chalk; the original composition extended and modified on the l. by an additional slip of paper containing the throne and the military commander, while the woman crouching with the lap-dog is drawn on yet another slip of paper superimposed on this; squared for transfer; 28·3 × 42·8 cm. (11⅛ × 16¾ in.).

PROV.: Sir Hans Sloane, Bart., by whom it was bequeathed to the B.M., 1753.
5214–249 (L.B.1).

BIBL.: *Sloane Cat.*, p. 161, No. 249.

The attribution presumably goes back at least to Sir Hans Sloane and thus must be respected. In appearance the drawing is rather French, which is not inconsistent with the painter's eclecticism, and would indicate that it was executed during, or after, his stay in France. It has little or nothing in common with the only known authentic drawing by Verrio, in the collection of Maître Soulié of Toulouse, which is a study for the picture of the Marriage of the Virgin now in the Musée des Augustins there. Maître Soulié's drawing is far more Italian in character and is in a completely different technique of black chalk heightened with white.

The subject of the present drawing has not been identified with certainty. It may be intended as an apotheosis of Charles II in something of the same vein as the *Sea Triumph* of that monarch at Hampton Court (*See* Collins Baker, *Hampton Court*, p. 156) and the ceilings at Windsor, but the principal personage bears little resemblance to the king.

WHITE, ROBERT

B. 1645: D. 1703

Portrait draughtsman and engraver

Born in London in 1645. Had a natural talent for drawing and etching, and drew a self-portrait at the age of 16 in 1661, noted by Vertue as in the collection of James West, who owned many of White's drawings. Studied under David Loggan (*q.v.*). His earliest plate, a portrait of Everard Maynwaring, must date from before 1666. Also early in his career, executed some topographical work, and, according to Vertue, drew for his master 'many buildings', which perhaps points to his having assisted in the publication of Loggan's *Oxonia illustrata*, 1675, and *Cantabrigia illustrata*, 1688. May also have worked with Loggan and 'Kickers' (a draughtsman mentioned by Vertue but otherwise unrecorded) in the preparation of Slezer's *Theatrum Scotiae*, eventually published in 1693. On his own account, at this period, drew and engraved a bird's-eye view of The Royal Exchange of London, 1671, in the style of his master. But his principal output was to be in the field of portrait engraving in line, of which he became the leading exponent of his day, publishing some 400 plates covering a period from about 1666 to 1702. Mentioned by Thomas Stringer, secretary to 1st Earl of Shaftesbury, in a letter to John Locke (April 30th, 1688) as having drawn Shaftesbury's 'face in black and white in order to engrave a plate [*B.M. Engraved Portraits*, IV, p. 59, No. 13] for a print of him' and as 'being a man of such eminency and reputation in that art'. Engraved after most of the well-known portrait painters of the time, such as Lely, Kneller, John Riley and Mary Beale, as well as his own *ad vivum* drawings, executed in Loggan's manner, in black lead on vellum with the faces occasionally tinted in pale brown wash. Usually charged about £4 a plate, but for the equestrian portrait of Charles XI of Sweden after Dahl, received £30. Also engraved a number of frontispieces, titles, and illustrations to books, including those to Sandford's *The Order and Ceremonies used for and at the*

Solemn Interment of George Duke of Albemarle (after Francis Barlow), 1670, Wood's *Historia et Antiquitates Universitatis Oxoniensis* (after A. D. Hennin), 1674, and the first *Oxford Almanack*, 1674. Several of his engraved portraits likewise used as frontispieces. Besides his early self-portrait, drew another at the age of 33, while Kneller is also said to have drawn or painted him. Lived in Bloomsbury Market where he eventually died in poverty in October, 1703, being buried on the 26th of that month at St.

Giles-in-the-Fields. Among his pupils were his son George (who finished some of his plates but who is principally known as a mezzotinter) and John Sturt.

BIBL.: *St. Giles-in-the-Fields, Burial Register* (*inf.* from the Rev. G. C. Taylor). *Walpole*, III, pp. 947–53. *D.N.B.*, LXI, 1900, p. 73. *Bell & Poole*, pp. 64–71. *Locke*, p. 265. *Long*, p. 460. *Johnson*, pp. 58–9. *Vertue, Index*, pp. 286–7.

1. HENRY HOWARD, 7th DUKE OF NORFOLK. Bust, turned half-l., with eyes looking to front. Wearing long curling hair or wig, and a cravat. Plate 287

Black lead on vellum, the shoulders only lightly indicated; 13 × 8·9 cm. (5⅛ × 3½ in.).

INSCR.: *Recto*, in the upper r.-hand corner, in ink, 46.
Verso, in the lower l.-hand corner, in black lead, by the artist, *R. White delin*, and below, *Duke of Norfolk* (partly obliterated).

PROV.: James West (?) (Sale, Langford, 26:i:1773, Lots 39–42, or 27:i:1773, Lots

34–38). Rev. C. M. Cracherode, by whom it was bequeathed to the B.M., 1799.
G.g.1–475 (L.B.3).

BIBL.: *Cracherode Cat.*, p. 103, No. 475. *Bell & Poole*, p. 69. *Long*, p. 460.

[Henry Howard, 7th Duke of Norfolk (B. 1665: D. 1701), son of the 6th Duke whom he succeeded in 1684. As a staunch Protestant was instrumental in winning over the Eastern Counties to the support of William III.]

2. THOMAS OSBORNE, 1st DUKE OF LEEDS. Bust, turned slightly to r., with eyes looking to front. Wearing a long curling wig, and cravat.

Black lead on vellum, the face touched with metal-point; 13 × 8·8 cm. (5⅛ × 3½ in.).

INSCR.: *Recto*, at the foot, in black lead, *Duke of Leeds*, and in the upper r.-hand corner, in ink, 39.
Verso, in the lower l.-hand corner, in black lead, by the artist, *R : White delin*.

PROV.: As for No. 1.
G.g.1–476 (L.B.7).

ENGR.: Study for the head of the bust portrait of the Duke engraved by Robert White (*ad Vivum delin: et sculpsit*) which shows the sitter, within an oval laurel-wreath border (*See B.M. Engraved Portraits*, III, p. 36). The

drawing is about three-quarters the size of the head in the engraving.

BIBL.: *Cracherode Cat.*, p. 103, No. 476. *D.N.B.*, XLII, 1895, p. 303. *Bell & Poole*, p. 68. *Long*, p. 460.

[Thomas Osborne (B. 1631: D. 1712). Successively Earl of Danby, Marquis of Carmarthen, and Duke of Leeds, being raised to the latter dignity in 1694. One of the leading statesmen of his time, governing the country as Lord Treasurer, 1673–8, and as virtual Prime Minister, 1690–5. Brought about the marriage of William of Orange and Princess Mary.]

White's engraving is undated, but the lettering on it refers to the Duke's being Lord Lieutenant of the Three Ridings of Yorkshire, a post which he relinquished in 1699. The engraving and the present preliminary drawing would thus have apparently been made between 1694, when the sitter became Duke of Leeds, and 1699, that is between the ages of 63 and 68. For other portraits, *See B.M. Engraved Portraits*, III, pp. 35—6.

3. KENNETH MACKENZIE, 4th EARL OF SEAFORTH. Head alone, turned slightly to r., with eyes looking to front. Wearing a long curling wig. Plate 287

Black lead on vellum, the face finished in metal-point; 13·2 × 10·3 cm. (5¼ × 4⅛ in.).

INSCR.: *Recto*, in the lower r.-hand corner, in black lead, *Lᵈ Seaforth*, and in the upper r.-hand corner, in ink, *16*.
Verso, in the lower l.-hand corner, in black lead, by the artist, *R. White f.*, and towards the r., *ob 1701* (referring to the sitter's death, and thus added later).

PROV.: As for No. 1.
G.g.1–480 (L.B.4).

ENGR.: Study for the head of the bust portrait of the Earl engraved by Robert White (*ad vivum delin. et sculp.*), which shows the sitter, wearing the Order of the Thistle, within an oval border wreathed with laurel (*See B.M. Engraved Portraits*, IV, p. 47). The drawing is the same size as the head in the engraving.

BIBL.: *Cracherode Cat.*, p. 104, No. 480. *Bell & Poole*, p. 69. *Long*, p. 460.

[Kenneth Mackenzie, 4th Earl of Seaforth (D. 1701). Succeeded to the earldom, 1678. Created a Privy Councillor, 1678, and a Companion of the Order of the Thistle, 1687. Was a supporter of James II, with whom he served, after the Revolution, in Ireland. Failed to come to terms with William III's government and was imprisoned. Was released in 1697 and went to France, where he eventually died in Paris.]
On White's engraving the Earl is described as a Privy Councillor and a Knight of the Thistle, which would suggest that it and the present drawing were made soon after 1687. According to the *D.N.B.* (Vol. XXXV, 1893, p. 158) there is another portrait of the Earl at Brahan Castle, seat of the Seaforths.

4. KING JAMES II. Head alone, turned slightly to r., with eyes looking to front. Wearing a long curling wig. Plate 286

Black lead on vellum, the face finished in metal-point; 12·6 × 8·9 cm. (5 × 3½ in.).

INSCR.: *Recto*, at the foot, in black lead, *King James the 2ᵈ*, and in the upper r.-hand corner, in ink, *54*.
Verso, in the lower l.-hand corner, in black lead, by the artist, *White f* and at the foot, *Jacobus R. Angliae* (?).

PROV.: As for No. 1.
G.g.1–481 (L.B.1).

BIBL.: *Cracherode Cat.*, p. 104, No. 481. *Bell & Poole*, p. 68. *Long*, p. 460.

White engraved several portraits of James II, both as Duke of York and as King (*See B.M. Engraved Portraits*, II, pp. 622–6). None of these, however, corresponds very closely with the present drawing, which is nearest in type to the one painted by Kneller in 1688 for Samuel Pepys, and subsequently engraved by Vertue. The Pepys portrait was sold at Sotheby's, 1:iv:1931, Lot 8, but its present whereabouts is unknown.

5. SIR JOHN VAUGHAN. Bust, turned slightly to r., eyes looking to front. Wearing long curling hair, moustache and slight tufted beard, skull cap and bands.

Black lead on vellum, the face finished in metal-point, the body and dress only lightly indicated, $13 \cdot 6 \times 9 \cdot 1$ cm. ($5\frac{3}{8} \times 3\frac{1}{2}$ in.).

INSCR.: *Recto*, at the foot, in black lead, Ld *Chief* . . . (nearly obliterated), and in the upper r.-hand corner, in ink, *3* (partly cut away).

      Verso, at the foot, in black lead, incorrectly, *Ld* (?) *Ch. Justice Hales.*

PROV.: As for No. 1.
G.g.1–482 (L.B.5, as 'Sir Matthew Hale').

ENGR.: Study probably for the engraving by Robert White, in the same sense but on a slightly smaller scale, showing the judge wearing his collar of office, which forms the frontispiece to *The Reports and Arguments of Sir J. Vaughan*, 1677 (See *B.M. Engraved Portraits*, IV, p. 337). The details of dress in the engraving do not correspond exactly with those in the drawing, which are actually

nearer in this respect to those in a painting of Vaughan, said to have been at 'Lleeswood' (Leeswood Hall (?), Flint) when it was engraved by W. Bond, for Philip Yorke's *Royal Tribes of Wales*, 1799.

BIBL. & REPR.: *Cracherode Cat.*, p. 104, No. 482. *B.M. Reproductions*, Pt. III, 1893, p. 3, No. 12 (B). *Bell & Poole*, p. 66. *Long*, p. 460.

[Sir John Vaughan (B. 1603: D. 1674). Chief Justice of the Common Pleas. Was a close friend of Lord Clarendon, with whom, however, he subsequently broke, being one of the chief promoters of Clarendon's impeachment in 1667.]

The old identification of this drawing with Sir Matthew Hale is explained by Robert White's having engraved a portrait of that judge after Michael Wright's painting in the Guildhall, which is superficially similar to the portraits of Vaughan.

6. WILLIAM, DUKE OF GLOUCESTER, AS A CHILD. Bust, turned slightly to l., with eyes looking to front. Wearing a plumed cap.

Plumbago on vellum, the face finished in metal-point, the body only lightly indicated; $12 \cdot 6 \times 8 \cdot 9$ cm. ($5 \times 3\frac{1}{2}$ in.).

INSCR.: *Recto*, at the foot, in black lead, *The Duke of Glocester*, and in the upper r.-hand corner, in ink, *32.* (twice)

      Verso, in the lower l.-hand corner, in black lead, by the artist, *R: White delin.*, and at the foot, . . . *of Gloceter* (?) (partly obliterated).

PROV.: As for No. 1.
G.g.1–484 (L.B.2).

BIBL.: *Cracherode Cat.*, p. 104, No. 484. *Bell & Poole*, p. 68. *Long*, p. 460.

[William, Duke of Gloucester (B. 1689: D. 1700). Son of Princess, later Queen Anne and Prince George of Denmark. Declared Duke of Gloucester by William III. Made K.G., 1695, and appointed to command William III's Dutch regiment of foot-guards, 1698.]

The present drawing should be compared with John Smith's mezzotint after Kneller, which according to *Chaloner Smith* (III, p. 1173, No. 111) dates from 1691, when the sitter was three years old. *Bell & Poole* (See *Bibl.*) list the drawing as '1695 (before)' (p. 68).

7. DR. JOHN EDWARDS. Bust, turned half-r., with eyes looking to front. Wearing curling dark-coloured wig, bands and gown. In an oval.   Plate 289

Black lead on vellum, the face finished in metal-point, the details of the dress unfinished; $11 \cdot 8 \times 8 \cdot 9$ cm. ($4\frac{5}{8} \times 3\frac{1}{2}$ in.).

INSCR.: *Recto*, in the lower r.-hand corner, in black lead, *Dr Edwards*, and in the upper r.-hand corner, in ink, *58*.

Verso, in the lower r.-hand corner, in black lead, *Harris / G (S?) T. P*, and below *D / Edwards* (partly obliterated).

PROV.: As for No. 1.
G.g.1–487 (L.B. 9).

ENGR.: By Robert White, in the same sense (*ad vivum sculp.*), as the frontispiece to Edwards's *Sermons on Special Occasions and Subjects*, 1698 (*See B.M. Engraved Portraits*, II, 134). In the engraving the details of the dress are finished.

BIBL.: *Cracherode Cat.*, p. 104, No. 487. *Bell & Poole*, p. 69. *Long*, p. 460.

[John Edwards (B. 1637: D. 1716). Calvinistic divine. Second son of Thomas Edwards, a divine of similar convictions. Was an opponent of Socianism, and, like his father, of the Arminians. Became D.D. in 1699.]

The present drawing is presumably contemporary with the engraving after it, prefixed to Edwards's *Sermons*, 1698, and would thus show the sitter aged about 61. A later portrait was engraved by George Vertue as the frontispiece to Edwards's *Theologia Reformata*, 1713.

The inscription *Harris* on the *verso* of the drawing may be an incorrect identification of the sitter with John Harris, D.D., F.R.S. (B. 1667 (?): D. 1719), whose portrait, also by Robert White, was engraved by George White (*See B.M. Engraved Portraits*, II, p. 452).

In the Pierpont Morgan Collection is a drawing by Robert White, inscribed *Dr. Edwards*. The sitter is an older man than the subject of the present drawing, but has some facial characteristics in common with him (*See* C. Fairfax Murray, *J. Pierpont Morgan Collection of Drawings* . . . , 1912, III, Pl. 14).

8. DR. NATHANIEL VINCENT. Bust, turned half-r., with eyes looking to front. Wearing close-curling wig, bands and gown. In an oval.   Plate 288

Black lead on vellum, the face finished in metal-point, the details of the dress unfinished; $13 \cdot 3 \times 8 \cdot 8$ cm. ($5\frac{1}{4} \times 3\frac{1}{2}$ in.).

INSCR.: *Recto*, at the foot, in black lead, *Dr Vincent*.

Verso, in the lower l.-hand corner, in black lead, by the artist, *R* [White] (mainly obliterated), and at the foot, *Dr Vincent P. Cla : Hall*.

PROV.: As for No. 1.
G.g.1–488 (L.B.8).

ENGR.: Study for the engraving by Robert White (*ad vivum sculp*), which is lettered round the oval frame *EFFIGIES NATHANAELIS VINCENTIJ S.T.P. A. CL. PR. SRS. ÆT. A. 58 A.D. 1694*. In the engraving the details of the dress are finished.

BIBL.: *Cracherode Cat.*, p. 104, No. 488. *Bell & Poole*, p. 68. *Long*, p. 460.

[Nathaniel Vincent (B. *c.* 1636: D. 1722). Divine. Admitted to Clare Hall, Cambridge, 1653, graduating as M.A. in 1660, and becoming a Fellow. In 1674 preached before Charles II at Newmarket 'in a long Periwig and Holland sleeves, the dress of Gentlemen', which scandalised that monarch. Was created S.T.P. and D.D. in 1679, and was also appointed a royal chaplain. In James II's reign showed Roman Catholic tendencies, but took the Oaths at the Revolution. Towards the end of his life suffered a certain amount of opprobium on account of his Jacobite sympathies (*See* J. R. Wardale, *Clare College*, 1899, pp. 134–6).]

The engraved portrait of Vincent described above from its format would seem, like so many other of White's productions, to have been intended for the frontispiece to a book, but so far this has not been identified.

Robert White also drew and engraved the portrait of another and better known Nathaniel Vincent (B. 1639 (?): D. 1697), a Nonconformist divine, which is lettered *R. White delin: et sculp: | The true Effigies of Mr. Nathanael Vincent, Minister of the Gospel*. It served as the frontispiece to this Vincent's *True Touchstone of Grace and Nature*, 1681 (*See* J. Granger, *A Bibliographical History of England*, 5th edn., 1824, V, p. 79). There is no impression of it in this Department. Subsequent authorities (including *B.M. Engraved Portraits*, IV, p. 376) have confused it with White's portrait of Nathaniel Vincent of Clare Hall.

9. JOHN BUNYAN. Bust, turned slightly to r., with eyes looking to front. Wearing long hair, moustache and small tufted beard, and a cassock with a small linen collar turned down over it. **Plate 286**

Black lead on vellum, the face finished in metal-point; 12·2 × 9 cm. (4¾ × 3½ in.).

INSCR.: *Recto*, at the foot, in black lead, *I. Bunion*.

Verso, in the lower l.-hand corner, in black lead, probably not by the artist, *R White*.

PROV.: As for No. 1.

G.g.1–493 (L.B.6).

ENGR. & ETCH.: (1) Study for the engraving, lettered *John Bunnyon*, by Robert White, in the same sense, as the frontispiece to Bunyan's *The Holy War*, 1682, with the cassock finished black. (2) By E. Whymper. (3) Etch. by William Strang, 1885 (*Binyon*, No. 81). (4) For other related engravings, *See B.M. Engraved Portraits*, I, p. 286.

BIBL. & REPR.: *Cracherode Cat.*, p. 105, No. 493. *B.M. Reproductions*, Pt. III, p. 3, No. 10 (A). *Bell & Poole*, p. 68. *Brown*, pp. 385–7, 412–14. *Long*, p. 460. *Harrison, Frontispiece*.

[John Bunyan (B. 1628: D. 1688). The celebrated author of *The Pilgrim's Progress*.]

According to Dr. Brown, the present drawing served as a study for the portrait of Bunyan asleep, engraved by White as the frontispiece to the third edition of *The Pilgrim's Progress*, 1679. From this Mr. Harrison deduces that the drawing was made when Bunyan was fifty years old (*i.e.* about 1678). Dr. Brown also states that White's drawing formed the basis of the full-length figure of Bunyan 'as the typical Mansoul', which appears in the unsigned engraving opposite p. 1 of *The Holy War*, 1682. Both of Dr. Brown's statements may be correct, but curiously enough neither he nor Mr. Harrison makes any reference to the engraved portrait of Bunyan which forms the frontispiece to *The Holy War*, and which is directly based on the present drawing (*See* Engr. & Etch. above).

White's drawing should also be compared with the oil-painting of Bunyan by Thomas Sadler in the National Portrait Gallery (No. 1311) which dates from 1685. Sadler's portrait shows a marked characteristic, a lateral squint of the sitter's l. eye, which is not apparent in White's drawing.

Yet another early portrait of Bunyan should be cited: that which forms the frontispiece, engraved by John Sturt, to William Marshall's edition of *The Works of . . . Mr. John Bunyan*, 1692. The head of this portrait corresponds fairly closely, though in reverse, with that in Sadler's picture, but some details, notably the pose of the body and the lace-edged linen collar are nearer to White's frontispiece to *The Holy War*. Charles Doe refers to Sturt's engraving in his *Relation to the Christian Reader*, which forms part of the 'Index' at the end of the 1692 edition of *The Works*: 'His [Bunyan's] Effigies was cut in copper from an Original paint done to the life (by his very good Friend a Limner) and those that desire it single to put in a Frame, may have it at this Bookseller's, Mr Marshall, . . .' Bunyan's limner friend has not been identified with any certainty, but he may be Thomas Sadler, in which case Sturt's engraving may be regarded as a modified reproduction of Sadler's painting.

In speaking of White's drawing Mr. Harrison affirms that the artist was a personal friend of Bunyan, but there is no contemporary evidence of this, and it is possible that his statement is based on a confused recollection of the passage from Charles Doe's *Relation* quoted above.

10. AN UNKNOWN GENTLEMAN. Bust, turned half-r., with eyes looking to front. Wearing a long curling wig, steenkirk, and coat open at the neck.

Plate 288

Black lead on vellum, the face finished in metal-point; oval; 12·5 × 10 cm. (5 × 4 in.).

INSCR.: *Recto*, on the r., in black lead, by the artist, *R White / delin / 1699.*

PROV.: Mr. Hamilton, from whom it was purchased by the B.M., 1866.
  1866–10–13–85 (L.B.10).

BIBL.: *Bell and Poole*, p. 69. *Long*, p. 460.

In view of its provenance, this drawing should be compared with a portrait, engraved by Robert White, of *Wᵐ. Hamilton Esquʳ* of Chilston (D. 1737), which appears in a plate together with four others, 1701, representing five Kentish gentlemen who were imprisoned in that same year for presenting a 'scandalous and insolent petition' to the House of Commons (*See B.M. Engraved Portraits*, V, p. 73). The present drawing does not represent the same person as the engraving, which is of an older man, but there are similarities in the pose of the figure and in the details of the dress, especially the twisted scarf and lyre-shaped fastenings on the coat, which suggest that the drawing may represent another member of this branch of the Hamilton family. White's original drawing of William Hamilton of Chilston was formerly in Lord Northwick's collection, and was sold at Sotheby's, iv:xi:1920, Lot 482 (*See Bell and Poole*, p. 69); it is now in the V. & A. M. (*Stephenson Bequest*, Pl. 111–1929).

11. AN ELDERLY DIVINE(?). Bust, turned half-r., with eyes looking to front, and a wart on his l. cheek. Wearing long white hair, bands, and doublet. **Plate 289**

Black lead on vellum; oval; 11·9 × 9·1 cm. (4¾ × 3⅝ in.).

INSCR.: *Recto*, on the r., in black lead, by the artist, *R White fec.*

PROV.: E. Daniell, from whom it was purchased by the B.M., 1872.
  1872–10–12–3429 (L.B.11).

BIBL.: *Bell and Poole*, p. 70. *Long*, p. 460.

12. AN UNKNOWN DIVINE(?). Bust, turned half-r., with eyes looking to front. Wearing a long curling wig, white cravat, and gown.

Black lead on vellum, the face finished in metal-point; oval; 12·2 × 10·2 cm. (4¾ × 4 in.).

INSCR.: *Recto*, on the r., in black lead, by the artist, *R. White / fecit 80*.

PROV.: Anon. coll. (Sale, Christie, 14:vii:1884, Lot 221, 'A Medallion Portrait of a Clergyman', purchased by Dr. John Percy). Dr. Percy (Sale, Christie, 24:iv:1890, Lot 1380, 'Portrait of David Loggan'). Purchased at the Percy Sale by the B.M., 1890.

1890–5–12–152 (L.B.12).

BIBL.: *Percy Cat.*, pp. 80–2. *Bell and Poole*, p. 67. *Long*, p. 460.

The identification of the sitter with David Loggan (*See* Prov.) is presumably not a traditional one. The drawing is not so described in Dr. Percy's own Catalogue, and only appeared with this title in his sale. Probably it is the drawing by Robert White 'stated to be a portrait of Loggan', which according to the *D.N.B.* (Vol. XXXIV, 1893, p. 89) is in the B.M.

13. AN UNKNOWN MAN. H.L., with body turned slightly to l., head slightly to r., and eyes looking to front. Wearing a long curling wig, cravat and coat.

Black lead on vellum; oval; 11·1 × 8·7 cm. (4⅜ × 3⅜ in.).

PROV.: E. Rawdon Smith, by whom it was presented to the B.M., 1954.

1954–11–3–428 (100).

WINDE, WILLIAM

B. Before 1648: D. 1722
Architect and cavalry officer

Grandson of Sir Robert Winde (D. 1652), Gentleman of the Privy Chamber to Charles I, and son of Henry Winde (D. 1658), an English Royalist who emigrated to Holland in 1647 and had his property sequestered by the Cromwellians. Probably born before his father left England and identical with the William Winde who was an ensign in command of English troops at Bergen-op-Zoom in 1658. Vertue gave 1648 as the date of his birth but this cannot be accepted. Came to England at the Restoration and in 1661 was made Gentleman Usher to Elizabeth, Queen of Bohemia. In 1667 bought a cornetcy in the King's Troop of the Royal Regiment of Horse. Promoted to Lieutenant in 1676 and, a year later, to the temporary rank of Captain. Sent to Jersey in command of his own troop of horse which was disbanded in 1679. On his return to England presented the King with a book 'with all the castles, landing places and several views of the Island (Jersey) set forth in colours', which he had drawn. Rewarded with a grant of the reversion of Sir Martin Beckman's (*q.v.*) post of second engineer to the ordnance. Fought at Sedgemoor and distinguished himself by routing the 'Green Regiment of the rebells and . . . taking a Colonel's Colours besides a Horse Colours'. Not promoted in spite of the memorials he sent the King in 1685 and 1688. Relinquished his military career after the revolution of 1688 and devoted the rest of his life to architecture. Sometimes called the 'pupil' of Sir Balthazar Gerbier (*q.v.*) who addressed the 39th dedication of the *Counsel and Advise to All Builders* to him and with whom he worked at Lord Craven's house at Hampstead Marshall from 1662 until Gerbier's death in 1667, finishing it in about 1688 (destroyed by fire, 1718). For the same patron rebuilt the centre and W. wing of Combe Abbey (1680–91). Married Magdalen, daughter of Sir James Bridgeman, brother of the Lord Keeper, Sir Orlando Bridgeman. For his wife's relations, Sir John and Lady Bridgeman, remodelled Castle Bromwich Hall between 1685 and 1690. For the Duke of Buckingham built Cliefden House (completed by Thomas Archer, but burnt down in 1795), and Buckingham House (1705) which became the model for many XVIII c. mansions. For the Marquess of Powis built a house in Lincoln's Inn Fields (1684–9), renamed Newcastle House after the Marquess had been outlawed for his Jacobite sympathies (the present building is an adaptation of Winde's original design by Sir Edwin Lutyens). In 1706 advised Lord Ashburnham on the decorations at Ampthill Park, Beds. Also practised gardening, and laid out the grounds of Castle Bromwich, Eastwell Park, Kent, and probably those of Buckingham House, a drawing for which is in the Soane Museum. Was a correspondent of Sir Hans Sloane and probably knew Wren. Was a Fellow of the Royal Society from 1662 until 1685 when he was expelled, presumably for failure to pay his subscription. Died in 1722 and was buried in St. Martin-in-the-Fields on April 28th. He left a son, William, who subsequently became Chamberlain to Princess Sophia and died in 1741. His drawings are straightforward working designs. His wife, Magdalen, is commemorated on the tombstone of Lady Howard of Eskrick, her sister, in Richmond Church, Surrey.

BIBL.: *T.-B.*, XXXVI, 1947, p. 50. *Vertue, Index*, p. 297 (under Wynne). *Colvin*, pp. 682–5.

DRAWINGS IN OTHER COLLECTIONS: Bodleian Library, Gough MS.: Designs for Hampstead Marshall and Combe Abbey.

1. DESIGN FOR A DOOR AT HAMPSTEAD MARSHALL. A wall-arcade of three bays, consisting of semi-parabolic arches springing from piers and restonels with Roman Doric caps and bases. The central bay occupied by a doorcase, composed of an architrave with cornice supported on two consoles, the side bays by window-openings with architraves. **Plate 291**

Pen and brown ink, ruled, with grey wash; 20·6 × 31·6 cm. (8⅛ × 12½ in.).

INSCR.: *Recto*, in the upper l.-hand corner, *1*, and along the top, *The doore of the Portico betwixt the Staircases At Hamptid Marshal 1672*.

PROV.: Richard Bull (Sale, Sotheby, 23:v:1881, Lot 52). Purchased at the Bull Sale by the B.M., 1881.

1881–6–11–154 (L.B.3, as by Gerbier).

Lord Craven in 1662 employed Sir Balthazar Gerbier to build a house on the site of a former mansion at least twice rebuilt previously. After Gerbier's death the work was finished by his pupil, Capt. William Winde. A Kip engraving shows it as it was just before 1709. It was destroyed by fire in 1718 and only the gate piers now remain. If, as has been suggested, Gerbier died in 1667, Winde must have been responsible for most of the building.

WISSING, WILLEM

B. 1656: D. 1687

Portrait painter

The essential details of the artist's life contained in a Latin inscription on his monument in St. Martin's Church, Stamford. Born in Amsterdam and received his early training at The Hague under Willem Doudijns (B. 1630: D. 1697), and A. van Ravesteijn (B. 1615: D. 1690), history and portrait painters. According to Vertue, also studied in Paris, which may explain traces of French-style ornament in the backgrounds and accessories of his portraits. Arrived in England by 1676, when he was admitted as a member of the Dutch Reformed Church in Austin Friars. Entered Lely's studio, either directly as a pupil or first as a 'livery man' (*i.e.* servant). Is specifically mentioned in Lely's Will as his assistant. After his master's death in 1680 was for a short time Kneller's principal rival, being patronized by Charles II and by James II whose favourite painter he became, and who, according to Buckeridge,

sent him to Holland to paint Princess Mary and her husband. Many of his portraits engraved by leading mezzotinters of the day. Among his later patrons were Sir John Brownlow of Belton (where there are portraits by Wissing of Lady Brownlow and their daughter Elizabeth Brownlow) and John, 5th Earl of Exeter, for whom he worked at Burghley House on the portrait of the young Lord Burghley. Died on Sept. 10th, 1687, soon after this was finished and was buried at St. Martin's, Stamford. One of his assistants, J. van der Vaart (*q.v.*), on Wissing's death took over his studio completing some of his unfinished portraits.

BIBL.: *Buckeridge*, pp. 435–6. *Walpole*, II, pp. 526–7. *T.-B.*, XXXVI, 1947, p. 111 (with *Bibl.*). *Vertue, Index*, p. 292. *Waterhouse*, p. 75 and note 35.

1. A LADY SEATED. W.L., seated in a chair to l., looking to front and leaning with her cheek in her r. hand, her l. hand in her lap. Wearing a *fontange*, gown and lace sleeves. **Plate 297**

Black chalk; 47·4 × 31·7 cm. (18⅝ × 12½ in.).

PROV.: Sir Hans Sloane, Bart., by whom it was bequeathed to the B.M., 1753.
5214–68.

BIBL.: *Sloane Cat.*, p. 137, No. 68.

The attribution to Wissing presumably dates from Sloane's time, but no other drawings by the artist are known which might substantiate this. The present example belongs to an intimate type of portrait-study which is common with Dutch *genre* painters, but is only found in England in the drawings of the younger Charles Beale (*q.v.*).

WREN, SIR CHRISTOPHER

B. 1632 : D. 1723

Architect and astronomer

Born on Oct. 20th, 1632, at East Knoyle, in Wiltshire, where his father, Christopher Wren (B. 1591: D. 1658), was Rector. Educated at Westminster School and Wadham College, Oxford. In 1653 was elected a Fellow of All Souls College and in February 1660/1 Savilian Professor of Astronomy. Helped in the foundation of the Royal Society in 1660 and was President from 1680–2. In 1661 was made assistant to the Surveyor General, Sir John Denham. His first buildings, the Sheldonian Theatre, Oxford, and the Chapel of Pembroke College, Cambridge, were begun in 1663. Left London during the Plague of 1665 and paid a visit of six months to Paris where he met Bernini and probably Guarino Guarini. After the Fire of London, Sept. 2nd–8th, 1666, laid before the King, on Sept. 12th, a plan of reconstruction, and soon after was appointed 'surveyor-general and principal architect for rebuilding the whole city'. Succeeded Denham as Surveyor General in 1669. In the same year married Faith Coghill (D. 1675) and secondly, in 1676, Jane, daughter of the 2nd Baron Fitzwilliam of Lifford. Died on February 25th, 1723, at his house in St. James's Street and was buried in St. Paul's Cathedral on March 5th.

His style as an architect derived from both Italian and French masters, as well as from his predecessor, Inigo Jones. After about 1690 also came under the influence of Borromini. His appreciation of the Gothic is seen in direct essays in that manner as well as in his adaptation of the spire to churches designed in the Renaissance or Baroque idiom. Most of the drawings attributed to him in the Wren Society volumes, though coming from his office, are probably the work of assistants.

BIBL.: *D.N.B.*, LXIII, 1900, p. 80. *Wren Memorial Volume. Wren Soc., passim.* T.-B., XXXVI, 1947, p. 274. *Vertue, Index*, pp. 294–5. *Colvin*, pp. 699–715.

1. **DESIGN FOR THE FINIAL OF 'THE MONUMENT'.** A phoenix on its blazing nest and, below, a collar of acanthus ornament, the whole surmounting a drum-shaped pedestal with a door in it. **Plate 293**

Pen and brown ink, with grey wash; 20 × 10·5 cm. ($7\frac{7}{8} \times 4\frac{1}{8}$ in.).

PROV.: Richard Bull (Sale, Sotheby, 23:v:1881, Lot 175). Purchased at the Bull Sale by the B.M., 1881.

1881–6–11–205 (L.B.2).

REPR.: *Wren Memorial Volume*, 1923, p. 130.

In 1667 Parliament passed an act 'that a Columne or Pillar of Brase or Stone be erected on or as neare unto the place where the said Fire soe unhappily began as Conveniently as may be. . . .' A tax of 12d. a ton on coal was granted for the purpose of this act. The first design seems to have been for an obelisk surmounted by a phoenix but this was abandoned in favour of a column which was begun in 1671, though it was not decided what the terminal should be. The design was based closely on Trajan's column as illustrated in Serlio, the original drawing for the base (B.M., Sloane MS. 5238, *f.* 72) being taken directly from the engraving (p. 78, Book II of the 1584 edition). In 1675

Wren, in a report to the City Lands Committee, recommended a statue 15 ft. high which 'would undoubtedly bee the noblest finishing . . .', but which would cost £1000. As an alternative he suggested 'a ball of Copper, nine foot diameter . . . with the Flames and guilt'. He remarked that a 'Phoenix was at first thought of, and is the ornament of the wooden Modell of the Pillar, which I caused to be made before it was begun; but, upon second thoughts I rejected it because it will be costly, not easily understood at that highth, and worse understood at a distance and lastly dangerous by reason of the sayle, the spread winges will carry in the winde'. Other designs for the Monument are at All Souls College and in the B.M., Sloane MS., 5238. This drawing seems to be later than the preliminary designs for an obelisk (Sloane, 5238/69) and was probably made after a column had been determined upon. Sir John Summerson's opinion is that the drawing is not by Wren but by one of the draughtsmen employed in his office.

2. DESIGN FOR THE CUPOLA OF ST. PAUL'S.
Two half-sections, drawn freehand to show the relation of the inner and outer domes. The finial to the dome of the r.-hand study is a ball supported by scrolls, that on the l. being similar but only faintly indicated. The r.-hand study is scaled vertically in eights from 8 to 64, the l.-hand across the base, in tens from 1 to 50. In the upper l.-hand corner, sketch of a cherub's head, scroll and pendant drapery, presumably for carving. **Plate 294**

Pen and brown ink; $21 \cdot 3 \times 24 \cdot 5$ cm. ($8\frac{3}{8} \times 9\frac{1}{2}$ in.).

INSCR.: *Recto*, at the foot, by Ralph Thoresby, *Sr. Chr: Wren's owne hand*; along top edge to the r. in a different hand, *For the Dome of St. Pauls Church.*

PROV.: Ralph Thoresby. Walpole by whom it was given to Richard Bull (Sale, Sotheby, 23:v:1881, Lot 174). Purchased at the Bull Sale by the B.M., 1881.

1881–6–11–203 (L.B.1).

REPR.: *Sir Christopher Wren Bicentenary Memorial Volume*, 1923, p. 53. Wren Soc., XV, dedicatory page.

3. DESIGN FOR A REREDOS IN HAMPTON COURT CHAPEL.
Alternative designs for an altarpiece to fit in the Tudor chapel at Hampton Court, the beams of which are shown at the top. In the centre, a communion table covered with a cloth on which stand two candlesticks, a chalice, ewer and alms-dish. The r. half shows a single Corinthian column supporting an entablature and segmental pediment. The l. half shows a pair of Corinthian columns supporting a similar pediment beneath which are two cherubim and a swag of fruit and flowers. On the l. side, a small niche. Beneath the design and corresponding with it, a plan of the sanctuary. **Plate 292**

Pen and brown ink, touched with watercolours; $28 \cdot 5 \times 19 \cdot 2$ cm. ($11\frac{1}{4} \times 7\frac{7}{8}$ in.).

INSCR.: *Recto*, in ink, by the artist, at the r. edge of the plan: *Vestry dore,* and at the foot of the plan: *Hampton Court Chappel Decr 5. 1710,* together with measurements.

PROV.: Richard Bull (Sale, Sotheby, 23:v:1881, Lot 174). Purchased at the Bull Sale by the B.M., 1881.

1881–6–11–165 (L.B.3, as William Kent).

BIBL.: *Wren Soc.*, IV, pp. 13–14, V, p. 12. H.M.C., Middlesex, p. 42a.

This drawing corresponds with one in the Soane Museum (formerly in a volume of drawings of the Wren school which are now mounted separately). It is a full development of the l.-hand alternative but without cherubs or swags; this is reproduced in *Wren Soc.*, IV, p. 13. Another design for the same chapel is reproduced in *Wren Soc.*, V, Pl. XLIV. The reredos as built seems to be influenced by both designs. No building accounts have been discovered relating to an alteration of the chapel in 1710.

WYCK, JAN

B. *c.* 1645: D. 1700

Battle, sporting and landscape painter and draughtsman

Born in Haarlem, son of the landscape painter Thomas Wyck. Nothing known of his upbringing, but probably trained by his father with whom he most likely came to England soon after the Restoration. Appeared before a Court of the Painter-Stainers on June 17th, 1674, and promised to pay his own and his father's 'quarterage'. On Nov. 22nd, 1676, a licence was issued by the Vicar-General for 'Jan Wick of St. Paul's Covent Garden, gent., widower, about 31, to marry Ann Skynner, of St. Martins in the Fields, spinster, about 19, her parents dead, at St. Mary Savoy', this suggesting that he was born in 1645, not 1640 (*Thieme-Becker*) or 1653 (*D.N.B.*). Yet another document, however, states that he was 'about 38' in 1688. Four children born between 1678 and 1683, but none of these survived and his wife died in 1687. On Nov. 24th, 1680, 'Mr. Wike', among others was 'added to the Com^tee of [Acting (?)] painters' of the Painter-Stainers' Company. Designed illustrations for Richard Blome's *Gentleman's Recreation*, 1686, two of the original drawings being in the Department (*See* Nos. 7 & 8 below). Probably lived in Durham Yard, Strand, until 1688, when he married, as his third wife, 'Elizabeth Holomberry of Mortlock, Surrey, spinster', and moved to Mortlake. To this wife two boys and one girl were born and baptized between 1689 and 1693 when she died. Visited Scotland and 'painted many views'; Vertue records a view of Stirling Castle by 'Lucas Vorsterman'—actually Johannes Vorsterman (B. *c.* 1643: D. 1699)—with 'figures by Wyke' (Welbeck Abbey). Vertue also credits him with views of 'The Ile of Jersey', which were also drawn by his pupil Sir Martin Beckman (*q.v.*) who became Chief Engineer and Master Gunner of England, under William III. Was the master of John Wootton (B. 1682 (?): D. 1765); an engraved portrait of Wyck by J. Faber after Kneller bears the inscription: *Optimi Ingenii Viro / Joanni Wootton / Joannis Wyck insignis Praeliorum Pictoris quondam Discipulo hanc Magistri Effigiem*. Died on May 17th, 1700, and was buried at Mortlake two days later. In his own day esteemed for his battle-pieces and sporting subjects and, as recorded by Vertue, was a 'Duch Battel-Painter of grate note. He has both in his Horses and Landskips, a grate Freedom of Pencilling and good Colour; as also a grate deal of Fire in most of his Designs, some of which are very large, especially those of Sieges and pitched Battels as at Namur, the Boyn, &c. His Hunting Pieces are also in grate Esteem among our Country-Gentry, for whom he often drew Horses & Dogs by the Life, in which he imitated the manner of Wouverman'. Of his battle-scenes, one, of *Bothwell Brig*, now at Drumlanrig, was probably painted for the Duke of Monmouth; another, of *William III and the Duke of Marl-*

borough, was in a private collection at Edinburgh; and two others are in the Holburne Museum at Bath. An equestrian portrait of William III at Torbay, dated 1688, is in the National Maritime Museum. Vertue also noted in Mr. Halstead's Sale, in 1726, a 'Turkish Procession to Mecca (whole length) "Jan Wyck 1688" a fine noble picture'. In the handling of the foliage in Nos. 6 and 7 below anticipates the early English water-colourist William Taverner (B. 1703: D. 1772).

BIBL.: *Painter-Stainers' Minutes*, II, pp. 170 & 258. *D.N.B.*, LXIII, 1900, p. 292. *Kendall. M'Naughton. Grant*, p. 10. *T.-B.*, XXXVI, 1947, p. 323. *Vertue, Index*, p. 296.

DRAWINGS IN OTHER COLLECTIONS: Dr. H. Wellesley (Sale, Sotheby, 5:vii:1866, Lots 1728—37, as Thomas Wyck, but Jan (?)). Oppé collection.

1. TWO CAVALIERS.
Two cavaliers riding into the foreground, the one on the l. on a road which curves round a wooded bank, the one on the r. approaching from a by-road.

Pen and brown ink, with grey wash; $18 \cdot 4 \times 20 \cdot 5$ cm. ($7\frac{1}{4} \times 8\frac{1}{8}$ in.).

PROV.: The Rev. C. M. Cracherode, by whom it was bequeathed to the B.M., 1799. **G.g.2–316** (L.B.1).

BIBL.: *Cracherode Cat.*, p. 73, No. 316.

2. THE 'BLANKET FAIR' ON THE THAMES DURING THE GREAT FROST IN THE WINTER OF 1683/4.
View from mid-stream, looking E. along the frozen Thames, from near Temple Stairs which appear on the l. In the foreground, groups of figures and a number of coaches on the ice, while from the r. a boat on wheels is dragged towards the centre by a chain of men. Beyond, the main line of booths, known as 'Temple Street', and beyond that, the river dotted with other figures and vehicles. In the distance, l., the Monument and the White Tower rising above the other buildings of the City; in the centre, London Bridge; and on the r., the tower of St. Mary Overy (now Southwark Cathedral).

Brush drawing, in grey wash over black lead; on two conjoined sheets; $23 \cdot 6 \times 70 \cdot 7$ cm. ($9\frac{1}{4} \times 27\frac{7}{8}$ in.).

INSCR.: *Recto*, in the upper r.-hand corner, *Munday February the 4: | Ao 168¾*.

PROV.: J. C. Crowle, by whom it was bequeathed, in an extra-illustrated copy of the 1793 edn. of Pennant's *London*, to the B.M., 1811.
    Crowle-Pennant, Pt. VIII, No. 239, (L.B.5).

ENGR.: By James Stow, 1825.

BIBL.: *B.M. MS. Maps . . . and Topographical Drawings*, II, p. 20.
    From early Dec., 1683, to Feb. 28th, 1684, the Thames above London Bridge (as upon other occasions) was frozen over. The ice was so thick that it enabled coaches to be driven over it, bear-baiting and other sports to take place, and a line of booths known as 'Temple Street' to be erected across the river between Temple Stairs and the 'Old King's Barge House' on the Surrey shore. The present drawing should be compared with Joseph Moxon's *MAP of the River | THAMES | Merrily Cal'd | BLANKET FAIR (See Crowle-Pennant,*

Pt. VIII, No. 230), and William Warter's *AN | Exact and lively Mapp | OR | REPRESEN-TATION | of Booths and all the varieties of showes and | Humours upon the Ice on the River | THAMES by London (See Crace Coll., Pf. VIII, No. 19), both of which were engraved and published at the time.

In the collection of H.R.H. the Duke of Kent was an oil-painting, attributed to Jan Wyck, representing the same subject and taken from the same point of view as the present drawing, but differing in the arrange-ment of the figures and other details. It appeared in the exhibition of *Old London*, at 45 Park Lane, in 1938, and is reproduced in the *Illustrated Souvenir*, p. 22. Another view of the Fair, also attributed to Wyck, taken from the Surrey shore opposite Temple Stairs, was with Messrs. Leggatt in 1926.

3. THE BATTLE OF THE BOYNE (?). View from high ground overlooking a river which is being crossed by attacking troops at three points, in the centre and in the distance, r. On the far bank the defending army, and in the distance, l., their encampment near a church spire. In the foreground, r., a general and his aide-de-camp, both on horseback. In a scrolled cartouche with a cherub's head at the top.

Pen and brown ink, with grey wash; indented for transfer; cut to the shape of the car-touche; 8·6 × 19·3 cm. (3⅜ × 7½ in.).

INSCR.: *Recto*, at the foot, by the artist, *I W fe.*

PROV.: Sir Walter C. Trevelyan, Bart., by whom It was presented to the B.M., 1871.

1871–12–9–6327 (L.B.2).

The traditional attribution to Jan Wyck is presumably based on the signature, which, however, only consists of initial letters. No doubt the engraving (most probably a book illustration), for which this drawing is a design, would provide a clue as to its author-ship and subject, but this has not yet been identified. Mr. Binyon suggests that the drawing may be intended for a representa-tion of the Battle of the Boyne, July 1st, 1690, and the manner in which the attacking army is fording the river in three separate places, is certainly not unlike that seen in the contemporary engraved view of the Battle of the Boyne by Theodor Maas.

A view of the Battle, but apparently taken from the 'Jacobite side', attributed to Jan Wyck, was in Lord Fitzwilliam's Sale at Christie's, 11:vi:49, Lot 198. Nagler (Vol. 22, p. 150) mentions a large mezzotint of the Battle of the Boyne with Wyck's name on it, which may have been engraved by the elder John Faber. No impression of it is in the Department.

4. TWO STUDIES OF EQUESTRIAN FIGURES. On the l., a cavalryman, seen partly from behind, his horse rearing towards the r. On the r., a woman, mounted side-saddle on a horse standing in profile to l., and beyond her, a man riding off over the slope of a hill.

Black lead; 18·1 × 29·2 cm. (7⅛ × 11½ in.).

PROV.: Richard Bull (Sale, Sotheby, 23:v:1881, Lot 177). Purchased at the Bull Sale, through A. W. Thibaudeau, by the B.M., 1881.

1881–6–11–206 (L.B.4).

The figures in this drawing much resemble those which occur in Wyck's battle and hunting compositions.

5. FORDING A STREAM. In the centre foreground, a horseman crossing the stream and holding under his arm a small greyhound at which a dog, leaping in the water, is barking. On the r., a man and a woman also on horseback about to enter the water, and beyond them, on a bank, three peasants with a donkey. On the l., a man and woman on foot wading into the stream, and a packhorse, standing in the water drinking, with a spaniel sitting on its back.

Black lead; 19 × 30·8 cm. (7½ × 12⅛ in.).   In the same manner as No. 4.

> PROV.: As for No. 4.
> 1881–6–11–207 (L.B.3).

6. DISTANT VIEW OF LONDON, LOOKING N.W. FROM BLACKHEATH. View looking from the top of the road now known as Croom's Hill, which runs from Greenwich to Blackheath up the W. side of Greenwich Park. On the l., broken ground, with a ploughed field and occasional trees and bushes, rising towards a low cliff. In the centre, the road with a sportsman and his dog and, further off, another figure descending it. On the r., the paling of Greenwich Park running up to a wooded bank on which a man is seated. In the distance, the Thames and London, rather faintly seen, with Westminster Abbey, the Tower, and Old St. Paul's. **Plate 290(b)**

Brush drawing in brown and grey wash over black lead; on two conjoined sheets of paper; 30 × 79·5 cm. (11¾ × 31¼ in.).

> INSCR.: *Recto*, above the respective landmarks in the distance, *London*, and *Westminster, den Toor* (?), *paules*.

> PROV.: Paul Sandby (*Lugt*, No. 2112. Sale, Christie, 17:iii:1812, Lot 92). G. Mayer, by whom it was presented to the B.M., 1897.
> 1897–8–31–1.

> ENGR.: By R. B. Godfrey, 1776.

> BIBL. & REPR.: *Hind, Dutch & Flemish Drawings*, IV, p. 118, No. 15, & Pl. LXVIII.

As the tower of St. Paul's is seen in the distance, this drawing would have been made early in 1666, the year of the Great Fire.

On Godfrey's engraving and in Sandby's Sale Catalogue, the author's name is given as 'Wyck' without any first name. The drawing was presented to the Museum as by Thomas Wyck, and was catalogued under that name by Mr. Hind. In the handling of the foliage and in other details, however, it is so reminiscent of the two designs by Jan Wyck for illustrations to Richard Blome's *The Gentleman's Recreation*, listed below at Nos. 7 & 8, that it has now been transferred to works by this younger artist.

7. THE DEATH OF THE HART. The dead hart lying on its side at the foot of a bank in the foreground, within a ring of baying hounds kept in check by three huntsmen with whips. To the l., another huntsman on horseback watching the scene, and in the centre, four others blowing a fanfare on straight hunting-horns. Further up the bank, r., a man on horseback holding three other horses. To the l., a group of trees, and in the background, a stag-hunt in progress. **Plate 295**

Pen and brown ink, with washes of brown and brownish grey; 29·8 × 21·cm. (11¾ × 8¼ in.). Old mount; 37·8 × 28·9 cm. (14¾ × 11⅛ in.).

INSCR.: *Recto*, on the old mount, at the foot, perhaps by the artist, *Wyke fe*.
    Verso, on the old mount, in black lead, *John Wyck or Wyke B. 1640 D. 1702 (signed) | Purchased at the Strawberry Hill Sale 1842*.

PROV.: Horace Walpole (Sale, Robins, 23:vi:1842, Lot 1266, No. 36, purchased by Henry Graves & Co.). Dr. Barry Delany (*Lugt*, No. 350). Apparently not in his sale, Sotheby, 5:vi:1872). E. H. Coles, and A. H. Coles, from whom it was purchased by the B.M., 1950.
    1950–10–14–1.

ENGR.: By Arthur Soly, with the lettering *The Death of the Hart*, in Richard Blome's *The Gentleman's Recreation*, 1686, between pp. 84 & 85.

BIBL.: *Vertue*, I, p. 161.

EXHIB.: London, 39, Grosvenor Square, 1937, *British Country Life*, No. 455.

This drawing is important as a representation of English sporting and country life in the late XVII c. It is interesting too in its relation to the work of Francis Barlow, who also provided some of the illustrations to the sporting section of Richard Blome's book.
    The handling of the foliage of the trees on the l. is very near to that in No. 6, the *View of London from Blackheath*, and is one of the principal reasons for now giving that drawing to Jan Wyck.

8. RABBIT CATCHING. View over a field with a rabbit warren. On the r., a lady and gentleman followed by two other gentlemen walking into the foreground, with a hound near them. In the centre, a man with two dead rabbits beside him, sitting on the grass and watching the entrance to a burrow above which prowls a ferret. Beyond, on the l., a man catching rabbits in a net. Further off, in the centre, a hound coursing, and to the l., three rabbits by a burrow, and others, dead, hung from a pole. In the background, centre, a dovecot backed by trees which surround, l., a mansion. On the r., horses and cattle by a fence beyond which is a distant park with deer in it. **Plate 296**

Pen and brown ink, with washes of grey and brown; 29·8 × 21·4 cm. (11¾ × 8⅜ in.). Old mount; 37·3 × 29 cm. (14¾ × 11⅜ in.).

INSCR.: *Recto*, on the old mount, at the foot, perhaps by the artist, *Wyke fe*.
    Verso, on the old mount, *John Wyck or Wyke B. 1640 D. 1702 (signed) | Purchased at the Strawberry Hill Sale 1842*.

PROV.: Horace Walpole (Sale, Robins, 23:vi:1842, Lot 1266, No. 35, purchased by Henry Graves & Co.). Dr. Barry Delany (*Lugt*, No. 350. Apparently not in his sale, Sotheby, 5:vi:1872). E. H. Coles, and A. H.

Coles, from whom it was purchased by the B.M., 1950.
    1950–10–14–2.

BIBL.: *Vertue*, I, p. 161.

EXHIB.: London, 39 Grosvenor Square, 1937, *British Country Life*, No. 456.

This drawing was intended as an illustration to Richard Blome's *The Gentleman's Recreation*, 1686, but was not apparently used. It corresponds with Chap. XIV of Part III of the book, *Hunting*, pp. 98–9, 'Of Taking and Hunting the CONEY or RABET, with Dogs, Nets and Ferrets, . . .'.

ADDITIONAL HANDLIST OF DRAWINGS BY FOREIGN ARTISTS

Appended is a list of drawings with British connexions by artists not included in the main sections of *British Artists* and *Foreign Artists working in Great Britain*. In each case only title, medium, measurements and registration number are given as the drawings either have already been described, or will be described in full detail in the catalogues devoted to the specific schools to which they belong.

ANON. DUTCH ARTIST

Working 17th c.

1. SATIRE ON CROMWELL'S GOVERN-MENT

Pen and brown ink, with grey wash.
26 × 32·5 cm. (10¼ × 12¾ in.).
1891–6–17–22 (H.67).

ANON. ITALIAN ARTIST

Working 17th c.

See under: HOLBEIN, Copies after

BISSCHOP, JAN DE

B. *c.* 1628: D. 1671

Not known to have come to England

See under HOLBEIN, Copies after

BLOOTELING, ABRAHAM

B. 1640: D. 1690

Came to England 1672; returned to Amsterdam by September 1678

1. CHARLES II. AFTER LELY
Brush drawing in grey wash.
21·9 × 18·5 cm. (8⅝ × 7¼ in.).
G.g.1–460.

2. EDWARD MONTAGUE, 2nd EARL OF SANDWICH. AFTER LELY

Brush drawing in grey; indented for trans-fer.
23·6 × 19·2 cm. (9¼ × 7½ in.).
G.g.1–464 (H.1).

3. NOAH BRYDGES
Black lead on vellum.
7·6 × 6·3 cm. (oval) (3 × 2½ in.).
G.g.1–501 (H.3).

CLOUET, FRANÇOIS

B. before 1522: D. 1572

Did not visit England

1. MARIE DE LORRAINE, QUEEN OF SCOTLAND
Red and black chalks.
30·4 × 22·5 cm. (12 × 8⅞ in.).
G.g.1–420.

2. MARY, QUEEN OF SCOTS
Red and black chalks.
25·8 × 21·5 cm. (10⅛ × 8½ in.).
1862–3–8–1.

DIEPENBECK, ABRAHAM VAN

(DIEPENBEECK)

B. 1596: D. 1675

Visited England, according to Vertue, V, 57, but date uncertain (See H., II, p. 100 ff.)

1. WILLIAM CAVENDISH, 1st DUKE OF NEWCASTLE, ON HORSEBACK, WITH BOLSOVER CASTLE IN THE BACKGROUND

Pen and brush drawing in brown ink, with grey wash and touches of white.

39·5 × 52 cm. (15½ × 20½ in.).

5236–112 (H.20).

2. WILLIAM CAVENDISH, 1st DUKE OF NEWCASTLE AND HIS FAMILY

Pen and brush drawing in brown ink, with washes of brown and grey, heightened with white.

18·2 × 16 cm. (7⅛ × 6¼ in.).

1858–4–17–1629 (H.14).

DÜRER, ALBRECHT

B. 1471: D. 1528

Did not visit England

1. HENRY PARKER, 8th BARON MORLEY

Black lead on green prepared paper.

37·9 × 30·5 cm. (14⅞ × 12 in.).

1890–5–12–155 (L.871 D.280).

Morley was sent to Nuremberg by Henry VIII in 1523 to confer the Order of the Garter on the Archduke Ferdinand.

EECKHOUT, GERBRAND VAN DEN

B. 1621: D. 1674

Not known to have come to England

1. ALLEGORY ON THE TRIPLE ALLIANCE OF ENGLAND, HOLLAND AND SWEDEN AGAINST FRANCE, 1668

Pen and brown ink, with brown wash.

29 × 22·7 cm. (11⅜ × 9 in.).

1836–8–11–240 (H.8).

ESSELENS, JACOB

B.1626: D. 1687

Spent some time in England

1. PANORAMIC VIEW OF CANTERBURY AND SURROUNDING COUNTRY LOOKING S.E.

Pen and brown ink, with washes of brown and grey.

18·5 × 104·8 cm. (7¼ × 41¼ in.).

1856–6–14–155 (Schellinks, H.11).

GRAVE, JOSUA DE

Working c. 1672–1711

Not known to have come to England

1–12. A SERIES OF VIEWS OF PLACES CONNECTED WITH MARLBOROUGH'S CAMPAIGN OF AUGUST 1711, AND THE INVESTMENT OF BOUCHAIN, NEAR DOUAI

Pen and grey ink, with grey wash.

About 14 × 18·5 cm. (5½ × 7¼ in.).

1922–7–10–1–12 (H.1–12).

HAGEN, CHRISTIAN

[HAGENS]

Working c. 1663–88

Not known to have visited England

1. SIR WILLIAM DAVIDSON, BART.

Black chalk on vellum.

30 × 23 cm. (11¾ × 9 in.).

1848–9–11–411 (H.1).

HOEFNAGEL, JORIS

B. 1542: D. 1600

Probably in England c. 1568 (Cf. drawing listed below, dated 1568)

1. NONSUCH PALACE

Pen and ink, with brown wash and watercolour.

22 × 46·4 cm. (8⅝ × 18¼ in.).

1943–10–9–35.

HOLBEIN, HANS

B. 1497: D. 1543

Worked in England from 1526 to 1528, and again from 1532 until his death

[1–3] *FIGURE STUDIES AND PORTRAITS*

1. A WOMAN SEATED ON A SETTLE WITH FOUR CHILDREN

Brush drawing in black ink, with grey wash.

13·3 × 16·9 cm. (5¼ × 6⅝ in.).

1852–5–9–1 (L.B.8; G.100).

2. STUDIES OF A LADY IN A PEAKED HEADDRESS

Brush drawing in ink, with black wash, tinted in pink.

15·9 × 10·9 cm. (6¼ × 4¼ in.).

1895–9–15–991 (L.B.11; G.150).

3. AN ENGLISH WOMAN, PERHAPS MARGARET ROPER

Black chalk, touched with red chalk and yellow water-colour, and heightened with white on pink prepared paper.

27·4 × 19·3 cm. (10⅞ × 7½ in.).

1910–2–12–105 (G.93).

[4–188] *DESIGNS FOR ORNAMENTS, ETC.*

4. THE END OF A JEWEL CASKET, flanked by pillars, decorated with arabesque ornament.

Pen and black ink, with washes of black and yellow.

11·5 × 7·9 cm. (4½ × 3⅛ in.).

5308–1 (L.B.31, c).

Cf. No. 8.

5. A MEDALLION of Time freeing Truth from the Rock, surrounded by the inscription, *Nihil est tectum qvod nō sit retegendv̄ et nihil occultv̄ qvod nō revelabitur.*

Pen and black ink, with grey wash.

Diam. 4·7 cm. (1⅞ in.).

5308–2 (L.B.35, d; G.263).

6. MONOGRAM OF THE LETTERS A.B.C.E

Pen and black ink.

2 × 2·6 cm. (¾ × 1 in.).

5308–3 (L.B.38, d; G.337).

Cf. Nos. 9 & 10.

7. MONOGRAM OF THE LETTERS E.N.L.R.A.O.D

Pen and black ink.

1·8 × 2·8 cm. (¾ × 1⅛ in.).

5308–4 (L.B.38, f; G.339).

8. THE END OF A JEWEL CASKET. Alternative design for No. 4.

Pen and black ink, with washes of black and yellow ochre.

11·3 × 7·8 cm. (4½ × 3⅛ in.).

5308–5 (L.B.31, d; G.403).

9. MONOGRAM OF THE LETTERS A.B.C.E. Alternative design for No. 6.

Pen and black ink.

2·3 × 2·8 cm. (⅞ × 1⅛ in.).

5308–6 (L.B.38, a; G.334).

10. MONOGRAM OF THE LETTERS A.B.C.E. Alternative design for No. 6.

Pen and black ink.

2·1 × 2·6 cm. (⅞ × 1 in.).

5308–7 (L.B.38, c; G.336).

11. DESIGN FOR A BINDING IN GOLD OR SILVER. Decorated with arabesque ornament incorporating the initials *T.I.W.*

Pen and black ink, with washes of black and yellow.

7·9 × 5·9 cm. (3⅛ × 2⅜ in.).

5308–8 (L.B.31, a; G.405).

Cf. No. 13.

12. MONOGRAM OF THE LETTERS A.T.L.H.E.N.R.S.I.G.K

Pen and ink, with black wash.

Diam. 2·9 cm. (1⅛ in.).

5308–9 (L.B.38, g; G.343).

13. DESIGN FOR A BINDING IN GOLD OR SILVER. An alternative design for No. 11.

Pen and black ink, with washes of black and yellow.

8·1 × 6 cm. (3⅛ × 2⅜ in.).

5308–10 (L.B.31, b; G.404).

14. MONOGRAM OF THE LETTERS H.I.S.A

Pen and black ink, with brown wash.
2·4 × 2·4 cm. (1 × 1 in.).
5308–11 (L.B.38, b; G.335).

15. DESIGN FOR A FOLIATED ORNA-MENT WITH A SATYR'S MASK

Pen and black ink, with grey wash.
3·1 × 3·5 cm. (1¼ × 1⅜ in.).
5308–12 (L.B.22, d; G.428).

16. A MEDALLION. In the centre the Trinity with the motto *TRINITATIS GLORIA STABILIMVR* and round it a border of red roses.

Pen and black ink, with water-colour.
Diam. 5·8 cm. (2¼ in.).
5308–13 (L.B.29, l; G.264).
Cf. No. 22.

17. MONOGRAM OF THE LETTERS H.N.A.V.G.R.S.X.D. set with 5 stones.

Pen and black ink.
3·2 × 2·9 cm. (1¼ × 1⅛ in.).
5308–14 (L.B.38, n; G.331).

18. DESIGN FOR A CIRCULAR PENDANT WITH A DEVICE. A man and woman lamenting over another figure on a funeral pyre, in the flames of which was to be set a stone, probably a ruby.

Pen and black ink, with grey wash, touched with yellow.
5·3 × 4·1 cm. (2⅛ × 1⅝ in.).
5308–15 (L.B.29, h; G.291).

19. DESIGN FOR A PENDANT with a leaf ornament twined with ribbons, and sur-mounted by a grotesque figure.

Pen and ink, with black wash.
6·7 × 4·1 cm. (2⅝ × 1⅝ in.).
5308–16 (L.B.28, l; G.316).

20. A MEDALLION OF ST. JOHN THE BAPTIST

Pen and brown ink, with water-colour.
Diam. 4·6 cm. (1⅞ in.).
5308–17 (L.B.35, c; G.390).

21. A LOZENGE-SHAPED JEWEL. The central stone set in open foliated work.

Pen and black ink, with washes of black and grey.
3 × 2·8 cm. (1¼ × 1⅛ in.).
5308–18 (L.B.37, o; G.354).

22. A MEDALLION. In the centre the Annunciation with the motto *ORIGO MVNDI MELIORIS*, with a border of mari-golds.

Pen and black ink, with water-colour.
Diam. 5·9 cm. (2¼ in.).
5308–19 (L.B.29, k; G.265).
Either the reverse of, or the alternative design for No. 16.

23. A CIRCULAR JEWEL. Central stone set in foliated scroll-work.

Pen and black ink, with grey wash.
Diam. 2·2 cm. (⅞ in.).
5308–20 (L.B.37, a; G.357).
Cf. Nos. 42, 48, 50 & 107.

24. DESIGN FOR A FINIAL. A winged female figure holding a mirror.

Pen and black ink.
4·3 × 2·9 cm. (1¾ × 1⅛ in.).
5308–21 (L.B.23, b; G.232).
Cf. Nos. 26 & 27.

25. A MEDALLION WITH A DEVICE. A hand issuing from a cloud and resting on a book which lies on a rock. Below on a car-touche, the motto *SERVAR VOGLIO QVEL CHE HO / GVIRATO*.

Pen and black ink, with grey wash.
5·5 × 5·5 cm. (2⅛ × 2⅛ in.).
5308–22 (L.B.29, b; G.388).
Cf. No. 37.

26. DESIGN FOR A FINIAL. A winged female figure holding a brush.

Pen and black ink.
4·4 × 2·9 cm. (1¾ × 1⅛ in.).
5308–23 (L.B.23, a; G.233).
Cf. Nos. 24 & 27.

27. DESIGN FOR A FINIAL. A winged female figure holding a comb.

Pen and black ink.

4·7 × 3·5 cm. ($1\frac{7}{8}$ × $1\frac{3}{8}$ in.).

5308–24 (L.B.23, c; G.234).

Cf. Nos. 24 & 26.

28. A MEDALLION WITH LOT AND HIS WIFE

Pen and black ink, with grey wash.

5 × 5 cm. (2 × 2 in.).

5308–25 (L.B.35, e; G.290).

29. DESIGN FOR A FINIAL. A winged male figure holding a battleaxe.

Pen and black ink, with grey wash.

4·7 × 3·7 cm. ($1\frac{7}{8}$ × $1\frac{1}{2}$ in.).

5308–26 (L.B.23, e; G.236).

Cf. Nos. 173 & 175.

30. A MEDALLION WITH A BLACK CARTOUCHE SURMOUNTED BY A RIBBON

Pen and black ink.

2·8 × 4·4 cm. ($1\frac{1}{8}$ × $1\frac{3}{4}$ in.).

5308–27 (L.B.30, d).

31. A MEDALLION WITH A DEVICE. A boy lying under a fountain, which jets its water over him.

Pen and black ink, with grey wash.

Diam. 5·4 cm. ($2\frac{1}{8}$ in.).

5308–28 (L.B.29, g; G.280).

32. A TAG OF A BELT (?). Three stones set in a foliated ornament.

Pen and black ink, with grey wash.

2·9 × 4·1 cm. ($1\frac{1}{8}$ × $1\frac{5}{8}$ in.).

5308–29 (L.B.37, n; G.330).

33. DESIGN FOR A HEART-SHAPED PENDANT, with two doves billing and the motto *TVRTVRIUM CONCORDIA* and three pearls.

Water-colour.

5·5 × 3·4 cm. ($2\frac{1}{8}$ × $1\frac{3}{8}$ in.).

5308–30 (L.B.27, b).

Design for the reverse of the pendant, No. 35.

34. DESIGN FOR A CURVED BORDER OF ROSES AND ACORNS

Pen and black ink.

2·1 × 4·1 cm. ($\frac{7}{8}$ × $1\frac{5}{8}$ in.).

5308–31 (L.B.34, p; G.367).

35. DESIGN FOR THE FRONT OF THE PENDANT, No. 33.

Water-colour and gold.

5·6 × 3·4 cm. ($2\frac{1}{4}$ × $1\frac{3}{8}$ in.).

5308–32 (L.B.27, c).

36. DESIGN FOR A LOZENGE-SHAPED PENDANT, twined with ribbon work and set with diamonds and pearls.

Pen and black ink, with washes of grey and light yellow.

6·3 × 4·1 cm. ($2\frac{1}{2}$ × $1\frac{5}{8}$ in.).

5308–33 (L.B.28, h; G.322).

37. ALTERNATIVE DESIGN FOR THE DEVICE, No. 29. Similarly inscribed.

Pen and black ink, with brown wash.

Diam. 5·5 cm. ($2\frac{1}{8}$ in.).

5308–34 (L.B.29, c; G.389).

Cf. No. 25.

38. DESIGN FOR A PENDANT, with ribbon work set with stones and pearls.

Pen and ink, with black wash.

5·8 × 4·9 cm. ($2\frac{1}{4}$ × $1\frac{7}{8}$ in.).

5308–35 (L.B.28, m; G.319).

39. MONOGRAM OF THE LETTERS E.S.H.N.K.P

Pen and black ink.

2·2 × 2·9 cm. ($\frac{7}{8}$ × $1\frac{1}{8}$ in.).

5308–36 (L.B.38, m; G.332).

40. DESIGN FOR A PENDANT, set with emeralds and a pearl.

Pen and black ink, with washes of grey and water-colour.

8·5 × 5·5 cm. ($3\frac{3}{8}$ × $2\frac{1}{8}$ in.).

5308–37 (L.B.27, d; G.313).

41. MONOGRAM OF THE LETTERS T.W.E.S

Pen and black ink.
2 × 3·1 cm. ($\frac{3}{4}$ × 1$\frac{1}{4}$ in.).
5308–38 (L.B.38, s; G.342).

42. A CIRCULAR JEWEL. Central stone set in a foliated scroll-work.

Pen and black ink, with grey wash.
Diam. 2·4 cm. (1 in.).
5308–39 (L.B.37, c; G.355).
Cf. Nos. 23, 48, 50 & 107.

43. A MEDALLION WITH A DEVICE. A pair of compasses, serpents, dolphins and cornucopias, all entwined with a ribbon inscribed, *PRVDENTEMENT ET PAR COMPAS INCONTINENT VIENDRAS.*

Pen and ink, with black wash.
4·9 × 5·1 cm. (1$\frac{7}{8}$ × 2 in.).
5308–40 (L.B.29, i).

44. A CIRCULAR JEWEL. Circular stone set in a foliated scroll-work.

Pen and black ink.
2·2 × 2·4 cm. ($\frac{7}{8}$ × 1 in.).
5308–41 (L.B.37, q; G.358).

45. A ROUNDEL CONTAINING HOLBEIN'S ARMS. Argent, a bull's head, with a ring in its nose and a mullet of six points between the horns, sable, on a shield. Mantling argent and sable, and a helm with the crest of a mullet of six points between a bull's horns, all on a blue blackground.

Pen and black ink, touched with gold and blue wash.
Diam. 4·3 cm. (1$\frac{3}{4}$ in.).
5308–42 (L.B.29, e; G.394).

46. DESIGN FOR A PENDANT. A half length figure of a lady in contemporary dress holding a tablet, inscribed *WELL / LAYDI / WELL*, with three pearls below.

Pen and black ink, with grey wash.
6·6 × 3·4 cm. (2$\frac{5}{8}$ × 1$\frac{3}{8}$ in.).
5308–43 (L.B.28, a; G.345).

47. DESIGN FOR A SEAL OF CHARLES BRANDON, DUKE OF SUFFOLK

Pen and black ink, with grey wash.
4·7 × 4·7 cm. (1$\frac{7}{8}$ × 1$\frac{7}{8}$ in.).
5308–44 (L.B.29, a; G.387).

48. A CIRCULAR JEWEL. Central stone set in a foliated scroll-work.

Pen and black ink, with grey wash.
Diam. 2·1 cm. ($\frac{3}{4}$ in.).
5308–45 (L.B.37, e; G.359).
Cf. Nos. 23, 42, 50 & 107.

49. PENDANT IN THE FORM OF A MONOGRAM R.E. Set with a single central stone and three pearls.

Pen and black ink.
5·4 × 4·2 cm. (2$\frac{1}{8}$ × 1$\frac{5}{8}$ in.).
5308–46 (L.B.38, l; G.327).

50. DESIGN FOR A CIRCULAR JEWEL. Central stone set in a foliated scroll-work.

Pen and black ink, with grey wash.
Diam. 2·1 cm. ($\frac{7}{8}$ in.).
5308–47 (L.B.37, f; G.360).
Cf. Nos. 23, 42, 48 and 107.

51. AN OVAL JEWEL WITH A FOLIATED BORDER

Pen and ink, with black wash, touched with light brown.
5·3 × 4·3 cm. (2$\frac{1}{8}$ × 1$\frac{3}{4}$ in.).
5308–48 (L.B.37, g; G.361).

52. TERMINAL FIGURES OF SATYRS SUPPORTING A BASE, AND THE DIAGRAM OF A SCREW ATTACHMENT

Pen and black ink, with grey wash.
7·5 × 3·9 cm. (3 × 1$\frac{1}{2}$ in.).
5308–49 (L.B.22, b; G.215).

53. DESIGN FOR A CRUCIFORM PENDANT

Pen and black ink.
6·8 × 5 cm. (2$\frac{3}{4}$ × 2 in.).
5308–50 (L.B.27, a; G.418).

54. A COLLAR WITH FOLIATED ORNAMENT SET WITH STONES AND PEARLS

Pen and black ink, with grey wash.
8·7 × 2·5 cm. (3$\frac{3}{8}$ × 1 in.).
5308–51 (L.B.35, a; G.375).

55. AN ORNAMENT SHAPED AS A VOLUTE

Pen and black ink, with grey wash.

3·5 × 1·8 cm. (1$\frac{3}{8}$ × $\frac{3}{4}$ in.).

5308–52 (L.B.35, k; G.431).

56. A COLLAR DECORATED WITH NYMPHS AND SATYRS SUPPORTING STONES AND PEARLS

Pen and ink, with brown wash.

1·9 × 6·3 cm. ($\frac{3}{4}$ × 2$\frac{1}{2}$ in.).

5308–53 (L.B.35, h; G.376).

57. LUCRETIA STABBING HERSELF

Pen and black ink.

2·9 × 2·2 cm. (1$\frac{1}{8}$ × $\frac{7}{8}$ in.).

5308–54.

58. A RING WITH THE DEVICE OF A RAM, and the inscription (on a separate slip), *ARCANVM CELA*.

Pen and black ink.

1·6 × 6·3 cm. ($\frac{5}{8}$ × 2$\frac{1}{2}$ in.); ·5 × 5 cm. ($\frac{1}{4}$ × 2 in.).

5308–55 (L.B.35, n; G.391).

59. DAGGER HILT

Pen and black ink, with grey wash.

5·2 × 4·6 cm. (2$\frac{1}{2}$ × 1$\frac{3}{4}$ in.).

5308–56 (L.B.20, a; G.441).

60. DAGGER HILT

Pen and black ink, with grey wash.

12·7 × 8·6 cm. (5 × 3$\frac{3}{8}$ in.).

5308–57 (L.B.20, c; G. 438).

61. DAGGER HILT

Pen and black ink, with grey wash.

5·3 × 4·6 cm. (2$\frac{1}{8}$ × 1$\frac{7}{8}$ in.).

5308–58 (L.B.20, b; G.439).

62. DAGGER HILT

Pen and black ink, with grey wash.

7·3 × 7·1 cm. (2$\frac{7}{8}$ × 2$\frac{3}{4}$ in.).

5308–59 (L.B.20, e; G.442).

63. DAGGER HILT

Pen and black ink, with grey wash.

6 × 7·8 cm. (2$\frac{3}{8}$ × 3 in.).

5308–60 (L.B.20, d; G.440).

64. CLASP OF A BELT

Pen and black ink, with washes of black and light brown.

3·8 × 9·9 cm. (1$\frac{1}{2}$ × 3$\frac{7}{8}$ in.).

5308–61 (L.B.21, k; G.453).

65. TAG OF A BELT

Pen and black ink, with washes of grey and black.

4·6 × 2·7 cm. (1$\frac{7}{8}$ × 1$\frac{1}{8}$ in.).

5308–62 (L.B.21, e).

66. BUCKLE OF A BELT

Pen and black ink, with washes of black and light brown.

4·5 × 4 cm. (1$\frac{3}{4}$ × 1$\frac{5}{8}$ in.).

5308–63 (L.B.21, h; G.452).

67. TAG OF A BELT

Pen and black ink, with washes of grey and black.

4·5 × 2·7 cm. (1$\frac{3}{4}$ × 1 in.).

5308–64 (L.B.21, b).

68. DETAIL OF A CURVED ARABESQUE ORNAMENT

Pen and black ink.

1·9 × 4·8 cm. ($\frac{3}{4}$ × 1$\frac{7}{8}$ in.).

5308–65 (L.B.34, n; G. 422).

69. BUCKLE AND TAG OF A BELT

Pen and black ink, with washes of black and light brown.

9·4 × 4·1 cm. (3$\frac{3}{4}$ × 1$\frac{5}{8}$ in.).

5308–66 (L.B.21, i; G.454).

70. DETAIL OF A CURVED ARABESQUE ORNAMENT

Pen and black ink.

2·9 × 4·3 cm. (1$\frac{1}{8}$ × 1$\frac{3}{4}$ in.).

5308–67 (L.B.34, m; G.421).

71. A STRIP OF ARABESQUE ORNAMENT

Pen and ink, with black wash.

5·8 × 1·6 cm. (2$\frac{1}{4}$ × $\frac{5}{8}$ in.).

5308–68 (L.B.35, g; G.380).

72. A SMALL CARTOUCHE ORNAMENT

Pen and black ink, touched with light brown wash.

1·6 × 2·6 cm. ($\frac{5}{8}$ × 1 in.).

5308–69 (L.B.37, d; G.427).

73. BUCKLE AND TAG OF A BELT

Pen and black ink, with washes of black and grey.

14·5 × 2·8 cm. (5$\frac{3}{4}$ × 1$\frac{1}{8}$ in.).

5308–70 (L.B.21, c; G.455).

74. A NECKLACE (?) FORMED OF OSTRICH PLUMES

Pen and black ink.

2·6 × 4·4 cm. (1 × 1$\frac{3}{4}$ in.).

5308–71 (L.B.30, c; G.402).

75. A NUDE WOMAN SEATED ON A GLOBE

Pen and black ink, with grey wash.

7·7 × 3·9 cm. (3 × 1$\frac{1}{2}$ in.).

5308–72 (L.B.22, c; G.238).

Cf. No. 76.

76. A NUDE WOMAN RECLINING ON A GLOBE

Pen and black ink, with grey wash.

5·1 × 4·5 cm. (2 × 1$\frac{3}{4}$ in.).

5308–73 (L.B.22, e; G.239).

Cf. No. 75.

77. A CHAIN OF INTERLACED AND FOLIATED ORNAMENT

Pen and ink, with black wash, tinted in water-colour.

1·5 × 5·7 cm. ($\frac{5}{8}$ × 2$\frac{1}{4}$ in.).

5308–74 (L.B.36, k; G.382).

Cf. Nos. 78, 90 & 182.

78. A CHAIN OF ARABESQUE ORNAMENT

Pen and ink, with black wash, tinted in water-colour.

1·6 × 5·3 cm. ($\frac{5}{8}$ × 2$\frac{1}{8}$ in.).

5308–75 (L.B.36, i; G.381).

Cf. Nos. 77, 90 & 182.

79. A CHAIN

Pen and ink, with black wash.

6·6 × 1·1 cm. (2$\frac{5}{8}$ × $\frac{1}{2}$ in.).

5308–76 (L.B.35, f; G.383).

80. JEWEL WITH THREE STONES, set in a scroll inscribed *MI / LADI / PRINSIS*.

Pen and black ink, with grey wash.

·7 × 6·1 cm. ($\frac{1}{2}$ × 2$\frac{3}{8}$ in.).

5308–77 (L.B.30, a; G.346).

81. A RING WITH THE CREST OF A DEMI-WOLF

Pen and black ink, with grey wash.

1·9 × 6·1 cm. ($\frac{3}{4}$ × 2$\frac{3}{8}$ in.).

5308–78 (L.B.35, m; G.392).

82. A SMALL SHIELD WITH THE MONOGRAM A.H

Pen and black ink.

3 × 3·1 cm. (1$\frac{1}{4}$ × 1$\frac{1}{4}$ in.).

5308–79 (L.B.38, p; G.424).

83. A BORDER: LAUREL LACED WITH THE GARTER

Pen and brown ink, with yellow wash and blue body-colour.

1·2 × 7·7 cm. ($\frac{1}{2}$ × 3 in.).

5308–82 (L.B.36, f; G.401).

84. A BORDER: THE GARTER TWINED WITH GOLDEN LAUREL

Pen and brown ink, with yellow wash and blue body-colour.

1·1 × 7·7 cm. ($\frac{3}{8}$ × 3 in.).

5308–82* (L.B.36, g; G.399).

85. A BORDER: A BAND OF CHAIN PATTERN

Pen and brown ink, with yellow wash and blue body-colour.

1 × 7·7 cm. ($\frac{3}{8}$ × 3 in.).

5308–82** (L.B.36, h; G.400).

86. A JEWEL WITH THREE STONES AND THREE PEARLS set in a scroll, inscribed *MI / LADI / PRINSIS*. Alternative design to No. 80.

Pen and black ink, with grey wash.
$3 \times 7 \cdot 2$ cm. ($1\frac{1}{4} \times 2\frac{7}{8}$ in.).
5308–84 (L.B.30, b; G.347).

87. BUCKLE AND TAG OF A BELT
Pen and black ink, with washes of grey and black.
$15 \cdot 2 \times 2 \cdot 8$ cm. ($6 \times 1\frac{1}{8}$ in.).
5308–85 (L.B.21, a; G.456).

88. TWO CUPIDS FOR A SUNDIAL
Pen and black ink, with grey wash.
$8 \cdot 3 \times 6 \cdot 7$ cm. ($3\frac{1}{4} \times 2\frac{5}{8}$ in.).
5308–86 (L.B.22, a; G.221).

89. BUCKLE AND TAG OF A BELT
Pen and black ink, with washes of grey and black.
$15 \times 3 \cdot 2$ cm. ($5\frac{7}{8} \times 1\frac{1}{4}$ in.).
5308–87 (L.B.21, g; G.457).

90. A CHAIN OF INTERLACED AND FOLIATED ORNAMENT
Pen and ink, with black wash, tinted in water-colour.
$1 \cdot 7 \times 6$ cm. ($\frac{5}{8} \times 2\frac{3}{8}$ in.).
5308–88 (L.B.36, l; G.385).
Cf. Nos. 77, 78 & 182.

91. DESIGN FOR A LYRE-SHAPED PENDANT, inscribed *QVAM ACCIPERE DARE MVLTO BEATIVS*.
Pen and ink, with black wash.
$6 \times 4 \cdot 2$ cm. ($2\frac{3}{8} \times 1\frac{5}{8}$ in.).
5308–89 (L.B.28, f; G.318).

92. DESIGN FOR A PENDANT, set with a central leaf ornament flanked by ribbons, set with stones and pearls.
Pen and ink, with black wash.
$5 \cdot 9 \times 4 \cdot 3$ cm. ($2\frac{3}{8} \times 1\frac{5}{8}$ in.).
5308–90 (L.B.28, i; G.315).

93. DESIGN FOR A PENDANT, set with sapphires and pearls.
Pen and black ink, with washes of black, grey and light brown, touched with white.

$12 \cdot 2 \times 6 \cdot 3$ cm. ($4\frac{7}{8} \times 2\frac{1}{2}$ in.).
5308–91 (L.B.26, e; G.309).
Cf. Nos. 97, 103, 106 & 109.

94. DESIGN FOR A PENDANT, set with a central stone and pearls.
Pen and ink, with black wash.
$4 \cdot 7 \times 4 \cdot 1$ cm. ($1\frac{7}{8} \times 1\frac{5}{8}$ in.).
5308–92 (L.B.28, d; G.314).

95. DESIGN FOR A PENDANT, set with stones.
Pen and ink, with black wash.
$5 \cdot 7 \times 4 \cdot 3$ cm. ($2\frac{1}{4} \times 1\frac{3}{4}$ in.).
5308–93 (L.B.28, e; G.320).

96. DESIGN FOR A PENDANT, with leaf ornament entwined with ribbons, and set with stones and pearls.
Pen and ink, with black wash.
$5 \cdot 6 \times 3 \cdot 9$ cm. ($2\frac{1}{8} \times 1\frac{1}{2}$ in.).
5308–94 (L.B.28, k; G.317).

97. DESIGN FOR A PENDANT, set with sapphires and pearls.
Pen and black ink, with washes of black, grey and light brown, touched with white.
$13 \cdot 5 \times 6 \cdot 6$ cm. ($5\frac{3}{8} \times 2\frac{5}{8}$ in.).
5308–95 (L.B.26, b; G.308).
Cf. Nos. 93, 103, 106, & 109.

98. DESIGN FOR A PENDANT: half-length female figure and two cornucopias set with stones and pearls.
Pen and ink, with black wash.
$5 \cdot 9 \times 4 \cdot 3$ cm. ($2\frac{1}{4} \times 1\frac{3}{4}$ in.).
5308–96 (L.B.28, g; G.321).

99. DESIGN FOR A PENDANT, set with a lozenge and an oval stone and three pearls.
Pen and black ink.
$5 \times 3 \cdot 2$ cm. ($2 \times 1\frac{1}{4}$ in.).
5308–97 (L.B.28, c; G.324).

100. DESIGN FOR A PENDANT, set with a lozenge and an oval stone and three pearls. An alternative design to No. 101.

Pen and black ink.
$5\cdot3 \times 3$ cm. ($2\frac{1}{8} \times 1\frac{1}{8}$ in.).
5308–98 (L.B.28, b; G.323).

101. AN OVAL JEWEL, the central stone set in foliated scroll-work, the upper and lower halves forming alternative designs.

Pen and black ink, with grey wash.
Each $1\cdot7 \times 4\cdot3$ cm. ($\frac{5}{8} \times 1\frac{3}{4}$ in.).
5308–99 and **99*** (L.B.37, l; G.350).
Cf. Nos. 102 & 105.

102. AN OVAL JEWEL, the central stone set in foliated scroll-work, the upper and lower halves forming alternative designs.

Pen and black ink, with grey wash.
Each $1\cdot7 \times 4\cdot2$ cm. ($\frac{3}{4} \times 1\frac{5}{8}$ in.).
5308–100 and **100*** (L.B.37, m; G.351).
Cf. Nos. 101 & 105.

103. DESIGN FOR A PENDANT, set with sapphires and pearls.

Pen and black ink, with washes of black, grey and light brown, touched with white.
$11\cdot2 \times 6\cdot2$ cm. ($4\frac{3}{8} \times 2\frac{1}{2}$ in.).
5308–101 (L.B.26, d; G.310).
Cf. Nos. 93, 97, 106 & 109.

104. A CIRCULAR JEWEL WITH A FOLIATED BORDER

Pen and black ink, with washes of black and light brown.
$2\cdot9 \times 4\cdot5$ cm. ($1\frac{1}{8} \times 1\frac{3}{4}$ in.).
5308–102 (L.B.37, h; G.368).

105. AN OVAL JEWEL, the central stone set in a foliated scroll-work.

Pen and black ink, with grey wash.
$1\cdot8 \times 4\cdot1$ cm. ($\frac{3}{4} \times 1\frac{5}{8}$ in.).
5308–103 (L.B.37, i; G.352).
Cf. Nos. 101 & 102.

106. DESIGN FOR A PENDANT, set with sapphires and pearls.

Pen and black ink, with washes of black, grey and light brown, touched with white.
$9 \times 5\cdot3$ cm. ($3\frac{1}{8} \times 2\frac{1}{8}$ in.).
5308–104 (L.B.26, c; G.312).
Cf. Nos. 93, 97, 103 & 109.

107. A CIRCULAR JEWEL. Central stone set in a foliated scroll-work.

Pen and black ink, with grey wash.
Diam. $2\cdot2$ cm. ($\frac{7}{8}$ in.).
5308–105 (L.B.37, b; G.356).
Cf. Nos. 23, 42, 48 & 50.

108. AN OVAL JEWEL. Central stone set in a foliated scroll-work.

Pen and black ink, with grey wash.
$2\cdot5 \times 2\cdot8$ cm. ($1 \times 1\frac{1}{8}$ in.).
5308–106 (L.B.37, k; G.353).

109. DESIGN FOR A PENDANT, set with a ruby, sapphires and pearls.

Pen and black ink, with washes of black, grey and water-colour, touched with white.
$11\cdot6 \times 6\cdot4$ cm. ($4\frac{5}{8} \times 2\frac{1}{2}$ in.).
5308–107 (L.B.26, a; G.311).
Cf. Nos. 93, 97, 103 & 106.

110. MONOGRAM OF THE LETTERS L.N.H.O.J.N.A.G

Pen and ink, with black wash.
Diam. $3\cdot6$ cm. ($1\frac{1}{2}$ in.).
5308–108 (L.B.38, i; G.344).

111. PART OF A LINK OF A CHAIN, set with two pearls.

Pen and black ink, with grey wash.
$1\cdot8 \times 2\cdot2$ cm. ($\frac{3}{4} \times \frac{7}{8}$ in.).
5308–109 (L.B.25, a; G.348).
Cf. No. 113.

112. MONOGRAM OF THE LETTERS T.H.E.O.S.I.B.L.A

Pen and black ink.
Diam. $4\cdot3$ cm. ($1\frac{3}{4}$ in.).
5308–110 (L.B.38, e; G.341).

113. FIVE DESIGNS FOR LINKS OF CHAINS, set with pearls.

Pen and black ink, with washes of grey and black.
$9\cdot3 \times 6\cdot9$ cm. ($3\frac{5}{8} \times 2\frac{3}{4}$ in.).
5308–111 (L.B.25, f; G.349).
Cf. No. 111.

114. DESIGN FOR A CIRCULAR ORNA-
MENT with roses and a carnation.

Pen and black ink, with grey wash.
Diam. 3·7 cm. (1½ in.).
5308–112 (L.B.25, d; G.425).

115. MONOGRAM OF THE LETTERS
M.T.H.F.N.R.A.D.O.G.V

Pen and black ink.
4·5 × 4·5 cm. (1¾ × 1¾ in.).
5308–113 (L.B.38, h; G.338).

116. PENDANT IN THE FORM OF A
MONOGRAM A.V.R.N.T.E.K.C.I.S. Set
with 10 stones.

Pen and black ink.
5·7 × 6·9 cm. (2¼ × 2¾ in.).
5308–114 (L.B.38, o; G.325).

117. PENDANT IN THE FORM OF A
MONOGRAM A.H. Set with a single central
stone.

Pen and black ink, with washes of grey and
yellow.
4·8 × 4·7 cm. (1⅞ × 1⅞ in.).
5308–115 (L.B.38, r; G.329).

118. DESIGN FOR A PENDANT IN THE
FORM OF A MONOGRAM H.I (for
Henry VIII and Jane Seymour (?)), set with
an emerald and three pearls.

Pen and brown ink, with water-colour.
7·2 × 4·8 cm. (2⅞ × 1⅞ in.).
5308–116 (L.B.27, f; G.326).

119. DESIGN FOR A PENDANT IN THE
FORM OF A MONOGRAM R.E, set with
two rubies, a sapphire, an emerald and three
pearls.

Pen and black ink, with water-colour.
8·4 × 4·1 cm. (3¼ × 1⅝ in.).
5308–117 (L.B.27, e; G.328).

120. PANEL OF FOLIATED ORNAMENT,
incorporating a medallion with the monogram L.M.A.R.Y, perhaps for the lid of a
casket.

Pen and black ink.
7·3 × 7·7 cm. (2⅞ × 3 in.).
5308–118 (L.B.33, f; G.406).

121. MONOGRAM OF THE LETTERS
A.H.N.L.I.O

Pen and black ink.
2·4 × 3·8 cm. (1 × 1½ in.).
5308–119 (L.B.38, q; G.340).

122. MONOGRAM OF THE LETTERS
C.T.P.N.A.E.S.O

Pen and black ink.
2·4 × 3·5 cm. (⅞ × 1⅜ in.).
5308–120 (L.B.38, k; G.333).

123. PANEL OF ARABESQUE ORNA-
MENT, probably for a gold or silver book-
binding.

Pen and ink, with black wash.
5·5 × 7·1 cm. (2⅛ × 2¾ in.).
5308–121 (L.B.33, g; G.420).

124. DESIGN FOR A SEGMENTAL
ARABESQUE ORNAMENT

Pen and black ink, with grey wash.
6·3 × 11·3 cm. (2½ × 4½ in.).
5308–122 (L.B.34, q; G.224).

125. DESIGN FOR A TASSEL

Pen and black ink, with grey wash.
15·4 × 3·5 cm. (6⅛ × 1⅜ in.).
5308–123 (L.B.25, e; G.430).

126. STEM OF A GOBLET

Pen and black ink, with grey wash.
10·7 × 12·6 cm. (4¼ × 5 in.).
5308–124 (L.B.22, f; G.214).

127. A CURVED GROTESQUE BORDER

Pen and black ink, with grey-brown wash.
2·3 × 8·5 cm. (⅞ × 3⅜ in.).
5308–124* (L.B.34, l; G.226).

128. DESIGN FOR A TASSEL

Pen and black ink, with grey wash.
10·3 × 3·1 cm. (4 × 1¼ in.).
5308–125 (L.B.25, g; G.429).

129. A MEDALLION DECORATED WITH ARABESQUE ORNAMENT

Pen and black ink.
Diam. 4·3 cm. (1¾ in.).
5308–126 (L.B.32, a; G.303).

130. A MEDALLION DECORATED WITH ARABESQUE ORNAMENT

Pen and black ink.
Diam. 4·3 cm. (1¾ in.).
5308–127 (L.B.32, b; G.304).

131. A MEDALLION DECORATED WITH ARABESQUE ORNAMENT surrounding a central cartouche.

Pen and ink, with black wash.
Diam. 8 cm. (3⅛ in.).
5308–128 (L.B.32, d; G.419).

132. A MEDALLION DECORATED WITH ARABESQUE ORNAMENT

Pen and black ink.
Diam. 4·3 cm. (1¾ in.).
5308–129 (L.B.32, f; G.301).

133. A MEDALLION DECORATED WITH AN INTERLACED ARABESQUE ORNAMENT

Brush drawing in black wash.
Diam. 4·3 cm. (1¾ in.).
5308–130 (L.B.32, e; G.302).

134. DESIGN FOR A SEGMENTAL ARABESQUE ORNAMENT

Pen and black ink.
6·2 × 9·3 cm. (2½ × 3⅝ in.).
5308–131 (L.B.34, o; G.231).

135. A BUTTON decorated with six fish circling round the centre.

Pen and black ink.
Diam. 2·5 cm. (1 in.).
5308–132 (L.B.32, c; G.306).

136. A CURVED ARABESQUE BORDER

Pen and black ink.
3·6 × 9·5 cm. (1½ × 3¾ in.).
5308–133 (L.B.34, k; G.229).

137. A CIRCULAR ORNAMENT, decorated with interlaced foliations.

Pen and black ink.
2·2 × 2·2 cm. (⅞ × ⅞ in.).
5308–134 (L.B.37, p; G.305).

138. A CURVED ARABESQUE BORDER

Pen and black ink.
2·2 × 3·6 cm. (⅞ × 1⅜ in.).
5308–135 (L.B.30, g; G.228).

139. DESIGN FOR A PENDANT (?) Pansies in a hanging bowl.

Pen and black ink.
5·6 × 6·3 cm. (2¼ × 2½ in.).
5308–136 (L.B.25, b; G.426).

140. A CURVED GROTESQUE BORDER

Pen and brown ink, with grey-brown wash.
2·7 × 4·5 cm. (1⅛ × 1¾ in.).
5308–137 (L.B.30, f; G.225).
Cf. No. 127.

141. PANEL OF ARABESQUE ORNAMENT, perhaps for the top mount of a scabbard.

Pen and black ink.
5·1 × 3·9 cm. (2 × 1⅝ in.).
5308–138 (L.B.33, b; G.411).

142. PANEL OF ARABESQUE ORNAMENT, alternative design to No. 143.

Pen and black ink.
4·9 × 4·1 cm. (2 × 1⅝ in.).
5308–139 (L.B.33, a; G.409).

143. PANEL OF ARABESQUE ORNAMENT, perhaps for the top mount of a scabbard.

Pen and black ink.
2·3 × 5·6 cm. (⅞ × 2¼ in.).
5308–140 (L.B.33, d; G.407).
Cf. No. 142.

144. PANEL OF ARABESQUE ORNAMENT, perhaps for the top mount of a scabbard.

Pen and black ink.
2·8 × 4·5 cm. (1⅛ × 1¾ in.).
5308–141 (L.B.33, e; G.408).

145. DETAIL OF A FOLIATED ORNAMENT

Pen and black ink.
1·9 × 2·6 cm. (¾ × 1 in.).
5308–142 (L.B.35, b; G.370).

146. DESIGN FOR BOOK CLASPS

Pen and black ink.
5·2 × 4·8 cm. (2 × 1⅞ in.).
5308–142* (L.B.30, e; G.415).

147. PANEL OF ARABESQUE ORNAMENT, perhaps for the top mount of a scabbard.

Pen and black ink.
4·8 × 4·4 cm. (1⅞ × 1¾ in.).
5308–143 (L.B.33, h; G.410).

148. A CHAIN DECORATED WITH ARABESQUE ORNAMENT

Pen and black ink, with washes of black and grey.
2·4 × 13·6 cm. (1 × 5⅜ in.).
5308–144 (L.B.30, h; G.374).

149. A CHAIN DECORATED WITH ARABESQUE ORNAMENT

Pen and black ink, with washes of black and grey.
2 × 7·5 cm. (¾ × 3 in.).
5308–145 (L.B.30, i; G.372).

150. AN ENAMEL CLASP

Pen and ink, with black wash, tinted in water-colour.
1·6 × 2·2 cm. (⅝ × ⅞ in.).
5308–146 (L.B.36, b; G.412).
Cf. Nos. 151, 154 & 155.

151. AN ENAMEL CLASP

Pen and ink, with black wash, tinted in water-colour.
1·7 × 2·1 cm. (⅝ × ⅞ in.).
5308–147 (L.B.36, a; G.415).
Cf. Nos. 150, 154 & 155.

152. PORTABLE SUNDIAL AND CALENDAR

Pen and black ink, with grey wash.
8·4 × 2·7 cm. (3⅜ × 1⅛ in.).
5308–148 (L.B.25, c; G.423).

153. A BUTTON WITH ARABESQUE ORNAMENT

Pen and black ink, with yellow wash.
1·5 × 2·8 cm. (⅝ × 1⅛ in.).
5308–149 (L.B.36, c; G.307).

154. AN ENAMEL CLASP

Pen and black ink.
1·9 × 2·5 cm. (¾ × 1 in.).
5308–150 (L.B.36, e; G.416).
Cf. Nos. 150, 151 & 155.

155. AN ENAMEL CLASP

Pen and ink, with black wash, tinted with water-colour.
1·6 × 2·6 cm. (⅝ × 1 in.).
5308–151 (L.B.36, d; G.414).
Cf. Nos. 150, 151 & 154.

156. A CHAIN DECORATED WITH ARABESQUE ORNAMENT

Pen and black ink, with grey wash.
2 × 12 cm. (¾ × 4¾ in.).
5308–152 (L.B.30, k; G.373).

157. AN ORNAMENT COVERED WITH A SCALE PATTERN

Pen and black ink.
3·9 × 1 cm. (1½ × ⅜ in.).
5308–153 (L.B.35, i; G.432).

158. SHIELD WITH HOLBEIN'S ARMS

Pen and black ink, with blue wash.
2·1 × 2·1 cm. (⅞ × ⅞ in.).
5308–154 (L.B.29, d; G.395).
Cf. No. 45.

159. A SMALL PANEL OF INTERLACED DAISIES

Pen and black ink.
3 × 1·5 cm. (1¼ × ⅝ in.).
5308–155 (L.B.35, l; G.386).

160. A CURVED ARABESQUE BORDER
Pen and black ink.
1·9 × 9·5 cm. ($\frac{3}{4} \times 3\frac{3}{4}$ in.).
5308–156 (L.B.34, g; G.227).

161. BORDER ORNAMENT
Pen and black ink, with grey wash.
1·5 × 2 cm. ($\frac{5}{8} \times \frac{3}{4}$ in.).
5308–157 (L.B.34, e; G. 362).

162. A CURVED ARABESQUE BORDER
Pen and black ink.
1·8 × 8·7 cm. ($\frac{3}{4} \times 3\frac{1}{2}$ in.).
5308–158 (L.B.34, d; G.230).

163. BORDER ORNAMENT
Pen and black ink, with grey wash.
1·3 × 1·8 cm. ($\frac{1}{2} \times \frac{3}{4}$ in.).
5308–159 (L.B.34, b; G.364).

164. BORDER ORNAMENT
Pen and black ink, with grey wash.
1·3 × 1·4 cm. ($\frac{1}{2} \times \frac{1}{2}$ in.).
5308–160 (L.B.34, c; G.363).

165. DESIGN FOR A CURVED ARABESQUE BORDER
Pen and black ink.
1·1 × 7·7 cm. ($\frac{1}{2} \times 3$ in.).
5308–161 (L.B.34, f; G.371).

166. BORDER ORNAMENT
Pen and black ink, with grey wash.
1·6 × 1·5 cm. ($\frac{5}{8} \times \frac{5}{8}$ in.).
5308 162 (L.B.34, a; G.365).

167. FRAGMENT OF A CURVED ARABESQUE BORDER
Pen and black ink.
1·7 × 3·4 cm. ($\frac{5}{8} \times 1\frac{3}{8}$ in.).
5308–163 (L.B.34, i; G.369).

168. SHIELD WITH HOLBEIN'S ARMS
Pen and black ink.
Diam. 2 cm. ($\frac{3}{4}$ in.).
5308–164 (L.B.29, f; G.393).
Cf. No. 45.

169. PANEL OF ARABESQUE ORNAMENT, perhaps for the upper mount of a scabbard.
Pen and black ink.
2·1 × 2·9 cm. ($\frac{7}{8} \times 1\frac{1}{8}$ in.).
5308–165 (L.B.33, c; G.413).

170. DESIGN FOR A CURVED ARABESQUE BORDER
Pen and black ink, with grey wash.
1·1 × 5·4 cm. ($\frac{1}{2} \times 2\frac{1}{8}$ in.).
5308–166 (L.B.34, h; G.366).

171. DESIGN FOR A FINIAL: a male half-figure in a cuirass.
Pen and black ink, with grey wash.
4·1 × 6·1 cm. ($1\frac{5}{8} \times 2\frac{3}{8}$ in.).
5308–167 (L.B.23, i; G.240).
Cf. Nos. 172 & 174.

172. DESIGN FOR A FINIAL: a male half-figure in a cuirass.
Pen and black ink, with grey wash.
4·6 × 6·3 cm. ($1\frac{7}{8} \times 2\frac{1}{2}$ in.).
5308–168 (L.B.23, g, G.242)'
Cf. Nos. 171 & 174.

173. DESIGN FOR A FINIAL: a winged male figure holding a jaw bone.
Pen and black ink, with grey wash.
4·7 × 3·6 cm. ($1\frac{7}{8} \times 1\frac{3}{8}$ in.).
5308–169 (L.B.23, f; G.235).
Cf. Nos. 29 & 175.

174. DESIGN FOR A FINIAL: a male half-figure in a cuirass.
Pen and black ink, with grey wash.
4·4 × 5·3 cm. ($1\frac{3}{4} \times 2\frac{1}{8}$ in.).
5308–170 (L.B.23, h; G.241).
Cf. Nos. 171 & 172.

175. DESIGN FOR A FINIAL: a winged male figure holding a club and a buckler.
Pen and black ink, with grey wash.
4·7 × 3·8 cm. ($1\frac{7}{8} \times 1\frac{1}{2}$ in.).
5308–171 (L.B.23, d; G. 237).
Cf. Nos. 29 & 173.

176. A WINGED STAG
Pen and black ink, with grey wash.
7·9 × 9·4 cm. (3⅛ × 3⅝ in.).
5308–172 (L.B.24, d; G.244).
Cf. No. 179.

177. DESIGN FOR CRESTS (?); a cock, a spread eagle, and a strawberry.
Pen and black ink.
4·2 × 5·2 cm. (1⅝ × 2 in.).
5308–173 (L.B.24, c; G.246).

178. DESIGN FOR A BADGE: a chained white hind.
Pen and black ink.
4·3 × 4·6 cm. (1¾ × 1⅞ in.).
5308–174 (L.B.24, b; G.245).

179. STUDIES OF GOATS
Pen and black ink, with grey wash.
8·6 × 10·8 cm. (3⅜ × 4¼ in.).
5308–175 (L.B.24, e).
Cf. No. 176.

180. A RAM'S HEAD
Pen and black ink, with grey wash.
2·5 × 2 cm. (1 × ¾ in.).
5308–176 (L.B.24, a; G.247).

181. DESIGN FOR A DAGGER SHEATH
Pen and brown ink, with grey wash.
22·5 × 6 cm. (8⅞ × 2⅜ in.).
5308–178 (L.B., p.342).

182. A CHAIN OF INTERLACED AND FOLIATED ORNAMENT
Pen and ink, with black wash, tinted in water-colour.
2·1 × 5·8 cm. (⅞ × 2¼ in.).
5308–179 (L.B.36, m; G.384).
Cf. Nos. 77, 78 & 90.

183. A BAND OF ORNAMENT (BELT SLIDE)
Pen and black ink, with grey wash.
·6 × 3·1 cm. (¼ × 1¼ in.).
5308–no number (L.B.21, d; G.459).

184. A BAND OF ORNAMENT (BELT SLIDE)
Pen and black ink, with grey wash.
·7 × 2·9 cm. (¼ × 1⅛ in.).
5308–no number (L.B.21, f; G.458).

185. DESIGN FOR A DAGGER, with the Triumph of Bellona on the scabbard.
Pen and black ink, with washes of black and greenish yellow.
34·7 × 7·6 cm. (13⅝ × 3 in.).
1848–11–25–8.

186. DESIGN FOR THE JANE SEYMOUR GOLD CUP
Pen and black ink.
37·6 × 14·3 cm. (14¾ × 5⅝ in.); old mount 44·5 × 23·8 cm. (17½ × 9¾ in.).
1848–11–25–9 (L.B.18; G.207).

187. DESIGN FOR A CLOCK, presented by Sir Anthony Denny to Henry VIII.
Pen and black ink, with grey wash.
41·1 × 21·4 cm. (16⅛ × 8½ in.).
1850–7–13–14 (L.B.17; G.220).

188. DESIGN FOR A CHIMNEY-PIECE, PROBABLY AT BRIDEWELL PALACE.
Pen, with washes of grey and water-colour.
54·1 × 42·7 cm. (21¼ × 16¾ in.).
1854–7–8–1 (L.B.16; G.123).

[189–191] ATTRIBUTED TO HOLBEIN

189. JOHN FISHER, BISHOP OF ROCHESTER
Pen and black ink, with grey wash over red and black chalk, on pink prepared paper.
32·8 × 26·1 cm. (12⅞ × 10¼ in.).
G.g.1–416 (L.B.9; under G.35).

190. MUSICIANS ON A BALCONY
Pen and black ink, with grey wash.
12·9 × 18·1 cm. (5⅛ × 7⅛ in.).
1852–5–19–2 (L.B.15; G.126).

191. KATHARINE, 4th WIFE OF CHARLES BRANDON, DUKE OF SUFFOLK

Black chalk, with touches of red and yellow chalk, strengthened with brush and black ink, on pink prepared paper.

29·2 × 20·6 cm. ($11\frac{1}{2} \times 8\frac{1}{8}$ in.).

1895–9–15–990 (L.B.10; G.C3).

[192–197] *COPIES AFTER HOLBEIN*

192. THOMAS HOWARD, 3rd DUKE OF NORFOLK. Copy by Lucas Vorsterman I.

Brush drawing in brown and grey wash, over red chalk.

24·9 × 19·5 cm. ($9\frac{3}{4} \times 7\frac{5}{8}$ in.).

1846–7–9–9 (H.11).

193. THE TRIUMPH OF RICHES. Copy by Jan de Bisschop.

Pen and ink, with brown wash, over a slight sketch in black chalk.

33·4 × 77·4 cm. ($13\frac{1}{8} \times 30\frac{1}{2}$ in.).

1854–6–28–19 and 20 (H.2).

194. THE TRIUMPH OF POVERTY. Copy by Jan de Bisschop.

Pen and ink, with brown wash, over a slight sketch in black chalk.

34·5 × 47·4 cm. ($13\frac{1}{2} \times 18\frac{5}{8}$ in.).

1854–6–28–21 (H.1).

195. THE TRIUMPH OF RICHES. Copy probably by an anonymous 17th c. Italian artist.

Pen and black ink, with grey wash.

24·8 × 58·8 cm. ($9\frac{3}{4} \times 23\frac{1}{8}$ in.).

1854–6–28–114 (L.B., p.342).

196. THE TRIUMPH OF POVERTY. Copy by Matthäus Merian II.

Left hand section, pen and ink, with brown wash; right hand section, pen and brown ink, with washes of brown and grey.

42·8 × 57·7 cm. ($16\frac{7}{8} \times 22\frac{3}{4}$ in.).

1864–6–11–148.

197. THE TRIUMPH OF POVERTY. Copy attributed to Lucas Vorsterman I.

Black and red chalk, pen and brown ink, with washes of brown and grey, and

heightened with white; the foliage green and the background blue body-colour.

43·7 × 58·5 cm. ($17\frac{1}{4} \times 23$ in.).

1894–7–21–2 (L.B., p.343; H.16).

KEIRINCX, ALEXANDER

B. 1600: D. *c.* 1652

Vertue (I, p. 127) saw two views of London by Keirincx dated 1625, and also states (V, p. 38) that he was employed by Charles I to draw views.

ATTRIBUTED TO KEIRINCX

1. VIEW OF THE THAMES LOOKING N.W. TOWARDS THE TOWER OF LONDON FROM THE BERMONDSEY SIDE

Pen and ink, with brown wash.

14·7 × 27·7 cm. ($5\frac{3}{4} \times 10\frac{7}{8}$ in.).

1855–7–14–60 (H.1).

MERIAN, MATTHÄUS II

B. 1621: D. 1687

Recommended in 1639 to Van Dyck in London; by 1641 in Paris

See under: HOLBEIN, Copies after

OVERBECK, M. VAN

[OVERBEEK]

Worked latter half of the 17th c. (See Hind, IV, pp. 22–3)

1. MARGATE, KENT, FROM THE S.E.

Pen and brown ink, with brown wash on tinted paper.

10·7 × 21·3 cm. ($4\frac{1}{4} \times 8\frac{3}{8}$ in.).

1929–5–11–22 (H.1).

2. WESTMINSTER FROM THE S.E., LOOKING ACROSS THE THAMES

Pen and brown ink, with brown wash on tinted paper.

20·6 × 33·2 cm. ($8\frac{1}{8} \times 13\frac{1}{8}$ in.).

Crowle Pennant, VIII, No. 245.

QUEBORN, CRISPIN VAN

B. 1604: D. 1652

Not known to have visited England

1. FREDERICK V, KING OF BOHEMIA

Pen and brown ink on vellum.

12 × 9·7 cm. ($4\frac{3}{4} \times 3\frac{7}{8}$ in.).

1895–9–15–1298 (a) (H.1).

2. ELIZABETH, QUEEN OF BOHEMIA

Pen and brown ink on vellum.

12·1 × 9·7 cm. ($4\frac{3}{4} \times 3\frac{7}{8}$ in.).

1895–9–15–1298 (b) (H.2).

RUBENS, SIR PETER PAUL

B. 1577: D. 1640

Visited England from 1629 to 1630

1. SIR THEODORE TURQUET DE MAYERNE

Oil colours, with grey wash and black chalk.

30·8 × 21·9 cm. ($12\frac{1}{8} \times 8\frac{5}{8}$ in.).

1860–6–16–36 (H.94).

[Mayerne (B.1573: D. 1655) was physician to James I and Charles I, residing in England from 1611 until his death.]

SCHELLINKS, WILLEM

B. 1627: D. 1678

Between July 14th, 1661, and August 24th, 1665, was travelling in Western Europe, during which time he visited England

1. EXTENSIVE VIEW OF MOUNT'S BAY, CORNWALL, WITH ST. MICHAEL'S MOUNT, MID-DISTANCE, L.

Pen and light brown ink over black chalk.

30·9 × 112 cm. ($12\frac{1}{8} \times 44\frac{1}{8}$ in.).

1856–8–9–1 (H.2).

2. *Recto*, ST. MICHAEL'S MOUNT, CORNWALL, FROM THE N.

Pen and black ink, with washes of brown over black lead.

Verso, THE SAME

Black lead.

20·3 × 61·3 cm. ($8 \times 24\frac{1}{8}$ in.).

1856–8–9–2 (H.3).

3. *Recto*, VIEW OF FOWEY, CORNWALL, FROM THE N.E.

Pen and brown ink, with brown wash, tinted in water-colour, over black lead.

Verso, STUDIES OF COTTAGES

Black lead.

19 × 88 cm. ($7\frac{1}{2} \times 34\frac{5}{8}$ in.).

1856–8–9–3 (H.4).

4. THE CHEESEWRING, NEAR LISKEARD, CORNWALL

Brush drawing in brown ink, with light brown wash, over black lead.

18·3 × 58·9 cm. ($7\frac{1}{4} \times 23\frac{1}{4}$ in.).

1856–8–9–4 (H.5).

5. THE CHEESEWRING, NEAR LISKEARD, CORNWALL

Brush drawing in brown ink, with light brown wash, over black lead.

18·3 × 58·7 cm. ($7\frac{1}{4} \times 23\frac{1}{8}$ in.).

1856–8–9–5 (H.6).

6. STONEHENGE

Pen and brown ink, with washes of brown and grey, over black lead.

18·5 × 55·6 cm. ($7\frac{1}{4} \times 21\frac{7}{8}$ in.).

1856–8–9–6 (H.7).

7. STONEHENGE AND SALISBURY PLAIN

Pen and brown ink, with grey-brown wash, over black lead.

19·3 × 71·8 cm. ($7\frac{5}{8} \times 28\frac{1}{4}$ in.).

1856–8–9–7 (H.8).

8. THE DUTCH FLEET IN THE MEDWAY, JUNE 1667. An extensive view of the River from Rochester to Sheerness.

Pen and brown ink, with washes of grey, brown and green, over black lead, touched with red chalk.

27·5 × 73 cm. ($10\frac{7}{8} \times 28\frac{5}{8}$ in.).

1869–7–10–9 (H.9).

Cf. No. 10.

9. PANORAMIC VIEW LOOKING N., SHOWING THE THAMES ESTUARY FROM GREENHITHE TO TILBURY

Pen and brown ink, with washes of grey and brown.

$34 \cdot 7 \times 95 \cdot 2$ cm. ($13\frac{5}{8} \times 37\frac{1}{2}$ in.).

1856–6–14–154 (H.10).

10. THE DUTCH ATTACK ON THE MEDWAY, JUNE 19–23, 1667.

Pen and brown ink, with grey wash, tinted in water-colour.

$7 \cdot 1 \times 27 \cdot 2$ cm. ($2\frac{3}{4} \times 10\frac{5}{8}$ in.).

1910–2–12–107.

Previously attributed to Hollar.

11. DISTANT VIEW OF DOVER AND THE CASTLE FROM THE S.W.

Pen and brown ink over black chalk.

$41 \cdot 4 \times 94 \cdot 3$ cm. ($16\frac{1}{4} \times 37\frac{1}{8}$ in.).

1955–10–8–1.

12. ARCHCLIFF FORT, DOVER, FROM THE S.W.

Pen and brown ink, with grey wash over black chalk.

$19 \cdot 4 \times 29 \cdot 9$ cm. ($7\frac{5}{8} \times 11\frac{3}{4}$ in.).

1955–10–8–2.

13. CHALK CLIFF, NEAR DOVER

Pen and brown ink, with washes of grey, brown and green, over black chalk.

$30 \cdot 7 \times 62 \cdot 2$ cm. ($12\frac{1}{8} \times 24\frac{1}{2}$ in.).

1955–10–8–3.

14. ROCHESTER AND THE MEDWAY FROM UPNOR CASTLE

Black chalk, with pen and brown ink; the central part of the drawing has been extended on three sides.

$19 \cdot 5 \times 53 \cdot 4$ cm. ($7\frac{5}{8} \times 21$ in.).

1955–10–8–4.

15. A FORESHORE WITH SHIPS RIDING AT ANCHOR

Brush drawing, with washes of brown and grey.

$20 \cdot 9 \times 51 \cdot 7$ cm. ($8\frac{1}{4} \times 20\frac{3}{8}$ in.).

1955–10–8–5.

ATTRIBUTED TO SCHELLINKS

16. DISTANT VIEW OF A CASTLE, PERHAPS CORFE, FROM THE N.E.

Black chalk and black lead.

$13 \cdot 7 \times 26$ cm. ($5\frac{3}{8} \times 10\frac{1}{4}$ in.).

5214–78 (H.14).

STORCK, JACOB

Fl. 1660–86
Not known to have visited England

1. SEA FIGHT BETWEEN THE ENGLISH AND DUTCH FLEETS, probably the Battle of the Texel, August 1673.

Pen and brown ink, with grey wash.

$17 \cdot 3 \times 23 \cdot 5$ cm. ($6\frac{7}{8} \times 9\frac{1}{4}$ in.).

1836–8–11–517 (H.1).

2. SEA FIGHT BETWEEN THE ENGLISH AND DUTCH FLEETS, probably the Battle of the Texel, August 1673.

Pen and brown ink, with grey wash.

$16 \cdot 3 \times 22 \cdot 1$ cm. ($6\frac{3}{8} \times 8\frac{3}{4}$ in.).

1836–8–11–516 (H.2).

VAN DYCK, SIR ANTHONY

B. 1599: D. 1641

Visited England from late 1620 until early 1621. Settled here in 1632, remaining until Autumn 1640, apart from a visit to Brussels from early 1634 until January 1635. Returned in May 1641, and again in November and died in London on December 9th, 1641

[1–31] *PORTRAIT STUDIES EXECUTED IN ENGLAND*

1. A YOUNG MAN

Black chalk touched with white on blue-grey paper.

$34 \cdot 3 \times 22 \cdot 3$ cm. ($13\frac{1}{2} \times 8\frac{3}{4}$ in.).

5227–112 (L.B.54; H.66).

2. A GENTLEMAN

Black chalk touched with white on blue-grey paper.

34·4 × 22·6 cm. ($13\frac{1}{2}$ × $8\frac{7}{8}$ in.).
5227–113 (L.B.51; H.63).

3. FRANCES BRYDGES, COUNTESS OF EXETER

Black chalk touched with white on blue-grey paper.

34·7 × 27·4 cm. ($13\frac{5}{8}$ × $10\frac{3}{4}$ in.).
G.g.1–423 (L.B.49; H.61).

4. ORAZIO GENTILESCHI

Black chalk, with grey wash and a few touches of pen and brown ink; indented for transfer.

23·6 × 17·9 cm. ($9\frac{3}{8}$ × 7 in.); old mount, 30·5 × 24·3 cm. (12 × $9\frac{1}{2}$ in.).
G.g.2–238 (L.B.28; H.35).

5. A LADY

Black chalk heightened with white on blue-grey paper.

52·7 × 34·3 cm. ($20\frac{3}{4}$ × $13\frac{1}{2}$ in.).
1845–12–8–6 (L.B.62; H.71).

6. *Recto*, A LADY
Verso, STUDY OF HANDS

Black chalk touched with white on blue-grey paper.

35·3 × 31·1 cm. ($13\frac{7}{8}$ × $12\frac{1}{4}$ in.).
1845–12–8–7 (L.B.66; H.75).

7. ROBERT DORMER, EARL OF CARNARVON, AND HIS WIFE, ANNE SOPHIA

Black chalk touched with white on buff paper.

49·2 × 29·3 cm. ($19\frac{3}{8}$ × $11\frac{1}{2}$ in.).
1845–12–8–9 (L.B.48; H.60).

8. LORD BERNARD STUART

Black chalk touched with white on blue-grey paper.

43·2 × 28·7 cm. (17 × $11\frac{1}{4}$ in.).
1845–12–8–10 (L.B.53; H.65).

9. SIR WILLIAM KILLIGREW (?)

Black chalk touched with white on blue-grey paper.

41·3 × 29·3 cm. ($16\frac{1}{4}$ × $11\frac{1}{2}$ in.).
1845–12–8–11 (L.B.50; H.62).

10. BUST OF A MAN

Black chalk touched with white on blue-grey paper.

20·1 × 18·5 cm. ($7\frac{7}{8}$ × $7\frac{1}{4}$ in.).
1845–12–24–2 (L.B.57; H.68).

11. THOMAS HOWARD, 2nd EARL OF ARUNDEL

Black chalk touched with white on blue-grey paper.

24·2 × 21·7 cm. ($9\frac{1}{2}$ × $8\frac{1}{2}$ in.).
1846–7–9–11 (L.B.40; H.52).

12. A LADY

Black chalk touched with white on blue-grey paper.

38·1 × 27 cm. (15 × $10\frac{5}{8}$ in.).
1846–7–9–12 (L.B.60; H.69).

13. ANN CARR, COUNTESS OF BEDFORD (?)

Black chalk heightened with white on buff paper.

41·9 × 24·1 cm. ($16\frac{1}{2}$ × $9\frac{1}{2}$ in.).
1846–7–9–13 (L.B.47; H.59).

14. LUCY PERCY, COUNTESS OF CARLISLE

Black chalk touched with white on blue-grey paper.

49·8 × 25·8 cm. ($19\frac{5}{8}$ × $10\frac{1}{8}$ in.).
1846–7–9–14 (L.B.61; H.70).

15. ANNE CROFTS, COUNTESS OF CLEVELAND

Black chalk heightened with white on buff paper.

45·1 × 28·6 cm. ($17\frac{3}{4}$ × $11\frac{1}{4}$ in.).
1846–7–9–15 (L.B.46; H.58).

16. A LADY

Black chalk touched with white on blue-grey paper.

52·3 × 34·3 cm. ($20\frac{5}{8}$ × $13\frac{1}{2}$ in.).
1850–4–13–126 (L.B.64; H.73).

17. A LADY

Black chalk touched with white on blue-grey paper.

45·1 × 27·3 cm. (17¾ × 10¾ in.).

1850–4–13–127 (L.B.65; H.74).

18. *Recto*, A LADY

Verso, A LADY AND A GENTLEMAN

Black chalk heightened with white on green-grey paper.

48·8 × 32·7 cm. (19¼ × 12⅞ in.).

1850–4–13–128 (L.B.63; H.72).

The verso may perhaps be a preparatory study for the portrait of Sir Kenelm Digby and his family, at Welbeck Abbey.

19. HENRY DANVERS, EARL OF DANBY

Black chalk touched with white on buff paper.

42·2 × 31·8 cm. (16⅝ × 12½ in.).

1852–4–24–167 (L.B.45; H.57).

20. ENDYMION PORTER WITH HIS SON

Black chalk touched with white on buff paper.

31·8 × 24·2 cm. (12½ × 9½ in.).

1854–5–13–15 (L.B.39; H.51).

21. THOMAS HOWARD, 2nd EARL OF ARUNDEL

Black chalk heightened with white on brown-grey paper.

48 × 35·6 cm. (18⅞ × 14 in.).

1854–5–13–16 (L.B.41; H.53).

22. STUDY FOR A HORSE, possibly connected with the portrait of Charles I on horseback with M. de St. Antoine, at Windsor.

Black chalk heightened with white on green-grey paper.

42·9 × 36·6 cm. (16⅞ × 14⅜ in.).

1874–8–8–22 (L.B.31; H.47).

23. *Recto*, LORD FRANCIS VILLIERS

Verso, TWO STUDIES OF LADIES

Black chalk touched with white on buff paper.

47·6 × 28 cm. (18¾ × 11 in.).

1874–8–8–138 (L.B.44; H.56).

24. CHARLES II, AS PRINCE OF WALES

Black chalk touched with white on blue-grey paper.

34·7 × 23·8 cm. (13⅝ × 9⅜ in.).

1874–8–8–140 (L.B.38; H.50).

25. STUDIES OF A GREYHOUND, for the portrait of James Stuart, 4th Duke of Lennox, 1st Duke of Richmond.

Black chalk touched with white on buff paper.

47 × 32·8 cm. (18½ × 12⅞ in.).

1874–8–8–141 (L.B.43; H.55).

26. JAMES STUART, 4th DUKE OF LENNOX AND 1st DUKE OF RICHMOND

Black chalk touched with white on buff paper.

47·7 × 28 cm. (18¾ × 11 in.).

1874–8–8–142 (L.B.42; H.54).

27. CHARLES I ON HORSEBACK WITH M. DE ST. ANTOINE

Black chalk touched with white on blue-grey paper.

39·8 × 28·3 cm. (15⅝ × 11⅛ in.).

1885–5–9–44 (L.B.30; H.46).

28. CHARLES I ON HORSEBACK

Pen and ink, with brown wash, heightened with white on blue-grey paper.

28·3 × 23·9 cm. (11⅛ × 9⅜ in.).

1885–5–9–45 (L.B.37; H.49).

29. ANN CECIL, COUNTESS OF NORTHUMBERLAND

Black chalk touched with white on blue-grey paper.

35·1 × 23·9 cm. (13⅞ × 9⅜ in.).

1895–9–15–1072 (L.B.55; H.67).

30. *Recto*, A LADY

Verso, NUDE STUDY OF A WOMAN

Black chalk touched with white on blue-grey paper.

46·5 × 27·5 cm. (18¼ × 10¾ in.).
1897–8–13–3(47) (H. add. 120).

31. STUDY OF THE LEFT FORE-LEG OF A HORSE, probably connected with the portrait of Charles I on horseback with M. de St. Antoine.

Black chalk on green-grey paper.
23·2 × 14·7 cm. (9⅛ × 5¾ in.).
1910–2–12–209 (H.48).

[32–38] *LANDSCAPE STUDIES*

The only drawing in the following series which can definitely be said to have been executed in England is the *Study of Plants*, No. 34, which is inscribed by the artist in English.

32. STUDY OF TREES

Pen and brown ink, with washes of brown and green.
19·5 × 23·6 cm. (7⅝ × 9¼ in.).
O.o.9–50 (L.B.71; H.82).

33. A FARMYARD

Pen and brown ink, with washes of brown and water-colour; touched with black lead (perhaps by another hand).
28 × 40·6 cm. (11 × 16 in.).
1885–5–9–46 (L.B.69; H.80).

34. STUDY OF PLANTS

Pen and ink, with brown wash.
21·3 × 32·7 cm. (8⅜ × 12⅞ in.).
1885–5–9–47 (L.B.75; H.85).

(Nos. 35–8). The following four drawings are clearly by the same hand and belong to a group executed in body-colour possibly of the same locality. Three of these come from a similar source, since they have identical inscriptions in a 17th c. hand (?) to Van Dyck. The fourth, No. 37, has an old inscription on the mount to I. Rademaker. No artist of this name with the initial I is recorded, and the work of Abraham Rade-

maker (B. 1675: D. 1733) does not have any affinity with these drawings.

35. A TREE BORDERED COUNTRY LANE BESIDE A STREAM

Body-colour on blue grey paper.
27 × 21·9 cm. (10⅝ × 8⅝in.).
1886–5–13–4 (L.B.67; H.86).

36. A COUNTRY LANE BESIDE A STREAM WITH A DISTANT VIEW OF A MEADOW

Water-colour and body-colour on blue-grey paper.
24·5 × 39·7 cm. (9⅝ × 15⅝ in.).
1895–9–15–1067 (L.B.68; H.87).

37. A TREE BORDERED COUNTRY LANE

Water-colour and body-colour on blue-grey paper.
28·2 × 45·3 cm. (11⅛ × 17⅞ in.); old mount, 32·1 × 47·7 cm. (12⅝ × 18¾ in.).
1932–10–12–2.

As far as can be discerned, the style of the black hood worn by the woman is consistent with the dress of the English woman *c.* 1640 (*Cf.* Hollar, *Parthey*, No. 1884).

38. VIEW FROM A FIELD, WITH TREES AND A SANDY BANK

Water-colour and body-colour on blue-grey paper.
24·1 × 38·7 cm. (9½ × 15¼ in.).
1936–10–10–22.

COPIES AFTER VAN DYCK

39. THOMAS WENTWORTH, EARL OF STRAFFORD, WITH HIS SECRETARY, SIR PHILIP MAINWARING

Red chalk.
21 × 27·8 cm. (8¼ × 10⅞ in.).
1846–5–9–214.

40. GEORGE DIGBY, 2nd EARL OF BRISTOL

Black chalk heightened with white on blue-grey paper.

$34\cdot8 \times 16\cdot9$ cm. ($13\frac{5}{8} \times 6\frac{5}{8}$ in.).

1846–7–9–17 (L.B.52; H.64).

Catalogued by Hind as an original study by Van Dyck, but heavily retouched by another hand. It has, however, all the characteristics of a copy after a painting.

41. QUEEN HENRIETTA MARIA WITH THE PRINCESS MARY

Black chalk heightened with white on blue-grey paper.

$37\cdot8 \times 24\cdot2$ cm. ($14\frac{7}{8} \times 9\frac{1}{2}$ in.).

1860–6–16–34 (L.B.29; H.45).

Catalogued by Hind as a preparatory study for the painting of Charles I with his family, at Windsor. It would appear, however, to be a copy after the painting.

42. THE EARL AND COUNTESS OF ARUNDEL AND FAMILY (?)

Brush drawing in brown wash, heightened with white oil colour, on brown paper.

$16\cdot2 \times 23\cdot3$ cm. ($6\frac{3}{8} \times 9\frac{1}{8}$ in.).

1926–7–14–1 (H. add. 116).

43. ANN, COUNTESS OF MORTON, AND ANN KIRK

Brush and grey ink heightened with white on green paper.

$22\cdot1 \times 28\cdot6$ cm. ($8\frac{3}{4} \times 11\frac{1}{4}$ in.).

1946–7–13–976.

VINNE, JAN VAN DER

B. 1663: D. 1721

In England some time in 1686; back in Holland by 1688

1. VIEW OF OXFORD FROM THE S.W.

Black lead, with brown wash.

$23\cdot6 \times 39\cdot8$ cm. ($9\frac{1}{4} \times 15\frac{5}{8}$ in.).

1879–3–8–1 (H.3).

VINNE, VINCENT LAURENSZ VAN DER

B. 1629: D. 1702

Not known to have visited England

1–14. THE ARTS AND SCIENCES AND THE OCCUPATIONS OF MEN

All in pen and ink, with occasional grey or black wash, over black lead.

All about $23\cdot5 \times 19\cdot1$ cm. ($9\frac{1}{4} \times 7\frac{1}{2}$ in.).

5237–151 to **164** (H.1–14).

Carried out for R.B., who is probably to be identified with Richard Blome. Seven of them are known in engravings (in reverse).

VISSCHER, CLAES JANSZ

B. 1586: D. 1652

Probably visited England in the early 17 c.

1. EXECUTION OF THE CONSPIRATORS IN THE GUNPOWDER PLOT, 1606.

Pen and brown ink, with light brown wash. Indented for transfer.

$23\cdot8 \times 34\cdot4$ cm. ($9\frac{3}{8} \times 13\frac{1}{2}$ in.).

1919–5–13–1 (H.1).

VLIEGER, SIMON DE

B. c. 1600: D. 1653

Not known to have visited England

1. VISIT OF HENRIETTA MARIA TO HEEMSTEDE, 1642.

Pen and brown ink, with grey wash.

$17\cdot7 \times 20\cdot2$ cm. ($6\frac{7}{8} \times 8$ in.).

1886–7–6–8 (H.13).

VORSTERMAN, LUCAS I

B. 1595: D. 1675

Arrived in England after April 1624, and returned to Antwerp before the end of 1630

1. CHARLES I AS PRINCE OF WALES

Pen and brown-grey ink.

$19\cdot8 \times 14\cdot7$ cm. ($7\frac{3}{4} \times 5\frac{3}{4}$ in.).

5227–9 (H.9).

2. GEORGE VILLIERS, DUKE OF BUCKINGHAM

Brush drawing in brown and grey wash, touched with red chalk over black chalk.

19·8 × 17 cm. (7¾ × 6⅝ in.).
1862–5–24–19 (H.10).

3. ANNE DACRE, COUNTESS OF ARUNDEL AND SURREY

Black and red chalk, with grey wash, heightened with white.

23·3 × 17·5 cm. (9⅛ × 6⅞ in.).
1940–4–13–71.

4. SIR FRANCIS CRANE

Black and red chalk.

17·9 × 14 cm. (7 × 5½ in.).
1849–3–28–3.

[Sir Francis Crane (D. 1636) was Director of the tapestry works at Mortlake].

See also: HOLBEIN, Copies after

ZEEMAN, REINIER

B. c. 1623: D. before 1667

Not known to have visited England

1. NAVAL ENGAGEMENT DURING THE 1st ANGLO-DUTCH WAR

Brush drawing in grey ink.

19·6 × 31·1 cm. (7¾ × 12¼ in.).
1836–8–11–598 (H.4).

2. NAVAL ENGAGEMENT DURING THE 1st ANGLO-DUTCH WAR

Brush drawing in grey ink; indented for transfer.

17·2 × 26 cm. (6¾ × 10¼ in.).
1836–8–11–606 (H.5).

ZUCCARO, FEDERICO

B. c. 1542: D. 1609

In England by the end of 1574, but was already back in Rome in October 1575

1. ELIZABETH I

Red and black chalk.

30·9 × 22·2 cm. (12⅛ × 8¾ in.); old mount, 42 × 32·9 cm. (16½ × 13 in.).
G.g.1–417.

2. ROBERT DUDLEY, EARL OF LEICESTER

Red and black chalk.

32·5 × 22 cm. (12¾ × 8⅝ in.); old mount, 43·5 × 32·8 cm. (17⅛ × 12⅞ in.).
G.g.1–418.

ABBREVIATIONS

L.B. Laurence Binyon, *Drawings by British Artists and Artists of Foreign Origin working in Great Britain, in the B.M.*, 1898–1907.

D. Campbell Dodgson, *Guide to the Woodcuts, Drawings and Engravings of Albrecht Dürer in the B.M.*, 1928.

H. A. M. Hind, *Drawings by Dutch and Flemish Artists in the B.M.*, I–IV (17th century), 1915–31.

G. Paul Ganz, *Die Handzeichnungen Hans Holbein d.J.*, 1937.

INDEX OF PROVENANCES

ADAIR, MISS (1903).
LOGGAN, 10.

ADAMS, READ (1889).
FAITHORNE, 5.

ALLAN-FRASER, PATRICK (D.1890). Artist. Married Elizabeth Fraser, whose ancestor was Place Parrott, a grandson of Francis Place.
MANBY, 1–4.

ALLEN, THOMAS, F.S.A. (B.1743: D.1807).
KNYFF, 2.

ANDERSON, WILLIAM (1908).
ASHFIELD, 1.

ANON. COLL., late XIX c.
R. WHITE, 12.

ANON. DUTCH COLL. (1763).
LELY, 1, 12, 16.

ANON. COLL. Unidentified. Lugt 2883ᵃ.
S. DU BOIS, 3–6.

ANON. COLL. In B.M. by 1837.
HILLIARD, 2.

ARGYLL, JOHN CAMPBELL, 5th Duke of (B.1723: D.1806). Field-Marshal.
I. OLIVER, 10.

ASHE, MISS CECILIA (1878).
MARSHALL, 1–33.

B. E. Unidentified collector (Lugt 827).
I. OLIVER, 12, 14, 15.

BAGFORD, JOHN (B.1650: D.1716). Shoemaker and book collector.
HOLLAR, 48.

BAKER, CHARLES HENRY COLLINS (B.1880). Keeper of the N.G. (1914–32); member of the research staff, Huntington Library, California (1932–49). Surveyor of the King's Pictures (1928–34).
TILSON, 1.

BARTLEMAN, JAMES (B.1769: D.1821). Well-known bass singer, London.
G. KNELLER, 10.

BECKFORD, WILLIAM (B.1759: D.1844). Author of *Vathek*, builder of Fonthill, and collector.
VAN DE VELDE, 48.

BENGER, F. B. (1954).
BARLOW, 137.

BERNAL, RALPH (D.1854). M.P. and collector.
ANON. DUTCH EARLY XVII C., 1.

BICKNELL, ELHANAN (B.1788: D.1861). Member of whale fishing firm and collector, Herne Hill.
C. BEALE, 17.

BLOFELD, J. C. (1909). Hoveton House, Norfolk. Sold the collection of drawings and other objects formed by his great-great-grandfather, Thomas Blofeld (B.1753: D.1817), and his son Thomas Calthorpe Blofeld (B.1777: D.1855).
SIBERECHTS, 1.

BRISTOW, WHISTON (1764).
LODGE, 1–3. PLACE, 26.

BROWN, ERNEST, AND PHILLIPS. Fine art dealers founded in 1902. London.
DAHL, 3.

BUCKINGHAM AND CHANDOS, RICHARD GRENVILLE, 1st Duke of (B.1776: D.1839). Statesman and collector of rare prints.
ANON., PERHAPS DUTCH MID XVII C., 1. ANON., AFTER 1677, 1. KNYFF, 2.

BUCKINGHAM AND CHANDOS, RICHARD GRENVILLE, 2nd Duke of (B.1797: D.1861). M.P. and historical writer.
ANON., PERHAPS DUTCH MID XVII C., 1. ANON. AFTER 1677, 1. KNYFF, 2.

BULL, RICHARD (D.1805). Collector, and correspondent of Horace Walpole. Ongar, Essex and North Court, Isle of Wight.
BARLOW, 5. BYNG, 1. DAHL, 4. GASCAR, 1. GIBBONS, 1. GIBSON, 1. LELY, 31. LUTTERELL, 2. MEDINA, 2. PIERCE, 1–6. WINDE, 1. WREN, 1–3. WYCK, 4, 5.

BUNNING, MRS. C. STUART (1955).
TILSON, 2–4.

579

DANIELL, EDWARD. Fine art dealer, London. Founded in 1827.

BARLOW, 6. BULFINCH, 2. FABER, 2. DE JONGH, 5. FORSTER, I. LODGE, I–3. PLACE, 26. RILEY, I. VAN DER MEULEN, I. VAN DER VELDE, 2, 10, 16–21, 34. R. WHITE, 11.

DASENT, CAPTAIN WALTER, R.N. (B.1880: D.1940).

VAN DE VELDE, 79–93.

DAVIES, RANDALL (B.1866: D.1946). Solicitor to L.N.E.R. Collector, principally of English drawings. Writer on art. Editor of *Old Water-colour Society's Club*.

CLEYN, 2.

DELANY, DR. BARRY (*fl. c.* 1875). Doctor at Kilkenny Lunatic Asylum, and collector.

RILEY, I. WYCK, 7, 8.

DENNEY, E. (1936).

THRUMPTON, I.

DERBY, EDWARD STANLEY, 18th Earl of (B.1918).

CHÉRON, 5.

DERBY, JAMES STANLEY, 10th Earl of (B. 1664: D.1735/6).

CHÉRON, 5.

DIMSDALE, THOMAS (B. 1758: D.1823). Banker and collector, London.

HOLLAR, 26.

DODGSON, CAMPBELL (B.1867: D.1949). Keeper of Prints and Drawings, B.M. (1912–32) and collector.

GREENHILL, 2.

DUNDAS, LADY JANE (D.1897). Daughter of the 8th Earl of Wemyss and wife of Col. Philip Dundas.

ANON. FLEMISH *fl.* EARLY XVI C., I.

ELLIOT, CAPTAIN JOHN (1933).

MEDINA, 3

ELLIS, SIR HENRY (B.1777: D.1869) Principal Librarian B.M., 1827–56.

GASSELIN, 2.

ELLIS AND WHITE, MESSRS. Fine art dealers *c.* 1881.

T. JOHNSON, I.

EMMETT, WILLIAM. For biography see pp. 304–5.

JONES, 11–18.

ESDAILE, WILLIAM (B.1758: D.1837). Banker and collector, London.

HOLLAR, 13, 16, 39, 40. LELY, 24. LOGGAN, 5.

EVANS, A. E. & SONS. Fine art dealers *c.* 1852–59.

BARLOW, 3, 131, 132. GYLES, I. LAROON II, 4–11. MEDINA, I. VAN DE VELDE, 9, 11–14, 22, 43, 47, 66–72, 125–127.

FALC, ABRAHAM (1763).

LELY, 16.

FARRER, MR. (1845).

LELY, 18.

FAWCETT, MR. (1888).

LELY, 33.

FAWKENER, WILLIAM (*fl.* middle of XVIII c.). Collector. Bequeathed his collection to B.M., 1769.

CHÉRON, 3, 4. VERELST, I.

FENWICK, THOMAS FITZROY PHILLIPPS (B.1856: D.1938). Grandson of Sir Thomas Phillipps, Bart.

BARLOW, 135. LUTTERELL, 4. I. OLIVER, 11.

FILMER family. Of East Sutton, purchased by Sir Edward Filmer in 1610.

ARGALL, I.

FLORENCE, H. L., FUND. Henry Louis Florence (B.1843/4: D.1916). Left a legacy to the B.M. in 1916, which was assigned to the Department of Prints and Drawings in 1919. Well-known collector, who also left bequests to the N.G. and V. & A. Museum.

CARTER, I. TILSON, I.

FOUNTAINE, SIR ANDREW (B.1676: D.1753). Virtuoso. Vice-chamberlain to Queen Caroline and tutor to Prince William. Collector.

BARLOW, 137. LELY, 28.

FOUQUET (1763).

LELY, I.

FRANCIS, JOHN DEFFETT (B.1815: D.1901). Portrait painter and collector, Swansea.

G. KNELLER, 15.

FRERE, MRS. V. (1951).

ANON. FLEMISH. EARLY XVI C., I.

GELLATLY, PETER (B.1831: D.1912). Solicitor and collector, Essex and London.

HILLIARD, I.

GELLATLY, MRS. PETER. Wife of Peter Gellatly (1831–1912).

HILLIARD, I.

GLOUCESTER, WILLIAM FREDERICK, 2nd Duke of (1776–1834). K.G., F.R.S., Nephew of George III.

LUTTERELL, I.

GOUPIL, MESSRS. Founded *c.* 1827. Fine art dealers, Paris and London.

GRIFFIER, I.

GRANT, A. G. (1956).

P. OLIVER, 2.

GRAVES, HENRY, & CO. Founded in 1752. Fine art dealers, London.

BARLOW, 4, 28, 35–38, 42–44, 48, 49, 52, 54–57, 60, 64, 65, 69, 72, 73, 76, 78–84, 86, 92, 93, 96, 100–2. BULFINCH, I. LAGUERRE, I, 2. LELY, 3–11. RILEY, I. WYCK, 7, 8.

GRIMSTON, JOHN (B.1725: D.1780). Of Kilnwick Hall, Yorks.

FABER, 5. LOGGAN, 12.

H. Unidentified mark, before 1857.

VAN DE VELDE, 47.

HAECKEN, JOSEPH VAN (B.1699?: D.1749). Portrait and history painter, and collector, London.

CHÉRON, 4.

HAMILTON, MR. (1866).

R. WHITE, 10.

HANKS, MISS E. (1867).

BARLOW, 17–27, 29–34, 39–41, 45–7, 50, 51, 53, 58, 59, 61–3, 66–8, 70, 71, 74, 77, 85, 87–91, 94, 95, 97–99, 103–130.

HARDING, G. R. (1897).

BACKER, I. EDWARD BYNG, 2–8. LAROON II, 2.

HARVEY, F. (1893).

TALMAN, I, 2.

HENDERSON, JOHN (B.1797: D.1878). F.S.A. Collector. Benefactor to the B.M. and the Ashmolean Museum.

CRADOCK, I–3. VAN DE VELDE, 26, 38, 52, 73–5, 128–132.

HESELTINE, JOHN POSTLE (B.1843: D.1929). Well-known collector and Trustee of the N.G., London.

HOLLAR, 6, 51.

HOGARTH, MESSRS. Fine art dealers, *c.* 1882.

FORSTER, 2. HOLLAR, 5. ENGLISH DRAUGHTSMAN *c.* 1680(?) I and 2.

HOLLIS, THOMAS (B.1720: D.1774). Friend of Consul Smith and patron of Canaletto when in England.

I. OLIVER, 10.

HOLLIS, THOMAS (formerly BRAND) (*fl. c.* 1748–1804). Changed his name on being left the property of his friend Thomas Hollis.

I. OLIVER, 10.

HOLLOWAY, MARSEILLE (D. *c.* 1910). Fine art dealer, London. Established *c.* 1860.

C. BEALE, 17. VAN DE VELDE, 41, 42, 50, 51, 133.

HONE, NATHANIEL (B.1718: D.1784). Portrait painter, miniaturist, and collector.

LELY, 29. P. OLIVER, I.

HOSPER, H. J. (1911).

EVELYN, 2.

HOWARD, HUGH (B. 1675: D.1737). Portrait painter and collector. Elder brother of Dr. Robert Howard, Bishop of Elphin.

BARLOW, 134. CLEYN, I. COOKE, I–3. DANCKERTS, 2. S. DU BOIS, I, 2. FULLER, I, 2. JONES, 3–10. G. KNELLER 26. LAROON II, I. LELY, 25–7. I. OLIVER, 8. PRINCE RUPERT, I, 2. VAN DER VAART, I. VAN DE VELDE, 24, 40, 53, 76, 77, 134.

HOWARD, DR. ROBERT (B.1683: D.1740). Bishop of Elphin. Younger brother of Hugh Howard, whose collection he inherited.

BARLOW, 134. CLEYN, I. COOKE, I–3. DANCKERTS, 2. S. DU BOIS, I, 2. FULLER, I, 2. JONES, 3–10. G. KNELLER, 26. LAROON II, I. LELY, 25–7. I. OLIVER, 7, 8. PRINCE RUPERT, I, 2. VAN DER VAART, I. VAN DE VELDE, 24, 40 53, 76, 77, 134.

HUME, (1820).

VAN DE VELDE, 48.

HUMPHRY, OZIAS (B.1742: D.1810). Miniature painter.

EVELYN, I.

IJVER. Fine art dealer *c.* 1763.

LELY, 12.

JACKSON, ROBERT (1889).

FABER, 3. GIBBONS, 2–6.

JANTZEN, DR. JOHANNES (1955).

LELY, 16.

JONES, E. PETER (1917).

ANON. PROBABLY GERMAN EARLY XVII C., I–20.

JOWETT, ALFRED (1935).

BECKMAN, I.

KEOGH, MR. (1879).

VAN DE VELDE, 36.

KNIGHT, RICHARD PAYNE (B.1750: D.1824). Collector, London. Trustee of the B.M. Writer on art and archaeology and pioneer of the Picturesque.

COLONIA, I, 2. DAHL, I. LELY, 17, 34. I. OLIVER, 4. P. OLIVER, I. VAN DE VELDE, 39, 64, 65, 117–121. VAN DIEST, I.

WHEELER, EWART (1950). Fine art dealer.

FAITHORNE, 5.

WHITE, The REV. F. O. (1881).

LOGGAN, 9.

WHITEHEAD, Mr. (1876).

BARLOW, 10, 12–14.

WICKLOW, CHARLES HOWARD, 5th Earl of (B.1839: D.1881). Last owner of the Wicklow collection.

BARLOW, 134. CLEYN, 1. COOKE, 1–3. DANCKERTS, 2. S. DU BOIS, 1, 2. FULLER, 1, 2. JONES, 3–10. G. KNELLER, 26. LAROON, 1. LELY, 25–27. I. OLIVER, 7, 8. PRINCE RUPERT, 1, 2. VAN DER VAART, 1. VAN DE VELDE, 24, 40, 53, 76, 77, 134.

WILKINS, SIR CHARLES (B.1749: D.1836). Orientalist. Grandson of Elizabeth Byng, sister of Edward Byng.

BYNG, 2–8.

WILLIAMS, IOLO (B.1890). Author and journalist. Museums correspondent of *The Times*. Collector of English drawings.

MANBY, 1–4. TOUROUDE, 1.

WILLIAMS, MISS MURIEL H. (1927).

ROUSSEAU, 1.

WILLIAMSON, DR. GEORGE CHARLES (B.1858: D.1942). Writer on art, especially the history of portrait miniatures, and collector of drawings and coins.

FAITHORNE, 5.

WILLIAMS-WYNN, Rt. Hon. SIR HENRY(B.1783: D.1856). Diplomat.

HOLLAR, 25.

WILLIAMS-WYNN, HENRY BERTIE (B.1820: D.1895). Son of the Rt. Hon. Sir Henry Williams-Wynn.

HOLLAR, 25.

WOODBURN, SAMUEL (B.1786: D.1853). Fine art dealer, St. Martin's Lane, London.

BARLOW, 135. GERBIER, 1. LUTTERELL, 4. I. OLIVER, 5, 10(?), 12. VAN DE VELDE, 8, 15, 35, 37.

WRAY, CHARLES (B.1718: D.1791). Of Bath. Son of Elizabeth Byng, sister of Edward Byng, said to have been of Hoare's Bank.

BYNG, 2–8.

WRAY, ELIZABETH (D.1759). Widow of Rev. William Wray. Sister of Edward Byng.

BYNG, 2–8.

WYNDHAM, FRANCES (PLACE). (Born between 1694 and 1727). Younger daughter of Francis Place's second marriage. Married Wadham Wyndham (see below).

PLACE, 1–25, 27–36.

WYNDHAM, WADHAM (*fl. c.*1636). Of Orchard Wyndham. Married Frances, daughter of Francis Place. Perhaps identical with the Captain Wadham Windham in the list of subscribers to Francis Drake's *Eboracum*.

PLACE, 1–25, 27–36.

YAXLEY, MRS. E. (1952).

I. OLIVER, 13.

LIST OF WORKS REFERRED TO IN AN ABBREVIATED FORM

Adams: Randolph G. Adams, *An Effort to Identify John White*, in *American Historical Review*, XLI, Oct., 1935, pp. 87–91

Admin., P.C.C., Middlesex: Somerset House, *Prerogative Court of Canterbury, Transcripts of Administrations,* MSS.

Airy: Osmund Airy, *Charles II*, 1901

Allen: Elsa G. Allen, *The History of American Ornithology Before Audubon*, in *Transactions of the American Philosophical Society*, n.s., XLI, 1951, pp. 386–591

Allen, XVI c. American Bird Paintings: Elsa G. Allen, *Some Sixteenth Century Paintings of American Birds*, in *The Auk*, n.s., LIII, 1936, pp. 17–21

Altena: J. Q. van Regteren Altena, *The Drawings of Jacques de Gheyn*, 1936

Andersen: Jurgen Andersen, *Kunster og Kolonisator. John Whites Tegninger fra Virginia*, in *Bogrennen*, no. 10, 1955

Anderson: R. C. Anderson, *Part I, English Ships, 1649–1702*, in *Lists of Men-of-War, 1650–1700.* No. 5 in the *Occasional Publications* of The Society for Nautical Research

Apollo: Apollo, *A Journal of the Arts*, etc., 1925–

Arch. Art. Français: Nouvelles Archives de l Art Français, 1872

Art Journal: The Art Journal, 1849–1912

Artisti Salentini: Mostra Retrospettiva degli Artisti Salentini, *Catalogo Generale*, 1939

Ashmolean Mus. Report, 1955: University of Oxford, Ashmolean Museum, *Report of the Visitors*, 1955

Auerbach: Erna Auerbach, *Tudor Artists*, 1954

Auerbach, Hilliard Studies: Erna Auerbach, articles on Hilliard in *Burl. Mag.* XCI, 1949, pp. 166 and 169; XCIV, 1952, pp. 326–30; XCV, 1953, pp. 197–205

Azzolini: Isidoro Ugurgieri Azzolini, *Le Pompe Sanesi . . .*, 1649

Bagford, Faithorne: B.M. Harleian MS. 5910. iv, *f.* 157. Being an MS. from Bagford's *Collectiana*

Baker & Constable: C. H. Collins Baker and W. G. Constable, *English Painting of the Sixteenth and Seventeenth Centuries*, 1930

Baker, Ashfield: C. H. Collins Baker, *Notes on Edmund Ashfield*, in *Walpole Soc.*, III, 1914, pp. 83–7

Baker, Chandos: C. H. Collins Baker and M. I. Baker, *The Life and Circumstances of James Brydges, 1st Duke of Chandos*, 1949

Baker, Hampton Court: C. H. Collins Baker, *Catalogue of the Pictures at Hampton Court*, 1929

Baker, Johnson: C. H. Collins Baker, *A Portrait Group by Cornelius Johnson*, in *Burl. Mag.*, XXXIX, 1921, p. 221

Baker, Lely: C. H. Collins Baker, *Lely and the Stuart Portrait Painters*, 1912

Baker, Lely and Kneller: C. H. Collins Baker, *Lely and Kneller*, in *Art Journal*, 1922, p. 40

Baker, Lely Drawings: C. H. Collins Baker, *Some Drawings by Lely*, in *Art Journal*, 1911, pp. 337–40

Baker, Petworth: C. H. Collins Baker, *Catalogue of the Petworth Collection of Pictures*, 1920

Baker, Tilson: C. H. Collins Baker, *An Unknown English (?) Portrait Draughtsman*, in *The Connoisseur*, LXXXVII, pp. 289–90, figs. 1 & 2

Baker, Verrio: C. H. Collins Baker, *Antonio Verrio and Thornhill's Early Portraiture*, in *The Connoisseur*, CXXXI, 1953, pp. 10–13

Bartsch: Adam Bartsch, *Le Peintre Graveur*, 1803–21

Beauties of England: A New Display of the Beauties of England, 3rd edn., 1776

Beckett: Francis Beckett, *The Painter Frantz Clein in Denmark*, in *D. Kgl. Danske Vidensk Selsk-Skrifter, Hist, og Filos.*, Afd., 7. Raekke, V. 2, 1936

Beckett, Lely: R. B. Beckett, *Lely*, 1951

Bell and Poole: C. F. Bell and Rachel Poole, *English Seventeenth-Century Portrait Drawings in Oxford Collections (Part II)*, in *Walpole Soc.* XIV, 1926; pp. 43–80,

Bell, Letter: C. F. Bell, Letter on *A Drawing Ascribed to Van Dyck* by R. Schwabe in *Burl. Mag.*, LIII, 1928, p. 208

Bell, Portrait Drawings: C. F. Bell, *English Seventeenth-Century Portrait Drawings in Oxford Collections*, in *Walpole Soc.* v, 1915–17, pp. 1–18 and Pls. I (a & b) and II (a & b)

Benisovich: Michel Benisovich, *Two Drawings by Peter Lely*, in *Burl. Mag.*, XCI, 1919, pp. 79–80

Benson and Hatcher: R. Benson and H. Hatcher, *Old and New Sarum or Salisbury*, 1843

B.F.A.C., British-born Artists: Burlington Fine Arts Club, *Catalogue of an Exhibition of Works of British-born Artists of the Seventeenth Century*, 1938

Bickham, Deliciae: George Bickham, *Deliciae Britannicae*, 2nd. edn., 1755

Bigges; Walter Bigges, *A summarie and True Discourse of Sir Frances Drakes West Indian voyage*, (with one general and four city maps). Richard Field, 1589 (B.M. copy G. 6509).

Binyon, Drawings of Englishwomen: Laurence Binyon, *Some Drawings of Englishwomen from Van Dyck to Kneller*, in *Burl. Mag.*, X, 1906–7, pp. 74–80, Pls. I–III

Binyon, English Water-colours: Laurence Binyon, *English Water-colours*, 2nd edn., 1944

Binyon, White: Laurence Binyon, *The Drawings of John White*, in *Walpole Soc.*, XIII, 1924–5, pp. 19–24

Biographie Toulousaine: Anon., *Biographie Toulousaine*, 1823

Birch: Thomas Birch, *The History of the Royal Society of London,* 1756–7

Blaauw: W. H. Blaauw, *John Dunstal,* in *Sussex Archaeological Collections,* VIII, 1856, p. 270

Blakiston Documents Noel Blakiston, *Nicholas Hilliard: Some Unpublished Documents,* in *Burl. Mag.,* XC, 1948, pp. 101–7; XCI, 1949, p. 169

Blofeld Cat.: MS. catalogue of drawings in the possession of the Blofeld family at Hoveton House, Wroxham, Norfolk

Blunt, French Drawings: Anthony Blunt, *The French Drawings in the Collection of H. M. at Windsor Castle,* 1945

Blunt: Wilfred Blunt, *Tulipomania,* 1950

Blunt, Botanical Illustration: Wilfred Blunt, *The Art of Botanical Illustration,* 1950

Bolton and Hendry: Arthur T. Bolton and H. Duncan Hendry, *Introduction. Sir Christopher Wren's Original Design for Hampton Court Palace in 1689,* in *Wren Society,* IV, 1927, p. 13–14

Borenius, Addenda: Tancred Borenius, *Addenda to the Work of Van Dyck,* in *Burl. Mag.,* LXXXIX, 1941, pp. 200–1

Borenius, Lely's Coll: [Tancred Borenius], *Sir Peter Lely's Collection* in *Burl. Mag.,* LXXXIII, 1943

Bramston: Autobiography of Sir John Bramston. Printed for the Camden Society, 1845

Braun & Hogenberg: G. Braun and F. Hogenberg, *Civitates Orbis Terrarum,* 1573–1618

Braun Reproductions: Adolph Braun, *Catalogue des Reproductions . . . D'après les Dessins des Grands Maîtres,* 1913

Bridgeman-Winde Letters: MS. *Letters from Capt. William Winde to Lady Bridgeman.* 1688–99/1700. (Earl of Bradford's Archives, Weston Park)

B.M., Additional MSS.: Catalogue of Additions to the Manuscripts in the British Museum, 1836–

B.M., Drawings Presented and Purchased: Catalogue of Drawings Presented and Purchased, c. 1856. MS. preserved in the Dept. of Prints and Drawings, British Museum

B.M., Eng. Topographical & Landscape Drawing: The Beginnings of English Topographical and Landscape Drawing. An exhibition held in the Department of Prints & Drawings, British Museum, 1949–50

B.M., Engraved Portraits: Freeman O'Donoghue and H. M. Hake, *Catalogue of Engraved British Portraits . . . in the British Museum,* 1908–25

B.M., Lansdowne MS. No. 655: The Last Will and Testament of Richard Busby, D.D., one of the Prebendaries of the Collegiate Church of S Peter in Westminster and Master of the King's School there Deceased

B.M., MS. Maps and Topographical Drawings: Catalogue of Manuscript Maps, Charts and Plans, and Topographical Drawings in the British Museum, 1844

B.M., P.R. Purchases: B.M., Print Room, *Reports of Purchases,* MS. & typescript

B.M. Postcards: Six postcard reproductions (Nos. 427–432 inclusive) of John White drawings published by the British Museum

B.M.Q.: British Museum Quarterly, 1926–

B.M., Raleigh & Hakluyt: Sir Walter Raleigh and Richard Hakluyt. Catalogue of an exhibition held in the King's Library, British Museum, July–Sept., 1952

B.M. Reproductions: Reproductions of Drawings of Old Masters in the British Museum, Pts. I–IV, 1888–94

B.M. Satires: F. G. Stephens & Mrs. M. D. George, *Catalogue of Political and Personal Satires,* 1870–1954

B.N., Belgique: Biographie nationale de Belgique, 1866–1938

Briquet: C. M. Briquet, *Les Filigranes. Dictionnaire Historique des Marques du Papier. . . .* 1907

Brooks: Eric St. John Brooks, *Sir Christopher Hatton,* 1946

Brown: John Brown, *John Bunyan* (ed. F. M. Harrison), 1928

Buckeridge: B. Buckeridge, *An Essay Towards an English School of Painters,* in Roger de Piles *The Art of Painting,* 3rd edn, 1750? [1st edn., 1704, 2nd edn., 1744]

Bull (?) Devizes: Henry Bull or James Waylen, *A History Military and Municipal of the Ancient Borough of the Devizes . . .* 1857

Burghley Cat.: The Marchioness of Exeter, *Catalogue of Pictures at Burghley House, Northamptonshire,* 1954

Burl. Mag.: The Burlington Magazine, 1903–

Bushnell, White: D. I. Bushnell, Jr., *John White—The First English Artist to Visit America, 1585,* in *Virginia Mag. of History and Biography,* XXXV, 1927, pp. 419–30 and XXXVI, 1928, pp. 17–26 and 124–34

C.S.P. Dom.: Calendar of State Papers. Domestic Series (1547–1704). Various Editors, 1856–1924

C.T.B.: Calendar of Treasury Books from 1660 ed. by William A. Shaw, 1904–

Callcott: J. W. Callcott, *Account of the Graduates' Meeting, a Society of Musical Professors, Established in London* Novr. 24, 1790. B.M. Add. MS. 27693, ff. 6–36

Camden Soc.: Publications of the Camden Society, 1840–97

Campbell, Vitruvius: Colen Campbell, *Vitruvius Britannicus,* 1717–25

C.C.L.: Commissary Court of London, Transcripts of Wills. Guildhall MS. 9172

Chaloner Smith (also *C.S.*): John Chaloner Smith, *British Mezzotinto Portraits,* 1883

Cheetham, Gerbier: F. H. Cheetham, *Hampstead Marshall and Sir Balthazar Gerbier,* in *N. & Q.,* 11th Series, VII, pp. 406–8

Chester Painters, Apprentices: Apprentice Records of the Painters, Glaziers, Embroiderers and Stationers' Company of Chester, 1571–1691. MS. in keeping of Dr. Skonce, Steward of the Company

Chester Painters, Expense Bk.: Expense Book of the Painters, Glaziers, Embroiderers and Stationers' Company of Chester, 1620–1707. MS. in keeping of Dr. Skonce, Steward of the Company

Chettle: G. H. Chettle *Marlborough House Chapel, St. James's Palace* in *Country Life,* LXXXIV, 1938, pp. 450–53

Christchurch, Newgate, Registers: The Registers of Christchurch, Newgate (Harl. Soc., Register 21), ed. W. A. Littledale, 1895

Chotzen and Draak: Th. M. Chotzen and A. M. Draak, *Beschrijving der Britsche Eilanden door Lucas de Heere,* 1937

Churchill: W. A. Churchill, *Watermarks in Paper in the XVII and XVIII Centuries,* 1935

Colby: F. C. Colby, *Visitation of the County of Somerset in the Year 1623* (Harl. Soc.), 1876

Colvin: H. M. Colvin, *Biographical Dictionary of Architects,* 1954

Colvin & Hind: Sidney Colvin, *Early Engraving and Engravers in England* . . . [with a list of Engravers' works by A. M. Hind], 1905

Connoisseur: The Connoisseur: a Magazine for Collectors, 1901–

Conway: Sir Martin Conway, *Drawings by Gerard David,* in *Burl. Mag.,* XIII, 1908, p. 155

Cooke: Robert Cooke, *The Visitation of London, 1568,* ed. J. J. Howard & G. J. Armytage (Harl. Soc.), 1869

Country Life: Country Life Magazine, 1897–

Cowfold Registers: The Parish Registers of Cowfold, Sussex (Sussex Record Society, XXII, ed. P. S. Godman, 1916)

Crace: J. G. Crace, *Some Account of the Worshipful Company of Painters,* 1880

Crace, Catalogue: Frederick Crace: *A Catalogue of Plans and Views of London, Westminster and Southwark,* 1878

Crace, Painter-Stainers: J. D. Crace, *A Catalogue of the Pictures . . . in Possession of the Worshipful Company of Painter-Stainers,* 1908

Cracherode Cat.: Catalogue of the Cracherode Collection of Drawings, 1845. MS. preserved in the Dept. of Prints and Drawings

Croft-Murray, Rubens: Edward Croft-Murray, *The Landscape Background in Rubens's 'St. George and the Dragon',* in *Burl. Mag.,* LXXXIX, 1947, pp. 89–93

Croft-Murray, Flemish Sketchbook: Edward Croft-Murray, *A Leaf from a Flemish Sketchbook of the Early Sixteenth Century,* in *B.M.Q.,* XVII, No. 1, 1952, pp. 8–10, Pl. I

Crowle, Pennant: Pennant, *Some Account of London Illustrated with Portraits, Views, Plans etc., by T. Chas. Crowle,* 1801

Crowle, Pennant, Index: Index of the Maps, Plans, Views, Portraits, Historical & other Subjects Contained in Pennant's Account of London with illustrations collected and inserted by T. Chas. Crowle and bequeathed to the B.M., 1811

Cruden: R. P. Cruden, *History of Gravesend,* 1843

Cumming: W. P. Cumming, *The Identity of John White, Governor of Virginia and John White the Artist,* in *North Carolina Historical Review,* XV, 1938, pp. 197–203

Cumming, Purcell: William H. Cumming, *Portraits of Purcell,* in *The Musical Times,* XXXVI, 1895, pp. 735–736

Cundall: H. M. Cundall, *Bygone Richmond,* 1925

Cust, Foreign Artists in London: Lionel Cust, *Foreign Artists . . . Working in London from about 1560 to 1660,* 1903. H. S. Proceedings, vii

Cust, Johnson: Lionel Cust, *Cornelius Janssen Van Ceulen,* in *Burl. Mag.,* XVI, 1910, pp. 280–1

Cust, Mary Queen of Scots: Lionel Cust, *Notes on the Authentic Portraits of Mary Queen of Scots,* 1903

Cust, Van Dyck: Lionel Cust, *Anthony Van Dyck,* 1900

D.A.B.: Dictionary of American Biography, 1928–44

De Boer: Dr. M. G. de Boer. *Balthazar Gerbier,* in *Oud Holland,* XXI, 1903, pp. 129–60

De Bruyn: Cornelis de Bruyn, *Reizen . . . Door de Vermaardste Deelen van Klein Asia,* 1698 (French edn., 1700)

De Bry, America, Pt. I: Theodor de Bry, *America, Pt. I,* 1590, being a reprint of Thomas Hariot, *A Briefe and True Report of the New Found Land of Virginia,* 1588

De Bry, America, Pt. II: Theodor de Bry, *America, Pt. II,* containing the *Brevis Narratio Eorum Quae in Florida . . . Gallis Acciderunt* by Jacques le Moyne, 1591

De Domenici: Bernardo de Domenici, *Vite dei Pittori, Scultori et Architetti Napolitani,* 1745 (2nd edn., 1840–6)

Delbanco: G. Delbanco, *Abraham Hondius,* in *Old Master Drawings,* V, 1930, pp. 40–1, Pls. 19–20

Derby Miniatures: The Earl of Derby's Miniatures in *Connoisseur,* June, 1958, pp. 43–46

Descamps: J. B. Descamps, *La Vie des Peintres Flamands, Allemands et Hollandois avec des Portraits,* 1754

De Simone: L. G. de Simone, *Lecce ei Suoi Monumenti,* 1874

Dézallier, Environs: Antoine Nicolas Dézallier d'Argenville, *Voyage Pittoresque des Environs de Paris,* 2nd edn., 1762

D.N.B.: George Smith (founder), *Dictionary of National Biography,* 1885–1949

Dobson: William Dobson, 1611–1649. An Exhibition of Paintings. Arts Council, 1951

Dodgson, Gaywood: Campbell Dodgson in 'Quarterly notes by the Editor,' *Print Collectors' Quarterly,* XV, 1928

Dodgson, Irish Seal: Campbell Dodgson, *A Design for the Irish Seal of Queen Elizabeth,* in *Burl. Mag.,* V, 1904, pp. 573–4, Pl. II

Dodgson, Ornamental Designs: Campbell Dodgson, *Ornamental Designs,* in *Proceedings of the Society of Antiquaries,* June 28, 1917

Dodgson, Woodcuts: Campbell Dodgson, *Guide to the Woodcuts, Drawings and Engravings of Albrecht Dürer in the B.M.,* 1928

Dostal: E. Dostal, *Vaclav (Venceslas) Hollar,* 1924

Drake: Francis Drake, *Eboracum or the History and Antiquities of the City of York . . . ,* 1736

Dugdale, Monasticon: Sir William Dugdale, *Monasticon Anglicanum,* 1655–73, 2nd edn., 1718

Duleep Singh: Prince Frederick Duleep Singh, *Portraits in Norfolk Houses* [c. 1927]

Dulwich Catalogue: Dulwich College Gallery Catalogue, 1892

Dumont: Jean Dumont, *A New Voyage to the Levant,* 1696

Eagleston: A. J. Eagleston, *The Channel Islands under Tudor Government, 1485–1642,* 1949

Edwards: Ralph Edwards, *Oil Miniatures by Cornelius Johnson,* in *Burl. Mag.,* LXI, 1932, pp. 131–2

Eggleston: Edward Eggleston, *John White's Drawings* in *The Nation,* LII, Apr., 1891, pp. 340–1

Elsum: John Elsum, *Epigrams Upon the Paintings of the Most Eminent Masters, Ancient and Modern,* 1700

Evelyn, Diary: John Evelyn, *Diary,* ed. E. S. de Beer, 1955

Evelyn, Sculptura: J. Evelyn, *Sculptura: or the History, and Art of Chalcography and Engraving in Copper . . . ,* ed., with the unpublished Second Part, by C. F. Bell, 1906

Fagan: Louis Fagan, *A Descriptive Catalogue of the Engraved Works of William Faithorne,* 1888

Farquhar: Helen Farquhar, *Nicholas Hilliard, Embosser of Medals of Gold,* in *Numismatic Chronicle,* Series IV, VIII, 1908, pp. 342, 346, 347, Pl. XXVI

Faulkner, Chelsea: Thomas Faulkner, *An Historical and Descriptive Account of the Royal Hospital . . . at Chelsea,* 1805

Fawkener Cat.: Catalogue of the Fawkener Collection of Drawings, 1845. MS. preserved in the Dept. of Prints & Drawings, B.M.

Fellowes: Edward H. Fellowes, *The Military Knights of Windsor,* 1944

Fiennes: Celia Fiennes, *Journeys,* ed. Christopher Morris, 1949

Finberg: A. J. Finberg, *A Chronological List of Portraits by Cornelius Johnson,* in *Walpole Soc.,* X, 1922, pp. 1–37

Fite & Freeman: Emerson D. Fite and Archibald Freeman, *A Book of Old Maps,* 1926

Flannery: Regina Flannery, *Analysis of coastal Algonquian Culture,* in Catholic University of America Anthropological Series, No. 7. 1939

Flindt, Entwürfe: Entwürfe zu Gefässen ünd Motiven für Goldschmiedarbeiten. Serie I. 33 Blatt in Lichtdruck nach Originalblättern in Punzmanier von Paul Flindt-Nürnberg [n.d.]

Fokker: T. H. Fokker, *Jan Siberechts, Peintre de la Paysanne Flamande,* 1931

Foster, Alumni: J. Foster, *Alumni Oxonienses. The Members of the University of Oxford, 1500–1714.* Arranged by Joseph Foster, 1892

Foster, Cooper: J. J. Foster, *Samuel Cooper and the English Miniature Painters of the XVII Century,* 1914–16

Foster, Cooper, Supplement: J. J. Foster, *A List Alphabetically Arranged of Works of English Miniature Painters of the XVII Century.* With a Description of the Same, Names of the Owners and Remarks. Supplementary to *Samuel Cooper and the English Miniature Painters of the XVII Century,* 1914–16

Foster, Licences: John Foster, *London Marriage Licences, 1521–1869,* 1887

Freeman, Dunstall: Philip Freeman, *On the Site of 'A Temple by Chichester' as Etched by John Dunstall,* in *Sussex Archaeological Collections,* VII, 1854, pp. 56–60

Freind Cat.: Catalogue of Prints and Drawings formerly in the collection of Dr. Robert Freind and later in that of William, 2nd Viscount Ashbrook. MS. preserved in Department of Prints and Drawings, B.M.

Gainsborough Exhibition: Gainsborough Exhibition Catalogue, Ipswich, 1927

Ganz: Paul Ganz, *Die Handzeichnungen Hans Holbein d. J.,* 1937

Gavin: C. M. Gavin, *Royal Yachts,* 1932

Glück, Reflections: Gustav Glück, *Reflections on Van Dyck's Early Death,* in *Burl. Mag.,* LXXIX, 1941, pp. 193–9

Glück, Van Dyck: Gustav Glück, *Van Dyck,* in *Klassiker Der Kunst,* 1931

Goldsmid: Edward Goldsmid, *Explanatory Notes of a Pack of Cavalier Playing Cards Temp. Charles II Forming A Complete Political Satire of the Commonwealth,* 1886

Gordon: D. J. Gordon, *Poet and Architect: The Intellectual Setting of the Quarrel Between Ben Jonson and Inigo Jones,* in *Warburg Journal,* XII, 1949, pp. 152–78

Gotch: J. A. Gotch, *Inigo Jones,* 1928

Gotch, Itinerary: J. A. Gotch, *Inigo Jones's Principal Visit to Italy in 1614. The Itinerary of His Journeys,* in the *Journal of the Royal Institute of British Architects,* third series, XLVI, pp. 85–6

Gotch, Whitehall: J. A. Gotch, *The Original Drawings for the Palace at Whitehall, Attributed to Inigo Jones,* in *The Architectural Review,* XXXI, 1912, pp. 333–64

Goulding: Richard W. Goulding, *Catalogue of the Pictures Belonging to his Grace the Duke of Portland,* 1936

Graham-Fresnoy: Richard Graham, *A Short Account of the most Eminent Painters both Ancient and Modern,* in *De Arte Graphica* by C. A. Du Fresnoy. Translated into English Together with an *Original Preface* containing a Parallel betwixt Painting and Poetry by Mr. Dryden, 1695

Granger: The Rev. James Granger, *A Biographical History of England,* 5th edn., 1824

Grant: M. H. Grant, *A Chronological History of the Old English Landscape Painters* [1926]–1947

Grove: Sir George Grove, *Dictionary of Music and Musicians,* 5th edn., ed. Eric Blom, VI, 1954

Guiffrey & Barthelemy: J. Guiffrey & J. Barthelemy, *Liste des Pensionnaires de l'Académie de France à Rome,* 1908

Gunther: R. T. Gunther, *The Architecture of Sir Roger Pratt,* 1928

Hake: H. M. Hake, *Some Contemporary Records Relating to Francis Place, Engraver and Draughtsman with a Catalogue of his Engraved Work,* in *Walpole Soc.,* X, 1922, pp. 39–69

Hakluyt: Richard Hakluyt, *The Principal Navigations, Voyages Traffiques & Discoveries of the English Nation,* 1598–1600

Hakluyt (MacLehose edn.): Richard Hakluyt, *The Principal Navigations, Voyages, Traffiques & Discoveries of the English Nation.* Published by James MacLehose & Sons, in 12 volumes, 1903–5

Ham House: Ralph Edwards & Peter Ward-Jackson, *Ham House, a Guide,* 1951

Harcourt-Bath: William Harcourt-Bath, *A History of the Family of Harcourt,* 1930

Harl. Soc.: Publications of the Harleian Society, 1869–

Harrison: F. M. Harrison, *A Bibliography of the Works of John Bunyan,* 1932

Hasted: Edward Hasted, *History of Kent,* 1778–99

Hatfield MS. No. 9: Notes on British Painting from Archives: I, in *Burl. Mag.,* XCVI, 1954, p. 323

Hauck: Karl Hauck, *Die Briefe der Kinder des Winterkönigs,* in *Neue Heidelberger Jahrbücher,* XV, 1908, pp. 129–30, 132–3, 133–4

Hayes: John Hayes, *Claude de Jongh,* in *Burl. Mag.,* XCVIII, 1956, pp. 3–11

Heawood: Edward Heawood, *Watermarks mainly of the 17th and 18th Centuries,* 1950, Vol. I of *Monumenta Chartæ Papyraceæ Historiam Illustrantia,* ed. E. J. Labarre

Heseltine, German School: J. P. Heseltine, *Original Drawings chiefly of the German School in the Collection of J. P. Heseltine,* 1912

Hind, Dutch & Flemish Drawings: A. M. Hind, *A Catalogue of Drawings by Dutch and Flemish Artists Preserved in the Department of Prints and Drawings, B.M., 1915–31*

Hind, Engraving in England, I: Arthur M. Hind, *Engraving in England in the Sixteenth & Seventeenth Centuries. Part I, the Tudor Period,* 1952

Hind, Hollar: A. M. Hind, *Wenceslaus Hollar and his Views of London and Windsor in the Seventeenth Century,* 1922

Hind, Miscellaneous: A. M. Hind, *Miscellaneous Drawings from the Heseltine Sale,* in *B.M.Q.,* x, 1935, p. 23 and Plate xa

Hind, Rembrandt's Etchings: A. M. Hind, *A Catalogue of Rembrandt's Etchings, Chronologically Arranged and Completely Illustrated,* two vols, 2nd edn., 1924

Hind, Studies: A. M. Hind, *Studies in English Engraving* I–VI, in *Connoisseur,* XCI, 1933, pp. 74–80, 223–33, 363–74; and XCII, 1933, pp. 92–105, 215–27, 382–91

Hind, Van Dyck: A. M. Hind, *A Landscape Drawing Attributed to Van Dyck,* in *B.M.Q.,* VII, 1932, p. 63, (repr. Pl. XXXVI)

Hind, Van Dyck and English Landscape: A. M. Hind, *Van Dyck and English Landscape,* in *Burl. Mag.,* LI, 1927, pp. 292–7

Hinton Portraits: Additional MS. 6391; a MS. catalogue of portraits in country houses arranged alphabetically in counties

Hist. MSS. Comm., Charlemont MSS.: Historical Manuscripts Commission, 3rd Report. (MSS. of House of Lords), 1872 [Ser. 2]
Charlemont MSS., II (1894). [Ser. 28.]

H.M.C., Middlesex: Royal Commission on Historical Monuments (England). *An Inventory of the Historical Monuments in Middlesex,* 1937

Hoare: Sir Richard Colt Hoare, *The History of Modern Wiltshire,* 1822–44

Hobson: R. L. Hobson, *Handbook of the Pottery and Porcelain of the Far East,* 1937

Hofer: Philip Hofer, *Francis Barlow's Aesop,* in *Harvard Library Bulletin,* II, No. 3, 1948 (with full *Bibl.*), pp. 279–95

Holland: W. J. Holland, *The First Picture of an American Butterfly,* in *Scientific Monthly,* XXIX (1926), pp. 45–8

Holland, Hatfield: L. G. Holland, *A Description & Historical Catalogue of the Collection of Pictures at Hatfield House . . . ,* 1891

Holmes: Sir Charles Holmes, *The Portraits of Arne and Purcell,* in *Burl. Mag.,* XXVII, 1915, p. 187, Pl. IIE

Holmes, Villiers: Sir Charles Holmes, *George and Francis Villiers by Van Dyck,* in *Burl. Mag.,* XL, 1922, pp. 54–6

Honour, Knyff: Hugh Honour, *Leonard Knyff,* in *Burl. Mag.,* XCVI, 1954, pp. 337–8, Figs. 2 & 5–8

Hooke: Robert Hooke, *Diary, 1672–80,* ed. H. W. Robinson and Walter Adams, 1935

Hope, Windsor: W. H. St. John Hope, *Windsor Castle,* 1913

Horsfield, Sussex: T. W. Horsfield, *The History, Antiquities, and Topography of the County of Sussex,* 1835

Hotson: L. Hotson, *The Commonwealth and Restoration Stage,* 1928

Houbraken: Arnold Houbraken, *Grosse Schouburgh,* ed. A. von Wurzbach, 1880

Howard & Campbell, Golden Grove: Rachel A. G Howard & K. S. Campbell, *A Catalogue of the Pictures at Golden Grove,* 1904

H.S., Proceedings: Proceedings of the Huguenot Society of London, 1885–

H.S., Publications: The Publications of the Huguenot Society, 1887–

Hulton: P. H. Hulton, *A Volume of Drawings by Francis Barlow,* in *B.M.Q.,* XX, No. 1, March, 1955

Hussey: Christopher Hussey, *Sprotborough Hall, Doncaster. The Seat of Brig.-Gen. Sir A. Bewicke-Copley, K.B.E.,* in *Country Life,* LI, 1922, pp. 174–80

Hussey, Dorney Court: Christopher Hussey, *Dorney Court, Buckinghamshire. The Seat of Brevet-Colonel C. H. D. Palmer,* in *Country Life,* LVI July–August, 1924, pp. 136–42, 176–83

Ilchester, Lely: Lord Ilchester, letter in *Burl. Mag.,* LXXXVII, 1945, p. 206

Immerzeel: J. Immerzeel, *De Levens en Werken der Hollandsche en Vlaamsche Kunst-schilders . . . ,* 1842

'J.B.': J. B. (James Burgess ?), *The Lives of the Most Eminent Modern Painters,* 1754

Jenkinson: H. Jenkinson, *The Great Seal of England: Deputed or Departmental Seals,* in *Archaeologia,* LXXXV, 1936, pp. 293–338

Johnson: Alfred Forbes Johnson, *A Catalogue of Engraved and Etched English Title-Pages,* 1934

Jones: Alfred Jones, *The Drinking Horns and Silver Plate in the National Museum at Copenhagen,* in *Burl. Mag.,* XV, 1909, pp. 221–32

Keith: William Grant Keith, *Inigo Jones as a Collector,* in the *Journal of the Royal Institute of British Architects,* third series, XXXIII, 1925, pp. 95–110

Kendall: G. E. Kendall, *Notes on the Life of John Wootton with a List of Engravings after his Pictures,* in *Walpole Soc.,* XXI, 1932, pp. 23–42

Kendrick: Sir Thomas Kendrick, *British Antiquity,* 1950

Keynes, Evelyn: G. Keynes, *John Evelyn, a Study in Bibliophily and a Bibliography of his Writings,* 1937

Killanin: Lord Killanin, *Sir Godfrey Kneller and his Times, 1646–1723,* 1948

Kingston Accounts: William, 4th Earl of Kingston, *Accounts,* in Nottingham University Library, MS. 4206

K der K: Klassiker der Kunst.

Kleinmann: H. Kleinmann (publisher), *Handzeichnungen Alter Meister der Hollandischen Schule* [c. 1900]

Knowles, Gyles: John A. Knowles, *Henry Gyles, Glasspainter of York,* in *Walpole Soc.,* XI, 1923, pp. 47–72

Knowles, Sundials: John A. Knowles, *Stained Glass Sundials,* in *Connoisseur,* LXXXV, 1930, pp. 227–31

L.B. See abbreviations, p. 578

L.C.C. Survey of London: L.C.C., *The Survey of London,* being the volume of the Register of the Committee of the Memorials of Greater London . . . Ed. C. R. Ashbee, 1900

Lecce, Registers: Lecce, Cathedral, *Liber Bapt.,* 1650–61, MS.

Le Conte: Pierre Le Conte, *French Ships, 1648–1700,* in *Lists of Men-of-War, 1650–1700.* No. 5 in the *Occasional Publications* of The Society of Nautical Research

Lee: Viscount Lee of Fareham, *Lely's Love Story*, in *Burl. Mag.*, LX, 1932, pp. 145–6, Pls. 147, 150

Lemaitre: Henri Lemaitre, *Le Paysage Anglais à l'Aquarelle, 1760–1851*, 1955

Lewis: H. C. Lewis, *Extracts from the Diaries and Correspondence of John Evelyn and Samuel Pepys Relating to Engraving*, 1915

Lille Catalogue: *Catalogue des Tableaux du Musée de Lille Précédé d'une Notice Historique par Jules Lenglart,* 1893

Locke: *The Correspondence of John Locke and Edward Clarke Edited with a Biographical Study by Benjamin Rand*, 1927

Loggan: David Loggan, *Cantabrigia Illustrata [c. 1676–1690]*, ed. A. Clarke, 1905

London, Monuments: Royal Commission on Historical Monuments (England), *An Inventory of the Historical Monuments in London*, 1924–

London Visitation: J. J. Howard and G. J. Armytage (ed.): *The Visitation of London in the year 1568, taken by Robert Cooke*, 1869
See also *Cooke*

Long: Basil Long, *British Miniaturists*, 1929

Lorant: Stefan Lorant, *The New World. The First Pictures of America Made by John White and Jacques le Moyne and Engraved by Theodore de Bry*, 1946

Lowndes: W. C. Lowndes, *Bibliographers' Manual*, 1857

Lugt, Dutch Catalogue, Berlin: Frits Lugt, *Beiträge zu Dem Katalog der niederlandischen Handzeichnungen in Berlin in Jahrbuch der Preussischen Kunstsammlungen*, LII, 1931, p. 47, S. 127, Fig. 13

Lugt: Frits Lugt, *Le Portrait Miniature Illustré par la Collection de S.M. la Reine des Pays Bas*, 1917

Lugt, Marques: Frits Lugt, *Les Marques de Collections de Dessins et D'estampes*, 1921, & *Supplément*, 1956

Mckerrow: R. B. Mckerrow and F. S. Ferguson, *Title-page Borders Used in England and Scotland, 1485–1640*, 1932

M'Naughton: Joseph M'Naughton, *Earliest View Painted of Stirling*, in *Stirling Natural History and Archaeological Society Transactions*, 1930–31, p. 146

Magazine of Art: *Magazine of Art*, May, 1878–Oct. 1902. New series, Nov., 1902–July, 1904

Maher: John Maher, *Francis Place in Dublin*, in *Journal of the Royal Society of Antiquaries of Ireland*, LXII, Pt. I, 1932, pp. 1–14

Maher, Drogheda: John Maher, *Francis Place in Drogheda, Kilkenny and Waterford, etc.*, in *Journal of the Royal Society of Antiquaries of Ireland*, LXIV, Pt. I, 1934, pp. 41–53

Maison: K. E. Maison, *Portraits by Cornelius Jonson in Scotland*, in *Burl. Mag.*, LXXIV, 1939, pp. 86–91

Maitland, Edinburgh: William Maitland, *The History of Edinburgh*, 1753

Malcolm Cat.: J. C. Robinson, *Descriptive Catalogue of Drawings by Old Masters Forming the Collection of John Malcolm of Portalloch*, 1876

Malliot: J. Malliot, *Recherches Historiques sur les Etablissmens et les Monumens de la Ville de Toulouse, et Vies de Quelques Artistes. . . .* Transcript by M. Couac from the original now lost. Toulouse, Bibliothèque Municipale, MS. 998

Manchée: W. H. Manchée, *Marylebone, and its Huguenot Associations*, in *Proceedings of the Huguenot Society, London*, XI, 1915–17

Marshall: George William Marshall, *Miscellanea Marescalliana*, 1883–88

Martyn: Thomas Martyn, *The English Connoisseur*, 2nd edn., 1767

Mayerne: Sir Theodore Mayerne, *Pictoria, Sculptoria, Tinctoria et quae subalternarum artium, 1620–46*. B. M. Sloane MS. 2052

Mercers' Accts.: Mercers' Co., *Second and Renter Wardens Accounts*, MS.

Metcalfe: Walter C. Metcalfe (ed.), *Visitation of the County of Buckinghamshire in 1566* (Harleian MS., 5867), 1883

Metcalfe, Essex: Walter C. Metcalfe, *The Visitations of Essex* (Harl. Soc. XIII), 1878

Millar: Oliver Millar, *An Attribution to Cornelius Johnson Reinstated*, in *Burl. Mag.*, XC, 1948, pp. 322–3

Millar, Charles I: Oliver Millar, *Charles I, Honthorst and Van Dyck*, in *Burl. Mag.*, XCVI, 1954, pp. 39–42, Figs. 1, 5

Millar, Dobson: Oliver Millar, *William Dobson, 1611–46*. Catalogue of an exhibition of paintings arranged by the Arts Council at the Tate Gallery, 1951

Mills: Weymer Mills, *Dutch Plumbagos. The Clements Collection*, in *Connoisseur*, XXXVII, 1913, pp. 153–60

Moens: W. J. C. Moens, *Registers . . . of the Dutch Reformed Church, Austin Friars*, 1884

Moffet: Thomas Moffet, *Insectorum Sive Minimorum Animalium Theatrum*, 1634

Monconys: Balthasar de Monconys, *Journal des Voyages (Voyage d'Angleterre)*, 1665–6

Montaiglon: Anatole de Montaiglon, *Procès-verbaux de l'Academie Royale de Peinture et de Sculpture, 1648–1792*, 1875–1892

Moorman: Theo Moorman, *Some Newly Discovered Drawings by Francis Place*, in *Burl. Mag.*, XCIV, 1952, pp. 159 and 160

Morgan: J. Pierpont Morgan Collection of Drawings; Reproductions, 1912

Morgan, Sarsaparilla: Edmund S. Morgan, *John White and the Sarsaparilla*, in *The William and Mary Quarterly*, XIV, July, 1957, pp. 414–7

Musaeum Tradescantianum: John Tradescant the Younger, *Musaeum Tradescantianum*, 1664, reprinted 1925

Musgrave: Sir William Musgrave, *Obituary, Prior to 1800*, ed. Sir George J. Armytage (Harl. Soc.), 1899–1901

N. & Q.: *Notes and Queries*, 1856–

Navy Records: Publications of the Navy Records Society

Neale: John Philip Neale, *Views of the Seats of Noblemen and Gentlemen in England, Wales, Scotland and Ireland*, Ser. I, 1818–23; Ser. II, 1824–9

Nichols: John Bowyers Nichols, *Anecdotes of William Hogarth Written by himself with Essays on his Life and Genius and Criticisms. . . . Selected from Walpole, Gilpin, J. Ireland, Lamb, Phillips and Others to which are added a Catalogue of his Prints . . . Lists of Paintings, Drawings, etc.*, 1833

Nichols & Bruce, Wills: *Wills from Doctors' Commons. A Selection from the Wills of Eminent Persons. . . .* Edited by John Gough Nichols and John Bruce (Camden Soc.), 1863

Nisser: Wilhelm Nisser, *Michael Dahl and the Contemporary Swedish School of Painting in England,* 1927

Norgate: Edward Norgate, *Miniatura or the Art of Limning,* ed. Martin Hardie, 1919

Norman, Hilliard: Nicholas Hilliard's Treatise concerning 'The Arte of Limning' with introduction and notes by Philip Norman, in *Walpole Soc.,* I, 1912, pp. 1–54

Norman Papers: Kent County Record Office, Maidstone, *Papers of the Norman Family,* MSS.

North, Lives: Roger North, *The Lives of the Right Hon. Francis North, Baron Guildford; The Hon. Sir Dudley North; and The Hon. and Rev. Dr. John North . . . ,* ed. Augustus Jessopp, D.D., 1890

Ogden: Henry and Margaret Ogden, *English Taste in Landscape in the Seventeenth Century,* 1955

Ogden, Lely's Coll.: Henry and Margaret Ogden, *Sir Peter Lely's Collection: Further Notes,* in *Burl. Mag.,* LXXXIV, 1944, p. 154

Old London Exhibition: Illustrated Souvenir of the Old London Exhibition at 45, Park Lane, 1938

O.M.D.: Old Master Drawings, A Quarterly Magazine for Students and Collectors, ed. K. T. Parker, 1926–40

Olrik: Jurgen Olrik, *Danske Guldsmedes Maerker,* 1919

Oppé, English Drawings: A. P. Oppé, *English Drawings—Stuart and Georgian periods—at Windsor Castle,* 1950

Osborne and Fisher: Edgar Osborne and Francis Fisher, *A Derbyshire Gibbons Monument,* in *Journal of the Derbyshire Archaeological Society and Natural History Society,* LXXI. (New Series LXIV), 1951, p. 81

Osborne, Letters: Letters of Dorothy Osborne to Sir William Temple, ed. G. C. Moore-Smith, 1928

Oswald: Arthur Oswald, *Albury Park, Surrey I. The Home of Helen, Duchess of Northumberland,* in *Country Life,* CVIII, May–August, 1950, pp. 598–602

Painter-Stainers' Minutes: Painter-Stainers' Company, *The Book of Orders and Constitutions, 1623–1649.* Guildhall MS. 5667/1

Painter-Stainers' Pictures: A Catalogue of the Pictures, Prints, Drawings etc. in possession of the Worshipful Company of Painter-Stainers at Painters' Hall, 1908

Palaprat: Jean Palaprat, *Oeuvres,* 2nd edn., 1711

Panettera: Andrea Panettera, *Cronache Della Città di Lecce,* in *Rivista Storica Salentina,* Appendix, p. 53

Parker: K. T. Parker, *Wenceslas Hollar (1607–1677). Study of a Lady's Muff,* in *Old Master Drawings,* VI, No. 22, 1931, p. 38, pl. 33

Parthey: Gustav Parthey. *Wenzel Hollar. Beschreibendes Verzeichniss Seiner Kupferstiche.* Berlin, 1853

Payne Cat.: Thomas Payne, *Sale Catalogue,* Langford & Son, London, March 3–4, 1768

Payne Knight Cat.: Catalogue of the Payne Knight Collection of Drawings, 1845. MS. preserved in the Dept. of Prints & Drawings, B.M.

P.C.C.: See *Will*

P.C.Q.: Print Collector's Quarterly, 1911–42

Peacham, Henry Peacham, *The Art of Drawing with the Pen, and Limning in Water Colours,* 1606

Peck: Francis Peck, *Desiderata Curiosa* (2nd edn.) 1779

Peckham, St Bartholemew, Chichester: W. D. Peckham, *St. Bartholemew, Chichester,* in *Sussex Notes and Queries,* XI, 1947, p. 112

Penrose: G. Penrose (Cornwall County Museum and Art Gallery, Truro). . . . *The Alfred A. de Pass Collection,* 1936

Percy Cat.: Dr. John Percy, MS. catalogue of his collection of drawings, in an interleaved copy of the B.F.A.C. Catalogue, *Drawings in Watercolours,* 1871, preserved in the Dept. of Prints & Drawings, B.M.

Philip: I. G. Philip, *Balthazar Gerbier and the Duke of Buckingham's Pictures,* in *Burl. Mag.,* XCIX, 1957, pp. 155–6

Piper: David Piper, *Lumley Inventory,* in *Burl. Mag.* XCIX, 1957, pp. 299–300

Planiscig: Leo Planiscig, *Die Bronzeplastiken im Kunsthistorisches Museum in Wien,* 1924. Publikationen aus den Sammlungen für Plastik und Kunstgewerbe. Ed. Julius Schlosser (Vol. IV)

Poole, Oxford Portraits: Rachel Lane Poole, *Catalogue of Portraits in . . . the University, Colleges, City and County of Oxford,* 1912–25

Poole, Pierce: Rachel Lane Poole, *Edward Pierce the Sculptor,* in *Walpole Soc.,* XI, 1923, pp. 38–45

Pope-Hennessy: John Pope-Hennessy, *Nicholas Hilliard and Mannerist Art Theory,* in *Warburg Journal,* VI, 1943, pp. 89–100

Pope-Hennessy, Hilliard: John Pope-Hennessy, *A Lecture on Nicholas Hilliard,* 1949

Popham, Fenwick: Catalogue of Drawings in the Collection formed by Sir Thomas Phillipps, Bart., F.R.S., now in the Possession of his Grandson, T. Fitzroy Phillipps Fenwick of Thirlestaine House, Cheltenham. Privately printed, 1935

Popham, Hollar: A. E. Popham, *Wenceslas Hollar (1607–1677),* in *Old Master Drawings,* No. 6, Sept. 1927, pp. 29–30, Pl. 33

Popham, Van Dyck: A. E. Popham, *Acquisitions at the Oppenheimer Sale,* in *B.M.Q.,* XI, 1936, p. 128

Portraits Transferred from Dept. of Antiquities: List of Portraits etc. Transferred from the Dept. of Antiquities to that of Prints, May 9th [and March], 1846. MS. preserved in the Dept. of Prints & Drawings, B.M.

Pote: Joseph Pote, *The History and Antiquity of Windsor Castle,* 1749

Preussischen Jahrbuch: Jahrbuch der Preussischen Kunst-Sammlungen, 1880–1943

Puyvelde: L. van Puyvelde, *Van Dyck and the Amsterdam Double Portrait,* in *Burl. Mag.,* LXXXIII, 1943, pp. 205–7

Puyvelde, Flemish Drawings: L. van Puyvelde, *Flemish Drawings at Windsor Castle,* 1942

Quinn: The Roanoke Voyages, 1584–1590. Documents to Illustrate the English Voyages to North America . . . ed. D. B. Quinn, Hakluyt Soc., Ser. II, CIV, 1955

Raven: C. E. Raven, *English Naturalists from Neckam to Ray,* 1947

Redgrave: S. Redgrave, *A Dictionary of Artists of the English School* (2nd edn.), 1878

Reitlinger: H. S. Reitlinger, *The Beale Drawings in the British Museum,* in *Burl. Mag.,* XLI, 1922, pp. 143–7 & Pls. A–D

Reynolds: Graham Reynolds, *Nicholas Hilliard and Isaac Oliver.* Monograph and catalogue for an exhibition held at the V. & A.M. to commemorate the 400th anniversary of the birth of Nicholas Hilliard, 1947

Reynolds, Flatman: Graham Reynolds, *A Miniature Self-Portrait by Thomas Flatman, Limner & Poet*, in Burl. Mag., LXXXIX, 1947, p. 67, Pl. IIe

Richmond, Registers: John Chaloner Smith, *The Parish Registers of Richmond, Surrey* (Surrey Parish Register Soc.), 1903–5

Ritchie: M. I. Ritchie, *English Drawings*, 1935

Roberts: W. Roberts, *Our National Museums and Galleries: Recent Acquisitions, The British Museum: The Print Room*, in Magazine of Art, 1901, pp. 316–7

Robinson: M. S. Robinson, *A Catalogue of Drawings in the National Maritime Museum made by the Elder and the Younger Willem Van de Velde*, 1958

Rooses: Max Rooses, *L'œuvre de P. P. Rubens*, 1886–92

Routh: E. M. G. Routh, *Tangier, England's Lost Atlantic Outpost*, 1912

Rowntree: Arthur Rowntree, *The History of Scarborough*, 1931

Rowse: A. L. Rowse, *Sir Richard Grenville of the Revenge*, 1937

Russell: C. E. Russell, *English Mezzotint Portraits and Their States*, 1926

Rylands: W. H. Rylands, *The Visitations of the County of Buckingham, 1634* (Harl. Soc.), 1909

Sainsbury: W. N. Sainsbury, *Original Unpublished Papers Illustrative of the Life of Sir P. P. Rubens . . .*, 1859

St. Botolph's Bishopsgate, Register: *Burial Register of St. Botolph's Church, Bishopsgate*, II, 1893

St. Bride's, Fleet Street, Register: *St. Bride's Church, Fleet Street, Register of Births, Deaths and Marriages*. Guildhall MS. 6540

St. Giles-in-the-Fields, Registers: *Burial Registers of St. Giles-in-the-Fields, London*. MS. preserved in the church

St. Martin-in-the-Fields, Registers: *The Registers of St. Martin-in-the-Fields, Pt. I, 1550–1619* (Harl. Soc.), ed. Thomas Mason, 1898; *Pt. II, 1619–36* (Harl. Soc.), ed. J. V. Kitto, 1936; remainder, 1636– still in MS. (Chester MSS. VI, VII at College of Arms)

St. Martin Orgars, Register: *Register of the Church of St. Martin Orgars with its History and That of Swallow Street*. (II. S. Publications XXXVII, 1935), ed. William & Susan Minet

St. Mary Magdalen, Bermondsey, Registers: *Burial Registers of St. Mary Magdalen, Bermondsey*. MS. preserved in the church

St. Paul's, Covent Garden, Registers: *The Registers of St. Paul's Church, Covent Garden* (Harl. Soc.), ed. Rev. W. H. Hunt, 1906–9

Sanderson: Sir William Sanderson, *Graphice*, 1638

Sandrart: Joachim von Sandrarts *Academie der Bau-, Bild- und Mahlerey-künste von 1675*, ed. A. R. Peltzer, 1925

Scharf, Blenheim: George Scharf, *Catalogue . . . of the pictures in Blenheim Palace*, 1862

Scharf, Water-colours: George Scharf, *Views of the Staircase, Montagu House, Old British Museum*, 1845. Water-colours in the B.M. Print Room, 1862.6.14, 629–31

Scharf, Woburn: George Scharf, *A descriptive and historical catalogue of the collection of pictures at Woburn Abbey*, 1890

Schneider: H. Schneider, *The Portraits of Cornelis Janssens Van Ceulen*, in Burl. Mag., XLV, 1924, pp. 295–6. Also (following on) James D. Milner, *Comments on Above Article*, pp. 296–7

Scholes: Percy A. Scholes, *The Great Doctor Burney*, 1948

Schreiber: *Playing Cards of Various Ages and Countries from the Collection of Lady Charlotte Schreiber*, 3 vols., 1892

Schwabe: Randolph Schwabe, *A Drawing Ascribed to Van Dyck*, in Burl. Mag., LIII, 1928, pp. 61–3, Figs. A, B

Seymour: June Seymour, *Edward Pierce, Baroque Sculptor of London*, in Guildhall Miscellany, Jan., 1952, pp. 10–17

Shaw Sparrow, Barlow: Walter Shaw Sparrow, *Francis Barlow: his Country Life and Field Sports*, in Apollo, XIX, 1934, pp. 25–9

Shaw Sparrow, British Etching: Walter Shaw Sparrow, *A Book of British Etching from Francis Barlow to Francis Seymour Haden*, 1926

Shaw Sparrow, British Sporting Artists: Walter Shaw Sparrow, *British Sporting Artists from Barlow to Herring*, 1922

Shaw Sparrow, Earliest Sporting Artist: Walter Shaw Sparrow, *Our Earliest Sporting Artist Francis Barlow —1626–1704*, in The Connoisseur, XCVIII, 1936, pp. 36–40

Sheepshanks Cat.: *Catalogue of the Sheepshanks Collection of Drawings*, 1845. MS. preserved in the Dept. of Prints and Drawings, B.M.

Sheppard: Edgar Sheppard, *Memorials of St. James's Palace*, 1894

Simpson & Bell: *Designs by Inigo Jones for Masques and Plays at Court. A Descriptive Catalogue of Drawings for Scenery & Costumes Mainly in the Collection of His Grace, The Duke of Devonshire With Introduction. Notes by Percy Simpson & C. F. Bell*, in Walpole Soc., XII, 1924

Sloane Antiquities, Pictures & Drawings: Sir Hans Sloane, *A Catalogue of Antiquities* [Pictures and Drawings]. Typescript, preserved in the Dept. of Prints & Drawings, of an original MS. in the Dept. of Ethnography

Sloane Cat.: *Catalogue of the Sloane Collection of Drawings*, 1845. MS. preserved in the Dept. of Prints and Drawings, B.M.

Smith; Dutch, Flemish & French Painters: John Smith, *A Catalogue Raisonné of . . . Dutch, Flemish, and French Painters*, 1829–42

Smith, Nollekens: J. C. Smith, *Nollekens and his Times*, 1828

Smith, Painting: Marshall Smith, *The Art of Painting According to the Theory and Practise of the Best Italian, French and German Masters*. Second edition by M. S. Gent, 1693

Smith, Westminster: J. T. Smith, *The Antiquities of Westminster*, 1807

Sprinzels: Franz Sprinzels, *Hollar Handzeichnungen*, 1938

Stevens: Henry Stevens, *Bibliotheca Historica*, 1870

Stevens, Hariot: Henry Stevens, *Thomas Hariot*, 1900

Stevens Report: Henry Stevens, *Report*, dated March 22,

1866, to A. Panizzi Esq. on one bound volume of drawings by John White and one of offprints from them, offered for sale to the Trustees of the B.M.

Strutt: Joseph Strutt, *A Biographical Dictionary of Engravers,* 1885

Stukeley, Memoirs: The Family Memoirs of the Rev. William Stukeley (Surtees Soc.), 1882–7

Summerson: John Summerson, *Architecture in Britain, 1530–1830,* 1953

Surtees: Robert Surtees, *The History and Antiquities of the County Palatine of Durham, Compiled from Original Records* . . . , 1816–40

Sutherland Cat.: Catalogue of the Sutherland Collection (2 vols.). Published by L. Payne & Foss and D. Colnaghi & Co., 1837

Symonds: Richard Symonds, *Notes on Painting 1650–1* (B.M., Egerton MS. 1636).

Tabernacle, Glasshouse Street Registers: The Registers of the Churches of The Tabernacle, Glasshouse Street and Leicester Fields, 1688–1783 (H.S. Publications, XXIX, 1926), ed. William & Susan Minet

Talman-Aldrich: John Talman, *Letter to Dr. Henry Aldrich, Dean of Christ Church, Giving an Account of the Collection of Drawings of Monsignor Marchetti, Bishop of Arezzo, Collected by Padre Resta,* 1758, in Talman's *Letter Book.* MS. preserved in Bodleian Library (Eng. Letters, c. 34)

Taylor: Eva G. R. Taylor, *The Original Writings & Correspondence of the Two Richard Hakluyts,* Hakluyt Soc., 2nd Ser., LXXVI, 1935

T.–B.: Ulrich Thieme and Felix Becker, *Allgemeines Lexikon der Bildenden Künstler* . . . , 1908–50

Thompson, A Lost Painting: Francis Thompson, *A Lost Painting of Chatsworth,* in Country Life, CXI, 1952, pp. 914–5

Thompson, Chatsworth: Francis Thompson, *A History of Chatsworth,* 1949

Thomson: W. G. Thomson, *A History of Tapestry,* 1930

Thoresby, Correspondence: Rev. Joseph Hunter, *The Correspondence of Ralph Thoresby,* 1832

Thoresby, Diary: Rev. Joseph Hunter, *The Diary of Ralph Thoresby (1677–1724),* 1830

Thoresby, Ducatus: Ralph Thoresby, *Ducatus Leodiensis,* 1715

Thoresby Society: Letters to Ralph Thoresby (Publications of The Thoresby Society (Leeds)), 1912, ed. W. T. Lancaster

Tipping: H. A. Tipping, *Grinling Gibbons and the Woodwork of his Age 1648–1720,* 1913

Toppin: Aubrey J. Toppin, *A Ceramic Miscellany,* No. 1 in The English Ceramic Circle Trs. (1951), 3, Pt. 1, pp. 65–8

Toulouse, Regre Pour les baptêmes, Mariage e Mortuaires Pour l'an 1668. MS. in Archives Municipales, GG 243

Toynbee, Early Portraits: Margaret Toynbee, *Some Early Portraits of Princess Mary* . . . , in Burl. Mag., LXXXII, 1943, pp. 101–3

Toynbee, Lely's Early Work: Margaret Toynbee, *The Early Work of Sir Peter Lely,* in Burl. Mag., LXXXVI, 1945, pp. 125–7

Turner: William Henry Turner, *The Visitations of the County of Oxford* (Harl. Soc.), 1871

Urzidil: Johannes Urzidil, *Hollar, A Czech Emigré in England,* 1942

Van der Waal: H. van der Waal, *Drie Eeuwen Vaderlandsche Geschied-uitbeelding 1500–1800,* 1952

Van Eeghen: Teekeningen van Oude Meisters Behoorende tot de Verzameling van Mr. Chr. P. van Eegen. Catalogue of an exhibition at the Museum Fodor, Autumn 1935, with foreword by J. Q. van Regteren Altena

Van Luttervelt: R. van Luttervelt, *Het Portret van Willem II en Maria Stuart in Het Rijksmusuem,* in Oud Holland, LXVIII, pp. 159–69, 1952

Van Rijsewijk, I: P. Haverkorn van Rijsewijk, *Willem van de Velde de Oude,* in Oud Holland, XVIII, 1900, pp. 21–44

Van Rijsewijk, II: P. Haverkorn van Rijsewijk, *Willem van de Velde de Oude,* in Oud Holland, XX, 1902, pp. 170–92

Van Rijsewijk, Schilders du Bois: P. Haverkorn van Rijsewijk, *De Rotterdamsche Schilders du Bois,* in Oud Holland, XVII, 1899, pp. 176–85, 240

Verrio, Burghley: Burghley House, *Accounts of Antonio Verrio and Others for Painting at Burghley, 1687–98.* MS.

Verrio, Windsor: Windsor Castle, Royal Library, *Accounts of Antonio Verrio and René Cousin for Painting and Gilding at Windsor, 1676–87.* MS. I.B. 3a

Versailles & Marly: Nouvelle Description des Chasteaux et Parcs de Versailles et de Marly, 1701

Vertue: George Vertue, *Note Books* I–VI, in Walpole Soc., XVIII, 1930; XX, 1932; XXII, 1934; XXIV, 1936; XXVI, 1938; XXX, 1955

Vertue, Index: Lord Ilchester, *Vertue Note Books, Index to Vols. I–V,* in Walpole Soc., XXIX, 1947

V. & A.M., Portrait Drawings: Victoria and Albert Museum. *Portrait Drawings,* 1953

Vreugdenhil: A Vreugdenhil, *Part IV, Ships of the United Netherlands, 1648–1702* in Lists of Men-of-War, 1650–1700. No. 5 in the Occasional Publications of the Society for Nautical Research

Walpole: Horace Walpole, *Anecdotes of Painting in England; with Some Account of the Principal Artists* . . . , ed. Ralph N. Wornum, 1862

Walpole (1786): Horace Walpole, *Anecdotes of Painting in England,* 4th edn., 1786

Walpole Soc.: Walpole Society [Publications], Volumes, 1912–

Walsh: Elizabeth Walsh, *Mrs. Mary Beale, Paintress,* in Connoisseur, CXXXI, March, 1953, pp. 3–8

Warburg Journal: Journal of the Warburg Institute, 1937–

Ward: Ned Ward, *The London Spy,* ed. A. L. Hayward, 1927

Warner, N. England: Rev. Richard Warner, *A Tour Through the Northern Counties of England, and the Borders of Scotland,* 1802

Waterhouse: Ellis K. Waterhouse, *Painting in Britain 1530–1790,* 1953

Waterhouse, John Greenhill: Ellis K. Waterhouse, *John Greenhill (1649–1676),* in O.M.D., XI, No. 44, 1936–8, pp. 69–70

Waterhouse, Van Dyck: Ellis K. Waterhouse, *Letter in Burl. Mag.,* LXXXVI, 1945, pp. 50–56

Watson: F. J. B. Watson, *On the Early History of Collecting in England,* in Burl. Mag., LXXXV, 1944, pp. 226, 227

Weale: J. Cyril M. Weale, *Registers of the Catholic Chapels Royal and the Portuguese Embassy Chapel, 1662–1829* (Cath. Rec. Soc.), 1941

Weale, Kunstbode: W. H. Weale, *Nederlandsche Kunstbode*, 1879

Weeks: S. B. Weeks, *Lane and White, the Governors of Roanoke*, in *North Carolina University Magazine*, IX, 1890, pp. 225–36

Weilbach: [Philip] *Weilbachs Kunstnerleksikon* (Dictionary of Danish Artists), 1947–52

Wellesley Cat.: Catalogue of the Miniatures and Portraits in Plumbago or Pencil Belonging to Francis & Minnie Wellesley, [n. d.]

Wellesley, Dunstall: H. Wellesley, *On Two Engravings by John Dunstall of 'A Temple by Chichester'*, in *Sussex Archaeological Collections*, V, 1852, pp. 278–280, Pl. facing p. 276

Wheatley & Cunningham: H. B. Wheatley and P. Cunningham, *London Past and Present*, 1891

Whinney: Margaret Whinney, *John Webb's Drawings for Whitehall Palace*, in *Walpole Society*, XXXI, pp. 45–107, Plates IX–XVI

Whitley: W. T. Whitley, *Artists and their Friends in England, 1700–1799*, 1928

Wiener Jahrbuch: Jahrbuch Der Kunsthistorischen Sammlungen in Wien. First published 1883. New Series 1926–

Will, London: Somerset House, *Commissary Court of London, Transcripts of Wills*, MSS.

Will: Somerset House, Prerogative Court of Canterbury, Transcripts of Wills, MSS.

Williams: Iolo A. Williams, *Early English Watercolours*, 1952

Williams, Manby: Iolo A. Williams, *Thomas Manby, a XVIIth Century Landscape Painter*, in *Apollo*, XXIII, 1936, pp. 276–7

Williamson Cat.: George C. Williamson, *Catalogue of Works of Art* (privately printed), 1909

Williamson, Portrait Miniatures: George C. Williamson, *The History of Portrait Miniatures*, 1904

Williamson, Stuart Portraits: Hugh Ross Williamson, *Four Stuart Portraits*, 1949

Wind, Shaftesbury: Edgar Wind, *Shaftesbury as a Patron of Art*, in *Warburg Journal*, II, 1938–9, pp. 185–8

Winde: MS. Letters from Capt. William Winde to Lady Bridgeman, 1688–1699/1700. (Earl of Bradford's Archives, Weston Park)

Winkler: F. Winkler, *Das Skizzenbuch Gerard Davids*, in *Pantheon*, III, Jan.–June 1929

Winter: Carl Winter, *Elizabethan Miniatures*, 1943

Winter, Hilliard: Carl Winter, *Hilliard and Elizabethan Miniatures*, in *Burl. Mag.*, LXXXIX, 1947, pp. 175–83

Witt Repr.: Sir Robert & Lady Witt, Library of Reproductions of Pictures, Courtauld Institute, University of London.

Wittkower: R. Wittkower, *Pseudo-Palladian Elements in English Neo-Classical Architecture*, in *Warburg Journal*, VI, 1943, pp. 154–64

Wittkower, Inigo Jones: R. Wittkower, *'Puritanissimo Fiero'*, in *Burl. Mag.*, XC, 1948, pp. 50–1

Wood, Athenae Oxon: Anthony à Wood, *Athenae Oxonienses—An exact history of all the writers and bishops who have had their education in the most antient . . . University of Oxford . . . from 1500 . . . to 1695*, 2 vols., 1721

Woodward: John Woodward, *Tudor and Stuart Drawings*, 1951

Wren Memorial Volume: Sir Christopher Wren Bicentenary Memorial Volume, ed. Rudolf Dircks, 1923

Wren Soc.: Publications of the Wren Society, I–XIX, 1923–43

Wren Soc., Index: Index to I–XIX of the *Wren Soc.*, in *Wren Soc.*, XX, 1943

Wright: Irene A. Wright, *Further English Voyages to Spanish America, 1583–1594*, Hakluyt Soc. Series II, XCIX, 1951

Wroth: W. & A. E. Wroth, *The London Pleasure Gardens of the Eighteenth Century*, 1896

Wurzbach: Alfred von Wurzbach, *Niederländisches Künstler Lexikon*, 1906–10

Young: Arthur Young, *A Six Months Tour Through the North of England*, 1770

Zimmerman: Franklin B. Zimmerman, *Purcell Portraiture* in *Organ and Choral Aspects and Prospects*, ed. Max. Hinnchsen, 1958, pp. 136–49

TABLE OF INDEXES

INDEXES

The references in this index are to the numbered entries under the artist's name.

ANCIENT HISTORY, ALLEGORY AND MYTHOLOGY

Achilles, tomb of, *Chéron* 5 (53)
Actaeon, *Chéron* 5 (44)
Aeneas, *Chéron* 5 (39), (45), (52)
Aeolus, *Chéron* 5 (40), (48)
Agamemnon, *Chéron* 5 (58)
Agave, *Chéron* 5 (29)
Alexander and Roxana, marriage of, *S. Du Bois* 3
allegorical composition, design for, *Verrio* 1
Angelica, *Chéron* 4
Antiope: *Chéron* 2 (a); *Colonia* 2v.; *I. Oliver* 7
Apollo: *Barlow* 82; *Chéron* 5 (10), (13), (16), (34), (41), (58); *Hollar* 47v.; *I. Oliver* 1
Aquarius, *Chéron* 5 (11)
Arcas, *Chéron* 5 (3), (11)
Argus, *Byng* 8 (75)–(77), (79), (80)
Ariadne, *Chéron* 5 (121)
Arts and Sciences, etc., *Vinne*, 1–14
Ascalaphus, *Chéron* 5 (31)
Athamas, *Chéron* 5 (22)

Bacchanalian scenes: *Anon. English c. 1596* 1r., p. 3; *Chéron* 5 (37), (38)
Bacchus: *Beale II* 121; *Chéron* 5 (36), (47), (55), (121)
Belides, the, *Chéron* 5 (22)
Bellona, triumph of (design for a dagger), *Holbein* 185

Callisto, *Chéron* 5 (3), (11)
casket of beauty, *S. Du Bois* 4
Centaurs, *See* Chiron and Nessus
Cerberus, *Chéron* 5 (22)
Ceres, *Chéron* 5 (28), (30), (31)
Charity, *Gibbons* 1
Chiron, *Chéron* 5 (11), (14)
Chryses, *Chéron* 5 (58)
Corone, *Chéron* 5 (21)
Coronis, *Chéron* 5 (16), (34)
Cupid: *Barlow* 67, 75, 76; *Beale II* 115; *S. Du Bois* 5; *Gascar* 1; *Holbein* 88; *John White* 78 f. 41v.
Cyane, *Chéron* 5 (35)

Daphne, *Chéron* 5 (41)
Death, *Barlow* 67, 96
Dejanira, *Chéron* 5 (19), (20), (46), (49)
Deluge, the, *Chéron* 5 (24), (25)
Deucalion, *Chéron* 5 (6)
Diana: *Byng* 7 f. 33v.; *Chéron* 5 (44), (108); *Kneller* 6v.; *I. Oliver* 2
Dido, *Chéron* 5 (45r. & v.)
Diomede, *Chéron* 5 (52)

Discord, *Chéron* 5 (2)
dragon's teeth, the, *Chéron* 5 (15)

Elements, the, *Chéron* 5 (3)
Evenus, *Chéron* 5 (19), (46)

Faith, *Pierce II* 1
Fame: *Pierce II* 1; *Touroude* 1
fleece, the golden, *Chéron* 5 (120)
Flora: *Chéron* 5 (18); *Verelst* 1 (?)
Fortitude, *Pierce II* 1
Fortuna, *Anon. German* (?) *early xvii c.* 12r., p. 12
Furies, the, *Chéron* 5 (22)

Galatea (?), *Chéron* 5 (57)
Ganymede, *Chéron* 5 (112)
Giants, the, *Chéron* 5 (9)
globe, nude woman on, *Holbein* 75, 76
Gods, the assembled: *Chéron* 5 (1), (2), (4), (109); *S. Du Bois* 5
Gorgon's head, the, *Chéron* 5 (26), (65r.)

Hades, *Chéron* 5 (22)
Harpies, *Anon. German* (?) *early xvii c.* 7, 9, pp. 10, 11
Hector, *Chéron* 5 (51)
Helicon, Mount, *Chéron* 5 (27), (42), (54)
Hercules: *Barlow* 60; *Beale II* 162–164; *Chéron* 1, 2, 5 (19), (20), (64), (75 (?)), (110); *Cleyn* 1; *Fuller* 1
Hermaphrodite, *Chéron* 5 (23)
Hero (?), *Anon. German* (?) *early xvii c.* 18, p. 13
History, *Touroude* 1
Hope, *Pierce II* 1
Hour, the First, *Chéron* 5 (16)
Humility, *Verrio* 1

Iris, *Chéron* 5 (25)

Janus, *Chéron* 5 (106)
Jason, *Chéron* 5 (15)
Juno: *Barlow* 80; *Chéron* 5 (18), (22), (40), (108), (113); *Laguerre* 1
Jupiter: *Barlow* 44; *Chéron* 5 (3), (11), (14), (17), (18), (24), (25), (50), (113); *Colonia* 2v.; *I. Oliver* 7
Justice: *Anon. German* (?) *early xvii c.* 11v., p. 12; *Byng* 1, 2 f. 11r.; *Cleyn* 1; *Van de Velde* (?) 83; *Verrio* 1

Leander (?), *Anon. German* (?) *early xvii c.* 18, p. 13
Lucretia, death of: *Holbein* 57; *Inigo Jones* 1

Mars, *Chéron* 5 (4)
maidens, the winged, *Chéron* 5 (111)
Medoro, *Chéron* 4
Medusa, *Chéron* 5 (33)

601

ARCHITECTURE AND SCULPTURE

HISTORICAL EVENTS AND PERSONS
(See also portrait index)

MISCELLANEOUS

NATURAL HISTORY

PORTRAITS

SHIPPING

TOPOGRAPHY